HAESE & HARRIS PUBLICATIONS

Specialists in mathema

Mathematics
for the international student
Mathematics HL (Core)
second edition

Paul Urban

David Martin

Robert Haese

Sandra Haese

Michael Haese

Mark Humphries

for use with
IB Diploma
Programme

MATHEMATICS FOR THE INTERNATIONAL STUDENT
Mathematics HL (Core) second edition

Paul Urban	B.Sc.(Hons.),B.Ec.
David Martin	B.A.,B.Sc.,M.A.,M.Ed.Admin.
Robert Haese	B.Sc.
Sandra Haese	B.Sc.
Michael Haese	B.Sc.(Hons.),Ph.D.
Mark Humphries	B.Sc.(Hons.)

Haese & Harris Publications
3 Frank Collopy Court, Adelaide Airport, SA 5950, AUSTRALIA
Telephone: +61 8 8355 9444, Fax: + 61 8 8355 9471
Email: info@haeseandharris.com.au
Web: www.haeseandharris.com.au

National Library of Australia Card Number & ISBN 978-1-876543-11-2

© Haese & Harris Publications 2008

Published by Raksar Nominees Pty Ltd.
3 Frank Collopy Court, Adelaide Airport, SA 5950, AUSTRALIA

First Edition	2004
Reprinted	2005 three times *(with minor corrections)*, 2006, 2007
Second Edition	2008
Reprinted	2009 *(with minor corrections)*, 2010, 2011

Cartoon artwork by John Martin. Artwork by Piotr Poturaj and David Purton.
Cover design by Piotr Poturaj.
Computer software by David Purton, Thomas Jansson and Troy Cruickshank.

Typeset in Australia by Susan Haese (Raksar Nominees). Typeset in Times Roman $10\frac{1}{2}/11\frac{1}{2}$.

The textbook and its accompanying CD have been developed independently of the International Baccalaureate Organization (IBO). The textbook and CD are in no way connected with, or endorsed by, the IBO.

Acknowledgements: While every attempt has been made to trace and acknowledge copyright, the authors and publishers apologise for any accidental infringement where copyright has proved untraceable. They would be pleased to come to a suitable agreement with the rightful owner.

Disclaimer: All the internet addresses (URL's) given in this book were valid at the time of printing. While the authors and publisher regret any inconvenience that changes of address may cause readers, no responsibility for any such changes can be accepted by either the authors or the publisher.

FOREWORD

Mathematics for the International Student: Mathematics HL has been written to reflect the syllabus for the two-year IB Diploma Mathematics HL course. It is not our intention to define the course. Teachers are encouraged to use other resources. We have developed the book independently of the International Baccalaureate Organization (IBO) in consultation with many experienced teachers of IB Mathematics. The text is not endorsed by the IBO.

This second edition builds on the strengths of the first edition. Many excellent suggestions were received from teachers around the world and these are reflected in the changes. In some cases sections have been consolidated to allow for greater efficiency. Changes have also been made in response to the introduction of a calculator-free examination paper. A large number of questions, including some to challenge even the best students, have been added. In particular, the final chapter contains over 200 miscellaneous questions, some of which require the use of a graphics calculator. These questions have been included to provide more difficult challenges for students and to give them experience at working with problems that may or may not require the use of a graphics calculator.

The combination of textbook and interactive Student CD will foster the mathematical development of students in a stimulating way. Frequent use of the interactive features on the CD is certain to nurture a much deeper understanding and appreciation of mathematical concepts.

The book contains many problems from the basic to the advanced, to cater for a wide range of student abilities and interests. While some of the exercises are simply designed to build skills, every effort has been made to contextualise problems, so that students can see everyday uses and practical applications of the mathematics they are studying, and appreciate the universality of mathematics.

Emphasis is placed on the gradual development of concepts with appropriate worked examples, but we have also provided extension material for those who wish to go beyond the scope of the syllabus. Some proofs have been included for completeness and interest although they will not be examined.

For students who may not have a good understanding of the necessary background knowledge for this course, we have provided printable pages of information, examples, exercises and answers on the Student CD. To access these pages, simply click on the 'Background knowledge' icons when running the CD.

It is not our intention that each chapter be worked through in full. Time constraints will not allow for this. Teachers must select exercises carefully, according to the abilities and prior knowledge of their students, to make the most efficient use of time and give as thorough coverage of work as possible.

Investigations throughout the book will add to the discovery aspect of the course and enhance student understanding and learning. Many Investigations could be developed into portfolio assignments. Teachers should follow the guidelines for portfolio assignments to ensure they set acceptable portfolio pieces for their students that meet the requirement criteria for the portfolios.

Review sets appear at the end of each chapter and a suggested order for teaching the two-year course is given at the end of this Foreword.

The extensive use of graphics calculators and computer packages throughout the book enables students to realise the importance, application and appropriate use of technology. No single aspect of technology has been favoured. It is as important that students work with a pen and paper as it is that they use their calculator or graphics calculator, or use a spreadsheet or graphing package on computer.

The interactive features of the CD allow immediate access to our own specially designed geometry packages, graphing packages and more. Teachers are provided with a quick and easy way to demonstrate concepts, and students can discover for themselves and re-visit when necessary.

Instructions appropriate to each graphic calculator problem are on the CD and can be printed for students. These instructions are written for Texas Instruments and Casio calculators.

In this changing world of mathematics education, we believe that the contextual approach shown in this book, with the associated use of technology, will enhance the students' understanding, knowledge and appreciation of mathematics, and its universal application.

We welcome your feedback.

Email: info@haeseandharris.com.au
Web: www.haeseandharris.com.au

PMU DCM RCH
SHH PMH MAH

ACKNOWLEDGEMENTS

The authors and publishers would like to thank all those teachers who have offered advice and encouragement. Many of them have read page proofs and made constructive comments and suggestions.

Particular thanks go to Stephen Hobbs who has given generously of his time in reviewing the first edition and making suggestions for improvement in this second edition. Thanks are also due to Dr. Andrzej Cichy, Peter Blythe, Brendan Watson, Myrricia Holmann, Jeff Jones, Mark Willis, John Poole and Marjut Mäenpää. We acknowledge the contributions of John Owen and Mark Bruce in the preparation of the first edition and we also want to thank others who provided assistance – they include: Cameron Hall, Fran O'Connor, Glenn Smith, Anne Walker, Malcolm Coad, Ian Hilditch, Phil Moore, Julie Wilson, Kerrie Clements, Margie Karbassioun, Brian Johnson, Carolyn Farr, Rupert de Smidt, Terry Swain, Marie-Therese Filippi, Nigel Wheeler, Sarah Locke, Rema George.

The publishers wish to make it clear that acknowledging these individual does not imply any endorsement of this book by any of them and all responsibility for content rests with the authors and publishers.

TEACHING THE TWO-YEAR COURSE – A SUGGESTED ORDER

Teachers are encouraged to carefully check the BACKGROUND KNOWLEDGE sections supplied on the accompanying CD to ensure that basics have been mastered relatively early in the two-year HL course. Some of these topics naturally occur at the beginning of a specific chapter, as indicated in the table of contents. Click on the BACKGROUND KNOWLEDGE active icons to access the printable pages on the CD.

Teachers will have their personal preferences for the order in which the chapters are tackled. A suggestion is to work progressively from Chapter 1 through to Chapter 20, but leave Chapters 9, 15 and, possibly, 16 for the second year. The remaining chapters can be worked through in order.

Alternatively, for the first year, students could work progressively from Chapter 1 to Chapter 23 but not necessarily including chapters 7, 15 and 16. Chapter 9 'Mathematical Induction' could also be attempted later, perhaps early in the second year. In some parts of the world, the topics of Polynomials, Complex Numbers, 3-D Vector Geometry and Calculus are not usually covered until the final year of school.

Another approach could be to teach just those topics that are included in the Mathematics SL syllabus in the first year and leave the remaining topics for completion in the second year.

However, it is acknowledged that there is no single best way for all teachers to work through the syllabus. Individual teachers have to consider particular needs of their students and other requirements and preferences that they may have.

USING THE INTERACTIVE STUDENT CD

The CD is ideal for independent study. Frequent use will nurture a deeper understanding of Mathematics. Students can revisit concepts taught in class and undertake their own revision and practice. The CD also has the text of the book, allowing students to leave the textbook at school and keep the CD at home.

The icon denotes an Interactive Link on the CD. Simply 'click' the icon to access a range of interactive features:

+ spreadsheets
+ video clips
+ graphing and geometry software
+ graphics calculator instructions
+ computer demonstrations and simulations
+ background knowledge (as printable pages)

INTERACTIVE LINK

For those who want to make sure they have the prerequisite levels of understanding for this course, printable pages of background information, examples, exercises and answers are provided on the CD. Click the 'Background knowledge' icon on pages 12 and 248.

Graphics calculators: Instructions for using graphics calculators are also given on the CD and can be printed. Instructions are given for Texas Instruments and Casio calculators. Click on the relevant icon (TI or C) to access printable instructions.

Examples in the textbook are not always given for both types of calculator. Where that occurs, click on the relevant icon to access the instructions for the other type of calculator.

NOTE ON ACCURACY

Students are reminded that in assessment tasks, including examination papers, unless otherwise stated in the question, all numerical answers must be given exactly or to three significant figures.

HL & SL COMBINED CLASSES

Refer to our website www.haeseandharris.com.au for guidance in using this textbook in HL and SL combined classes.

HL OPTIONS

This is a companion to the **Mathematics HL (Core)** textbook. It offers coverage of each of the following options:

+ Topic 8 – Statistics and probability
+ Topic 9 – Sets, relations and groups
+ Topic 10 – Series and differential equations
+ Topic 11 – Discrete mathematics

In addition, coverage of the Geometry option for students undertaking the IB Diploma course **Further Mathematics** is presented on the CD that accompanies the **HL Options** book.

SUPPLEMENTARY BOOKS

A separate book of WORKED SOLUTIONS gives the fully worked solutions for every question (discussions, investigations and projects excepted) in each chapter of the **Mathematics HL (Core)** textbook. The HL (CORE) EXAMINATION PREPARATION & PRACTICE GUIDE offers additional questions and practice exams to help students prepare for the Mathematics HL examination. For more information email info@haeseandharris.com.au

TABLE OF CONTENTS

SYMBOLS AND NOTATION USED IN THIS BOOK

$\mathbb{N}$ — the set of positive integers and zero, $\{0, 1, 2, 3, ...\}$

$\mathbb{Z}$ — the set of integers, $\{0, \pm 1, \pm 2, \pm 3, ...\}$

$\mathbb{Z}^+$ — the set of positive integers, $\{1, 2, 3, ...\}$

$\mathbb{Q}$ — the set of rational numbers

$\mathbb{Q}^+$ — the set of positive rational numbers, $\{x \mid x > 0, \ x \in \mathbb{Q}\}$

$\mathbb{R}$ — the set of real numbers

$\mathbb{R}^+$ — the set of positive real numbers, $\{x \mid x > 0, \ x \in \mathbb{R}\}$

$\mathbb{C}$ — the set of complex numbers, $\{a + bi \mid a, b \in \mathbb{R}\}$

i — $\sqrt{-1}$

z — a complex number

z^* — the complex conjugate of z

$|z|$ — the modulus of z

$\arg z$ — the argument of z

$\mathcal{Re}\, z$ — the real part of z

$\mathcal{Im}\, z$ — the imaginary part of z

$\{x_1, x_2, ...\}$ — the set with elements $x_1, x_2, ...$

$n(A)$ — the number of elements in the finite set A

$\{x \mid ......$ — the set of all x such that

$\in$ — is an element of

$\notin$ — is not an element of

$\varnothing$ — the empty (null) set

U — the universal set

$\cup$ — union

$\cap$ — intersection

$\subseteq$ — is a subset of

A' — the complement of the set A

$a^{\frac{1}{n}}, \sqrt[n]{a}$ — a to the power of $\frac{1}{n}$, nth root of a (if $a \geqslant 0$ then $\sqrt[n]{a} \geqslant 0$)

$a^{\frac{1}{2}}, \sqrt{a}$ — a to the power $\frac{1}{2}$, square root of a (if $a \geqslant 0$ then $\sqrt{a} \geqslant 0$)

$|x|$ — the modulus or absolute value of x, that is $\begin{cases} x \text{ for } x \geqslant 0 & x \in \mathbb{R} \\ -x \text{ for } x < 0 & x \in \mathbb{R} \end{cases}$

$\equiv$ — identity or is equivalent to

$\approx$ — is approximately equal to

$>$ — is greater than

$\geq$ or $\geqslant$ — is greater than or equal to

$<$ — is less than

$\leq$ or $\leqslant$ — is less than or equal to

$\not>$ — is not greater than

$\not<$ — is not less than

$[a, b]$ — the closed interval $a \leqslant x \leqslant b$

$]a, b[$ — the open interval $a < x < b$

u_n — the nth term of a sequence or series

d — the common difference of an arithmetic sequence

r — the common ratio of a geometric sequence

S_n — the sum of the first n terms of a sequence, $u_1 + u_2 + ... + u_n$

S_∞ or S — the sum to infinity of a sequence, $u_1 + u_2 + ...$

$\displaystyle\sum_{i=1}^{n} u_i$ — $u_1 + u_2 + ... + u_n$

$\displaystyle\binom{n}{r}$ — $\dfrac{n!}{r!(n-r)!}$

$f : A \rightarrow B$ — f is a function under which each element of set A has an image in set B

$f : x \mapsto y$ — f is a function under which x is mapped to y

$f(x)$ — the image of x under the function f

f^{-1} — the inverse function of the function f

$f \circ g$ — the composite function of f and g

$\displaystyle\lim_{x \to a} f(x)$ — the limit of $f(x)$ as x tends to a

$\dfrac{dy}{dx}$ — the derivative of y with respect to x

$f'(x)$ — the derivative of $f(x)$ with respect to x

$\dfrac{d^2y}{dx^2}$ — the second derivative of y with respect to x

$f''(x)$ — the second derivative of $f(x)$ with respect to x

$\dfrac{d^n y}{dx^n}$ — the nth derivative of y with respect to x

$f^{(n)}(x)$ — the nth derivative of $f(x)$ with respect to x

$\displaystyle\int y \, dx$ — the indefinite integral of y with respect to x

$\displaystyle\int_a^b y \, dx$ — the definite integral of y with respect to x between the limits $x = a$ and $x = b$

e^x — exponential function of x

$\log_a x$ — logarithm to the base a of x

$\ln x$	the natural logarithm of x, $\log_e x$	$P(A)$	probability of event A
sin, cos, tan	the circular functions	$P'(A)$	probability of the event "not A"
arcsin, arccos, arctan	the inverse circular functions	$P(A \mid B)$	probability of the event A given B
		$x_1, x_2, ...$	observations of a variable
csc, sec, cot	the reciprocal circular functions	$f_1, f_2, ...$	frequencies with which the observations $x_1, x_2, x_3, ...$ occur
$A(x, y)$	the point A in the plane with Cartesian coordinates x and y	p_x	probability distribution function $P(X = x)$ of the discrete random variable X
[AB]	the line segment with end points A and B	$f(x)$	probability density function of the continuous random variable X
AB	the length of [AB]		
(AB)	the line containing points A and B	$E(X)$	the expected value of the random variable X
$\widehat{A}$	the angle at A	$\text{Var}(X)$	the variance of the random variable X
$\widehat{CAB}$ or $C\widehat{A}B$	the angle between [CA] and [AB]	μ	population mean
$\triangle ABC$	the triangle whose vertices are A, B and C	σ	population standard deviation
$\mathbf{v}$	the vector $\mathbf{v}$	σ^2	population variance
$\overrightarrow{AB}$	the vector represented in magnitude and direction by the directed line segment from A to B	$\overline{x}$	sample mean
		s_n^2	sample variance
		s_n	standard deviation of the sample
$\mathbf{a}$	the position vector $\overrightarrow{OA}$	s_{n-1}^2	unbiased estimate of the population variance
$\mathbf{i}, \mathbf{j}, \mathbf{k}$	unit vectors in the directions of the Cartesian coordinate axes	$B(n, p)$	binomial distribution with parameters n and p
$|\mathbf{a}|$	the magnitude of vector $\mathbf{a}$	$Po(m)$	Poisson distribution with mean m
$|\overrightarrow{AB}|$	the magnitude of $\overrightarrow{AB}$	$N(\mu, \sigma^2)$	normal distribution with mean μ and variance σ^2
$\mathbf{v} \bullet \mathbf{w}$	the scalar product of $\mathbf{v}$ and $\mathbf{w}$	$X \sim B(n, p)$	the random variable X has a binomial distribution with parameters n and p
$\mathbf{v} \times \mathbf{w}$	the vector product of $\mathbf{v}$ and $\mathbf{w}$		
$\mathbf{A}^{-1}$	the inverse of the non-singular matrix $\mathbf{A}$	$X \sim Po(m)$	the random variable X has a Poisson distribution with mean m
$\det\mathbf{A}$ or $|\mathbf{A}|$	the determinant of the square matrix $\mathbf{A}$	$X \sim N(\mu, \sigma^2)$	the random variable X has a normal distribution with mean μ and variance σ^2
$\mathbf{I}$	the identity matrix		

BACKGROUND KNOWLEDGE

Before starting this course you can make sure that you have a good understanding of the necessary background knowledge. Click on the icon alongside to obtain a printable set of exercises and answers on this background knowledge.

Click on the icon to access printable facts about number sets

SUMMARY OF CIRCLE PROPERTIES

- A **circle** is a set of points which are equidistant from a fixed point, which is called its **centre**.

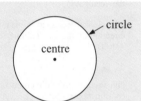

- The **circumference** is the distance around the entire circle boundary.

- An **arc** of a circle is any continuous part of the circle.

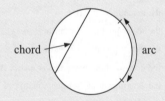

- A **chord** of a circle is a line segment joining any two points of a circle.

- A **semi-circle** is a half of a circle.

- A **diameter** of a circle is any chord passing through its centre.

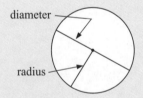

- A **radius** of a circle is any line segment joining its centre to any point on the circle.

- A **tangent** to a circle is any line which touches the circle in exactly one point.

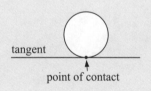

Click on the appropriate icon to revisit these well known theorems.

Name of theorem	Statement	Diagram
Angle in a semi-circle	The angle in a semi-circle is a right angle.	$A\widehat{B}C = 90^o$ GEOMETRY PACKAGE
Chords of a circle	The perpendicular from the centre of a circle to a chord bisects the chord.	$AM = BM$ GEOMETRY PACKAGE
Radius-tangent	The tangent to a circle is perpendicular to the radius at the point of contact.	$O\widehat{A}T = 90^o$ GEOMETRY PACKAGE
Tangents from an external point	Tangents from an external point are equal in length.	$AP = BP$ GEOMETRY PACKAGE
Angle at the centre	The angle at the centre of a circle is twice the angle on the circle subtended by the same arc.	$A\widehat{O}B = 2 \times A\widehat{C}B$ GEOMETRY PACKAGE
Angles subtended by the same arc	Angles subtended by an arc on the circle are equal in size.	$A\widehat{D}B = A\widehat{C}B$ GEOMETRY PACKAGE
Angle between a tangent and a chord	The angle between a tangent and a chord at the point of contact is equal to the angle subtended by the chord in the alternate segment.	$B\widehat{A}S = B\widehat{C}A$ GEOMETRY PACKAGE

SUMMARY OF MEASUREMENT FACTS

PERIMETER FORMULAE

The distance around a closed figure is its **perimeter**.

For some shapes we can derive a formula for perimeter. The formulae for the most common shapes are given below:

> The length of an arc is a fraction of the circumference of a circle.

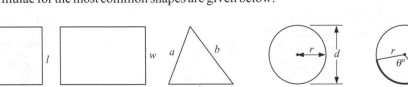

square	rectangle	triangle	circle	arc
$P = 4l$	$P = 2(l + w)$	$P = a + b + c$	$C = 2\pi r$ or $C = \pi d$	$l = \left(\frac{\theta}{360}\right)2\pi r$

AREA FORMULAE

Shape	Figure	Formula
Rectangle	width, length	**Area = length × width**
Triangle	height, base, base	**Area $= \frac{1}{2}$base × height**
Parallelogram	height, base	**Area = base × height**
Trapezium or **Trapezoid**	a, h, b	**Area $= \left(\dfrac{a+b}{2}\right) \times h$**
Circle	r	**Area $= \pi r^2$**
Sector	θ, r	**Area $= \left(\dfrac{\theta}{360}\right) \times \pi r^2$**

SURFACE AREA FORMULAE

RECTANGULAR PRISM

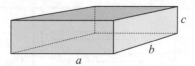

$$A = 2(ab + bc + ac)$$

CYLINDER

Object	Outer surface area
Hollow cylinder hollow h r hollow	$A = 2\pi rh$ (no ends)
Open can hollow h r solid	$A = 2\pi rh + \pi r^2$ (one end)
Solid cylinder solid h r solid	$A = 2\pi rh + 2\pi r^2$ (two ends)

CONE

Object	Outer surface area
Open cone r s	$A = \pi rs$ (no base)
Solid cone r s	$A = \pi rs + \pi r^2$ (solid)

SPHERE

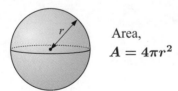

Area,
$$A = 4\pi r^2$$

VOLUME FORMULAE

Object	Figure	Volume
Solids of uniform cross-section	height — end — height — end	**Volume of uniform solid = area of end × length**
Pyramids and cones	height — base — height — h — base	**Volume of a pyramid or cone = $\frac{1}{3}$(area of base × height)**
Spheres	r	**Volume of a sphere = $\frac{4}{3}\pi r^3$**

Chapter 1

Functions

Contents:

RELATIONS AND FUNCTIONS

The charges for parking a car in a short-term car park at an airport are given in the table shown alongside.

There is an obvious relationship between the time spent in the car park and the cost. The cost is *dependent* on the length of time the car is parked.

Looking at this table we might ask: How much would be charged for *exactly* one hour? Would it be $5 or $9?

To make the situation clear, and to avoid confusion, we could adjust the table and draw a graph. We need to indicate that 2-3 hours really means a time over 2 hours up to and including 3 hours, i.e., $2 < t \leqslant 3$.

Car park charges	
Period (h)	*Charge*
0 - 1 hours	$5.00
1 - 2 hours	$9.00
2 - 3 hours	$11.00
3 - 6 hours	$13.00
6 - 9 hours	$18.00
9 - 12 hours	$22.00
12 - 24 hours	$28.00

So, we now have

Car park charges	
Period	*Charge*
$0 < t \leqslant 1$ hours	$5.00
$1 < t \leqslant 2$ hours	$9.00
$2 < t \leqslant 3$ hours	$11.00
$3 < t \leqslant 6$ hours	$13.00
$6 < t \leqslant 9$ hours	$18.00
$9 < t \leqslant 12$ hours	$22.00
$12 < t \leqslant 24$ hours	$28.00

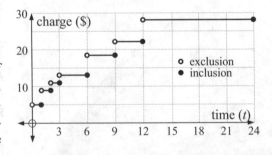

In mathematical terms, because we have a relationship between two variables, time and cost, the schedule of charges is an example of a **relation**.

A relation may consist of a finite number of ordered pairs, such as $\{(1, 5), (-2, 3), (4, 3), (1, 6)\}$ or an infinite number of ordered pairs.

The parking charges example is clearly the latter as any real value of time (t hours) in the interval $0 < t \leqslant 24$ is represented.

The set of possible values of the variable on the horizontal axis is called the **domain** of the relation.

For example: • $\{t: \ 0 < t \leqslant 24\}$ is the domain for the car park relation
            • $\{-2, 1, 4\}$ is the domain of $\{(1, 5), (-2, 3), (4, 3), (1, 6)\}$.

The set which describes the possible y-values is called the **range** of the relation.

For example: • the range of the car park relation is $\{5, 9, 11, 13, 18, 22, 28\}$
            • the range of $\{(1, 5), (-2, 3), (4, 3), (1, 6)\}$ is $\{3, 5, 6\}$.

We will now look at relations and functions more formally.

RELATIONS

> A **relation** is any set of points on the Cartesian plane.

A relation is often expressed in the form of an **equation** connecting the **variables** x and y.
For example $y = x + 3$ and $x = y^2$ are the equations of two relations.
These equations generate sets of ordered pairs.

Their graphs are:

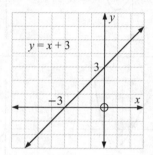
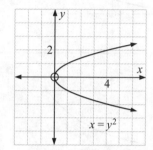

However, a relation may not be able to be defined by an equation. Below are two examples which show this:

(1)
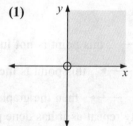
All points in the first quadrant are a relation.
$x > 0, y > 0$

(2)
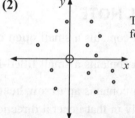
These 13 points form a relation.

FUNCTIONS

> A **function**, sometimes called a **mapping**, is a relation in which no two different ordered pairs have the same x-coordinate (first member).

We can see from the above definition that a function is a special type of relation.

TESTING FOR FUNCTIONS

Algebraic Test:

> If a relation is given as an equation, and the substitution of any value for x results in one and only one value of y, we have a function.

For example:
- $y = 3x - 1$ is a function, as for any value of x there is only one value of y
- $x = y^2$ is not a function since if $x = 4$, say, then $y = \pm 2$.

Geometric Test or "Vertical Line Test":

> If we draw all possible vertical lines on the graph of a relation, the relation:
> - is a function if each line cuts the graph no more than once
> - is not a function if at least one line cuts the graph more than once.

Example 1

Which of the following relations are functions?

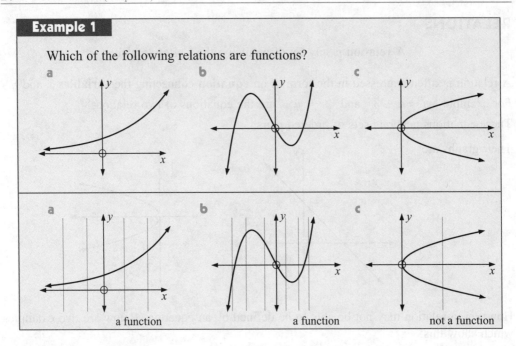

GRAPHICAL NOTE

- If a graph contains a small **open circle** such as ─○─ , this point is **not included**.

- If a graph contains a small **filled-in circle** such as ──● , this point **is included**.

- If a graph contains an **arrow head** at an end such as ──→ then the graph continues indefinitely in that general direction, or the shape may repeat as it has done previously.

EXERCISE 1A

1 Which of the following sets of ordered pairs are functions? Give reasons.

a   {(1, 3), (2, 4), (3, 5), (4, 6)}   b   {(1, 3), (3, 2), (1, 7), (−1, 4)}
c   {(2, −1), (2, 0), (2, 3), (2, 11)}   d   {(7, 6), (5, 6), (3, 6), (−4, 6)}
e   {(0, 0), (1, 0), (3, 0), (5, 0)}   f   {(0, 0), (0, −2), (0, 2), (0, 4)}

2 Use the vertical line test to determine which of the following relations are functions:

a   b   c   d

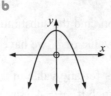

e   f   g   h

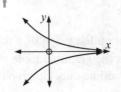

3 Will the graph of a straight line always be a function? Give evidence.

4 Give algebraic evidence to show that the relation $x^2 + y^2 = 9$ is not a function.

B   FUNCTION NOTATION, DOMAIN AND RANGE

Function machines are sometimes used to illustrate how functions behave.

For example:

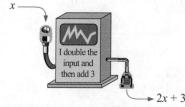

So, if 4 is fed into the machine,
$2(4) + 3 = 11$ comes out.

The above 'machine' has been programmed to perform a particular function.
If f is used to represent that particular function we can write:

   f is the function that will convert x into $2x + 3$.

So, f would convert 2 into $2(2) + 3 = 7$ and
$\qquad\qquad\qquad -4$ into $2(-4) + 3 = -5$.

This function can be written as:

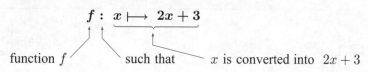

Two other equivalent forms we use are: $f(x) = 2x + 3$ or $y = 2x + 3$

So, $f(x)$ is the value of y for a given value of x,   i.e., $y = f(x)$.

Notice that for $f(x) = 2x + 3$, $f(2) = 2(2) + 3 = 7$ and $f(-4) = 2(-4) + 3 = -5$.

Consequently, $f(2) = 7$ indicates that the point $(2, 7)$
lies on the graph of the function.

Likewise $f(-4) = -5$ indicates that the point
$(-4, -5)$ also lies on the graph.

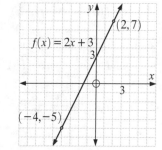

Note:

- $f(x)$ is read as "f of x".

- f is the function which converts x into $f(x)$,
  i.e., $f : x \mapsto f(x)$.

- $y = f(x)$ is sometimes called the **image** of x.

Example 2

If $f : x \mapsto 2x^2 - 3x$, find the value of: **a** $f(5)$ **b** $f(-4)$

$f(x) = 2x^2 - 3x$

a $f(5) = 2(5)^2 - 3(5)$ {replacing x by (5)}

$= 2 \times 25 - 15$

$= 35$

b $f(-4) = 2(-4)^2 - 3(-4)$ {replacing x by (-4)}

$= 2(16) + 12$

$= 44$

Example 3

If $f(x) = 5 - x - x^2$, find in simplest form: **a** $f(-x)$ **b** $f(x+2)$

a $f(-x) = 5 - (-x) - (-x)^2$ {replacing x by $(-x)$}

$= 5 + x - x^2$

b $f(x+2) = 5 - (x+2) - (x+2)^2$ {replacing x by $(x+2)$}

$= 5 - x - 2 - [x^2 + 4x + 4]$

$= 3 - x - x^2 - 4x - 4$

$= -x^2 - 5x - 1$

EXERCISE 1B.1

1 If $f : x \mapsto 3x + 2$, find the value of:

    a $f(0)$ **b** $f(2)$ **c** $f(-1)$ **d** $f(-5)$ **e** $f(-\frac{1}{3})$

2 If $f : x \mapsto 3x - x^2 + 2$, find the value of:

    a $f(0)$ **b** $f(3)$ **c** $f(-3)$ **d** $f(-7)$ **e** $f(\frac{3}{2})$

3 If $f(x) = 7 - 3x$, find in simplest form:

    a $f(a)$ **b** $f(-a)$ **c** $f(a+3)$ **d** $f(b-1)$ **e** $f(x+2)$ **f** $f(x+h)$

4 If $F(x) = 2x^2 + 3x - 1$, find in simplest form:

    a $F(x+4)$ **b** $F(2-x)$ **c** $F(-x)$ **d** $F(x^2)$ **e** $F(x^2-1)$ **f** $F(x+h)$

5 If $G(x) = \dfrac{2x+3}{x-4}$:   **a** evaluate   **i** $G(2)$ **ii** $G(0)$ **iii** $G(-\frac{1}{2})$

                      b find a value of x where $G(x)$ does not exist

                      c find $G(x+2)$ in simplest form

                      d find x if $G(x) = -3$.

6 f represents a function. What is the difference in meaning between f and $f(x)$?

7 If the value of a photocopier t years after purchase is given by $V(t) = 9650 - 860t$ euros:

   a find $V(4)$ and state what $V(4)$ means

   b find t when $V(t) = 5780$ and explain what this represents

   c find the original purchase price of the photocopier.

8 On the same set of axes draw the graphs of three different functions $f(x)$ such that $f(2) = 1$ and $f(5) = 3$.

9 Find a linear function $f(x) = ax + b$ for which $f(2) = 1$ and $f(-3) = 11$.

10 Given $T(x) = ax^2 + bx + c$, find a, b and c if $T(0) = -4$, $T(1) = -2$ and $T(2) = 6$.

DOMAIN AND RANGE

The **domain** of a relation is the set of permissible values that x may have.

The **range** of a relation is the set of permissible values that y may have.

For example:

(1)

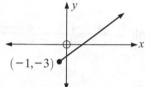

All values of $x \geqslant -1$ are permissible.

So, the domain is $\{x \mid x \geqslant -1\}$ or $x \in [-1, \infty[$.

All values of $y \geqslant -3$ are permissible.

So, the range is $\{y \mid y \geqslant -3\}$ or $y \in [-3, \infty[$.

(2)

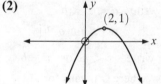

x can take any value.

So, the domain is $\{x \mid x \text{ is in } \mathbb{R}\}$ or $x \in \mathbb{R}$.

y cannot be > 1.

So, the range is $\{y \mid y \leqslant 1\}$ or $y \in]-\infty, 1]$.

(3)

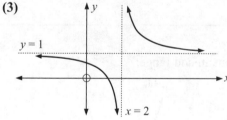

x can take all values except $x = 2$.

So, the domain is $\{x \mid x \neq 2\}$.

Likewise, the range is $\{y \mid y \neq 1\}$.

The domain and range of a relation are often described using **interval notation**.

For example:

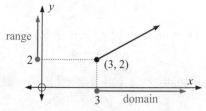

The domain consists of all real x such that $x \geqslant 3$ and we write this as

$$\{x \mid x \geqslant 3\} \quad \text{or} \quad x \in [3, \infty[.$$

the set of all x such that $x \geqslant 3$

Likewise the range would be

$\{y \mid y \geqslant 2\}$ or $y \in [2, \infty[$.

For the profit function alongside:

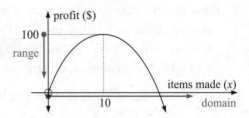

- the domain is $\{x \mid x \geqslant 0\}$

  or $x \in [0, \infty[$

- the range is $\{y \mid y \leqslant 100\}$

  or $y \in]-\infty, 100]$.

Intervals have corresponding graphs.   For example:

$\{x \mid x \geqslant 3\}$ or $x \in [3, \infty[$ | is read "the set of all x such that x is greater than or equal to 3" and has number line graph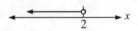

$\{x \mid x < 2\}$ or $x \in]-\infty, 2[$ | has number line graph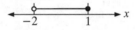

$\{x \mid -2 < x \leqslant 1\}$ or $x \in]-2, 1]$ | has number line graph

$\{x \mid x \leqslant 0 \text{ or } x > 4\}$

i.e., $x \in]-\infty, 0]$ or $]4, \infty[$ | has number line graph

Note: for numbers *between* a and b we write $a < x < b$

or $x \in]a, b[$.

for numbers '*outside*' a and b we write $x < a$ or $x > b$

i.e., $x \in]-\infty, a[\cup]b, \infty[$ where $\cup$ means 'or'.

Example 4

For each of the following graphs state the domain and range:

a

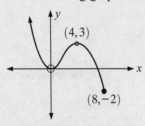

b

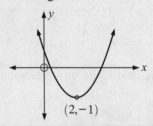

a   Domain is $\{x \mid x \leqslant 8\}$

or $x \in]-\infty, 8]$

Range is $\{y \mid y \geqslant -2\}$

or $y \in [-2, \infty[$

b   Domain is $\{x \mid x \text{ is in } \mathbb{R}\}$

or $x \in \mathbb{R}$

Range is $\{y \mid y \geqslant -1\}$

or $y \in [-1, \infty[$

EXERCISE 1B.2

1 Write down the domain and range for each of the following functions:

   a $\{(1, 3), (2, 5), (3, 7)\}$
      b $\{(-1, 3), (0, 3), (2, 5)\}$

   c $\{(-3, 1), (-2, 1), (-1, 1), (3, 1)\}$
   d $\{(x, y) \mid x^2 + y^2 = 4, \ x \in \mathbb{Z}, \ y \geqslant 0\}$

2 For each of the following graphs find the domain and range:

a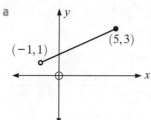
b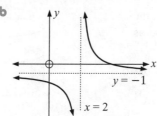
c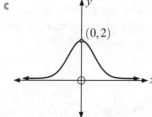

d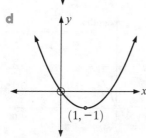
e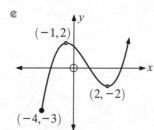
f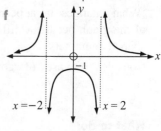

3 Find the domain and range of each of the following functions:

   a $f : x \mapsto 2x - 1$
   b $f : x \mapsto 3$
   c $f(x) = |3x - 1| + 2$

   d $f : x \mapsto \sqrt{x^2 + 4}$
   e $y = \sqrt{x^2 - 4}$
   f $y = \dfrac{5}{x - 2}$

   g $f(x) = \sqrt{2 - x}$
   h $f(x) = \dfrac{3}{\sqrt{2x - 5}}$
   i $f : x \mapsto 2 + \dfrac{3}{5 - x}$

4 Use a graphics calculator to help sketch graphs of the following functions. Find the domain and range of each.

   a $f(x) = \sqrt{x}$
      b $f : x \mapsto \dfrac{1}{x^2}$

   c $f : x \mapsto \sqrt{4 - x}$
      d $y = x^2 - 7x + 10$

   e $f : x \mapsto 5x - 3x^2$
      f $f : x \mapsto x + \dfrac{1}{x}$

   g $y = \dfrac{x + 4}{x - 2}$
      h $y = x^3 - 3x^2 - 9x + 10$

   i $f : x \mapsto \dfrac{3x - 9}{x^2 - x - 2}$
      j $y = x^2 + x^{-2}$

   k $y = x^3 + \dfrac{1}{x^3}$
      l $f : x \mapsto x^4 + 4x^3 - 16x + 3$

INVESTIGATION 1   FLUID FILLING FUNCTIONS

 When water is added at a **constant rate** to a cylindrical container, the depth of water in the container is a linear function of time. This is because the volume of water added is directly proportional to the time taken to add it. If water was not added at a constant rate the direct proportionality would not exist.

The depth-time graph for the case of a cylinder would be as shown alongside:

DEMO

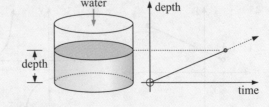

The question arises:
'What changes in appearance of the graph occur for different shaped containers?'

Consider a vase of conical shape.

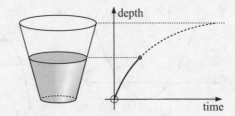

What to do:

1   For each of the following containers, draw a 'depth v time' graph as water is added:

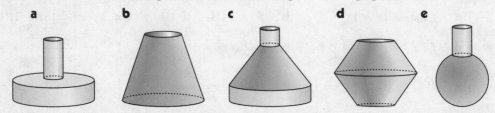

2   Use the water filling demonstration to check your answers to question **1**.

3   Write a brief report on the connection between the shape of a vessel and the corresponding shape of its depth-time graph. You may wish to discuss this in parts. For example, first examine cylindrical containers, then conical, then other shapes. Gradients of curves must be included in your report.

4   Draw possible containers as in question **1** which have the following 'depth v time' graphs:

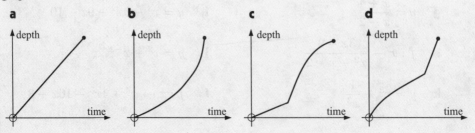

C COMPOSITE FUNCTIONS, $f \circ g$

Given $f : x \mapsto f(x)$ and $g : x \mapsto g(x)$, then the **composite function** of f and g will convert x into $f(g(x))$.

$f \circ g$ is used to represent the composite function of f and g.

$f \circ g$ means "f following g" and $(f \circ g)(x) = f(g(x))$ i.e., $f \circ g : x \mapsto f(g(x))$.

Consider $f : x \mapsto x^4$ and $g : x \mapsto 2x + 3$.

$f \circ g$ means that g converts x to $2x + 3$ and then f converts $(2x + 3)$ to $(2x + 3)^4$.

This is illustrated by the two function machines below.

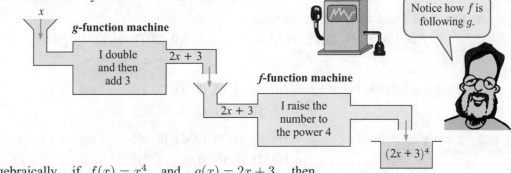

Algebraically, if $f(x) = x^4$ and $g(x) = 2x + 3$, then

$$(f \circ g)(x) = f(g(x))$$
$$= f(2x + 3) \quad \{g \text{ operates on } x \text{ first}\}$$
$$= (2x + 3)^4 \quad \{f \text{ operates on } g(x) \text{ next}\}$$

and $(g \circ f)(x) = g(f(x))$
$$= g(x^4)$$
$$= 2(x^4) + 3$$
$$= 2x^4 + 3$$

So, in general, $f(g(x)) \neq g(f(x))$.

The ability to break down functions into composite functions is useful in **differential calculus**.

Example 5

Given $f : x \mapsto 2x + 1$ and $g : x \mapsto 3 - 4x$ find in simplest form:

a $(f \circ g)(x)$

b $(g \circ f)(x)$

$f(x) = 2x + 1$ and $g(x) = 3 - 4x$

a $\therefore (f \circ g)(x) = f(g(x))$
$$= f(3 - 4x)$$
$$= 2(3 - 4x) + 1$$
$$= 6 - 8x + 1$$
$$= 7 - 8x$$

b $(g \circ f)(x) = g(f(x))$
$$= g(2x + 1)$$
$$= 3 - 4(2x + 1)$$
$$= 3 - 8x - 4$$
$$= -8x - 1$$

Note: If $f(x) = 2x + 1$ then
$$f(\Delta) = 2(\Delta) + 1,$$
$$f(*) = 2(*) + 1,$$
$$f(3x - 4) = 2(3x - 4) + 1.$$

Note: If $F(x) = (f \circ g)(x)$, the domain of F is the domain of g excluding any values
of x such that $g(x) = u$ where $f(u)$ is undefined.

EXERCISE 1C

1 Given $f : x \mapsto 2x + 3$ and $g : x \mapsto 1 - x$, find in simplest form:

   a $(f \circ g)(x)$ **b** $(g \circ f)(x)$ **c** $(f \circ g)(-3)$

2 Given $f : x \mapsto x^2$ and $g : x \mapsto 2 - x$ find $(f \circ g)(x)$ and $(g \circ f)(x)$.
Find also the domain and range of $f \circ g$ and $g \circ f$.

3 Given $f : x \mapsto x^2 + 1$ and $g : x \mapsto 3 - x$, find in simplest form:

   a $(f \circ g)(x)$ **b** $(g \circ f)(x)$ **c** x if $(g \circ f)(x) = f(x)$

4 Functions f and g are defined as follows:

$$f = \{(0, 2), (1, 3), (2, 0), (3, 1)\} \qquad g = \{(0, 3), (1, 2), (2, 1), (3, 0)\}$$

   Find **a** $f \circ g$ **b** $g \circ f$ **c** $f \circ f$

5 f and g are defined as: $f = \{(0, 3), (1, 0), (2, 1), (3, 2)\}$ Find $f \circ g$

                                    $g = \{(0, 1), (1, 2), (2, 3), (3, 0)\}$

6 f and g are defined as: $f = \{(0, 2), (1, 5), (2, 7), (3, 9)\}$ Find **a** $f \circ g$

                                    $g = \{(2, 2), (5, 0), (7, 1), (9, 3)\}$ **b** $g \circ f$

7 Given $f(x) = \dfrac{x + 3}{x + 2}$ and $g(x) = \dfrac{x + 1}{x - 1}$, find in simplest form:

   a $(f \circ g)(x)$ **b** $(g \circ f)(x)$ **c** $(g \circ g)(x)$

   In each case, find the domain of the composite function.

8 **a** If $ax + b = cx + d$ for all values of x, show that $a = c$ and $b = d$.

      Hint: If it is true for all x, it is true for $x = 0$ and $x = 1$.

   b Given $f(x) = 2x + 3$ and $g(x) = ax + b$ and that $(f \circ g)(x) = x$ for all
      values of x, deduce that $a = \frac{1}{2}$ and $b = -\frac{3}{2}$.

   c Is the result in **b** true if $(g \circ f)(x) = x$ for all x?

D   SIGN DIAGRAMS

Sometimes we do not wish to draw a time-consuming graph of a function but wish to know
when the function is positive, negative, zero or undefined. A *sign diagram* enables us to do
this and is relatively easy to construct.

A **sign diagram** consists of:

- a **horizontal line** which is really the x-axis
- **positive** (+) and **negative** (−) signs indicating that the graph is **above** and **below** the
  x-axis respectively
- **critical values**, the numbers written below the line, which are the graph's x-intercepts
  or where it is undefined.

Consider the three functions given below.

Function	$y = (x+2)(x-1)$	$y = -2(x-1)^2$	$y = \dfrac{4}{x}$
Graph	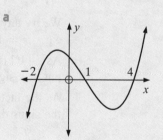		
Sign diagram			

(Graphs and sign diagrams shown in table.)

Notice that:
- A sign change occurs about a critical value for single factors such as $(x+2)$ and $(x-1)$, indicating **cutting** of the x-axis.
- No sign change occurs about the critical value for squared factors such as $(x-1)^2$, indicating **touching** of the x-axis.
- ⋮ shows a function is **undefined** at $x = 0$.
  0

In general:
- when a factor has an **odd power** there is a change of sign about that critical value
- when a factor has an **even power** there is no sign change about that critical value.

Example 6

Draw sign diagrams for:

a

b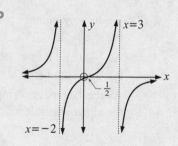

a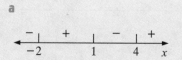

b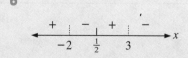

Example 7

Draw a sign diagram of: **a** $(x+3)(x-1)$ **b** $2(2x+5)(3-x)$

a $(x+3)(x-1)$ has critical values of -3 and 1.

We try any number > 1, e.g., $x = 2$

As $(5)(1) > 0$
we put a $+$ sign here.

As the factors are 'single' the signs alternate giving:

b $2(2x+5)(3-x)$ has critical values of $-\frac{5}{2}$ and 3.

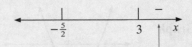

We try any number > 3, e.g., $x = 5$

As $2(15)(-2) < 0$
we put a $-$ sign here.

As the factors are 'single' the signs alternate giving:

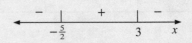

Example 8

Draw a sign diagram of: **a** $12 - 3x^2$ **b** $-4(x-3)^2$

a $12 - 3x^2 = -3(x^2 - 4)$
$\qquad\qquad = -3(x+2)(x-2)$
which has critical values of -2 and 2

We try any number > 2
e.g., $x = 3$.
As $-3(5)(1)$ is < 0 we put a $-$ sign here.
As the factors are 'single' the signs alternate.

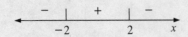

b $-4(x-3)^2$
has a critical value of 3.

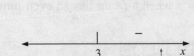

We try any number > 3
e.g., $x = 4$.
As $-4(1)^2$ is < 0 we put a $-$ sign here.
As the factor is 'squared' the signs do not change.

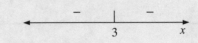

Example 9

Draw a sign diagram for $\dfrac{x-1}{2x+1}$.

$\dfrac{x-1}{2x+1}$ is zero when $x=1$ and undefined when $x=-\frac{1}{2}$.

So,

For $x=10$, $\dfrac{x-1}{2x+1}=\dfrac{9}{21}>0$

Since $(x-1)$ and $(2x+1)$ are single factors the signs alternate.

$\therefore$ sign diagram is

EXERCISE 1D

1 From the graphs below, draw corresponding sign diagrams:

a
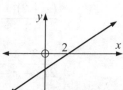

b
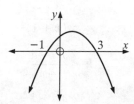

c
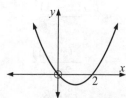

d
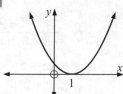

e
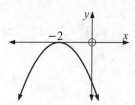

f
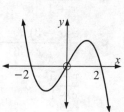

g
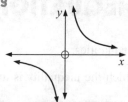

h
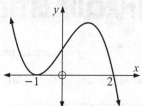

i
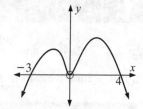

j
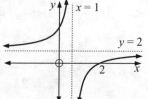

k
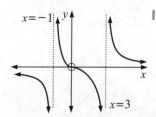

l
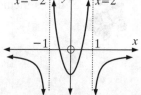

2 Draw sign diagrams for:

   a $(x+4)(x-2)$ **b** $x(x-3)$ **c** $x(x+2)$

   d $-(x+1)(x-3)$ **e** $(2x-1)(3-x)$ **f** $(5-x)(1-2x)$

   g x^2-9 **h** $4-x^2$ **i** $5x-x^2$

   j x^2-3x+2 **k** $2-8x^2$ **l** $6x^2+x-2$

   m $6-16x-6x^2$ **n** $-2x^2+9x+5$ **o** $-15x^2-x+2$

3 Draw sign diagrams for:

   a $(x+2)^2$ **b** $(x-3)^2$ **c** $-(x+2)^2$

   d $-(x-4)^2$ **e** x^2-2x+1 **f** $-x^2+4x-4$

   g $4x^2-4x+1$ **h** $-x^2-6x-9$ **i** $-4x^2+12x-9$

4 Draw sign diagrams for:

   a $\dfrac{x+2}{x-1}$ **b** $\dfrac{x}{x+3}$ **c** $\dfrac{2x+3}{4-x}$

   d $\dfrac{4x-1}{2-x}$ **e** $\dfrac{3x}{x-2}$ **f** $\dfrac{-8x}{3-x}$

   g $\dfrac{(x-1)^2}{x}$ **h** $\dfrac{4x}{(x+1)^2}$ **i** $\dfrac{(x+2)(x-1)}{3-x}$

   j $\dfrac{x(x-1)}{2-x}$ **k** $\dfrac{x^2-4}{-x}$ **l** $\dfrac{3-x}{2x^2-x-6}$

   m $\dfrac{x^2-3}{x+1}$ **n** $\dfrac{x^2+1}{x}$ **o** $\dfrac{x^2+2x+4}{x+1}$

   p $\dfrac{-(x-3)^2(x^2+2)}{x+3}$ **q** $\dfrac{-x^2(x+2)}{5-x}$ **r** $\dfrac{x^2+4}{(x-3)^2(x-1)}$

   s $\dfrac{x-5}{x+1}+3$ **t** $\dfrac{x-2}{x+3}-4$ **u** $\dfrac{3x+2}{x-2}-\dfrac{x-3}{x+3}$

E   INEQUALITIES (INEQUATIONS)

$2x+3>11-x$ and $\dfrac{2x-1}{x} \leqslant \dfrac{x+3}{5}$ are examples of inequalities.

In this section we aim to find all values of the unknown for which the inequality is true.

GROUP INVESTIGATION   SOLVING INEQUALITIES

Jon's method of solving $\dfrac{3x+2}{1-x}>4$ was:

If $\dfrac{3x+2}{1-x}>4$,   then

$$3x+2>4(1-x)$$
$$\therefore \quad 3x+2>4-4x$$
$$\therefore \quad 7x>2$$
$$\therefore \quad x>\tfrac{2}{7}$$

However, Sarah pointed out that if $x = 5$, $\dfrac{3x+2}{1-x} = \dfrac{17}{-4} = -4\frac{1}{4}$ and $-4\frac{1}{4}$ is **not** greater than 4.

They concluded that there was something wrong with the method of solution.

A graph also highlighted an error.

It seems that the correct answer is $\frac{2}{7} < x < 1$.

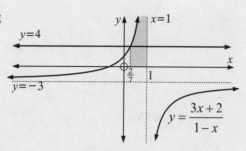

Questions:

1 At what step was Jon's method wrong?

2 Suggest an algebraic method which does give the correct answer.

From the **Investigation** above you should have concluded that multiplying both sides of an inequality by an unknown can lead to incorrect results. We therefore need an alternative method.

To solve inequalities we use these steps:

- Make the RHS zero by shifting all terms to the LHS.
- Fully factorise the LHS.
- Draw a sign diagram for the LHS.
- Determine the values required from the sign diagram.

Note:

- if $a > b$ and $c \in \mathbb{R}$, then $a + c > b + c$
- if $a > b$ and $c > 0$, then $ac > bc$
- if $a > b$ and $c < 0$, then $ac < bc$
- if $a > b > 0$, then $a^2 > b^2$

Example 10

Solve for x: **a** $3x^2 + 5x \geqslant 2$ **b** $x^2 + 9 < 6x$

a
$$3x^2 + 5x \geqslant 2$$
$$\therefore \quad 3x^2 + 5x - 2 \geqslant 0 \qquad \text{\{making RHS zero\}}$$
$$\therefore \quad (3x - 1)(x + 2) \geqslant 0 \qquad \text{\{fully factorising LHS\}}$$

Sign diagram of LHS is

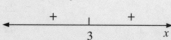

So,   for LHS $\geqslant 0$, $x \in\ ]-\infty, -2]$ or $x \in [\frac{1}{3}, \infty[$.

b
$$x^2 + 9 < 6x$$
$$\therefore \quad x^2 - 6x + 9 < 0 \qquad \text{\{make RHS zero\}}$$
$$\therefore \quad (x - 3)^2 < 0 \qquad \text{\{fully factorising LHS\}}$$

Sign diagram of LHS is

So, the inequality is *never true*.

Example 11

Solve for x: **a** $\dfrac{3x+2}{x-4} \leqslant 1$ **b** $\dfrac{1}{x} \leqslant 10$

a
$$\frac{3x+2}{x-4} \leqslant 1$$

$$\therefore \quad \frac{3x+2}{x-4} - 1 \leqslant 0$$

$$\therefore \quad \left(\frac{3x+2}{x-4}\right) - 1\left(\frac{x-4}{x-4}\right) \leqslant 0$$

$$\therefore \quad \frac{3x+2-(x-4)}{x-4} \leqslant 0$$

$$\therefore \quad \frac{2x+6}{x-4} \leqslant 0$$

$$\therefore \quad x \in [-3, 4[$$

b
$$\frac{1}{x} \leqslant 10$$

$$\therefore \quad \frac{1}{x} - 10 \leqslant 0$$

$$\therefore \quad \frac{1}{x} - 10\left(\frac{x}{x}\right) \leqslant 0$$

$$\therefore \quad \frac{1-10x}{x} \leqslant 0$$

Thus, $x \in]-\infty, 0[$ or $[\frac{1}{10}, \infty[$.

Example 12

Solve for x:

$$\frac{3x+1}{x-1} > \frac{3x}{x+1}$$

$$\frac{3x+1}{x-1} > \frac{3x}{x+1}$$

$$\therefore \quad \frac{3x+1}{x-1} - \frac{3x}{x+1} > 0$$

$$\therefore \quad \frac{(3x+1)(x+1) - 3x(x-1)}{(x-1)(x+1)} > 0$$

$$\therefore \quad \frac{7x+1}{(x-1)(x+1)} > 0$$

Sign diagram
of LHS is:

Thus, $x \in]-1, -\frac{1}{7}[$ or $]1, \infty[$.

EXERCISE 1E

1 Solve for x:

    a $(2-x)(x+3) \geqslant 0$ **b** $(x-1)^2 < 0$ **c** $(2x+1)(3-x) > 0$

    d $x^2 \geqslant x$ **e** $x^2 \geqslant 3x$ **f** $3x^2 + 2x < 0$

    g $x^2 < 4$ **h** $2x^2 \geqslant 4$ **i** $x^2 + 4x + 4 > 0$

    j $2x^2 \geqslant x + 3$ **k** $4x^2 - 4x + 1 < 0$ **l** $6x^2 + 7x < 3$

    m $3x^2 > 8(x+2)$ **n** $2x^2 - 4x + 2 > 0$ **o** $6x^2 + 1 \leqslant 5x$

    p $1 + 5x < 6x^2$ **q** $12x^2 \geqslant 5x + 2$ **r** $2x^2 + 9 > 9x$

2 Solve for x:

a $\dfrac{x+4}{2x-1} > 0$

b $\dfrac{x+1}{4-x} < 0$

c $\dfrac{x+3}{2x+3} \geqslant 0$

d $\dfrac{2x}{x-3} \geqslant 1$

e $\dfrac{x+2}{x-1} \geqslant -3$

f $\dfrac{x+2}{2x-1} < \dfrac{1}{2}$

g $\dfrac{1}{x} > 100$

h $\dfrac{x}{2x-1} \geqslant 5$

i $\dfrac{1-x}{1+x} < 4$

j $\dfrac{2}{2x-5} < \dfrac{1}{x+7}$

k $\dfrac{x^2-2x}{x+3} > 0$

l $\dfrac{x^2+5x}{x^2-4} \leqslant 0$

m $\dfrac{x}{x+2} > \dfrac{1}{x}$

n $x > \dfrac{4}{x}$

o $\dfrac{1}{x} \leqslant x$

p $x^3 \geqslant x$

q $\dfrac{2x-3}{x+2} < \dfrac{2x}{x-2}$

r $\dfrac{x^2}{3x-2} \leqslant 1$

F   THE MODULUS FUNCTION

The **modulus** of a real number x is its distance from 0 on the number line.

Because the modulus is a distance, it cannot be negative.

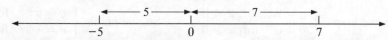

So, the modulus of 7 is 7,   which is written as $|7| = 7$
and the modulus of -5 is 5,   which is written as $|-5| = 5$.

Thus, $|x|$ is the distance of x from 0 on the number line.

If $x > 0$ If $x < 0$

ALGEBRAIC DEFINITION

The modulus of x, $|x| = \begin{cases} x & \text{if } x \geqslant 0 \\ -x & \text{if } x < 0 \end{cases}$

$y = |x|$ has graph

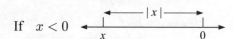

This branch
is $y = -x$, $x < 0$.

This branch
is $y = x$, $x \geqslant 0$.

Notice that $\sqrt{7^2} = \sqrt{49} = 7$ and $\sqrt{(-5)^2} = \sqrt{25} = 5$

Thus $|x| = \sqrt{x^2}$ is an equivalent definition of $|x|$.

Example 13

If $a = -3$ and $b = 4$ find:

a $|7 + a|$ b $|ab|$ c $|a^2 + 2b|$

a $|7 + a|$
$= |7 + (-3)|$
$= |4|$
$= 4$

b $|ab|$
$= |(-3)(4)|$
$= |-12|$
$= 12$

c $|a^2 + 2b|$
$= |(-3)^2 + 2(4)|$
$= |9 + 8|$
$= |17|$
$= 17$

Example 14

By replacing $|x|$ with x for $x \geqslant 0$ and $-x$ for $x < 0$, write the following functions without the modulus sign and hence graph each function:

a $f(x) = x - |x|$ b $f(x) = x|x|$

a If $x < 0$, $f(x) = x - (-x) = 2x$.
If $x \geqslant 0$, $f(x) = x - x = 0$.

So, we graph $\begin{cases} y = 2x & \text{for } x < 0 \\ y = 0 & \text{for } x \geqslant 0. \end{cases}$

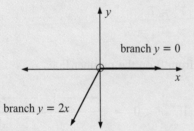

b If $x \geqslant 0$, $f(x) = x(x) = x^2$.
If $x < 0$, $f(x) = x(-x) = -x^2$.

So, we graph $\begin{cases} y = x^2 & \text{for } x \geqslant 0 \\ y = -x^2 & \text{for } x < 0. \end{cases}$

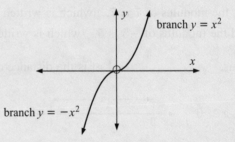

EXERCISE 1F.1

1 If $a = -2$, $b = 3$, $c = -4$ find the value of:

a $|a|$ b $|b|$ c $|a||b|$ d $|ab|$

e $|a - b|$ f $|a| - |b|$ g $|a + b|$ h $|a| + |b|$

i $|a|^2$ j a^2 k $\left|\dfrac{c}{a}\right|$ l $\dfrac{|c|}{|a|}$

2 If $x = -3$, find the value of:

a $|5 - x|$ b $|5| - |x|$ c $\left|\dfrac{2x + 1}{1 - x}\right|$ d $|3 - 2x - x^2|$

3 a Is $|a + b| = |a| + |b|$?   b Is $|a - b| = |a| - |b|$?

4 Copy and complete:

a	b	$\lvert ab \rvert$	$\lvert a \rvert \lvert b \rvert$	$\left\lvert \dfrac{a}{b} \right\rvert$	$\dfrac{\lvert a \rvert}{\lvert b \rvert}$
6	2				
6	−2				
−6	2				
−6	−2				

What do you suspect?

5 Use the fact that $\lvert x \rvert = \sqrt{x^2}$ to prove that:

a $\lvert ab \rvert = \lvert a \rvert \lvert b \rvert$ **b** $\left\lvert \dfrac{a}{b} \right\rvert = \dfrac{\lvert a \rvert}{\lvert b \rvert}, \quad b \neq 0$ **c** $\lvert a - b \rvert = \lvert b - a \rvert$

6 Using $\lvert a \rvert = a$ if $a \geqslant 0$ and $-a$ if $a < 0$, write the following functions without modulus signs and hence graph each function:

a $y = \lvert x - 2 \rvert$ **b** $y = \lvert x + 1 \rvert$ **c** $y = -\lvert x \rvert$

d $y = \lvert x \rvert + x$ **e** $y = \dfrac{\lvert x \rvert}{x}$ **f** $y = x - 2\lvert x \rvert$

g $y = \lvert x \rvert + \lvert x - 2 \rvert$ **h** $y = \lvert x \rvert - \lvert x - 1 \rvert$ **i** $y = \lvert x^2 + 1 \rvert$

j $y = \lvert x^2 - 1 \rvert$ **k** $y = \lvert x^2 - 2x \rvert$ **l** $y = \lvert x^2 + 3x + 2 \rvert$

MODULUS EQUATIONS

From the previous exercise you should have discovered these **properties of modulus**:

- $\lvert x \rvert \geqslant 0$ for all x
- $\lvert x \rvert^2 = x^2$ for all x
- $\left\lvert \dfrac{x}{y} \right\rvert = \dfrac{\lvert x \rvert}{\lvert y \rvert}$ for all x and y, $y \neq 0$
- $\lvert -x \rvert = \lvert x \rvert$ for all x
- $\lvert xy \rvert = \lvert x \rvert \lvert y \rvert$ for all x and y
- $\lvert a - b \rvert = \lvert b - a \rvert$ for all a and b.

It is clear that $\lvert x \rvert = 2$ has two solutions, $x = 2$ and $x = -2$.

In general, if $\lvert x \rvert = a$ where $a > 0$, then $x = \pm a$.

We use this rule to solve modulus equations.

Example 15

Solve for x: **a** $\lvert 2x + 3 \rvert = 7$ **b** $\lvert 3 - 2x \rvert = -1$

a $\lvert 2x + 3 \rvert = 7$
$\therefore \quad 2x + 3 = \pm 7$
$\therefore \quad 2x = 7 - 3$ or $-7 - 3$
$\therefore \quad 2x = 4$ or -10
$\therefore \quad x = 2$ or -5

b $\lvert 3 - 2x \rvert = -1$
has no solution as LHS is never negative.

Example 16

Solve for x: $\left| \dfrac{3x+2}{1-x} \right| = 4$

$\left| \dfrac{3x+2}{1-x} \right| = 4$ $\therefore$ $\dfrac{3x+2}{1-x} = \pm 4$

If $\dfrac{3x+2}{1-x} = 4$ If $\dfrac{3x+2}{1-x} = -4$

then $3x + 2 = 4(1-x)$ then $3x + 2 = -4(1-x)$

$\therefore$ $3x + 2 = 4 - 4x$ $\therefore$ $3x + 2 = -4 + 4x$

$\therefore$ $7x = 2$ $\therefore$ $6 = x$

$\therefore$ $x = \frac{2}{7}$

So, $x = \frac{2}{7}$ or 6.

Also notice that if $|x| = |b|$ then $x = \pm b.$

Example 17

Solve for x: $|x+1| = |2x-3|$

If $|x+1| = |2x-3|$,   then $x + 1 = \pm(2x - 3)$ {using property above}

If $x + 1 = 2x - 3$ If $x + 1 = -(2x - 3)$

then $4 = x$ then $x + 1 = -2x + 3$

$\therefore$ $3x = 2$

$\therefore$ $x = \frac{2}{3}$ So, $x = \frac{2}{3}$ or 4.

EXERCISE 1F.2

1 Solve for x:

a $|x| = 3$ b $|x| = -5$ c $|x| = 0$

d $|x - 1| = 3$ e $|3 - x| = 4$ f $|x + 5| = -1$

g $|3x - 2| = 1$ h $|3 - 2x| = 3$ i $|2 - 5x| = 12$

2 Solve for x:

a $\left| \dfrac{x}{x-1} \right| = 3$ b $\left| \dfrac{2x-1}{x+1} \right| = 5$ c $\left| \dfrac{x+3}{1-3x} \right| = \dfrac{1}{2}$

3 Solve for x:

a $|x+1| = |2-x|$ b $|x| = |5-x|$ c $|3x-1| = |x+2|$

d $|2x+5| = |1-x|$ e $|1-4x| = 2|x-1|$ f $|3x+2| = 2|2-x|$

4 Solve for x using   i a graphical method   ii an algebraic method:

a $|x+2| = 2x+1$ b $|2x+3| = 3|x|-1$ c $|x-2| = \frac{2}{5}x+1$

MODULUS INEQUALITIES

Notice that if $|x| < 2$ then x lies between -2 and 2

i.e., if $|x| < 2$, then $-2 < x < 2$.

Likewise, if $|x| > 2$, then $x > 2$ or $x < -2$.

In general,
- if $|x| < k$ where $k > 0$, then $-k < x < k$
- if $|x| > k$ where $k > 0$, then $x < -k$ or $x > k$

Example 18

Solve for x: **a** $|3x - 7| < 10$ **b** $|3 - 2x| \geqslant 4$

a $\quad |3x - 7| < 10$

$\therefore \quad -10 < 3x - 7 < 10$

$\therefore \quad -3 < 3x < 17$ {adding 7 to each part}

$\therefore \quad -\frac{3}{3} < x < \frac{17}{3}$

$\therefore \quad x \in]-1, \frac{17}{3}[$

b $\quad |3 - 2x| \geqslant 4$

$\therefore \quad |2x - 3| \geqslant 4$ {using $|a - b| = |b - a|$}

$\therefore \quad 2x - 3 \geqslant 4$ or $2x - 3 \leqslant -4$

$\therefore \quad 2x \geqslant 7$ or $2x \leqslant -1$

$\therefore \quad x \geqslant \frac{7}{2}$ or $x \leqslant -\frac{1}{2}$ i.e., $x \in]-\infty, -\frac{1}{2}]$ or $[\frac{7}{2}, \infty[$

Notice that **a** and **b** above could be solved by a different method.

In $|3x - 7| < 10$, we see that both sides are non-negative

$\therefore \quad |3x - 7|^2 < 100$ {squaring both sides}

$\therefore \quad (3x - 7)^2 - 10^2 < 0$ {$|a|^2 = a^2$ for all a}

$\therefore \quad [3x - 7 + 10][3x - 7 - 10] < 0$

$\therefore \quad [3x + 3][3x - 17] < 0$

The LHS has sign diagram: so $x \in]-1, \frac{17}{3}[$.

Example 19   Find exactly where $2|x - 1| \geqslant |3 - x|$.

Both sides of the inequality $2|x - 1| \geqslant |3 - x|$ are non-negative.

$\therefore$ we square both sides to get $4|x - 1|^2 \geqslant |3 - x|^2$

$\therefore \quad 4(x - 1)^2 - (3 - x)^2 \geqslant 0$ {as $|a|^2 = a^2$ for $a \in \mathbb{R}$}

$\therefore \quad [2(x - 1) + (3 - x)][2(x - 1) - (3 - x)] \geqslant 0$

$\therefore \quad (x + 1)(3x - 5) \geqslant 0$

The critical values are $x = -1, \frac{5}{3}$ with sign diagram:

$\therefore \quad x \in]-\infty, -1]$ or $[\frac{5}{3}, \infty[$ (check with GDC)

Sometimes a graphical solution is easier.

Example 20

Solve graphically: $|1 - 2x| > x + 1$.

We draw graphs of $y = |1 - 2x|$ and $y = x + 1$ on the same set of axes.

$$y = |1 - 2x| = \begin{cases} 1 - 2x & \text{for} \quad 1 - 2x \geqslant 0, \quad \text{i.e.,} \quad x \leqslant \tfrac{1}{2} \\ -1 + 2x & \text{for} \quad 1 - 2x < 0, \quad \text{i.e.,} \quad x > \tfrac{1}{2} \end{cases}$$

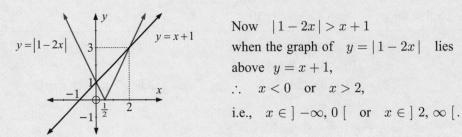

Now $|1 - 2x| > x + 1$
when the graph of $y = |1 - 2x|$ lies
above $y = x + 1$,

$\therefore \quad x < 0 \quad \text{or} \quad x > 2$,

i.e., $x \in]-\infty, 0[\quad \text{or} \quad x \in]2, \infty[$.

EXERCISE 1F.3

1   Solve for x:

   a $|x| < 4$

   b $|x| \geqslant 3$

   c $|x + 3| \leqslant 1$

   d $|x + 4| \geqslant 2$

   e $|2x - 1| < 3$

   f $|3 - 4x| > 2$

   g $|2x + 1| < 4$

   h $2 \geqslant |x - 1|$

   i $|3 - 7x| < 4$

   j $|2 - 7x| \geqslant 5$

   k $|5 - 3x| \leqslant 1$

   l $5 \geqslant |3 - x|$

2   Solve:

   a $|x - 3| \leqslant 4$

   b $|2x - 1| \leqslant 3$

   c $|3x + 1| > 2$

   d $|5 - 2x| \geqslant 7$

   e $|x| \geqslant |2 - x|$

   f $3|x| \leqslant |1 - 2x|$

   g $\left| \dfrac{x}{x - 2} \right| \geqslant 3$

   h $\left| \dfrac{2x + 3}{x - 1} \right| \geqslant 2$

3   Solve graphically:

   a $|2x - 3| < x$

   b $2x - 3 < |x|$

   c $|x^2 - x| > 2$

   d $|x| - 2 \geqslant |4 - x|$

4   Graph the function $f(x) = \dfrac{|x|}{x - 2}$, and hence find all values of x for which $\dfrac{|x|}{x - 2} \geqslant -\tfrac{1}{2}$.

5   a   Draw the graph of $y = |x + 5| + |x + 2| + |x| + |x - 3|$.

   b

   A ————•———————————•———————————O———————————•———— B
         P   Q   R
        −5   −2   3

P, Q and R are factories which are 5, 2 and 3 km away from factory O respectively.

A security service wishes to know where it should locate its premises along AB so that the total length of cable to the 4 factories is a minimum.

  i   Explain why the total length of cable is given by

$$|x+5| + |x+2| + |x| + |x-3| \quad \text{where } x \text{ is the position of the security}$$

service on AB.

  ii   Where should the security service set up to minimise the length of cable to all 4 factories? What is the minimum length of cable?

  iii   If a fifth factory at S, located 7 km right of O, also requires the security service, where should the security service locate its premises for minimum cable length?

6 Which of these is true?   Give proof.

  a $|x+y| \leqslant |x| + |y|$ for all x, y **b** $|x-y| \geqslant |x| - |y|$ for all x, y

G   THE RECIPROCAL FUNCTION $x \mapsto \frac{1}{x}$

$$x \mapsto \frac{1}{x} \quad \text{or} \quad f(x) = \frac{1}{x} \quad \text{is defined as the \textbf{reciprocal function}.}$$

It has graph:

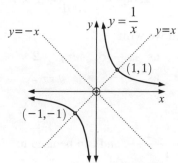

Notice that:

- $f(x) = \dfrac{1}{x}$ is undefined when $x = 0$

- The graph of $f(x) = \dfrac{1}{x}$ exists in the first and third quadrants only.

- $f(x) = \dfrac{1}{x}$ is symmetric about $y = x$ and $y = -x$

- as $x \to \infty$, $\quad f(x) \to 0$ (from above)
  as $x \to -\infty$, $\quad f(x) \to 0$ (from below)
  as $x \to 0$ (from right), $y \to \infty$
  as $x \to 0$ (from left), $\quad y \to -\infty$

$\to$ reads "*approaches*" or "*tends to*"

- $f(x) = \dfrac{1}{x}$ is **asymptotic** to the x-axis

  and to the y-axis.

  The graph gets closer to the axes as it gets further from the origin.

EXERCISE 1G

1 Sketch the graphs of $f(x) = \dfrac{1}{x}$, $g(x) = \dfrac{2}{x}$, $h(x) = \dfrac{4}{x}$ on the same set of axes.

Comment on any similarities and differences.

2 Sketch the graphs of $f(x) = -\dfrac{1}{x}$, $g(x) = -\dfrac{2}{x}$, $h(x) = -\dfrac{4}{x}$ on the same set of axes.

Comment on any similarities and differences.

ASYMPTOTES OF OTHER RATIONAL FUNCTIONS

Consider the function $f(x) = \dfrac{2x+1}{x-1}$.

Its graph is:

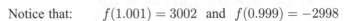

Notice that at $x = 1$, $f(x)$ is undefined.

As the graph approaches the vertical line $x = 1$, we say that $x = 1$ is a *vertical asymptote*.

Notice that: $f(1.001) = 3002$ and $f(0.999) = -2998$

We write: as $x \to 1$ (from the left), $f(x) \to -\infty$

as $x \to 1$ (from the right), $f(x) \to \infty$

or alternatively, as $x \to 1^-$, $f(x) \to -\infty$

as $x \to 1^+$, $f(x) \to \infty$

We also notice that $f(1000) = \dfrac{2001}{999} \doteqdot 2.003$ and $f(-1000) = \dfrac{-1999}{-1001} \doteqdot 1.997$

This indicates that $y = 2$ is a *horizontal asymptote* and we write:

as $x \to \infty$, $y \to 2$ (from above)   *or*   as $x \to \infty$, $y \to 2^+$

as $x \to -\infty$, $y \to 2$ (from below)   as $x \to -\infty$, $y \to 2^-$

Notice that   as $|x| \to \infty$, $f(x) \to 2$

The sign diagram of $y = \dfrac{2x+1}{x-1}$ is   and can be used to discuss

the function near its vertical asymptote without having to graph the function.

Now consider the function $f(x) = x + 1 + \dfrac{3}{x-2}$

Its graph is:

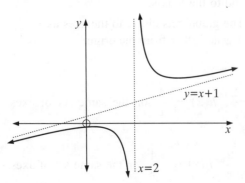

$x = 2$ is a vertical asymptote.

At $x = 2$, $f(x)$ is undefined.

As $x \to 2^-$, $f(x) \to -\infty$

as $x \to 2^+$, $f(x) \to \infty$

Notice that $\dfrac{3}{x-2} \to 0$ as $|x| \to \infty$

So, as $x \to \infty$, $f(x) \to x + 1$ (from above)

as $x \to -\infty$, $f(x) \to x + 1$ (from below)

Thus $y = x + 1$ is an *oblique asymptote*.

DISCUSSION   ASYMPTOTES

What would be the asymptotes of

- $y = \dfrac{2x^2}{(x-1)(x-4)}$ • $y = x^2 + \dfrac{1}{x}$?

INVESTIGATION 2   FINDING ASYMPTOTES

Use the **graphing package** supplied or a **graphics calculator** to examine the following functions for asymptotes:

GRAPHING PACKAGE

a $y = -1 + \dfrac{3}{x-2}$ **b** $y = \dfrac{3x+1}{x+2}$ **c** $y = \dfrac{3x-9}{(x-2)(x+1)}$

d $y = \dfrac{2x}{x^2-4}$ **e** $y = \dfrac{1-x}{(x+2)^2}$ **f** $y = \dfrac{x^2+4}{x-1}$

g $y = \dfrac{x^2-1}{x^2+1}$ **h** $y = \dfrac{x^2-6x+5}{(x+1)^2}$ **i** $y = x^2 + \dfrac{2}{x}$

Further examples of asymptotic behaviour are seen in exponential, logarithmic and some trigonometric functions.

Note: A function may cross a horizontal or oblique asymptote, but never a vertical asymptote.

EXERCISE 1H

1   For the following functions:
   i   determine the asymptotes
   ii   discuss the behaviour of the function as it approaches its asymptotes
   iii sketch the graph of the function
   iv   find the coordinates of all points where the function crosses its asymptotes.

   a $f : x \mapsto \dfrac{3}{x-2}$ **b** $f(x) = 2 - \dfrac{3}{x+1}$

   c $f : x \mapsto \dfrac{x+3}{(x+1)(x-2)}$ **d** $f(x) = x + \dfrac{2}{x-3}$

   e $y = \dfrac{x^2-4}{x^2+4}$ **f** $y = \dfrac{2x^2+1}{x^2-4}$

   g $f : x \mapsto x + 2 + \dfrac{x-2}{x+1}$ **h** $g : x \mapsto 2x - \dfrac{2x}{x^2+1}$

   i $y = \dfrac{4x}{x^2-4x-5}$ **j** $y = x^2 - \dfrac{4}{x}$

INVERSE FUNCTIONS

The operations of $+$ and $-$, $\times$ and $\div$, squaring and finding the square root, are **inverse operations** as one undoes what the other does.

For example, $x + 3 - 3 = x$, $x \times 3 \div 3 = x$ and $\sqrt{8^2} = 8$.

A function $y = f(x)$ *may or may not* have an inverse function.

If $y = f(x)$ has an **inverse function**, this new function $f^{-1}(x)$

- must indeed be a function, i.e., satisfy the vertical line test
- must be the reflection of $y = f(x)$ in the line $y = x$
- must satisfy the condition that $f^{-1} : f(x) \mapsto x$

The function $y = x$, defined as $f : x \mapsto x$,   is the **identity function**.

This means that, for any function f that has an inverse function f^{-1}, $f \circ f^{-1}$ and $f^{-1} \circ f$ must always equal the identity function. So, $(f \circ f^{-1})(x) = (f^{-1} \circ f)(x) = x$, so the inverse function undoes the effect of the function on x.

If (x, y) lies on f, then (y, x) lies on f^{-1}. So reflecting the function in $y = x$ has the algebraic effect of interchanging x and y.

For example, $f : y = 5x + 2$ becomes $f^{-1} : x = 5y + 2$.

Consider:

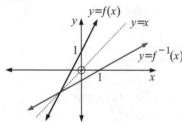

$y = f^{-1}(x)$ is the inverse of
$y = f(x)$ as

- it is also a function
- it is the reflection of $y = f(x)$
  in the oblique line $y = x$.

This is the reflection of $y = f(x)$ in $y = x$, but it is *not* the inverse function of $y = f(x)$ as it fails the vertical line test.

We say that the function $y = f(x)$ does not have an inverse.

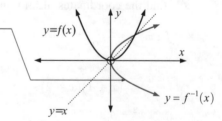

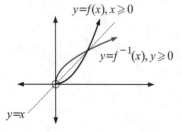

However, consider the same function $y = f(x)$ but with the domain $x \geqslant 0$.

The function does now have an inverse function, as drawn alongside.

$y = f(x)$ subject to $x \leqslant 0$ would also have an inverse function.

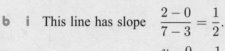

Consider $f : x \mapsto 2x + 3$.

a On the same axes, graph f and its inverse function f^{-1}.

b Find $f^{-1}(x)$ using   **i**   coordinate geometry and the slope of $f^{-1}(x)$ from **a**

                        ii   variable interchange.

c Check that $(f \circ f^{-1})(x) = (f^{-1} \circ f)(x) = x$

---

a $f(x) = 2x + 3$ passes through $(0, 3)$ and $(2, 7)$.

   $\therefore$ $f^{-1}(x)$ passes through $(3, 0)$ and $(7, 2)$.

b **i** This line has slope $\dfrac{2 - 0}{7 - 3} = \dfrac{1}{2}$.

So, its equation is $\dfrac{y - 0}{x - 3} = \dfrac{1}{2}$

             i.e., $y = \dfrac{x - 3}{2}$

$\therefore$ $f^{-1}(x) = \dfrac{x - 3}{2}$

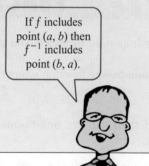

ii f is $y = 2x + 3$, so f^{-1} is $x = 2y + 3$

                      $\therefore$ $x - 3 = 2y$

                      $\therefore$ $\dfrac{x - 3}{2} = y$ i.e., $f^{-1}(x) = \dfrac{x - 3}{2}$

c $(f \circ f^{-1})(x)$ and $(f^{-1} \circ f)(x)$

$= f(f^{-1}(x))$ $= f^{-1}(f(x))$

$= f\left(\dfrac{x - 3}{2}\right)$ $= f^{-1}(2x + 3)$

$= 2\left(\dfrac{x - 3}{2}\right) + 3$ $= \dfrac{(2x + 3) - 3}{2}$

$= x$ $= \dfrac{2x}{2}$

                             $= x$

> If f includes point (a, b) then f^{-1} includes point (b, a).

EXERCISE 1I

1 For each of the following functions f

   i   on the same axes graph $y = x$, f and f^{-1}

   ii   find $f^{-1}(x)$ using coordinate geometry and **i**

   iii   find $f^{-1}(x)$ using variable interchange:

      a $f : x \mapsto 3x + 1$

      b $f : x \mapsto \dfrac{x + 2}{4}$.

2 For each of the following functions f

    i find $f^{-1}(x)$ **ii** sketch $y = f(x)$, $y = f^{-1}(x)$ and $y = x$ on the same axes

    iii show that $f^{-1} \circ f = f \circ f^{-1} = x$, the identity function:

   a $f : x \mapsto 2x + 5$ **b** $f : x \mapsto \dfrac{3 - 2x}{4}$ **c** $f : x \mapsto x + 3$

3 Copy the graphs of the following functions and in each case include the graphs of $y = x$ and $y = f^{-1}(x)$:

a

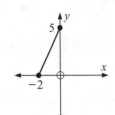

b

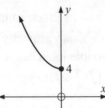

c

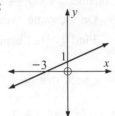

d

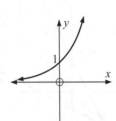

e

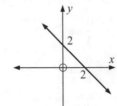

f

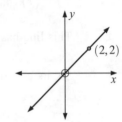

4 **a** Sketch the graph of $f : x \mapsto x^2 - 4$ and reflect it in the line $y = x$.

  b Does f have an inverse function?

  c Does f with restricted domain $x \geqslant 0$ have an inverse function?

5 Sketch the graph of $f : x \mapsto x^3$ and its inverse function $f^{-1}(x)$.

J | FUNCTIONS WHICH HAVE INVERSES

It is important to understand the distinction between one-to-one and many-to-one functions.

> A **one-to-one** function is any function where • for each x there is only one value of y and
> • for each y there is only one value of x.

Functions that are **one-to-one** satisfy both the '**vertical line test**' and the '**horizontal line test**'.

This means that: • no vertical line can meet the graph more than once
                    • no horizontal line can meet the graph more than once.

Functions that are not one-to-one are called **many-to-one**. While these functions must satisfy the '**vertical line test**' they *do not satisfy* the '**horizontal line test**', i.e., at least one y-value has more than one corresponding x-value.

> • If the function $y = f(x)$ is **one-to-one**, it will have an inverse function $y = f^{-1}(x)$.
> • If a function $y = f(x)$ is **many-to-one**, it *will not* have an inverse function.
> • Many-to-one functions can have inverse functions for a restricted part of the domain (see **Example 22**).

Example 22

Consider $f : x \mapsto x^2$.

a   Explain why the function defined above does not have an inverse function.

b   Does $f : x \mapsto x^2$ where $x \geqslant 0$ have an inverse function?

c   Find $f^{-1}(x)$ for $f : x \mapsto x^2$, $x \geqslant 0$.

d   Sketch $y = f(x)$, $y = x$ and $y = f^{-1}(x)$ for f in **b** and f^{-1} in **c**.

a $f : x \mapsto x^2$ has domain $x \in \mathbb{R}$ and is many-to-one.
It does not pass the 'horizontal line test'.

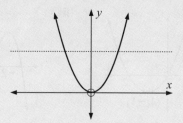

b   If we restrict the domain to $x \geqslant 0$ or $x \in [0, \infty[$, or in fact any domain which makes f one-to-one, it satisfies the 'horizontal line test' and so has an inverse function.

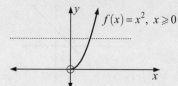

c f is defined by $y = x^2$, $x \geqslant 0$
$\therefore\ f^{-1}$ is defined by $x = y^2$, $y \geqslant 0$
$\therefore\quad y = \pm\sqrt{x}$, $y \geqslant 0$
$\therefore\quad y = \sqrt{x}$
$\{$as $-\sqrt{x}$ is $\leqslant 0\}$
So, $f^{-1}(x) = \sqrt{x}$

d
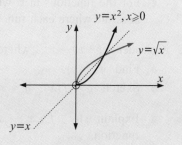

Note: The function $f(x) = \dfrac{1}{x}$, $x \neq 0$,   is called the **reciprocal function**.

It is said to be a **self-inverse function** as $f = f^{-1}$.

This is because the graph of $y = \dfrac{1}{x}$ is symmetrical about the line $y = x$.

Any function with a graph which is symmetrical about the line $y = x$ must be a **self-inverse function**.

EXERCISE 1J

Note: If the domain of a function is the set of all real numbers, then the statement $x \in \mathbb{R}$ will be omitted.

1   Which of the following functions have inverses? In each of these cases, write down the inverse function.

a $\{(1, 2), (2, 4), (3, 5)\}$

b $\{(-1, 3), (0, 2), (1, 3)\}$

c $\{(2, 1), (-1, 0), (0, 2), (1, 3)\}$

d $\{(-1, -1), (0, 0), (1, 1)\}$

2 **a** Show that $f : x \mapsto \dfrac{1}{x}$ has an inverse function for all $x \neq 0$.

    b Find f^{-1} algebraically and show that f is a self-inverse function.

3 Show that $f : x \mapsto \dfrac{3x - 8}{x - 3}$, $x \neq 3$ is a self-inverse function by:

    a reference to its graph   **b** using algebra.

4 The '**horizontal line test**' says that:

for a function to have an inverse function, no horizontal line can cut it more than once.

    a Explain why this is a valid test for the existence of an inverse function.

    b Which of the following functions have an inverse function?

    i 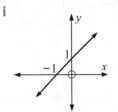   **ii** 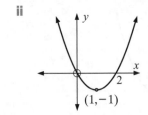   **iii**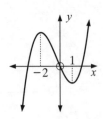

    c For the functions in **b** which do not have an inverse, specify domains as wide as possible where each function does have an inverse.

5 Consider $f : x \mapsto x^2$ where $x \leqslant 0$.

    a Find $f^{-1}(x)$.

    b Sketch $y = f(x)$, $y = x$ and $y = f^{-1}(x)$ on the same set of axes.

6 **a** Explain why $f : x \mapsto x^2 - 4x + 3$ is a function but does not have an inverse function.

    b Explain why f for $x \geqslant 2$ has an inverse function.

    c Show that the inverse function of the function in **b** is $f^{-1}(x) = 2 + \sqrt{1 + x}$.

    d If the domain of f is restricted to $x \geqslant 2$, state the domain and range of

      i f **ii** f^{-1}.

    e Show that $f \circ f^{-1} = f^{-1} \circ f = x$, the identity function.

7 Given $f : x \mapsto (x + 1)^2 + 3$ where $x \geqslant -1$:

    a find the defining equation of f^{-1}

    b sketch, using technology, the graphs of $y = f(x)$, $y = x$ and $y = f^{-1}(x)$

    c state the domain and range of   **i** f **ii** f^{-1}.

8 Consider the functions $f : x \mapsto 2x + 5$ and $g : x \mapsto \dfrac{8 - x}{2}$.

    a Find $g^{-1}(-1)$.   **b** Solve for x if $(f \circ g^{-1})(x) = 9$.

9 Given $f : x \mapsto 5^x$ and $g : x \mapsto \sqrt{x}$:

    a find **i** $f(2)$ **ii** $g^{-1}(4)$ **b** solve the equation $(g^{-1} \circ f)(x) = 25$.

10 Given $f : x \mapsto 2x$ and $g : x \mapsto 4x - 3$ show that $(f^{-1} \circ g^{-1})(x) = (g \circ f)^{-1}(x)$.

11 Which of these functions is a self-inverse function, i.e., $f^{-1}(x) = f(x)$?

     a $f(x) = 2x$ **b** $f(x) = x$ **c** $f(x) = -x$ **d** $f(x) = \dfrac{2}{x}$ **e** $f(x) = -\dfrac{6}{x}$

12 Show that $(f \circ f^{-1})(x) = (f^{-1} \circ f)(x) = x$ for:

     a $f(x) = 3x + 1$ **b** $f(x) = \dfrac{x+3}{4}$ **c** $f(x) = \sqrt{x}$

13

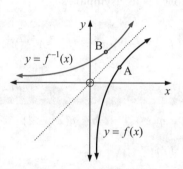

    a   B is the image of A under a reflection in the line $y = x$.
    If A is $(x, f(x))$, what are the coordinates of B under the reflection?

    b   Substitute your result from **a** into $y = f^{-1}(x)$. What result do you obtain?

    c   Explain how to establish that $f(f^{-1}(x)) = x$ also.

REVIEW SET 1A

1 If $f(x) = 2x - x^2$ find: **a** $f(2)$ **b** $f(-3)$ **c** $f(-\tfrac{1}{2})$

2 For each of the following graphs determine:

     i   the range and domain   **ii**   the x and y-intercepts

     iii   whether it is a function   **iv**   if it has an inverse function

   a

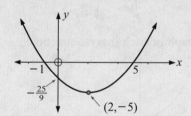

   b

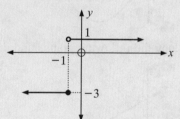

3 Find a, b and c if $f(0) = 5$, $f(-2) = 21$ and $f(3) = -4$ and $f(x) = ax^2 + bx + c$.

4 Draw a sign diagram for:

     a $(3x + 2)(4 - x)$ **b** $\dfrac{x - 3}{x^2 + 4x + 4}$

5 If $f(x) = 2x - 3$ and $g(x) = x^2 + 2$, find: **a** $f(g(x))$ **b** $g(f(x))$

6 Solve for x:

     a $\dfrac{x(x + 8)}{x + 2} \leqslant 5$ **b** $\dfrac{3}{x - 1} > \dfrac{5}{2x + 1}$

7 Consider $x \mapsto 2x - 7$.

    a   On the same set of axes graph $y = x$, f and f^{-1}.

    b   Find $f^{-1}(x)$ using variable interchange.

    c   Show that $f \circ f^{-1} = f^{-1} \circ f = x$, the identity function.

8 Solve for x:

  a $\left| \dfrac{2x+1}{x-2} \right| = 3$ **b** $|3x-2| \geqslant |2x+3|$

9 For $f : x \mapsto \dfrac{4x+1}{x^2+x-6}$

  a determine the asymptotes
  b discuss the behaviour of the function as it approaches its asymptotes
  c sketch the graph.

10 Given $f : x \mapsto 3x+6$ and $h : x \mapsto \dfrac{x}{3}$, show that $(f^{-1} \circ h^{-1})(x) = (h \circ f)^{-1}(x)$.

REVIEW SET 1B

1 If $g(x) = x^2 - 3x$, find in simplest form   **a** $g(x+1)$ **b** $g(x^2 - 2)$

2 For each of the following functions $f(x)$ find $f^{-1}(x)$:

  a $f(x) = 7 - 4x$ **b** $f(x) = \dfrac{3+2x}{5}$

3 For each of the following graphs, find the domain and range.

  a 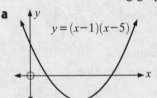   **b**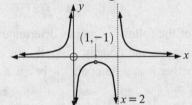

4 Copy the following graphs and draw the graph of each inverse function:

  a 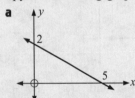   **b**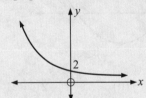

5 Draw a sign diagram for:

  a $\dfrac{x^2 - 6x - 16}{x - 3}$ **b** $\dfrac{x+9}{x+5} + x$

6 Solve for x:

  a $2x^2 + x \leqslant 10$ **b** $\dfrac{x^2 - 3x - 4}{x + 2} > 0$

7 Find an f and a g function given that:

  a $f(g(x)) = \sqrt{1 - x^2}$ **b** $g(f(x)) = \left(\dfrac{x-2}{x+1} \right)^2$

8 Solve for x:

  a $|4x - 2| = |x + 7|$ **b** $|7 - 3x| \geqslant 8$

9 For $f(x) = 3 + \dfrac{3x - 2}{x^2 - 4}$

    a determine the asymptotes

    b discuss the behaviour of the function as it approaches its asymptotes

    c sketch the graph

    d find the coordinates of all points where the function crosses its asymptotes.

10 Given $h : x \mapsto (x - 4)^2 + 3, \quad x \in [4, \infty[$

    a find the defining equation of h^{-1} **b** show that $h \circ h^{-1} = h^{-1} \circ h = x$

REVIEW SET 1C

1 If $h(x) = 7 - 3x$:

    a find in simplest form $h(2x - 1)$ **b** find x if $h(2x - 1) = -2$

2 For each of the following graphs find the domain and range:

    a   **b**

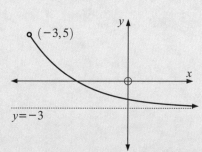 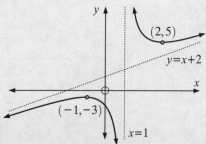

3 If $f(x) = 1 - 2x$ and $g(x) = \sqrt{x}$:

    a find in simplest form   **i** $(f \circ g)(x)$ **ii** $(g \circ f)(x)$

    b What is the domain and range of $f \circ g$ and $g \circ f$?

4 Solve for x:

    a $\dfrac{x^2 - 3}{x - 2} < 6$ **b** $\dfrac{2x + 1}{x - 1} \geqslant \dfrac{2x + 3}{x + 2}$

5 Consider $f(x) = \dfrac{1}{x^2}$.   **a** For what value of x is $f(x)$ meaningless?

                               b Sketch the graph of this function using technology.

                               c State the domain and range of the function.

6   **a** Solve graphically: $|2x - 6| > x + 3$

    b Graph the function $f(x) = \dfrac{x}{|x| + 1}$ and hence find all values of x for

        which $\dfrac{x}{|x| + 1} \geqslant \dfrac{1}{3}$

7   **a** Draw a sign diagram for $\dfrac{(x + 2)(x - 3)}{x - 1}$.

    b Hence, solve for x: $\dfrac{x^2 + x - 8}{x - 1} < 2$

8 For $f(x) = x - 2 + \dfrac{5}{(x-1)^2}$

   a determine the asymptotes
   b discuss the behaviour of the function as it approaches its asymptotes
   c sketch the graph.

9 Find $f^{-1}(x)$ given that $f(x)$ is: **a** $4x + 2$ **b** $\dfrac{3 - 5x}{4}$

10 **a** Sketch the graph of $g : x \mapsto x^2 + 6x + 7$.
   b Explain why g for $x \in \,] - \infty, \, -3]$ has an inverse function g^{-1}.
   c Find algebraically, the equation of g^{-1}.   **d** Sketch the graph of g^{-1}.
   e Find the range of g and hence the domain and range of g^{-1}.

Chapter 2

Sequences and series

Contents:

A   NUMBER PATTERNS

An important skill in mathematics is to:
- **recognise** a pattern in a set of numbers,
- **describe** the pattern in words, and
- **continue** the pattern.

A list of numbers where there is a pattern is called a **number sequence**.
The numbers in the sequence are said to be its **members** or its **terms**.

For example,   3, 7, 11, 15, ... form a number sequence.

The first term is 3,   the second term is 7,   the third term is 11,   and so on.

We describe this pattern in words:

"*The sequence starts at 3 and each term is 4 more than the previous one.*"

Thus, the fifth term is 19, the sixth term is 23, and so on.

Example 1

Describe the sequence: 14, 17, 20, 23, ... and write down the next two terms.

The sequence starts at 14 and each term is 3 more than the previous term.
The next two terms are 26 and 29.

EXERCISE 2A

1   Write down the first four terms of the sequence if you start with:
   a   4 and add 9 each time
   b   45 and subtract 6 each time
   c   2 and multiply by 3 each time
   d   96 and divide by 2 each time.

2   For each of the following write a description of the sequence and find the next 2 terms:
   a   8, 16, 24, 32, ...
   b   2, 5, 8, 11, ...
   c   36, 31, 26, 21, ...
   d   96, 89, 82, 75, ...
   e   1, 4, 16, 64, ...
   f   2, 6, 18, 54, ...
   g   480, 240, 120, 60, ...
   h   243, 81, 27, 9, ...
   i   50 000, 10 000, 2000, 400, ...

3   Describe the following number patterns and write down the next 3 terms:
   a   1, 4, 9, 16, ...
   b   1, 8, 27, 64, ...
   c   2, 6, 12, 20, ...

B   SEQUENCES OF NUMBERS

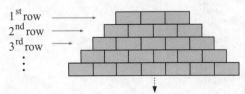

1st row
2nd row
3rd row

Consider the illustrated tower of bricks. The top row, or first row, has three bricks. The second row has four bricks, and the third row has five bricks.

If u_n represents the number of bricks in row n (from the top)
then $u_1 = 3$, $u_2 = 4$, $u_3 = 5$, $u_4 = 6$, ...

The number pattern: 3, 4, 5, 6, ... is called a **sequence** of numbers.

This sequence can be specified by:

- **Using words**

  "The top row has three bricks and each successive row under it has one more brick."

- **Using an explicit formula** $u_n = n + 2$ is the **general term** (or **nth term**) formula for $n = 1, 2, 3, 4, 5, ...$

  Check: $u_1 = 1 + 2 = 3$ ✓ $u_2 = 2 + 2 = 4$ ✓
  $u_3 = 3 + 2 = 5$ ✓   etc.

Early members of a sequence can be graphed. Each term is represented by a dot.

The dots *must not* be joined. Why?

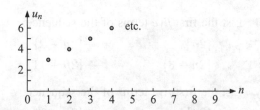

OPENING PROBLEM

A circular stadium consists of sections as illustrated, with aisles in between. The diagram shows the 13 tiers of concrete steps for the final section, **Section K**. Seats are to be placed along every concrete step, with each seat being 0.45 m wide. AB, the arc at the front of the first row, is 14.4 m long, while CD, the arc at the back of the back row, is 20.25 m long.

For you to consider:

1 How wide is each concrete step?

2 What is the length of the arc of the back of Row 1, Row 2, Row 3, etc?

3 How many seats are there in Row 1, Row 2, Row 3, ..., Row 13?

4 How many sections are there in the stadium?

5 What is the total seating capacity of the stadium?

6 What is the radius of the 'playing surface'?

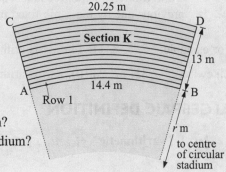

To solve problems like the **Opening Problem** and many others, a detailed study of **sequences** and their sums (called **series**) is required.

NUMBER SEQUENCES

A **number sequence** is a set of numbers defined by a rule that is valid for positive integers.

A number sequence is a function whose domain is the set of positive integers.

Sequences may be defined in one of the following ways:

- using a formula which represents the **general term** (or **nth term**)
- giving a description in words
- listing the first few terms and assuming that the pattern represented continues indefinitely.

THE GENERAL TERM

u_n, T_n, t_n, A_n, etc. can all be used to represent the **general term** (or **nth term**) of a sequence and are defined for $n = 1, 2, 3, 4, 5, 6, \ldots$.

$\{u_n\}$ represents the sequence that can be generated by using u_n as the **nth term**.

$\{u_n\}$ is a function, i.e., $n \mapsto u_n$, $n \in \mathbb{Z}^+$

For example, $\{2n + 1\}$ generates the sequence $3, 5, 7, 9, 11, \ldots$.

EXERCISE 2B

1 List the first *five* terms of the sequence:

    a $\{2n\}$ b $\{2n + 2\}$ c $\{2n - 1\}$ d $\{2n - 3\}$

    e $\{2n + 3\}$ f $\{2n + 11\}$ g $\{3n + 1\}$ h $\{4n - 3\}$

2 List the first *five* terms of the sequence:

    a $\{2^n\}$ b $\{3 \times 2^n\}$ c $\{6 \times (\tfrac{1}{2})^n\}$ d $\{(-2)^n\}$

3 List the first *five* terms of the sequence $\{15 - (-2)^n\}$.

C   ARITHMETIC SEQUENCES

An **arithmetic sequence** is a sequence in which each term differs from the previous one by the same fixed number.

For example: $2, 5, 8, 11, 14, \ldots$ is arithmetic as $5 - 2 = 8 - 5 = 11 - 8 = 14 - 11$, etc.

Likewise, $31, 27, 23, 19, \ldots$ is arithmetic as $27 - 31 = 23 - 27 = 19 - 23$, etc.

ALGEBRAIC DEFINITION

$\{u_n\}$ is **arithmetic** $\Leftrightarrow$ $u_{n+1} - u_n = d$ for all positive integers n where d is a constant (the **common difference**).

Note:
- $\Leftrightarrow$ is read as 'if and only if'
- If $\{u_n\}$ is arithmetic then $u_{n+1} - u_n$ is a constant *and* if $u_{n+1} - u_n$ is a constant then $\{u_n\}$ is arithmetic.

THE NAME 'ARITHMETIC'

If a, b and c are any consecutive terms of an arithmetic sequence then

$$b - a = c - b \quad \text{\{equating common differences\}}$$
$$\therefore \quad 2b = a + c$$
$$\therefore \quad b = \frac{a + c}{2}$$

So, the middle term is the **arithmetic mean** of the terms on either side of it.

THE GENERAL TERM FORMULA

Suppose the first term of an arithmetic sequence is u_1 and the common difference is d.

Then $u_2 = u_1 + d$, $u_3 = u_1 + 2d$, $u_4 = u_1 + 3d$,   and so on.

Hence $u_n = u_1 + \underbrace{(n-1)}d$

The coefficient of d is one less than the subscript.

So,   for an **arithmetic sequence** with **first term u_1** and **common difference d** the **general term** (or **nth term**) is $u_n = u_1 + (n-1)d$.

Example 2

Consider the sequence   2, 9, 16, 23, 30, ...

a   Show that the sequence is arithmetic.

b   Find the formula for the general term u_n.

c   Find the 100th term of the sequence.

d   Is   i   828   ii   2341   a member of the sequence?

a $9 - 2 = 7$ So, assuming that the pattern continues,
      $16 - 9 = 7$ consecutive terms differ by 7.
      $23 - 16 = 7$ $\therefore$ the sequence is arithmetic with $u_1 = 2$, $d = 7$.
      $30 - 23 = 7$

b $u_n = u_1 + (n-1)d$ $\therefore$ $u_n = 2 + 7(n-1)$ i.e., $u_n = 7n - 5$

c   If $n = 100$, $u_{100} = 7(100) - 5 = 695$.

d   i   Let $u_n = 828$ ii   Let $u_n = 2341$
    $\therefore$ $7n - 5 = 828$ $\therefore$ $7n - 5 = 2341$
    $\therefore$ $7n = 833$ $\therefore$ $7n = 2346$
    $\therefore$ $n = 119$ $\therefore$ $n = 335\frac{1}{7}$

    $\therefore$ 828 is a term of the sequence.   which is not possible as n must be an
    In fact it is the 119th term.   integer. $\therefore$ 2341 cannot be a term.

Example 3

Find k given that $3k + 1$, k and -3 are consecutive terms of an arithmetic sequence.

Since the terms are consecutive, $k - (3k + 1) = -3 - k$ {equating differences}
    $\therefore$ $k - 3k - 1 = -3 - k$
    $\therefore$ $-2k - 1 = -3 - k$
    $\therefore$ $-1 + 3 = -k + 2k$
    $\therefore$ $k = 2$

Example 4

Find the general term u_n for an arithmetic sequence with $u_3 = 8$ and $u_8 = -17$.

$u_3 = 8$ $\therefore$ $u_1 + 2d = 8$ .... (1) $\{u_n = u_1 + (n-1)d\}$

$u_8 = -17$ $\therefore$ $u_1 + 7d = -17$ .... (2)

We now solve (1) and (2) simultaneously:

$$-u_1 - 2d = -8$$
$$\underline{u_1 + 7d = -17}$$
$$\therefore \quad 5d = -25 \qquad \{\text{adding the equations}\}$$
$$\therefore \quad d = -5$$

So in (1) $u_1 + 2(-5) = 8$

$\therefore$ $u_1 - 10 = 8$

$\therefore$ $u_1 = 18$

Now $u_n = u_1 + (n-1)d$

$\therefore$ $u_n = 18 - 5(n-1)$

$\therefore$ $u_n = 18 - 5n + 5$

$\therefore$ $u_n = 23 - 5n$

Check:

$u_3 = 23 - 5(3)$
$= 23 - 15$
$= 8$ $\checkmark$

$u_8 = 23 - 5(8)$
$= 23 - 40$
$= -17$ $\checkmark$

Example 5

Insert four numbers between 3 and 12 so that all six numbers are in arithmetic sequence.

If the numbers are $3, \ 3 + d, \ 3 + 2d, \ 3 + 3d, \ 3 + 4d, \ 12$

then $3 + 5d = 12$

$\therefore$ $5d = 9$

$\therefore$ $d = \frac{9}{5} = 1.8$

So, we have   3, 4.8, 6.6, 8.4, 10.2, 12.

EXERCISE 2C

1   Consider the sequence   6, 17, 28, 39, 50, ...

   a   Show that the sequence is arithmetic.   b   Find the formula for its general term.

   c   Find its 50th term.   d   Is 325 a member?

   e   Is 761 a member?

2   Consider the sequence 87, 83, 79, 75, ...

   a   Show that the sequence is arithmetic.   b   Find the formula for its general term.

   c   Find the 40th term.   d   Is -143 a member?

3 A sequence is defined by $u_n = 3n - 2$.

    a Prove that the sequence is arithmetic.   **Hint:** Find $u_{n+1} - u_n$.

    b Find u_1 and d.   **c** Find the 57th term.

    d What is the least term of the sequence which is greater than 450?

4 A sequence is defined by $u_n = \dfrac{71 - 7n}{2}$.

    a Prove that the sequence is arithmetic.   **b** Find u_1 and d.   **c** Find u_{75}.

    d For what values of n are the terms of the sequence less than -200?

5 Find k given the consecutive arithmetic terms:

    a $32, k, 3$ **b** $k + 1, 2k + 1, 13$ **c** $5, k, k^2 - 8$

6 Find the general term u_n for an arithmetic sequence given that:

    a $u_7 = 41$ and $u_{13} = 77$ **b** $u_5 = -2$ and $u_{12} = -12\frac{1}{2}$

    c the seventh term is 1 and the fifteenth term is -39

    d the eleventh and eighth terms are -16 and $-11\frac{1}{2}$ respectively.

7   **a** Insert three numbers between 5 and 10 so that all five numbers are in arithmetic sequence.

    b Insert six numbers between -1 and 32 so that all eight numbers are in arithmetic sequence.

8 Consider the finite arithmetic sequence $36, 35\frac{1}{3}, 34\frac{2}{3}, ..., -30$.

    a Find u_1 and d.   **b** How many terms does the sequence have?

9 An arithmetic sequence starts $23, 36, 49, 62, ...$ What is the first term of the sequence to exceed $100\,000$?

D   GEOMETRIC SEQUENCES

A sequence is **geometric** if each term can be obtained from the previous one by multiplying by the same non-zero constant.

For example: $2, 10, 50, 250, ...$ is a geometric sequence as

$$2 \times 5 = 10 \quad \text{and} \quad 10 \times 5 = 50 \quad \text{and} \quad 50 \times 5 = 250.$$

Notice that $\frac{10}{2} = \frac{50}{10} = \frac{250}{50} = 5$,   so each term divided by the previous one gives the same constant.

Algebraic definition:

> $\{u_n\}$ is **geometric** $\Leftrightarrow \dfrac{u_{n+1}}{u_n} = r$ for all positive integers n
>
> where r is a **constant** called the **common ratio**.

For example: • $2, 10, 50, 250, ...$ is geometric with $r = 5$.

               • $2, -10, 50, -250, ...$ is geometric with $r = -5$.

THE NAME 'GEOMETRIC'

If a, b and c are any consecutive terms of a geometric sequence then $\dfrac{b}{a} = \dfrac{c}{b}$.

$\therefore \quad b^2 = ac \quad$ and so $\quad b = \pm\sqrt{ac} \quad$ where $\sqrt{ac}$ is the **geometric mean** of a and c.

THE GENERAL TERM

Suppose the first term of a geometric sequence is u_1 and the common ratio is r.

Then $\quad u_2 = u_1 r, \quad u_3 = u_1 r^2, \quad u_4 = u_1 r^3, \quad$ and so on.

$\qquad$ Hence $\quad u_n = u_1 r^{n-1}$

$\qquad\qquad\qquad$ The power of r is one less than the subscript.

So, $\qquad$ for a **geometric sequence** with **first term u_1** and **common ratio r**,

$\qquad$ the **general term** (or **nth term**) is $\quad u_n = u_1 r^{n-1}$.

Example 6

For the sequence $\quad 8, 4, 2, 1, \frac{1}{2}, \ldots\ldots$

a $\quad$ Show that the sequence is geometric. $\qquad$ b $\quad$ Find the general term u_n.

c $\quad$ Hence, find the 12th term as a fraction.

---

a $\quad \dfrac{4}{8} = \dfrac{1}{2} \qquad \dfrac{2}{4} = \dfrac{1}{2} \qquad \dfrac{1}{2} = \dfrac{1}{2} \qquad \dfrac{\frac{1}{2}}{1} = \dfrac{1}{2}$

So, assuming the pattern continues, consecutive terms have a common ratio of $\frac{1}{2}$

$\therefore \quad$ the sequence is geometric with $\quad u_1 = 8 \quad$ and $\quad r = \frac{1}{2}$.

b $\quad u_n = u_1 r^{n-1} \qquad \therefore \quad u_n = 8\left(\frac{1}{2}\right)^{n-1} \quad or \quad u_n = 2^3 \times (2^{-1})^{n-1}$

$\qquad\qquad\qquad\qquad\qquad\qquad\qquad\qquad\qquad\qquad = 2^3 \times 2^{-n+1}$

c $\quad u_{12} = 8 \times \left(\frac{1}{2}\right)^{11} \qquad\qquad\qquad\qquad\qquad = 2^{3+(-n+1)}$

$\qquad\quad = \dfrac{1}{256} \qquad\qquad\qquad\qquad\qquad\qquad\quad = 2^{4-n}$

Example 7

$k - 1$, $2k$ and $21 - k$ are consecutive terms of a geometric sequence. Find k.

Since the terms are geometric, $\qquad \dfrac{2k}{k-1} = \dfrac{21-k}{2k} \qquad$ {equating r's}

$\qquad\qquad\qquad\qquad \therefore \quad 4k^2 = (21-k)(k-1)$

$\qquad\qquad\qquad\qquad \therefore \quad 4k^2 = 21k - 21 - k^2 + k$

$\qquad\qquad\qquad \therefore \quad 5k^2 - 22k + 21 = 0$

$\qquad\qquad\qquad \therefore \quad (5k-7)(k-3) = 0 \quad$ and so $k = \frac{7}{5}$ or 3

Check: $\qquad$ If $\quad k = \frac{7}{5} \quad$ the terms are: $\frac{2}{5}, \frac{14}{5}, \frac{98}{5}$. $\checkmark \quad \{r = 7\}$

$\qquad\qquad\qquad$ If $\quad k = 3 \quad$ the terms are: $2, 6, 18$. $\checkmark \quad \{r = 3\}$

Example 8

A geometric sequence has $u_2 = -6$ and $u_5 = 162$. Find its general term.

$$u_2 = u_1 r = -6 \quad \dots (1)$$
$$\text{and} \quad u_5 = u_1 r^4 = 162 \quad \dots (2)$$

So, $\dfrac{u_1 r^4}{u_1 r} = \dfrac{162}{-6} \qquad \{(2) \div (1)\}$

$\therefore \quad r^3 = -27$

$\therefore \quad r = \sqrt[3]{-27}$

$\therefore \quad r = -3$

and so in (1) $\quad u_1(-3) = -6$

$\therefore \quad u_1 = 2$

Thus $\quad u_n = 2 \times (-3)^{n-1}$.

Note:

$(-3)^{n-1} \neq -3^{n-1}$

as we do not know the value of n.

If n is odd, then $\quad (-3)^{n-1} = 3^{n-1}$

If n is even, then $\quad (-3)^{n-1} = -3^{n-1}$

$\therefore$ we cannot simplify the answer.

Example 9

Find the first term of the geometric sequence $6, 6\sqrt{2}, 12, 12\sqrt{2}, \dots$ which exceeds 1400.

Now $u_1 = 6$ and $r = \sqrt{2}$

$\therefore \quad u_n = 6 \times (\sqrt{2})^{n-1}$.

Next we need to find n such that $u_n > 1400$.

Using a graphics calculator with $Y_1 = 6 \times (\sqrt{2})^{\wedge}(n-1)$, we view a *table of values:*

X	Y₁
15	768
16	1086.1
17	1536
18	2172.2
19	3072
20	4344.5
21	6144

X=15

So, the first term to exceed 1400 is u_{17} where $u_{17} = 1536$.

Note: Later we can solve problems like this one using logarithms.

EXERCISE 2D.1

1 For the geometric sequence with first two terms given, find b and c:

   a $\quad 2, 6, b, c, \dots$ b $\quad 10, 5, b, c, \dots$ c $\quad 12, -6, b, c, \dots$

2   a Show that the sequence $5, 10, 20, 40, \dots$ is geometric.

   b Find u_n and hence find the 15th term.

3   a Show that the sequence $12, -6, 3, -\frac{3}{2}, \dots$ is geometric.

   b Find u_n and hence find the 13th term (as a fraction).

4 Show that the sequence $8, -6, 4.5, -3.375, ...$ is geometric and hence find the 10th term as a decimal.

5 Show that the sequence $8, 4\sqrt{2}, 4, 2\sqrt{2}, ...$ is geometric. Hence find, in simplest form, the general term u_n.

6 Find k given that the following are consecutive terms of a geometric sequence:

    a $7, k, 28$ **b** $k, 3k, 20 - k$ **c** $k, k + 8, 9k$

7 Find the general term u_n of the geometric sequence which has:

    a $u_4 = 24$ and $u_7 = 192$ **b** $u_3 = 8$ and $u_6 = -1$

    c $u_7 = 24$ and $u_{15} = 384$ **d** $u_3 = 5$ and $u_7 = \frac{5}{4}$

8   **a** Find the first term of the sequence $2, 6, 18, 54, ...$ which exceeds $10\,000$.

    b Find the first term of the sequence $4, 4\sqrt{3}, 12, 12\sqrt{3}, ...$ which exceeds 4800.

    c Find the first term of the sequence $12, 6, 3, 1.5, ...$ which is less than 0.0001.

COMPOUND INTEREST

Consider the following: You invest $1000 in the bank. You leave the money in the bank for 3 years. You are paid an interest rate of 10% p.a. The interest is added to your investment each year.

An interest rate of 10% p.a. is paid, *increasing the value* of your investment yearly.

Your percentage increase each year is 10%, so at the end of the year you will have $100\% + 10\% = 110\%$ of the value at its start. This corresponds to a *multiplier* of 1.1.

After one year your investment is worth $1000 \times 1.1 = \$1100$

After two years it is worth
$$\$1100 \times 1.1$$
$$= \$1000 \times 1.1 \times 1.1$$
$$= \$1000 \times (1.1)^2 = \$1210$$

After three years it is worth
$$\$1210 \times 1.1$$
$$= \$1000 \times (1.1)^2 \times 1.1$$
$$= \$1000 \times (1.1)^3$$

This suggests that if the money is left in your account for n years it would amount to $\$1000 \times (1.1)^n$.

Observe that:
$$u_1 = \$1000 \qquad = \text{initial investment}$$
$$u_2 = u_1 \times 1.1 \qquad = \text{amount after 1 year}$$
$$u_3 = u_1 \times (1.1)^2 = \text{amount after 2 years}$$
$$u_4 = u_1 \times (1.1)^3 = \text{amount after 3 years}$$
$$\vdots$$
$$u_{n+1} = u_1 \times (1.1)^n = \text{amount after } n \text{ years}$$

In general,   we can use the compound interest formula $\boldsymbol{u_{n+1} = u_1 \times r^n}$

where $u_1 = $ initial investment $n = $ number of years

           $r = $ growth multiplier $u_{n+1} = $ amount after n years.

Example 10

$5000 is invested for 4 years at 7% p.a. compound interest, compounded annually. What will it amount to at the end of this period?

$u_5 = u_1 \times r^4$ is the amount after 4 years

$\quad\quad = 5000 \times (1.07)^4$ {for a 7% increase 100% becomes 107%}

$\quad\quad \approx 6553.98$ {5000 $\boxed{\times}$ 1.07 $\boxed{\wedge}$ 4 $\boxed{\text{ENTER}}$ }

So, it amounts to $6553.98.

Example 11

How much should I invest now if I want the maturing value to be $10 000 in 4 years' time, if I am able to invest at 8.5% p.a. compounded annually?

$u_1 = ?, \quad u_5 = 10\,000, \quad r = 1.085$

$\quad\quad\quad u_5 = u_1 \times r^4$ {using $u_{n+1} = u_1 \times r^n$}

$\therefore \quad 10\,000 = u_1 \times (1.085)^4$

$\therefore \quad u_1 = \dfrac{10\,000}{(1.085)^4}$

$\therefore \quad u_1 \approx 7215.74$ {10 000 $\boxed{\div}$ 1.085 $\boxed{\wedge}$ 4 $\boxed{\text{ENTER}}$ }

So, you should invest $7215.74 now.

EXERCISE 2D.2

1   **a**   What will an investment of $3000 at 10% p.a. compound interest amount to after 3 years?

   b   What part of this is interest?

2   How much compound interest is earned by investing €20 000 at 12% p.a. if the investment is over a 4 year period?

3   **a**   What will an investment of 30 000 Yen at 10% p.a. compound interest amount to after 4 years?

   b   What part of this is interest?

4   How much compound interest is earned by investing $80 000 at 9% p.a., if the investment is over a 3 year period?

5   What will an investment of 100 000 Yen amount to after 5 years if it earns 8% p.a. compounded twice annually?

6   What will an investment of £45 000 amount to after 21 months if it earns 7.5% p.a. compounded quarterly?

7   How much money must be invested now if you require $20 000 for a holiday in 4 years' time and the money can be invested at a fixed rate of 7.5% p.a. compounded annually?

8   What initial investment is required to produce a maturing amount of £15 000 in 60 months' time given that a fixed rate of 5.5% p.a. compounded annually is guaranteed?

9   How much should I invest now if I want a maturing amount of €25 000 in 3 years' time and the money can be invested at a fixed rate of 8% p.a. compounded quarterly?

10 What initial investment is required to produce a maturing amount of 40 000 Yen in 8 years' time if your money can be invested at 9% p.a., compounded monthly?

OTHER GEOMETRIC SEQUENCE PROBLEMS

Example 12

The initial population of rabbits on a farm was 50.
The population increased by 7% each week.
a   How many rabbits were present after:
   i   15 weeks   ii   30 weeks?
b   How long would it take for the population to reach 500?

We notice that $u_1 = 50$ and $r = 1.07$
$$u_2 = 50 \times 1.07 = \text{the population after 1 week}$$

a   i $u_{n+1} = u_1 \times r^n$ ii   and
   $\therefore \quad u_{16} = 50 \times (1.07)^{15}$ $u_{31} = 50 \times (1.07)^{30}$
   ≈ 137.95 ≈ 380.61
   i.e.,   138 rabbits   i.e.,   381 rabbits

b $u_{n+1} = u_1 \times (1.07)^n$ after n weeks
   So, we need to find when $50 \times (1.07)^n = 500$.
   Trial and error on your calculator gives $n \approx 34$ weeks
   or   using the **Equation Solver** gives $n \approx 34.03$

or   by finding the **point of intersection**
of $Y_1 = 50 \times 1.07^{\wedge}X$ and $Y_2 = 500$
on a graphics calculator, the solution is
≈ 34.03 weeks.

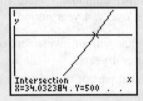

Intersection
X=34.032384 . Y=500

EXERCISE 2D.3

1   A nest of ants initially consists of 500 ants.
   The population is increasing by 12% each week.

   a   How many ants will there be after
      i   10 weeks   ii   20 weeks?

   b   Use technology to find how many weeks it
      will take for the ant population to reach 2000.

2 The animal *Eraticus* is endangered. Since 1992 there has only been one colony remaining and in 1992 the population of the colony was 555. Since then the population has been steadily decreasing at 4.5% per year. Find:

 a the population in the year 2007

 b the year in which we would expect the population to have declined to 50.

E   SERIES

A **series** is the addition of the terms of a sequence,

i.e., $u_1 + u_2 + u_3 + ... + u_n$ is a series.

The **sum** of a series is the result when we perform the addition.

Given a series which includes the first n terms of a sequence, its sum is

$S_n = u_1 + u_2 + u_3 + ... + u_n$.

Example 13

For the sequence 1, 4, 9, 16, 25, ...

 a Write down an expression for S_n.   **b** Find S_n for $n = 1, 2, 3, 4$ and 5.

a $S_n = 1^2 + 2^2 + 3^2 + 4^2 + ... + n^2$ {all terms are perfect squares}	**b** $S_1 = 1$ $S_2 = 1 + 4 = 5$ $S_3 = 1 + 4 + 9 = 14$ $S_4 = 1 + 4 + 9 + 16 = 30$ $S_5 = 1 + 4 + 9 + 16 + 25 = 55$

SIGMA NOTATION

$u_1 + u_2 + u_3 + u_4 + ... + u_n$ can be written more compactly using **sigma notation**.

$\sum$, which is called **sigma**, is the equivalent of capital S in the Greek alphabet.

We write $u_1 + u_2 + u_3 + u_4 + ... + u_n$ as $\displaystyle\sum_{k=1}^{n} u_k$.

So, $\displaystyle\sum_{k=1}^{n} u_k$ reads "the **sum of all numbers** of the form u_k where $k = 1, 2, 3, ...,$ up to n".

Example 14

Expand and evaluate: **a** $\displaystyle\sum_{k=1}^{7} (k+1)$ **b** $\displaystyle\sum_{k=1}^{5} \frac{1}{2^k}$

a $\displaystyle\sum_{k=1}^{7} (k+1)$ $= 2 + 3 + 4 + 5 + 6 + 7 + 8$ $= 35$	**b** $\displaystyle\sum_{k=1}^{5} \frac{1}{2^k}$ $= \frac{1}{2} + \frac{1}{4} + \frac{1}{8} + \frac{1}{16} + \frac{1}{32}$ $= \frac{31}{32}$

Note:

$$\sum_{k=1}^{n} (a_k + b_k) = \sum_{k=1}^{n} a_k + \sum_{k=1}^{n} b_k$$

If c is a constant, $\quad \sum_{k=1}^{n} ca_k = c \sum_{k=1}^{n} a_k \quad$ and $\quad \sum_{k=1}^{n} c = cn$

EXERCISE 2E.1

1 For the following sequences:

    i write down an expression for S_n **ii** find S_5.

   a $\quad 3, 11, 19, 27, \; ....$ **b** $\quad 42, 37, 32, 27, \; ....$ **c** $\quad 12, 6, 3, 1\frac{1}{2}, \; ....$

   d $\quad 2, 3, 4\frac{1}{2}, 6\frac{3}{4}, \; ....$ **e** $\quad 1, \frac{1}{2}, \frac{1}{4}, \frac{1}{8}, \; ....$ **f** $\quad 1, 8, 27, 64, \; ....$

2 Expand and evaluate:

   a $\displaystyle\sum_{k=1}^{4} (3k - 5)$ **b** $\displaystyle\sum_{k=1}^{5} (11 - 2k)$ **c** $\displaystyle\sum_{k=1}^{7} k(k + 1)$ **d** $\displaystyle\sum_{k=1}^{5} 10 \times 2^{k-1}$

3 For $u_n = 3n - 1$, write $u_1 + u_2 + u_3 + ... + u_{20}$ using sigma notation and evaluate the sum.

4 Show that:

   a $\displaystyle\sum_{k=1}^{n} c = cn$ **b** $\displaystyle\sum_{k=1}^{n} ca_k = c \sum_{k=1}^{n} a_k$ **c** $\displaystyle\sum_{k=1}^{n} (a_k + b_k) = \sum_{k=1}^{n} a_k + \sum_{k=1}^{n} b_k$

5 **a** Explain why $\displaystyle\sum_{k=1}^{n} (3k^2 + 4k - 3) = 3\sum_{k=1}^{n} k^2 + 4\sum_{k=1}^{n} k - 3n$

   b Given that $\displaystyle\sum_{k=1}^{n} k = \frac{n(n + 1)}{2}$ and $\displaystyle\sum_{k=1}^{n} k^2 = \frac{n(n + 1)(2n + 1)}{6}$

    find in simplest form $\displaystyle\sum_{k=1}^{n} (k + 1)(k + 2)$.

    Check your answer in the case when $n = 10$.

ARITHMETIC SERIES

An **arithmetic series** is the addition of successive terms of an arithmetic sequence.

For example: $21, 23, 25, 27, ..., 49$ is an arithmetic sequence.

So, $21 + 23 + 25 + 27 + ... + 49$ is an arithmetic series.

SUM OF AN ARITHMETIC SERIES

If the first term is u_1 and the common difference is d, then the terms are:
$u_1, \; u_1 + d, \; u_1 + 2d, \; u_1 + 3d,$ etc.

Suppose that u_n is the final term of an arithmetic series.

So, $S_n = u_1 + (u_1 + d) + (u_1 + 2d) + ... + (u_n - 2d) + (u_n - d) + u_n$

But $S_n = u_n + (u_n - d) + (u_n - 2d) + ... + (u_1 + 2d) + (u_1 + d) + u_1$ {reversing them}

Adding these two equations vertically we get

$$2S_n = \underbrace{(u_1 + u_n) + (u_1 + u_n) + (u_1 + u_n) + ... + (u_1 + u_n) + (u_1 + u_n) + (u_1 + u_n)}_{n \text{ of these}}$$

$\therefore\quad 2S_n = n(u_1 + u_n)$

$\therefore\quad S_n = \dfrac{n}{2}(u_1 + u_n)$ where $u_n = u_1 + (n-1)d$

$$\text{So,}\qquad \boldsymbol{S_n = \dfrac{n}{2}(u_1 + u_n)}\qquad or \qquad \boldsymbol{S_n = \dfrac{n}{2}(2u_1 + (n-1)d)}$$

Example 15

Find the sum of $4 + 7 + 10 + 13 + ...$ to 50 terms.

The series is arithmetic with $u_1 = 4$, $d = 3$ and $n = 50$.

So, $S_{50} = \dfrac{50}{2}(2 \times 4 + 49 \times 3)$ $\{$using $S_n = \dfrac{n}{2}(2u_1 + (n-1)d)\}$

$\qquad\quad = 3875$

Example 16

Find the sum of $-6 + 1 + 8 + 15 + ... + 141$.

The series is arithmetic with $u_1 = -6$, $d = 7$ and $u_n = 141$.

First we need to find n.

Now $u_n = u_1 + (n-1)d = 141$

$\therefore\quad -6 + 7(n-1) = 141$

$\therefore\quad 7(n-1) = 147$

$\therefore\quad n - 1 = 21$

$\therefore\quad n = 22$

Using $S_n = \frac{n}{2}(u_1 + u_n)$,

$S_{22} = \frac{22}{2}(-6 + 141)$

$\qquad = 11 \times 135$

$\qquad = 1485$

EXERCISE 2E.2

1 Find the sum of:

    a $\quad 3 + 7 + 11 + 15 + ...$ to 20 terms

    b $\quad \frac{1}{2} + 3 + 5\frac{1}{2} + 8 + ...$ to 50 terms

    c $\quad 100 + 93 + 86 + 79 + ...$ to 40 terms

    d $\quad 50 + 48\frac{1}{2} + 47 + 45\frac{1}{2} + ...$ to 80 terms

2 Find the sum of:

    a $\quad 5 + 8 + 11 + 14 + ... + 101$

    b $\quad 50 + 49\frac{1}{2} + 49 + 48\frac{1}{2} + ... + (-20)$

    c $\quad 8 + 10\frac{1}{2} + 13 + 15\frac{1}{2} + ... + 83$

3 Evaluate these arithmetic series:

    a $\sum_{k=1}^{10} (2k+5)$ **b** $\sum_{k=1}^{15} (k-50)$ **c** $\sum_{k=1}^{20} \left(\dfrac{k+3}{2}\right)$

4 An arithmetic series has seven terms. The first term is 5 and the last term is 53. Find the sum of the series.

5 An arithmetic series has eleven terms. The first term is 6 and the last term is -27. Find the sum of the series.

6

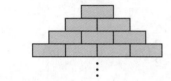

A bricklayer builds a triangular wall with layers of bricks as shown. If the bricklayer uses 171 bricks, how many layers did he build?

7 Each section of a soccer stadium has 44 rows with 22 seats in the first row, 23 in the second row, 24 in the third row, and so on. How many seats are there in:

    a row 44   **b** each section   **c** the stadium which has 25 sections?

8 Find the sum of:

    a the first 50 multiples of 11   **b** the multiples of 7 between 0 and 1000

    c the integers between 1 and 100 which are not divisible by 3.

9 Prove that the sum of the first n positive integers is $\frac{1}{2}n(n+1)$.

10 Consider the series of odd numbers $1+3+5+7+\ldots$.

    a What is the nth odd number u_n?

    b Prove that "the sum of the first n odd numbers is n^2".

    c Check your answer to **b** by finding S_1, S_2, S_3 and S_4.

11 Find the first two terms of an arithmetic sequence where the sixth term is 21 and the sum of the first seventeen terms is 0.

12 Three consecutive terms of an arithmetic sequence have a sum of 12 and a product of -80. Find the terms.   **Hint:** Let the terms be $x-d$, x and $x+d$.

13 Five consecutive terms of an arithmetic sequence have a sum of 40. The product of the middle and the two end terms is 224. Find the terms of the sequence.

GEOMETRIC SERIES

> A **geometric series** is the addition of successive terms of a geometric sequence.

For example,   1, 2, 4, 8, 16, ..., 1024   is a geometric sequence.

So, $1+2+4+8+16+\ldots+1024$ is a geometric series.

SUM OF A GEOMETRIC SERIES

If the first term is u_1 and the common ratio is r, then the terms are:

$$u_1, \ u_1 r, \ u_1 r^2, \ u_1 r^3, \ \ldots \quad \text{etc.}$$

So,
$$S_n = u_1 + u_1r + u_1r^2 + u_1r^3 + \ .... \ + u_1r^{n-2} + u_1r^{n-1}$$

$$\uparrow \qquad \uparrow \qquad \uparrow \qquad\qquad \uparrow \qquad \uparrow$$
$$u_2 \qquad u_3 \qquad u_4 \qquad\qquad u_{n-1} \qquad u_n$$

and for $r \neq 1$,
$$S_n = \frac{u_1(r^n - 1)}{r - 1} \quad or \quad S_n = \frac{u_1(1 - r^n)}{1 - r}.$$

Proof: If $S_n = u_1 + u_1r + u_1r^2 + u_1r^3 + ... + u_1r^{n-2} + u_1r^{n-1}$ .... (1)

then $rS_n = (u_1r + u_1r^2 + u_1r^3 + u_1r^4 + ... + u_1r^{n-1}) + u_1r^n$

$\therefore \ rS_n = (S_n - u_1) + u_1r^n$ {from (1)}

$\therefore \ rS_n - S_n = u_1r^n - u_1$

$\therefore \ S_n(r - 1) = u_1(r^n - 1)$ and so $S_n = \dfrac{u_1(r^n - 1)}{r - 1}$ or $\dfrac{u_1(1 - r^n)}{1 - r}$ for $r \neq 1$.

Discuss the case $r = 1$.

Example 17

Find the sum of $2 + 6 + 18 + 54 + ...$ to 12 terms.

The series is geometric with $u_1 = 2$, $r = 3$ and $n = 12$.

So, $S_{12} = \dfrac{2(3^{12} - 1)}{3 - 1}$ {using $S_n = \dfrac{u_1(r^n - 1)}{r - 1}$}

$= 531\,440$

Example 18

Find a formula for S_n for $9 - 3 + 1 - \frac{1}{3} + ...$ to n terms.

The series is geometric with $u_1 = 9$, $r = -\frac{1}{3}$, "n" $= n$.

So, $S_n = \dfrac{u_1(1 - r^n)}{1 - r} = \dfrac{9(1 - (-\frac{1}{3})^n)}{\frac{4}{3}}$

$\therefore \ S_n = \frac{27}{4}(1 - (-\frac{1}{3})^n)$

This answer cannot be simplified as we do not know if n is odd or even.

EXERCISE 2E.3

1 Find the sum of the following series:

   a $12 + 6 + 3 + 1.5 + ...$ to 10 terms

   b $\sqrt{7} + 7 + 7\sqrt{7} + 49 + ...$ to 12 terms

   c $6 - 3 + 1\frac{1}{2} - \frac{3}{4} + ...$ to 15 terms

   d $1 - \frac{1}{\sqrt{2}} + \frac{1}{2} - \frac{1}{2\sqrt{2}} + ...$ to 20 terms

2 Find a formula for S_n for:

    a $\sqrt{3} + 3 + 3\sqrt{3} + 9 + ...$ to n terms

    b $12 + 6 + 3 + 1\frac{1}{2} + ...$ to n terms

    c $0.9 + 0.09 + 0.009 + 0.0009 + ...$ to n terms

    d $20 - 10 + 5 - 2\frac{1}{2} + ...$ to n terms

3 Evaluate these geometric series:

    a $\displaystyle\sum_{k=1}^{10} 3 \times 2^{k-1}$ **b** $\displaystyle\sum_{k=1}^{12} (\tfrac{1}{2})^{k-2}$ **c** $\displaystyle\sum_{k=1}^{25} 6 \times (-2)^{k}$

4 Each year a salesperson is paid a bonus of $2000 which is banked into the same account. It earns a fixed rate of interest of 6% p.a. with interest being paid annually. The amount at the end of each year in the account is calculated as follows:

$$A_0 = 2000$$
$$A_1 = A_0 \times 1.06 + 2000$$
$$A_2 = A_1 \times 1.06 + 2000 \quad \text{etc.}$$

    a Show that $A_2 = 2000 + 2000 \times 1.06 + 2000 \times (1.06)^2$.

    b Show that $A_3 = 2000[1 + 1.06 + (1.06)^2 + (1.06)^3]$.

    c Find the total bank balance after 10 years, assuming there are no fees or charges.

5 Consider $S_n = \frac{1}{2} + \frac{1}{4} + \frac{1}{8} + \frac{1}{16} + ... + \frac{1}{2^n}$.

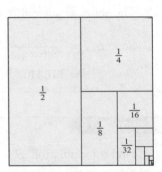

    a Find S_1, S_2, S_3, S_4 and S_5 in fractional form.

    b From **a** guess the formula for S_n.

    c Find S_n using $S_n = \dfrac{u_1(1 - r^n)}{1 - r}$.

    d Comment on S_n as n gets very large.

    e What is the relationship between the given diagram and **d**?

SUM OF AN INFINITE GEOMETRIC SERIES

Sometimes it is necessary to consider $S_n = \dfrac{u_1(1 - r^n)}{1 - r}$ when n gets very large. What happens to S_n in this situation?

If $|r| > 1$, the series is said to be **divergent** and the sum becomes infinitely large.

If $-1 < r < 1$, i.e., $|r| < 1$, then r^n approaches 0 for very large n.

This means that S_n will get closer and closer to $\dfrac{u_1}{1 - r}$.

We say that the series **converges** and we write its sum as

$$S = \frac{u_1}{1 - r} \quad \text{for } |r| < 1$$

We call this the **limiting sum** of the series.

This result can be used to find the value of recurring decimals.

Example 19

Write $0.\bar{7}$ as a rational number.

$0.\bar{7} = \frac{7}{10} + \frac{7}{100} + \frac{7}{1000} + \frac{7}{10\,000} + ...$

which is a geometric series with infinitely many terms

$$\therefore \quad S = \frac{u_1}{1-r} = \frac{\frac{7}{10}}{1 - \frac{1}{10}} = \frac{7}{9}$$

So, $0.\bar{7} = \frac{7}{9}$

EXERCISE 2E.4

1 Consider $0.\bar{3} = \frac{3}{10} + \frac{3}{100} + \frac{3}{1000} + ...$ which is an infinite geometric series.

   a What are **i** u_1 and **ii** r?

   b Using **a**, show that $0.\bar{3} = \frac{1}{3}$.

2 Write as a rational number: **a** $0.\bar{4}$ **b** $0.\overline{16}$ **c** $0.\overline{312}$

3 Use $S = \dfrac{u_1}{1-r}$ to check your answers to **Exercise 2E.3**, question **5d**.

4 Find the sum of each of the following infinite geometric series:

   a $18 + 12 + 8 + ...$ **b** $18.9 - 6.3 + 2.1 - ......$

5 Find each of the following:

   a $\displaystyle\sum_{k=1}^{\infty} \frac{3}{4^k}$ **b** $\displaystyle\sum_{k=0}^{\infty} 6\left(-\frac{2}{5}\right)^k$

6 Determine whether each of the following series is convergent. If so, find the sum of the series. If not, find the smallest value of n for which the sum of the first n terms of the series exceeds 100.

   a $18 - 9 + 4.5 - ......$ **b** $1.2 + 1.8 + 2.7 + ...$

7 The sum of the first three terms of a convergent geometric series is 19. The sum of the series is 27. Find the first term and the common ratio.

8 The second term of a convergent geometric series is $\frac{8}{5}$.

   The sum of the series is 10. Show that there are two possible series and find the first term and the common ratio in each case.

9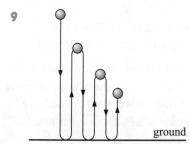

A ball takes 1 second to hit the ground when dropped. It then takes 90% of this time to rebound to its new height and this continues until the ball comes to rest.

   a Show that the total time of motion is given by $1 + 2(0.9) + 2(0.9)^2 + 2(0.9)^3 + ...$

   b Find S_n for the series in **a**.

   c How long does it take for the ball to come to rest?

   ground

Note: This diagram is inaccurate as the motion is really up and down on the same spot. It has been separated out to help us visualise what is happening.

F   MISCELLANEOUS PROBLEMS

EXERCISE 2F

1 Henk starts a new job selling TV sets. He hopes to sell 11 sets in the first week, 14 in the next, 17 in the next, and so on in arithmetic sequence. In what week does Henk hope to sell his 2000th TV set?

2 A computer is bought for \$2795 and depreciates at a rate of 2% per month. After how many months will its value reduce to \$500?

3 A geometric series has a second term of 6 and the sum of its first three terms is -14. Find its fourth term.

4 When a ball falls vertically off a table it rebounds 75% of its height after each bounce. If it travels a total distance of 490 cm, how high was the table top above the floor?

5 An arithmetic and a geometric sequence both have a first term of 1 and their second terms are equal. The 14th term of the arithmetic sequence is three times the third term of the geometric sequence. Find the twentieth term of each sequence.

6 Evaluate: **a** $\displaystyle\sum_{k=1}^{5} k(k+1)(k+2)$ **b** $\displaystyle\sum_{k=6}^{12} 100 \times (1.2)^{k-3}$

7 Find n given that: **a** $\displaystyle\sum_{k=1}^{n} (2k+3) = 1517$ **b** $\displaystyle\sum_{k=1}^{n} 2 \times 3^{k-1} = 177\,146$

8 Find x if $\displaystyle\sum_{k=1}^{\infty} \left(\frac{3x}{2}\right)^{k-1} = 4$.

9 The sum of the first n terms of an arithmetic sequence is $\dfrac{n(3n+11)}{2}$.

   a Find its first two terms.   **b** Find the twentieth term of the sequence.

10 **Mortgage repayments:**

   \$8000 is borrowed over a 2-year period at a rate of 12% p.a. Quarterly repayments are made and the interest is adjusted each quarter, which means that the amount repaid in the period is deducted and the interest is charged on the new amount owed.

   There are $2 \times 4 = 8$ repayments and the interest per quarter is $\frac{12\%}{4} = 3\%$.

   At the end of the first quarter the amount owed, A_1, is given by   \$8000 $\times 1.03 - R$, where R is the amount of each repayment.

   At the end of the second quarter the amount owed, A_2, is given by:

   $$\begin{aligned} A_2 &= A_1 \times 1.03 - R \\ &= (\$8000 \times 1.03 - R) \times 1.03 - R \\ &= \$8000 \times (1.03)^2 - 1.03R - R \end{aligned}$$

   a Find a similar expression for the amount owed at the end of the third quarter, A_3.

   b Write down an expression for the amount owed at the end of the 8th quarter, A_8, and hence deduce the value of R. **Hint:** What value do we want A_8 to have?

   c If the amount borrowed at adjusted interest conditions is \$P, the interest rate is $r\%$ per repayment interval, and there are m repayments, show that the amount of each repayment is $R = \dfrac{P(1 + \frac{r}{100})^m \times \frac{r}{100}}{(1 + \frac{r}{100})^m - 1}$.

INVESTIGATION   VON KOCH'S SNOWFLAKE CURVE

  ,  ,  , 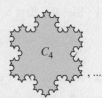 , ...

In this investigation we consider a **limit curve** named after the Swedish mathematician Niels Fabian Helge von Koch (1870 - 1924).

To draw **Von Koch's Snowflake curve** we

- start with an equilateral triangle, C_1
- then divide each side into 3 equal parts
- then on each middle part draw an equilateral triangle
- then delete the side of the smaller triangle which lies on C_1.

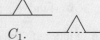

The resulting curve is C_2, and C_3, C_4, C_5, ... are found by 'pushing out' equilateral triangles on each edge of the previous curve as we did with C_1 to get C_2.

We get a sequence of special curves C_1, C_2, C_3, C_4, ... and Von Koch's curve is the limiting case when n is infinitely large.

Your task is to investigate the perimeter and area of Von Koch's curve.

What to do:

1   Suppose C_1 has a perimeter of 3 units. Find the perimeter of C_2, C_3, C_4 and C_5.

    Hint: ——•——•—— becomes ——／\＼—— so 3 parts become 4 parts.

    Remembering that Von Koch's curve is C_n, where n is infinitely large, find the perimeter of Von Koch's curve.

2   Suppose the area of C_1 is 1 unit^2. Explain why the areas of C_2, C_3, C_4 and C_5 are

$$A_2 = 1 + \tfrac{1}{3} \text{ units}^2 \qquad\qquad A_3 = 1 + \tfrac{1}{3}[1 + \tfrac{4}{9}] \text{ units}^2$$

$$A_4 = 1 + \tfrac{1}{3}[1 + \tfrac{4}{9} + (\tfrac{4}{9})^2] \text{ units}^2 \qquad A_5 = 1 + \tfrac{1}{3}[1 + \tfrac{4}{9} + (\tfrac{4}{9})^2 + (\tfrac{4}{9})^3] \text{ units}^2.$$

    Use your calculator to find A_n where $n = 1, 2, 3, 4, 5, 6, 7$, etc., giving answers which are as accurate as your calculator permits.

    What do you think will be the area within Von Koch's snowflake curve?

3   Is there anything remarkable about your answers to **1** and **2**?

4   Similarly, investigate the sequence of curves obtained by 'pushing out' squares on successive curves from the middle third of each side,

    i.e., the curves C_1, C_2, C_3, C_4, etc.

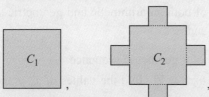 , 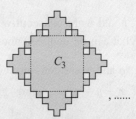 , ...

Region contains 8 holes.

REVIEW SET 2A

1 List the first four members of the sequences defined by:

    a $u_n = 3^{n-2}$ **b** $u_n = \dfrac{3n+2}{n+3}$ **c** $u_n = 2^n - (-3)^n$

2 A sequence is defined by $u_n = 68 - 5n$.

    a Prove that the sequence is arithmetic.

    b Find u_1 and d.

    c Find the 37th term.

    d What is the first term of the sequence less than -200?

3   **a** Show that the sequence   3, 12, 48, 192, ...   is geometric.

    b Find u_n and hence find u_9.

4 Find k if $3k$, $k-2$ and $k+7$ are consecutive terms of an arithmetic sequence.

5 Find the general term of an arithmetic sequence given that $u_7 = 31$ and $u_{15} = -17$. Hence, find the value of u_{34}.

6 A sequence is defined by $u_n = 6(\tfrac{1}{2})^{n-1}$.

    a Prove that the sequence is geometric.   **b** Find u_1 and r.

    c Find the 16th term to 3 significant figures.

7 Show that   28, 23, 18, 13, ...   is arithmetic and hence find u_n and the sum S_n of the first n terms in simplest form.

8 Find k given that 4, k and $k^2 - 1$ are consecutive geometric terms.

9 Determine the general term of a geometric sequence given that its sixth term is $\frac{16}{3}$ and its tenth term is $\frac{256}{3}$.

10 Find the sum of each of the following infinite geometric series:

    a $1.21 - 1.1 + 1 - \ldots\ldots$ **b** $\frac{14}{3} + \frac{4}{3} + \frac{8}{21} + \ldots\ldots$

11 $x + 3$ and $x - 2$ are the first two terms of a geometric series. Find the values of x for which the series converges.

12 The sum of the first two terms of a geometric series is 90. The third term is 24.

    a Show that there are two possible series and find the first term and the common ratio in each case.

    b Show that both series converge and find their respective sums.

13 a, b and c are consecutive terms of both an arithmetic and geometric sequence. What can be deduced about a, b and c?

14 x, y and z are consecutive terms of a geometric sequence. If $x + y + z = \frac{7}{3}$ and $x^2 + y^2 + z^2 = \frac{91}{9}$, find the values of x, y and z.

REVIEW SET 2B

1 a Determine the number of terms in the sequence $24, 23\frac{1}{4}, 22\frac{1}{2}, ..., -36$.

 b Find the value of u_{35} for the sequence in **a**.

 c Find the sum of the terms of the sequence in **a**.

2 Insert six numbers between 23 and 9 so that all eight numbers are in arithmetic sequence.

3 Find the formula for u_n, the general term of:

 a $86, 83, 80, 77, ...$ **b** $\frac{3}{4}, 1, \frac{7}{6}, \frac{9}{7}, ...$ **c** $100, 90, 81, 72.9, ...$

 Note: One of these sequences is neither arithmetic nor geometric.

4 Write down the expansion of: **a** $\displaystyle\sum_{k=1}^{7} k^2$ **b** $\displaystyle\sum_{k=1}^{8} \frac{k+3}{k+2}$

5 Write in the form $\displaystyle\sum_{k=1}^{n} (.....)$:

 a $4 + 11 + 18 + 25 + ...$ for n terms   **b** $\frac{1}{4} + \frac{1}{8} + \frac{1}{16} + \frac{1}{32} + ...$ for n terms.

6 Find the sum of:

 a $3 + 9 + 15 + 21 + ...$ to 23 terms   **b** $24 + 12 + 6 + 3 + ...$ to 12 terms.

7 Calculate: **a** $\displaystyle\sum_{k=1}^{8} \left(\frac{31 - 3k}{2} \right)$ **b** $\displaystyle\sum_{k=1}^{15} 50(0.8)^{k-1}$

8 Find the first term of the sequence $5, 10, 20, 40, ...$ which exceeds $10\,000$.

9 What will an investment of €6000 at 7% p.a. compound interest amount to after 5 years if the interest is compounded:

 a annually   **b** quarterly   **c** monthly?

10 Find the sum of each of the following infinite geometric series:

 a $18 - 12 + 8 - ......$ **b** $8 + 4\sqrt{2} + 4 + ...$

11 $2x$ and $x - 2$ are the first two terms of a convergent geometric series. If the sum of the series is $\frac{18}{7}$, find x, clearly explaining why there is only one possible value.

12 Find $\displaystyle\sum_{k=7}^{\infty} 5 \left(\frac{2}{5} \right)^{k-1}$.

13 a, b, c, d and e are consecutive terms of an arithmetic sequence.

 Prove that $a + e = b + d = 2c$.

14 Find the sum of the n consecutive geometric terms which can be inserted between 1 and 2.

15 Suppose an arithmetic sequence and a geometric sequence with common ratio r have the same first two terms. Show that the third term of the geometric sequence is $\dfrac{r^2}{2r - 1}$ times the third term of the arithmetic sequence.

REVIEW SET 2C

1 A geometric sequence has $u_6 = 24$ and $u_{11} = 768$. Determine the general term of the sequence and hence find:

    a u_{17} **b** the sum of the first 15 terms.

2 How many terms of the series $11 + 16 + 21 + 26 + ...$ are needed to exceed a sum of 450?

3 Find the first term of the sequence $24, 8, \frac{8}{3}, \frac{8}{9}, ...$ which is less than 0.001.

4 **a** Determine the number of terms in the sequence $128, 64, 32, 16, ..., \frac{1}{512}$.

    b Find the sum of these terms.

5 $12 500 is invested in an account which pays 8.25% p.a. compounded. Find the value of the investment after 5 years if the interest is compounded:

    a half-yearly   **b** monthly.

6 How much should be invested at a fixed rate of 9% p.a. compounded interest if you wish it to amount to $20 000 after 4 years with interest paid monthly?

7 In 2004 there were 3000 koalas on Koala Island. Since then, the population of koalas on the island has increased by 5% each year.

    a How many koalas were on the island in 2007?

    b In what year will the population first exceed 5000?

8 A ball bounces from a height of 2 metres and returns to 80% of its previous height on each bounce. Find the total distance travelled by the ball until it stops bouncing.

9 **a** Under what conditions will the series $\displaystyle\sum_{k=1}^{\infty} 50(2x-1)^{k-1}$ converge? Explain!

    b Find $\displaystyle\sum_{k=1}^{\infty} 50(2x-1)^{k-1}$ if $x = 0.3$.

10 The sum of the first n terms of a sequence is $\dfrac{3n^2 + 5n}{2}$.

    a Find the nth term.

    b Prove that the sequence is arithmetic.

11 a, b and c are consecutive terms of an arithmetic sequence. Prove that the following are also consecutive terms of an arithmetic sequence:

    a $b+c$, $c+a$ and $a+b$ **b** $\dfrac{1}{\sqrt{b}+\sqrt{c}}$, $\dfrac{1}{\sqrt{c}+\sqrt{a}}$ and $\dfrac{1}{\sqrt{a}+\sqrt{b}}$

12 Show that $\underbrace{(111111......1)}_{2n\ 1\text{'s}} - \underbrace{(22222......2)}_{n\ 2\text{'s}}$ is a perfect square.

    (For example: $11 - 2 = 9 = 3^2$ and $1111 - 22 = 1089 = 33^2$.)

Chapter 3

Exponentials

Contents:

We often deal with numbers that are repeatedly multiplied together. Mathematicians use **indices** or **exponents** to represent such expressions. For example, $5 \times 5 \times 5 = 5^3$.

Indices have many applications in areas such as finance, engineering, physics, electronics, biology and computer science. Problems encountered in these areas may involve situations where quantities increase or decrease over time. Such problems are often examples of **exponential growth** or **decay**.

OPENING PROBLEM   LEGEND OF THE
AMBALAPPUZHA PAAL PAYASAM

According to Hindu legend, Lord Krishna once appeared as a sage before the king who ruled a region of India, and challenged him to a game of chess. The prize if Lord Krishna won was based on the chessboard: that the king would provide him with a single grain of rice for the first square, two grains of rice for the second square, four grains of rice for the third square, and so on doubling the rice on each successive square on the board. Lord Krishna of course did win, and the king was most unhappy when he realised he owed more rice than there was in the world.

Consider the following questions:
  1 Is there a function which describes the number of grains of rice on each square?
  2 How many grains of rice would there be on the 40th square?
  3 Using your knowledge of series, find the total number of grains of rice that the king owed.

A   INDEX NOTATION

Rather than writing $3 \times 3 \times 3 \times 3 \times 3$, we can write such a product as 3^5.

3^5 reads "three to the power of five" or "three with index five".

Thus $4^3 = 4 \times 4 \times 4$ and $5^6 = 5 \times 5 \times 5 \times 5 \times 5 \times 5$.

$$3^5$$

power, index or exponent

base   exponent

If n is a positive integer, then a^n is the product of n factors of a.

$$a^n = \underbrace{a \times a \times a \times a \times \ \dots\dots\ \times a}_{n \text{ factors}}$$

EXERCISE 3A

1 List the first six powers of:
    a 2   **b** 3   **c** 4

2 Copy and complete the values of these common powers:
    a $5^1 = \dots.$, $5^2 = \dots.$, $5^3 = \dots.$, $5^4 = \dots$
    b $6^1 = \dots.$, $6^2 = \dots.$, $6^3 = \dots.$, $6^4 = \dots$
    c $7^1 = \dots.$, $7^2 = \dots.$, $7^3 = \dots.$, $7^4 = \dots$

B   EVALUATING POWERS

So far we have only considered **positive** bases raised to a power.

We will now briefly look at **negative** bases. Consider the statements below:

$(-1)^1 = -1$ $(-2)^1 = -2$

$(-1)^2 = -1 \times -1 = 1$ $(-2)^2 = -2 \times -2 = 4$

$(-1)^3 = -1 \times -1 \times -1 = -1$ $(-2)^3 = -2 \times -2 \times -2 = -8$

$(-1)^4 = -1 \times -1 \times -1 \times -1 = 1$ $(-2)^4 = -2 \times -2 \times -2 \times -2 = 16$

From the patterns above we can see that:

A **negative** base raised to an **odd** power is **negative**.

A **negative** base raised to an **even** power is **positive**.

CALCULATOR USE

Although different calculators vary in the appearance of keys, they all perform operations of raising to powers in a similar manner.

Power keys $\boxed{x^2}$ squares the number in the display.

       $\boxed{\wedge}$ 3   raises the number in the display to the power 3.

       $\boxed{\wedge}$ 5   raises the number in the display to the power 5.

       $\boxed{\wedge}$ $\boxed{(-)}$ 4   raises the number in the display to the power -4.

Example 1

Find, using your calculator: a 6^5 b $(-5)^4$ c -7^4

		Answer
a	Press: 6 $\boxed{\wedge}$ 5 **ENTER**	7776
b	Press: $\boxed{(}$ $\boxed{(-)}$ 5 $\boxed{)}$ $\boxed{\wedge}$ 4 **ENTER**	625
c	Press: $\boxed{(-)}$ 7 $\boxed{\wedge}$ 4 **ENTER**	-2401

Note: You will need to check if your calculator uses the same key sequence as in the examples. If not, work out the sequence which gives you the correct answers.

Example 2

Find using your calculator, and comment on: **a** 5^{-2} **b** $\dfrac{1}{5^2}$

		Answer
a	Press: 5 $\boxed{\wedge}$ $\boxed{(-)}$ 2 $\boxed{\text{ENTER}}$	0.04
b	Press: 1 $\boxed{\div}$ 5 $\boxed{\wedge}$ 2 $\boxed{\text{ENTER}}$	0.04

The answers indicate that $5^{-2} = \dfrac{1}{5^2}$.

EXERCISE 3B

1 Simplify, then use a calculator to check your answer:

   a $(-1)^5$ **b** $(-1)^6$ **c** $(-1)^{14}$ **d** $(-1)^{19}$

   e $(-1)^8$ **f** -1^8 **g** $-(-1)^8$ **h** $(-2)^5$

   i -2^5 **j** $-(-2)^6$ **k** $(-5)^4$ **l** $-(-5)^4$

2 Use your calculator to find the value of the following, recording the entire display:

   a 4^7 **b** 7^4 **c** -5^5 **d** $(-5)^5$ **e** 8^6

   f $(-8)^6$ **g** -8^6 **h** 2.13^9 **i** -2.13^9 **j** $(-2.13)^9$

3 Use your calculator to find the values of the following:

   a 9^{-1} **b** $\dfrac{1}{9^1}$ **c** 6^{-2} **d** $\dfrac{1}{6^2}$

   e 3^{-4} **f** $\dfrac{1}{3^4}$ **g** 17^0 **h** $(0.366)^0$

   What do you notice?

4 Consider $3^1, 3^2, 3^3, 3^4, 3^5$ ....   Look for a pattern and find the last digit of 3^{101}.

5 What is the last digit of 7^{217}?

6 Answer the **Opening Problem** on page **78**.

C   INDEX LAWS

The following are **laws of indices** for $m, n \in \mathbb{Z}$:

- $a^m \times a^n = a^{m+n}$
- $\dfrac{a^m}{a^n} = a^{m-n}$ $(a \neq 0)$
- $\left(\dfrac{a}{b}\right)^n = \dfrac{a^n}{b^n}$ $(b \neq 0)$

- $(a^m)^n = a^{mn}$
- $(ab)^n = a^n b^n$
- $a^0 = 1$ for all $a \neq 0$

- a^{-n} and a^n are reciprocals, i.e., $a^{-n} = \dfrac{1}{a^n}$ for all $a \neq 0$.

Example 3

Write as powers of 2:

a $\quad 16$ b $\quad \frac{1}{16}$ c $\quad 1$ d $\quad 4 \times 2^n$ e $\quad \frac{2^m}{8}$

a $\quad 16$	b $\quad \frac{1}{16}$	c $\quad 1$	d $\quad 4 \times 2^n$	e $\quad \frac{2^m}{8}$
$= 2 \times 2 \times 2 \times 2$	$= \frac{1}{2^4}$	$= 2^0$	$= 2^2 \times 2^n$	$= \frac{2^m}{2^3}$
$= 2^4$	$= 2^{-4}$		$= 2^{2+n}$	$= 2^{m-3}$

Example 4

Write without negative indices: $\quad \dfrac{a^{-3}b^2}{c^{-1}}$

$$\frac{a^{-3}b^2}{c^{-1}} = \frac{b^2 c}{a^3} \qquad \{as \quad a^{-3} = \frac{1}{a^3}, \quad \frac{1}{c^{-1}} = c^1\}$$

Example 5

Write $\dfrac{1}{2^{1-n}}$ in non-fractional form.

$$\frac{1}{2^{1-n}} = 2^{-(1-n)}$$
$$= 2^{-1+n}$$
$$= 2^{n-1}$$

EXERCISE 3C.1

1 Write as powers of 2:

a $\quad 4$ b $\quad \frac{1}{4}$ c $\quad 8$ d $\quad \frac{1}{8}$ e $\quad 32$ f $\quad \frac{1}{32}$

g $\quad 2$ h $\quad \frac{1}{2}$ i $\quad 64$ j $\quad \frac{1}{64}$ k $\quad 128$ l $\quad \frac{1}{128}$

2 Write as powers of 3:

a $\quad 9$ b $\quad \frac{1}{9}$ c $\quad 27$ d $\quad \frac{1}{27}$ e $\quad 3$ f $\quad \frac{1}{3}$

g $\quad 81$ h $\quad \frac{1}{81}$ i $\quad 1$ j $\quad 243$ k $\quad \frac{1}{243}$

3 Write as a single power of 2:

a $\quad 2 \times 2^a$ b $\quad 4 \times 2^b$ c $\quad 8 \times 2^t$ d $\quad (2^{x+1})^2$ e $\quad (2^{1-n})^{-1}$

f $\quad \frac{2^c}{4}$ g $\quad \frac{2^m}{2^{-m}}$ h $\quad \frac{4}{2^{1-n}}$ i $\quad \frac{2^{x+1}}{2^x}$ j $\quad \frac{4^x}{2^{1-x}}$

4 Write as a single power of 3:

a $\quad 9 \times 3^p$ b $\quad 27^a$ c $\quad 3 \times 9^n$ d $\quad 27 \times 3^d$ e $\quad 9 \times 27^t$

f $\quad \frac{3^y}{3}$ g $\quad \frac{3}{3^y}$ h $\quad \frac{9}{27^t}$ i $\quad \frac{9^a}{3^{1-a}}$ j $\quad \frac{9^{n+1}}{3^{2n-1}}$

5 Write without negative indices:

a ab^{-2} b $(ab)^{-2}$ c $(2ab^{-1})^2$ d $(3a^{-2}b)^2$ e $\dfrac{a^2b^{-1}}{c^2}$

f $\dfrac{a^2b^{-1}}{c^{-2}}$ g $\dfrac{1}{a^{-3}}$ h $\dfrac{a^{-2}}{b^{-3}}$ i $\dfrac{2a^{-1}}{d^2}$ j $\dfrac{12a}{m^{-3}}$

6 Write in non-fractional form:

a $\dfrac{1}{a^n}$ b $\dfrac{1}{b^{-n}}$ c $\dfrac{1}{3^{2-n}}$ d $\dfrac{a^n}{b^{-m}}$ e $\dfrac{a^{-n}}{a^{2+n}}$

RATIONAL INDICES

Notice that $a^{\frac{1}{2}} \times a^{\frac{1}{2}} = a^{\frac{1}{2}+\frac{1}{2}} = a^1 = a$ {for index laws to be obeyed}

and $\sqrt{a} \times \sqrt{a} = a$ also.

So, $a^{\frac{1}{2}} = \sqrt{a}$ {by direct comparison}

Likewise $a^{\frac{1}{3}} \times a^{\frac{1}{3}} \times a^{\frac{1}{3}} = a^1 = a$

and $\sqrt[3]{a} \times \sqrt[3]{a} \times \sqrt[3]{a} = a$

suggests $a^{\frac{1}{3}} = \sqrt[3]{a}$

Thus in general, $a^{\frac{1}{n}} = \sqrt[n]{a}$ where $\sqrt[n]{a}$ reads "the nth root of a".

Notice also that $a^{\frac{2}{3}} \times a^{\frac{2}{3}} \times a^{\frac{2}{3}} = a^2$

$\therefore \left(a^{\frac{2}{3}}\right)^3 = a^2$ {if $(a^m)^n = a^{mn}$ is to be used}

$\therefore a^{\frac{2}{3}} = \sqrt[3]{a^2}.$

In general, $a^{\frac{m}{n}} = \sqrt[n]{a^m}$

Example 6

Write as a single power of 2:   a $\sqrt[3]{2}$ b $\dfrac{1}{\sqrt{2}}$ c $\sqrt[5]{4}$

a $\sqrt[3]{2}$
$= 2^{\frac{1}{3}}$

b $\dfrac{1}{\sqrt{2}}$
$= \dfrac{1}{2^{\frac{1}{2}}}$
$= 2^{-\frac{1}{2}}$

c $\sqrt[5]{4}$
$= (2^2)^{\frac{1}{5}}$
$= 2^{2\times\frac{1}{5}}$
$= 2^{\frac{2}{5}}$

Example 7

Use your calculator to evaluate $2^{\frac{7}{5}}$.

Calculator:	*Answer:*
For $2^{\frac{7}{5}}$ press: $2 \boxed{\wedge} \boxed{(} 7 \boxed{\div} 5 \boxed{)} \boxed{\textbf{ENTER}}$	$\approx 2.639\,015$

Example 8

Without using a calculator, write in simplest rational form: **a** $8^{\frac{4}{3}}$ **b** $27^{-\frac{2}{3}}$

a $8^{\frac{4}{3}}$

$= (2^3)^{\frac{4}{3}}$

$= 2^{3 \times \frac{4}{3}}$ $\{(a^m)^n = a^{mn}\}$

$= 2^4$

$= 16$

b $27^{-\frac{2}{3}}$

$= (3^3)^{-\frac{2}{3}}$

$= 3^{3 \times -\frac{2}{3}}$

$= 3^{-2}$

$= \frac{1}{9}$

EXERCISE 3C.2

1 Write as a single power of 2:

   a $\sqrt[5]{2}$ **b** $\dfrac{1}{\sqrt[5]{2}}$ **c** $2\sqrt{2}$ **d** $4\sqrt{2}$ **e** $\dfrac{1}{\sqrt[3]{2}}$

   f $2 \times \sqrt[3]{2}$ **g** $\dfrac{4}{\sqrt{2}}$ **h** $(\sqrt{2})^3$ **i** $\dfrac{1}{\sqrt[3]{16}}$ **j** $\dfrac{1}{\sqrt{8}}$

2 Write as a single power of 3:

   a $\sqrt[3]{3}$ **b** $\dfrac{1}{\sqrt[3]{3}}$ **c** $\sqrt[4]{3}$ **d** $3\sqrt{3}$ **e** $\dfrac{1}{9\sqrt{3}}$

3 Write the following in the form a^x where a is a prime number and x is rational:

   a $\sqrt[3]{7}$ **b** $\sqrt[4]{27}$ **c** $\sqrt[5]{16}$ **d** $\sqrt[3]{32}$ **e** $\sqrt[7]{49}$

   f $\dfrac{1}{\sqrt[3]{7}}$ **g** $\dfrac{1}{\sqrt[4]{27}}$ **h** $\dfrac{1}{\sqrt[5]{16}}$ **i** $\dfrac{1}{\sqrt[3]{32}}$ **j** $\dfrac{1}{\sqrt[7]{49}}$

4 Use your calculator to find:

   a $3^{\frac{3}{4}}$ **b** $2^{\frac{7}{8}}$ **c** $2^{-\frac{1}{3}}$ **d** $4^{-\frac{3}{5}}$

5 Use your calculator to evaluate in three different ways:

   a $\sqrt{9}$ **b** $\sqrt[4]{8}$ **c** $\sqrt[5]{27}$ **d** $\dfrac{1}{\sqrt[3]{7}}$

6 Without using a calculator, write in simplest rational form:

   a $4^{\frac{3}{2}}$ **b** $8^{\frac{5}{3}}$ **c** $16^{\frac{3}{4}}$ **d** $25^{\frac{3}{2}}$ **e** $32^{\frac{2}{5}}$

   f $4^{-\frac{1}{2}}$ **g** $9^{-\frac{3}{2}}$ **h** $8^{-\frac{4}{3}}$ **i** $27^{-\frac{4}{3}}$ **j** $125^{-\frac{2}{3}}$

D   ALGEBRAIC EXPANSION AND FACTORISATION

EXPANSION LAWS

$$(a+b)(c+d) = ac + ad + bc + bd$$
$$(a+b)(a-b) = a^2 - b^2$$
$$(a+b)^2 = a^2 + 2ab + b^2$$
$$(a-b)^2 = a^2 - 2ab + b^2$$

Example 9

Expand and simplify: $x^{-\frac{1}{2}}(x^{\frac{3}{2}} + 2x^{\frac{1}{2}} - 3x^{-\frac{1}{2}})$

$x^{-\frac{1}{2}}(x^{\frac{3}{2}} + 2x^{\frac{1}{2}} - 3x^{-\frac{1}{2}})$

$= x^{-\frac{1}{2}} \times x^{\frac{3}{2}} + x^{-\frac{1}{2}} \times 2x^{\frac{1}{2}} - x^{-\frac{1}{2}} \times 3x^{-\frac{1}{2}}$ {each term is $\times$ by $x^{-\frac{1}{2}}$}

$= x^1 + 2x^0 - 3x^{-1}$ {adding indices}

$= x + 2 - \dfrac{3}{x}$

Example 10

Expand and simplify: a $(2^x + 3)(2^x + 1)$ b $(e^x + e^{-x})^2$

a $(2^x + 3)(2^x + 1)$
$= 2^x \times 2^x + 2^x + 3 \times 2^x + 3$
$= 2^{2x} + 4 \times 2^x + 3$
$= 4^x + 2^{2+x} + 3$

b $(e^x + e^{-x})^2$
$= (e^x)^2 + 2e^x \times e^{-x} + (e^{-x})^2$
$= e^{2x} + 2e^0 + e^{-2x}$
$= e^{2x} + 2 + e^{-2x}$

EXERCISE 3D.1

1   Expand and simplify:

a $x^2(x^3 + 2x^2 + 1)$ b $2^x(2^x + 1)$ c $x^{\frac{1}{2}}(x^{\frac{1}{2}} + x^{-\frac{1}{2}})$

d $e^x(e^x + 2)$ e $3^x(2 - 3^{-x})$ f $x^{\frac{1}{2}}(x^{\frac{3}{2}} + 2x^{\frac{1}{2}} + 3x^{-\frac{1}{2}})$

g $2^{-x}(2^x + 5)$ h $5^{-x}(5^{2x} + 5^x)$ i $x^{-\frac{1}{2}}(x^2 + x + x^{\frac{1}{2}})$

2   Expand and simplify:

a $(2^x + 1)(2^x + 3)$ b $(3^x + 2)(3^x + 5)$ c $(5^x - 2)(5^x - 4)$

d $(2^x + 3)^2$ e $(3^x - 1)^2$ f $(4^x + 7)^2$

g $(x^{\frac{1}{2}} + 2)(x^{\frac{1}{2}} - 2)$ h $(2^x + 3)(2^x - 3)$ i $(x^{\frac{1}{2}} + x^{-\frac{1}{2}})(x^{\frac{1}{2}} - x^{-\frac{1}{2}})$

j $(x + \dfrac{2}{x})^2$ k $(e^x - e^{-x})^2$ l $(5 - 2^{-x})^2$

FACTORISATION AND SIMPLIFICATION

Example 11

Factorise: **a** $2^{n+3} + 2^n$ **b** $2^{n+3} + 8$ **c** $2^{3n} + 2^{2n}$

a $\quad 2^{n+3} + 2^n$
$= 2^n 2^3 + 2^n$
$= 2^n (2^3 + 1)$
$= 2^n \times 9$

b $\quad 2^{n+3} + 8$
$= 2^n 2^3 + 8$
$= 8(2^n) + 8$
$= 8(2^n + 1)$

c $\quad 2^{3n} + 2^{2n}$
$= 2^{2n} 2^n + 2^{2n}$
$= 2^{2n} (2^n + 1)$

Example 12

Factorise: **a** $4^x - 9$ **b** $9^x + 4(3^x) + 4$

a $\quad 4^x - 9$
$= (2^x)^2 - 3^2 \qquad$ {difference of two squares}
$= (2^x + 3)(2^x - 3)$

b $\quad 9^x + 4(3^x) + 4$
$= (3^x)^2 + 4(3^x) + 4 \qquad$ {compare $\quad a^2 + 4a + 4$}
$= (3^x + 2)^2 \qquad$ {as $\quad a^2 + 4a + 4 = (a+2)^2$}

Example 13

Simplify: **a** $\dfrac{6^n}{3^n}$ **b** $\dfrac{4^n}{6^n}$

a $\quad \dfrac{6^n}{3^n} \qquad$ **or** $\qquad \dfrac{6^n}{3^n}$

$= \dfrac{2^n 3^x}{3^n{}_1} \qquad\qquad = \left(\dfrac{6}{3}\right)^n$

$= 2^n \qquad\qquad\qquad = 2^n$

b $\quad \dfrac{4^n}{6^n} \qquad$ **or** $\qquad \dfrac{4^n}{6^n}$

$= \dfrac{2^n 2^n}{2^n 3^n} \qquad\qquad = \left(\dfrac{4}{6}\right)^n$

$= \dfrac{2^n}{3^n} \qquad\qquad\quad = \left(\dfrac{2}{3}\right)^n$

Example 14

Simplify: **a** $\dfrac{3^n + 6^n}{3^n}$ **b** $\dfrac{2^{m+2} - 2^m}{2^m}$ **c** $\dfrac{2^{m+3} + 2^m}{9}$

a $\quad \dfrac{3^n + 6^n}{3^n}$

$= \dfrac{3^n + 2^n 3^n}{3^n}$

$= \dfrac{3^n (1 + 2^n)}{3^n{}_1}$

$= 1 + 2^n$

b $\quad \dfrac{2^{m+2} - 2^m}{2^m}$

$= \dfrac{2^m 2^2 - 2^m}{2^m}$

$= \dfrac{2^m (4 - 1)}{2^m{}_1}$

$= 3$

c $\quad \dfrac{2^{m+3} + 2^m}{9}$

$= \dfrac{2^m 2^3 + 2^m}{9}$

$= \dfrac{2^m (8 + 1)}{9{}_1}$

$= 2^m$

Example 15

Solve for x: $4^x + 2^x - 20 = 0$

$$4^x + 2^x - 20 = 0$$
$$\therefore \quad (2^x)^2 + 2^x - 20 = 0 \qquad \{\text{compare} \quad a^2 + a - 20 = 0\}$$
$$\therefore \quad (2^x - 4)(2^x + 5) = 0 \qquad \{\text{as} \quad a^2 + a - 20 = (a-4)(a+5)\}$$
$$\therefore \quad 2^x = 4 \quad \text{or} \quad 2^x = -5$$
$$\therefore \quad 2^x = 2^2 \qquad \{2^x \text{ cannot be negative}\}$$
$$\therefore \quad x = 2$$

EXERCISE 3D.2

1 Factorise:

a $5^{2x} + 5^x$
b $3^{n+2} + 3^n$
c $e^n + e^{3n}$

d $5^{n+1} - 5$
e $6^{n+2} - 6$
f $4^{n+2} - 16$

g $3(2^n) + 2^{n+1}$
h $2^{n+2} + 2^{n+1} + 2^n$
i $3^{n+1} + 2(3^n) + 3^{n-1}$

2 Factorise:

a $9^x - 4$
b $4^x - 25$
c $16 - 9^x$

d $25 - 4^x$
e $9^x - 4^x$
f $4^x + 6(2^x) + 9$

g $9^x + 10(3^x) + 25$
h $4^x - 14(2^x) + 49$
i $25^x - 4(5^x) + 4$

3 Factorise:

a $4^x + 9(2^x) + 18$
b $4^x - 2^x - 20$
c $9^x + 9(3^x) + 14$

d $9^x + 4(3^x) - 5$
e $25^x + 5^x - 2$
f $49^x - 7^{x+1} + 12$

4 Simplify:

a $\dfrac{12^n}{6^n}$
b $\dfrac{20^a}{2^a}$
c $\dfrac{6^b}{2^b}$
d $\dfrac{4^n}{20^n}$

e $\dfrac{35^x}{7^x}$
f $\dfrac{6^a}{8^a}$
g $\dfrac{5^{n+1}}{5^n}$
h $\dfrac{5^{n+1}}{5}$

5 Simplify:

a $\dfrac{6^m + 2^m}{2^m}$
b $\dfrac{2^n + 12^n}{2^n}$
c $\dfrac{8^n + 4^n}{2^n}$

d $\dfrac{6^n + 12^n}{1 + 2^n}$
e $\dfrac{5^{n+1} - 5^n}{4}$
f $\dfrac{5^{n+1} - 5^n}{5^n}$

g $\dfrac{2^n - 2^{n-1}}{2^n}$
h $\dfrac{2^n + 2^{n-1}}{2^n + 2^{n+1}}$
i $\dfrac{3^{n+1} - 3^n}{3^n + 3^{n-1}}$

6 Simplify:

a $2^n(n+1) + 2^n(n-1)$
b $3^n\left(\dfrac{n-1}{6}\right) - 3^n\left(\dfrac{n+1}{6}\right)$

7 Solve for x:

a $4^x - 6(2^x) + 8 = 0$
b $4^x - 2^x - 2 = 0$
c $9^x - 12(3^x) + 27 = 0$

d $9^x = 3^x + 6$
e $25^x - 23(5^x) - 50 = 0$
f $49^x + 1 = 2(7^x)$

E EXPONENTIAL EQUATIONS

An **exponential equation** is an equation in which the unknown occurs as part of the index or exponent.

For example: $2^x = 8$ and $30 \times 3^x = 7$ are both exponential equations.

If $2^x = 8$,   then $2^x = 2^3$.   Thus $x = 3$,   and this is the only solution.

Hence: If $a^x = a^k$,   then $x = k$.

So, if the base numbers are the same, we can **equate indices**.

Example 16

Solve for x: **a** $2^x = 16$ **b** $3^{x+2} = \frac{1}{27}$

Once we have the same base we then equate the indices.

a $\quad 2^x = 16$	**b** $\qquad 3^{x+2} = \frac{1}{27}$
$\therefore \quad 2^x = 2^4$	$\therefore \quad 3^{x+2} = 3^{-3}$
$\therefore \quad x = 4$	$\therefore \quad x + 2 = -3$
	$\therefore \quad x = -5$

Example 17

Solve for x:

a $4^x = 8$

b $9^{x-2} = \frac{1}{3}$

a $\qquad 4^x = 8$	**b** $\qquad 9^{x-2} = \frac{1}{3}$
$\therefore \quad (2^2)^x = 2^3$	$\therefore \quad (3^2)^{x-2} = 3^{-1}$
$\therefore \quad 2^{2x} = 2^3$	$\therefore \quad 3^{2(x-2)} = 3^{-1}$
$\therefore \quad 2x = 3$	$\therefore \quad 2x - 4 = -1$
$\therefore \quad x = \frac{3}{2}$	$\therefore \quad 2x = 3$
	$\therefore \quad x = \frac{3}{2}$

Remember to use the index laws correctly!

EXERCISE 3E

1 Solve for x:

  a $2^x = 2$ **b** $2^x = 4$ **c** $3^x = 27$ **d** $2^x = 1$

  e $2^x = \frac{1}{2}$ **f** $3^x = \frac{1}{3}$ **g** $2^x = \frac{1}{8}$ **h** $2^{x+1} = 8$

  i $2^{x-2} = \frac{1}{4}$ **j** $3^{x+1} = \frac{1}{27}$ **k** $2^{x+1} = 64$ **l** $2^{1-2x} = \frac{1}{2}$

2 Solve for x:

  a $4^x = 32$ **b** $8^x = \frac{1}{4}$ **c** $9^x = \frac{1}{3}$ **d** $49^x = \frac{1}{7}$

  e $4^x = \frac{1}{8}$ **f** $25^x = \frac{1}{5}$ **g** $8^{x+2} = 32$ **h** $8^{1-x} = \frac{1}{4}$

  i $4^{2x-1} = \frac{1}{2}$ **j** $9^{x-3} = 3$ **k** $(\frac{1}{2})^{x+1} = 2$ **l** $(\frac{1}{3})^{x+2} = 9$

  m $4^x = 8^{-x}$ **n** $(\frac{1}{4})^{1-x} = 8$ **o** $(\frac{1}{7})^x = 49$ **p** $(\frac{1}{2})^{x+1} = 32$

3 Solve for x:

   a $4^{2x+1} = 8^{1-x}$ **b** $9^{2-x} = (\frac{1}{3})^{2x+1}$ **c** $2^x \times 8^{1-x} = \frac{1}{4}$

4 Solve for x:

   a $3 \times 2^x = 24$ **b** $7 \times 2^x = 56$ **c** $3 \times 2^{x+1} = 24$

   d $12 \times 3^{-x} = \frac{4}{3}$ **e** $4 \times (\frac{1}{3})^x = 36$ **f** $5 \times (\frac{1}{2})^x = 20$

F | GRAPHS OF EXPONENTIAL FUNCTIONS

We have learned to deal with b^n where $n \in \mathbb{Q}$, i.e., n is any rational number.

But what about b^n where $n \in \mathbb{R}$, i.e., where n is not necessarily a rational?

To answer this question, we can look at graphs of exponential functions.

> The most simple general **exponential function** has the form $y = b^x$ where $b > 0$, $b \neq 1$.

For example, $y = 2^x$ is an exponential function.

Table of values:

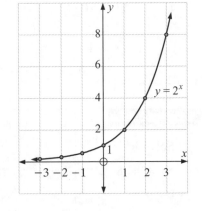

x	-3	-2	-1	0	1	2	3
y	$\frac{1}{8}$	$\frac{1}{4}$	$\frac{1}{2}$	1	2	4	8

We notice that for $x = -10$, say, $y = 2^{-10} \approx 0.001$

Also when $x = -50$, $y = 2^{-50} \approx 8.88 \times 10^{-16}$

So, it appears that as x becomes large and negative, the graph of $y = 2^x$ approaches the x-axis from above it.

We say that $y = 2^x$ is 'asymptotic to the x-axis', or '$y = 0$ is a **horizontal asymptote**'.

INVESTIGATION 1   EXPONENTIAL GRAPHS

We will investigate families of exponential functions.

GRAPHING PACKAGE

What to do:

1   **a** On the same set of axes, use a **graphing package** or **graphics calculator** to graph the following functions: $y = 2^x$, $y = 3^x$, $y = 10^x$, $y = (1.3)^x$.

    b The functions in **a** are all members of the family $y = b^x$.

      i What effect does changing b values have on the shape of the graph?

      ii What is the y-intercept of each graph?

     iii What is the horizontal asymptote of each graph?

2   **a**   On the same set of axes, use a **graphing package** or **graphics calculator** to graph the following functions: $y = 2^x$, $y = 2^x + 1$, $y = 2^x - 2$.

   b   The functions in **a** are all members of the family $y = 2^x + d$ where d is a constant.

   i   What effect does changing d values have on the position of the graph?
   ii   What effect does changing d values have on the shape of the graph?
   iii   What is the horizontal asymptote of each graph?
   iv   What is the horizontal asymptote of $y = 2^x + d$?

   c   To graph $y = 2^x + d$ from $y = 2^x$ what transformation is used?

3   **a**   On the same set of axes, use a **graphing package** or **graphics calculator** to graph the following functions: $y = 2^x$, $y = 2^{x-1}$, $y = 2^{x+2}$, $y = 2^{x-3}$.

   b   The functions in **a** are all members of the family $y = 2^{x-c}$.

   i   What effect does changing c values have on the position of the graph?
   ii   What effect does changing c values have on the shape of the graph?
   iii   What is the horizontal asymptote of each graph?

   c   To graph $y = 2^{x-c}$ from $y = 2^x$,   what transformation is used?

4   **a**   On the same set of axes, use a **graphing package** or **graphics calculator** to graph the functions $y = 2^x$ and $y = 2^{-x}$.

   b   **i**   What is the y-intercept of each graph?
   ii   What is the horizontal asymptote of each graph?
   iii   What transformation moves $y = 2^x$ to $y = 2^{-x}$?

5   **a**   On the same set of axes, use a **graphing package** or **graphics calculator** to graph the following functions:
   i $y = 2^x$, $y = 3 \times 2^x$, $y = \frac{1}{2} \times 2^x$ **ii** $y = -2^x$, $y = -3 \times 2^x$, $y = -\frac{1}{2} \times 2^x$

   b   The functions in **a** are all members of the family $y = a \times 2^x$ where a is a constant. Comment on the effect on the graph when **i** $a > 0$ **ii** $a < 0$.

   c   What is the horizontal asymptote of each graph? Why?

From your investigation you should have discovered that:

For the general exponential function $y = a \times b^{x-c} + d$

▶ b controls how steeply the graph increases or decreases
▶ c controls horizontal translation
▶ d controls vertical translation and $y = d$ is the equation of the horizontal asymptote.
▶   • If $a > 0$, $b > 1$
         the function is
         increasing.
      • If $a > 0$, $0 < b < 1$
         the function is
         decreasing.
      • If $a < 0$, $b > 1$
         the function is
         decreasing.
      • If $a < 0$, $0 < b < 1$
         the function is
         increasing.

We can sketch reasonably accurate graphs of
exponential functions using:

- the horizontal asymptote
- the y-intercept
- two other points, say when
  $x = 2$, $x = -2$

All exponential graphs
are similar in shape
and have a horizontal
asymptote.

Example 18

Sketch the graph of $y = 2^{-x} - 3$.

For $y = 2^{-x} - 3$
the horizontal asymptote is $y = -3$

When $x = 0$, $\begin{aligned} y &= 2^0 - 3 \\ &= 1 - 3 \\ &= -2 \end{aligned}$

$\therefore$ the y-intercept is -2

When $x = 2$, $\begin{aligned} y &= 2^{-2} - 3 \\ &= \tfrac{1}{4} - 3 \\ &= -2\tfrac{3}{4} \end{aligned}$

When $x = -2$, $y = 2^2 - 3 = 1$

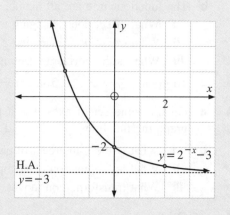

We now have a well-defined meaning for b^n where $b, n \in \mathbb{R}$ because simple exponential
functions have smooth increasing or decreasing graphs.

EXERCISE 3F

1 Given the graph of $y = 2^x$ we can find
approximate values of 2^x for various x
values.

For example:

- $2^{1.8} \approx 3.5$ (see point A)
- $2^{2.3} \approx 5$ (see point B)

Use the graph to determine approximate
values of:

a $2^{\frac{1}{2}}$ or $\sqrt{2}$ b $2^{0.8}$
c $2^{1.5}$ d $2^{-1.6}$
e $2^{\sqrt{2}}$ f $2^{-\sqrt{2}}$

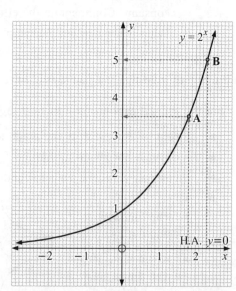

2 Draw freehand sketches of the following pairs of graphs using your observations from

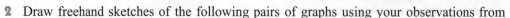

the previous investigation:

   a $y = 2^x$ and $y = 2^x - 2$ b $y = 2^x$ and $y = 2^{-x}$

   c $y = 2^x$ and $y = 2^{x-2}$ d $y = 2^x$ and $y = 2(2^x)$

3   Check your answers to 2 using technology.

GRAPHING PACKAGE

4   Draw freehand sketches of the following pairs of graphs:

   a $y = 3^x$ and $y = 3^{-x}$ b $y = 3^x$ and $y = 3^x + 1$

   c $y = 3^x$ and $y = -3^x$ d $y = 3^x$ and $y = 3^{x-1}$

5   Sketch the graphs of:

   a $y = 2^x + 1$ b $y = 2 - 2^x$ c $y = 2^{-x} + 3$ d $y = 3 - 2^{-x}$

6   Use your GDC to graph the functions in question 5 above and find y when $x = \sqrt{2}$.

7   For the graphs of the functions in question 5 above, discuss the behaviour of y as $x \to \pm\infty$. Hence determine the horizontal asymptotes for each graph.

G   GROWTH AND DECAY

In this exercise we will examine situations where quantities are either increasing or decreasing exponentially. These situations are known as **growth** and **decay**, and occur frequently in the world around us.

For example, populations of animals, people, and bacteria usually *grow* in an exponential way. Radioactive substances and items that depreciate usually *decay* exponentially.

GROWTH

Consider a population of 100 mice which under favourable conditions is increasing by 20% each week. To increase a quantity by 20%, we multiply it by 120% or 1.2.

So, if P_n is the population after n weeks, then

$P_0 = 100$ {the *original* population}
$P_1 = P_0 \times 1.2 = 100 \times 1.2$
$P_2 = P_1 \times 1.2 = 100 \times (1.2)^2$
$P_3 = P_2 \times 1.2 = 100 \times (1.2)^3$, etc

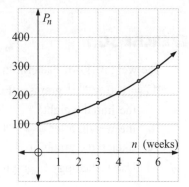

and from this pattern we see that $P_n = 100 \times (1.2)^n$.

Alternatively:

This is an example of a *geometric sequence* and we could find the rule to generate it.
Clearly $r = 1.2$ and so as $P_n = P_0 r^n$, then $P_n = 100 \times (1.2)^n$ for $n = 0, 1, 2, 3, \ldots$

Example 19

An entomologist monitoring a grasshopper plague notices that the area affected by the grasshoppers is given by $A_n = 1000 \times 2^{0.2n}$ hectares, where n is the number of weeks after the initial observation.

a   Find the original affected area.

b   Find the affected area after   **i** 5 weeks   **ii** 10 weeks.

c   Find the affected area after 12 weeks.

d   Draw the graph of A_n against n.

a $A_0 = 1000 \times 2^0$
$\quad\quad = 1000 \times 1$
$\quad\quad = 1000 \quad\quad \therefore$ original area was 1000 ha.

b   **i** $A_5 = 1000 \times 2^1$ **ii** $A_{10} = 1000 \times 2^2$
$\quad\quad\quad = 2000$ $\quad\quad\quad\quad = 4000$
$\quad\quad$ i.e., area is 2000 ha. $\quad\quad\quad$ i.e., area is 4000 ha.

c $A_{12} = 1000 \times 2^{0.2 \times 12}$
$\quad\quad\quad = 1000 \times 2^{2.4}$ {*Press:* 1000 ⊠ 2 ∧ 2.4 **ENTER** }
$\quad\quad\quad \approx 5278$

$\quad\quad \therefore$ after 12 weeks, area affected   **d**
$\quad\quad$ is about 5300 ha.

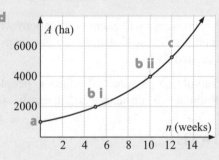

EXERCISE 3G.1

1 The weight W_t of bacteria in a culture t hours after establishment is given by $W_t = 100 \times 2^{0.1t}$ grams.   Find:

   a the initial weight

   b the weight after   **i** 4 hours   **ii** 10 hours   **iii** 24 hours.

   c Sketch the graph of W_t against t using the results of **a** and **b** only.

   d Use technology to graph $Y_1 = 100 \times 2^{0.1X}$ and check your answers to **a**, **b** and **c**.

2 A breeding program to ensure the survival of pygmy possums was established with an initial population of 50 (25 pairs). From a previous program, the expected population P_n in n years' time is given by $P_n = P_0 \times 2^{0.3n}$.

   a What is the value of P_0?

   b What is the expected population after: **i** 2 years   **ii** 5 years   **iii** 10 years?

   c Sketch the graph of P_n against n using **a** and **b** only.

   d Use technology to graph $Y_1 = 50 \times 2^{0.3X}$ and check your answers in **b**.

3 The speed V_t of a chemical reaction is given by $V_t = V_0 \times 2^{0.05t}$ where t is the temperature in °C. Find:

    a the speed at 0°C   **b** the speed at 20°C

    c the percentage increase in speed at 20°C compared with the speed at 0°C.

    d Find $\left(\dfrac{V_{50} - V_{20}}{V_{20}} \right) \times 100\%$. What does this calculation represent?

4 A species of bear is introduced to a large island off Alaska where previously there were no bears. 6 pairs of bears were introduced in 1998. It is expected that the population will increase according to $B_t = B_0 \times 2^{0.18t}$ where t is the time since the introduction.

    a Find B_0.   **b** Find the expected bear population in 2018.

    c Find the expected percentage increase from 2008 to 2018.

DECAY

Now consider a radioactive substance of original weight 20 grams which *decays* or reduces by 5% each year. The multiplier is now 95% or 0.95.

So, if W_n is the weight after n years, then:

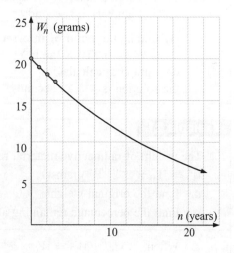

$W_0 = 20$ grams

$W_1 = W_0 \times 0.95 = 20 \times 0.95$ grams

$W_2 = W_1 \times 0.95 = 20 \times (0.95)^2$ grams

$W_3 = W_2 \times 0.95 = 20 \times (0.95)^3$ grams

$\vdots$

$W_{20} = 20 \times (0.95)^{20} \approx 7.2$ grams

$\vdots$

$W_{100} = 20 \times (0.95)^{100} \approx 0.1$ grams

and from this pattern we see that $W_n = 20 \times (0.95)^n$.

Alternatively:

Once again we have a *geometric sequence* with $W_0 = 20$ and $r = 0.95$, and consequently $W_n = 20 \times (0.95)^n$ for $n = 0, 1, 2, 3, \ldots$.

Example 20

When a diesel-electric generator is switched off, the current dies away according to the formula $I(t) = 24 \times (0.25)^t$ amps, where t is the time in seconds.

    a Find $I(t)$ when $t = 0, 1, 2$ and 3.

    b What current flowed in the generator at the instant when it was switched off?

    c Plot the graph of $I(t)$ for $t \geqslant 0$ using the information above.

    d Use your graph and/or technology to find how long it takes for the current to reach 4 amps.

a $I(t) = 24 \times (0.25)^t$ amps

$I(0)$	$I(1)$	$I(2)$	$I(3)$
$= 24 \times (0.25)^0$	$= 24 \times (0.25)^1$	$= 24 \times (0.25)^2$	$= 24 \times (0.25)^3$
$= 24$ amps	$= 6$ amps	$= 1.5$ amps	$= 0.375$ amps

b   When $t = 0$, $I(0) = 24$ $\quad \therefore$ 24 amps of current flowed.

c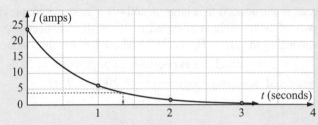

d   From the graph above, the approximate time to reach 4 amps is 1.3 seconds.   *or*

By finding the **point of intersection** of
$Y_1 = 24 \times (0.25)^{\wedge}X$ and $Y_2 = 4$
on a graphics calculator,
the solution is ≈ 1.29 seconds.

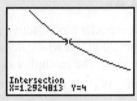

Example 21

The weight of radioactive material remaining after t years is given by
$W_t = W_0 \times 2^{-0.001t}$ grams.
a   Find the original weight.
b   Find the percentage remaining after 200 years.

a   When $t = 0$, $W_0 = W_0 \times 2^0 = W_0$
$\therefore$ W_0 is the original weight.

b   When $t = 200$, $\begin{aligned} W_{200} &= W_0 \times 2^{-0.001 \times 200} \\ &= W_0 \times 2^{-0.2} \\ &\approx W_0 \times 0.8706 \\ &\approx 87.06\% \text{ of } W_0 \quad \therefore \quad 87.1\% \text{ remains.} \end{aligned}$

EXERCISE 3G.2

1   The weight of a radioactive substance t years after being set aside is given by
$W(t) = 250 \times (0.998)^t$ grams.
   a   How much radioactive substance was put aside?
   b   Determine the weight of the substance after:
      i   400 years   ii   800 years   iii   1200 years.
   c   Sketch the graph of $W(t)$ for $t \geqslant 0$, using the above information.
   d   Use your graph or graphics calculator to find how long it takes for the substance to decay to 125 grams.

2   The temperature T of a liquid which has been placed in a refrigerator is given by
$T(t) = 100 \times 2^{-0.02t}$ °C   where t is the time in minutes. Find:
  a   the initial temperature
  b   the temperature after:
      i   15 minutes   ii   20 minutes   iii   78 minutes.
  c   Sketch the graph of $T(t)$ for $t \geqslant 0$ using a and b only.

3   The weight W_t grams of radioactive substance remaining after t years is given by
$W_t = 1000 \times 2^{-0.03t}$ grams.   Find:
  a   the initial weight
  b   the weight after:
      i   10 years   ii   100 years   iii   1000 years.
  c   Graph W_t against t using a and b only.

4   The weight W_t of radioactive uranium remaining after t years is given by the formula
$W_t = W_0 \times 2^{-0.0002t}$ grams, $t \geqslant 0$.   Find:
  a   the original weight   b   the percentage weight loss after 1000 years.

H   THE NATURAL EXPONENTIAL 'e'

We have seen that the simplest exponential functions are of the form $f(x) = b^x$ where
$b > 0$, $b \neq 1$.

Below are some graphs of simple exponential functions.

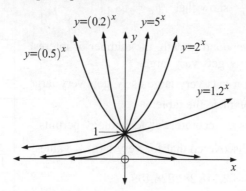

We can see that for all positive values of the base b, the graph is always positive.

Hence $b^x > 0$ for all $b > 0$.

There are a vast number of possible choices for the base number.

However, where exponential data is examined in science, engineering, and other areas, the
base $e \approx 2.7183$ is commonly used.

e is a special number in mathematics. It is irrational like π, and just as π is the ratio of a
circle's circumference to its diameter, e also has a physical meaning. We explore this meaning
in the following investigation.

96   EXPONENTIALS   (Chapter 3)

INVESTIGATION 2   CONTINUOUS COMPOUND INTEREST

A formula for calculating the amount to which an investment grows is

$u_n = u_0(1 + i)^n$ where

u_n is the **final amount** u_0 is the **initial amount**

i is the **interest rate per compounding period**

n is the **number of periods** or number of times the interest is compounded.

We will investigate the final value of an investment for various values of n, and allow n to get extremely large.

What to do:

1 Suppose $1000 is invested for one year at a fixed rate of 6% p.a. Use your calculator to find the final amount or *maturing value* if the interest is paid:

   a   annually ($n = 1$, $i = 6\% = 0.06$)   **b**   quarterly ($n = 4$, $i = \frac{6\%}{4} = 0.015$)

   c   monthly   **d**   daily   **e**   by the second   **f**   by the millisecond.

2 Comment on your answers obtained in **1**.

3 If r is the percentage rate per year, t is the number of years,   and

   N is the number of interest payments per year,   then $i = \dfrac{r}{N}$ and $n = Nt$.

   This means that the growth formula becomes $u_n = u_0 \left(1 + \dfrac{r}{N}\right)^{Nt}$

   If we let $a = \dfrac{N}{r}$,   show that $u_n = u_0 \left[\left(1 + \dfrac{1}{a}\right)^a\right]^{rt}$.

4 For continuous compound growth, the number of interest payments per year N gets very large.

   a   Explain why a gets very large as N gets very large.

   b   Copy and complete the table:

   Give answers as accurately as technology permits.

a	$\left(1 + \dfrac{1}{a}\right)^a$
10	
100	
1000	
10 000	
100 000	
$\vdots$	

5 You should have discovered that for very large a values,

   $$\left(1 + \frac{1}{a}\right)^a \approx 2.718\,281\,828\,459......$$

6 Now use the $\boxed{e^x}$ key of your calculator to find the value of e^1,

   i.e.,   press 1 $\boxed{e^x}$ $\boxed{=}$ or $\boxed{e^x}$ 1 $\boxed{=}$.   What do you notice?

7 For continuous growth, $u_n = u_0 e^{rt}$ where u_0 is the initial amount

   r is the annual percentage rate

   t is the number of years

   Use this formula to find the final value if $1000 is invested for 4 years at a fixed rate of 6% p.a., where the interest is calculated continuously.

From **Investigation 2** we observe that:

"If interest is paid continuously (instantaneously) then the formula for calculating a compounding amount $u_n = u_0(1 + i)^n$ can be replaced by $u_n = u_0 e^{rt}$, where r is the percentage rate p.a. and t is the number of years."

RESEARCH   RESEARCHING e

What to do:

1 The 'bell curve' which models statistical distributions is shown alongside. Research the equation of this curve.

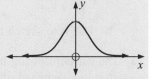

2 $e^{i\pi} + 1 = 0$ is called **Euler's equation** where i is the *imaginary* number $\sqrt{-1}$. Research the significance of this equation.

3 The series $f(x) = 1 + x + \frac{1}{2}x^2 + \frac{1}{2\times 3}x^3 + \frac{1}{2\times 3\times 4}x^4 + \ldots\ldots$ has infinitely many terms. It has been shown that $f(x) = e^x$.

Check this statement by finding an approximation for $f(1)$ using its first 20 terms.

EXERCISE 3H

1 Use the $\boxed{e^x}$ key on a calculator to find the value of e to as many digits as possible.

2 Sketch, on the same set of axes, the graphs of $y = 2^x$, $y = e^x$ and $y = 3^x$. Comment on any observations.

GRAPHING PACKAGE

3 Sketch, on the same set of axes, the graphs of $y = e^x$ and $y = e^{-x}$. What is the geometric connection between these two graphs?

4 For the general exponential function $y = ae^{kx}$, what is the y-intercept?

5 Consider $y = 2e^x$.

   a Explain why y can never be < 0.   **b** Find y if: **i** $x = -20$ **ii** $x = 20$.

6 Find, to 3 significant figures, the value of:

   a e^2 **b** e^3 **c** $e^{0.7}$ **d** $\sqrt{e}$ **e** e^{-1}

7 Write the following as powers of e:

   a $\sqrt{e}$ **b** $e\sqrt{e}$ **c** $\dfrac{1}{\sqrt{e}}$ **d** $\dfrac{1}{e^2}$

8 Simplify:

   a $\left(e^{0.36}\right)^{\frac{1}{2}}$ **b** $\left(e^{0.064}\right)^{\frac{t}{16}}$ **c** $\left(e^{-0.04}\right)^{\frac{t}{8}}$ **d** $\left(e^{-0.836}\right)^{\frac{t}{5}}$

9 Find, to five significant figures, the values of:

   a $e^{2.31}$ **b** $e^{-2.31}$ **c** $e^{4.829}$ **d** $e^{-4.829}$

   e $50e^{-0.1764}$ **f** $80e^{-0.6342}$ **g** $1000e^{1.2642}$ **h** $0.25e^{-3.6742}$

10 On the same set of axes, sketch and clearly label the graphs of:

$$f : x \mapsto e^x, \qquad g : x \mapsto e^{x-2}, \qquad h : x \mapsto e^x + 3$$

State the domain and range of each function.

11 On the same set of axes, sketch and clearly label the graphs of:

$f : x \mapsto e^x, \qquad g : x \mapsto -e^x, \qquad h : x \mapsto 10 - e^x$

State the domain and range of each function.

12 The weight of bacteria in a culture is given by $W(t) = 2e^{\frac{t}{2}}$ grams where t is the time in hours after the culture was set to grow.

  a What is the weight of the culture at:

    i $t = 0$ **ii** $t = 30$ min   **iii** $t = 1\frac{1}{2}$ hours   **iv** $t = 6$ hours?

  b Use **a** to sketch the graph of $W(t) = 2e^{\frac{t}{2}}$.

13 The current flowing in an electrical circuit t seconds after it is switched off is given by
$I(t) = 75e^{-0.15t}$ amps.

  a What current is still flowing in the circuit after:

    i $t = 1$ sec   **ii** $t = 10$ sec?

  b Use your graphics calculator to sketch
$I(t) = 75e^{-0.15t}$ and $I = 1$.

  c Find how long it would take for the current to fall to 1 amp.

14   **a** Given $f : x \mapsto e^x$, find the defining equation of f^{-1}.

    b Sketch the graphs of $y = e^x$, $y = x$ and $y = f^{-1}(x)$ on the same set of axes.

REVIEW SET 3A

1 Simplify: **a** $-(-1)^{10}$ **b** $-(-3)^3$ **c** $3^0 - 3^{-1}$

2 Simplify using the index laws:

  a $a^4 b^5 \times a^2 b^2$ **b** $6xy^5 \div 9x^2 y^5$ **c** $\dfrac{5(x^2 y)^2}{(5x^2)^2}$

3 Write the following as a power of 2:

  a 2×2^{-4} **b** $16 \div 2^{-3}$ **c** 8^4

4 Write without brackets or negative indices:

  a b^{-3} **b** $(ab)^{-1}$ **c** ab^{-1}

5 Find the value of x, without using your calculator: **a** $2^{x-3} = \frac{1}{32}$ **b** $9^x = 27^{2-2x}$

6 Evaluate without using a calculator: **a** $8^{\frac{2}{3}}$ **b** $27^{-\frac{2}{3}}$

7 Evaluate, correct to 3 significant figures, using your calculator:

  a $3^{\frac{3}{4}}$ **b** $27^{-\frac{1}{5}}$ **c** $\sqrt[4]{100}$

8 If $f(x) = 3 \times 2^x$, find the value of: **a** $f(0)$ **b** $f(3)$ **c** $f(-2)$

9 On the same set of axes draw the graphs of   **a** $y = 2^x$ **b** $y = 2^x - 4$, stating the y-intercept and the equation of the horizontal asymptote.

10 The temperature of a liquid t minutes after it was heated is given by
$T = 80 \times (0.913)^t$ °C. Find:

    a the initial temperature of the liquid

    b the temperature after **i** $t = 12$ **ii** $t = 24$ **iii** $t = 36$ minutes.

    c Draw the graph of T against t for $t \geqslant 0$, using the above or technology.

    d Hence, find the time taken for the temperature to reach 25°C.

REVIEW SET 3B

1 Simplify: **a** $-(-2)^3$ **b** $5^{-1} - 5^0$

2 Simplify using the index laws:

    a $(a^7)^3$ **b** $pq^2 \times p^3q^4$ **c** $\dfrac{8ab^5}{2a^4b^4}$

3 Write as powers of 2: **a** $\frac{1}{16}$ **b** $2^x \times 4$ **c** $4^x \div 8$

4 Write without brackets or negative indices:

    a $x^{-2} \times x^{-3}$ **b** $2(ab)^{-2}$ **c** $2ab^{-2}$

5 Solve for x without using a calculator: **a** $2^{x+1} = 32$ **b** $4^{x+1} = \left(\frac{1}{8}\right)^x$

6 Write as powers of 3: **a** 81 **b** 1 **c** $\frac{1}{27}$ **d** $\frac{1}{243}$

7 Write as a single power of 3: **a** $\dfrac{27}{9^a}$ **b** $(\sqrt{3})^{1-x} \times 9^{1-2x}$

8 For $y = 3^x - 5$:

    a find y when $x = 0, \pm1, \pm2$ **b** discuss y as $x \to \infty$ and as $x \to -\infty$

    c sketch the graph of $y = 3^x - 5$ **d** state the equation of any asymptote.

9 Without using a calculator, solve for x: **a** $27^x = 3$ **b** $9^{1-x} = 27^{x+2}$

10 On the same set of axes, sketch and clearly label the graphs of:
$$f : x \mapsto e^x, \quad g : x \mapsto e^{x-1}, \quad h : x \mapsto 3 - e^x$$
State the domain and range of each function.

REVIEW SET 3C

1 **a** Write 4×2^n as a power of 2.

    b Evaluate $7^{-1} - 7^0$.

    c Write $\left(\frac{2}{3}\right)^{-3}$ in simplest fractional form.

    d Simplify $\left(\dfrac{2a^{-1}}{b^2}\right)^2$. Do not have negative indices or brackets in your answer.

2 **a** Write 288 as a product of prime numbers in index form. **b** Simplify $\dfrac{2^{x+1}}{2^{1-x}}$.

3 Write as powers of 5 in simplest form:

    a 1 **b** $5\sqrt{5}$ **c** $\dfrac{1}{\sqrt[4]{5}}$ **d** 25^{a+3}

4 Simplify:

    a $-(-2)^2$ **b** $(-\frac{1}{2}a^{-3})^2$ **c** $(-3b^{-1})^{-3}$

5 Expand and simplify:

    a $e^x(e^{-x} + e^x)$ **b** $(2^x + 5)^2$ **c** $(x^{\frac{1}{2}} - 7)(x^{\frac{1}{2}} + 7)$

6 Expand and simplify:

    a $(3 - 2^a)^2$ **b** $(\sqrt{x} + 2)(\sqrt{x} - 2)$ **c** $2^{-x}(2^{2x} + 2^x)$

7 Solve for x: **a** $6 \times 2^x = 192$ **b** $4 \times (\frac{1}{3})^x = 324$

8 The weight of a radioactive substance after t years is given by
$W = 1500 \times (0.993)^t$ grams.

    a   Find the original amount of radioactive material.

    b   Find the amount of radioactive material remaining after:

        i   400 years   **ii**   800 years.

    c   Sketch the graph of W against t, $t \geqslant 0$, using the above or technology.

    d   Hence, find the time taken for the weight to reduce to 100 grams.

9 If $4^a 2^b = 1$ and $\dfrac{8^a}{4^b} = \dfrac{1}{128}$, find $\dfrac{16^a}{2^b}$.

10 For $y = 2e^{-x} + 1$:

    a   find y when $x = 0$, ± 1, ± 2 **b**   discuss y as $x \to \infty$ and as $x \to -\infty$

    c   sketch the graph of $y = 2e^{-x} + 1$ **d**   state the equation of any asymptote.

Chapter 4

Logarithms

Contents:

OPENING PROBLEM

Paulo knows that when he invests €12 000 for n years at an interest rate of 8.35% p.a. compounded annually, the value of the investment at the end of this period is given by $A_{n+1} = 12\,000 \times (1.0835)^n$ euros.

Consider the following questions:

1 What is the value of A_1 and what is its interpretation?

2 How would we find the value of the investment after 5 years?

3 If we let $n = 2.25$, $A_{3.25} = 12\,000 \times (1.0835)^{2.25}$. Does the power 2.25 have a meaning? What is the interpretation of the value of $A_{3.25}$?

4 How long would it take for the investment to double in value?

5 What would the graph of A_{n+1} against n look like?

After studying the concepts of this chapter, you should be able to answer the questions above.

A   LOGARITHMS

HISTORICAL NOTE

In the late 16th century, astronomers spent a large part of their working lives doing the complex and tedious calculations of spherical trigonometry needed to understand the movement of celestial bodies.

A Scotsman, **John Napier**, discovered a method of simplifying these calculations using logarithms. So effective was Napier's method that it was said he effectively doubled the life of an astronomer by reducing the time required to do these calculations.

Consider the function $f : x \mapsto 10^x$.

The defining equation of f is $f(x) = 10^x$ or $y = 10^x$.

Now consider the graph of f and its inverse function f^{-1}.

The question arises:

How can we write f^{-1} in functional form, or, what is the defining function of f^{-1}?

As f is defined by $y = 10^x$,

f^{-1} is defined by $x = 10^y$.

{interchanging x and y}

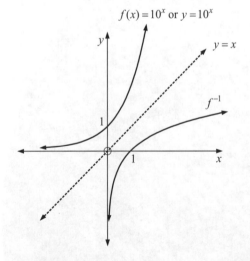

$f(x) = 10^x$ or $y = 10^x$

So, y is the exponent to which 10 (the base) is raised in order to get x.

We write this as $y = \log_{10} x$

and say that   "y is the logarithm of x in base 10."

So,
- if $f(x) = 10^x$,   then $f^{-1}(x) = \log_{10} x$
- if $f(x) = b^x$,   then $f^{-1}(x) = \log_b x$

LOGARITHMS IN BASE b

In general: If $A = b^n$, $b \neq 1$, $b > 0$, we say that n is the logarithm of A in base b, and that $A = b^n \Leftrightarrow n = \log_b A$, $A > 0$.

$A = b^n \Leftrightarrow n = \log_b A$ is a short way of writing:
"if $A = b^n$ then $n = \log_b A$, and if $n = \log_b A$ then $A = b^n$".

We say that $A = b^n$ and $n = \log_b A$ are *equivalent* or *interchangeable* statements.

For example:
- $8 = 2^3$ means that $3 = \log_2 8$ and vice versa.
- $\log_5 25 = 2$ means that $25 = 5^2$ and vice versa.

If $y = b^x$ then $x = \log_b y$, and so $x = \log_b b^x$.

If $x = b^y$ then $y = \log_b x$, and so $x = b^{\log_b x}$ provided $x > 0$.

Example 1

a Write an equivalent exponential statement for $\log_{10} 1000 = 3$.
b Write an equivalent logarithmic statement for $3^4 = 81$.

a From $\log_{10} 1000 = 3$ we deduce that $10^3 = 1000$.
b From $3^4 = 81$ we deduce that $\log_3 81 = 4$.

Example 2

Find: **a** $\log_{10} 100$ **b** $\log_2 32$ **c** $\log_5(0.2)$

a To find $\log_{10} 100$ we ask "What power must 10 be raised to, to get 100?"
As $10^2 = 100$, then $\log_{10} 100 = 2$.

b As $2^5 = 32$, then $\log_2 32 = 5$.

c As $5^{-1} = \frac{1}{5} = 0.2$, then $\log_5(0.2) = -1$.

EXERCISE 4A

1 Write an equivalent exponential statement for:
a $\log_{10} 10\,000 = 4$ **b** $\log_{10}(0.1) = -1$ **c** $\log_{10} \sqrt{10} = \frac{1}{2}$
d $\log_2 8 = 3$ **e** $\log_2(\frac{1}{4}) = -2$ **f** $\log_3 \sqrt{27} = 1.5$

2 Write an equivalent logarithmic statement for:

    a $2^2 = 4$ **b** $2^{-3} = \frac{1}{8}$ **c** $10^{-2} = 0.01$

    d $7^2 = 49$ **e** $2^6 = 64$ **f** $3^{-3} = \frac{1}{27}$

3 Find:

    a $\log_{10} 100\,000$ **b** $\log_{10}(0.01)$ **c** $\log_3 \sqrt{3}$ **d** $\log_2 8$

    e $\log_2 64$ **f** $\log_2 128$ **g** $\log_5 25$ **h** $\log_5 125$

    i $\log_2(0.125)$ **j** $\log_9 3$ **k** $\log_4 16$ **l** $\log_{36} 6$

    m $\log_3 243$ **n** $\log_2 \sqrt[3]{2}$ **o** $\log_a a^n$ **p** $\log_8 2$

    q $\log_t \left(\frac{1}{t}\right)$ **r** $\log_6 6\sqrt{6}$ **s** $\log_4 1$ **t** $\log_9 9$

4 Use your calculator to find:

    a $\log_{10} 152$ **b** $\log_{10} 25$ **c** $\log_{10} 74$ **d** $\log_{10} 0.8$

5 Solve for x:

    a $\log_2 x = 3$ **b** $\log_4 x = \frac{1}{2}$ **c** $\log_x 81 = 4$ **d** $\log_2(x - 6) = 3$

6 **a** Prove that $\log_a a^n = n$.

    b Hence, find:

       i $\log_4 16$ **ii** $\log_2 4$ **iii** $\log_3 \left(\frac{1}{3}\right)$ **iv** $\log_{10} \sqrt[5]{100}$

       v $\log_2 \left(\frac{1}{\sqrt{2}}\right)$ **vi** $\log_5(25\sqrt{5})$ **vii** $\log_3 \left(\frac{1}{\sqrt{3}}\right)$ **viii** $\log_4 \left(\frac{1}{2\sqrt{2}}\right)$

B   LOGARITHMS IN BASE 10

Many positive numbers can be easily written in the form 10^x.

For example,

$$10\,000 = 10^4$$
$$1000 = 10^3$$
$$100 = 10^2$$
$$10 = 10^1$$
$$1 = 10^0$$
$$0.1 = 10^{-1}$$
$$0.01 = 10^{-2}$$
$$0.001 = 10^{-3} \quad \text{etc.}$$

Numbers like $\sqrt{10}$, $10\sqrt{10}$ and $\dfrac{1}{\sqrt[5]{10}}$ can also be written in the form 10^x as follows:

$$\sqrt{10}$$
$$= 10^{\frac{1}{2}}$$
$$= 10^{0.5}$$

$$10\sqrt{10}$$
$$= 10^1 \times 10^{0.5}$$
$$= 10^{1.5}$$

$$\dfrac{1}{\sqrt[5]{10}}$$
$$= 10^{-\frac{1}{5}}$$
$$= 10^{-0.2}$$

In fact, all positive numbers can be written in the form 10^x by using logarithms in base 10.

> The **logarithm in base 10** of a positive number is its power of 10.

For example:

- Since $1000 = 10^3$,   we write $\log_{10} 1000 = 3$ or $\log 1000 = 3$.

- Since $0.01 = 10^{-2}$,   we write $\log_{10}(0.01) = -2$ or $\log(0.01) = -2$.

In algebraic form, $a = 10^{\log a}$ for any $a > 0$.

Notice that a must be positive since $10^x > 0$ for all $x \in \mathbb{R}$.

Notice also that $\log 1000 = \log 10^3 = 3$

and $\log 0.01 = \log 10^{-2} = -2$

give us the useful alternative $\log 10^x = x$

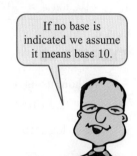

If no base is indicated we assume it means base 10.

Example 3

a   Without using a calculator, find: i $\log 100$ ii $\log(\sqrt[4]{10})$.
b   Check your answers using technology.

a   i $\log 100 = \log 10^2 = 2$ ii $\log(\sqrt[4]{10}) = \log(10^{\frac{1}{4}}) = \frac{1}{4}$

b   i   press   log 100) **ENTER**   *Answer:* 2

   ii   press   log 10 ^ 0.25) **ENTER**   *Answer:* 0.25

Example 4

Use your calculator to write the following in the form 10^x where x is correct to 4 decimal places: a   8   b   800   c   0.08

a   8   b   800   c   0.08
  $= 10^{\log 8}$ $= 10^{\log 800}$ $= 10^{\log 0.08}$
  $\approx 10^{0.9031}$ $\approx 10^{2.9031}$ $\approx 10^{-1.0969}$

Example 5

a   Use your calculator to find: i $\log 2$ ii $\log 20$
b   Explain why $\log 20 = \log 2 + 1$.

a   i $\log 2 \approx 0.3010$ b $\log 20 = \log(2 \times 10)$

   ii $\log 20 \approx 1.3010$ $\approx \log(10^{0.3010} \times 10^1)$
        {calculator} $\approx \log 10^{1.3010}$ {adding indices}
                                                   ≈ 1.3010
                                                   $\approx \log 2 + 1$

Example 6				
Find x if:	**a**	$x = 10^{\log x}$	**b**	$x = 10^{\log x}$
a $\log x = 3$	$\therefore$	$x = 10^3$	$\therefore$	$x \approx 10^{-0.271}$
b $\log x \approx -0.271$	$\therefore$	$x = 1000$	$\therefore$	$x \approx 0.536$

EXERCISE 4B

1 Without using a calculator, find:

    a $\log 10\,000$ **b** $\log 0.001$ **c** $\log 10$ **d** $\log 1$

    e $\log \sqrt{10}$ **f** $\log(\sqrt[3]{10})$ **g** $\log\left(\frac{1}{\sqrt[4]{10}}\right)$ **h** $\log 10\sqrt{10}$

    i $\log \sqrt[3]{100}$ **j** $\log\left(\frac{100}{\sqrt{10}}\right)$ **k** $\log(10 \times \sqrt[3]{10})$ **l** $\log 1000\sqrt{10}$

    m $\log 10^n$ **n** $\log(10^a \times 100)$ **o** $\log\left(\frac{10}{10^m}\right)$ **p** $\log\left(\frac{10^a}{10^b}\right)$

2 Find using a calculator:

    a $\log 10\,000$ **b** $\log 0.001$ **c** $\log \sqrt{10}$ **d** $\log \sqrt[3]{10}$

    e $\log \sqrt[3]{100}$ **f** $\log 10\sqrt{10}$ **g** $\log\left(\frac{1}{\sqrt{10}}\right)$ **h** $\log\left(\frac{1}{\sqrt[4]{10}}\right)$

3 Use your calculator to write these in the form 10^x where x is correct to 4 decimal places:

    a 6   **b** 60   **c** 6000   **d** 0.6   **e** 0.006

    f 15   **g** 1500   **h** 1.5   **i** 0.15   **j** 0.000 15

4   **a** Use your calculator to find: **i** $\log 3$ **ii** $\log 300$

    b Explain why $\log 300 = \log 3 + 2$.

5   **a** Use your calculator to find: **i** $\log 5$ **ii** $\log 0.05$

    b Explain why $\log 0.05 = \log 5 - 2$.

6 Find x if:

    a $\log x = 2$ **b** $\log x = 1$ **c** $\log x = 0$ **d** $\log x = -1$

    e $\log x = \frac{1}{2}$ **f** $\log x = -\frac{1}{2}$ **g** $\log x \approx 0.8351$ **h** $\log x \approx -3.1997$

C   LAWS OF LOGARITHMS

INVESTIGATION   DISCOVERING THE LAWS OF LOGARITHMS

What to do:

1 Use your calculator to find:

    a $\log 2 + \log 3$ **b** $\log 3 + \log 7$ **c** $\log 4 + \log 20$

    d $\log 6$ **e** $\log 21$ **f** $\log 80$

From your answers, suggest a possible simplification for $\ln a + \ln b$.

2 Use your calculator to find:

   a $\log 6 - \log 2$ **b** $\log 12 - \log 3$ **c** $\log 3 - \log 5$

   d $\log 3$ **e** $\log 4$ **f** $\log(0.6)$

From your answers, suggest a possible simplification for $\ln a - \ln b$.

3 Use your calculator to find:

   a $3 \log 2$ **b** $2 \log 5$ **c** $-4 \log 3$

   d $\log(2^3)$ **e** $\log(5^2)$ **f** $\log(3^{-4})$

From your answers, suggest a possible simplification for $n \log a$.

From the investigation, you should have discovered the three important **laws of logarithms**:

If A and B are both positive then:

- $\log A + \log B = \log(AB)$
- $\log A - \log B = \log\left(\dfrac{A}{B}\right)$
- $n \log A = \log\left(A^n\right)$

More generally, in any base c we have these **laws of logarithms**:

If A and B are both positive then:

- $\log_c A + \log_c B = \log_c(AB)$
- $\log_c A - \log_c B = \log_c\left(\dfrac{A}{B}\right)$
- $n \log_c A = \log_c\left(A^n\right)$

These laws are easily established using the first three index laws.

Example 7

Use the laws of logarithms to write the following as a single logarithm:

   a $\log 5 + \log 3$ **b** $\log 24 - \log 8$ **c** $\log 5 - 1$

   a $\log 5 + \log 3$
$= \log(5 \times 3)$
$= \log 15$

   b $\log 24 - \log 8$
$= \log\left(\frac{24}{8}\right)$
$= \log 3$

   c $\log 5 - 1$
$= \log 5 - \log 10^1$
$= \log\left(\frac{5}{10}\right)$
$= \log\left(\frac{1}{2}\right)$

Example 8

Write as a single logarithm in the form $\log a$, $a \in \mathbb{Q}$.

   a $2 \log 7 - 3 \log 2$

   b $2 \log 3 - 1$

   a $2 \log 7 - 3 \log 2$
$= \log(7^2) - \log(2^3)$
$= \log 49 - \log 8$
$= \log\left(\frac{49}{8}\right)$

   b $2 \log 3 - 1$
$= \log(3^2) - \log 10^1$
$= \log 9 - \log 10$
$= \log(0.9)$

Example 9

Simplify $\dfrac{\log 8}{\log 4}$ without using a calculator.

$\dfrac{\log 8}{\log 4} = \dfrac{\log 2^3}{\log 2^2}$

$= \dfrac{3\log 2}{2\log 2}$

$= \frac{3}{2}$

Example 10

Show that:

a $\log\left(\frac{1}{9}\right) = -2\log 3$

b $\log 500 = 3 - \log 2$

a $\log\left(\frac{1}{9}\right)$

$= \log(3^{-2})$

$= -2\log 3$

b $\log 500$

$= \log\left(\frac{1000}{2}\right)$

$= \log 1000 - \log 2$

$= \log 10^3 - \log 2$

$= 3 - \log 2$

EXERCISE 4C.1

1   Write as a single logarithm:

   a $\log 8 + \log 2$ b $\log 8 - \log 2$ c $\log 40 - \log 5$

   d $\log 4 + \log 5$ e $\log 5 + \log(0.4)$ f $\log 2 + \log 3 + \log 4$

   g $1 + \log 3$ h $\log 4 - 1$ i $\log 5 + \log 4 - \log 2$

   j $2 + \log 2$ k $\log 40 - 2$ l $\log 6 - \log 2 - \log 3$

   m $\log 50 - 4$ n $3 - \log 50$ o $\log\left(\frac{4}{3}\right) + \log 3 + \log 7$

2   Write as a single logarithm or integer:

   a $5\log 2 + \log 3$ b $2\log 3 + 3\log 2$ c $3\log 4 - \log 8$

   d $2\log 5 - 3\log 2$ e $\frac{1}{2}\log 4 + \log 3$ f $\frac{1}{3}\log\left(\frac{1}{8}\right)$

   g $3 - \log 2 - 2\log 5$ h $1 - 3\log 2 + \log 20$ i $2 - \frac{1}{2}\log 4 - \log 5$

3   Simplify without using a calculator:

   a $\dfrac{\log 4}{\log 2}$ b $\dfrac{\log 27}{\log 9}$ c $\dfrac{\log 8}{\log 2}$

   d $\dfrac{\log 3}{\log 9}$ e $\dfrac{\log 25}{\log(0.2)}$ f $\dfrac{\log 8}{\log(0.25)}$

   Check your answers using a calculator.

4   Show that:

   a $\log 9 = 2\log 3$ b $\log\sqrt{2} = \frac{1}{2}\log 2$ c $\log\left(\frac{1}{8}\right) = -3\log 2$

   d $\log\left(\frac{1}{5}\right) = -\log 5$ e $\log 5 = 1 - \log 2$ f $\log 5000 = 4 - \log 2$

5   If $p = \log_b 2$, $q = \log_b 3$ and $r = \log_b 5$ write in terms of p, q and r:

   a $\log_b 6$ b $\log_b 108$ c $\log_b 45$

   d $\log_b\left(\frac{5\sqrt{3}}{2}\right)$ e $\log_b\left(\frac{5}{32}\right)$ f $\log_b(0.\overline{2})$

6 If $\log_2 P = x$, $\log_2 Q = y$ and $\log_2 R = z$ write in terms of x, y and z:

   a $\log_2(PR)$ **b** $\log_2(RQ^2)$ **c** $\log_2\left(\dfrac{PR}{Q}\right)$

   d $\log_2(P^2\sqrt{Q})$ **e** $\log_2\left(\dfrac{Q^3}{\sqrt{R}}\right)$ **f** $\log_2\left(\dfrac{R^2\sqrt{Q}}{P^3}\right)$

7 If $\log_t M = 1.29$ and $\log_t N^2 = 1.72$ find:

   a $\log_t N$ **b** $\log_t(MN)$ **c** $\log_t\left(\dfrac{N^2}{\sqrt{M}}\right)$

LOGARITHMIC EQUATIONS

Example 11

Write these as logarithmic equations (in base 10):   **a** $y = a^2 b$ **b** $y = \dfrac{a}{b^3}$ **c** $P = \dfrac{20}{\sqrt{n}}$

a $\qquad y = a^2 b$

$\therefore \quad \log y = \log(a^2 b)$

$\therefore \quad \log y = \log a^2 + \log b$

$\therefore \quad \log y = 2\log a + \log b$

b $\qquad y = \dfrac{a}{b^3}$

$\therefore \quad \log y = \log\left(\dfrac{a}{b^3}\right)$

$\therefore \quad \log y = \log a - \log b^3$

$\therefore \quad \log y = \log a - 3\log b$

c $P = \left(\dfrac{20}{\sqrt{n}}\right) \quad \therefore \quad \log P = \log\left(\dfrac{20}{n^{\frac{1}{2}}}\right)$ and so $\log P = \log 20 - \frac{1}{2}\log n$

Example 12

Write the following equations without logarithms: **a** $\log A = \log b + 2\log c$

                                                 b $\log M = 3\log a - 1$

a $\qquad \log A = \log b + 2\log c$

$\therefore \quad \log A = \log b + \log c^2$

$\therefore \quad \log A = \log(bc^2)$

$\therefore \qquad A = bc^2$

b $\qquad \log M = 3\log a - 1$

$\therefore \quad \log M = \log a^3 - \log 10^1$

$\therefore \quad \log M = \log\left(\dfrac{a^3}{10}\right)$

$\therefore \qquad M = \dfrac{a^3}{10}$

EXERCISE 4C.2

1 Write the following as logarithmic equations (in base 10):

   a $y = 2^x$ **b** $y = 20b^3$ **c** $M = ad^4$ **d** $T = 5\sqrt{d}$

   e $R = b\sqrt{l}$ **f** $Q = \dfrac{a}{b^n}$ **g** $y = ab^x$ **h** $F = \dfrac{20}{\sqrt{n}}$

   i $L = \dfrac{ab}{c}$ **j** $N = \sqrt{\dfrac{a}{b}}$ **k** $S = 200 \times 2^t$ **l** $y = \dfrac{a^m}{b^n}$

2 Write the following equations without logarithms:

a $\log D = \log e + \log 2$

b $\log F = \log 5 - \log t$

c $\log P = \frac{1}{2}\log x$

d $\log M = 2\log b + \log c$

e $\log B = 3\log m - 2\log n$

f $\log N = -\frac{1}{3}\log p$

g $\log P = 3\log x + 1$

h $\log Q = 2 - \log x$

3 Solve for x:

a $\log_3 27 + \log_3(\frac{1}{3}) = \log_3 x$

b $\log_5 x = \log_5 8 - \log_5(6 - x)$

c $\log_5 125 - \log_5 \sqrt{5} = \log_5 x$

d $\log_{20} x = 1 + \log_{20} 10$

e $\log x + \log(x + 1) = \log 30$

f $\log(x + 2) - \log(x - 2) = \log 5$

D   NATURAL LOGARITHMS

In **Chapter 3** we came across the **natural exponential** $e \approx 2.718\,28$.

If f is the exponential function $x \mapsto e^x$ (i.e., $f(x) = e^x$ or $y = e^x$) then its inverse function, f^{-1} is $x = e^y$ or $y = \log_e x$.

So, $y = \log_e x$ is the reflection of $y = e^x$ in the mirror line $y = x$.

$\ln x$ is used to represent $\log_e x$. $\ln x$ is called the **natural logarithm** of x.

Notice that: $\ln 1 = \ln e^0 = 0$ $\ln e = \ln e^1 = 1$ $\ln e^2 = 2$

$\ln \sqrt{e} = \ln e^{\frac{1}{2}} = \frac{1}{2}$ and $\ln\left(\frac{1}{e}\right) = \ln e^{-1} = -1$

In general, $\ln e^x = x$ and $e^{\ln x} = x.$

Also, since $a^x = \left(e^{\ln a}\right)^x = e^{x\ln a},$ $a^x = e^{x\ln a}.$

Example 13

Use your calculator to write the following in the form e^k where k is correct to 4 decimal places: a   50   b   0.005

a   50

$= e^{\ln 50}$ {using $x = e^{\ln x}$}

$\approx e^{3.9120}$

b   0.005

$= e^{\ln 0.005}$

$\approx e^{-5.2983}$

Example 14

Find x if:

a $\ln x = 2.17$

b $\ln x = -0.384$

a $\ln x = 2.17$

$\therefore \ x = e^{2.17}$

$\therefore \ x \approx 8.76$

b $\ln x = -0.384$

$\therefore \ x = e^{-0.384}$

$\therefore \ x \approx 0.681$

Example 15

Use the laws of logarithms to write the following as a single logarithm:

a $\ln 5 + \ln 3$ b $\ln 24 - \ln 8$ c $\ln 5 - 1$

a $\ln 5 + \ln 3$	b $\ln 24 - \ln 8$	c $\ln 5 - 1$
$= \ln(5 \times 3)$	$= \ln\left(\frac{24}{8}\right)$	$= \ln 5 - \ln e^1$
$= \ln 15$	$= \ln 3$	$= \ln\left(\frac{5}{e}\right)$

Example 16

Use the laws of logarithms to simplify:

a $2\ln 7 - 3\ln 2$

b $2\ln 3 - 1$

a $2\ln 7 - 3\ln 2$

$= \ln(7^2) - \ln(2^3)$

$= \ln 49 - \ln 8$

$= \ln\left(\frac{49}{8}\right)$

b $2\ln 3 - 1$

$= \ln(3^2) - \ln e$

$= \ln 9 - \ln e$

$= \ln\left(\frac{9}{e}\right)$

Example 17

Show that:

a $\ln\left(\frac{1}{9}\right) = -2\ln 3$

b $\ln 500 \approx 6.9078 - \ln 2$

a $\ln\left(\frac{1}{9}\right)$

$= \ln(3^{-2})$

$= -2\ln 3$

b $\ln 500 = \ln\left(\dfrac{1000}{2}\right)$

$= \ln 1000 - \ln 2$

$\approx 6.9078 - \ln 2$

Example 18

Write the following equations without logarithms:

a $\ln A = 2\ln c + 3$

b $\ln M = 3\ln a - 2$

a $\ln A = 2\ln c + 3$

$\therefore \ \ln A - 2\ln c = 3$

$\therefore \ \ln A - \ln c^2 = 3$

$\therefore \ \ln\left(\dfrac{A}{c^2}\right) = 3$

$\therefore \ \dfrac{A}{c^2} = e^3$

$\therefore \ A = e^3 c^2$

b $\ln M = 3\ln a - 2$

$\therefore \ \ln M - 3\ln a = -2$

$\therefore \ \ln M - \ln a^3 = -2$

$\therefore \ \ln\left(\dfrac{M}{a^3}\right) = -2$

$\therefore \ \dfrac{M}{a^3} = e^{-2}$

$\therefore \ M = a^3 e^{-2}$ or $M = \dfrac{a^3}{e^2}$

EXERCISE 4D

1 Without using a calculator find:

a $\ln e^3$ b $\ln 1$ c $\ln \sqrt[3]{e}$ d $\ln\left(\dfrac{1}{e^2}\right)$

2 Check your answers to question **1** using a calculator.

3 Explain why $\ln(-2)$ and $\ln 0$ cannot be found.

4 Simplify:

    a $\ln e^a$ **b** $\ln(e \times e^a)$ **c** $\ln\left(e^a \times e^b\right)$ **d** $\ln(e^a)^b$ **e** $\ln\left(\dfrac{e^a}{e^b}\right)$

5 Use your calculator to write these in the form e^x where x is correct to 4 dec. places:

    a 6   **b** 60   **c** 6000   **d** 0.6   **e** 0.006

    f 15   **g** 1500   **h** 1.5   **i** 0.15   **j** 0.000 15

6 Find x if:

    a $\ln x = 3$ **b** $\ln x = 1$ **c** $\ln x = 0$ **d** $\ln x = -1$

    e $\ln x = -5$ **f** $\ln x \approx 0.835$ **g** $\ln x \approx 2.145$ **h** $\ln x \approx -3.2971$

7 Write as a single logarithm:

    a $\ln 15 + \ln 3$ **b** $\ln 15 - \ln 3$ **c** $\ln 20 - \ln 5$

    d $\ln 4 + \ln 6$ **e** $\ln 5 + \ln(0.2)$ **f** $\ln 2 + \ln 3 + \ln 5$

    g $1 + \ln 4$ **h** $\ln 6 - 1$ **i** $\ln 5 + \ln 8 - \ln 2$

    j $2 + \ln 4$ **k** $\ln 20 - 2$ **l** $\ln 12 - \ln 4 - \ln 3$

8 Write in the form $\ln a, \ a \in \mathbb{Q}$:

    a $5\ln 3 + \ln 4$ **b** $3\ln 2 + 2\ln 5$ **c** $3\ln 2 - \ln 8$

    d $3\ln 4 - 2\ln 2$ **e** $\frac{1}{3}\ln 8 + \ln 3$ **f** $\frac{1}{3}\ln\left(\frac{1}{27}\right)$

    g $-\ln 2$ **h** $-\ln\left(\frac{1}{2}\right)$ **i** $-2\ln\left(\frac{1}{4}\right)$

9 Show that:

    a $\ln 27 = 3\ln 3$ **b** $\ln\sqrt{3} = \frac{1}{2}\ln 3$ **c** $\ln\left(\frac{1}{16}\right) = -4\ln 2$

    d $\ln\left(\frac{1}{6}\right) = -\ln 6$ **e** $\ln\left(\frac{1}{\sqrt{2}}\right) = -\frac{1}{2}\ln 2$ **f** $\ln\left(\frac{e}{5}\right) = 1 - \ln 5$

    g $\ln\sqrt[3]{5} = \frac{1}{3}\ln 5$ **h** $\ln\left(\frac{1}{32}\right) = -5\ln 2$ **i** $\ln\left(\frac{1}{\sqrt[5]{2}}\right) = -\frac{1}{5}\ln 2$

10 Write the following equations without logarithms:

    a $\ln D = \ln x + 1$ **b** $\ln F = -\ln p + 2$ **c** $\ln P = \frac{1}{2}\ln x$

    d $\ln M = 2\ln y + 3$ **e** $\ln B = 3\ln t - 1$ **f** $\ln N = -\frac{1}{3}\ln g$

    g $\ln Q \approx 3\ln x + 2.159$ **h** $\ln D \approx 0.4\ln n - 0.6582$

E   EXPONENTIAL EQUATIONS USING LOGARITHMS

In **Chapter 3** we found solutions to simple exponental equations by creating equal bases and then equating indices. However, it is not always easy to make the bases the same. In these situations we use **logarithms** to find the solution.

Example 19

Solve for x, giving your answer to 3 significant figures: $2^x = 30$.

$$2^x = 30$$
$$\therefore \quad \log 2^x = \log 30 \quad \text{\{find the logarithm of each side\}}$$

$$\therefore \quad x \log 2 = \log 30 \qquad \{\log a^n = n \log a\}$$
$$\therefore \quad x = \frac{\log 30}{\log 2}$$
$$\therefore \quad x \approx 4.91 \quad (3 \text{ s.f.})$$

Example 20

Solve for t to 3 significant figures: $200 \times 2^{0.04t} = 6$.

$$200 \times 2^{0.04t} = 6$$
$$\therefore \quad 2^{0.04t} = \frac{6}{200} \qquad \{\text{dividing both sides by } 200\}$$
$$\therefore \quad 2^{0.04t} = 0.03$$
$$\therefore \quad \log 2^{0.04t} = \log 0.03 \qquad \{\text{find the logarithm of each side}\}$$
$$\therefore \quad 0.04t \times \log 2 = \log 0.03 \qquad \{\log a^n = n \log a\}$$
$$\therefore \quad t = \frac{\log 0.03}{0.04 \times \log 2} \approx -126 \quad (3 \text{ s.f.})$$

EXERCISE 4E

1 Solve for x, giving your answer correct to 3 significant figures:

  a $2^x = 10$ **b** $3^x = 20$ **c** $4^x = 100$

  d $(1.2)^x = 1000$ **e** $2^x = 0.08$ **f** $3^x = 0.000\,25$

  g $(\frac{1}{2})^x = 0.005$ **h** $(\frac{3}{4})^x = 10^{-4}$ **i** $(0.99)^x = 0.000\,01$

2 Find the solution to the following correct to 4 significant figures:

  a $200 \times 2^{0.25t} = 600$ **b** $20 \times 2^{0.06t} = 450$ **c** $30 \times 3^{-0.25t} = 3$

  d $12 \times 2^{-0.05t} = 0.12$ **e** $50 \times 5^{-0.02t} = 1$ **f** $300 \times 2^{0.005t} = 1000$

To solve exponential equations of the form $e^x = a$ we simply use the property:

If $e^x = a$ then $x = \ln a$.

This rule is clearly true, because if $e^x = a$

$$\text{then} \quad \ln e^x = \ln a \quad \{\text{finding ln of both sides}\}$$
$$\therefore \quad x = \ln a \quad \{\ln e^x = x\}$$

Example 21

Find x to 4 s.f. if: **a** $e^x = 30$ **b** $e^{\frac{x}{3}} = 21.879$ **c** $20e^{4x} = 0.0382$

  a $e^x = 30$
$$\therefore \quad x = \ln 30$$
$$\therefore \quad x \approx 3.401$$

  b $e^{\frac{x}{3}} = 21.879$
$$\therefore \quad \frac{x}{3} = \ln 21.879$$
$$\therefore \quad x \approx 9.257$$

  c $20e^{4x} = 0.0382$
$$\therefore \quad e^{4x} = 0.001\,91$$
$$\therefore \quad 4x = \ln 0.001\,91$$
$$\therefore \quad 4x \approx -6.2607$$
$$\therefore \quad x \approx -1.565$$

3 Solve for x, giving answers correct to 4 significant figures:

a $e^x = 10$

b $e^x = 1000$

c $e^x = 0.008\,62$

d $e^{\frac{x}{2}} = 5$

e $e^{\frac{x}{3}} = 157.8$

f $e^{\frac{x}{10}} = 0.016\,82$

g $20 \times e^{0.06x} = 8.312$

h $50 \times e^{-0.03x} = 0.816$

i $41.83e^{0.652x} = 1000$

Note: Remember that you may not need to use logs when solving exponential equations. It is usually much easier if you can get the same base on both sides.

F   THE CHANGE OF BASE RULE

If $\log_b A = x$,   then $b^x = A$

$\therefore \quad \log_c b^x = \log_c A$ {taking logarithms in base c}

$\therefore \quad x\log_c b = \log_c A$ {power law of logarithms}

$\therefore \quad x = \dfrac{\log_c A}{\log_c b}$

So, $\log_b A = \dfrac{\log_c A}{\log_c b}$

Example 22

Find $\log_2 9$ by: **a**   letting $\log_2 9 = x$

b   using the rule $\log_b A = \dfrac{\log_c A}{\log_c b}$ with:

i $c = 10$ **ii** $c = e$

a   Let $\log_2 9 = x$

$\therefore \quad 9 = 2^x$

$\therefore \quad \log 2^x = \log 9$

$\therefore \quad x\log 2 = \log 9$

$\therefore \quad x = \dfrac{\log 9}{\log 2} \approx 3.17$

b i $\log_2 9 = \dfrac{\log_{10} 9}{\log_{10} 2}$

≈ 3.17

ii $\log_2 9 = \dfrac{\ln 9}{\ln 2}$

≈ 3.17

Example 23

Solve for x: $8^x - 5(4^x) = 0$

$8^x - 5(4^x) = 0$

$\therefore \quad 2^{3x} - 5(2^{2x}) = 0$

$\therefore \quad 2^{2x}(2^x - 5) = 0$

$\therefore \quad 2^x = 5$ {as $2^{2x} > 0$ for all x}

$\therefore \quad x = \log_2 5$

$\therefore \quad x = \dfrac{\log 5}{\log 2} \approx 2.32$ {Check this using technology.}

EXERCISE 4F

1 Use the rule $\log_b A = \dfrac{\log_{10} A}{\log_{10} b}$ to find, correct to 3 significant figures:

    a $\log_3 12$ **b** $\log_{\frac{1}{2}} 1250$ **c** $\log_3 (0.067)$ **d** $\log_{0.4}(0.006\,984)$

2 Use the rule $\log_b A = \dfrac{\ln A}{\ln b}$ to solve, correct to 3 significant figures:

    a $2^x = 0.051$ **b** $4^x = 213.8$ **c** $3^{2x+1} = 4.069$

    Hint: In **2a** $2^x = 0.051$ implies that $x = \log_2(0.051)$.

3 Solve for x:

    a $25^x - 3(5^x) = 0$ **b** $8(9^x) - 3^x = 0$

4 Solve for x:

    a $\log_4 x^3 + \log_2 \sqrt{x} = 8$ **b** $\log_{16} x^5 = \log_{64} 125 - \log_4 \sqrt{x}$

5 Find the exact value of x for which $4^x \times 5^{4x+3} = 10^{2x+3}$

G   GRAPHS OF LOGARITHMIC FUNCTIONS

Consider the general exponential function $f : x \mapsto a^x,\ \ a > 0,\ \ a \neq 1$.

The defining equation of f is $f(x) = a^x$ (or $y = a^x$).   The graph of $y = a^x$ is:

For $0 < a < 1$:   For $a > 1$:

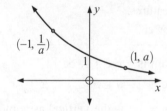 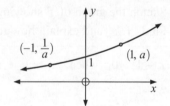

These functions have the **horizontal asymptote** $y = 0$ (the x-axis). They have domain $\mathbb{R}$ (all real numbers) and range $\{y : y > 0\}$ or $y \in\ ]\,0,\,\infty\,[$.

Obviously the function $y = a^x$ is one-to-one and has an inverse function f^{-1}.

So, if f is $y = a^x$, then f^{-1} is $x = a^y$, i.e., $y = \log_a x$.

$$\text{If}\ \ f(x) = a^x \ \ \text{then}\ \ f^{-1}(x) = \log_a x.$$

Note: •   The domain of f^{-1} is $\{x : x > 0\}$ or $x \in\ ]\,0,\,\infty\,[$.

                The range of f^{-1} is $y \in \mathbb{R}$.

      •   The domain of f = the range of f^{-1}.

                The range of f = the domain of f^{-1}.

LOGARITHMIC GRAPHS

The graphs of $y = \log_a x$ are:

For $0 < a < 1$:

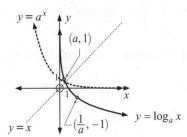

For $a > 1$:

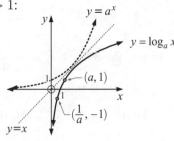

Note:
- both graphs are reflections of $y = a^x$ in the line $y = x$
- both functions have domain $\{x : \ x > 0\}$ or $x \in \,]\,0, \infty\,[$
- we can only find **logarithms of positive numbers**
- both graphs have the vertical asymptote $x = 0$ (the y-axis)
- for $0 < a < 1$, as $x \to \infty$, $y \to -\infty$ and as $x \to 0$ (from right), $y \to \infty$
  for $a > 1$, \quad as $x \to \infty$, $y \to \infty$ \quad and as $x \to 0$ (from right), $y \to -\infty$
- to find the **domain** of $\log_a g(x)$, we find the solutions of $g(x) > 0$.

Example 24

Consider the function $f : x \mapsto \log_2(x - 1) + 1$.
a Find the domain and range of f.
b Find any asymptotes and axis intercepts.
c Sketch the graph of f showing all important features.
d Find f^{-1} and explain how to verify your answer.

---

a $x - 1 > 0$ when $x > 1$ \qquad So, the domain is $x \in \,]\,1, \infty\,[$
\hspace{10em} and the range is \quad $y \in \mathbb{R}$

b As $x \to 1$ from the right, $y \to -\infty$. $\therefore$ $x = 1$ is the vertical asymptote.
As $x \to \infty$, $y \to \infty$.
When $x = 0$, y is undefined \qquad $\therefore$ there is no y-intercept.
When $y = 0$, $\log_2(x - 1) = -1$ \quad $\therefore$ $x - 1 = 2^{-1}$ $\therefore$ $x = 1\frac{1}{2}$
So, the x-intercept is $1\frac{1}{2}$

c To graph using your calculator we
will need to change the base.

So, we graph $y = \dfrac{\log(x - 1)}{\log 2} + 1$

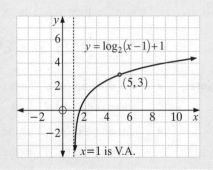

d \qquad f is defined by $y = \log_2(x - 1) + 1$
$\therefore$ f^{-1} is defined by $x = \log_2(y - 1) + 1$
$\therefore$ $x - 1 = \log_2(y - 1)$

$$\therefore \quad y - 1 = 2^{x-1}$$
$$\therefore \quad y = 2^{x-1} + 1$$
$$\therefore \quad f^{-1}(x) = 2^{x-1} + 1 \quad \text{which has a H.A. of } y = 1 \quad \checkmark$$
$$\text{Its domain is } x \in \mathbb{R}, \text{ range is } y \in \,]1, \infty[.$$

Graphics calculator tip:

When graphing f, f^{-1} and $y = x$ on the same axes, it is best to set the scale so that $y = x$ makes a 45° angle with both axes.   Why?

To ensure the graphs are not distorted, use a square window.

Recall that: • inverse functions are formed by interchanging x and y
   • $y = f^{-1}(x)$ is the reflection of $y = f(x)$ in the line $y = x$.

Example 25

Given $f : x \mapsto e^{x-3}$

a   find the defining equation of f^{-1}
b   sketch the graphs of f and f^{-1} on the same set of axes
c   state the domain and range of f and f^{-1}
d   find any asymptotes and intercepts.

a
$$f(x) = e^{x-3}$$
$$\therefore \quad f^{-1} \text{ is } x = e^{y-3}$$
$$\therefore \quad y - 3 = \ln x$$
$$\therefore \quad y = 3 + \ln x$$

b
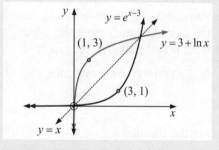

c
	f	f^{-1}
domain	$x \in \mathbb{R}$	$x > 0$
range	$y > 0$	$y \in \mathbb{R}$

d   For f: HA is $y = 0$,   for f^{-1}:   VA is $x = 0$.
For f: y-int is $(0, e^{-3})$,   for f^{-1}: x-int is $(e^{-3}, 0)$.

EXERCISE 4G.1

1   For the following functions f:
   i   Find the domain and range.
   ii   Find any asymptotes and axes intercepts.
   iii   Sketch the graph of $y = f(x)$ showing all important features.
   iv   Solve $f(x) = -1$ algebraically and check the solution on your graph.
   v   Find f^{-1} and explain how to verify your answer.

   a $f : x \mapsto \log_3(x + 1)$
   b $f : x \mapsto 1 - \log_3(x + 1)$
   c $f : x \mapsto \log_5(x - 2) - 2$
   d $f : x \mapsto 1 - \log_5(x - 2)$
   e $f : x \mapsto 1 - \log_2 x^2$
   f $f : x \mapsto \log_2(x^2 - 3x - 4)$

2 For the following functions:

      i find the defining equation of f^{-1}

      ii sketch the graphs of f and f^{-1} on the same set of axes

      iii state the domain and range of f and f^{-1}.

      iv Find any asymptotes.

  a $f : x \mapsto e^x + 5$ **b** $f : x \mapsto e^{x+1} - 3$

  c $f : x \mapsto \ln x - 4$ where $x > 0$ **d** $f : x \mapsto \ln(x-1) + 2$ where $x > 1$

3 Given $f : x \mapsto e^{2x}$ and $g : x \mapsto 2x - 1$, find the defining equations of:

  a $(f^{-1} \circ g)(x)$ **b** $(g \circ f)^{-1}(x)$

4 Consider the graphs A and B. One of them is the graph of $y = \ln x$ and the other is the graph of $y = \ln(x - 2)$.

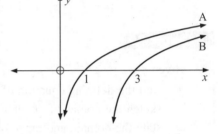

  a Identify which is which. Give evidence for your answer.

  b Redraw the graphs on a new set of axes and add to them the graph of $y = \ln(x + 2)$.

  c Find the equation of the vertical asymptote for each graph.

5 Kelly said that in order to graph $y = \ln(x^2)$, you could first graph $y = \ln x$ and then double the distances away from the x-axis. Connecting these points will give the graph of $y = \ln x^2$.

Is she correct? Give evidence.

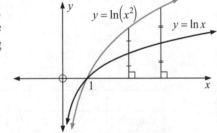

6 For the function $f : x \mapsto e^{x+3} + 2$

  a Find the defining equation for f^{-1}.

  b Find the values of x for which:

    i $f(x) < 2.1$ **ii** $f(x) < 2.01$ **iii** $f(x) < 2.001$ **iv** $f(x) < 2.0001$

    and hence conjecture the horizontal asymptote for the graph of f.

  c Determine the horizontal asymptote of $f(x)$ by discussing the behaviour of $f(x)$ as $x \to \pm\infty$.

  d Hence, determine the vertical asymptote and the domain of f^{-1}.

FURTHER INEQUALITIES

We have seen on many occasions what it means to *solve* an equation. Usually the equations have been presented to us in one of the forms $f(x) = 0$ or $f(x) = g(x)$.

Simply, it means we must find all possible values of the pronumeral, x in this case, that make the equation true.

For equations of the form $f(x) = 0$, we can graph $f(x)$ and then find where the graph meets the x-axis.

For equations of the form $f(x) = g(x)$, we can either graph $f(x)$ and $g(x)$ separately and find the x-coordinate(s) of their point(s) of intersection, or, we can graph $y = f(x) - g(x)$ and find where this graph meets the x-axis.

We can use these same principles in order to solve inequalities.

Note that when solving inequalities, only real number solutions are possible.

Example 26

Solve for x: a $e^x = 2x^2 + x + 1$ b $e^x \geqslant 2x^2 + x + 1$

a   We graph $f(x) = e^x$
and $g(x) = 2x^2 + x + 1$.

Using technology we find the points of intersection of $f(x)$ and $g(x)$.

∴ $x = 0$ and $x \approx 3.21$ are solutions.

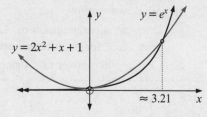

Note: We need to be sure that the graphs will not meet again. We could graph $f(x) - g(x)$ and find where the graph meets the x-axis.

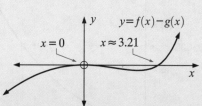

b   Using the same graphs as above, we seek values of x for which $f(x) - g(x) \geqslant 0$.
This is where the graph of $f(x)$ either meets or is higher than the graph of $g(x)$.

The solution is $x = 0$ or $x \geqslant 3.21$

We could even graph the solution set:

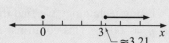

and could describe it as $x = 0$ *or* $x \in [3.21, \infty[$.

EXERCISE 4G.2

1   Solve for x:

   a $x^2 > e^x$ b $x^3 < e^{-x}$ c $5 - x > \ln x$

2   State the domain of $f : x \mapsto x^2 \ln x$.   Hence find where $f(x) \leqslant 0$.

3   a   Use technology to sketch the graph of $f : x \mapsto \dfrac{2}{x} - e^{2x^2 - x + 1}$.

   b   State the domain and range of this function.

   c   Hence find all $x \in \mathbb{R}$ for which $e^{2x^2 - x + 1} > \dfrac{2}{x}$.

GROWTH AND DECAY

In **Chapter 3** we showed how exponential functions can be used to model a variety of growth and decay situations. These included the growth of populations and the decay of radioactive substances. In this section we consider more growth and decay problems, focussing particularly on how logarithms can be used in their solution.

POPULATION GROWTH

Example 27

A farmer monitoring an insect plague notices that the area affected by the insects is given by $A_n = 1000 \times 2^{0.7n}$ hectares, where n is the number of weeks after the initial observation.

a Draw an accurate graph of A_n against n and use your graph to estimate the time taken for the affected area to reach 5000 ha.

b Check your answer to **a** using logarithms and using suitable technology.

a
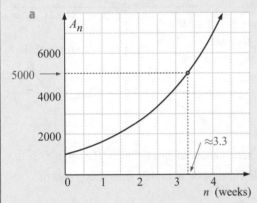

b When $A_n = 5000$,

$$1000 \times 2^{0.7n} = 5000$$
$$\therefore \quad 2^{0.7n} = 5$$
$$\therefore \quad \log 2^{0.7n} = \log 5$$
$$\therefore \quad 0.7n \log 2 = \log 5$$
$$\therefore \quad n = \frac{\log 5}{0.7 \times \log 2}$$
$$\therefore \quad n \approx 3.32$$

$\therefore$ it takes about 3 weeks and 2 more days.

Using technology we find the intersection of $y = 1000 \times 2^{0.7x}$ and $y = 5000$. This confirms $n \approx 3.32$.

EXERCISE 4H.1

1 The weight W_t of bacteria in a culture t hours after establishment is given by $W_t = 20 \times 2^{0.15t}$ grams. Find the time for the weight of the culture to reach:

   a 30 grams   **b** 100 grams.

2 The mass M_t of bacteria in a culture t hours after establishment is given by $M_t = 25 \times e^{0.1t}$ grams. Find the time for the mass of the culture to reach:

   a 50 grams   **b** 100 grams.

3 A biologist monitoring a fire ant infestation notices that the area affected by the ants is given by $A_n = 2000 \times e^{0.57n}$ hectares, where n is the number of weeks after the initial observation.

   a Draw an accurate graph of A_n against n and use your graph to estimate the time taken for the infested area to reach 10 000 ha.

b Find the answer to **a** using logarithms.

c Check your answer to **b** using suitable technology.

FINANCIAL GROWTH

Suppose an amount u_1 is invested at a rate of $r\%$ each compounding period. In this case the value of the investment after n periods is given by $u_{n+1} = u_1 \times r^n$. In order to find n, the **period** of the investment, we need to use **logarithms**.

Example 28

Iryna has €5000 to invest in an account that pays 5.2% p.a. interest compounded annually. How long will it take for her investment to reach €20 000?

$u_{n+1} = 20\,000$ after n years

$u_1 = 5000$

$r = 105.2\% = 1.052$

Now $u_{n+1} = u_1 \times r^n$

$\therefore \quad 20\,000 = 5000 \times (1.052)^n$

$\therefore \quad (1.052)^n = 4$

$\therefore \quad \log(1.052)^n = \log 4$

$\therefore \quad n \times \log 1.052 = \log 4$

$\therefore \quad n = \dfrac{\log 4}{\log 1.052} \approx 27.3$ years

$\therefore$ it will take at least 28 years.

EXERCISE 4H.2

1 A house is expected to increase in value at an average rate of 7.5% p.a. If the house is worth £160 000 now, how long is it expected to take for the value to reach £250 000?

2 Thabo has $10 000 to invest in an account that pays 4.8% p.a. compounded annually. How long will it take for his investment to grow to $15 000?

3 Dien invests $15 000 at 8.4% p.a. compounded *monthly*. He will withdraw his money when it reaches $25 000, at which time he plans to travel. The formula $u_{n+1} = u_1 \times r^n$ can be used to calculate the time needed where n is the time in months.

  a Explain why $r = 1.007$.

  b After how many months can he withdraw the money?

4 Revisit the **Opening Problem** on page **102** and answer the questions posed.

DECAY

EXERCISE 4H.3

1 The mass M_t of radioactive substance remaining after t years is given by $M_t = 1000 \times e^{-0.04t}$ grams. Find the time taken for the mass to:

  a halve   **b** reach 25 grams   **c** reach 1% of its original value.

2 A man jumps from an aeroplane and his speed of descent is given by $V = 50(1-e^{-0.2t})$ m s^{-1} where t is the time in seconds. Find the time taken for his speed to reach 40 m s^{-1}.

3 The temperature T of a liquid which has been placed in a refrigerator is given by $T = 4 + 96 \times e^{-0.03t}$ °C, where t is the time in minutes. Find the time required for the temperature to reach: **a**   25°C **b**   5°C.

4 The weight W_t of radioactive substance remaining after t years is given by $W_t = 1000 \times 2^{-0.04t}$ grams.   Find the time taken for the weight to:

  a halve   **b**   reach 20 grams   **c**   reach 1% of its original value.

5 The weight $W(t)$ of radioactive uranium remaining after t years is given by the formula $W(t) = W_0 \times 2^{-0.0002t}$ grams, $t \geqslant 0$.   Find the time taken for the original weight to fall to: **a**   25% of its original value   **b**   0.1% of its original value.

6 The current I flowing in a transistor radio t seconds after it is switched off is given by $I = I_0 \times 2^{-0.02t}$ amps.   Find the time taken for the current to drop to 10% of its original value.

7 A parachutist jumps from the basket of a stationary hot air balloon. His speed of descent is given by $V = 50(1 - 2^{-0.2t})$ m s^{-1} where t is the time in seconds. Find the time taken for his speed to reach 40 m s^{-1}.

REVIEW SET 4A

1 Find the following *without* using a calculator. Show all working.

  a $\log_4 64$ **b** $\log_2 256$ **c** $\log_2(0.25)$ **d** $\log_{25} 5$ **e** $\log_8 1$

  f $\log_6 6$ **g** $\log_{81} 3$ **h** $\log_9(0.\overline{1})$ **i** $\log_{27} 3$ **j** $\log_k \sqrt{k}$

2 Without using a calculator, find: **a** $\log \sqrt{10}$ **b** $\log \dfrac{1}{\sqrt[3]{10}}$ **c** $\log(10^a \times 10^{b+1})$

3 Find x if: **a** $\log_2 x = -3$ **b** $\log_5 x \approx 2.743$ **c** $\log_3 x \approx -3.145$

4 Write as logarithmic equations: **a** $P = 3 \times b^x$ **b** $m = \dfrac{n^3}{p^2}$

5 Write the following equations without logarithms:

  a $\log_2 k \approx 1.699 + x$ **b** $\log_a Q = 3 \log_a P + \log_a R$

  c $\log A \approx 5 \log B - 2.602$

6 Solve for x, giving your answer correct to 4 significant figures:

  a $5^x = 7$ **b** $20 \times 2^{2x+1} = 500$

7 The weight of radioactive substance after t years is $W_t = 2500 \times 3^{-\frac{t}{3000}}$ grams.

  a Find the initial weight.

  b Find the time taken for the weight to reduce to 30% of its original value.

  c Find the percentage weight loss after 1500 years.

  d Sketch the graph of W_t against t.

8 Solve for x: $16^x - 5 \times 8^x = 0$

9 Solve the equation $\log_3(10x^2 - x - 2) = 2 + 2 \log_3 x$

10 Find the *exact* value of a which satisfies the equation $5^{3a} \times 4^{2a+1} = 10^{3a+2}$

  Give your answer in the form $\dfrac{\ln x}{\ln y}$ where $x, y \in \mathbb{Z}$.

REVIEW SET 4B

1 Without using a calculator, find the base 10 logarithms of: **a** $\sqrt{1000}$ **b** $\dfrac{10}{\sqrt[3]{10}}$ **c** $\dfrac{10^a}{10^{-b}}$

2 Solve for x:

    a $\log x = 3$ **b** $\log_3(x+2) = 1.732$ **c** $\log_2(\dfrac{x}{10}) = -0.671$

3 Write as a single logarithm:

    a $\log 16 + 2\log 3$ **b** $\log_2 16 - 2\log_2 3$ **c** $2 + \log_4 5$

4 Write the following equations without logarithms:

    a $\log T = 2\log x - \log y$ **b** $\log_2 K = \log_2 n + \frac{1}{2}\log_2 t$

5 Solve for x: **a** $3^x = 300$ **b** $30 \times 5^{1-x} = 0.15$ **c** $3^{x+2} = 2^{1-x}$

6 If $A = \log_2 2$ and $B = \log_2 3$, write the following in terms of A and B:

    a $\log_2 36$ **b** $\log_2 54$ **c** $\log_2(8\sqrt{3})$ **d** $\log_2(20.25)$ **e** $\log_2(0.\bar{8})$

7 For the function $g : x \mapsto \log_3(x+2) - 2$:

    a Find the domain and range.

    b Find any asymptotes and axes intercepts for the graph of the function.

    c Sketch the graph of $y = g(x)$.

    d Find g^{-1}. Explain how to verify your answer for g^{-1}.

    e Sketch the graphs of g, g^{-1} and $y = x$ on the same axes.

8 Solve exactly for a in the equation $\log_4 a^5 + \log_2 a^{\frac{3}{2}} = \log_8 625$.

9 A straight line has equation $y = mx + c$. Its gradient is -2 and it passes through the point $\left(1, \ \log_5 \frac{3}{25}\right)$.

    a Find the equation of the line.

    b If $y = \log_5 M$, find an expression for M in terms of x.

    c Hence, find the value of x when $M = 25$.

10 Solve simultaneously for x and y: $4^x \times 2^y = 16$ and $8^x = 2^{\frac{y}{2}}$.

11 Solve $\log_8 \sqrt[4]{x^2 + 7} = \frac{1}{3}$

REVIEW SET 4C

1   **a** On the same set of axes sketch and clearly label graphs of:

      $f : x \mapsto e^x$, $g : x \mapsto e^{-x}$ and $h : x \mapsto -e^{-x}$.

    b What is the geometric connection between: **i** f and g **ii** g and h?

2 Sketch on the same set of axes the graphs of $y = e^x$ and $y = 3e^x$.

3 A particle moves in a straight line such that its displacement from the origin O is given by $s(t) = 120t - 40e^{-\frac{t}{5}}$ metres, where t is the time in seconds, $t \geqslant 0$.

    a Find the position of the particle at   **i** $t = 0$ **ii** $t = 5$ **iii** $t = 20$.

    b Hence sketch the graph of $s(t) = 120t - 40e^{-\frac{t}{5}}$ for $t \geqslant 0$.

4 Without using a calculator, find: **a** $\ln(e^5)$ **b** $\ln(\sqrt{e})$ **c** $\ln\left(\dfrac{1}{e}\right)$

5 Simplify: **a** $\ln(e^{2x})$ **b** $\ln(e^2 e^x)$ **c** $\ln\left(\dfrac{e}{e^x}\right)$

6 Write as a single logarithm:
   a $\ln 6 + \ln 4$ **b** $\ln 60 - \ln 20$ **c** $\ln 4 + \ln 1$ **d** $\ln 200 - \ln 8 + \ln 5$

7 Write in the form $a \ln k$ where a and k are positive whole numbers and k is prime:
   a $\ln 32$ **b** $\ln 125$ **c** $\ln 729$

8 Solve for x, giving answers correct to 3 significant figures:
   a $e^x = 400$ **b** $e^{2x+1} = 11$ **c** $25e^{\frac{x}{2}} = 750$ **d** $e^{2x} = 7e^x - 12$

9 Solve $12(2^x) = 7 + \dfrac{10}{2^x}$ giving your answer in the form $m + \log_2 n$, $m,\, n \in \mathbb{Z}$.

REVIEW SET 4D

1 On the same set of axes, sketch and clearly label the graphs of:
   $f : x \mapsto e^x, \qquad g : x \mapsto e^{-x}, \qquad h : x \mapsto e^{-x} - 4.$
   State the domain and range of each function.

2 Sketch on the same set of axes, the graphs of $y = e^x$ and $y = e^{3x}$.

3 Without using a calculator, find:

   a $\ln(e\sqrt{e})$ **b** $\ln\left(\dfrac{1}{e^3}\right)$ **c** $\ln\left(\dfrac{e}{\sqrt{e^5}}\right)$

4 Write in the form e^x: **a** 20 **b** 3000 **c** 0.075

5 Simplify:
   a $4\ln 2 + 2\ln 3$ **b** $\frac{1}{2}\ln 9 - \ln 2$ **c** $2\ln 5 - 1$ **d** $\frac{1}{4}\ln 81$

6 Write the following equations without logarithms:
   a $\ln P = 1.5 \ln Q + \ln T$ **b** $\ln M = 1.2 - 0.5 \ln N$

7 Consider $g : x \mapsto 2e^x - 5$.
   a Find the defining equation of g^{-1}.
   b Sketch the graphs of g and g^{-1} on the same set of axes.
   c State the domain and range of g and g^{-1}.

8 The weight W_t grams of radioactive substance remaining after t weeks is given by
   $W_t = 8000 \times e^{-\frac{t}{20}}$ grams.   Find the time for the weight to:
   a halve   **b** reach 1000 g   **c** reach 0.1% of its original value.

9 The function f is defined for $x > 4$ by $f(x) = \ln(x^2 - 16) - \ln x - \ln(x - 4)$

   a Express $f(x)$ in the form $\ln\left(\dfrac{x + a}{x}\right)$, stating the value of $a \in \mathbb{Z}$.
   b Find an expression for $f^{-1}(x)$.

Chapter 5

Graphing and transforming functions

Contents:

A   FAMILIES OF FUNCTIONS

There are several families of functions that you are already familiar with. These include:

Name	General form	Function notation
Linear	$f(x) = ax + b, \quad a \neq 0$	$f : x \mapsto ax + b, \quad a \neq 0$
Quadratic	$f(x) = ax^2 + bx + c, \quad a \neq 0$	$f : x \mapsto ax^2 + bx + c, \quad a \neq 0$
Cubic	$f(x) = ax^3 + bx^2 + cx + d, a \neq 0$	$f : x \mapsto ax^3 + bx^2 + cx + d, a \neq 0$
Absolute value	$f(x) = \lvert x \rvert$	$f : x \mapsto \lvert x \rvert$
Exponential	$f(x) = a^x, \quad a > 0, \quad a \neq 1$	$f : x \mapsto a^x, \quad a > 0, \quad a \neq 1$
Logarithmic	$f(x) = \log_e x \quad \text{or} \quad f(x) = \ln x$	$f : x \mapsto \ln x$
Reciprocal	$f(x) = \dfrac{k}{x}, \quad x \neq 0$	$f : x \mapsto \dfrac{k}{x}, \quad x \neq 0$

These families of functions have different and distinctive graphs. We can compare them by considering important graphical features such as:

- the axes intercepts   (where the graph cuts the x and y-axes)
- slopes
- turning points   (maxima and minima)
- values of x where the function does not exist
- the presence of asymptotes   (lines or curves that the graph approaches).

INVESTIGATION   FUNCTION FAMILIES

In this investigation you are encouraged to use the graphing package supplied. Click on the icon to access this package.

GRAPHING
PACKAGE

What to do:

1   From the menu, graph on the same set of axes:
   $y = 2x + 1, \quad y = 2x + 3, \quad y = 2x - 1$
   Comment on all lines of the form $y = 2x + b$.

2   From the menu, graph on the same set of axes:
   $y = x + 2, \quad y = 2x + 2, \quad y = 4x + 2, \quad y = -x + 2, \quad y = -\frac{1}{2}x + 2$
   Comment on all lines of the form $y = ax + 2$.

3   On the same set of axes graph:
   $y = x^2, \quad y = 2x^2, \quad y = \frac{1}{2}x^2, \quad y = -x^2, \quad y = -3x^2, \quad y = -\frac{1}{5}x^2$
   Comment on all functions of the form $y = ax^2, \quad a \neq 0$.

4   On the same set of axes graph:
   $y = x^2, \quad y = (x - 1)^2 + 2, \quad y = (x + 1)^2 - 3, \quad y = (x - 2)^2 - 1$
   and other functions of the form $y = (x - h)^2 + k$ of your choice.
   Comment on the functions of this form.

5 On the same set of axes, graph these absolute value functions:

    a $y = |x|$, $y = 2|x|$, $y = |2x|$

    b $y = |x|$, $y = |x| + 2$, $y = |x| - 3$

    c $y = |x|$, $y = |x - 2|$, $y = |x + 3|$, $y = |x - 1| + 2$

Write a brief report on your discoveries.

6 On the same set of axes, graph these functions:

    a $y = \dfrac{1}{x}$, $y = \dfrac{3}{x}$, $y = \dfrac{10}{x}$
        b $y = \dfrac{-1}{x}$, $y = \dfrac{-2}{x}$, $y = \dfrac{-5}{x}$

    c $y = \dfrac{1}{x}$, $y = \dfrac{1}{x-2}$, $y = \dfrac{1}{x+3}$
        d $y = \dfrac{1}{x}$, $y = \dfrac{1}{x} + 2$, $y = \dfrac{1}{x} - 2$

    e $y = \dfrac{2}{x}$, $y = \dfrac{2}{x-1} + 2$, $y = \dfrac{2}{x+2} - 1$

Write a brief report on your discoveries.

Example 1

If $f(x) = x^2$, find in simplest form:

    a $f(2x)$ **b** $f\left(\dfrac{x}{3}\right)$ **c** $2f(x) + 1$ **d** $f(x+3) - 4$

a $f(2x)$	**b** $f\left(\dfrac{x}{3}\right)$	**c** $2f(x) + 1$	**d** $f(x+3) - 4$
$= (2x)^2$	$= \left(\dfrac{x}{3}\right)^2$	$= 2x^2 + 1$	$= (x+3)^2 - 4$
$= 4x^2$	$= \dfrac{x^2}{9}$		$= x^2 + 6x + 9 - 4$
			$= x^2 + 6x + 5$

EXERCISE 5A

1 If $f(x) = x$, find in simplest form:

    a $f(2x)$ **b** $f(x) + 2$ **c** $\frac{1}{2}f(x)$ **d** $2f(x) + 3$

2 If $f(x) = x^3$, find in simplest form:

    a $f(4x)$ **b** $\frac{1}{2}f(2x)$ **c** $f(x+1)$ **d** $2f(x+1) - 3$

    Note: $(x+1)^3 = x^3 + 3x^2 + 3x + 1$.   See the binomial theorem, **Chapter 8**.

3 If $f(x) = 2^x$, find in simplest form:

    a $f(2x)$ **b** $f(-x) + 1$ **c** $f(x-2) + 3$ **d** $2f(x) + 3$

4 If $f(x) = \dfrac{1}{x}$, find in simplest form:

    a $f(-x)$ **b** $f(\frac{1}{2}x)$ **c** $2f(x) + 3$ **d** $3f(x-1) + 2$

For the following questions, use the graphing package or your graphics calculator to graph and find the key features of the functions.

GRAPHING PACKAGE

5 Consider $f : x \mapsto 2x + 3$ or $y = 2x + 3$.

  a Graph the function.

  b Find algebraically, the: **i** x-axis intercept **ii** y-axis intercept **iii** slope.

  c Use technology to check the axes intercepts found in **b**.

6 Consider $f : x \mapsto (x - 2)^2 - 9$.

  a Graph the function.

  b Find algebraically the x and y axes intercepts.

  c Use technology to check that:

  i the x-axis intercepts are -1 and 5 **ii** the y-intercept is -5

  iii the vertex is $(2, -9)$.

7 Consider $f : x \mapsto 2x^3 - 9x^2 + 12x - 5$.

  a Graph the function.

  b Check that: **i** the x-intercepts are 1 and $2\frac{1}{2}$ **ii** the y-intercept is -5

  iii the minimum turning point is at $(2, -1)$

  iv the maximum turning point is at $(1, 0)$.

8 Sketch the graph of $y = |x|$.

  Note: $|x| = x$ if $x \geqslant 0$ and $|x| = -x$ if $x < 0$.

9 Consider $f : x \mapsto 2^x$. Graph the function and check these key features:

  a as $x \to \infty$, $2^x \to \infty$

  b as $x \to -\infty$, $2^x \to 0$ (from above)

  c the y-intercept is 1

  d 2^x is > 0 for all x.

$\to$ reads 'approaches' or 'tends to'

10 Consider $f : x \mapsto \log_e x$.

  Graph the function and then check that:

  a as $x \to \infty$, $\ln x \to \infty$ **b** as $x \to 0$ (from the right), $\ln x \to -\infty$

  c $\ln x$ only exists if $x > 0$ **d** the x-intercept is 1

  e the y-axis is an asymptote.

B   TRANSFORMATIONS OF GRAPHS

In the next exercise you should discover the graphical connection between $y = f(x)$ and functions of the form:

- $y = f(x) + b$, b is a constant
- $y = f(x - a)$, a is a constant
- $y = p\,f(x)$, p is a positive constant
- $y = f(kx)$, k is a positive constant
- $y = -f(x)$
- $y = f(-x)$

TYPES $y = f(x) + b$ AND $y = f(x - a)$

EXERCISE 5B.1

1 **a** Sketch the graph of $f(x) = x^2$.

  b On the same set of axes sketch the graphs of:

   i $y = f(x) + 2$, i.e., $y = x^2 + 2$ **ii** $y = f(x) - 3$, i.e., $y = x^2 - 3$

  c What is the connection between the graphs of $y = f(x)$ and $y = f(x) + b$ if:

   i $b > 0$ **ii** $b < 0$?

2 For each of the following functions f, sketch on the same set of axes $y = f(x)$, $y = f(x) + 1$ and $y = f(x) - 2$.

  a $f(x) = |x|$ **b** $f(x) = 2^x$ **c** $f(x) = x^3$ **d** $f(x) = \dfrac{1}{x}$

  Summarise your observations by describing the graphical transformation of $y = f(x)$ as it becomes $y = f(x) + b$.

3 **a** On the same set of axes, graph: $f(x) = x^2$, $y = f(x - 3)$ and $y = f(x + 2)$.

  b What is the connection between the graphs of $y = f(x)$ and $y = f(x - a)$ if:

   i $a > 0$ **ii** $a < 0$?

4 For each of the following functions f, sketch on the same set of axes the graphs of $y = f(x)$, $y = f(x - 1)$ and $y = f(x + 2)$.

  a $f(x) = |x|$ **b** $f(x) = x^3$ **c** $f(x) = \ln x$ **d** $f(x) = \dfrac{1}{x}$

  Summarise your observations by describing the geometrical transformation of $y = f(x)$ as it becomes $y = f(x - a)$.

5 For each of the following functions sketch:

  $y = f(x)$, $y = f(x - 2) + 3$ and $y = f(x + 1) - 4$ on the same set of axes.

  a $f(x) = x^2$ **b** $f(x) = e^x$ **c** $f(x) = \dfrac{1}{x}$

6 Copy these functions and then draw the graph of $y = f(x - 2) - 3$.

  a
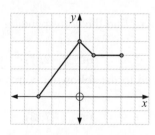

  b
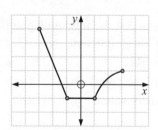

7 Given $f(x) = x^2$ is transformed to $g(x) = (x - 3)^2 + 2$:

  a find the images of the following points on $f(x)$:

   i $(0, 0)$ **ii** where $x = -3$ **iii** where $x = 2$

  b find the points on $f(x)$ which correspond to the following points on $g(x)$:

   i $(1, 6)$ **ii** $(-2, 27)$ **iii** $(1\frac{1}{2}, 4\frac{1}{4})$

TYPES $y = p\,f(x)\,,\,p > 0$ AND $y = f(kx)\,,\,k > 0$

EXERCISE 5B.2

1 Sketch on the same set of axes, the graphs of $y = f(x)$, $y = 2\,f(x)$ and $y = 3\,f(x)$
for each of:

    a $f(x) = x^2$ **b** $f(x) = |x|$ **c** $f(x) = x^3$

    d $f(x) = e^x$ **e** $f(x) = \ln x$ **f** $f(x) = \dfrac{1}{x}$

2 Sketch on the same set of axes, the graphs of $y = f(x)$, $y = \frac{1}{2}f(x)$ and $y = \frac{1}{4}f(x)$
for each of:

    a $f(x) = x^2$ **b** $f(x) = x^3$ **c** $f(x) = e^x$

3 Using **1** and **2**, summarise your observations by describing the graphical transformation
of $y = f(x)$ to $y = p\,f(x)$ for $p > 0$.

4 Sketch on the same set of axes, the graphs of $y = f(x)$ and $y = f(2x)$ for each of:

    a $y = x^2$ **b** $y = (x-1)^2$ **c** $y = (x+3)^2$

5 Sketch on the same set of axes, the graphs of $y = f(x)$ and $y = f(3x)$ for each of:

    a $y = x$ **b** $y = x^2$ **c** $y = e^x$

6 Sketch on the same set of axes, the graphs of $y = f(x)$ and $y = f\left(\frac{x}{2}\right)$ for each of:

    a $y = x^2$ **b** $y = 2x$ **c** $y = (x+2)^2$

7 Using **4**, **5** and **6**, summarise your observations by describing the graphical transformation
of $y = f(x)$ to $y = f(kx)$ for $k > 0$.

8 Consider the function $f : x \mapsto x^2$.
On the same set of axes sketch the graphs of:

    a $y = f(x)$, $y = 3\,f(x-2)+1$ and $y = 2\,f(x+1)-3$

    b $y = f(x)$, $y = f(x-3)$, $y = f\left(\frac{x}{2}-3\right)$, $y = 2\,f\left(\frac{x}{2}-3\right)$ and $y = 2\,f\left(\frac{x}{2}-3\right)+4$

    c $y = f(x)$ and $y = \frac{1}{4}\,f(2x+5)+1$.

9 **a** Given that the following points lie on $y = f(x)$, find the corresponding points on
the image function $y = 3f(2x)$:

        i $(3, -5)$ **ii** $(1, 2)$ **iii** $(-2, 1)$

    b Find the points on $y = f(x)$ which are moved to the following points under the
transformation $y = 3f(2x)$:

        i $(2, 1)$ **ii** $(-3, 2)$ **iii** $(-7, 3)$

10 The function $y = f(x)$ is transformed to the function $g(x) = 3 + 2f(\frac{1}{2}x + 1)$.

    a Fully describe the transformation that maps $f(x)$ onto $g(x)$.

    b Using **a**, find the image points of the following points on $f(x)$:

        i $(1, -3)$ **ii** $(2, 1)$ **iii** $(-1, -2)$

    c Find the points on $f(x)$ which correspond to the following points on $g(x)$:

        i $(-2, -5)$ **ii** $(1, -1)$ **iii** $(5, 0)$

TYPES $y = -f(x)$ AND $y = f(-x)$

EXERCISE 5B.3

1   On the same set of axes, sketch the graphs of:

   a $y = 3x$ and $y = -3x$
   b $y = e^x$ and $y = -e^x$

   c $y = x^2$ and $y = -x^2$
   d $y = \ln x$ and $y = -\ln x$

   e $y = x^3 - 2$ and $y = -x^3 + 2$
   f $y = 2(x + 1)^2$ and $y = -2(x + 1)^2$

2   Based on question **1**, what transformation moves $y = f(x)$ to $y = -f(x)$?

3   **a**   Find $f(-x)$ for:

   i $f(x) = 2x + 1$ **ii** $f(x) = x^2 + 2x + 1$ **iii** $f(x) = |x - 3|$

   b   Graph $y = f(x)$ and $y = f(-x)$ for:

   i $f(x) = 2x + 1$ **ii** $f(x) = x^2 + 2x + 1$ **iii** $f(x) = |x - 3|$

4   Based on question **3**, what transformation moves $y = f(x)$ to $y = f(-x)$?

5   The function $y = f(x)$ is transformed to $g(x) = -f(x)$.

   a   Find the points on $g(x)$ corresponding to the following points on $f(x)$:
   i $(3, 0)$ **ii** $(2, -1)$ **iii** $(-3, 2)$

   b   Find the points on $f(x)$ that have been transformed to the following points on $g(x)$:
   i $(7, -1)$ **ii** $(-5, 0)$ **iii** $(-3, -2)$

6   The function $y = f(x)$ is transformed to $h(x) = f(-x)$.

   a   Find the image points on $h(x)$ for the following points on $f(x)$:
   i $(2, -1)$ **ii** $(0, 3)$ **iii** $(-1, 2)$

   b   Find the points on $f(x)$ corresponding to the following points on $h(x)$:
   i $(5, -4)$ **ii** $(0, 3)$ **iii** $(2, 3)$

7   A function $y = f(x)$ is transformed to the function $y = -f(-x) = g(x)$.

   a   Describe the nature of the transformation.

   b   If $(3, -7)$ lies on $y = f(x)$,   find the transformed point on $g(x)$.

   c   Find the point on $f(x)$ that transforms to the point $(-5, -1)$.

Summary of graphical transformations on $y = f(x)$

▶   For $y = f(x) + b$,   the effect of b is to **translate** the graph **vertically** through b units.

   •   If $b > 0$ it moves **upwards**.   •   If $b < 0$ it moves **downwards**.

▶   For $y = f(x - a)$,   the effect of a is to **translate** the graph **horizontally** through a units.

   •   If $a > 0$ it moves to the **right**.   •   If $a < 0$ it moves to the **left**.

▶   For $y = f(x - a) + b$,   the graph is translated horizontally a units and vertically b units. We say it is translated by the vector $\begin{bmatrix} a \\ b \end{bmatrix}$.

continued next page

continued from previous page

▶   For $y = p\,f(x)$, $p > 0$,   the effect of p is to **vertically stretch** the graph by a factor of p.

  • If $p > 1$ it moves points of $y = f(x)$ **further away** from the x-axis.
  • If $0 < p < 1$ it moves points of $y = f(x)$ **closer** to the x-axis.

▶   For $y = f(kx)$, $k > 0$, the effect of k is to **horizontally compress** the graph by a factor of k.

  • If $k > 1$ it moves points of $y = f(x)$ **closer** to the y-axis.
  • If $0 < k < 1$ it moves points of $y = f(x)$ **further away** from the y-axis.

▶   For $y = -f(x)$, the effect is to **reflect** $y = f(x)$ **in the x-axis**.

▶   For $y = f(-x)$, the effect is to **reflect** $y = f(x)$ **in the y-axis**.

Note: Stretching by a factor of $\frac{1}{p}$ is equivalent to compressing by a factor of p.

For example, $y = \frac{1}{3} f(x)$ indicates that $y = f(x)$ is vertically stretched by a factor of $\frac{1}{3}$, or compressed by a factor of 3.

Likewise, $y = f(\frac{1}{4}x)$ indicates that $y = f(x)$ is horizontally compressed by a factor of $\frac{1}{4}$, or stretched by a factor of 4.

EXERCISE 5B.4

1   Copy the following graphs for $y = f(x)$ and sketch the graphs of $y = -f(x)$ on the same axes.

a 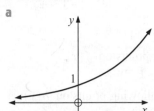   **b** 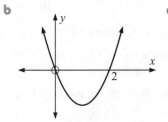   **c**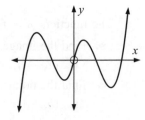

2   Given the following graphs of $y = f(x)$,   sketch graphs of $y = f(-x)$:

a 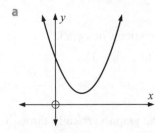   **b** 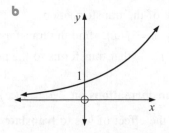   **c**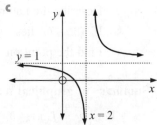

3   The scales on the graphs below are the same. Match each equation to its graph.

A $y = x^4$ **B** $y = 2x^4$ **C** $y = \frac{1}{2}x^4$ **D** $y = 6x^4$

a 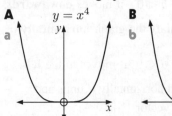   **b** 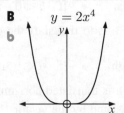   **c** 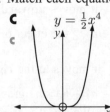   **d**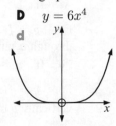

4 For the graph of $y = f(x)$ given, draw sketches of:

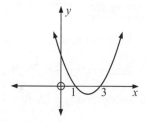

   a $y = 2f(x)$ **b** $y = \frac{1}{2}f(x)$

   c $y = f(x + 2)$ **d** $y = f(2x)$

   e $y = f(\frac{1}{2}x)$

5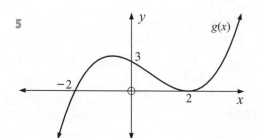

For the graph of $y = g(x)$ given, draw sketches of:

   a $y = g(x) + 2$ **b** $y = -g(x)$

   c $y = g(-x)$ **d** $y = g(x + 1)$

6 For the graph of $y = h(x)$ given, draw sketches of:

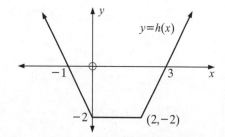

   a $y = h(x) + 1$ **b** $y = \frac{1}{2}h(x)$

   c $y = h(-x)$ **d** $y = h\left(\frac{x}{2}\right)$

C   SIMPLE RATIONAL FUNCTIONS

> Any function $x \mapsto \dfrac{ax + b}{cx + d}$, $x \neq -\dfrac{d}{c}$ where a, b, c and d are constants
>
> is called a **simple rational function**.

These functions are characterised by the presence of both a **horizontal asymptote** (HA) and a **vertical asymptote** (VA).

Any graph of a simple rational function can be obtained from the reciprocal function $x \mapsto \dfrac{1}{x}$ by a combination of transformations including:

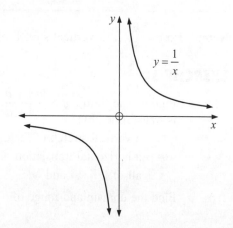

- a **translation**
  (vertical and/or horizontal)

- **stretches** and **compressions**
  (vertical and/or horizontal)

Example 2

a   Find the function $y = g(x)$ that results when transforming the reciprocal

function, $x \mapsto \dfrac{1}{x}$ by: a vertical stretch with factor 2 then a horizontal

compression with factor 3, then a translation of $\begin{bmatrix} 3 \\ -2 \end{bmatrix}$.

b   Find the asymptotes of each function found in a.

c   Is the function found in a a self inverse function? Explain.

a   Under a vertical stretch $\dfrac{1}{x}$ becomes $2\left(\dfrac{1}{x}\right)$ $\{2f(x)\}$
with factor 2,

Under a horizontal com- $\dfrac{2}{x}$ becomes $\dfrac{2}{(3x)}$ $\{f(3x)\}$
pression with factor 3,

Under a translation of $\begin{bmatrix} 3 \\ -2 \end{bmatrix}$, $\dfrac{2}{3x}$ becomes $\dfrac{2}{3(x-3)} - 2$ $\{f(x-3)-2\}$

$$\therefore \quad f(x) = \frac{2}{3x-9} - 2 = \frac{2}{3x-9} - \frac{2(3x-9)}{3x-9} = \frac{-6x+20}{3x-9}$$

b   The asymptotes of $y = \dfrac{1}{x}$ are: VA $x = 0$,   HA $y = 0$

$\therefore$ for the new function   VA is $x = 3$,   HA is $y = -2$ $\{$as translated $\begin{bmatrix} 3 \\ -2 \end{bmatrix}\}$

c

From a graphics calculator the graph is found as shown.

It is not symmetrical about $y = x$.
Hence, it is *not* a self inverse function.

Note: $f(x) = \dfrac{k}{x}$ is a vertical stretch of $x \mapsto \dfrac{1}{x}$ with factor k.

EXERCISE 5C

1   a   Find, in the form $y = \dfrac{ax+b}{cx+d}$,   the function that results when $x \mapsto \dfrac{1}{x}$
is transformed by:

   i   a vertical stretch of factor $\frac{1}{2}$ ii   a horizontal stretch of factor 3

   iii   a horizontal translation of -3 iv   a vertical translation of 4

   v   all of i, ii, iii and iv.

b   Find the domain and range of $y = \dfrac{ax+b}{cx+d}$ as found in a v.

Example 3

For the function $f : x \mapsto \dfrac{2x - 6}{x + 1}$,   find:

a the asymptotes   **b** how to transform the function to give $x \mapsto \dfrac{1}{x}$

a $f(x) = \dfrac{2x - 6}{x + 1} = \dfrac{2(x + 1) - 8}{x + 1} = 2 - \dfrac{8}{x + 1} = \dfrac{-8}{x + 1} + 2$

This represents a translation of $\begin{bmatrix} -1 \\ 2 \end{bmatrix}$ from $f(x) = \dfrac{-8}{x}$ which has VA $x = 0$ and   HA $y = 0$.

So, $f(x) = \dfrac{2x - 6}{x + 1}$ has VA $x = -1$ and   HA $y = 2$.

Note: • $\dfrac{2x - 6}{x + 1}$ is undefined when $x = -1$

• as $|x| \to \infty$, $f(x) \to 2$

• the domain of $f(x) = \dfrac{2x - 6}{x + 1}$ is $\{x : x \neq -1\}$

the range of $f(x) = \dfrac{2x - 6}{x + 1}$ is $\{y : y \neq 2\}$

b To get $f(x) = \dfrac{2x - 6}{x + 1}$ from $f(x) = \dfrac{1}{x}$ we

vertically stretch by a factor of 8 $\{\dfrac{1}{x}$ becomes $8\left(\dfrac{1}{x}\right) = \dfrac{8}{x}\}$

then reflect in the x-axis $\{\dfrac{8}{x}$ becomes $-\dfrac{8}{x}\}$

then translate by $\begin{bmatrix} -1 \\ 2 \end{bmatrix}$ $\{\dfrac{-8}{x}$ becomes $\dfrac{-8}{x + 1} + 2\}$

So, to do the **opposite** we

translate by $\begin{bmatrix} 1 \\ -2 \end{bmatrix}$, then reflect in the x-axis, then vertically stretch by factor $\frac{1}{8}$.

Check: $y = \dfrac{2x - 6}{x + 1}$ becomes $y = \dfrac{2(x - 1) - 6}{(x - 1) + 1} - 2 = \dfrac{2x - 8}{x} - 2 = -\dfrac{8}{x}$

then $-\dfrac{8}{x}$ becomes $\dfrac{8}{x}$ and $\dfrac{8}{x}$ becomes $\dfrac{8}{(8x)} = \dfrac{1}{x}$.

2 For these functions find:

i the asymptotes   **ii** how to transform $f(x)$ to give the function $x \mapsto \dfrac{1}{x}$.

a $f : x \mapsto \dfrac{2x + 4}{x - 1}$ **b** $f : x \mapsto \dfrac{3x - 2}{x + 1}$ **c** $f : x \mapsto \dfrac{2x + 1}{2 - x}$

Example 4

Consider $f(x) = \dfrac{4x+3}{x-2}$.

a Find the asymptotes of $y = f(x)$.
b Find the axes intercepts.

c Discuss the behaviour of f near its   **i** VA.   **ii** HA.
d Sketch the graph of the function.
e Describe the transformations which move $x \mapsto \dfrac{1}{x}$ to $x \mapsto \dfrac{4x+3}{x-2}$.

---

a $y = \dfrac{4x+3}{x-2} = \dfrac{4(x-2)+11}{x-2} = 4 + \dfrac{11}{x-2}$

So, the function has   VA $x = 2$ {where y is undefined}

and has   HA $y = 4$ {as $|x| \to \infty$, $y \to 4$}

b When $x = 0$, $y = \frac{3}{-2}$ $\therefore$ y-intercept is $-1\frac{1}{2}$

when $y = 0$, $4x + 3 = 0$

$x = -\frac{3}{4}$ $\therefore$ x-intercept is $-\frac{3}{4}$

c **i** as $x \to 2$ (from the left), $y \to -\infty$ **ii** as $x \to -\infty$, $y \to 4$ (from below)
as $x \to 2$ (from the right), $y \to \infty$ as $x \to \infty$, $y \to 4$ (from above)

d

e $\dfrac{1}{x}$ becomes $\dfrac{11}{x}$ under a vertical stretch with factor 11, and then

$\dfrac{11}{x}$ becomes $\dfrac{4x+3}{x-2}$ under a

translation of $\begin{bmatrix} 2 \\ 4 \end{bmatrix}$

---

3 For the following functions:

i find the asymptotes   **ii** find the axes intercepts
iii discuss the graph's behaviour near its VA and its HA
iv sketch the graph.
v Describe the transformations which move $x \mapsto \dfrac{1}{x}$ to the given function.

a $y = \dfrac{2x+3}{x+1}$ **b** $y = \dfrac{3}{x-2}$ **c** $y = \dfrac{2x-1}{3-x}$ **d** $y = \dfrac{5x-1}{2x+1}$

4 In order to remove noxious weeds from her property Helga sprays with a weedicide. The chemical is slow acting and the number of weeds per hectare remaining after t days is modelled by $N = 20 + \dfrac{100}{t+2}$ weeds/ha.

a How many weeds per ha were alive before the spraying?
b How many weeds will be alive after 8 days?
c How long will it take for the number of weeds still alive to be 40/ha?
d Sketch the graph of N against t
e According to the model, is the spraying going to eradicate all weeds?

Graphics calculator tips:

- To find the **zeros** of a function $y = f(x)$, simply **graph** the function and find its x-**intercepts**.

  This is equivalent to finding the **roots** or **solutions** of the equation $f(x) = 0$.

- To check that you have found the correct asymptotes (VA and HA):
  - ▶ Try to find y for the x-asymptote value. It should be undefined.
  - ▶ Try to find y for large x values, e.g., $\pm 10^9$. It should give a value close to the y-asymptote value.

D FURTHER GRAPHICAL TRANSFORMATIONS

In this exercise you should discover the graphical connection between $y = f(x)$ and functions of the form $y = \dfrac{1}{f(x)}$, $y = |f(x)|$ and $y = f(|x|)$.

THE RECIPROCAL FUNCTION $y = \dfrac{1}{f(x)}$

Example 5

Graph on the same set of axes:

a $y = x - 2$ and $y = \dfrac{1}{x - 2}$ **b** $y = x^2$ and $y = \dfrac{1}{x^2}$

a
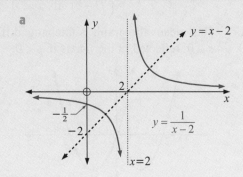

b
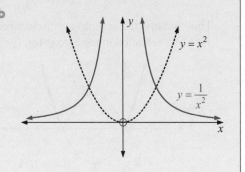

EXERCISE 5D.1

1 Graph on the same set of axes:

a $y = -x^2$ and $y = \dfrac{-1}{x^2}$ **b** $y = (x-1)(x-3)$ and $y = \dfrac{1}{(x-1)(x-3)}$

2 **Invariant points** are points which do not move under a transformation.

Show that if $y = f(x)$ is transformed to $y = \dfrac{1}{f(x)}$, invariant points occur at $y = \pm 1$.

Check your results in question **1** for invariant points.

DISCUSSION

THE GRAPHICAL CONNECTION BETWEEN $y = f(x)$ AND $y = \frac{1}{f(x)}$

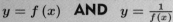

True or false?   Discuss:

- The zeros of $f(x)$ become VA values of $\frac{1}{f(x)}$ and the VA values of $f(x)$ become the zeros of $\frac{1}{f(x)}$.

- Maximum values of $f(x)$ become minimum values of $\frac{1}{f(x)}$ and the minimum values of $f(x)$ become maximum values of $\frac{1}{f(x)}$.

- When $f(x) > 0$, $\frac{1}{f(x)} > 0$ also and when $f(x) < 0$, $\frac{1}{f(x)} < 0$ also.

- When $f(x) \to 0$, $\frac{1}{f(x)} \to \pm\infty$ and when $\frac{1}{f(x)} \to 0$, $f(x) \to \pm\infty$.

THE MODULUS FUNCTIONS $y = |f(x)|$ AND $y = f(|x|)$

Example 6

Draw the graph of $f(x) = 3x(x - 2)$ and on the same axes draw the graphs of:

a $y = |f(x)|$ **b** $y = f(|x|)$

a $y = |f(x)| = \begin{cases} f(x) & \text{if } f(x) \geqslant 0 \\ -f(x) & \text{if } f(x) < 0 \end{cases}$

b $y = f(|x|) = \begin{cases} f(x) & \text{if } x \geqslant 0 \\ f(-x) & \text{if } x < 0 \end{cases}$

This means the graph is unchanged for $f(x) \geqslant 0$, reflected in the x-axis for $f(x) < 0$.

This means the graph is unchanged if $x \geqslant 0$, reflected in the y-axis if $x < 0$.

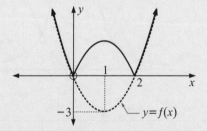

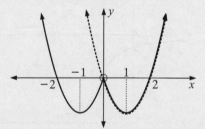

DISCUSSION

THE GRAPHICAL CONNECTION BETWEEN $y = f(x)$, $y = |f(x)|$ AND $y = f(|x|)$

True or false?   Discuss:

- $y = |f(x)| \Rightarrow y = f(x)$ for $f(x) \geqslant 0$ and $y = -f(x)$ for $f(x) < 0$

- The graph of $y = |f(x)|$ can be obtained from the graph of $y = f(x)$ by reflecting in the x-axis. (Try **a** $y = x^2$ **b** $y = e^x - 2$ **c** $y = \ln(x + 2)$)

- Points on the y-axis are invariant for $f(x) \rightarrow |f(x)|$
- The graph of $y = f(|x|)$ can be obtained from the graph of $y = f(x)$ by reflecting in the y-axis.
- $y = f(|x|)$ $\Rightarrow$ $y = f(x)$ for $x \geqslant 0$ and $y = f(-x)$ for $x < 0$.
- Points on the x-axis are invariant for $f(x) \rightarrow f(|x|)$

EXERCISE 5D.2

1 Draw $y = x(x+2)$ and on the same set of axes graph:

a $y = |f(x)|$
b $y = f(|x|)$

2 Copy the following graphs for $y = f(x)$ and on the same axes graph $y = \dfrac{1}{f(x)}$:

a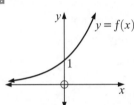

b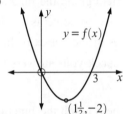

c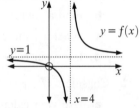

3 Copy the following graphs for $y = f(x)$ and on the same axes graph $y = |f(x)|$:

a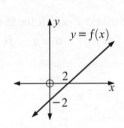

b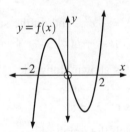

c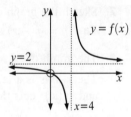

4 Repeat question **3**, but this time graph $y = f(|x|)$ instead of $y = |f(x)|$.

5 Suppose the function $f(x)$ is transformed to $|f(x)|$.
For the following points on $f(x)$ find the image points on $|f(x)|$:

a $(3, 0)$ b $(5, -2)$ c $(0, 7)$ d $(2, 2)$

6 Suppose the function $f(x)$ is transformed to $f(|x|)$.

a For the following points on $f(x)$ find the image points:

i $(0, 3)$ ii $(1, 3)$ iii $(7, -4)$

b For the points on $f(|x|)$ find the points on $f(x)$ that have been transformed:

i $(0, 3)$ ii $(-1, 3)$ iii $(10, -8)$

REVIEW SET 5A

1 If $f(x) = x^2 - 2x$, find in simplest form:

   a $f(3)$ **b** $f(-2)$ **c** $f(2x)$ **d** $f(-x)$ **e** $3f(x) - 2$

2 If $f(x) = 5 - x - x^2$, find in simplest form:

   a $f(4)$ **b** $f(-1)$ **c** $f(x-1)$ **d** $f\left(\dfrac{x}{2}\right)$ **e** $2f(x) - f(-x)$

3 Consider the function $f : x \mapsto x^2$. On the same set of axes graph:

   a $y = f(x)$ **b** $y = f(x+2)$ **c** $y = 2f(x+2)$ **d** $y = 2f(x+2) - 3$

4 The graph of $f(x) = 3x^3 - 2x^2 + x + 2$ is translated to its image $g(x)$ by the vector $\begin{bmatrix} 1 \\ -2 \end{bmatrix}$. Write the equation of $g(x)$ in the form $g(x) = ax^3 + bx^2 + cx + d$.

5 Consider $f(x) = (x+1)^2 - 4$.

   a Use your calculator to help graph the function.

   b Find algebraically **i** the x-intercepts   **ii** the y-intercept.

   c What are the coordinates of the vertex of the function?

   d Use your calculator to check your answers to **b** and **c**.

6 Consider $f : x \mapsto 2^{-x}$.

   a Use your calculator to help graph the function.

   b True or false: **i** as $x \to \infty$, $2^{-x} \to 0$ **ii** as $x \to -\infty$, $2^{-x} \to 0$

              iii the y-intercept is $\frac{1}{2}$ **iv** $2^{-x} > 0$ for all x?

7 Sketch the graph of $f(x) = -x^2$, and on the same set of axes sketch the graph of:

   a $y = f(-x)$ **b** $y = -f(x)$ **c** $y = f(2x)$ **d** $y = f(x-2)$

8 The graph of $y_1 = f(x)$ is shown alongside.

The x-axis is a tangent to $f(x)$ at $x = a$ and $f(x)$ cuts the x-axis at $x = b$.

On the same diagram sketch the graph of $y_2 = f(x-c)$ where $0 < c < b - a$. Indicate the coordinates of the points of intersection of y_2 with the x-axis.

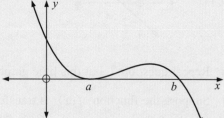

9 The graph of $f(x)$ is drawn alongside.

   a Copy the graph of $f(x)$ and draw the graph of $|f(x)|$ on the same set of axes.

   b Find the y-intercept of $\dfrac{1}{f(x)}$.

   c Show on the diagram the points that are invariant for the function $\dfrac{1}{f(x)}$.

   d Draw the graph of $y = \dfrac{1}{f(x)}$ on the same set of axes.

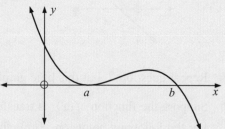

10 **a** If $f(x) = x + 2$, find the equation of the function F obtained by *stretching* the function f *vertically* by a factor of 2 and compressing the function *horizontally* by a factor of 2, followed by a translation of $\frac{1}{2}$ horizontally and -3 vertically.

  b **i** Check that the point $(1, 3)$ remains invariant under the transformation described in part **a**.

  ii What happens to the points $(0, 2)$ and $(-1, 1)$ under the transformation given in part **a**?

  iii Show that the points in **ii** lie on the graph of $y = F(x)$.

11 The graph of $f(x) = x^2$ is transformed to the graph of $g(x)$ by a reflection and a translation as illustrated in the diagram alongside.

Find the equation of $y = g(x)$ in the form $ax^2 + bx + c$.

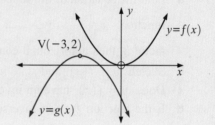

REVIEW SET 5B

1 If $f(x) = \dfrac{4}{x}$, find in simplest form:

  a $f(-4)$ **b** $f(2x)$ **c** $f\left(\dfrac{x}{2}\right)$ **d** $4f(x + 2) - 3$

2 Consider $f(x) : x \mapsto 3x - 2$.

  a Sketch the function f.

  b Find algebraically the **i** x-intercept **ii** y-intercept **iii** slope.

  c **i** Find y when $x = 0.3$ **ii** Find x when $y = 0.7$

3 For what values of x, where a is a positive real number, is $|x - a| = |x| - a$?

4 Let $f(x) = \dfrac{c}{x + c}$, $x \neq -c$, $c > 0$.

  a On a set of axes like those shown, sketch the graph of $f(x)$. Label clearly any points of intersection with the axes and any asymptotes.

  b On the same set of axes, sketch the graph of $\dfrac{1}{f(x)}$.

Label clearly any points of intersection with the axes.

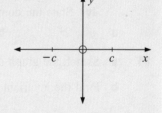

5 For the graph of $y = f(x)$, sketch graphs of:

  a $y = f(-x)$ **b** $y = -f(x)$

  c $y = f(x + 2)$ **d** $y = f(x) + 2$

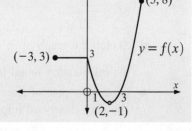

6 The graph of $y = f(x)$ is given.

On the same set of axes graph each pair of functions:

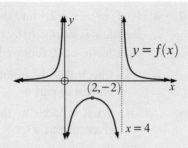

  a $y = f(x)$ and $y = f(x-2)+1$

  b $y = f(x)$ and $y = \dfrac{1}{f(x)}$

  c $y = f(x)$ and $y = |f(x)|$

7 **a** Find the equation of the function $y = f(x)$ that results from transforming the function $x \mapsto \dfrac{1}{x}$ by: a reflection in the y-axis, then a vertical stretch of factor 3, then a horizontal compression of factor 2, then a translation of $\begin{bmatrix} 1 \\ 1 \end{bmatrix}$.

  b Sketch $y = f(x)$ and state its domain and range.

  c Does $y = f(x)$ have an inverse function? Explain.

  d Is the function f a self-inverse function? Give graphical and algebraic evidence.

8 Discuss and sketch the graph of $y = \dfrac{2x-3}{3x+5}$.

Your discussion should include: the asymptote equations, axes intercepts, and what happens near the asymptotes.

9 The graph alongside is that of a rational relation.

Find its equation in the form $y = \dfrac{ax+b}{cx+d}$.

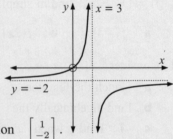

10 For each of the following functions:

  i find $y = f(x)$, the result of a translation $\begin{bmatrix} 1 \\ -2 \end{bmatrix}$.

  ii Sketch the original function and its translated function on the same set of axes.

  iii Clearly state any asymptotes of each function.

  iv State the domain and range of each function.

  a $y = 2^x$ **b** $y = \log_4 x$

11 **a** Sketch the graph of $f(x) = -2x + 3$, clearly showing the axis intercepts.

  b Find the invariant points for the graph of $y = \dfrac{1}{f(x)}$.

  c State the equation of the vertical asymptote and find the y-intercept of the graph of $y = \dfrac{1}{f(x)}$.

  d Sketch the graph of $y = \dfrac{1}{f(x)}$ on the same axes as in part **a**, showing clearly the information found in parts **b** and **c**.

  e On a new pair of axes, sketch the graphs of $y = |f(x)|$ and $y = f(|x|)$ showing clearly all important features.

Chapter 6

Quadratic equations and functions

Contents:

QUADRATICS

A **quadratic equation** is an equation of the form $ax^2 + bx + c = 0$ where a, b and c are constants, $a \neq 0$.

A **quadratic function** is a function of the form $f(x) = ax^2 + bx + c$, $a \neq 0$.
Alternatively, it can be written as $f : x \mapsto ax^2 + bx + c$, $a \neq 0$.

Quadratic functions are members of the family of **polynomials**.

$f : x \mapsto ax^3 + bx^2 + cx + d$, $a \neq 0$ is a *cubic polynomial*.

$f : x \mapsto ax^4 + bx^3 + cx^2 + dx + e$, $a \neq 0$ is a *quartic polynomial*.

HISTORICAL NOTE

Galileo Galilei (1564 - 1642) was born in Pisa, Tuscany. He was a philosopher who played a significant role in the scientific revolution of that time.

Within his research he conducted a series of experiments on the paths of projectiles, attempting to find a mathematical description of falling bodies.

Two of Galileo's experiments consisted of rolling a ball down a grooved ramp that was placed at a fixed height above the floor and inclined at a fixed angle to the horizontal. In one experiment the ball left the end of the ramp and descended to the floor. In the second, a horizontal shelf was placed at the end of the ramp, and the ball travelled along this shelf before descending to the floor.

In each experiment Galileo altered the release height (h) of the ball and measured the distance (d) the ball travelled before landing. The units of measurement were called 'punti' (points).

In both experiments Galileo found that once the ball left the ramp or shelf, its path was parabolic and could therefore be modelled by a quadratic function.

Galileo

OPENING PROBLEM

Farmer Brown wishes to construct a rectangular pen for her chickens using her barn for one of the sides. The other three sides will be constructed out of 80 m of chicken wire as illustrated.

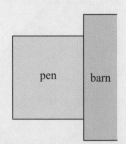

She can make the pen long and thin, or short and fat, or any rectangular shape in between, as long as she uses exactly 80 m of chicken wire. However, what she really wants to know is which rectangular shape will give her chickens the maximum area.

Can you:

- decide on a suitable variable to use and construct an area function in terms of this variable

- use the area function to find the maximum area that the pen may have and the shape of the pen when this occurs?

A   SOLVING QUADRATIC EQUATIONS (REVIEW)

Acme Leather Jacket Co. makes and sells x leather jackets each week and their profit function is given by $P = -12.5x^2 + 550x - 2125$ dollars.

How many jackets must be made and sold each week in order to obtain a weekly profit of $3000?

Clearly we need to solve the equation:

$$-12.5x^2 + 550x - 2125 = 3000$$
$$\text{i.e.,} \quad 12.5x^2 - 550x + 5125 = 0$$

This equation is of the form $ax^2 + bx + c = 0$ and is thus a quadratic equation.

To solve quadratic equations we can:

- **factorise** the quadratic and use the **Null Factor law**: "if $ab = 0$ then $a = 0$ or $b = 0$"
- **complete the square**
- use the **quadratic formula**
- use **technology**.

Definition:

> The **roots** or **solutions** of $ax^2 + bx + c = 0$ are the values of x which satisfy the equation, i.e., make it true.

For example, $x = 2$ is a root of $x^2 - 3x + 2 = 0$ since, when $x = 2$,
$$x^2 - 3x + 2 = (2)^2 - 3(2) + 2 = 4 - 6 + 2 = 0 \quad \checkmark$$

SOLVING BY FACTORISATION

Step 1: Make one side of the equation 0 by transferring all terms to one side.

Step 2: Fully factorise the other side.

Step 3: Use the 'Null Factor law': "if $ab = 0$ then $a = 0$ or $b = 0$".

Step 4: Solve the resulting elementary linear equations.

Example 1

Solve for x: **a** $3x^2 + 5x = 0$ **b** $x^2 = 5x + 6$

a $\quad 3x^2 + 5x = 0$	**b** $\qquad\qquad x^2 = 5x + 6$
$\therefore \quad x(3x + 5) = 0$	$\therefore \quad x^2 - 5x - 6 = 0$
$\therefore \quad x = 0 \text{ or } 3x + 5 = 0$	$\therefore \quad (x - 6)(x + 1) = 0$
$\therefore \quad x = 0 \text{ or } x = -\frac{5}{3}$	$\therefore \quad x - 6 = 0 \text{ or } x + 1 = 0$
	$\therefore \quad x = 6 \text{ or } -1$

Example 2

Solve for x: **a** $4x^2 + 1 = 4x$ **b** $6x^2 = 11x + 10$

a
$$4x^2 + 1 = 4x$$
$$\therefore \quad 4x^2 - 4x + 1 = 0$$
$$\therefore \quad (2x-1)^2 = 0$$
$$\therefore \quad x = \tfrac{1}{2}$$

b
$$6x^2 = 11x + 10$$
$$\therefore \quad 6x^2 - 11x - 10 = 0$$
$$\therefore \quad (2x-5)(3x+2) = 0$$
$$\therefore \quad x = \tfrac{5}{2} \quad \text{or} \quad -\tfrac{2}{3}$$

Example 3

Solve for x:

$$3x + \frac{2}{x} = -7$$

$$3x + \frac{2}{x} = -7$$
$$\therefore \quad x\left(3x + \frac{2}{x}\right) = -7x \qquad \text{\{multiply both sides by } x\text{\}}$$
$$\therefore \quad 3x^2 + 2 = -7x \qquad \text{\{expand the brackets\}}$$
$$\therefore \quad 3x^2 + 7x + 2 = 0 \qquad \text{\{make the RHS 0\}}$$
$$\therefore \quad (x+2)(3x+1) = 0 \qquad \text{\{factorising\}}$$
$$\therefore \quad x = -2 \quad \text{or} \quad -\tfrac{1}{3}$$

EXERCISE 6A.1

1 Solve the following by factorisation:

    a $4x^2 + 7x = 0$ **b** $6x^2 + 2x = 0$ **c** $3x^2 - 7x = 0$

    d $2x^2 - 11x = 0$ **e** $3x^2 = 8x$ **f** $9x = 6x^2$

    g $x^2 - 5x + 6 = 0$ **h** $x^2 = 2x + 8$ **i** $x^2 + 21 = 10x$

    j $9 + x^2 = 6x$ **k** $x^2 + x = 12$ **l** $x^2 + 8x = 33$

2 Solve the following by factorisation:

    a $9x^2 - 12x + 4 = 0$ **b** $2x^2 - 13x - 7 = 0$ **c** $3x^2 = 16x + 12$

    d $3x^2 + 5x = 2$ **e** $2x^2 + 3 = 5x$ **f** $3x^2 = 4x + 4$

    g $3x^2 = 10x + 8$ **h** $4x^2 + 4x = 3$ **i** $4x^2 = 11x + 3$

    j $12x^2 = 11x + 15$ **k** $7x^2 + 6x = 1$ **l** $15x^2 + 2x = 56$

3 Solve for x:

    a $(x+1)^2 = 2x^2 - 5x + 11$ **b** $(x+2)(1-x) = -4$

    c $5 - 4x^2 = 3(2x+1) + 2$ **d** $x + \dfrac{2}{x} = 3$

    e $2x - \dfrac{1}{x} = -1$ **f** $\dfrac{x+3}{1-x} = -\dfrac{9}{x}$

SOLVING BY 'COMPLETING THE SQUARE'

As you would be aware by now, not all quadratics factorise easily. For example, $x^2 + 4x + 1$ cannot be factorised by using a simple factorisation approach. This means that we need a different approach in order to solve $x^2 + 4x + 1 = 0$.

One way is to use the 'completing the square' technique.

Equations of the form $ax^2 + bx + c = 0$ can be converted to the form $(x + p)^2 = q$ from which the solutions are easy to obtain.

> Notice that if $X^2 = a$, then $X = \pm\sqrt{a}$.

Example 4

Solve exactly for x: **a** $(x + 2)^2 = 7$ **b** $(x - 1)^2 = -5$

a $(x + 2)^2 = 7$
$\therefore \quad x + 2 = \pm\sqrt{7}$
$\therefore \quad x = -2 \pm \sqrt{7}$

b $(x - 1)^2 = -5$
has no real solutions since the perfect square $(x - 1)^2$ cannot be negative.

Example 5

Solve for exact values of x: $x^2 + 4x + 1 = 0$

$x^2 + 4x + 1 = 0$
$\therefore \quad x^2 + 4x = -1$ {put the constant on the RHS}
$\therefore \quad x^2 + 4x + 2^2 = -1 + 2^2$ {completing the square}
$\therefore \quad (x + 2)^2 = 3$ {factorising}
$\therefore \quad x + 2 = \pm\sqrt{3}$
$\therefore \quad x = -2 \pm \sqrt{3}$

> The squared number we add to both sides is
> $$\left(\frac{\text{coefficient of } x}{2}\right)^2$$

EXERCISE 6A.2

1 Solve for exact values of x:

  a $(x + 5)^2 = 2$ **b** $(x + 6)^2 = -11$ **c** $(x - 4)^2 = 8$

  d $(x - 8)^2 = 7$ **e** $2(x + 3)^2 = 10$ **f** $3(x - 2)^2 = 18$

  g $(x + 1)^2 + 1 = 11$ **h** $(2x + 1)^2 = 3$ **i** $(1 - 3x)^2 - 7 = 0$

2 Solve for exact values of x by completing the square:

  a $x^2 - 4x + 1 = 0$ **b** $x^2 + 6x + 2 = 0$ **c** $x^2 - 14x + 46 = 0$

  d $x^2 = 4x + 3$ **e** $x^2 + 6x + 7 = 0$ **f** $x^2 = 2x + 6$

  g $x^2 + 6x = 2$ **h** $x^2 + 10 = 8x$ **i** $x^2 + 6x = -11$

If the coefficient of x^2 is not 1, we first divide throughout to make it 1.

For example, $2x^2 + 10x + 3 = 0$ becomes $x^2 + 5x + \frac{3}{2} = 0$

$-3x^2 + 12x + 5 = 0$ becomes $x^2 - 4x - \frac{5}{3} = 0$

3 Solve for exact values of x by completing the square:

a $2x^2 + 4x + 1 = 0$ b $2x^2 - 10x + 3 = 0$ c $3x^2 + 12x + 5 = 0$

d $3x^2 = 6x + 4$ e $5x^2 - 15x + 2 = 0$ f $4x^2 + 4x = 5$

THE QUADRATIC FORMULA

Many quadratic equations cannot be solved by factorising, and completing the square can be rather tedious. Consequently, the **quadratic formula** has been developed. This formula is:

$$\text{If}\quad ax^2 + bx + c = 0, \quad \text{then}\quad x = \frac{-b \pm \sqrt{b^2 - 4ac}}{2a}.$$

Proof: If $ax^2 + bx + c = 0$,

then $x^2 + \dfrac{b}{a}x + \dfrac{c}{a} = 0$ {dividing each term by a, as $a \neq 0$}

$\therefore\quad x^2 + \dfrac{b}{a}x\quad = -\dfrac{c}{a}$

$\therefore\quad x^2 + \dfrac{b}{a}x + \left(\dfrac{b}{2a}\right)^2 = -\dfrac{c}{a} + \left(\dfrac{b}{2a}\right)^2$ {completing the square on LHS}

$\therefore\quad \left(x + \dfrac{b}{2a}\right)^2 = \dfrac{b^2 - 4ac}{4a^2}$

$\therefore\quad x + \dfrac{b}{2a} = \pm\sqrt{\dfrac{b^2 - 4ac}{4a^2}}$

$\therefore\quad x = \dfrac{-b \pm \sqrt{b^2 - 4ac}}{2a}$

For example, consider the Acme Leather Jacket Co. equation from page **145**.

We need to solve: $12.5x^2 - 550x + 5125 = 0$

so in this case $a = 12.5, \quad b = -550, \quad c = 5125$

$\therefore\quad x = \dfrac{550 \pm \sqrt{(-550)^2 - 4(12.5)(5125)}}{2(12.5)}$

$= \dfrac{550 \pm \sqrt{46\,250}}{25}$

$\approx 30.60 \quad \text{or} \quad 13.40$

Trying to factorise this equation or using 'completing the square' would not be easy.

However, x needs to be a whole number, so $x = 13$ or 31 would produce a profit of around \$3000 each week.

Example 6

Solve for x: **a** $x^2 - 2x - 6 = 0$ **b** $2x^2 + 3x - 6 = 0$

a $x^2 - 2x - 6 = 0$ has
$a = 1$, $b = -2$, $c = -6$

$\therefore x = \dfrac{-(-2) \pm \sqrt{(-2)^2 - 4(1)(-6)}}{2(1)}$

$\therefore x = \dfrac{2 \pm \sqrt{4 + 24}}{2}$

$\therefore x = \dfrac{2 \pm \sqrt{28}}{2}$

$\therefore x = \dfrac{2 \pm 2\sqrt{7}}{2}$

$\therefore x = 1 \pm \sqrt{7}$

Solutions are: $1 + \sqrt{7}$ and $1 - \sqrt{7}$.

b $2x^2 + 3x - 6 = 0$ has
$a = 2$, $b = 3$, $c = -6$

$\therefore x = \dfrac{-3 \pm \sqrt{3^2 - 4(2)(-6)}}{2(2)}$

$\therefore x = \dfrac{-3 \pm \sqrt{9 + 48}}{4}$

$\therefore x = \dfrac{-3 \pm \sqrt{57}}{4}$

Solutions are:

$\dfrac{-3 + \sqrt{57}}{4}$ and $\dfrac{-3 - \sqrt{57}}{4}$.

EXERCISE 6A.3

1 Use the quadratic formula to solve exactly for x:

   a $x^2 - 4x - 3 = 0$ **b** $x^2 + 6x + 7 = 0$ **c** $x^2 + 1 = 4x$

   d $x^2 + 4x = 1$ **e** $x^2 - 4x + 2 = 0$ **f** $2x^2 - 2x - 3 = 0$

   g $x^2 - 2\sqrt{2}x + 2 = 0$ **h** $(3x + 1)^2 = -2x$ **i** $(x + 3)(2x + 1) = 9$

2 Use the quadratic formula to solve exactly for x:

   a $(x+2)(x-1) = 2-3x$ **b** $(2x + 1)^2 = 3 - x$ **c** $(x - 2)^2 = 1 + x$

   d $\dfrac{x-1}{2-x} = 2x + 1$ **e** $x - \dfrac{1}{x} = 1$ **f** $2x - \dfrac{1}{x} = 3$

B   THE DISCRIMINANT OF A QUADRATIC

In the quadratic formula, the quantity $b^2 - 4ac$ under the square root sign is called the **discriminant**.

The symbol **delta** Δ is used to represent the discriminant,   so $\Delta = b^2 - 4ac$.

The quadratic formula becomes $x = \dfrac{-b \pm \sqrt{\Delta}}{2a}$ where Δ replaces $b^2 - 4ac$.

Note:
- If $\Delta = 0$, $x = \dfrac{-b}{2a}$ is the **only solution** (a **repeated** or **double root**)

- If $\Delta > 0$, $\sqrt{\Delta}$ is a positive real number, so there are **two distinct real**

  roots: $\dfrac{-b + \sqrt{\Delta}}{2a}$ and $\dfrac{-b - \sqrt{\Delta}}{2a}$

- If $\Delta < 0$, $\sqrt{\Delta}$ is not a real number and so there are **no real roots**.

- If a, b and c are rational and Δ is a **perfect square** then the equation has two rational roots which can be found by factorisation.

Example 7

Use the discriminant to determine the nature of the roots of:

a $2x^2 - 2x + 3 = 0$ b $3x^2 - 4x - 2 = 0$

---

a $\Delta = b^2 - 4ac$
    $= (-2)^2 - 4(2)(3)$
    $= -20$ which is < 0

∴   there are no real roots

b $\Delta = b^2 - 4ac$
    $= (-4)^2 - 4(3)(-2)$
    $= 40$ which is > 0

40 is not a perfect square so there are 2 distinct irrational roots.

Example 8

For $x^2 - 2x + m = 0$,   find Δ and hence find the values of m for which the equation has: a   a repeated root   b   2 distinct real roots   c   no real roots.

$x^2 - 2x + m = 0$ has $a = 1$, $b = -2$ and $c = m$
∴ $\Delta = b^2 - 4ac = (-2)^2 - 4(1)(m) = 4 - 4m$

a   For a repeated root
    $\Delta = 0$
    ∴ $4 - 4m = 0$
    ∴ $4 = 4m$
    ∴ $m = 1$

b   For 2 distinct real roots
    $\Delta > 0$
    ∴ $4 - 4m > 0$
    ∴ $-4m > -4$
    ∴ $m < 1$

c   For no real roots
    $\Delta < 0$
    ∴ $4 - 4m < 0$
    ∴ $-4m < -4$
    ∴ $m > 1$

Notice:

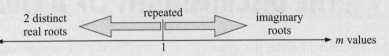

2 distinct real roots ← repeated → imaginary roots, m values, 1

Summary:

Roots of quadratic	Discriminant value
two real distinct roots	$\Delta > 0$
two identical real roots (repeated)	$\Delta = 0$
two real roots	$\Delta \geqslant 0$
no real roots	$\Delta < 0$

Example 9

For the equation $kx^2 + [k+3]x = 1$ find the discriminant Δ and draw a sign diagram for it. Hence, find the value of k for which the equation has:

 a two distinct real roots   b two real roots

 c a repeated root   d no real roots.

For $kx^2 + [k+3]x - 1 = 0$, $a = k,\ b = k+3,\ c = -1$

So, $\Delta = b^2 - 4ac$
$= (k+3)^2 - 4(k)(-1)$ and has sign diagram:
$= k^2 + 6k + 9 + 4k$
$= k^2 + 10k + 9$
$= (k+9)(k+1)$

```
   +        -         +
<----+----------+-------->  k
    -9         -1
```

 a For two distinct real roots, $\Delta > 0$ $\therefore$ $k < -9$ or $k > -1$.
 b For two real roots, $\Delta \geqslant 0$ $\therefore$ $k \leqslant -9$ or $k \geqslant -1$.
 c For a repeated root, $\Delta = 0$ $\therefore$ $k = -9$ or $k = -1$.
 d For no real roots, $\Delta < 0$ $\therefore$ $-9 < k < -1$.

EXERCISE 6B

1 By using the discriminant only, state the nature of the solutions of:

 a $x^2 + 7x - 3 = 0$ b $x^2 + 2\sqrt{3}x + 3 = 0$ c $3x^2 + 2x - 1 = 0$
 d $5x^2 + 4x - 3 = 0$ e $x^2 + x + 5 = 0$ f $16x^2 - 8x + 1 = 0$

2 By using the discriminant only, determine which of the following quadratic equations have rational roots which can be found by factorisation.

 a $6x^2 - 5x - 6 = 0$ b $2x^2 - 7x - 5 = 0$ c $3x^2 + 4x + 1 = 0$
 d $6x^2 - 47x - 8 = 0$ e $4x^2 - 3x + 2 = 0$ f $8x^2 + 2x - 3 = 0$

3 For the following quadratic equations, determine Δ in simplest form and draw a sign diagram for it. Hence find the value of m for which the equation has:

 i a repeated root   ii two distinct real roots   iii no real roots.

 a $x^2 + 4x + m = 0$ b $mx^2 + 3x + 2 = 0$ c $mx^2 - 3x + 1 = 0$

4 For the following quadratic equations, find the discriminant Δ and hence draw a sign diagram for it. Find all k values for which the equation has:

 i two distinct real roots   ii two real roots   iii a repeated root   iv no real roots.

 a $2x^2 + kx - k = 0$ b $kx^2 - 2x + k = 0$
 c $x^2 + [k+2]x + 4 = 0$ d $2x^2 + [k-2]x + 2 = 0$
 e $x^2 + [3k-1]x + [2k+10] = 0$ f $[k+1]x^2 + kx + k = 0$

C   THE SUM AND PRODUCT OF THE ROOTS

If $ax^2 + bx + c = 0$ has roots α and β then $\alpha + \beta = -\dfrac{b}{a}$ and $\alpha\beta = \dfrac{c}{a}$.

For example: if α and β are the roots of $2x^2 - 2x - 1 = 0$
then $\alpha + \beta = 1$ and $\alpha\beta = -\tfrac{1}{2}$.

Proof:

Method 1 (Quadratic formula)

Let $\alpha = \dfrac{-b + \sqrt{\Delta}}{2a}$, $\beta = \dfrac{-b - \sqrt{\Delta}}{2a}$

$\therefore \quad \alpha + \beta = \dfrac{-b + \sqrt{\Delta} - b - \sqrt{\Delta}}{2a}$

$\qquad = \dfrac{-2b}{2a} = -\dfrac{b}{a}$

and $\quad \alpha\beta = \left(\dfrac{-b + \sqrt{\Delta}}{2a}\right)\left(\dfrac{-b - \sqrt{\Delta}}{2a}\right)$

$\qquad = \dfrac{b^2 - \Delta}{4a^2} = \dfrac{b^2 - (b^2 - 4ac)}{4a^2} = \dfrac{4ac}{4a^2} = \dfrac{c}{a}$

Method 2

As $\quad ax^2 + bx + c = a(x - \alpha)(x - \beta)$,
$\qquad ax^2 + bx + c = a(x^2 - [\alpha + \beta]x + \alpha\beta)$
$\therefore \quad x^2 + \dfrac{b}{a}x + \dfrac{c}{a} = x^2 - [\alpha + \beta]x + \alpha\beta$

Equating coefficients,

$\qquad \alpha + \beta = -\dfrac{b}{a}$ and $\alpha\beta = \dfrac{c}{a}$

Example 10

Find the sum and product of the roots of $25x^2 - 20x + 1 = 0$.
Check your answer by solving the quadratic.

If α and β are the roots then $\quad \alpha + \beta = -\dfrac{b}{a} = \dfrac{20}{25} = \dfrac{4}{5}$

and $\quad \alpha\beta = \dfrac{c}{a} = \dfrac{1}{25}$

Check: $25x^2 - 20x + 1 = 0$ has roots

$\dfrac{20 \pm \sqrt{400 - 4(25)(1)}}{50} = \dfrac{20 \pm \sqrt{300}}{50} = \dfrac{20 \pm 10\sqrt{3}}{50} = \dfrac{2 \pm \sqrt{3}}{5}$

These have sum $= \dfrac{2 + \sqrt{3}}{5} + \dfrac{2 - \sqrt{3}}{5} = \dfrac{4}{5}$ ✓

and product $= \left(\dfrac{2 + \sqrt{3}}{5}\right)\left(\dfrac{2 - \sqrt{3}}{5}\right) = \dfrac{4 - 3}{25} = \dfrac{1}{25}$ ✓

EXERCISE 6C

1   Find the sum and product of the roots of:

    a $3x^2 - 2x + 7 = 0$ **b** $x^2 + 11x - 13 = 0$ **c** $5x^2 - 6x - 14 = 0$

2 The equation $kx^2 - (1+k)x + (3k+2) = 0$ is such that the sum of its roots is twice their product. Find k and the two roots.

3 $ax^2 - 6x + a - 2 = 0$, $a \neq 0$ has one root which is double the other.

    a Let the roots be α and 2α and find two equations involving α.

    b Find a and the two roots of the quadratic equation.

4 $kx^2 + (k-8)x + (1-k) = 0$ has one root which is two more than the other. Find k and the two roots.

5 The roots of the equation $x^2 - 6x + 7 = 0$ are α and β.

    Find the simplest quadratic equation with roots $\alpha + \dfrac{1}{\beta}$ and $\beta + \dfrac{1}{\alpha}$.

6 The roots of $2x^2 - 3x - 5 = 0$ are p and q.

    Find *all* quadratic equations with roots $p^2 + q$ and $q^2 + p$.

7 $kx^2 + [k+2]x - 3 = 0$ has roots which are real and positive.

    Find the possible values that k may have.

D | GRAPHING QUADRATIC FUNCTIONS

REVIEW OF TERMINOLOGY

The equation of a **quadratic function** is given by $y = ax^2 + bx + c$, where $a \neq 0$.

The graph of a quadratic function is called a **parabola**. The point where the graph 'turns' is called the **vertex**.

If the graph opens upward, the y-coordinate of the vertex is the **minimum** and the graph is concave upwards.

If the graph opens downward, the y-coordinate of the vertex is the **maximum** and the graph is concave downwards.

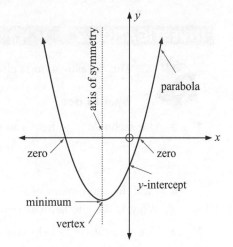

The vertical line that passes through the vertex is called the **axis of symmetry**. All parabolas are symmetrical about the axis of symmetry.

The point where the graph crosses the y-axis is the **y-intercept**.

The points (if they exist) where the graph crosses the x-axis are called the **x-intercepts**, and correspond to the **zeros** of the function.

INVESTIGATION 1   GRAPHING $y = a(x-\alpha)(x-\beta)$

 This investigation is best done using a **graphing package** or **graphics calculator**.

What to do:

1 a Use technology to help you to sketch:

$$y = (x-1)(x-3), \qquad y = 2(x-1)(x-3), \qquad y = -(x-1)(x-3),$$
$$y = -3(x-1)(x-3) \qquad \text{and} \qquad y = -\tfrac{1}{2}(x-1)(x-3)$$

b Find the x-intercepts for each function in **a**.

c What is the geometrical significance of a in $y = a(x-1)(x-3)$?

2 a Use technology to help you to sketch:

$$y = 2(x-1)(x-4), \qquad y = 2(x-3)(x-5), \qquad y = 2(x+1)(x-2),$$
$$y = 2x(x+5) \qquad \text{and} \qquad y = 2(x+2)(x+4)$$

b Find the x-intercepts for each function in **a**.

c What is the geometrical significance of α and β in $y = 2(x-\alpha)(x-\beta)$?

3 a Use technology to help you to sketch:

$$y = 2(x-1)^2, \qquad y = 2(x-3)^2, \qquad y = 2(x+2)^2, \qquad y = 2x^2$$

b Find the x-intercepts for each function in **a**.

c What is the geometrical significance of α in $y = 2(x-\alpha)^2$?

4 Copy and complete:

- If a quadratic has factorisation $y = a(x-\alpha)(x-\beta)$ it ...... the x-axis at ......
- If a quadratic has factorisation $y = a(x-\alpha)^2$ it ...... the x-axis at ......

INVESTIGATION 2   GRAPHING $y = a(x-h)^2 + k$

 This investigation is also best done using technology.

What to do:

1 a Use technology to help you to sketch:

$$y = (x-3)^2 + 2, \qquad y = 2(x-3)^2 + 2, \qquad y = -2(x-3)^2 + 2,$$
$$y = -(x-3)^2 + 2 \qquad \text{and} \qquad y = -\tfrac{1}{3}(x-3)^2 + 2$$

b Find the coordinates of the vertex for each function in **a**.

c What is the geometrical significance of a in $y = a(x-3)^2 + 2$?

2 a Use technology to help you to sketch:

$$y = 2(x-1)^2 + 3, \qquad y = 2(x-2)^2 + 4, \qquad y = 2(x-3)^2 + 1,$$
$$y = 2(x+1)^2 + 4, \qquad y = 2(x+2)^2 - 5 \qquad \text{and} \qquad y = 2(x+3)^2 - 2$$

b Find the coordinates of the vertex for each function in **a**.

c What is the geometrical significance of h and k in $y = 2(x-h)^2 + k$?

3 Copy and complete:

If a quadratic is in the form $y = a(x-h)^2 + k$ then its vertex has coordinates ......

From **Investigations 1** and **2** you should have discovered that:

- The coefficient of x^2 (which is a) controls the degree of width of the graph and whether it opens upwards or downwards.

  ▶ $a > 0$ produces ⋃ or concave up. $a < 0$ produces ⋂ or concave down.

  ▶   If $-1 < a < 1$, $a \neq 0$ the graph is wider than $y = x^2$.
       If $a < -1$ or $a > 1$ the graph is narrower than $y = x^2$.

Quadratic form, $a \neq 0$	*Graph*	*Facts*
• $y = a(x - \alpha)(x - \beta)$ α, β are real		x-intercepts are α and β axis of symmetry is $x = \frac{\alpha + \beta}{2}$ vertex is $\left(\frac{\alpha + \beta}{2}, f\left(\frac{\alpha + \beta}{2}\right) \right)$
• $y = a(x - \alpha)^2$ α is real		touches x-axis at α axis of symmetry is $x = \alpha$ vertex is $(\alpha, 0)$
• $y = a(x - h)^2 + k$		axis of symmetry is $x = h$ vertex is (h, k)
• $y = ax^2 + bx + c$ (general quadratic form)		axis of symmetry is $x = \dfrac{-b}{2a}$ x-intercepts for $\Delta \geqslant 0$ are $\dfrac{-b \pm \sqrt{\Delta}}{2a}$ where $\Delta = b^2 - 4ac$

Note: $-\dfrac{b}{2a}$ is the **average** of $\dfrac{-b - \sqrt{\Delta}}{2a}$ and $\dfrac{-b + \sqrt{\Delta}}{2a}$ irrespective of the sign of Δ.

SKETCHING GRAPHS USING KEY FACTS

Example 11

Using axes intercepts only, sketch the graphs of:

a $\quad y = 2(x+3)(x-1)$ b $\quad y = -2(x-1)(x-2)$ c $\quad y = \frac{1}{2}(x+2)^2$

a $\quad y = 2(x+3)(x-1)$
has x-intercepts -3, 1

When $x = 0$,
$$y = 2(3)(-1)$$
$$= -6$$
$\therefore$ y-intercept is -6

b $\quad y = -2(x-1)(x-2)$
has x-intercepts 1, 2

When $x = 0$,
$$y = -2(-1)(-2)$$
$$= -4$$
$\therefore$ y-intercept is -4

c $\quad y = \frac{1}{2}(x+2)^2$
touches x-axis at -2

When $x = 0$,
$$y = \frac{1}{2}(2)^2$$
$$= 2$$
$\therefore$ y-intercept is 2

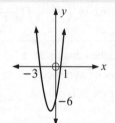 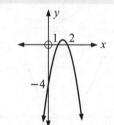 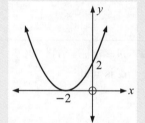

Example 12

Use the vertex, axis of symmetry and y-intercept to graph $\quad y = -2(x+1)^2 + 4$.

The vertex is $(-1, 4)$.

The axis of symmetry is $x = -1$.

When $x = 0$, $\quad y = -2(1)^2 + 4$
$$= 2$$

$a < 0 \quad \therefore \quad \cap$ shape

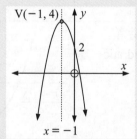

Example 13

For the quadratic $\quad y = 2x^2 + 6x - 3$, find:

a   the equation of the axis of symmetry   b   the coordinates of the vertex

c   the axes intercepts.

d   Hence, sketch the graph.

For $y = 2x^2 + 6x - 3$, $a = 2$, $b = 6$, $c = -3$. $a > 0$ $\therefore$ $\bigvee$ shape

a $\dfrac{-b}{2a} = \dfrac{-6}{4} = -\dfrac{3}{2}$

$\therefore$ axis of symmetry is $x = -\dfrac{3}{2}$.

b When $x = -\dfrac{3}{2}$,

$\begin{aligned} y &= 2(-\tfrac{3}{2})^2 + 6(-\tfrac{3}{2}) - 3 \\ &= -7\tfrac{1}{2} \quad \text{\{simplifying\}} \end{aligned}$

$\therefore$ vertex is $(-\tfrac{3}{2}, -7\tfrac{1}{2})$.

c When $x = 0$, $y = -3$

$\therefore$ y-intercept is -3.

When $y = 0$, $2x^2 + 6x - 3 = 0$

$\therefore$ $x = \dfrac{-6 \pm \sqrt{36 - 4(2)(-3)}}{4}$

$\therefore$ $x \approx -3.44$ or 0.44

d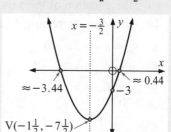

Example 14

Determine the coordinates of the vertex of $y = 2x^2 - 8x + 1$.

$y = 2x^2 - 8x + 1$ has $a = 2$, $b = -8$, $c = 1$

and so $\dfrac{-b}{2a} = \dfrac{-(-8)}{2 \times 2} = 2$

$\therefore$ equation of axis of symmetry is $x = 2$

and when $x = 2$, $y = 2(2)^2 - 8(2) + 1$

$= -7$

$\therefore$ the vertex has coordinates $(2, -7)$.

The vertex is called the **maximum turning point** or the **minimum turning point** depending on whether the graph is concave down or concave up.

EXERCISE 6D.1

1 Using axes intercepts only, sketch the graphs of:

  a $y = (x - 4)(x + 2)$ **b** $y = -(x - 4)(x + 2)$ **c** $y = 2(x + 3)(x + 5)$

  d $y = -3x(x + 4)$ **e** $y = 2(x + 3)^2$ **f** $y = -\tfrac{1}{4}(x + 2)^2$

2 What is the axis of symmetry of each graph in question **1**?

3 Use the vertex, axis of symmetry and y-intercept to graph:

  a $y = (x - 1)^2 + 3$ **b** $y = 2(x + 2)^2 + 1$ **c** $y = -2(x - 1)^2 - 3$

  d $y = \tfrac{1}{2}(x - 3)^2 + 2$ **e** $y = -\tfrac{1}{3}(x - 1)^2 + 4$ **f** $y = -\tfrac{1}{10}(x + 2)^2 - 3$

4 Find the turning point or vertex for the following quadratic functions:

  a $y = x^2 - 4x + 2$ **b** $y = x^2 + 2x - 3$ **c** $y = 2x^2 + 4$

  d $y = -3x^2 + 1$ **e** $y = 2x^2 + 8x - 7$ **f** $y = -x^2 - 4x - 9$

  g $y = 2x^2 + 6x - 1$ **h** $y = 2x^2 - 10x + 3$ **i** $y = -\tfrac{1}{2}x^2 + x - 5$

5 Find the x-intercepts for:

a	$y = x^2 - 9$	**b**	$y = 2x^2 - 6$	**c**	$y = x^2 + 7x + 10$
d	$y = x^2 + x - 12$	**e**	$y = 4x - x^2$	**f**	$y = -x^2 - 6x - 8$
g	$y = -2x^2 - 4x - 2$	**h**	$y = 4x^2 - 24x + 36$	**i**	$y = x^2 - 4x + 1$
j	$y = x^2 + 4x - 3$	**k**	$y = x^2 - 6x - 2$	**l**	$y = x^2 + 8x + 11$

6 For the following quadratics, find:

   i   the equation of the axis of symmetry   **ii**   the coordinates of the vertex

  iii   the axes intercepts, if they exist.   **iv**   Hence, sketch the graph.

a	$y = x^2 - 2x + 5$	**b**	$y = x^2 + 4x - 1$	**c**	$y = 2x^2 - 5x + 2$
d	$y = -x^2 + 3x - 2$	**e**	$y = -3x^2 + 4x - 1$	**f**	$y = -2x^2 + x + 1$
g	$y = 6x - x^2$	**h**	$y = -x^2 - 6x - 8$	**i**	$y = -\frac{1}{4}x^2 + 2x + 1$

SKETCHING GRAPHS BY COMPLETING THE SQUARE

If we wish to find the vertex of a quadratic given in general form $y = ax^2 + bx + c$ then one approach is to convert it to the form $y = a(x - h)^2 + k$ where we can read off the vertex (h, k). To do this we may choose to '**complete the square**'.

Example 15

Write $y = x^2 + 4x + 3$ in the form $y = (x - h)^2 + k$ by completing the square. Hence sketch $y = x^2 + 4x + 3$, stating the coordinates of the vertex.

$y = x^2 + 4x + 3$

$\therefore \quad y = x^2 + 4x + 2^2 + 3 - 2^2$

$\therefore \quad y = (x + 2)^2 - 1$

              ↓   ↓

      shift 2   shift 1

    units left   unit down

Vertex is $(-2, -1)$ and y-intercept is 3.

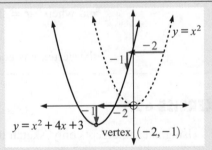

Example 16

Convert $y = 3x^2 - 4x + 1$ into the form $y = a(x - h)^2 + k$ by 'completing the square'. Hence, write down the coordinates of its vertex and sketch the graph of the function.

$y = 3x^2 - 4x + 1$

$ = 3[x^2 - \frac{4}{3}x + \frac{1}{3}]$ {take out a factor of 3}

$ = 3[x^2 - 2(\frac{2}{3})x + (\frac{2}{3})^2 - (\frac{2}{3})^2 + \frac{1}{3}]$ {complete the square}

$ = 3[(x - \frac{2}{3})^2 - \frac{4}{9} + \frac{1}{3}]$ {write as a perfect square}

$$= 3[(x - \tfrac{2}{3})^2 - \tfrac{1}{9}]$$
$$= 3(x - \tfrac{2}{3})^2 - \tfrac{1}{3} \qquad \text{\{expand to desired form\}}$$

So the vertex is $(\tfrac{2}{3}, -\tfrac{1}{3})$.

The y-intercept is 1.

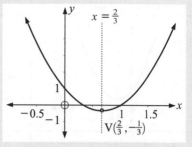

We can use technology to confirm this. For example:

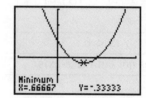

EXERCISE 6D.2

1 Write the following quadratics in the form $y = (x - h)^2 + k$ by 'completing the square'. Hence sketch each function, stating the vertex:

    a $y = x^2 - 2x + 3$ **b** $y = x^2 + 4x - 2$ **c** $y = x^2 - 4x$

    d $y = x^2 + 3x$ **e** $y = x^2 + 5x - 2$ **f** $y = x^2 - 3x + 2$

    g $y = x^2 - 6x + 5$ **h** $y = x^2 + 8x - 2$ **i** $y = x^2 - 5x + 1$

2 For each of the following quadratics:

    i convert into the form $y = a(x - h)^2 + k$ by 'completing the square'

    ii state the coordinates of the vertex

    iii find the y-intercept.

    iv Hence, sketch the graph of the quadratic.

    v Use technology to check your answer.

> a is always the factor to be 'taken out'.

    a $y = 2x^2 + 4x + 5$ **b** $y = 2x^2 - 8x + 3$

    c $y = 2x^2 - 6x + 1$ **d** $y = 3x^2 - 6x + 5$

    e $y = -x^2 + 4x + 2$ **f** $y = -2x^2 - 5x + 3$

3 Use your **graphing package** or **graphics calculator** to graph each of the following functions. Hence write each function in the form $y = a(x - h)^2 + k$.

> GRAPHING PACKAGE

    a $y = x^2 - 4x + 7$ **b** $y = x^2 + 6x + 3$ **c** $y = -x^2 + 4x + 5$

    d $y = 2x^2 + 6x - 4$ **e** $y = -2x^2 - 10x + 1$ **f** $y = 3x^2 - 9x - 5$

THE DISCRIMINANT AND THE QUADRATIC GRAPH

Consider the graphs of: $y = x^2 - 2x + 3$, $y = x^2 - 2x + 1$, $y = x^2 - 2x - 3$.

All of these curves have the same axis of symmetry: $x = 1$.

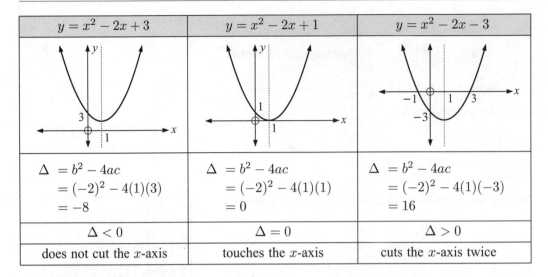

$y = x^2 - 2x + 3$	$y = x^2 - 2x + 1$	$y = x^2 - 2x - 3$
$\Delta = b^2 - 4ac$ $= (-2)^2 - 4(1)(3)$ $= -8$	$\Delta = b^2 - 4ac$ $= (-2)^2 - 4(1)(1)$ $= 0$	$\Delta = b^2 - 4ac$ $= (-2)^2 - 4(1)(-3)$ $= 16$
$\Delta < 0$	$\Delta = 0$	$\Delta > 0$
does not cut the x-axis	touches the x-axis	cuts the x-axis twice

The **discriminant** Δ determines if the graph:

- does not cut the x-axis $(\Delta < 0)$
- touches the x-axis $(\Delta = 0)$
- cuts the x-axis twice $(\Delta > 0)$.

Example 17

Use the discriminant to determine the relationship between the graph and the x-axis for: **a** $y = x^2 + 3x + 4$ **b** $y = -2x^2 + 5x + 1$

a $a = 1$, $b = 3$, $c = 4$

$\therefore \quad \Delta = b^2 - 4ac$ $a > 0$ $\therefore$ concave up
$\qquad = 9 - 4(1)(4)$
$\qquad = -7$ which is < 0

The graph does not cut the x-axis.   It lies entirely above the x-axis.

b $a = -2$, $b = 5$, $c = 1$

$\therefore \quad \Delta = b^2 - 4ac$ $a < 0$ $\therefore$ concave down
$\qquad = 25 - 4(-2)(1)$
$\qquad = 33$ which is > 0 $\therefore$ the graph cuts the x-axis twice.

POSITIVE DEFINITE AND NEGATIVE DEFINITE QUADRATICS

Positive definite quadratics are quadratics which are positive for all values of x,   i.e., $ax^2 + bx + c > 0$ for all $x \in \mathbb{R}$.

Negative definite quadratics are quadratics which are negative for all values of x,   i.e., $ax^2 + bx + c < 0$ for all $x \in \mathbb{R}$.

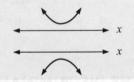

Tests:

- A quadratic is **positive definite** if $a > 0$ and $\Delta < 0$.
- A quadratic is **negative definite** if $a < 0$ and $\Delta < 0$.

EXERCISE 6D.3

1 Use the discriminant to determine the relationship between the graph and x-axis for:

    a $y = x^2 + 7x - 2$ **b** $y = x^2 + 4\sqrt{2}x + 8$ **c** $y = -2x^2 + 3x + 1$

    d $y = 6x^2 + 5x - 4$ **e** $y = -x^2 + x + 6$ **f** $y = 9x^2 + 6x + 1$

2 Show that:

    a $x^2 - 3x + 6 > 0$ for all x **b** $4x - x^2 - 6 < 0$ for all x

    c $2x^2 - 4x + 7$ is positive definite   **d** $-2x^2 + 3x - 4$ is negative definite

3 Explain why $3x^2 + kx - 1$ is never positive definite for any value of k.

4 Under what conditions is $2x^2 + kx + 2$ positive definite?

E   FINDING A QUADRATIC FROM ITS GRAPH

If we are given sufficient information on or about a graph we can determine the quadratic function in whatever form is required.

Example 18

Find the equation of the quadratic with graph:

a 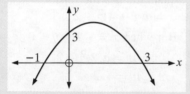   **b**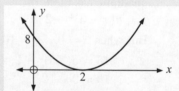

  a   Since the x-intercepts are -1 and 3,   **b**   Since it touches at 2,

      $y = a(x+1)(x-3), \quad a < 0.$ $y = a(x-2)^2, \quad a > 0.$

      But when $x = 0, \quad y = 3$ But when $x = 0, \quad y = 8$

      $\therefore \quad 3 = a(1)(-3)$ $\therefore \quad 8 = a(-2)^2$

      $\therefore \quad a = -1$ $\therefore \quad a = 2$

     So, $\quad y = -(x+1)(x-3).$ So, $\quad y = 2(x-2)^2.$

Example 19

Find the equation of the quadratic with graph:

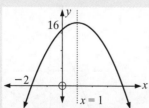

The axis of symmetry is $x = 1$, so the other x-intercept is 4

$$\therefore \quad y = a(x+2)(x-4)$$

But when $x = 0, \quad y = 16$

$$\therefore \quad 16 = a(2)(-4)$$

$$\therefore \quad a = -2$$

$\therefore$ the quadratic is $y = -2(x+2)(x-4)$

Example 20

Find, in the form $y = ax^2 + bx + c$, the equation of the quadratic whose graph cuts the x-axis at 4 and -3 and passes through the point $(2, -20)$.

Since the x-intercepts are 4 and -3, the equation is
$$y = a(x - 4)(x + 3) \quad \text{where} \quad a \neq 0.$$
But when $x = 2$, $y = -20$ $\quad \therefore \quad -20 = a(2 - 4)(2 + 3)$
$$\therefore \quad -20 = a(-2)(5)$$
$$\therefore \quad a = 2$$
$\therefore$ the equation is $y = 2(x - 4)(x + 3)$, or $y = 2x^2 - 2x - 24$

Example 21

Find the equation of the quadratic given its graph is:

a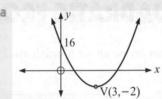

b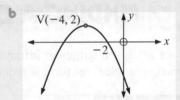

a For a vertex $(3, -2)$ the quadratic has the form
$y = a(x - 3)^2 - 2$

But when $x = 0$, $y = 16$
$\therefore \quad 16 = a(-3)^2 - 2$
$\therefore \quad 16 = 9a - 2$
$\therefore \quad 9a = 18$
$\therefore \quad a = 2$
So, $y = 2(x - 3)^2 - 2$

b For a vertex $(-4, 2)$ the quadratic has the form
$y = a(x + 4)^2 + 2$

But when $x = -2$, $y = 0$
$\therefore \quad 0 = a(2)^2 + 2$
$\therefore \quad 4a = -2$
$\therefore \quad a = -\frac{1}{2}$
So, $y = -\frac{1}{2}(x + 4)^2 + 2$

EXERCISE 6E

1 Find the equation of the quadratic with graph:

a

b

c

d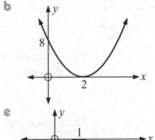

e

f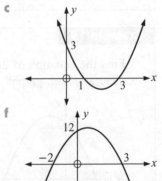

2 Find the quadratic with graph:

a

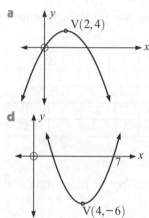

b **c**

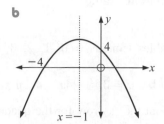

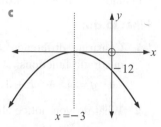

3 Find, in the form $y = ax^2 + bx + c$, the equation of the quadratic whose graph:

   a cuts the x-axis at 5 and 1, and passes through $(2, -9)$

   b cuts the x-axis at 2 and $-\frac{1}{2}$, and passes through $(3, -14)$

   c touches the x-axis at 3 and passes through $(-2, -25)$

   d touches the x-axis at -2 and passes through $(-1, 4)$

   e cuts the x-axis at 3, passes through $(5, 12)$ and has axis of symmetry $x = 2$

   f cuts the x-axis at 5, passes through $(2, 5)$ and has axis of symmetry $x = 1$.

4 If V is the vertex, find the equation of the quadratic given its graph is:

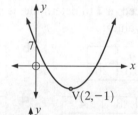

       FINDING QUADRATIC FUNCTIONS

$y = 2x^2 + 3x + 7$ is a quadratic function from which the following table of values is obtained:

x	0	1	2	3	4	5
y	7	12	21	34	51	72

Consider adding two further rows to this table:

   a row called Δ_1 which gives differences between successive y-values, and

   a row called Δ_2 which gives differences between successive Δ_1-values.

So, we have:

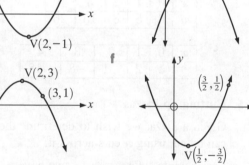

This table is known as a **difference table**.

What to do:

1 Construct difference tables (for $x = 0, 1, 2, 3, 4, 5$) for each of the following quadratic functions:

    a $y = x^2 + 4x + 3$ **b** $y = 3x^2 - 4x$ **c** $y = 5x - x^2$ **d** $y = 4x^2 - 5x + 2$

2 What do you notice about the Δ_2 row for the quadratic functions in **1**?

3 Consider the general quadratic $y = ax^2 + bx + c$, $a \neq 0$.

    a Copy and complete the following difference table:

x	0	1	2	3	4	5
y	ⓒ	$a + b + c$	$4a + 2b + c$	......	......	......
Δ_1	◯		......		......	......	......
Δ_2		◯		......		......	......

    b Comment on the Δ_2 row.

    c What can the encircled numbers be used for?

4 Use what you have noticed in **3** to determine, if possible, the quadratic functions with the following tables of values:

a

x	0	1	2	3	4
y	6	5	8	15	26

b

x	0	1	2	3	4
y	8	10	18	32	52

c

x	0	1	2	3	4
y	1	2	-1	-8	-18

d

x	0	1	2	3	4
y	5	3	-1	-7	-15

5 **Cutting up Pizzas**

Given a pizza, we wish to determine the **maximum** number of pieces into which it can be cut using n cuts across it.

For example, for $n = 1$ we have   i.e., 2 pieces

            for $n = 3$ we have   i.e., 7 pieces

    a Copy and complete:

Number of cuts, n	0	1	2	3	4	5
Maximum number of pieces, P_n						

    b Complete Δ_1 and Δ_2 rows and hence determine (if possible) a quadratic formula for P_n.

    c For a huge pizza with 12 cuts across it, find the maximum number of pieces resulting.

F   WHERE FUNCTIONS MEET

Consider the graphs of a quadratic function and a linear function on the same set of axes.

Notice that we could have:

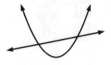

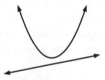

cutting	**touching**	**missing**
(2 points of intersection)	(1 point of intersection)	(no points of intersection)

If the graphs meet, the coordinates of the points of intersection of the graphs of the two functions can be found by *solving the two equations simultaneously.*

Example 22

Find the coordinates of the points of intersection of the graphs with equations
$y = x^2 - x - 18$ and $y = x - 3$.

$y = x^2 - x - 18$ meets $y = x - 3$ where

$$x^2 - x - 18 = x - 3$$
$$\therefore \quad x^2 - 2x - 15 = 0 \qquad \{\text{RHS} = 0\}$$
$$\therefore \quad (x - 5)(x + 3) = 0 \qquad \{\text{factorising}\}$$
$$\therefore \quad x = 5 \text{ or } -3$$

Substituting into $y = x - 3$,   when $x = 5$, $y = 2$ and   when $x = -3$, $y = -6$.

$\therefore$ the graphs meet at $(5, 2)$ and $(-3, -6)$.

Example 23

$y = 2x + c$ is a tangent to $y = 2x^2 - 3x + 4$.   Find c.

$y = 2x + c$ meets $y = 2x^2 - 3x + 4$ where
$$2x^2 - 3x + 4 = 2x + c$$
$$\therefore \quad 2x^2 - 5x + (4 - c) = 0$$

Now this quadratic has $\Delta = 0$ since the graphs touch.
$$\therefore \quad (-5)^2 - 4(2)(4 - c) = 0$$
$$\therefore \quad 8(4 - c) = 25$$
$$\therefore \quad 4 - c = 3\tfrac{1}{8}$$
$$\therefore \quad c = \tfrac{7}{8}$$

EXERCISE 6F

1 Find the coordinates of the point(s) of intersection of the graphs with equations:

   a $y = x^2 - 2x + 8$ and $y = x + 6$ **b** $y = -x^2 + 3x + 9$ and $y = 2x - 3$

   c $y = x^2 - 4x + 3$ and $y = 2x - 6$ **d** $y = -x^2 + 4x - 7$ and $y = 5x - 4$

2 Use a **graphing package** or a **GDC** to find the coordinates of the points of intersection (to 2 decimal places) of the graphs with equations:

GRAPHING PACKAGE

   a $y = x^2 - 3x + 7$ and $y = x + 5$ **b** $y = x^2 - 5x + 2$ and $y = x - 7$

   c $y = -x^2 - 2x + 4$ and $y = x + 8$ **d** $y = -x^2 + 4x - 2$ and $y = 5x - 6$

3 Find, by algebraic means, the points of intersection of the graphs with equations:

   a $y = x^2$ and $y = x + 2$ **b** $y = x^2 + 2x - 3$ and $y = x - 1$

   c $y = 2x^2 - x + 3$ and $y = 2 + x + x^2$ **d** $xy = 4$ and $y = x + 3$

4 Use technology to check your solutions to the questions in **3**.

5 Find possible values of c for which the lines $y = 3x + c$ are tangents to the parabola with equation $y = x^2 - 5x + 7$.

6 Find the values of m for which the lines $y = mx - 2$ are tangents to the curve with equation $y = x^2 - 4x + 2$.

7 Find the slopes of the lines with y-intercept $(0, 1)$ that are tangents to the curve $y = 3x^2 + 5x + 4$.

8   **a**   For what values of c do the lines $y = x + c$ never meet the parabola with equation $y = 2x^2 - 3x - 7$?

   b.   Choose one of the values of c found in part **a** above and sketch the graphs using technology to illustrate that these curves never meet.

INVESTIGATION 4   **THE PARABOLA** $y^2 = 4ax$

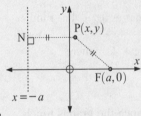

A **parabola** is defined as the locus of all points which are equidistant from a fixed point called the *focus* and a fixed line called the *directrix*.

Suppose the focus is F$(a, 0)$ and the directrix is the vertical line $x = -a$.

What to do:

1 Suggest a reason or reasons why we would let the focus be at $(a, 0)$ and the directrix be the line $x = -a$.

PRINTABLE GRAPH PAPER

2 Use the circular-linear graph paper provided to graph the parabola which has focus F$(2, 0)$ and directrix $x = -2$.

3 Use the definition given above to show that the equation of the parabola is $y^2 = 4ax$.

4 Let $y = mx + c$ be a tangent to $y^2 = 4ax$ at the point P.

Use quadratic theory to show that:

a $a = mc$

b P is at $\left(\dfrac{a}{m^2}, \dfrac{2a}{m}\right)$.

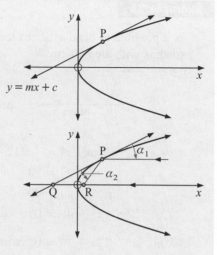

5 Suppose a ray of light comes in parallel to the axis of symmetry (the x-axis). It strikes a parabolic mirror at P and is reflected to cut the x-axis at R(k, 0).

$\alpha_1 = \alpha_2$ by the Reflection Principle.

a Deduce that triangle PQR is isosceles.

b Hence, deduce that $k = a$.

6 Clearly state what special result follows from **5 b**.

7 List real life examples of where the result in **6** has been utilised.

G ▌ PROBLEM SOLVING WITH QUADRATICS

When solving some problems algebraically, a quadratic equation results. We are generally only interested in any **real solutions** which result. If the resulting quadratic equation has no real roots then the problem has no real solution.

Any answer we obtain must be checked to see if it is reasonable. For example:

- if we are finding a length then it must be positive and we reject any negative solutions
- if we are finding 'how many people are present' then clearly a fractional answer would be unacceptable.

General problem solving method:

Step 1: If the information is given in words, translate it into algebra using a pronumeral such as x for the unknown. Write down the resulting equation.

Step 2: Solve the equation by a suitable method.

Step 3: Examine the solutions carefully to see if they are acceptable.

Step 4: Give your answer in a sentence.

Example 24

A rectangle has length 3 cm longer than its width. Its area is 42 cm^2. Find its width.

If the width is x cm, then the length is $(x + 3)$ cm.

Therefore $x(x + 3) = 42$ {equating areas}

$\therefore\ x^2 + 3x - 42 = 0$

$\therefore\ x \approx -8.15$ or 5.15 {using technology}

We reject the negative solution as lengths are positive $\therefore$ width ≈ 5.15 cm.

Example 25

Is it possible to bend a 12 cm length of wire to form the legs of a right angled triangle with area 20 cm²?

$\overline{\qquad\text{12 cm}\qquad}$ becomes

area 20 cm²

$$\text{Area,} \quad A = \tfrac{1}{2}x(12 - x)$$
$$\therefore \quad \tfrac{1}{2}x(12 - x) = 20$$
$$\therefore \quad x(12 - x) = 40$$
$$\therefore \quad 12x - x^2 - 40 = 0$$
$$\therefore \quad x^2 - 12x + 40 = 0 \quad \text{which gives} \quad x = \frac{12 \pm \sqrt{-16}}{2}$$

There are no real solutions, indicating the **impossibility**.

Example 26

A wall is 12 m long. It is timber panelled using vertical sheets of panelling of equal width. If the sheets had been 0.2 m wider, 2 less sheets would have been required. What is the width of the timber panelling used?

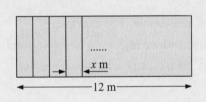

Let x m be the width of each panel.

$\therefore \quad \dfrac{12}{x}$ is the number of sheets needed.

Now if the sheets are $\left(x + \tfrac{1}{5}\right)$ m in width

$\left(\dfrac{12}{x} - 2\right)$ sheets are needed.

So, $\left(x + \tfrac{1}{5}\right)\left(\dfrac{12}{x} - 2\right) = 12$ {length of wall}

$\therefore \quad 12 - 2x + \dfrac{12}{5x} - \tfrac{2}{5} = 12$ {expanding LHS}

$\therefore \quad -2x + \dfrac{12}{5x} - \tfrac{2}{5} = 0$

$\therefore \quad -10x^2 + 12 - 2x = 0$ {× each term by $5x$}

$\therefore \quad 5x^2 + x - 6 = 0$ {÷ each term by -2}

$\therefore \quad (5x + 6)(x - 1) = 0$

$\therefore \quad x = -\tfrac{6}{5}$ or 1 where $x > 0$

$\therefore$ each sheet is 1 m wide.

EXERCISE 6G

1   Two integers differ by 12 and the sum of their squares is 74. Find the integers.

2 The sum of a number and its reciprocal is $5\frac{1}{5}$. Find the number.

3 The sum of a natural number and its square is 210. Find the number.

4 The product of two consecutive even numbers is 360. Find the numbers.

5 The product of two consecutive odd numbers is 255. Find the numbers.

6 The number of diagonals of an n-sided polygon is given by the formula $\;D = \dfrac{n}{2}(n-3)$. A polygon has 90 diagonals. How many sides does it have?

7 The length of a rectangle is 4 cm longer than its width. Find its width given that its area is 26 cm^2.

8 A rectangular box has a square base, and its height is 1 cm longer than the length of each side of its base.

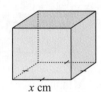

    a If each side of its base has length x cm, show that its total surface area is given by $\;A = 6x^2 + 4x$ cm^2.

    b If the total surface area is 240 cm^2, find the dimensions of the box.

9

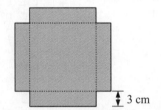

An open box contains 80 cm^3. It is made from a square piece of tinplate with 3 cm squares cut from each of its 4 corners. Find the dimensions of the original piece of tinplate.

10 Is it possible to bend a 20 cm length of wire into the shape of a rectangle which has an area of 30 cm^2?

11 The *golden rectangle* is the rectangle defined by the following statement:

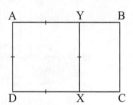

The **golden rectangle** can be divided into a square and a smaller rectangle by a line which is parallel to its shorter sides, the smaller rectangle being **similar** to the original rectangle.

Thus, if ABCD is the golden rectangle, ADXY is a square and BCXY is similar to ABCD.

The ratio of $\dfrac{AB}{AD}$ for the golden rectangle is called the **golden ratio**.

Show that the golden ratio is $\dfrac{1 + \sqrt{5}}{2}$.   **Hint:**   Let $AB = x$ units and $AD = 1$ unit.

12

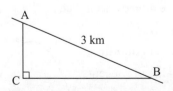

A triangular paddock has a road AB forming its longest side. AB is 3 km long. The fences AC and CB are at right angles. If BC is 400 m longer than AC, find the area of the paddock in hectares.

13 Find the width of a uniform concrete path placed around a 30 m by 40 m rectangular lawn, given that the concrete has area one quarter of the lawn.

14 Chuong and Hassan both drive 40 km from home to work each day. One day Chuong said to Hassan, "If you drive home at your usual speed, I will average 40 km h^{-1} faster than you and arrive home in 20 minutes less time." Find Hassan's speed.

15 If the average speed of a small aeroplane had been 120 km h^{-1} less, it would have taken a half an hour longer to fly 1000 km. Find the speed of the plane.

16 Two trains travel a 160 km track each day. The express travels 10 km h^{-1} faster and takes 30 minutes less than the normal train. Find the speed of the express.

17
A group of elderly citizens chartered a bus for $160. However, at the last minute 8 of them fell ill and had to miss the trip.

As a consequence, the other citizens had to pay an extra $1 each. How many elderly citizens went on the trip?

18 A tunnel is parabolic in shape with dimensions shown:

A truck carrying a wide load is 4.8 m high and 3.9 m wide, and needs to pass through the tunnel.

Determine whether the truck will fit.

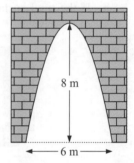

8 m

6 m

19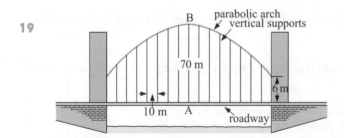

parabolic arch
vertical supports

B

70 m

10 m A

6 m

roadway

AB is the longest vertical support of a bridge which contains a parabolic arch. The vertical supports are 10 m apart. The arch meets the vertical end supports 6 m above the road.

a If axes are drawn on the diagram of the bridge above, with x-axis the road and y-axis on AB, find the equation of the parabolic arch in the form $y = ax^2 + c$.

b Hence, determine the lengths of all other vertical supports.

H   QUADRATIC OPTIMISATION

For a quadratic function $y = ax^2 + bx + c$, we have already seen that:

- if $a > 0$,
  the **minimum**
  value of y occurs
  at $x = -\dfrac{b}{2a}$.

  $x = -\dfrac{b}{2a}$
  $y_{\min}$

- if $a < 0$,
  the **maximum**
  value of y occurs
  at $x = -\dfrac{b}{2a}$.

  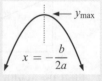
  $y_{\max}$
  $x = -\dfrac{b}{2a}$

The process of finding the maximum or minimum value of a function is called **optimisation**.

Optimisation is a very useful tool when looking at such issues as:
- maximising profits
- minimising costs

Example 27

Find the maximum or minimum value of the following quadratics, and the corresponding value of x: **a** $y = x^2 + x - 3$ **b** $y = 3 + 3x - 2x^2$

a For $y = x^2 + x - 3$
$a = 1$, $b = 1$, $c = -3$.

As $a > 0$, shape is $\smile$

$\therefore$ the minimum value occurs

when $x = \dfrac{-b}{2a} = -\dfrac{1}{2}$

and $y = (-\tfrac{1}{2})^2 + (-\tfrac{1}{2}) - 3$

$= -3\tfrac{1}{4}$

$\therefore$ the minimum value of y is $-3\tfrac{1}{4}$

occurring when $x = -\tfrac{1}{2}$.

b For $y = -2x^2 + 3x + 3$
$a = -2$, $b = 3$, $c = 3$.

As $a < 0$, shape is $\frown$

$\therefore$ the maximum value occurs

when $x = \dfrac{-b}{2a} = \dfrac{-3}{-4} = \tfrac{3}{4}$

and $y = -2(\tfrac{3}{4})^2 + 3(\tfrac{3}{4}) + 3$

$= 4\tfrac{1}{8}$

$\therefore$ the maximum value of y is $4\tfrac{1}{8}$

occurring when $x = \tfrac{3}{4}$.

Example 28

A vegetable gardener has 40 m of fencing to enclose a rectangular garden plot where one side is an existing brick wall. If the two equal sides are x m long:

a show that the area enclosed is given by $A = x(40 - 2x)$ m^2

b find the dimensions of the vegetable garden of maximum area.

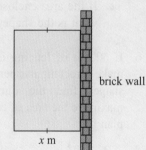

brick wall

x m

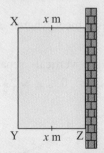

X x m

Y x m   Z

a Side XY $= 40 - 2x$ m.

Now area $=$ length $\times$ width

$\therefore$ $A = x(40 - 2x)$ m^2.

b $A = 40x - 2x^2 = -2x^2 + 40x$

is a quadratic in x, with $a = -2$, $b = 40$, $c = 0$.

As $a < 0$, shape is $\frown$

The max. area occurs when $x = \dfrac{-b}{2a} = \dfrac{-40}{-4} = 10$

$\therefore$ the area is maximised when YZ $= 10$ m and XY $= 20$ m.

EXERCISE 6H

1 Find the maximum or minimum values of the following quadratics, and the corresponding values of x:

   a $y = x^2 - 2x$ **b** $y = 7 - 2x - x^2$ **c** $y = 8 + 2x - 3x^2$

   d $y = 2x^2 + x - 1$ **e** $y = 4x^2 - x + 5$ **f** $y = 7x - 2x^2$

2 The profit in manufacturing x refrigerators per day, is given by the profit relation $P = -3x^2 + 240x - 800$ dollars. How many refrigerators should be made each day to maximise the total profit? What is the maximum profit?

3 A rectangular plot is enclosed by 200 m of fencing and has an area of A square metres. Show that:

   a $A = 100x - x^2$ where x m is the length of one of its sides

   b   the area is maximised when the rectangle is a square.

4 A rectangular paddock to enclose horses is to be made with one side being a straight water drain. If 1000 m of fencing is available for the other 3 sides, what dimensions should be used for the paddock so that it encloses the maximum possible area?

5 1800 m of fencing is available to fence six identical pig pens as shown in the diagram.

   a   Explain why $\quad 9x + 8y = 1800$.

   b   Show that the total area of each pen is given by $\quad A = -\frac{9}{8}x^2 + 225x$ m^2.

   c   If the area enclosed is to be maximised, what is the shape of each pen?

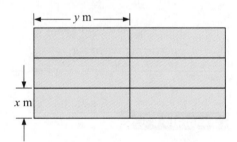

6 If 500 m of fencing is available to make 4 rectangular pens of identical shape, find the dimensions that maximise the area of each pen if the plan is:

   a 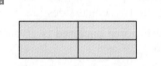   **b**

7

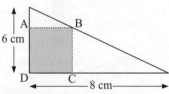

The graphs of $\ y = x^2 - 3x \ $ and $\ y = 2x - x^2$ are illustrated.

   a   Prove that the graphs meet where $\ x = 0$ and $\ x = 2\frac{1}{2}$.

   b   Find the maximum vertical separation between the curves for $\ 0 \leqslant x \leqslant 2\frac{1}{2}$.

8 Infinitely many rectangles may be inscribed within the right angled triangle shown alongside. One of them is illustrated.

   a   Let $\ AB = x$ cm and $\ BC = y$ cm. Use similar triangles to find y in terms of x.

   b   Find the dimensions of rectangle ABCD of maximum area.

9 A manufacturer of pot-belly stoves has the following situation to consider.

If x are made per week, each one will cost $(50 + \frac{400}{x})$ dollars and the total receipts per week for selling them would be $(550x - 2x^2)$ dollars.

How many pot-belly stoves should be made per week in order to maximise profits?

10 The total cost of producing x toasters per day is given by $C = (\frac{1}{10}x^2 + 20x + 25)$ euros, and the selling price of each toaster is $(44 - \frac{1}{5}x)$ euros. How many toasters should be produced each day in order to maximise the total profit?

11 A manufacturer of barbeques knows that if x of them are made each week then each one will cost $(60 + \frac{800}{x})$ pounds and the total receipts per week will be $(1000x - 3x^2)$ pounds. How many barbeques should be made per week to maximise profits?

12

The points $P_1(a_1, b_1)$, $P_2(a_2, b_2)$, $P_3(a_3, b_3)$, ..., $P_n(a_n, b_n)$ are obtained by experiment.

These points are believed to be close to linear through the origin $O(0, 0)$.

To find the equation of the 'line of best fit' through the origin we decide to minimise

$(P_1M_1)^2 + (P_2M_2)^2 + (P_3M_3)^2 + ... + (P_nM_n)^2$

where $[P_iM_i]$ is the vertical line segment connecting each point P_i with the line.

Find the slope of the 'line of best fit' in terms of a_i and b_i $(i = 1, 2, 3, 4, ..., n)$.

13 Write $f(x) = (x - a - b)(x - a + b)(x + a - b)(x + a + b)$ in expanded form and hence determine the least value of $f(x)$. Assume that a and b are real constants.

14 By considering $f(x) = (a_1x - b_1)^2 + (a_2x - b_2)^2$, use quadratic theory to prove the Cauchy-Schwarz inequality: $|a_1b_1 + a_2b_2| \leqslant \sqrt{a_1^2 + a_2^2} \sqrt{b_1^2 + b_2^2}$.

15 b_1, c_1, b_2 and c_2 are real numbers such that $b_1b_2 = 2(c_1 + c_2)$. Show that at least one of the equations $x^2 + b_1x + c_1 = 0$, $x^2 + b_2x + c_2 = 0$ has two real roots.

REVIEW SET 6A

1 For $y = -2(x + 2)(x - 1)$:

   a state the x-intercepts   **b** state the equation of the axis of symmetry

   c find the coordinates of the vertex   **d** find the y-intercept

   e sketch the graph of the function   **f** use technology to check your answers.

2 For $y = \frac{1}{2}(x - 2)^2 - 4$:

   a state the equation of the axis of symmetry

   b find the coordinates of the vertex   **c** find the y-intercept

   d sketch the graph of the function   **e** use technology to check your answers.

3 For $y = 2x^2 + 6x - 3$:

    a   convert into the form $y = a(x - h)^2 + k$ by 'completing the square'

    b   state the coordinates of the vertex   **c**   find the y-intercept

    d   sketch the graph   **e**   use technology to check your answers.

4 Solve the following equations, giving exact answers:

    a $x^2 - 11x = 60$ **b** $3x^2 - x - 10 = 0$ **c** $3x^2 - 12x = 0$

5 Solve the following equations:

    a $x^2 + 10 = 7x$ **b** $x + \dfrac{12}{x} = 7$ **c** $2x^2 - 7x + 3 = 0$

6 Solve the following equation by completing the square: $x^2 + 7x - 4 = 0$

7 Solve the following using the quadratic formula:

    a $x^2 - 7x + 3 = 0$ **b** $2x^2 - 5x + 4 = 0$

8   **a**   For what values of c do the lines with equations $y = 3x + c$ intersect the parabola $y = x^2 + x - 5$ in two distinct points?

    b   Choose one such value of c from part **a** and find the points of intersection.

9 The roots of $2x^2 - 3x = 4$ are α and β. Find the simplest quadratic equation which has roots $\dfrac{1}{\alpha}$ and $\dfrac{1}{\beta}$.

REVIEW SET 6B

1 Draw the graph of $y = -x^2 + 2x$.

2 Find the equation of the axis of symmetry and the vertex of $y = -3x^2 + 8x + 7$.

3 Use the discriminant only to determine the number of solutions to:

    a $3x^2 - 5x + 7 = 0$ **b** $-2x^2 - 4x + 3 = 0$

4 Find the maximum or minimum value of the relation $y = -2x^2 + 4x + 3$ and the value of x for which the maximum or minimum occurs.

5 Find the points of intersection of $y = x^2 - 3x$ and $y = 3x^2 - 5x - 24$.

6 For what values of k does the graph of $y = -2x^2 + 5x + k$ not cut the x-axis?

7 60 m of chicken wire is available to construct a chicken enclosure against an existing wall. The enclosure is to be rectangular.

    a   If $BC = x$ m, show that the area of rectangle ABCD is given by $A = (30x - \frac{1}{2}x^2)$ m².

    b   Find the dimensions of the enclosure which will maximise the area enclosed.

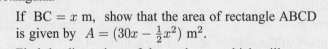
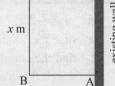

8 For what values of m are the lines $y = mx - 10$ tangents to the parabola $y = 3x^2 + 7x + 2$?

9 One of the roots of $kx^2 + (1 - 3k)x + (k - 6) = 0$ is the negative reciprocal of the other root. Find k and the two roots.

REVIEW SET 6C

1 Solve using the quadratic formula: **a** $x^2 + 5x + 3 = 0$ **b** $3x^2 + 11x - 2 = 0$

2 Solve the following equations: **a** $x^2 - 5x - 3 = 0$ **b** $2x^2 - 7x - 3 = 0$

3 Use technology to solve: **a** $(x-2)(x+1) = 3x - 4$ **b** $2x - \dfrac{1}{x} = 5$

4 Using the discriminant only, determine the nature of the solutions of:

   a $2x^2 - 5x - 7 = 0$ **b** $3x^2 - 24x + 48 = 0$

5 Find the values of m for which $2x^2 - 3x + m = 0$ has:

   a   a repeated root   **b**   two distinct real roots   **c**   no real roots

6 If AB is the same length as CD, BC is 2 cm shorter than AB, and BE is 7 cm in length, find the length of AB.

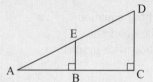

7 Find the length of the hypotenuse of a right angled triangle with one leg 7 cm longer than the other and the hypotenuse 2 cm longer than the longer leg.

8 Find the y-intercept of the line with slope -3 that is tangential to the parabola $y = 2x^2 - 5x + 1$.

9 $ax^2 + [3 - a]x - 4 = 0$ has roots which are real and positive. What values can a have?

REVIEW SET 6D

1 Use the vertex, axis of symmetry and y-intercept to graph:

   a $y = (x - 2)^2 - 4$ **b** $y = -\frac{1}{2}(x + 4)^2 + 6$

2 For the quadratic $y = 2x^2 + 4x - 1$,   find:

   a   the equation of the axis of symmetry   **b**   the coordinates of the vertex

   c   the axes intercepts.   **d**   Hence sketch the graph.

3 Use the discriminant only to find the relationship between the graph and the x-axis for:

   a $y = 2x^2 + 3x - 7$ **b** $y = -3x^2 - 7x + 4$

4 Determine if the quadratic functions are positive definite, negative definite or neither:

   a $y = -2x^2 + 3x + 2$ **b** $y = 3x^2 + x + 11$

5 Find the equation of the quadratic relation with graph:

   a   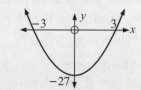   **b**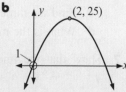

6 The sum of a number and its reciprocal is $2\frac{1}{30}$.   Find the number.

7 An open square container is made by cutting 4 cm square pieces out of a piece of tinplate. If the capacity is 120 cm^3, find the size of the original piece of tinplate.

8 Find the points where $y = -x^2 - 5x + 3$ and $y = x^2 + 3x + 11$ meet.

9 Show that no line with a y-intercept of (0, 10) will ever be tangential to the curve with equation $y = 3x^2 + 7x - 2$.

10 Find *all* quadratic equations which have roots $m - \dfrac{1}{n}$ and $n - \dfrac{1}{m}$ given that m and n are the roots of $3x^2 - 2x - 2 = 0$.

REVIEW SET 6E

1 Find the equation of the quadratic relation with graph:

a
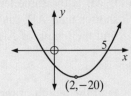

b
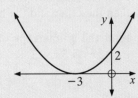

c

d

2 Find an expression for a quadratic which cuts the x-axis at 3 and -2 and has y-intercept 24. Give your answer in the form $y = ax^2 + bx + c$.

3 Find, in the form $y = ax^2 + bx + c$, the equation of the quadratic whose graph:
  a touches the x-axis at 4 and passes through (2, 12).
  b has vertex $(-4, 1)$ and passes through (1, 11).

4 Find the maximum or minimum value of the following quadratics, and the corresponding value of x: **a** $y = 3x^2 + 4x + 7$ **b** $y = -2x^2 - 5x + 2$

5 For what values of k would the graph of $y = x^2 - 2x + k$ cut the x-axis twice? Check your answer(s) using technology.

6 600 m of fencing are used to construct 6 rectangular animal pens as shown.
  a Show that $y = \dfrac{600 - 8x}{9}$.
  b Find the area A of each pen in terms of x.
  c Find the dimensions of each pen if each pen is to have maximum area.
  d What is the maximum area of each pen?

7 Show that the lines with equations $y = -5x + k$ are tangents to the parabola $y = x^2 - 3x + c$ if and only if $c - k = 1$.

8 $4x^2 - 3x - 3 = 0$ has roots p, q. Find *all* quadratic equations with roots p^3 and q^3.

Chapter 7

Complex numbers and polynomials

Contents:

A   SOLUTIONS OF REAL QUADRATICS WITH $\Delta < 0$

In **Chapter 6**, we determined that:

If $ax^2 + bx + c = 0$, $a \neq 0$ and a, b, $c \in \mathbb{R}$, then the solutions or roots are found using the formula $x = \dfrac{-b \pm \sqrt{\Delta}}{2a}$ where $\Delta = b^2 - 4ac$ is known as the **discriminant**.

We also observed that if:

- $\Delta > 0$ we have two real *distinct* solutions
- $\Delta = 0$ we have two real *identical* solutions
- $\Delta < 0$ we have no real solutions.

However, it is in fact possible to write down two solutions for the case where $\Delta < 0$. To do this we need **imaginary numbers**.

In 1572, Rafael Bombelli defined the imaginary number $i = \sqrt{-1}$. It is called 'imaginary' because we cannot place it on a number line. With i defined, we can write down solutions for quadratic equations with $\Delta < 0$. They are called *complex* solutions because they include a real and an imaginary part.

Any number of the form $a + bi$ where a and b are real and $i = \sqrt{-1}$ is called a **complex number**.

Example 1

Solve the quadratic equations: **a** $x^2 = -4$ **b** $z^2 + z + 2 = 0$

a
$$x^2 = -4$$
$$\therefore \quad x = \pm\sqrt{-4}$$
$$\therefore \quad x = \pm\sqrt{4}\sqrt{-1}$$
$$\therefore \quad x = \pm 2i$$

b
$$\Delta = 1 - 8 = -7$$
Now $z = \dfrac{-1 \pm \sqrt{-7}}{2}$ {quadratic formula}
$$\therefore \quad z = \dfrac{-1 \pm \sqrt{7}i}{2} = -\tfrac{1}{2} \pm \tfrac{\sqrt{7}}{2}i$$

In **Example 1** above, notice that $\Delta < 0$ in both cases. In each case we have found two complex solutions of the form $a + bi$, where a and b are real.

HISTORICAL NOTE

18th century mathematicians enjoyed playing with these new 'imaginary' numbers, but they were regarded as little more than interesting curiosities until the work of **Gauss** (1777 - 1855), the German mathematician, astronomer and physicist.

For centuries mathematicians attempted to find a method of trisecting an angle using a compass and straight edge. Gauss put an end to this when he used complex numbers to prove the impossibility of such a construction. From his systematic use of complex numbers and the special results, he was able to convince mathematicians of their usefulness.

Early last century **Steinmetz** (an American engineer) used complex numbers to solve electrical problems, illustrating that complex numbers did have a practical application.

Complex numbers are now used extensively in electronics, engineering, and various scientific fields, especially physics.

Example 2

Write as a product of linear factors:

a $x^2 + 4$ b $x^2 + 11$

a $x^2 + 4$
$= x^2 - 4i^2$
$= (x + 2i)(x - 2i)$

b $x^2 + 11$
$= x^2 - 11i^2$
$= (x + i\sqrt{11})(x - i\sqrt{11})$

Example 3

Solve for x:

a $x^2 + 9 = 0$

b $x^3 + 2x = 0$

a $x^2 + 9 = 0$
$\therefore \quad x^2 - 9i^2 = 0$
$(x + 3i)(x - 3i) = 0$
$\therefore \quad x = \pm 3i$

b $x^3 + 2x = 0$
$\therefore \quad x(x^2 + 2) = 0$
$\therefore \quad x(x^2 - 2i^2) = 0$
$x(x + i\sqrt{2})(x - i\sqrt{2}) = 0$
$\therefore \quad x = 0 \text{ or } \pm i\sqrt{2}$

Example 4

Solve for x:
$x^2 - 4x + 13 = 0$

$x^2 - 4x + 13 = 0 \quad \therefore \quad x = \dfrac{4 \pm \sqrt{16 - 4(1)(13)}}{2}$

$\therefore \quad x = \dfrac{4 \pm \sqrt{-36}}{2}$

$\therefore \quad x = \dfrac{4 \pm 6i}{2}$

$\therefore \quad x = 2 + 3i \text{ or } 2 - 3i$

Example 5

Solve for x:
$x^4 + x^2 = 6$

$x^4 + x^2 = 6$
$\therefore \quad x^4 + x^2 - 6 = 0$
$\therefore \quad (x^2 + 3)(x^2 - 2) = 0$
$\therefore \quad (x + i\sqrt{3})(x - i\sqrt{3})(x + \sqrt{2})(x - \sqrt{2}) = 0$
$\therefore \quad x = \pm i\sqrt{3} \text{ or } \pm\sqrt{2}$

EXERCISE 7A

1 Write in terms of i:

a $\sqrt{-9}$ b $\sqrt{-64}$ c $\sqrt{-\frac{1}{4}}$ d $\sqrt{-5}$ e $\sqrt{-8}$

2   Write as a product of linear factors:

a $x^2 - 9$	**b** $x^2 + 9$	**c** $x^2 - 7$	**d** $x^2 + 7$
e $4x^2 - 1$	**f** $4x^2 + 1$	**g** $2x^2 - 9$	**h** $2x^2 + 9$
i $x^3 - x$	**j** $x^3 + x$	**k** $x^4 - 1$	**l** $x^4 - 16$

3   Solve for x:

a $x^2 - 25 = 0$	**b** $x^2 + 25 = 0$	**c** $x^2 - 5 = 0$	**d** $x^2 + 5 = 0$
e $4x^2 - 9 = 0$	**f** $4x^2 + 9 = 0$	**g** $x^3 - 4x = 0$	**h** $x^3 + 4x = 0$
i $x^3 - 3x = 0$	**j** $x^3 + 3x = 0$	**k** $x^4 - 1 = 0$	**l** $x^4 = 81$

4   Solve for x:

a $x^2 - 10x + 29 = 0$	**b** $x^2 + 6x + 25 = 0$	**c** $x^2 + 14x + 50 = 0$
d $2x^2 + 5 = 6x$	**e** $x^2 - 2\sqrt{3}x + 4 = 0$	**f** $2x + \dfrac{1}{x} = 1$

5   Solve for x:

a $x^4 + 2x^2 = 3$	**b** $x^4 = x^2 + 6$	**c** $x^4 + 5x^2 = 36$
d $x^4 + 9x^2 + 14 = 0$	**e** $x^4 + 1 = 2x^2$	**f** $x^4 + 2x^2 + 1 = 0$

B   COMPLEX NUMBERS

FORMAL DEFINITION OF A COMPLEX NUMBER (IN CARTESIAN FORM)

Any number of the form $a + bi$ where a **and** b **are real** and $i = \sqrt{-1}$ is called a **complex number**.

Notice that **real** numbers are complex numbers in the special case where $b = 0$.

A complex number of the form bi where $b \neq 0$ is called **purely imaginary**.

THE 'SUM OF TWO SQUARES'

Notice that:

$$a^2 + b^2$$
$$= a^2 - b^2 i^2 \qquad \{\text{as } i^2 = -1\}$$
$$= (a + bi)(a - bi)$$

Compare: $a^2 - b^2 = (a + b)(a - b)$ {the difference of two squares factorisation}

and $a^2 + b^2 = (a + bi)(a - bi)$ {the sum of two squares factorisation}

REAL AND IMAGINARY PARTS OF COMPLEX NUMBERS

If we write $z = a + bi$ where a **and** b **are real** then:

- a is the **real part** of z and we write $a = \mathcal{Re}(z)$,
- b is the **imaginary part** of z and we write $b = \mathcal{Im}(z)$.

So,   if $z = 2 + 3i$, $\mathcal{Re}(z) = 2$ and $\mathcal{Im}(z) = 3$

if $z = -\sqrt{2}i$, $\mathcal{Re}(z) = 0$ and $\mathcal{Im}(z) = -\sqrt{2}$.

OPERATIONS WITH COMPLEX NUMBERS

Notice that: for radicals, $(2 + \sqrt{3}) + (4 + 2\sqrt{3}) = (2 + 4) + (1 + 2)\sqrt{3} = 6 + 3\sqrt{3}$

and for complex numbers, $(2 + i)\ \ \ + (4 + 2i)\ \ \ . = (2 + 4) + (1 + 2)i\ \ \ = 6 + 3i$

Also, notice that $(2 + \sqrt{3})(4 + 2\sqrt{3}) = 8 + 4\sqrt{3} + 4\sqrt{3} + 2(\sqrt{3})^2 = 8 + 8\sqrt{3} + 6$

and $(2 + i)(4 + 2i) = 8 + 4i\ \ \ + 4i\ \ \ + 2i^2\ \ \ = 8 + 8i\ \ - 2$

In fact the operations with complex numbers are identical to those with radicals, but with $i^2 = -1$ rather than $(\sqrt{2})^2 = 2$ or $(\sqrt{3})^2 = 3$.

So, we can **add**, **subtract**, **multiply** and **divide** complex numbers in the same way we perform these operations with radicals:

$$(a + bi) + (c + di) = (a + c) + (b + d)i \qquad \textbf{addition}$$
$$(a + bi) - (c + di) = (a - c) + (b - d)i \qquad \textbf{subtraction}$$
$$(a + bi)(c + di) = ac + adi + bci + bdi^2 \qquad \textbf{multiplication}$$
$$\frac{a + bi}{c + di} = \left(\frac{a + bi}{c + di}\right)\left(\frac{c - di}{c - di}\right) = \frac{ac - adi + bci - bdi^2}{c^2 + d^2} \qquad \textbf{division}$$

Notice how division can be performed using a multiplication technique to obtain a real number in the denominator.

Example 6

If $z = 3 + 2i$ and $w = 4 - i$ find:

a $z + w$ **b** $z - w$ **c** zw

a $z + w$	**b** $z - w$	**c** zw
$= (3 + 2i) + (4 - i)$	$= (3 + 2i) - (4 - i)$	$= (3 + 2i)(4 - i)$
$= 7 + i$	$= 3 + 2i - 4 + i$	$= 12 - 3i + 8i - 2i^2$
	$= -1 + 3i$	$= 12 + 5i + 2$
		$= 14 + 5i$

Example 7

If $z = 3 + 2i$ and $w = 4 - i$ find $\dfrac{z}{w}$ in the form $a + bi$, where a and b are real.

$$\frac{z}{w} = \frac{3 + 2i}{4 - i}$$

$$= \left(\frac{3 + 2i}{4 - i}\right)\left(\frac{4 + i}{4 + i}\right)$$

$$= \frac{12 + 3i + 8i + 2i^2}{16 - i^2}$$

$$= \frac{10 + 11i}{17}$$

$$= \tfrac{10}{17} + \tfrac{11}{17}i$$

EXERCISE 7B.1

1 Copy and complete:

z	$\mathcal{Re}(z)$	$\mathcal{Im}(z)$	z	$\mathcal{Re}(z)$	$\mathcal{Im}(z)$
$3 + 2i$			$-3 + 4i$		
$5 - i$			$-7 - 2i$		
3			$-11i$		
0			$i\sqrt{3}$		

2 If $z = 5 - 2i$ and $w = 2 + i$, find in simplest form:

   a $z + w$ **b** $2z$ **c** iw **d** $z - w$

   e $2z - 3w$ **f** zw **g** w^2 **h** z^2

3 For $z = 1 + i$ and $w = -2 + 3i$, find in simplest form:

   a $z + 2w$ **b** z^2 **c** z^3 **d** iz

   e w^2 **f** zw **g** $z^2 w$ **h** izw

4 Simplify i^n for $n = 0, 1, 2, 3, 4, 5, 6, 7, 8, 9$ and also for $n = -1, -2, -3, -4$, and -5.   Hence, simplify i^{4n+3} where n is any integer.

5 Write $(1 + i)^4$ in simplest form and hence find $(1 + i)^{101}$ in simplest form.

6 Suppose $(a + bi)^2 = -16 - 30i$ where a and b are real.
Find the possible values of a and b, given that $a > 0$.

7 For $z = 2 - i$ and $w = 1 + 3i$, find in the form $a + bi$ where a and b are real:

   a $\dfrac{z}{w}$ **b** $\dfrac{i}{z}$ **c** $\dfrac{w}{iz}$ **d** z^{-2}

8 Simplify: **a** $\dfrac{i}{1 - 2i}$ **b** $\dfrac{i(2 - i)}{3 - 2i}$ **c** $\dfrac{1}{2 - i} - \dfrac{2}{2 + i}$

9 If $z = 2 + i$ and $w = -1 + 2i$, find:

   a $\mathcal{Im}(4z - 3w)$ **b** $\mathcal{Re}(zw)$ **c** $\mathcal{Im}(iz^2)$ **d** $\mathcal{Re}\left(\dfrac{z}{w}\right)$

10 Check your answers to questions **1** to **4** and **7** to **9** using technology.

EQUALITY OF COMPLEX NUMBERS

Two complex numbers are **equal** when their **real parts** are equal and their **imaginary parts** are equal.
$$a + bi = c + di \iff a = c \text{ and } b = d.$$

Proof: Suppose $b \neq d$. Now if $a + bi = c + di$ where a, b, c and d are real,

then $bi - di = c - a$

$\therefore \quad i(b - d) = c - a$

$\therefore \quad i = \dfrac{c - a}{b - d} \quad$ {as $b \neq d$}

and this is false as the RHS is real and the LHS is imaginary.

Thus, the supposition is false and hence $b = d$ and furthermore $a = c$.

Example 8

If $(x + yi)(2 - i) = -i$ and x, y are real, determine the values of x and y.

If $(x + yi)(2 - i) = -i$, then $x + yi = \dfrac{-i}{2 - i}$

$$\text{i.e.,} \quad x + yi = \left(\dfrac{-i}{2 - i}\right)\left(\dfrac{2 + i}{2 + i}\right)$$

$$\therefore \quad x + yi = \dfrac{-2i - i^2}{4 + 1} = \dfrac{1 - 2i}{5}$$

$$\therefore \quad x + yi = \tfrac{1}{5} - \tfrac{2}{5}i$$

$$\text{and so} \quad x = \tfrac{1}{5}, \quad y = -\tfrac{2}{5}.$$

Example 9

Find real numbers x and y for which $(x + 2i)(1 - i) = 5 + yi$

$$(x + 2i)(1 - i) = 5 + yi$$
$$\therefore \quad x - xi + 2i + 2 = 5 + yi$$
$$\therefore \quad [x + 2] + [2 - x]i = 5 + yi$$
$$\therefore \quad x + 2 = 5 \quad \text{and} \quad 2 - x = y \quad \text{\{equating real and imaginary parts\}}$$
$$\therefore \quad x = 3 \quad \text{and} \quad y = -1$$

EXERCISE 7B.2

1   Find real numbers x and y such that:

     a $2x + 3yi = -x - 6i$
     b $x^2 + xi = 4 - 2i$
     c $(x + yi)(2 - i) = 8 + i$
     d $(3 + 2i)(x + yi) = -i$

2   Find x and y if x, $y \in \mathbb{R}$ and:

     a $2(x + yi) = x - yi$
     b $(x + 2i)(y - i) = -4 - 7i$
     c $(x + i)(3 - iy) = 1 + 13i$
     d $(x + yi)(2 + i) = 2x - (y + 1)i$

3   Write z in the form $a + bi$ where a, $b \in \mathbb{R}$ and $i = \sqrt{-1}$, if the complex number z satisfies the equation $3z + 17i = iz + 11$

4   The complex number z is a solution of the equation $\sqrt{z} = \dfrac{4}{1 + i} + 7 - 2i$.
    Express z in the form $a + bi$ where a and $b \in \mathbb{Z}$.

5   Find the real values of m and n for which $3(m + ni) = n - 2mi - (1 - 2i)$.

6   Express $z = \dfrac{3i}{\sqrt{2} - i} + 1$ in the form $a + bi$ where a, $b \in \mathbb{R}$, giving the *exact* values of the real and imaginary parts of z.

COMPLEX CONJUGATES

Complex numbers $a + bi$ and $a - bi$ are called **complex conjugates**.

If $z = a + bi$ we write its conjugate as $z^* = a - bi$.

Recall from page **181** that the conjugate is important for division:

$\dfrac{z}{w} = \dfrac{z}{w}\dfrac{w^*}{w^*} = \dfrac{zw^*}{ww^*}$ which makes the denominator real.

Complex conjugates appear as the solutions of real quadratic equations of the form $ax^2 + bx + c = 0$ where the discriminant $\Delta = b^2 - 4ac$ is **negative**.

For example:
- $x^2 - 2x + 5 = 0$ has $\Delta = (-2)^2 - 4(1)(5) = -16$

  and the solutions are $x = 1 + 2i$ and $1 - 2i$
- $x^2 + 4 = 0$ has $\Delta = 0^2 - 4(1)(4) = -16$

  and the solutions are $x = 2i$ and $-2i$

Note:
- Quadratics with real coefficients are called **real quadratics**. This does not necessarily mean that its zeros are real.
- If a quadratic equation has **rational coefficients** and an **irrational root** of the form $c + d\sqrt{n}$, then $c - d\sqrt{n}$ is also a root. These roots are **radical conjugates**.
- If a real quadratic equation has $\Delta < 0$ and $c + di$ is a complex root then $c - di$ is also a root. These roots are **complex conjugates**.

Theorem: If $c + di$ and $c - di$ are roots of a quadratic equation, then the quadratic equation is $a(x^2 - 2cx + (c^2 + d^2)) = 0$ for some constant $a \neq 0$.

Proof: The sum of the roots $= 2c$ and the product $= (c + di)(c - di) = c^2 + d^2$

$\therefore\ x^2 - (\text{sum})x + (\text{product}) = 0$

$\therefore\ x^2 - 2cx + (c^2 + d^2) = 0$

Alternatively: If $c + di$ and $c - di$ are roots then

$(x - [c + di])(x - [c - di]) = 0$

$\therefore\ (x - c - di)(x - c + di) = 0$

$\therefore\ (x - c)^2 - d^2 i^2 = 0$

$\therefore\ x^2 - 2cx + c^2 + d^2 = 0$

In general, $a(x^2 - 2cx + c^2 + d^2) = 0$ for some constant $a \neq 0$.

Example 10

Find all quadratic equations with real coefficients having $1 - 2i$ as a root.

As $1 - 2i$ is a root, $1 + 2i$ is also a root.

Sum of roots $= 1 - 2i + 1 + 2i$ Product of roots $= (1 - 2i)(1 + 2i)$

$= 2$ $= 1 + 4$

So, as $x^2 - (\text{sum})x + (\text{product}) = 0$, $= 5$

$a(x^2 - 2x + 5) = 0,\ a \neq 0$ gives all possible equations.

Note: The sum of complex conjugates $c + di$ and $c - di$ is $2c$ which is **real**.

The product is $(c + di)(c - di) = c^2 + d^2$ which is also **real**.

Example 11

Find exact values of a and b if $\sqrt{2} + i$ is a root of $x^2 + ax + b = 0$, $a, b \in \mathbb{R}$.

Since a and b are real, the quadratic has real coefficients

$\therefore$ $\sqrt{2} - i$ is also a root

$\therefore$ sum of roots $= \sqrt{2} + i + \sqrt{2} - i = 2\sqrt{2}$

product of roots $= (\sqrt{2} + i)(\sqrt{2} - i) = 2 + 1 = 3$

Thus $a = -2\sqrt{2}$ and $b = 3$.

EXERCISE 7B.3

1 Find all quadratic equations with real coefficients and roots of:

a $3 \pm i$	**b** $1 \pm 3i$	**c** $-2 \pm 5i$	**d** $\sqrt{2} \pm i$
e $2 \pm \sqrt{3}$	**f** 0 and $-\frac{2}{3}$	**g** $\pm i\sqrt{2}$	**h** $-6 \pm i$

2 Find exact values of a and b if:

a $3 + i$ is a root of $x^2 + ax + b = 0$, where a and b are real

b $1 - \sqrt{2}$ is a root of $x^2 + ax + b = 0$, where a and b are rational

c $a + ai$ is a root of $x^2 + 4x + b = 0$ where a and b are real. [Careful!]

INVESTIGATION 1   PROPERTIES OF CONJUGATES

The purpose of this investigation is to discover any properties that complex conjugates might have.

What to do:

1 Given $z_1 = 1 - i$ and $z_2 = 2 + i$ find:

a $z_1{}^*$ **b** $z_2{}^*$ **c** $(z_1{}^*)^*$ **d** $(z_2{}^*)^*$ **e** $(z_1 + z_2)^*$ **f** $z_1{}^* + z_2{}^*$

g $(z_1 - z_2)^*$ **h** $z_1{}^* - z_2{}^*$ **i** $(z_1 z_2)^*$ **j** $z_1{}^* z_2{}^*$ **k** $\left(\dfrac{z_1}{z_2}\right)^*$ **l** $\dfrac{z_1{}^*}{z_2{}^*}$

m $(z_1^2)^*$ **n** $(z_1{}^*)^2$ **o** $(z_2^3)^*$ **p** $(z_2{}^*)^3$

2 Repeat **1** with z_1 and z_2 of your choice.

3 From **1** and **2** formulate possible rules of conjugates.

PROPERTIES OF CONJUGATES

From **Investigation 1** you should have found the following rules for complex conjugates:

- $(z^*)^* = z$

- $(z_1 + z_2)^* = z_1{}^* + z_2{}^*$ and $(z_1 - z_2)^* = z_1{}^* - z_2{}^*$

- $(z_1 z_2)^* = z_1{}^* \times z_2{}^*$ and $\left(\dfrac{z_1}{z_2}\right)^* = \dfrac{z_1{}^*}{z_2{}^*}$, $z_2 \neq 0$

- $(z^n)^* = (z^*)^n$ for integers $n = 1, 2$ and 3
- $z + z^*$ and zz^* are real.

Example 12

Show that $(z_1 + z_2)^* = z_1{}^* + z_2{}^*$ for all complex numbers z_1 and z_2.

Let $z_1 = a + bi$ and $z_2 = c + di$ $\therefore$ $z_1^* = a - bi$ and $z_2^* = c - di$

Now $z_1 + z_2 = (a + c) + (b + d)i$ $\therefore$ $(z_1 + z_2)^* = (a + c) - (b + d)i$
$$= a + c - bi - di$$
$$= a - bi + c - di$$
$$= z_1{}^* + z_2{}^*$$

Example 13

Show that
$(z_1 z_2)^* = z_1{}^* \times z_2{}^*$
for all complex numbers
z_1 and z_2.

Let $z_1 = a + bi$ and $z_2 = c + di$
$$\therefore \quad z_1 z_2 = (a + bi)(c + di)$$
$$= ac + adi + bci + bdi^2$$
$$= [ac - bd] + i[ad + bc]$$

Thus $(z_1 z_2)^* = [ac - bd] - i[ad + bc]$ ...... (1)

Now $z_1{}^* \times z_2{}^* = (a - bi)(c - di)$
$$= ac - adi - bci + bdi^2$$
$$= [ac - bd] - i[ad + bc]$$ ...... (2)

From (1) and (2), $(z_1 z_2)^* = z_1{}^* \times z_2{}^*$

EXERCISE 7B.4

1   Show that $(z_1 - z_2)^* = z_1{}^* - z_2{}^*$ for all complex numbers z_1 and z_2.

2   Simplify the expression $(w^* - z)^* - (w - 2z^*)$ using the properties of conjugates.

3   It is known that a complex number z satisfies the equation $z^* = -z$.
    Show that z is either purely imaginary or zero.

4   If $z_1 = a + bi$ and $z_2 = c + di$:

   a   find $\dfrac{z_1}{z_2}$ (in form $X + Yi$)   b   show that $\left(\dfrac{z_1}{z_2}\right)^* = \dfrac{z_1{}^*}{z_2{}^*}$ for all z_1 and $z_2 \neq 0$.

5   An easier way of proving $\left(\dfrac{z_1}{z_2}\right)^* = \dfrac{z_1{}^*}{z_2{}^*}$ is to start with $\left(\dfrac{z_1}{z_2}\right)^* \times z_2{}^*$.

   Show how this can be done, remembering we have already proved that
   "the conjugate of a product is the product of the conjugates" in **Example 13**.

6   Prove that for all complex numbers z and w:

   a $zw^* + z^*w$ is always real   b $zw^* - z^*w$ is purely imaginary or zero.

7 **a** If $z = a + bi$ find z^2 in the form $X + Yi$.

    b Hence, show that $(z^2)^* = (z^*)^2$ for all complex numbers z.

    c Repeat **a** and **b** but for z^3 instead of z^2.

8 $w = \dfrac{z - 1}{z^* + 1}$ where $z = a + bi$. Find the conditions under which:

    a w is real   **b** w is purely imaginary.

CONJUGATE GENERALISATIONS

Notice that $(z_1 + z_2 + z_3)^* = (z_1 + z_2)^* + z_3^*$ {treating $z_1 + z_2$ as one complex number}

$$= z_1^* + z_2^* + z_3^* \quad ...... \text{ (1)}$$

Likewise $(z_1 + z_2 + z_3 + z_4)^* = (z_1 + z_2 + z_3)^* + z_4^*$

$$= z_1^* + z_2^* + z_3^* + z_4^* \quad \{\text{from (1)}\}$$

Since there is no reason why this process cannot continue for the conjugate of 5, 6, 7, ... complex numbers we generalise to:

$$(z_1 + z_2 + z_3 + ... + z_n)^* = z_1^* + z_2^* + z_3^* + ... + z_n^*.$$

The process of obtaining the general case from observing the simpler cases when $n = 1, 2, 3, 4, ...$ is called **mathematical induction**.

Proof by the Principle of Mathematical Induction is an exercise that could be undertaken after the completion of **Chapter 9**. This is a more formal treatment and constitutes a proper proof.

EXERCISE 7B.5

1 **a** Assuming $(z_1 z_2)^* = z_1^* z_2^*$, explain why $(z_1 z_2 z_3)^* = z_1^* z_2^* z_3^*$.

    b Show that $(z_1 z_2 z_3 z_4)^* = z_1^* z_2^* z_3^* z_4^*$ from **a**.

    c What is the inductive generalisation of your results in **a** and **b**?

    d What is the result of letting all z_i values be equal to z in **c**?

SUMMARY OF CONJUGATE DISCOVERIES

- If z is any complex number then $z + z^*$ is real and zz^* is real.
- $(z^*)^* = z$
- If z_1 and z_2 are any complex numbers then

    ▶ $(z_1 + z_2)^* = z_1^* + z_2^*$ ▶ $(z_1 - z_2)^* = z_1^* - z_2^*$

    ▶ $(z_1 z_2)^* = z_1^* z_2^*$ ▶ $\left(\dfrac{z_1}{z_2}\right)^* = \dfrac{z_1^*}{z_2^*}$

- $(z^n)^* = (z^*)^n$ for all positive integers n
- $(z_1 + z_2 + z_3 + ... + z_n)^* = z_1^* + z_2^* + z_3^* + ... + z_n^*$

    and $(z_1 z_2 z_3 .... z_n)^* = z_1^* z_2^* z_3^* .... z_n^*$

C   REAL POLYNOMIALS

Up to this point we have studied linear and quadratic polynomial functions at some depth, with perhaps occasional reference to cubic and quartic polynomials. We now turn our attention to general polynomials with real coefficients.

The **degree** of a polynomial is its highest power of the variable.

Polynomials	Degree	Name
$ax + b, \quad a \neq 0$	1	**linear**
$ax^2 + bx + c, \quad a \neq 0$	2	**quadratic**
$ax^3 + bx^2 + cx + d, \quad a \neq 0$	3	**cubic**
$ax^4 + bx^3 + cx^2 + dx + e, \quad a \neq 0$	4	**quartic**

a is the **leading coefficient** and the term not containing the **variable** x is the **constant term**.

A **real polynomial** has all its coefficients as real numbers. (They do not contain i where $i = \sqrt{-1}$.)

OPERATIONS WITH POLYNOMIALS

ADDITION AND SUBTRACTION

To **add** (or **subtract**) two polynomials we **add** (or **subtract**) 'like terms'.

Example 14

If $P(x) = x^3 - 2x^2 + 3x - 5$ and $Q(x) = 2x^3 + x^2 - 11$
find: **a** $P(x) + Q(x)$ **b** $P(x) - Q(x)$

> It is a good idea to place brackets around expressions which are subtracted.

a
$$P(x) + Q(x)$$
$$= \quad x^3 - 2x^2 + 3x - 5$$
$$+ 2x^3 + x^2 \qquad - 11$$
$$= \quad 3x^3 - x^2 + 3x - 16$$

b
$$P(x) - Q(x)$$
$$= x^3 - 2x^2 + 3x - 5 - [2x^3 + x^2 - 11]$$
$$= x^3 - 2x^2 + 3x - 5 - 2x^3 - x^2 + 11$$
$$= -x^3 - 3x^2 + 3x + 6$$

SCALAR MULTIPLICATION

To **multiply** a polynomial by a **scalar** (constant) we multiply each term by the scalar.

Example 15

If $P(x) = x^4 - 2x^3 + 4x + 7$ find: **a** $3P(x)$ **b** $-2P(x)$

a
$$3P(x)$$
$$= 3(x^4 - 2x^3 + 4x + 7)$$
$$= 3x^4 - 6x^3 + 12x + 21$$

b
$$-2P(x)$$
$$= -2(x^4 - 2x^3 + 4x + 7)$$
$$= -2x^4 + 4x^3 - 8x - 14$$

POLYNOMIAL MULTIPLICATION

To **multiply** two polynomials, we multiply every term of the first polynomial by every term of the second polynomial and then collect like terms.

Example 16

If $P(x) = x^3 - 2x + 4$ and $Q(x) = 2x^2 + 3x - 5$, find $P(x) Q(x)$.

$$
\begin{aligned}
P(x)Q(x) &= (x^3 - 2x + 4)(2x^2 + 3x - 5) \\
&= x^3(2x^2 + 3x - 5) - 2x(2x^2 + 3x - 5) + 4(2x^2 + 3x - 5) \\
&= 2x^5 + 3x^4 - 5x^3 \\
&\qquad\quad - 4x^3 - 6x^2 + 10x \\
&\qquad\qquad\quad + 8x^2 + 12x - 20 \\
&= 2x^5 + 3x^4 - 9x^3 + 2x^2 + 22x - 20
\end{aligned}
$$

EXERCISE 7C.1

1 If $P(x) = x^2 + 2x + 3$ and $Q(x) = 4x^2 + 5x + 6$, find in simplest form:

  a $\quad 3P(x)$ b $\quad P(x) + Q(x)$ c $\quad P(x) - 2Q(x)$ d $\quad P(x)Q(x)$

2 If $f(x) = x^2 - x + 2$ and $g(x) = x^3 - 3x + 5$, find in simplest form:

  a $\quad f(x) + g(x)$ b $\quad g(x) - f(x)$ c $\quad 2f(x) + 3g(x)$

  d $\quad g(x) + xf(x)$ e $\quad f(x)g(x)$ f $\quad [f(x)]^2$

3 Expand and simplify:

  a $\quad (x^2 - 2x + 3)(2x + 1)$ b $\quad (x - 1)^2(x^2 + 3x - 2)$

  c $\quad (x + 2)^3$ d $\quad (2x^2 - x + 3)^2$

  e $\quad (2x - 1)^4$ f $\quad (3x - 2)^2(2x + 1)(x - 4)$

NOTE ON SYNTHETIC MULTIPLICATION (OPTIONAL)

Polynomial multiplication can be performed using the coefficients only.

For example, for $(x^3 + 2x - 5)(2x + 3)$ we detach coefficients and multiply. It is different from the ordinary multiplication of large numbers because we sometimes have negative coefficients and because we do not carry tens into the next column.

$$
\begin{array}{rrrrr}
1 & 0 & 2 & -5 & \quad\longleftarrow \text{ coefficients of } x^3 + 2x - 5 \\
\times & 2 & 3 & & \quad\longleftarrow \text{ coefficients of } 2x + 3 \\
\hline
3 & 0 & 6 & -15 & \\
2 & 0 & 4 & -10 & \\
\hline
2 & 3 & 4 & -4 & -15 \\
x^4 & x^3 & x^2 & x & \text{constants}
\end{array}
$$

So $(x^3 + 2x - 5)(2x + 3)$
$= 2x^4 + 3x^3 + 4x^2 - 4x - 15$.

4 Find the following products:

  a $\quad (2x^2 - 3x + 5)(3x - 1)$ b $\quad (4x^2 - x + 2)(2x + 5)$

  c $\quad (2x^2 + 3x + 2)(5 - x)$ d $\quad (x - 2)^2(2x + 1)$

e $(x^2 - 3x + 2)(2x^2 + 4x - 1)$ **f** $(3x^2 - x + 2)(5x^2 + 2x - 3)$

g $(x^2 - x + 3)^2$ **h** $(2x^2 + x - 4)^2$ **i** $(2x + 5)^3$ **j** $(x^3 + x^2 - 2)^2$

DIVISION OF POLYNOMIALS

The division of polynomials is a more difficult process. We can divide a polynomial by another polynomial using an algorithm similar to that used for division of whole numbers.

The division process is only sensible if we divide a polynomial of degree n by another of degree n or less.

DIVISION BY LINEARS

Consider $(2x^2 + 3x + 4)(x + 2) + 7$.

If we expand this expression we get $(2x^2 + 3x + 4)(x + 2) + 7 = 2x^3 + 7x^2 + 10x + 15$.

Now consider $2x^3 + 7x^2 + 10x + 15$ divided by $x + 2$

i.e., $\dfrac{2x^3 + 7x^2 + 10x + 15}{x + 2} = \dfrac{(2x^2 + 3x + 4)(x + 2) + 7}{x + 2}$

$\therefore \dfrac{2x^3 + 7x^2 + 10x + 15}{x + 2} = \dfrac{(2x^2 + 3x + 4)(x + 2)}{x + 2} + \dfrac{7}{x + 2}$

$\therefore \dfrac{2x^3 + 7x^2 + 10x + 15}{x + 2} = \underbrace{2x^2 + 3x + 4}_{\text{quotient}} + \dfrac{7}{x + 2}$ ← remainder / divisor

DIVISION ALGORITHM

Division may be performed directly using the following **algorithm**:

Step 1: What do we multiply x by to get $2x^3$? The answer is $2x^2$, and $2x^2(x + 2) = 2x^3 + 4x^2$.

Step 2: Subtract $2x^3 + 4x^2$ from $2x^3 + 7x^2$. The answer is $3x^2$.

Step 3: Bring down the $10x$ to obtain $3x^2 + 10x$.

Return to *Step 1* with the question: "What must we multiply x by to get $3x^2$?" The answer is $3x$, and $3x(x + 2) = 3x^2 + 6x$ etc.

The result can also be achieved by leaving out the variable, as shown alongside.

Either way, $\quad \dfrac{2x^3 + 7x^2 + 10x + 15}{x + 2} = 2x^2 + 3x + 4 + \dfrac{7}{x + 2},$

$$\text{where} \quad x + 2 \quad \text{is called the } \textbf{divisor},$$
$$2x^2 + 3x + 4 \quad \text{is called the } \textbf{quotient},$$
$$\text{and} \quad 7 \quad \text{is called the } \textbf{remainder}.$$

In general, if $P(x)$ is divided by $ax + b$ until a constant remainder R is obtained,

$$\dfrac{P(x)}{ax + b} = Q(x) + \dfrac{R}{ax + b} \quad \text{where} \quad ax + b \quad \text{is the } \textbf{divisor},$$
$$Q(x) \quad \text{is the } \textbf{quotient}, \text{ and}$$
$$R \quad \text{is the } \textbf{remainder}.$$

Notice that $P(x) = Q(x) \times (ax + b) + R.$

Example 17

Find the quotient and remainder for $\dfrac{x^3 - x^2 - 3x - 5}{x - 3}.$

$$
\begin{array}{r}
x^2 + 2x + 3 \\
x - 3 \overline{\smash{\big)}\ x^3 - x^2 - 3x - 5} \\
-(x^3 - 3x^2) \\
\hline
2x^2 - 3x \\
-(2x^2 - 6x) \\
\hline
3x - 5 \\
-(3x - 9) \\
\hline
4
\end{array}
$$

$\therefore$ quotient is $x^2 + 2x + 3$ and remainder is 4.

Thus $\dfrac{x^3 - x^2 - 3x - 5}{x - 3} = x^2 + 2x + 3 + \dfrac{4}{x - 3}$

So, $x^3 - x^2 - 3x - 5 = (x^2 + 2x + 3)(x - 3) + 4.$

(Check by expanding and simplifying the RHS.)

Example 18

Perform the division $\dfrac{x^4 + 2x^2 - 1}{x + 3}.$

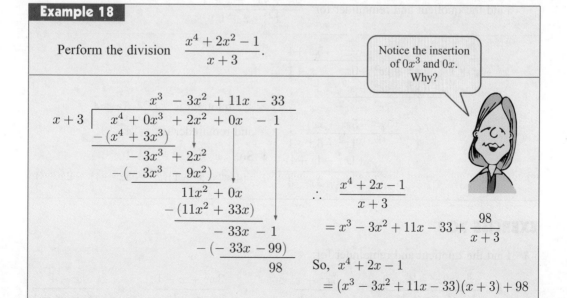

Notice the insertion of $0x^3$ and $0x$. Why?

$$
\begin{array}{r}
x^3 - 3x^2 + 11x - 33 \\
x + 3 \overline{\smash{\big)}\ x^4 + 0x^3 + 2x^2 + 0x - 1} \\
-(x^4 + 3x^3) \\
\hline
-3x^3 + 2x^2 \\
-(-3x^3 - 9x^2) \\
\hline
11x^2 + 0x \\
-(11x^2 + 33x) \\
\hline
-33x - 1 \\
-(-33x - 99) \\
\hline
98
\end{array}
$$

$\therefore \quad \dfrac{x^4 + 2x - 1}{x + 3}$

$= x^3 - 3x^2 + 11x - 33 + \dfrac{98}{x + 3}$

So, $x^4 + 2x - 1$

$= (x^3 - 3x^2 + 11x - 33)(x + 3) + 98$

EXERCISE 7C.2

1 Find the quotient and remainder for:

   a $\dfrac{x^2 + 2x - 3}{x + 2}$ **b** $\dfrac{x^2 - 5x + 1}{x - 1}$ **c** $\dfrac{2x^3 + 6x^2 - 4x + 3}{x - 2}$

2 Perform the divisions:

   a $\dfrac{x^2 - 3x + 6}{x - 4}$ **b** $\dfrac{x^2 + 4x - 11}{x + 3}$ **c** $\dfrac{2x^2 - 7x + 2}{x - 2}$

   d $\dfrac{2x^3 + 3x^2 - 3x - 2}{2x + 1}$ **e** $\dfrac{3x^3 + 11x^2 + 8x + 7}{3x - 1}$ **f** $\dfrac{2x^4 - x^3 - x^2 + 7x + 4}{2x + 3}$

3 Perform the divisions:

   a $\dfrac{x^2 + 5}{x - 2}$ **b** $\dfrac{2x^2 + 3x}{x + 1}$ **c** $\dfrac{3x^2 + 2x - 5}{x + 2}$

   d $\dfrac{x^3 + 2x^2 - 5x + 2}{x - 1}$ **e** $\dfrac{2x^3 - x}{x + 4}$ **f** $\dfrac{x^3 + x^2 - 5}{x - 2}$

DIVISION BY QUADRATICS

As with division by linears we can use the **division algorithm** to divide polynomials by quadratics. The division process stops when the remainder has degree less than that of the divisor,

$$\text{i.e.,} \quad \frac{P(x)}{a^2 + bx + c} = Q(x) + \frac{ex + f}{ax^2 + bx + c}$$

The remainder will be linear if $e \neq 0$ or constant if $e = 0$.

Example 19

Find the quotient and remainder for $\dfrac{x^4 + 4x^3 - x + 1}{x^2 - x + 1}$.

$$
\begin{array}{r}
x^2 +5x +4 \\
x^2 - x + 1 \enclose{longdiv}{x^4 +4x^3 +0x^2 -x +1} \\
-(x^4 -x^3 + x^2) \\
\hline
5x^3 - x^2 -x \\
-(5x^3 -5x^2 +5x) \\
\hline
4x^2 -6x +1 \\
-(4x^2 -4x+4) \\
\hline
-2x -3
\end{array}
$$

$\therefore$ quotient is $x^2 + 5x + 4$

and remainder is $-2x - 3$

So, $x^4 + 4x^3 - x + 1$
$= (x^2 - x + 1)(x^2 + 5x + 4) - 2x - 3$

EXERCISE 7C.3

1 Find the quotient and remainder for:

   a $\dfrac{x^3 + 2x^2 + x - 3}{x^2 + x + 1}$ **b** $\dfrac{3x^2 - x}{x^2 - 1}$ **c** $\dfrac{3x^3 + x - 1}{x^2 + 1}$ **d** $\dfrac{x - 4}{x^2 + 2x - 1}$

2 Carry out the following divisions and also write each in the form
$P(x) = D(x)Q(x) + R(x)$:

a $\dfrac{x^2 - x + 1}{x^2 + x + 1}$

b $\dfrac{x^3}{x^2 + 2}$

c $\dfrac{x^4 + 3x^2 + x - 1}{x^2 - x + 1}$

d $\dfrac{2x^3 - x + 6}{(x - 1)^2}$

e $\dfrac{x^4}{(x + 1)^2}$

f $\dfrac{x^4 - 2x^3 + x + 5}{(x - 1)(x + 2)}$

3 $P(x) = (x - 2)(x^2 + 2x + 3) + 7$. What is the quotient and remainder when $P(x)$ is divided by $x - 2$?

4 Given that $f(x) = (x - 1)(x + 2)(x^2 - 3x + 5) + 15 - 10x$, find the quotient and remainder when $f(x)$ is divided by $x^2 + x - 2$.

SYNTHETIC DIVISION (OPTIONAL)

PRINTABLE SECTION

Click on the icon for an exercise involving a synthetic division process for the division of a polynomial by a linear.

D   ROOTS, ZEROS AND FACTORS

ROOTS AND ZEROS

A **zero** of a polynomial is a value of the variable which makes the polynomial equal to zero. The **roots** of a polynomial **equation** are values of the variable which satisfy or are solutions to the equation.

The **roots** of $P(x) = 0$ are the **zeros** of $P(x)$ and the x-intercepts of the graph of $y = P(x)$.

If $x = 2$, $x^3 + 2x^2 - 3x - 10$

$\qquad\qquad = 8 + 8 - 6 - 10 \qquad\qquad \therefore$ 2 is a zero of $x^3 + 2x^2 - 3x - 10$

$\qquad\qquad = 0 \qquad\qquad\qquad\quad$ and   2 is a root of $x^3 + 2x^2 - 3x - 10 = 0$.

Note:

$\qquad\qquad \alpha$ is a **zero** of polynomial $P(x) \quad \Leftrightarrow \quad P(\alpha) = 0$.

$\qquad\qquad \alpha$ is a **root** (or **solution**) of $P(x) = 0 \quad \Leftrightarrow \quad P(\alpha) = 0$.

Example 20

Find the zeros of: a $x^2 - 4x + 53$ b $z^3 + 3z$

a   We wish to find x such that

$\qquad x^2 - 4x + 53 = 0$

$\qquad \therefore \quad x = \dfrac{4 \pm \sqrt{16 - 4(1)(53)}}{2}$

$\qquad \therefore \quad x = \dfrac{4 \pm 14i}{2} = 2 \pm 7i$

b   We wish to find z such that

$\qquad\qquad z^3 + 3z = 0$

$\qquad \therefore \quad z(z^2 + 3) = 0$

$\qquad \therefore \quad z(z + i\sqrt{3})(z - i\sqrt{3}) = 0$

$\qquad \therefore \quad z = 0$ or $\pm i\sqrt{3}$

If $P(x) = (x + 1)(2x - 1)(x + 2)$, then $(x + 1)$, $(2x - 1)$ and $(x + 2)$ are its **linear factors**.

Likewise $P(x) = (x+3)^2(2x+3)$ has been factorised into 3 linear factors, one of which is repeated.

In general, $(x-\alpha)$ is a **factor** of polynomial $P(x)$ $\Leftrightarrow$ there exists a polynomial $Q(x)$ such that $P(x) = (x-\alpha)Q(x)$.

Example 21

Factorise: a $z^2 + 4z + 9$ b $2z^3 + 5z^2 - 3z$?

a $z^2 + 4z + 9$ is zero when

$$\therefore \quad z = \frac{-4 \pm \sqrt{16 - 4(1)(9)}}{2} = -2 \pm i\sqrt{5}$$

$\therefore \quad z^2 + 4z + 9 = (z - [-2 + i\sqrt{5}])(z - [-2 - i\sqrt{5}])$

$\qquad\qquad\qquad = (z + 2 - i\sqrt{5})(z + 2 + i\sqrt{5})$

b $2z^3 + 5z^2 - 3z$
$= z(2z^2 + 5z - 3)$
$= z(2z - 1)(z + 3)$

Example 22   Find *all* cubic polynomials with zeros $\frac{1}{2}$, $-3 \pm 2i$.

The zeros $-3 \pm 2i$ have   sum $= -3 + 2i - 3 - 2i = -6$ and
$$\text{product} = (-3 + 2i)(-3 - 2i) = 13$$
and $\therefore$ come from the quadratic factor $z^2 + 6z + 13$
$\frac{1}{2}$ comes from the linear factor $2z - 1$
$\therefore \quad P(z) = a(2z - 1)(z^2 + 6z + 13), \quad a \neq 0.$

Example 23   Find *all* quartic polynomials with zeros of $2, -\frac{1}{3},   -1 \pm \sqrt{5}$.

The zeros $-1 \pm \sqrt{5}$ have   sum $= -1 + \sqrt{5} - 1 - \sqrt{5} = -2$ and
$$\text{product} = (-1 + \sqrt{5})(-1 - \sqrt{5}) = -4$$
and $\therefore$ come from the quadratic factor $z^2 + 2z - 4$
The zeros 2 and $-\frac{1}{3}$ come from the linear factors $(z - 2)$ and $(3z + 1)$
$\therefore \quad P(z) = a(z - 2)(3z + 1)(z^2 + 2z - 4), \quad a \neq 0.$

EXERCISE 7D.1

1   Find the zeros of:

    a $2x^2 - 5x - 12$ b $x^2 + 6x + 10$ c $z^2 - 6z + 6$

    d $x^3 - 4x$ e $z^3 + 2z$ f $z^4 + 4z^2 - 5$

2   Find the roots of:

    a $5x^2 = 3x + 2$ b $(2x + 1)(x^2 + 3) = 0$ c $-2z(z^2 - 2z + 2) = 0$

    d $x^3 = 5x$ e $z^3 + 5z = 0$ f $z^4 = 3z^2 + 10$

3 Find the linear factors of:

    a $2x^2 - 7x - 15$ **b** $z^2 - 6z + 16$ **c** $x^3 + 2x^2 - 4x$

    d $6z^3 - z^2 - 2z$ **e** $z^4 - 6z^2 + 5$ **f** $z^4 - z^2 - 2$

4 If $P(x) = a(x - \alpha)(x - \beta)(x - \gamma)$ then α, β and γ are its zeros.

Check that the above statement is correct by finding $P(\alpha)$, $P(\beta)$ and $P(\gamma)$.

5 Find *all* cubic polynomials with zeros of:

    a $\pm 2, 3$ **b** $-2, \pm i$ **c** $3, -1 \pm i$ **d** $-1, -2 \pm \sqrt{2}$

6 Find *all* quartic polynomials with zeros of:

    a $\pm 1, \pm \sqrt{2}$ **b** $2, -1, \pm i\sqrt{3}$ **c** $\pm \sqrt{3}, 1 \pm i$ **d** $2 \pm \sqrt{5}, -2 \pm 3i$

POLYNOMIAL EQUALITY

Polynomials are equal if and only if they generate the same y-value for each x-value. This means that graphs of equal polynomials should be identical.

> Two polynomials are **equal** if and only if they have the **same degree** (order) and corresponding terms have equal coefficients.

For example, if $2x^3 + 3x^2 - 4x + 6 = ax^3 + bx^2 + cx + d,$ then
$$a = 2, \quad b = 3, \quad c = -4 \quad \text{and} \quad d = 6.$$

EQUATING COEFFICIENTS

If we know that two polynomials are **equal** then we can 'equate coefficients' in order to find unknown coefficients.

Example 24

Find constants a, b and c given that:
$$6x^3 + 7x^2 - 19x + 7 = (2x - 1)(ax^2 + bx + c) \quad \text{for all } x.$$

    If $\quad 6x^3 + 7x^2 - 19x + 7 = (2x - 1)(ax^2 + bx + c)$

then $\quad 6x^3 + 7x^2 - 19x + 7 = 2ax^3 + 2bx^2 + 2cx - ax^2 - bx - c$

$\therefore \quad 6x^3 + 7x^2 - 19x + 7 = 2ax^3 + [2b - a]x^2 + [2c - b]x - c$

Since this is true for all x, we equate coefficients

$\therefore \quad \underbrace{2a = 6}_{x^3 \text{ s}}, \quad \underbrace{2b - a = 7}_{x^2 \text{ s}}, \quad \underbrace{2c - b = -19}_{x \text{ s}} \quad \text{and} \quad \underbrace{7 = -c}_{\text{constants}}$

$\therefore \quad a = 3$ and $c = -7$ and consequently $\underbrace{2b - 3 = 7 \quad \text{and} \quad -14 - b = -19}_{b = 5}$

So, $a = 3$, $b = 5$ and $c = -7$.   in both equations

Example 25

Find a and b if $z^4 + 9 = (z^2 + az + 3)(z^2 + bz + 3)$ for all z.

When solving more equations than unknowns simultaneously, we must check that any solutions fit **all** equations. If they do not, there are **no solutions**.

$$z^4 + 9 = (z^2 + az + 3)(z^2 + bz + 3) \quad \text{for all } z$$
$$\therefore \quad z^4 + 9 = z^4 + bz^3 + 3z^2$$
$$+ az^3 + abz^2 + 3az$$
$$+ 3z^2 + 3bz + 9$$
$$\therefore \quad z^4 + 9 = z^4 + [a+b]z^3 + [ab+6]z^2 + [3a+3b]z + 9 \quad \text{for all } z$$

Equating coefficients gives
$$\begin{cases} a + b = 0 & \text{...... (1)} \quad \{z^3 \text{ s}\} \\ ab + 6 = 0 & \text{...... (2)} \quad \{z^2 \text{ s}\} \\ 3a + 3b = 0 & \text{...... (3)} \quad \{z \text{ s}\} \end{cases}$$

From (1) and (3) we see that $b = -a$

So, in (2)
$$a(-a) + 6 = 0$$
$$\therefore \quad a^2 = 6$$
$$\therefore \quad a = \pm\sqrt{6} \quad \text{and so} \quad b = \mp\sqrt{6}$$
$$\therefore \quad a = \sqrt{6}, \ b = -\sqrt{6} \quad or \quad a = -\sqrt{6}, \ b = \sqrt{6}$$

Example 26

$x + 3$ is a factor of $P(x) = x^3 + ax^2 - 7x + 6$. Find a and the other factors.

Since $x + 3$ is a factor,
$$x^3 + ax^2 - 7x + 6 = (x+3)(x^2 + bx + 2) \quad \text{for some constant } b$$
$$= x^3 + bx^2 + 2x + 3x^2 + 3bx + 6$$
$$= x^3 + [b+3]x^2 + [3b+2]x + 6$$

Equating coefficients gives $\quad 3b + 2 = -7 \quad$ and $\quad a = b + 3$
$$\therefore \quad b = -3 \quad \text{and} \quad \therefore \quad a = 0$$
$$\therefore \quad P(x) = (x+3)(x^2 - 3x + 2)$$
$$= (x+3)(x-1)(x-2)$$

Example 27

$2x + 3$ and $x - 1$ are factors of $2x^4 + ax^3 - 3x^2 + bx + 3$.
Find a and b and all zeros of the polynomial.

Since $2x + 3$ and $x - 1$ are factors,
$$2x^4 + ax^3 - 3x^2 + bx + 3 = (2x+3)(x-1)(\text{a quadratic})$$
$$= (2x^2 + x - 3)(x^2 + cx - 1) \quad \text{for some } c$$

Equating coefficients of x^2 gives: $\quad -3 = -2 + c - 3$
$$\therefore \quad c = 2$$

Equating coefficients of x^3: $a = 2c + 1 = 4 + 1 = 5$

Equating coefficients of x: $b = -1 - 3c$

$\therefore \quad b = -1 - 6 = -7$

$\therefore \quad P(x) = (2x + 3)(x - 1)(x^2 + 2x - 1)$ which has zeros of:

$-\frac{3}{2}, 1$ and $\dfrac{-2 \pm \sqrt{4 - 4(1)(-1)}}{2} = \dfrac{-2 \pm 2\sqrt{2}}{2} = -1 \pm \sqrt{2}$

$\therefore$ the zeros are $-\frac{3}{2}$, 1 and $-1 \pm \sqrt{2}$.

EXERCISE 7D.2

1 Find constants a, b and c given that:

    a $2x^2 + 4x + 5 = ax^2 + [2b - 6]x + c$ for all x

    b $2x^3 - x^2 + 6 = (x - 1)^2(2x + a) + bx + c$ for all x.

2 Find a and b if:

    a $z^4 + 4 = (z^2 + az + 2)(z^2 + bz + 2)$ for all z

    b $2z^4 + 5z^3 + 4z^2 + 7z + 6 = (z^2 + az + 2)(2z^2 + bz + 3)$ for all z

3 Show that $z^4 + 64$ can be factorised into two real quadratic factors of the form $z^2 + az + 8$ and $z^2 + bz + 8$,   but cannot be factorised into two real quadratic factors of the form $z^2 + az + 16$ and $z^2 + bz + 4$.

4 Find real numbers a and b such that $x^4 - 4x^2 + 8x - 4 = (x^2 + ax + 2)(x^2 + bx - 2)$, and hence solve the equation $x^4 + 8x = 4x^2 + 4$.

5 **a** $2z - 3$ is a factor of $2z^3 - z^2 + az - 3$.   Find a and all zeros of the cubic.

    b $3z + 2$ is a factor of $3z^3 - z^2 + [a + 1]z + a$.   Find a and all the zeros of the cubic.

6 **a** Both $2x + 1$ and $x - 2$ are factors of $P(x) = 2x^4 + ax^3 + bx^2 - 12x - 8$. Find a and b and all zeros of $P(x)$.

    b $x + 3$ and $2x - 1$ are factors of $2x^4 + ax^3 + bx^2 + ax + 3$. Find a and b and hence determine all zeros of the quartic.

7 **a** $x^3 + 3x^2 - 9x + c$ has two identical linear factors. Prove that c is either 5 or -27 and factorise the cubic into linear factors in each case.

    b $3x^3 + 4x^2 - x + m$ has two identical linear factors. Find m and find the zeros of the polynomial in all possible cases.

THE REMAINDER THEOREM

Consider the cubic polynomial $P(x) = x^3 + 5x^2 - 11x + 3$.   If we divide $P(x)$ by $x - 2$, we find that:

$$\frac{x^3 + 5x^2 - 11x + 3}{x - 2} = x^2 + 7x + 3 + \frac{9}{x - 2} \longleftarrow \text{remainder}$$

so on division by $x - 2$,   the remainder is 9.

Notice also that $P(2) = 8 + 20 - 22 + 3$
$= 9$,   which is the remainder.

By considering other examples like the one above we formulate the **Remainder theorem**.

THE REMAINDER THEOREM

When a polynomial $P(x)$ is divided by $x - k$ until a constant remainder R is obtained then $R = P(k)$.

Proof: By the division algorithm, $P(x) = Q(x)(x - k) + R$
Now, letting $x = k$, $P(k) = Q(k) \times 0 + R$
$\therefore$ $P(k) = R$

Example 28

Use the Remainder theorem to find the remainder when $x^4 - 3x^3 + x - 4$
is divided by $x + 2$.

If $P(x) = x^4 - 3x^3 + x - 4$,   then

$P(-2) = (-2)^4 - 3(-2)^3 + (-2) - 4$
$= 16 + 24 - 2 - 4$
$= 34$

$\therefore$ when $P(x)$ is divided by $x + 2$, the remainder is 34. {Remainder theorem}

Example 29

When $P(x)$ is divided by $x^2 - 3x + 7$ the quotient is $x^2 + x - 1$ and the remainder $R(x)$ is unknown. However, when $P(x)$ is divided by $x - 2$ the remainder is 29 and when divided by $x + 1$ the remainder is -16. Find $R(x)$ in the form $ax + b$.

As the divisor is $x^2 - 3x + 7$,

$$P(x) = \underbrace{(x^2 + x - 1)}_{Q(x)} \underbrace{(x^2 - 3x + 7)}_{D(x)} + \underbrace{ax + b}_{R(x)}$$

But $P(2) = 29$ and $P(-1) = -16$ {Remainder theorem}
$\therefore$ $(2^2 + 2 - 1)(2^2 - 6 + 7) + 2a + b = 29$
and $((-1)^2 + (-1) - 1)((-1)^2 - 3(-1) + 7) + (-a + b) = -16$

$\therefore$ $(5)(5) + 2a + b = 29$
$(-1)(11) - a + b = -16$

$\therefore$ $2a + b = 4$
$-a + b = -5$

Solving these gives $a = 3$ and $b = -2$, so $R(x) = 3x - 2$.

When using the Remainder theorem, it is important to realise that

- $P(x) = (x+2)Q(x) + 3$
- $P(-2) = 3$
- '$P(x)$ divided by $x + 2$ leaves a remainder of 3'

are all **equivalent statements**.

EXERCISE 7D.3

1   Write two equivalent statements for:

    a If $P(2) = 7$, then ......   **b** If $P(x) = (x+3)Q(x) - 8$, then ......

    c If $P(x)$ divided by $x - 5$ has a remainder of 11 then ......

2   Without performing division, find the remainder when:

    a $x^3 + 2x^2 - 7x + 5$ is divided by $x - 1$

    b $x^4 - 2x^2 + 3x - 1$ is divided by $x + 2$.

3   Find a given that:

    a when $x^3 - 2x + a$ is divided by $x - 2$, the remainder is 7

    b when $2x^3 + x^2 + ax - 5$ is divided by $x + 1$, the remainder is -8.

4   Find a and b given that when $x^3 + 2x^2 + ax + b$ is divided by $x - 1$ the remainder is 4, and when divided by $x + 2$ the remainder is 16.

5   $2x^n + ax^2 - 6$ leaves a remainder of -7 when divided by $x - 1$, and 129 when divided by $x + 3$. Find a and n given that $n \in \mathbb{Z}^+$.

6   When $P(z)$ is divided by $z^2 - 3z + 2$ the remainder is $4z - 7$.
    Find the remainder when $P(z)$ is divided by: **a** $z - 1$ **b** $z - 2$.

7   When $P(z)$ is divided by $z + 1$ the remainder is -8 and when divided by $z - 3$ the remainder is 4. Find the remainder when $P(z)$ is divided by $(z-3)(z+1)$.

8   If $P(x)$ is divided by $(x-a)(x-b)$, prove that the remainder is: $\left(\dfrac{P(b) - P(a)}{b - a}\right) \times (x - a) + P(a)$.

THE FACTOR THEOREM

k is a zero of $P(x)$ $\Leftrightarrow$ $(x - k)$ is a factor of $P(x)$.

Proof: k is a zero of $P(x) \Leftrightarrow P(k) = 0$ {definition of a zero}
                             $\Leftrightarrow R = 0$ {Remainder theorem}
                             $\Leftrightarrow P(x) = Q(x)(x - k)$ {division algorithm}
                             $\Leftrightarrow (x - k)$ is a factor of $P(x)$ {definition of factor}

The **Factor theorem** says that if 2 is a zero of $P(x)$ then $(x - 2)$ is a factor of $P(x)$ and vice versa.

Example 30

Find k given that $x - 2$ is a factor of $x^3 + kx^2 - 3x + 6$.   Hence, fully factorise $x^3 + kx^2 - 3x + 6$.

Let $P(x) = x^3 + kx^2 - 3x + 6$

By the Factor theorem, as $x - 2$ is a factor then $P(2) = 0$

$$\therefore \quad (2)^3 + k(2)^2 - 3(2) + 6 = 0$$
$$\therefore \quad 8 + 4k = 0 \quad \text{and so} \quad k = -2$$

Now $x^3 - 2x^2 - 3x + 6 = (x - 2)(x^2 + ax - 3)$ for some constant a.

Equating coefficients of x^2 gives: $-2 = -2 + a$ i.e., $a = 0$

Equating coefficients of x gives: $-3 = -2a - 3$ i.e., $a = 0$

$$\therefore \quad x^3 - 2x^2 - 3x + 6 = (x - 2)(x^2 - 3)$$
$$= (x - 2)(x + \sqrt{3})(x - \sqrt{3})$$

or   Using synthetic division

2	1	k	-3	6
	0	2	$2k + 4$	$4k + 2$
	1	$k + 2$	$2k + 1$	$4k + 8$

$\therefore \quad P(2) = 4k + 8$ and since $P(2) = 0$, $k = -2$

Now $P(x) = (x - 2)(x^2 + [k + 2]x + [2k + 1])$
$$= (x - 2)(x^2 - 3)$$
$$= (x - 2)(x + \sqrt{3})(x - \sqrt{3})$$

EXERCISE 7D.4

1 Find k and hence factorise the polynomial if:

   a $2x^3 + x^2 + kx - 4$ has a factor of $x + 2$

   b $x^4 - 3x^3 - kx^2 + 6x$ has a factor of $x - 3$.

2 Find a and b given that $2x^3 + ax^2 + bx + 5$ has factors of $x - 1$ and $x + 5$.

3 **a** 3 is a zero of $P(z) = z^3 - z^2 + [k - 5]z + [k^2 - 7]$.
   Find k and hence find all zeros of $P(z)$.

   b Show that $z - 2$ is a factor of $P(z) = z^3 + mz^2 + (3m - 2)z - 10m - 4$ for all values of m. For what values of m is $(z - 2)^2$ a factor of $P(z)$?

4 **a** Consider $P(x) = x^3 - a^3$ where a is real.

   i Find $P(a)$.   What is the significance of this result?

   ii Factorise $x^3 - a^3$ as the product of a real linear and a quadratic factor.

   b Now consider $P(x) = x^3 + a^3$,   where a is real.

   i Find $P(-a)$.   What is the significance of this result?

   ii Factorise $x^3 + a^3$ as the product of a real linear and a quadratic factor.

5 **a** Prove that "$x + 1$ is a factor of $x^n + 1$ $\Leftrightarrow$ n is odd."

   b Find the real number a such that $x - 1 - a$ is a factor of $P(x) = x^3 - 3ax - 9$.

E   GRAPHING POLYNOMIALS

In this section we are obviously only concerned with graphing **real** polynomials. Remember that these are polynomials for which all coefficients are real.

Use of a **graphics calculator** or the **graphing package** provided will help in this section.

INVESTIGATION 2   CUBIC GRAPHS

Every cubic polynomial can be categorised into one of four types:

Type 1: Three real, distinct zeros: $P(x) = a(x - \alpha)(x - \beta)(x - \gamma)$, $a \neq 0$

Type 2: Two real zeros, one repeated: $P(x) = a(x - \alpha)^2(x - \beta)$, $a \neq 0$

Type 3: One real zero repeated three times: $P(x) = a(x - \alpha)^3$, $a \neq 0$

Type 4: One real and two imaginary zeros:
$$P(x) = (x - \alpha)(ax^2 + bx + c), \quad \Delta = b^2 - 4ac < 0, \quad a \neq 0$$

What to do:

1 Experiment with the graphs of *Type 1* cubics. Clearly state the effect of changing both the size and sign of a. What is the geometrical significance of α, β, and γ?

2 Experiment with the graphs of *Type 2* cubics. What is the geometrical significance of the squared factor?

3 Experiment with the graphs of *Type 3* cubics. Do not forget to consider $a > 0$ and $a < 0$. What is the geometrical significance of α?

GRAPHING
PACKAGE

4 Experiment with the graphs of *Type 4* cubics. What is the geometrical significance of α and the quadratic factor which has imaginary zeros?

From **Investigation 2** you should have discovered that:

- If $a > 0$, the graph has shape or . If $a < 0$ it is or .

- All cubics are continuous smooth curves.

- Every cubic polynomial must cut the x-axis at least once, and so has at least one real zero.

- For a cubic of the form $P(x) = a(x - \alpha)(x - \beta)(x - \gamma)$ the graph has three distinct x-intercepts corresponding to the three real, distinct zeros α, β and γ. The graph crosses over or **cuts** the x-axis at these points, as shown opposite.

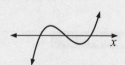

- For a cubic of the form $P(x) = a(x - \alpha)^2(x - \beta)$ the graph **touches** the x-axis at the repeated zero α and **cuts** it at the other x-intercept β, as shown opposite.

- For a cubic of the form $P(x) = a(x - \alpha)^3$, the graph has only one x-intercept, α. The graph is horizontal at this point, and the x-axis is a tangent to the curve, even though the curve crosses over it.

- For a cubic of the form $P(x) = (x - \alpha)(ax^2 + bx + c)$ where $\Delta < 0$, there is only one x-intercept, α. The graph cuts the x-axis at this point. The other two zeros are imaginary and so do not show up on the graph.

Example 31

Find the equation of the cubic with graph:

a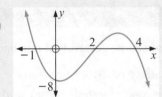

b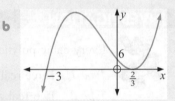

a The x-intercepts are $-1, 2, 4$

$\therefore \quad y = a(x + 1)(x - 2)(x - 4)$

But when $x = 0$, $y = -8$

$\therefore \quad a(1)(-2)(-4) = -8$

$\therefore \quad a = -1$

So, $y = -(x + 1)(x - 2)(x - 4)$

b Touching at $\frac{2}{3}$ indicates a squared factor $(3x - 2)^2$. Other x-intercept is -3, so $y = a(3x - 2)^2(x + 3)$

But when $x = 0$, $y = 6$

So, $a(-2)^2(3) = 6$ and $\therefore \quad a = \frac{1}{2}$

So, $y = \frac{1}{2}(3x - 2)^2(x + 3)$

Note:
- If an x-intercept is not given, use

$P(x) = (x - k)^2 \underbrace{(ax + b)}_{\text{most general form of a linear}}$.

Using $P(x) = a(x - k)^2(x + b)$ is more complicated.

- If there is clearly only one x-intercept and that is given, use

$P(x) = (x - k) \underbrace{(ax^2 + bx + c)}_{\text{most general form of a quadratic}}$.

What can you say about this quadratic?

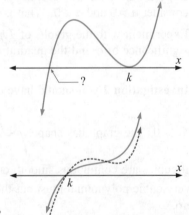

Either graph is possible.

Example 32

Find the equation of the cubic which cuts the x-axis at 2, -3 and -4 and passes through the point $(1, -40)$.

The zeros are 2, -3 and -4, so $y = a(x - 2)(x + 3)(x + 4)$, $a \neq 0$.

But when $x = 1$, $y = -40$ $\therefore \quad a(-1)(4)(5) = -40$

$\therefore \quad -20a = -40$

$\therefore \quad a = 2$

So, the equation is $y = 2(x - 2)(x + 3)(x + 4)$.

EXERCISE 7E.1

1 What is the geometrical significance of:
   a a single factor in $P(x)$, such as $(x - \alpha)$
   b a squared factor in $P(x)$, such as $(x - \alpha)^2$
   c a cubed factor in $P(x)$, such as $(x - \alpha)^3$?

2 Find the equation of the cubic with graph:

a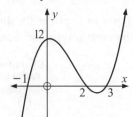
b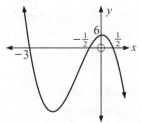
c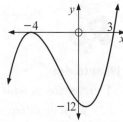
d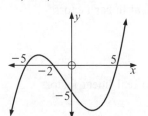
e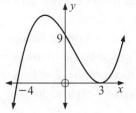
f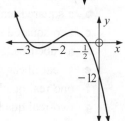

3 Find the equation of the cubic whose graph:
   a cuts the x-axis at 3, 1, -2 and passes through $(2, -4)$
   b cuts the x-axis at -2, 0 and $\frac{1}{2}$ and passes through $(-3, -21)$
   c touches the x-axis at 1, cuts the x-axis at -2 and passes through $(4, 54)$
   d touches the x-axis at $-\frac{2}{3}$, cuts the x-axis at 4 and passes through $(-1, -5)$.

4 Match the given graphs to the corresponding cubic function:
   a $y = 2(x-1)(x+2)(x+4)$ b $y = -(x+1)(x-2)(x-4)$
   c $y = (x-1)(x-2)(x+4)$ d $y = -2(x-1)(x+2)(x+4)$
   e $y = -(x-1)(x+2)(x+4)$ f $y = 2(x-1)(x-2)(x+4)$

A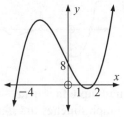
B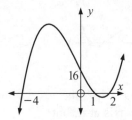
C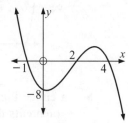
D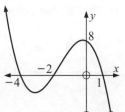
E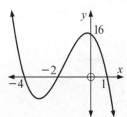
F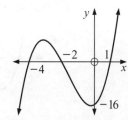

5 Find the equation of a real cubic polynomial which cuts:

    a the x-axis at $\frac{1}{2}$ and -3, cuts the y-axis at 30 and passes through $(1, -20)$

    b the x-axis at 1, touches the x-axis at -2 and cuts the y-axis at $(0, 8)$

    c the x-axis at 2, the y-axis at -4 and passes through $(1, -1)$ and $(-1, -21)$.

INVESTIGATION 3   QUARTIC GRAPHS

There are considerably more possible factor types to consider for quartic functions. We will consider quartics containing certain types of factors.

GRAPHING PACKAGE

What to do:

1 Experiment with quartics which have:

    a four different real linear factors

    b a squared real linear factor and two different real linear factors

    c two squared real linear factors

    d a cubed factor and one real linear factor

    e a real linear factor raised to the fourth power

    f one real quadratic factor with $\Delta < 0$ and two real linear factors

    g two real quadratic factors each with $\Delta < 0$.

From **Investigation 3** you should have discovered that:

- For a quartic polynomial in which a is the coefficient of x^4:

  ▶ If $a > 0$ the graph opens upwards.

  ▶ If $a < 0$ the graph opens downwards.

- If a quartic with $a > 0$ is fully factorised into real linear factors, for:

  ▶ a **single factor** $(x - \alpha)$, the graph **cuts** the x-axis at α

  e.g.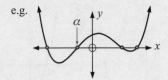

  ▶ a **squared factor** $(x - \alpha)^2$, the graph **touches** the x-axis at α

  e.g.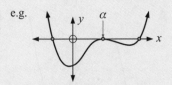

  ▶ a **cubed factor** $(x - \alpha)^3$, the graph **cuts** the x-axis at α, but is 'flat' at α

  e.g.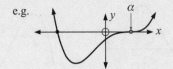

  ▶ a **quadruple factor** $(x - \alpha)^4$, the graph **touches** the x-axis but is 'flat' at that point

  e.g.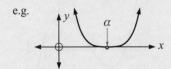

- If a quartic with $a > 0$ has one real quadratic factor with $\Delta < 0$ we could have:

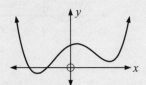

- If a quartic with $a > 0$ has two real quadratic factors both with $\Delta < 0$ we have:

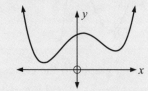

The graph does not meet the x-axis at all.

Example 33

Find the equation of the quartic with graph:

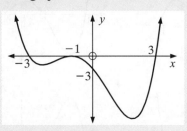

The graph touches the x-axis at -1 and cuts it at -3 and 3, so
$$y = a(x+1)^2(x+3)(x-3)$$
But when $x = 0$, $y = -3$
$$\therefore \quad -3 = a(1)^2(3)(-3)$$
$$\therefore \quad -3 = -9a$$
$$\therefore \quad a = \tfrac{1}{3}$$
$$\therefore \quad y = \tfrac{1}{3}(x+1)^2(x+3)(x-3)$$

Example 34

Find the quartic which touches the x-axis at 2, cuts it at -3, and also passes through $(1, -12)$ and $(3, 6)$.

$(x-2)^2$ is a factor as the graph *touches* the x-axis at 2.

$(x+3)$ is a factor as the graph *cuts* the x-axis at -3.

So $P(x) = (x-2)^2(x+3)(ax+b)$ where a and b are constants.

Now $P(1) = -12$, $\therefore$ $(-1)^2(4)(a+b) = -12$ i.e., $a+b = -3$ ...... (1)

and $P(3) = 6$, $\therefore$ $1^2(6)(3a+b) = 6$ i.e., $3a+b = 1$ ...... (2)

Solving (1) and (2) simultaneously gives $a = 2$, $b = -5$

$\therefore$ $P(x) = (x-2)^2(x+3)(2x-5)$

EXERCISE 7E.2

1 Find the equation of the quartic with graph:

a

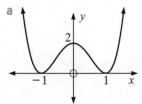

b

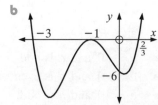

c

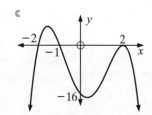

d
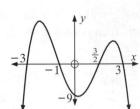

e
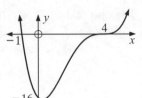

f
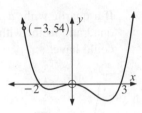

2 Match the given graphs to the corresponding quartic functions:

   a $y = (x - 1)^2(x + 1)(x + 3)$ **b** $y = -2(x - 1)^2(x + 1)(x + 3)$

   c $y = (x - 1)(x + 1)^2(x + 3)$ **d** $y = (x - 1)(x + 1)^2(x - 3)$

   e $y = -\frac{1}{3}(x - 1)(x + 1)(x + 3)^2$ **f** $y = -(x - 1)(x + 1)(x - 3)^2$

A
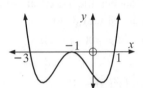

B
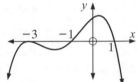

C
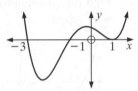

D
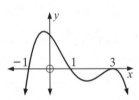

E
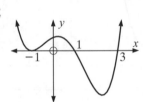

F
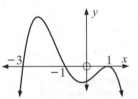

3 Find the equation of the quartic whose graph:

   a   cuts the x-axis at -4 and $\frac{1}{2}$, touches it at 2, and passes through the point $(1, 5)$

   b   touches the x-axis at $\frac{2}{3}$ and -3, and passes through the point $(-4, 49)$

   c   cuts the x-axis at $\pm\frac{1}{2}$ and ± 2, and passes through the point $(1, -18)$

   d   touches the x-axis at 1, cuts the y-axis at -1, and passes through the points $(-1, -4)$ and $(2, 15)$.

DISCUSSION   GENERAL POLYNOMIALS

What happens to $P(x) = a_n x^n + a_{n-1} x^{n-1} + \ldots + a_1 x + a_0,$ $a_n \neq 0$ a polynomial of degree n, $n \in \mathbb{N}$ as $|x| \to \infty$, i.e., as $x \to -\infty$ and as $x \to +\infty$?

Notice that as $|x| \to \infty$, the term $a_n x^n$ dominates the value of $P(x)$ and the values of the other terms become insignificant.

So, if $a_n > 0$ and n is even, $P(x) \to +\infty$, as $x \to +\infty$

                            and $P(x) \to +\infty$, as $x \to -\infty$.

Discuss the cases where: • $a_n > 0$ and n is odd

                           • $a_n < 0$ and n is even

                           • $a_n < 0$ and n is odd.

We have already seen that every real cubic polynomial must cut the x-axis at least once, and so has at least one real zero.

If the exact value of the zero is difficult to find, we can use technology to help us. We can then factorise the cubic as a linear factor times a quadratic, and if necessary use the quadratic formula to find the other zeros.

This method is particularly useful if we have one rational zero and two irrational zeros that are radical conjugates.

Example 35

Find all zeros of $P(x) = 3x^3 - 14x^2 + 5x + 2$.

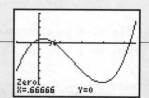

Using the calculator we search for any rational zero.
In this case $x \approx 0.666\,667$ or $0.\overline{6}$ indicates
$x = \frac{2}{3}$ is a zero and $\therefore$ $(3x - 2)$ is a factor

So, $3x^3 - 14x^2 + 5x + 2 = (3x - 2)(x^2 + ax - 1)$
$$= 3x^3 + [3a - 2]x^2 + [-3 - 2a]x + 2$$

Equating coefficients: $3a - 2 = -14$ and $-3 - 2a = 5$
$$\therefore \quad 3a = -12 \quad \text{and} \quad -2a = 8$$
$$\therefore \quad a = -4$$
$$\therefore \quad P(x) = (3x - 2)(x^2 - 4x - 1)$$
which has zeros $\frac{2}{3}$ and $2 \pm \sqrt{5}$ {quadratic formula}

TI
C
**GRAPHING
PACKAGE**

Example 36

Find all roots of $6x^3 + 13x^2 + 20x + 3 = 0$

$x \approx -0.166\,666\,67 = \frac{1}{6}$ is a zero, so $(6x + 1)$ is a factor.
$\therefore$ $(6x + 1)(x^2 + ax + 3) = 0$ for some constant a.
Equating coefficients of x^2: $1 + 6a = 13$ $\therefore$ $6a = 12$ $\therefore$ $a = 2$
Equating coefficients of x: $a + 18 = 20$ $\checkmark$
$\therefore$ $(6x + 1)(x^2 + 2x + 3) = 0$ and $x = -\frac{1}{6}$ or $-1 \pm i\sqrt{2}$ {quadratic formula}

For a quartic polynomial $P(x)$ we first need to establish if there are any x-intercepts at all. If there are not then the polynomial must have four complex zeros. If there *are* x-intercepts then we can try to identify linear or quadratic factors.

EXERCISE 7E.3

1 Find all zeros of:

    a $x^3 - 3x^2 - 3x + 1$

    b $x^3 - 3x^2 + 4x - 2$

    c $2x^3 - 3x^2 - 4x - 35$

    d $2x^3 - x^2 + 20x - 10$

    e $4x^4 - 4x^3 - 25x^2 + x + 6$

    f $x^4 - 6x^3 + 22x^2 - 48x + 40$

2 Find the roots of:

    a $x^3 + 2x^2 + 3x + 6 = 0$ **b** $2x^3 + 3x^2 - 3x - 2 = 0$

    c $x^3 - 6x^2 + 12x - 8 = 0$ **d** $2x^3 + 18 = 5x^2 + 9x$

    e $x^4 - x^3 - 9x^2 + 11x + 6 = 0$ **f** $2x^4 - 13x^3 + 27x^2 = 13x + 15$

3 Factorise into linear factors:

    a $x^3 - 3x^2 + 4x - 2$ **b** $x^3 + 3x^2 + 4x + 12$

    c $2x^3 - 9x^2 + 6x - 1$ **d** $x^3 - 4x^2 + 9x - 10$

    e $4x^3 - 8x^2 + x + 3$ **f** $3x^4 + 4x^3 + 5x^2 + 12x - 12$

    g $2x^4 - 3x^3 + 5x^2 + 6x - 4$ **h** $2x^3 + 5x^2 + 8x + 20$

4 The following cubics will not factorise. Find their zeros using technology.

    a $x^3 + 2x^2 - 6x - 6$ **b** $x^3 + x^2 - 7x - 8$

F | THEOREMS FOR REAL POLYNOMIALS

The following theorems are formal statements of discoveries we have made:

- **Unique Factorisation theorem**
  Every **real** polynomial of degree n can be factorised into n complex linear factors, some of which may be repeated.

- **Factor theorem**
  k is a zero of $P(x)$ $\Leftrightarrow$ $(x - k)$ is a factor of $P(x)$.

- Every real polynomial can be expressed as a product of **real** linear and **real** irreducible quadratic factors (where $\Delta < 0$).

- If $p + qi$ $(q \neq 0)$ is a zero of a **real** polynomial then its complex conjugate $p - qi$ is also a zero.

- Every **real** polynomial of odd degree has at least one real zero.

- All **real** polynomials of degree n have n zeros, some of which may be repeated. These zeros are real and/or complex zeros that occur in conjugate pairs.

Example 37

If $-3 + i$ is a zero of $P(x) = ax^3 + 9x^2 + ax - 30$ where a is real, find a and hence find all zeros of the cubic.

As $P(x)$ is real, both $-3 + i$ and $-3 - i$ are zeros.

These have sum of -6 and product of $(-3 + i)(-3 - i) = 10$,

so the zeros $-3 \pm i$ come from the quadratic $x^2 + 6x + 10$.

Consequently, $ax^3 + 9x^2 + ax - 30 = (x^2 + 6x + 10)(ax - 3)$.

                                                 ax^3 -30

To find a we equate coefficients of x^2 and x

$\therefore$ $9 = 6a - 3$ and $a = 10a - 18$ and $a = 2$ in both cases

$\therefore$ $a = 2$ and the other two zeros are $-3 - i$ and $\frac{3}{2}$.

         the linear factor is $(ax - 3)$ i.e., $(2x - 3)$

Example 38

One zero of $ax^3 + [a+1]x^2 + 10x + 15,   a \in \mathbb{R}$, is purely imaginary.
Find a and the zeros of the polynomial.

Let the purely imaginary zero be bi, $b \neq 0$.

$P(x)$ is real since its coefficients are all real, and so $-bi$ is also a zero.

For bi and $-bi$, their sum $= 0$ and their product $= -b^2 i^2 = b^2$

$\therefore$ these two zeros come from $x^2 + b^2$.

So, $ax^3 + [a+1]x^2 + 10x + 15 = (x^2 + b^2)\left(ax + \dfrac{15}{b^2}\right)$

$$= ax^3 + \left[\dfrac{15}{b^2}\right]x^2 + b^2 ax + 15$$

Consequently $a + 1 = \dfrac{15}{b^2}$ ...... (1)   and $b^2 a = 10$ ...... (2)

$\therefore$ $b^2 a + b^2 = 15$ {using (1)}

$\therefore$ $10 + b^2 = 15$ {using (2)}

$\therefore$ $b^2 = 5$ and so $b = \pm\sqrt{5}$

In (2), as $b^2 = 5$, $5a = 10$ $\therefore$ $a = 2$.

The linear factor is $ax + \dfrac{15}{b^2}$ or $2x + 3$

$\therefore$ $a = 2$ and the zeros are $\pm i\sqrt{5}$, $-\frac{3}{2}$.

EXERCISE 7F

1 Find all third degree real polynomials with zeros of $-\frac{1}{2}$ and $1 - 3i$.

2 $p(x)$ is a real cubic polynomial in which $p(1) = p(2 + i) = 0$ and $p(0) = -20$.
  Find $p(x)$ in expanded form.

3 $2 - 3i$ is a zero of $P(z) = z^3 + pz + q$ where p and q are real. Using conjugate
  pairs, find p and q and the other two zeros. Check your answer by solving for p and q
  using $P(2 - 3i) = 0$.

4 $3 + i$ is a root of $z^4 - 2z^3 + az^2 + bz + 10 = 0$, where a and b are real. Find a and
  b and the other roots of the equation.

5 One zero of $P(z) = z^3 + az^2 + 3z + 9$ is purely imaginary. If a is real, find a and
  hence factorise $P(z)$ into linear factors.

6 At least one zero of $P(x) = 3x^3 + kx^2 + 15x + 10$ is purely imaginary. Given that
  k is real, find k and hence resolve $P(x)$ into a product of linear factors.

7 A scientist working for Crash Test Barriers, Inc. is trying to design a crash test barrier
  whose ideal characteristics are shown graphically below. The independent variable t
  is the time after impact, measured in milliseconds, such that $0 \leqslant t \leqslant 700$. The

dependent variable is the distance that the barrier has been depressed because of the impact, measured in millimetres.

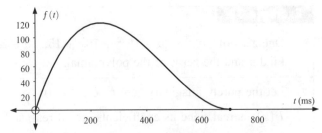

a The equation for this graph is of the form $f(t) = kt(t - a)^2$, $0 \leqslant t \leqslant 700$. From the graph, what is the value of a? What does it represent?

b If the ideal crash barrier is depressed by 85 mm after 100 milliseconds, find the value of k, and hence find the equation of the graph given.

c What is the maximum amount of depression, and when does it occur?

8 In the last year (starting 1st January), the volume of water (in megalitres) in a particular dam after t months could be described by the model $V(t) = -t^3 + 30t^2 - 131t + 250$.

The dam authority rules that if the volume falls below 100 ML, irrigation is prohibited. During which months, if any, was irrigation prohibited in the last twelve months? Include in your answer a neat sketch of any graphs you may have used.

9 A ladder of length 10 metres is leaning up against a wall so that it is just touching a cube shaped box of edge length one metre, that is resting on the ground against the wall. What height up the wall does the ladder reach?

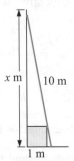

REVIEW SET 7A

1 Find real numbers a and b such that:

    a $a + ib = 4$ **b** $(1 - 2i)(a + bi) = -5 - 10i$ **c** $(a + 2i)(1 + bi) = 17 - 19i$

2 If $z = 3 + i$ and $w = -2 - i$, find in simplest form:

    a $2z - 3w$ **b** $\dfrac{z^*}{w}$ **c** z^3

3 Find the *exact* values of the real and imaginary parts of z if $z = \dfrac{3}{i + \sqrt{3}} + \sqrt{3}$

4 Find a complex number z such that $2z - 1 = iz - i$. Write your answer in the form $z = a + bi$ where $a, b \in \mathbb{R}$.

5 Prove that $zw^* - z^*w$ is purely imaginary or zero for all complex numbers z and w.

6 Given $w = \dfrac{z + 1}{z^* + 1}$ where $z = a + bi$, $a, b \in \mathbb{R}$, write w in the form $x + yi$ where $x, y \in \mathbb{R}$ and hence determine the conditions under which w is purely imaginary.

7 Expand and simplify: **a** $(3x^3 + 2x - 5)(4x - 3)$ **b** $(2x^2 - x + 3)^2$

8 Carry out the following divisions: **a** $\dfrac{x^3}{x + 2}$ **b** $\dfrac{x^3}{(x + 2)(x + 3)}$

9 State and prove the Remainder theorem.

10 $-2 + bi$ is a solution to $z^2 + az + [3 + a] = 0$. Find a and b given that they are real.

11 Find all zeros of $2z^4 - 5z^3 + 13z^2 - 4z - 6$.

12 Factorise $z^4 + 2z^3 - 2z^2 + 8$ into linear factors.

13 Find a quartic polynomial with rational coefficients having $2 - i\sqrt{3}$ and $\sqrt{2} + 1$ as two of its zeros.

14 If $f(x) = x^3 - 3x^2 - 9x + b$ has $(x - k)^2$ as a factor, show that there are two possible values of k. For each of these two values of k, find the corresponding value for b and hence solve $f(x) = 0$.

15 Find k if the line with equation $y = 2x + k$ does not meet the circle with equation $x^2 + y^2 + 8x - 4y + 2 = 0$.

16 When $P(x) = x^n + 3x^2 + kx + 6$ is divided by $x + 1$ the remainder is 12. When $P(x)$ is divided by $x - 1$ the remainder is 8. Find k and n given that $34 < n < 38$.

17 If α and β are two of the roots of $x^3 - x + 1 = 0$, show that $\alpha\beta$ is a root of $x^3 + x^2 - 1 = 0$. **Hint:** Let $x^3 - x + 1 = (x - \alpha)(x - \beta)(x - \gamma)$.

REVIEW SET 7B

1 Find $x, y \in \mathbb{Z}$ such that $z = x + yi$ satisfies the equation $\sqrt[3]{z} = \dfrac{5}{2 - i} - 3 - 2i$.

2 Without using a calculator, find $\sqrt{5 - 12i}$. Check your answer using a calculator.

3 Prove that if z is a complex number then both $z + z^*$ and zz^* are real.

4 If $z = 4 + i$ and $w = 3 - 2i$ find $2w^* - iz$.

5 Find rationals a and b such that $\dfrac{2 - 3i}{2a + bi} = 3 + 2i$.

6 $a + ai$ is a root of $x^2 - 6x + b = 0$ where $a, b \in \mathbb{R}$.
Explain why b has two possible values. Find a in each case.

7 Find the remainder when $x^{47} - 3x^{26} + 5x^3 + 11$ is divided by $x + 1$.

8 A quartic polynomial $P(x)$ has graph $y = P(x)$ which touches the x-axis at $(-2, 0)$, cuts it at $(1, 0)$, cuts the y-axis at $(0, 12)$, and passes through $(2, 80)$.

Find an expression for $P(x)$ in factored form and hence sketch the graph of $y = P(x)$.

9 If $P(x)$ has remainder 2 when divided by $x - 3$ and remainder -13 when divided by $x + 2$, find the remainder when $P(x)$ is divided by $x^2 - x - 6$.

10 Find *all* polynomials of *least* degree with rational coefficients that have $3 - i\sqrt{2}$ and $1 - \sqrt{2}$ as two zeros.

11 Factorise $2z^3 + z^2 + 10z + 5$ as a product of linear factors.

12 Find the general form of all polynomials of least degree which are real and have zeros of $2 + i$ and $-1 + 3i$.

13 $3 - 2i$ is a zero of $z^4 + kz^3 + 32z + 3k - 1$, where k is real.
Find k and all zeros of the quartic.

14 Find all the zeros of the polynomial $z^4 + 2z^3 + 6z^2 + 8z + 8$ given that one of the zeros is purely imaginary.

15 When a polynomial $P(x)$ is divided by $x^2 - 3x + 2$ the remainder is $2x + 3$.
Find the remainder when $P(x)$ is divided by $x - 2$.

REVIEW SET 7C

1 Find real numbers x and y such that $(3x + 2yi)(1 - i) = (3y + 1)i - x$.

2 Solve the equation: $z^2 + iz + 10 = 6z$

3 Prove that $zw^* + z^*w$ is real for all complex numbers z and w.

4 Find real x and y such that:

    a $x + iy = 0$ **b** $(3 - 2i)(x + i) = 17 + yi$ **c** $(x + iy)^2 = x - iy$

5 z and w are non-real complex numbers with the property that both $z + w$ and zw are real. Prove that $z^* = w$.

6 Find z if $\sqrt{z} = \dfrac{2}{3 - 2i} + 2 + 5i$

7 Find the remainder when $2x^{17} + 5x^{10} - 7x^3 + 6$ is divided by $x - 2$.

8 $5 - i$ is a zero of $2z^3 + az^2 + 62z + [a - 5]$, where a is real. Find a and the other two zeros.

9 Find, in general form, all polynomials of least degree which are real, and have zeros of:

    a $i\sqrt{2}$ and $\frac{1}{2}$ **b** $1 - i$ and $-3 - i$.

10 $P(x) = 2x^3 + 7x^2 + kx - k$ is the product of 3 linear factors, 2 of which are identical. Show that k can take 3 distinct values and resolve $P(x)$ into linear factors when k takes the largest of these 3 values.

11 Find all roots of $2z^4 - 3z^3 + 2z^2 = 6z + 4$.

12 Suppose k is real. For what values of k does $z^3 + az^2 + kz + ka = 0$ have:

    a one real root   **b** 3 real roots?

13 $3x + 2$ and $x - 2$ are factors of $6x^3 + ax^2 - 4ax + b$. Find a and b.

14 Find the exact values of k for which the line $y = x - k$ is a tangent to the circle with equation $(x - 2)^2 + (y + 3)^2 = 4$.

15 Find the quotient and remainder when $x^4 + 3x^3 - 7x^2 + 11x - 1$ is divided by $x^2 + 2$. Hence, find a and b for which $x^4 + 3x^3 - 7x^2 + (2 + a)x + b$ is exactly divisible by $x^2 + 2$.

Chapter 8

Counting and the binomial expansion

Contents:

OPENING PROBLEM

At an IB Mathematics Teachers' Conference there are 273 delegates present. The organising committee consists of 10 people.

- If each committee member shakes hands with every other committee member, how many handshakes take place?

    Can a 10-sided convex polygon be used to solve this problem?

- If all 273 delegates shake hands with all other delegates, how many handshakes take place now?

The **Opening Problem** is an example of a **counting** problem.

The following exercises will help us to solve counting problems without having to list and count the possibilities one by one. To do this we will examine:

- the product principle   •   counting permutations   •   counting combinations

A ▌ THE PRODUCT PRINCIPLE

Suppose that there are three towns A, B and C and that 4 different roads could be taken from A to B and two different roads from B to C.

We can show this in a diagram:

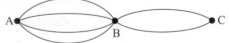

How many different pathways are there from A to C going through B?

If we take road 1, there are two alternative roads to complete our trip.

If we take road 2, there are two alternative roads to complete our trip, ... and so on.

So, there are $2 + 2 + 2 + 2 = 4 \times 2$ different pathways.

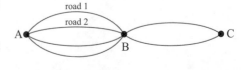

Notice that the 4 corresponds to the number of roads from A to B and the 2 corresponds to the number of roads from B to C.

Similarly, for:

there would be $4 \times 2 \times 3 = 24$ different pathways from A to D passing through B and C.

THE PRODUCT PRINCIPLE

If there are m different ways of performing an operation and for each of these there are n different ways of performing a second **independent** operation, then there are mn different ways of performing the two operations in succession.

The product principle can be extended to three or more successive operations.

Example 1

It is possible to take five different paths from Pauline's to Quinton's, 4 different paths from Quinton's to Reiko's and 3 different paths from Reiko's to Sam's. How many different pathways could be taken from Pauline's to Sam's via Quinton's and Reiko's?

The total number of different pathways $= 5 \times 4 \times 3 = 60$.   {product principle}

EXERCISE 8A

1 The illustration shows the possible map routes for a bus service which goes from P to S through both Q and R.

How many different routes are possible?

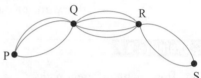

2

It is decided to label the vertices of a rectangle with the letters A, B, C and D.

In how many ways is this possible if:

   a they are to be in clockwise alphabetical order

   b they are to be in alphabetical order

   c they are to be in random order?

3 The figure alongside is box-shaped and made of wire.

An ant crawls along the wire from A to B.

How many different paths of shortest length lead from A to B?

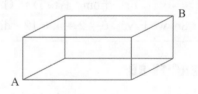

4 In how many different ways can the top two positions be filled in a table tennis competition of 7 teams?

5 A football competition is organised between 8 teams. In how many ways is it possible to fill the top 4 places in order of premiership points obtained?

6 How many 3-digit numbers can be formed using the digits 2, 3, 4, 5 and 6:

   a as often as desired   **b** once only?

7 How many different alpha-numeric plates for motor car registration can be made if the first 3 places are English alphabet letters and those remaining are 3 digits from 0 to 9?

8 In how many ways can:

   a 2 letters be mailed into 2 mail boxes   **b** 2 letters be mailed into 3 mail boxes

   c 4 letters be mailed into 3 mail boxes?

B   COUNTING PATHS

Consider the following road system leading from
P to Q:

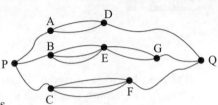

From A to Q there are 2 paths.
From B to Q there are $3 \times 2 = 6$ paths.
From C to Q there are 3 paths.

Thus, from P to Q there are $2 + 6 + 3 = 11$ paths.

Notice that: ▶ when going from B to G, we go from B to E **and** then from E to G, and we **multiply** the possibilities,

▶ when going from P to Q, we must first go from P to A, **or** P to B or P to C, and we **add** the possibilities.

Consequently:
- the word **and** suggests multiplying the possibilities
- the word **or** suggests adding the possibilities.

Example 2

How many different paths
lead from P to Q?

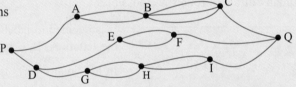

Going   from P to A to B to C to Q   there are $2 \times 3 = 6$ paths
or from P to D to E to F to Q   there are 2 paths
or from P to D to G to H to I to Q there are $2 \times 2 = 4$ paths.

So, we have $6 + 2 + 4 = 12$ different paths.

EXERCISE 8B

1   How many different paths lead from P to Q?

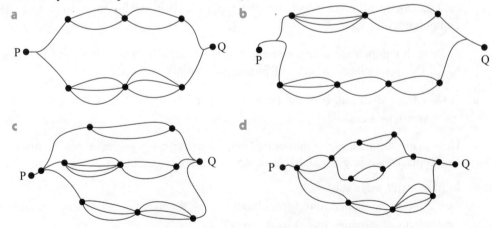

C   FACTORIAL NOTATION

In problems involving counting, products of consecutive positive integers are common.

For example, $8 \times 7 \times 6$ or $6 \times 5 \times 4 \times 3 \times 2 \times 1$.

FACTORIAL NOTATION

For convenience, we introduce **factorial numbers** to represent the products of consecutive positive integers.

For example, the product $6 \times 5 \times 4 \times 3 \times 2 \times 1$ can be written as $6!$.

In general,   for $n \geqslant 1$, $n!$ is the product of the first n positive integers.

$$n! = n(n-1)(n-2)(n-3).... \times 3 \times 2 \times 1$$

$n!$ is read   "n factorial".

Notice that $8 \times 7 \times 6$ can be written using factorial numbers only as

$$8 \times 7 \times 6 = \frac{8 \times 7 \times 6 \times 5 \times 4 \times 3 \times 2 \times 1}{5 \times 4 \times 3 \times 2 \times 1} = \frac{8!}{5!}$$

PROPERTIES OF FACTORIAL NUMBERS

The **factorial rule** is $n! = n \times (n-1)!$ for $n \geqslant 1$

which can be extended to $n! = n(n-1)(n-2)!$ and so on.

Using the factorial rule with $n = 1$,   we have $1! = 1 \times 0!$

We hence define $0! = 1$

Example 3

What integer is equal to: **a** $4!$ **b** $\dfrac{5!}{3!}$ **c** $\dfrac{7!}{4! \times 3!}$?

a $4! = 4 \times 3 \times 2 \times 1 = 24$ **b** $\dfrac{5!}{3!} = \dfrac{5 \times 4 \times 3 \times 2 \times 1}{3 \times 2 \times 1} = 5 \times 4 = 20$

c $\dfrac{7!}{4! \times 3!} = \dfrac{7 \times 6 \times 5 \times 4 \times 3 \times 2 \times 1}{4 \times 3 \times 2 \times 1 \times 3 \times 2 \times 1} = 35$

Example 4

Express in factorial form: **a** $10 \times 9 \times 8 \times 7$ **b** $\dfrac{10 \times 9 \times 8 \times 7}{4 \times 3 \times 2 \times 1}$

a $10 \times 9 \times 8 \times 7 = \dfrac{10 \times 9 \times 8 \times 7 \times 6 \times 5 \times 4 \times 3 \times 2 \times 1}{6 \times 5 \times 4 \times 3 \times 2 \times 1} = \dfrac{10!}{6!}$

b $\dfrac{10 \times 9 \times 8 \times 7}{4 \times 3 \times 2 \times 1} = \dfrac{10 \times 9 \times 8 \times 7 \times 6 \times 5 \times 4 \times 3 \times 2 \times 1}{4 \times 3 \times 2 \times 1 \times 6 \times 5 \times 4 \times 3 \times 2 \times 1} = \dfrac{10!}{4! \times 6!}$

Example 5

Write the following sums and differences as a product by factorising:

    a $8! + 6!$ **b** $10! - 9! + 8!$

a $8! + 6!$	**b** $10! - 9! + 8!$
$= 8 \times 7 \times 6! \ + \ 6!$	$= 10 \times 9 \times 8! \ - \ 9 \times 8! \ + \ 8!$
$= 6!(8 \times 7 + 1)$	$= 8!(90 - 9 + 1)$
$= 6! \times 57$	$= 8! \times 82$

Example 6

Simplify $\dfrac{7! - 6!}{6}$ using factorisation.

$$\dfrac{7! - 6!}{6}$$

$$= \dfrac{7 \times 6! - 6!}{6}$$

$$= \dfrac{6!(7 - 1)^{\,1}}{\cancel{6}_{\,1}}$$

$$= 6!$$

EXERCISE 8C

1 Find $n!$ for $n = 0, 1, 2, 3, ..., 10$.

2 Simplify without using a calculator:

    a $\dfrac{6!}{5!}$ **b** $\dfrac{6!}{4!}$ **c** $\dfrac{6!}{7!}$ **d** $\dfrac{4!}{6!}$ **e** $\dfrac{100!}{99!}$ **f** $\dfrac{7!}{5! \times 2!}$

3 Simplify: **a** $\dfrac{n!}{(n-1)!}$ **b** $\dfrac{(n+2)!}{n!}$ **c** $\dfrac{(n+1)!}{(n-1)!}$

4 Express in factorial form:

    a $7 \times 6 \times 5$ **b** 10×9 **c** $11 \times 10 \times 9 \times 8 \times 7$

    d $\dfrac{13 \times 12 \times 11}{3 \times 2 \times 1}$ **e** $\dfrac{1}{6 \times 5 \times 4}$ **f** $\dfrac{4 \times 3 \times 2 \times 1}{20 \times 19 \times 18 \times 17}$

5 Write as a product using factorisation:

    a $5! + 4!$ **b** $11! - 10!$ **c** $6! + 8!$ **d** $12! - 10!$

    e $9! + 8! + 7!$ **f** $7! - 6! + 8!$ **g** $12! - 2 \times 11!$ **h** $3 \times 9! + 5 \times 8!$

6 Simplify using factorisation:

    a $\dfrac{12! - 11!}{11}$ **b** $\dfrac{10! + 9!}{11}$ **c** $\dfrac{10! - 8!}{89}$ **d** $\dfrac{10! - 9!}{9!}$

    e $\dfrac{6! + 5! - 4!}{4!}$ **f** $\dfrac{n! + (n-1)!}{(n-1)!}$ **g** $\dfrac{n! - (n-1)!}{n-1}$ **h** $\dfrac{(n+2)! + (n+1)!}{n+3}$

D PERMUTATIONS

A **permutation** of a group of symbols is *any arrangement* of those symbols in a definite *order*.

For example, BAC is a permutation on the symbols A, B and C in which all three of them are used. We say the symbols are "taken 3 at a time".

Notice that   ABC, ACB, BAC, BCA, CAB, CBA   are all the different permutations on the symbols A, B and C taken 3 at a time.

In this exercise we are concerned with the listing of all permutations, and then learning to count how many permutations there are without having to list them all.

Example 7

List all the permutations on the symbols P, Q and R when they are taken:
a   1 at a time   b   2 at a time   c   3 at a time.

a   P, Q, R   b   PQ   QP   RP   c   PQR   QPR   RPQ
                        PR   QR   RQ   PRQ   QRP   RQP

Example 8

List all permutations on the symbols W, X, Y and Z taken 4 at a time.

WXYZ   WXZY   WYXZ   WYZX   WZXY   WZYX
XWYZ   XWZY   XYWZ   XYZW   XZYW   XZWY
YWXZ   YWZX   YXWZ   YXZW   YZWX   YZXW
ZWXY   ZWYX   ZXWY   ZXYW   ZYWX   ZYXW   i.e.,   24 of them.

For large numbers of symbols listing the complete set of permutations is absurd. However, we can still count them in the following way.

In **Example 8** there were 4 positions to fill:

In the 1st position, any of the 4 symbols could be used.

This leaves any of 3 symbols to go in the 2nd position,
which leaves any of 2 symbols to go in the 3rd position.

The remaining symbol must go in the 4th position.

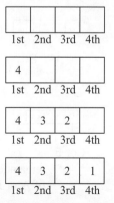

So, the   total number of permutations $= 4 \times 3 \times 2 \times 1$ {product principle}
$= 24$

Example 9

If a chess association has 16 teams, in how many different ways could the top 8 positions be filled on the competition ladder?

Any of the 16 teams could fill the 'top' position.
Any of the remaining 15 teams could fill the 2nd position.
Any of the remaining 14 teams could fill the 3rd position.
$\vdots$
Any of the remaining 9 teams could fill the 8th position.

i.e.,

16	15	14	13	12	11	10	9
1st	2nd	3rd	4th	5th	6th	7th	8th

$\therefore$ total number $= 16 \times 15 \times 14 \times 13 \times 12 \times 11 \times 10 \times 9$
$= 518\,918\,400$

Example 10

Suppose you have the alphabet blocks A, B, C, D and E and they are placed in a row. For example you could have: $\boxed{\text{D}\,\text{A}\,\text{E}\,\text{C}\,\text{B}}$

a How many different permutations could you have?
b How many permutations end in C?
c How many permutations have the form $\boxed{...\,\text{A}\,...\,\text{B}\,...}$?
d How many begin and end with a vowel, i.e., A or E?

a There are 5 letters taken 5 at a time.
   $\therefore$ total number $= 5 \times 4 \times 3 \times 2 \times 1 = 120$.

b $\boxed{4\,3\,2\,1\,1}$

   any others here

   C here

C must be in the last position (1 way) and the other 4 letters could go into the remaining 4 places in 4! ways.

   $\therefore$ total number $= 1 \times 4! = 24$ ways.

c $\boxed{3\,1\,2\,1\,1}$

   A   B

A goes into 1 place, B goes into 1 place and the remaining 3 letters go into the remaining 3 places in 3! ways.

   $\therefore$ total number $= 1 \times 1 \times 3! = 6$ ways.

d $\boxed{2\,3\,2\,1\,1}$

   A or E

   remainder of A or E

A or E could go into the 1st position, and after that one is placed, the other one goes into the last position.

The remaining 3 letters could be arranged in 3! ways in the 3 remaining positions.

   $\therefore$ total number $= 2 \times 1 \times 3! = 12$.

Example 11

There are 6 different books arranged in a row on a shelf. In how many ways can two of the books, A and B be together?

Method 1:   We could have any of the following locations for A and B

```
A  B  ×  ×  ×  ×
B  A  ×  ×  ×  ×
×  A  B  ×  ×  ×
×  B  A  ×  ×  ×
×  ×  A  B  ×  ×
×  ×  B  A  ×  ×
×  ×  ×  A  B  ×
×  ×  ×  B  A  ×
×  ×  ×  ×  A  B
×  ×  ×  ×  B  A
```
} 10 of these

If we consider any one of these, the remaining 4 books could be placed in 4! different orderings

$\therefore$ total number of ways
$= 10 \times 4! = 240$.

Method 2:

A and B can be put together in 2! ways   (i.e., AB or BA).
Now consider this pairing as one book (effectively tying a string around them) which together with the other 4 books can be ordered in 5! different ways.

$$\therefore \quad \text{total number} = 2! \times 5! = 240.$$

EXERCISE 8D

1   List the set of all permutations on the symbols W, X, Y and Z taken:
   a   1 at a time   b   two at a time   c   three at a time.
   Note: Example 8 has them taken 4 at a time.

2   List the set of all permutations on the symbols A, B, C, D and E taken:
   a   2 at a time   b   3 at a time.

3   In how many ways can:
   a   5 different books be arranged on a shelf
   b   3 different paintings, from a collection of 8, be chosen and hung in a row
   c   a signal consisting of 4 coloured flags be made if there are 10 different flags to choose from?

4   Suppose you have 4 different coloured flags. How many different signals could you make using:
   a   2 flags only   b   3 flags only   c   2 or 3 flags?

5   How many different permutations of the letters A, B, C, D, E and F are there if each letter can be used once only? How many of these:
   a   end in ED   b   begin with F and end with A
   c   begin and end with a vowel   (i.e., A or E)?

6   How many 3-digit numbers can be constructed from the digits 1, 2, 3, 4, 5, 6 and 7 if each digit may be used:
   a   as often as desired   b   only once   c   once only and the number is odd?

7 In how many ways can 3 boys and 3 girls be arranged in a row of 6 seats? In how many of these ways do the boys and girls alternate?

8 3-digit numbers are constructed from the digits 0, 1, 2, 3, 4, 5, 6, 7, 8 and 9 using each digit at most once. How many such numbers:

    a   can be constructed   **b**   end in 5   **c**   end in 0   **d**   are divisible by 5?

9 In how many ways can 5 different books be arranged on a shelf if:

    a   there are no restrictions   **b**   books X and Y must be together

    c   books X and Y are never together?

10 A group of 10 students sit randomly in a row of 10 chairs. In how many ways can this be done if:

    a   there are no restrictions   **b**   3 students A, B and C are always seated together?

11 How many three-digit numbers, in which no two digits are the same, can be made using the digits 0, 1, 3, 5, 8 if:

    a   there are no restrictions

    b   the numbers must be less than 500

    c   the numbers must be even and greater than 300?

12 How many different arrangements of four letters chosen from the letters of the word MONDAY are possible if:

    a   there are no restrictions

    b   at least one vowel (A or O) must be used

    c   no two vowels are adjacent?

13 Nine boxes are each labelled with a different whole number from 1 to 9. Five people are allowed to take one box each. In how many different ways can this be done if:

    a   there are no restrictions

    b   the first three people decide that they will take even numbered boxes?

14 Alice has booked ten adjacent front-row seats for a basketball game for herself and nine friends. Altogether, there are five boys and five girls.

    a   Assuming they all arrive, how many different arrangements are there if:

        i   there are no restrictions

        ii   boys and girls are to sit alternately?

    b   Due to a severe snowstorm, only five of Alice's friends are able to join her for the game. How many different ways are there of seating in the 10 seats if:

        i   there are no restrictions

        ii   any two of Alice's friends are to sit next to her?

15 At a restaurant, a rectangular table seats eight people, four on each of the longer sides. Eight diners sit at the table. How many different seating arrangements are there if:

    a   there are no restrictions

    b   two particular people wish to sit directly opposite each other

    c   two particular people wish to sit on the same side of the table, next to each other?

INVESTIGATION 1   PERMUTATIONS IN A CIRCLE

There are 6 permutations on the symbols A, B and C **in a line**.

These are: ABC   ACB   BAC   BCA   CAB   CBA.

However **in a circle** there are only 2 different permutations on these 3 symbols. These are:

A⟲B C   and   A⟲C B   as they are the only possibilities with different right-hand and left-hand neighbours.

Notice that

A⟲B C   C⟲A B   B⟲C A   are the same cyclic permutations.

What to do:

1 Draw diagrams showing different cyclic permutations for:
   a one symbol: A   **b** two symbols: A and B
   c three symbols: A, B and C   **d** four symbols: A, B, C and D

2 Copy and complete:

Number of symbols	Permutations in a line	Permutations in a circle
1		
2		
3	$6 = 3!$	$2 = 2!$
4		

3 If there are n symbols to be permuted in a circle, how many different orderings are possible?

E   COMBINATIONS

A **combination** is a selection of objects *without* regard to order or arrangement.

For example, the possible teams of 3 people selected from A, B, C, D and E are

    ABC   ABD   ABE   ACD   ACE   ADE
    BCD   BCE   BDE
    CDE   i.e.,   10 different combinations.

C_r^n is the number of combinations on n distinct or different symbols taken r at a time.

$$C_r^n \longleftarrow \text{the number up for selection}$$
$$ \longleftarrow \text{the number of positions needed to be filled.}$$

C_r^n may also be written as $_nC_r$ or as the **binomial coefficient** $\binom{n}{r}$.

From the teams example above we know that $C_3^5 = 10$.

However, we know the number of permutations of three people from the 5 possibilities is $5 \times 4 \times 3 = 60$,   so why is this answer 6 or 3! times larger than C_3^5 ?

This can be seen if we consider one of these teams, ABC say.

There are 3! ways in which the members of team ABC can be placed in a definite order, i.e., ABC, ACB, BAC, BCA, CAB, CBA and if this is done for all 10 possible teams we get all possible permutations of the 5 people taken 3 at a time.

So, $5 \times 4 \times 3 = C_3^5 \times 3!$ $\therefore$ $C_3^5 = \dfrac{5 \times 4 \times 3}{3 \times 2 \times 1}$ or $\dfrac{5!}{3! \times 2!}$.

In general, $C_r^n = \underbrace{\dfrac{n\,(n-1)(n-2)\,....\,(n-r+3)\,(n-r+2)\,(n-r+1)}{r\,(r-1)\,(r-2)\,....\qquad 3\qquad\quad 2\qquad\quad 1}}_{\text{Factor form}} = \underbrace{\dfrac{n!}{r!\,(n-r)!}}_{\text{Factorial form}}$

Values of C_r^n can be calculated from your calculator. For example, to find C_3^{10} :

TI-83:   Press 10 [MATH] [◀] **3** to select **3:n Cr** from the PRB menu, then 3 [ENTER]

Casio: Press 10 [OPTN] [F6] [F3] (PROB) [F3] (n Cr) 3 [EXE]

Example 12

How many different teams of 4 can be selected from a squad of 7 if:

a   there are no restrictions   b   the teams must include the captain?

---

a   There are 7 players up for selection and we want any 4 of them.
    This can be done in $C_4^7 = 35$ ways.

b   If the captain must be included *and* we need any 3 of the other 6, this can be done in $C_1^1 \times C_3^6 = 20$ ways.

Example 13

A committee of 4 is chosen from 7 men and 6 women. How many different committees can be chosen if:

a   there are no restrictions   b   there must be 2 of each sex

c   at least one of each sex is needed?

---

a   For no restrictions there are $7 + 6 = 13$ people up for selection and we want any 4 of them. $\therefore$ total number $= C_4^{13} = 715$.

b   The 2 men can be chosen in C_2^7 ways *and* the 2 women can be chosen in C_2^6 ways. $\therefore$ total number $= C_2^7 \times C_2^6 = 315$.

c   Total number
    $=$ number with   (3 M *and* 1 W)   *or*   (2 M *and* 2 W)   *or*   (1 M *and* 3 W)
    $= C_3^7 \times C_1^6 \; + \; C_2^7 \times C_2^6 \; + \; C_1^7 \times C_3^6$
    $= 665$

    Alternatively,   total number $= C_4^{13} - C_4^7 \times C_0^6 - C_0^7 \times C_4^6$.

EXERCISE 8E

1 Evaluate using factor form: **a** C_1^8 **b** C_2^8 **c** C_3^8 **d** C_6^8 **e** C_8^8.
Check each answer using your calculator.

2 In question **1** you probably noticed that $C_2^8 = C_6^8$.
In general, $C_r^n = C_{n-r}^n$. Prove using factorial form that this statement is true.

3 Find k if $\binom{9}{k} = 4\binom{7}{k-1}$.

4 List the different teams of 4 that can be chosen from a squad of 6 (named A, B, C, D, E and F). Check that the formula for C_r^n gives the total number of teams.

5 How many different teams of 11 can be chosen from a squad of 17?

6 Candidates for an examination are required to do 5 questions out of 9. In how many ways can this be done? If question 1 was compulsory, how many selections would be possible?

7 How many different committees of 3 can be selected from 13?
How many of these committees consist of the president and 2 others?

8 How many different teams of 5 can be selected from a squad of 12?
How many of these teams contain:
   a the captain and vice-captain **b** exactly one of the captain or the vice-captain?

9 A team of 9 is selected from a squad of 15. 3 of the players are *certainties* who must be included, and another must be excluded because of injury. In how many ways can this be done?

10 In how many ways can 4 people be selected from 10 if:
   a one person is always in the selection **b** 2 are excluded from every selection
   c 1 is always included and 2 are always excluded?

11 A committee of 5 is chosen from 10 men and 6 women. Determine the number of ways of selecting the committee if:
   a there are no restrictions **b** it must contain 3 men and 2 women
   c it must contain all men **d** it must contain at least 3 men
   e it must contain at least one of each sex.

12 A committee of 5 is chosen from 6 doctors, 3 dentists and 7 others.
Determine the number of ways of selecting the committee if it is to contain:
   a 2 doctors and 1 dentist **b** 2 doctors **c** at least one of the two professions.

13 How many diagonals has a 20-sided convex polygon?

14 There are 12 distinct points A, B, C, D, ..., L on a circle. Lines are drawn between each pair of points.
   a How many lines **i** are there in total **ii** pass through B?
   b How many triangles **i** are determined by the lines **ii** have one vertex B?

15 How many 4-digit numbers can be constructed where the digits are in ascending order from left to right? **Note:** You cannot start with 0.

16 **a** Give an example which demonstrates that:

$$C_0^5 \times C_4^6 + C_1^5 \times C_3^6 + C_2^5 \times C_2^6 + C_3^5 \times C_1^6 + C_4^5 \times C_0^6 = C_4^{11}.$$

b Copy and complete:

$$C_0^m \times C_r^n + C_1^m \times C_{r-1}^n + C_2^m \times C_{r-2}^n + \dots + C_{r-1}^m \times C_1^n + C_r^m \times C_0^n = \dots$$

17 In how many ways can 12 people be divided into:

a two equal groups   **b** three equal groups?

18 Line A contains 10 points and line B contains 7 points. If all points on line A are joined to all points on line B, determine the maximum number of points of intersection between A and B.

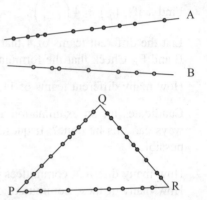

19 10 points are located on [PQ], 9 on [QR] and 8 on [RP].

All possible lines connecting these 27 points are drawn. Determine the maximum number of points of intersection of these lines which lie within triangle PQR.

F   BINOMIAL EXPANSIONS

> The sum $a + b$ is called a **binomial** as it contains two terms.
>
> Any expression of the form $(a + b)^n$ is called a **power of a binomial**.

Consider the following algebraic expansions of the powers $(a + b)^n$.

$(a + b)^1 = a + b$

$(a + b)^2 = a^2 + 2ab + b^2$

$(a + b)^3 = (a + b)(a + b)^2$

$\qquad\quad = (a + b)(a^2 + 2ab + b^2)$

$\qquad\quad = a^3 + 2a^2b + ab^2 + a^2b + 2ab^2 + b^3$

We say that:

$\qquad\quad = a^3 + 3a^2b + 3ab^2 + b^3$

> $a^2 + 2ab + b^2$ is the **binomial expansion** of $(a + b)^2$
>
> $a^3 + 3a^2b + 3ab^2 + b^3$ is the **binomial expansion** of $(a + b)^3$

INVESTIGATION 2   THE BINOMIAL EXPANSION OF $(a+b)^n$, $n \geqslant 4$

What to do:

1 Expand $(a + b)^4$ in the same way as for $(a + b)^3$ above.

2 Similarly, expand algebraically $(a + b)^5$ using your answer for the expansion of $(a + b)^4$ from **1**.

3 Expand $(a + b)^6$ using your expansion for $(a + b)^5$.

4 The $(a + b)^3 = a^3 + 3a^2b + 3ab^2 + b^3$ expansion contains 4 terms:

$a^3, 3a^2b, 3ab^2$ and b^3.   The coefficients of these terms are: 1   3   3   1

a What can be said about the powers of a and b in each term of the expansion of $(a+b)^n$ for $n = 0, 1, 2, 3, 4, 5$ and 6?

b Write down the triangle of coefficients to row 6:

$n = 0$				1		
$n = 1$			1		1	
$n = 2$		1		2		1
$n = 3$	1		3		3		1 ⟵ row 3

$\vdots$ etc.

5 This triangle of coefficients is called **Pascal's triangle**. Investigate:

   a the predictability of each row from the previous one

   b a formula for finding the sum of the numbers in the nth row of Pascal's triangle.

6 Use your results from **5** to predict the elements of the 7th row of Pascal's triangle and hence write down the binomial expansion of $(a+b)^7$.

Check your result algebraically by using $(a+b)^7 = (a+b)(a+b)^6$ and your results from **3** above.

From **Investigation 2** we obtained
$$(a+b)^4 = a^4 + 4a^3b + 6a^2b^2 + 4ab^3 + b^4$$
$$= a^4 + 4a^3b^1 + 6a^2b^2 + 4a^1b^3 + b^4$$

Notice that:
- As we look from left to right across the expansion, the powers of a decrease by 1 and the powers of b increase by 1.
- The sum of the powers of a and b in each term of the expansion is 4.
- The number of terms in the expansion is $4 + 1 = 5$.

In general, for the expansion of $(a+b)^n$ where $n = 1, 2, 3, 4, 5, \ldots$:
- As we look from left to right across the expansion, the powers of a decrease by 1 whilst the powers of b increase by 1.
- The sum of the powers of a and b in each term of the expansion is n.
- The number of terms in the expansion is $n + 1$.

The expansion $(a+b)^3 = a^3 + 3a^2b + 3ab^2 + b^3$ can be used to expand other cubes.

Example 14

Using $(a+b)^3 = a^3 + 3a^2b + 3ab^2 + b^3$, find the binomial expansion of:

a $(2x+3)^3$ **b** $(x-5)^3$

a In the expansion of $(a+b)^3$ we substitute $a = (2x)$ and $b = (3)$

$\therefore \quad (2x+3)^3 = (2x)^3 + 3(2x)^2(3) + 3(2x)^1(3)^2 + (3)^3$

$\qquad\qquad = 8x^3 + 36x^2 + 54x + 27$ on simplifying

b This time we substitute $a = (x)$ and $b = (-5)$

$\therefore \quad (x-5)^3 = (x)^3 + 3(x)^2(-5) + 3(x)(-5)^2 + (-5)^3$

$\qquad\qquad = x^3 - 15x^2 + 75x - 125$

Example 15

Find the: a 5th row of Pascal's triangle   b   binomial expansion of $\left(x - \frac{2}{x}\right)^5$.

a
$$1 \longleftarrow \text{the 0th row, for } (a+b)^0$$
$$1 \quad 1 \longleftarrow \text{the 1st row, for } (a+b)^1$$
$$1 \quad 2 \quad 1$$
$$1 \quad 3 \quad 3 \quad 1$$
$$1 \quad 4 \quad 6 \quad 4 \quad 1$$
$$1 \quad 5 \quad 10 \quad 10 \quad 5 \quad 1 \longleftarrow \text{the 5th row}$$

b   So, $(a+b)^5 = a^5 + 5a^4b + 10a^3b^2 + 10a^2b^3 + 5ab^4 + b^5$

and we let $a = (x)$ and $b = \left(\frac{-2}{x}\right)$

$\therefore$ $\left(x - \frac{2}{x}\right)^5 = (x)^5 + 5(x)^4\left(\frac{-2}{x}\right) + 10(x)^3\left(\frac{-2}{x}\right)^2 + 10(x)^2\left(\frac{-2}{x}\right)^3$

$$+ 5(x)\left(\frac{-2}{x}\right)^4 + \left(\frac{-2}{x}\right)^5$$

$$= x^5 - 10x^3 + 40x - \frac{80}{x} + \frac{80}{x^3} - \frac{32}{x^5}$$

EXERCISE 8F

1 Use the binomial expansion of $(a+b)^3$ to expand and simplify:

a $(x+1)^3$ b $(3x-1)^3$ c $(2x+5)^3$ d $\left(2x + \frac{1}{x}\right)^3$

2 Use $(a+b)^4 = a^4 + 4a^3b + 6a^2b^2 + 4ab^3 + b^4$ to expand and simplify:

a $(x-2)^4$ b $(2x+3)^4$ c $\left(x + \frac{1}{x}\right)^4$ d $\left(2x - \frac{1}{x}\right)^4$

3   a   Write down the 6th row of Pascal's triangle.

b   Find the binomial expansion of:

i $(x+2)^6$ ii $(2x-1)^6$ iii $\left(x + \frac{1}{x}\right)^6$

4 Expand and simplify:

a $(1+\sqrt{2})^3$ b $(1+\sqrt{5})^4$ c $(2-\sqrt{2})^5$

5   a   Expand $(2+x)^6$.

b   Use the expansion of a to find the value of $(2.01)^6$.

6 Expand and simplify $(2x+3)(x+1)^4$.

7 Find the coefficient of:

a a^3b^2 in the expansion of $(3a+b)^5$ b a^3b^3 in the expansion of $(2a+3b)^6$.

G   THE GENERAL BINOMIAL EXPANSION

$$(a+b)^n = \binom{n}{0}a^n + \binom{n}{1}a^{n-1}b + \binom{n}{2}a^{n-2}b^2 + \ldots + \binom{n}{n-1}ab^{n-1} + \binom{n}{n}b^n$$

where $\binom{n}{r} = C_r^n$ is the **binomial coefficient** of $a^{n-r}b^r$ and $r = 0, 1, 2, 3, \ldots, n$.

The **general term**, or $(r+1)$th term is $\; T_{r+1} = \binom{n}{r}a^{n-r}b^r$.

Example 16

Write down the first 3 and last 2 terms of the expansion of $\left(2x + \frac{1}{x}\right)^{12}$.

$\left(2x + \frac{1}{x}\right)^{12} = (2x)^{12} + \binom{12}{1}(2x)^{11}\left(\frac{1}{x}\right) + \binom{12}{2}(2x)^{10}\left(\frac{1}{x}\right)^2 + \ldots$

$\ldots + \binom{12}{11}(2x)\left(\frac{1}{x}\right)^{11} + \binom{12}{12}\left(\frac{1}{x}\right)^{12}$

Example 17

Find the 7th term of $\left(3x - \frac{4}{x^2}\right)^{14}$.

Do not simplify.

$a = (3x), \quad b = \left(\frac{-4}{x^2}\right) \quad$ and $\quad n = 14$

So, as $\; T_{r+1} = \binom{n}{r}a^{n-r}b^r$, we let $r = 6$

$\therefore \quad T_7 = \binom{14}{6}(3x)^8\left(\frac{-4}{x^2}\right)^6$

Example 18

In the expansion of $\left(x^2 + \frac{4}{x}\right)^{12}$, find:

a   the coefficient of x^6

b   the constant term

$a = (x^2), \quad b = \left(\frac{4}{x}\right) \quad$ and $\quad n = 12 \quad \therefore \quad T_{r+1} = \binom{12}{r}(x^2)^{12-r}\left(\frac{4}{x}\right)^r$

$$= \binom{12}{r}x^{24-2r}\frac{4^r}{x^r}$$

$$= \binom{12}{r}4^r x^{24-3r}$$

a   If $\; 24 - 3r = 6$

then $\; 3r = 18$

$\therefore \; r = 6$

$\therefore \; T_7 = \binom{12}{6}4^6 x^6$

$\therefore \;$ the coefficient of x^6 is

$\binom{12}{6}4^6 \;$ or $\; 3\,784\,704$.

b   If $\; 24 - 3r = 0$

then $\; 3r = 24$

$\therefore \; r = 8$

$\therefore \; T_9 = \binom{12}{8}4^8 x^0$

$\therefore \;$ the constant term is

$\binom{12}{8}4^8 \;$ or $\; 32\,440\,320$.

Example 19

Find the coefficient of x^5 in the expansion of $(x+3)(2x-1)^6$.

$(x+3)(2x-1)^6$

$= (x+3)[(2x)^6 + \binom{6}{1}(2x)^5(-1) + \binom{6}{2}(2x)^4(-1)^2 + ...]$

$= (x+3)(2^6x^6 - \binom{6}{1}2^5x^5 + \binom{6}{2}2^4x^4 - ....)$

So, the terms containing x^5 are $\binom{6}{2}2^4x^5$ from (1)

and $-3\binom{6}{1}2^5x^5$ from (2)

$\therefore$ the coefficient of x^5 is $\binom{6}{2}2^4 - 3\binom{6}{1}2^5$ $= -336$

EXERCISE 8G

1 Write down the first three and last two terms of the binomial expansion of:

   a $(1+2x)^{11}$ **b** $\left(3x + \frac{2}{x}\right)^{15}$ **c** $\left(2x - \frac{3}{x}\right)^{20}$

2 Without simplifying, find:

   a the 6th term of $(2x+5)^{15}$ **b** the 4th term of $\left(x^2 + \frac{5}{x}\right)^9$

   c the 10th term of $\left(x - \frac{2}{x}\right)^{17}$ **d** the 9th term of $\left(2x^2 - \frac{1}{x}\right)^{21}$

3 Find the coefficient of:

   a x^{10} in the expansion of $(3 + 2x^2)^{10}$ **b** x^3 in the expansion of $\left(2x^2 - \frac{3}{x}\right)^6$

   c x^{12} in the expansion of $\left(2x^2 - \frac{1}{x}\right)^{12}$

4 Find the constant term in:

   a the expansion of $\left(x + \frac{2}{x^2}\right)^{15}$ **b** the expansion of $\left(x - \frac{3}{x^2}\right)^9$

5 **a** Write down the first 5 rows of Pascal's triangle.

   b What is the sum of the numbers in:

      i row 1   **ii** row 2   **iii** row 3   **iv** row 4   **v** row 5?

   c Copy and complete:

   The sum of the numbers in row n of Pascal's triangle is ......

   d Show that $(1+x)^n = \binom{n}{0} + \binom{n}{1}x + \binom{n}{2}x^2 + ... + \binom{n}{n-1}x^{n-1} + \binom{n}{n}x^n$

   Hence deduce that $\binom{n}{0} + \binom{n}{1} + \binom{n}{2} + ... + \binom{n}{n-1} + \binom{n}{n} = 2^n$

6 **a** Find the coefficient of x^5 in the expansion of $(x+2)(x^2+1)^8$

   b Find the coefficient of x^6 in the expansion of $(2-x)(3x+1)^9$

7 Expand $(1 + 2x - x^2)^5$ in ascending powers of x as far as the term containing x^4.

8 **a** Show that $\binom{n}{1} = n$ and $\binom{n}{2} = \dfrac{n(n-1)}{2}$ are true statements.

   b The third term of $(1+x)^n$ is $36x^2$. Find the fourth term.

   c If $(1 + kx)^n = 1 - 12x + 60x^2 - .....$, find the values of k and n.

9 Find a if the coefficient of x^{11} in the expansion of $(x^2 + \dfrac{1}{ax})^{10}$ is 15.

10 From the binomial expansion of $(1+x)^n$, deduce that:

    a $\binom{n}{0} - \binom{n}{1} + \binom{n}{2} - \binom{n}{3} + \ldots\ldots + (-1)^n \binom{n}{n} = 0$

    b $\binom{2n+1}{0} + \binom{2n+1}{1} + \binom{2n+1}{2} + \ldots\ldots + \binom{2n+1}{n} = 4^n$

11 By considering the binomial expansion of $(1+x)^n$, find $\displaystyle\sum_{r=0}^{n} 2^r \binom{n}{r}$.

12 $(x^2 - 3x + 1)^2 = x^4 - 6x^3 + 11x^2 - 6x + 1$ and the sum of its coefficients is $1 - 6 + 11 - 6 + 1$ which is 1.

    What is the sum of the coefficients of $(x^3 + 2x^2 + 3x - 7)^{100}$?

13 By considering $(1+x)^n (1+x)^n = (1+x)^{2n}$, show that

    $\binom{n}{0}^2 + \binom{n}{1}^2 + \binom{n}{2}^2 + \binom{n}{3}^2 + \ldots\ldots + \binom{n}{n}^2 = \binom{2n}{n}$.

14   **a** Prove that $r\binom{n}{r} = n\binom{n-1}{r-1}$.

    b Hence show that $\binom{n}{1} + 2\binom{n}{2} + 3\binom{n}{3} + 4\binom{n}{4} + \ldots\ldots + n\binom{n}{n} = n2^{n-1}$

    c Suppose numbers P_r are defined by

        $P_r = \binom{n}{r} p^r (1-p)^{n-r}$ for $r = 0, 1, 2, 3, \ldots\ldots, n$.

    Prove that   **i** $\displaystyle\sum_{r=0}^{n} P_r = 1$ **ii** $\displaystyle\sum_{r=1}^{n} r P_r = np$

REVIEW SET 8A

1 Alpha-numeric number plates have two letters followed by four digits. How many plates are possible if:

    a there are no restrictions   **b** the first letter must be a vowel

    c no letter or digit may be repeated?

2 Ten points are located on a 2-dimensional plane. If no three points are collinear:

    a how many line segments joining two points can be drawn

    b how many different triangles can be drawn by connecting all 10 points with line segments in any possible way?

3 Simplify: **a** $\dfrac{n!}{(n-2)!}$ **b** $\dfrac{n! + (n+1)!}{n!}$

4   **a** How many committees of five can be selected from eight men and seven women?

    b How many of the committees contain two men and three women?

    c How many contain at least one man?

5 Eight people enter a room and each person shakes hands with every other person. How many hand shakes are made?

6 Use the binomial expansion to find: **a** $(x - 2y)^3$ **b** $(3x + 2)^4$

7 A team of five is chosen from six men and four women.

    a How many different teams are possible with no restrictions?

    b How many contain at least one of each sex?

8 The letters P, Q, R, S and T are to be arranged in a row. How many of the possible arrangements:

    a end with T   **b** begin with P and end with T?

9 Find the coefficient of x^3 in the expansion of $(2x+5)^6$.

10 Find the constant term in the expansion of $\left(2x^2 - \frac{1}{x}\right)^6$.

11 The first three terms in the expansion of $(1+kx)^n$, in ascending powers of x, are $1 - 4x + \frac{15}{2}x^2$. Find k and n.

12 Eight people enter a room and sit at random in a row of eight chairs. In how many ways can the sisters Cathy, Robyn and Jane sit together in the row?

13   **a** How many three digit numbers can be formed using the digits 0 to 9?

    b How many of these numbers are divisible by 5?

REVIEW SET 8B

1 A team of eight is chosen from 11 men and 7 women. How many different teams are possible if there are:

    a no restrictions   **b** four of each sex on the team

    c at least two women on the team?

2 A four digit number is constructed using the digits 0, 1, 2, 3, ..., 9 once only.

    a How many numbers are possible?   **b** How many are divisible by 5?

3 Use Pascal's triangle to expand $(a+b)^6$.

    Hence, find the binomial expansion of: **a** $(x-3)^6$ **b** $\left(1+\frac{1}{x}\right)^6$

4 Expand and simplify $(\sqrt{3}+2)^5$ giving your answer in the form $a+b\sqrt{3}$, $a, b \in \mathbb{Z}$.

5 Use the expansion of $(4+x)^3$ to find the exact value of $(4.02)^3$.

6 Find the constant term in the expansion of $\left(3x^2 + \frac{1}{x}\right)^8$.

7 Find the coefficient of x^{-6} in the expansion of $\left(2x - \frac{3}{x^2}\right)^{12}$.

8 Find the coefficient of x^5 in the expansion of $(2x+3)(x-2)^6$.

9 Find the possible values of a if the coefficient of x^3 in $\left(2x + \frac{1}{ax^2}\right)^9$ is 288.

10 Find the term independent of x in the expansion of $\left(3x - \frac{2}{x^2}\right)^6$.

11 Find the possible values of q if the constant terms in the expansions of $\left(x^3 + \frac{q}{x^3}\right)^8$ and $\left(x^3 + \frac{q}{x^3}\right)^4$ are equal.

Chapter 9

Mathematical induction

Contents:

A   THE PROCESS OF INDUCTION

The process of formulating a general result from a close examination of the simplest cases is called **mathematical induction**.

For example,   the first positive even number is $2 = 2 \times 1$
the second positive even number is $4 = 2 \times 2$
the third positive even number is $6 = 2 \times 3$
the fourth positive even number is $8 = 2 \times 4$

and from these results we *induce* that

the nth positive even number is $2 \times n$ or $2n$.

The statement that "the nth positive even number is $2n$" is a summary of the observations of the simple cases $n = 1, 2, 3, 4$ and is a statement which we **believe** is true. We call such a statement a **conjecture** or **proposition**.

We need to **prove** a conjecture before we can regard it as a fact.

Consider the following argument for finding the sum of the first n odd numbers:

$$1 = 1 = 1^2$$
$$1 + 3 = 4 = 2^2$$
$$1 + 3 + 5 = 9 = 3^2$$
$$1 + 3 + 5 + 7 = 16 = 4^2$$
$$\underbrace{1 + 3 + 5 + 7 + 9}_{\text{5 of these}} = 25 = 5^2$$

It seems that   "the sum of the first n odd numbers is n^2".

This pattern may continue or it may not. We require proof of the fact for all positive integers n. A formal statement of our conjecture may be:

" $\underbrace{1 + 3 + 5 + 7 + 9 + \dots..}_{n \text{ of these}} = n^2$ for all $n \in \mathbb{Z}^+$"

The nth odd number is $(2n - 1)$, so we could also write the proposition as:

"$1 + 3 + 5 + 7 + 9 + \dots.. + (2n - 1) = n^2$ for all $n \in \mathbb{Z}^+$"

One direct proof of the proposition is to note that the series is arithmetic with $u_1 = 1$, $d = 2$ and "n" $= n$.

$$\text{Hence} \quad S_n = \frac{n}{2}(2(1) + (n - 1)2) \quad \{\text{using } \frac{n}{2}(2u_1 + (n - 1)d)\}$$

$$= \frac{n}{2} \times 2n$$

$$= n^2$$

Example 1

By examining the cases $n = 1, 2, 3$ and 4, make a conjecture about the sum

of $S_n = \frac{1}{1\times2} + \frac{1}{2\times3} + \frac{1}{3\times4} + \frac{1}{4\times5} + \ldots + \frac{1}{n(n+1)}$.

$S_1 = \frac{1}{1\times2} = \frac{1}{2}$

$S_2 = \frac{1}{1\times2} + \frac{1}{2\times3} = \frac{1}{2} + \frac{1}{6} = \frac{2}{3}$

$S_3 = \frac{1}{1\times2} + \frac{1}{2\times3} + \frac{1}{3\times4} = \frac{2}{3} + \frac{1}{12} = \frac{3}{4}$

$S_4 = \frac{1}{1\times2} + \frac{1}{2\times3} + \frac{1}{3\times4} + \frac{1}{4\times5} = \frac{3}{4} + \frac{1}{20} = \frac{4}{5}$

From these results we conjecture that:

$$S_n = \frac{n}{n+1}.$$

Note:
- If the result in **Example 1** is true, then:

  $\frac{1}{1\times2} + \frac{1}{2\times3} + \frac{1}{3\times4} + \frac{1}{4\times5} + \ldots + \frac{1}{1000\times1001} = \frac{1000}{1001}$ {case $n = 1000$}

- The great Swiss mathematician **Euler** proposed that $P(n) = n^2 + n + 41$ was a formula for generating prime numbers. People who read his statement probably checked it for $n = 1, 2, 3, 4, 5, \ldots, 10$ and agreed with him.

  However, it was found to be incorrect as, for example

  $P(41) = 41^2 + 41 + 41 = 41(41 + 1 + 1) = 41 \times 43$,   a composite.

  So, not all propositions are true.

EXERCISE 9A

1 By examining the following using substitutions like $n = 1, 2, 3, 4, \ldots$, complete the proposition or conjecture.

 a The nth term of the sequence $3, 7, 11, 15, 19, \ldots$ is [   ] for $n = 1, 2, 3, 4, \ldots$

 b $3^n > 1 + 2n$ for [   ]

 c $11^n - 1$ is divisible by [ ] for [   ]

 d $2 + 4 + 6 + 8 + 10 + \ldots + 2n = $ [ ] for [   ]

 e $1! + 2 \times 2! + 3 \times 3! + 4 \times 4! + \ldots + n \times n! = $ [ ] for [   ]

 f $\dfrac{1}{2!} + \dfrac{2}{3!} + \dfrac{3}{4!} + \dfrac{4}{5!} + \ldots + \dfrac{n}{(n+1)!} = $ [ ] for [   ]

 g $7^n + 2$ is divisible by [ ] for [   ]

 h $\left(1 - \frac{1}{2}\right)\left(1 - \frac{1}{3}\right)\left(1 - \frac{1}{4}\right)\ldots\left(1 - \frac{1}{n+1}\right) = $ [ ] for [   ]

 i $\dfrac{1}{2\times5} + \dfrac{1}{5\times8} + \dfrac{1}{8\times11} + \ldots$ to n terms $= $ [ ] for [   ]

2 n points are placed inside a triangle.

Non-intersecting line segments are drawn connecting the 3 vertices of the triangle and the points within it, to partition the given triangle into smaller triangles. Make a proposition concerning the number of triangles obtained in the general case.

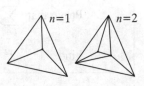

B   THE PRINCIPLE OF MATHEMATICAL INDUCTION

PROPOSITION NOTATION

We use P_n to represent a proposition which is defined for every integer n where $n \geqslant a$, $a \in \mathbb{Z}$.

For example, in the case of **Example 1**, our proposition P_n is

$$\text{``} \frac{1}{1 \times 2} + \frac{1}{2 \times 3} + \frac{1}{3 \times 4} ..... + \frac{1}{n(n+1)} = \frac{n}{n+1} \text{''} \quad \text{for all } n \in \mathbb{Z}^+.$$

Notice that P_1 is $\text{``} \dfrac{1}{1 \times 2} = \dfrac{1}{2} \text{''}$ and $P_2$ is $\text{``} \dfrac{1}{1 \times 2} + \dfrac{1}{2 \times 3} = \dfrac{2}{3} \text{''}$

and P_k is $\text{``} \dfrac{1}{1 \times 2} + \dfrac{1}{2 \times 3} + \dfrac{1}{3 \times 4} + ... + \dfrac{1}{k(k+1)} = \dfrac{k}{k+1} \text{''}$.

THE PRINCIPLE OF MATHEMATICAL INDUCTION

> Suppose P_n is a proposition which is defined for every integer $n \geqslant a$, $a \in \mathbb{Z}$.
>
> Now if
> - P_a is true, and
> - P_{k+1} is true whenever P_k is true,
>
> then P_n is true for all $n \geqslant a$.

This means that for $a = 1$, say, if the two above conditions hold, then the truth of P_1 implies that P_2 is true, which implies that P_3 is true, which implies that P_4 is true, and so on.

The **principle of mathematical induction** constitutes a formal proof that a particular proposition is true.

One can liken the principle of mathematical induction to the **domino effect**. We imagine an infinite set of dominoes all lined up.

Provided that:

- the first one topples to the right, and
- the $(k+1)$th domino will topple if the kth domino topples,

then eventually all will topple.

DEMO

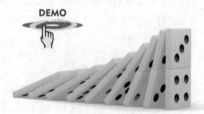

SUMS OF SERIES

Example 2

a Prove that $\displaystyle\sum_{i=1}^{n} i^2 = \frac{n(n+1)(2n+1)}{6}$ for all $n \in \mathbb{Z}^+$.

b Find $1^2 + 2^2 + 3^2 + 4^2 + ... + 100^2$.

a P_n is: "$1^2 + 2^2 + 3^2 + 4^2 + ... + n^2 = \dfrac{n(n+1)(2n+1)}{6}$,"   for all $n \in \mathbb{Z}^+$.

Proof: (By the principle of mathematical induction)

(1)   If $n = 1$,   LHS $= 1^2 = 1$ and   RHS $= \dfrac{1 \times 2 \times 3}{6} = 1$

$\therefore$ P_1 is true

(2)   If P_k is true, then

$$\sum_{i=1}^{k} i^2 = 1^2 + 2^2 + 3^2 + 4^2 + ... + k^2 = \dfrac{k(k+1)(2k+1)}{6}$$

Thus $1^2 + 2^2 + 3^2 + 4^2 + ... + k^2 + (k+1)^2$

$$= \dfrac{k(k+1)(2k+1)}{6} + (k+1)^2 \quad \{\text{using } P_k\}$$

$$= \dfrac{k(k+1)(2k+1)}{6} + (k+1)^2 \times \dfrac{6}{6}$$

$$= \dfrac{(k+1)[k(2k+1) + 6(k+1)]}{6}$$

$$= \dfrac{(k+1)(2k^2 + k + 6k + 6)}{6}$$

$$= \dfrac{(k+1)(2k^2 + 7k + 6)}{6}$$

$$= \dfrac{(k+1)(k+2)(2k+3)}{6}$$

$$= \dfrac{(k+1)([k+1]+1)(2[k+1]+1)}{6}$$

Always look for common factors.

Thus P_{k+1} is true whenever P_k is true. Since P_1 is true,

P_n is true for all $n \in \mathbb{Z}^+$.   {Principle of mathematical induction}

b $1^2 + 2^2 + 3^2 + 4^2 + ... + 100^2 = \dfrac{100 \times 101 \times 201}{6} = 338\,350$ {as $n = 100$}

EXERCISE 9B

1   Use the principle of mathematical induction to prove that the following propositions (conjectures) are true for all positive integers n:

a $\displaystyle\sum_{i=1}^{n} i = \dfrac{n(n+1)}{2}$

b $\displaystyle\sum_{i=1}^{n} i(i+1) = \dfrac{n(n+1)(n+2)}{3}$

c $\displaystyle\sum_{i=1}^{n} 3i(i+4) = \dfrac{n(n+1)(2n+13)}{2}$

d $\displaystyle\sum_{i=1}^{n} i^3 = \dfrac{n^2(n+1)^2}{4}$

Note: You should remember the result from **a**:

$$1 + 2 + 3 + ... + n = \dfrac{n(n+1)}{2} \quad \text{for all } n \text{ in } \mathbb{Z}^+.$$

2 Prove that the following proposition is true for all positive integers n:

$$\sum_{i=1}^{n} i \times 2^{i-1} = (n-1) \times 2^n + 1$$

Example 3

Prove that:

$$\sum_{i=1}^{n} \frac{1}{(3i-1)(3i+2)} = \frac{n}{6n+4} \quad \text{for all } n \in \mathbb{Z}^+.$$

P_n is: " $\dfrac{1}{2 \times 5} + \dfrac{1}{5 \times 8} + \cdots\cdots + \dfrac{1}{(3n-1)(3n+2)} = \dfrac{n}{6n+4}$ " for all $n \in \mathbb{Z}^+.$

Proof: (By the principle of mathematical induction)

(1) If $n = 1$,   LHS $= \dfrac{1}{2 \times 5} = \frac{1}{10}$ and   RHS $= \dfrac{1}{6 \times 1 + 4} = \frac{1}{10}$

  $\therefore$ P_1 is true.

(2) If P_k is true, then

$$\sum_{i=1}^{k} \frac{1}{(3i-1)(3i+2)} = \frac{1}{2 \times 5} + \frac{1}{5 \times 8} + \cdots\cdots + \frac{1}{(3k-1)(3k+2)} = \frac{k}{6k+4}$$

Now $\dfrac{1}{2 \times 5} + \dfrac{1}{5 \times 8} + \cdots\cdots + \dfrac{1}{(3k-1)(3k+2)} + \dfrac{1}{(3k+2)(3k+5)}$

$= \dfrac{k}{6k+4} + \dfrac{1}{(3k+2)(3k+5)}$ {using P_k}

$= \dfrac{k}{2(3k+2)} + \dfrac{1}{(3k+2)(3k+5)}$

$= \dfrac{k}{2(3k+2)} \times \left(\dfrac{3k+5}{3k+5}\right) + \dfrac{1}{(3k+2)(3k+5)} \times \left(\dfrac{2}{2}\right)$

$= \dfrac{3k^2 + 5k + 2}{2(3k+2)(3k+5)}$

$= \dfrac{(3k+2)(k+1)}{2(3k+2)(3k+5)}$

$= \dfrac{k+1}{6k+10}$

$= \dfrac{[k+1]}{6[k+1]+4}$

Thus P_1 is true, and P_{k+1} is true whenever P_k is true.

$\therefore$ P_n is true for all $n \in \mathbb{Z}^+$.   {Principle of mathematical induction}

3 Prove that the following propositions are true for $n \in \mathbb{Z}^+$:

a $\dfrac{1}{1 \times 2} + \dfrac{1}{2 \times 3} + \dfrac{1}{3 \times 4} + \ldots + \dfrac{1}{n(n+1)} = \dfrac{n}{n+1}$

and hence find $\dfrac{1}{10 \times 11} + \dfrac{1}{11 \times 12} + \dfrac{1}{12 \times 13} + \ldots + \dfrac{1}{20 \times 21}$

b $\dfrac{1}{1 \times 2 \times 3} + \dfrac{1}{2 \times 3 \times 4} + \ldots + \dfrac{1}{n(n+1)(n+2)} = \dfrac{n(n+3)}{4(n+1)(n+2)}$

4 Prove that the following propositions are true for $n \in \mathbb{Z}^+$:

a $1 \times 1! + 2 \times 2! + 3 \times 3! + 4 \times 4! + \ldots + n \times n! = (n+1)! - 1$

where $n!$ is the product of the first n positive integers.

b $\dfrac{1}{2!} + \dfrac{2}{3!} + \dfrac{3}{4!} + \dfrac{4}{5!} + \ldots + \dfrac{n}{(n+1)!} = \dfrac{(n+1)! - 1}{(n+1)!}$, and hence find the sum

$\dfrac{1}{2!} + \dfrac{2}{3!} + \dfrac{3}{4!} + \dfrac{4}{5!} + \ldots + \dfrac{9}{10!}$ in rational form.

5 Prove that the following conjecture is true:

$n + 2(n-1) + 3(n-2) + \ldots + (n-2)3 + (n-1)2 + n = \dfrac{n(n+1)(n+2)}{6}$

for all integers $n \geqslant 1$.

Hint: $1 \times 6 + 2 \times 5 + 3 \times 4 + 4 \times 3 + 5 \times 2 + 6 \times 1$
$= 1 \times 5 + 2 \times 4 + 3 \times 3 + 4 \times 2 + 5 \times 1 + (1 + 2 + 3 + 4 + 5 + 6)$

DIVISIBILITY

Consider the expression $4^n + 2$ for $n = 0, 1, 2, 3, 4, 5, \ldots$

$4^0 + 2 = 3 = 3 \times 1$

$4^1 + 2 = 6 = 3 \times 2$

$4^2 + 2 = 18 = 3 \times 6$ We observe that each of the answers is divisible

$4^3 + 2 = 66 = 3 \times 22$ by 3 and so we make the conjecture

$4^4 + 2 = 258 = 3 \times 86$ "$4^n + 2$ is divisible by 3 for all $n \in \mathbb{Z}^+$."

This proposition may or may not be true. If it is true, then we should be able to prove it using the principle of mathematical induction.

Note: $4^n + 2$ can be proven to be divisible by 3 by using the binomial expansion. We observe that

$4^n + 2$

$= (1 + 3)^n + 2$

$= 1^n + \binom{n}{1}3 + \binom{n}{2}3^2 + \binom{n}{3}3^3 + \binom{n}{4}3^4 + \ldots + \binom{n}{n-1}3^{n-1} + \binom{n}{n}3^n + 2$

$= 3 + \binom{n}{1}3 + \binom{n}{2}3^2 + \binom{n}{3}3^3 + \binom{n}{4}3^4 + \ldots + \binom{n}{n-1}3^{n-1} + \binom{n}{n}3^n$

$= 3\left(1 + \binom{n}{1} + \binom{n}{2}3 + \binom{n}{3}3^2 + \binom{n}{3}3^3 + \ldots + \binom{n}{n-1}3^{n-2} + \binom{n}{n}3^{n-1}\right)$

where the contents of the brackets is an integer.

Example 4

Prove that $4^n + 2$ is divisible by 3 for $n \in \mathbb{Z}$, $n \geqslant 0$.

P_n is: "$4^n + 2$ is divisible by 3" for $n \in \mathbb{Z}$, $n \geqslant 0$.

Proof: (By the principle of mathematical induction)

(1) If $n = 0$, $4^0 + 2 = 3 = 1 \times 3$ $\therefore$ P_0 is true.

(2) If P_k is true, then $4^k + 2 = 3A$ where A is an integer

Now $4^{k+1} + 2$

$= 4^1 4^k + 2$

$= 4(3A - 2) + 2$ {using P_k}

$= 12A - 8 + 2$

$= 12A - 6$

$= 3(4A - 2)$ where $4A - 2$ is an integer as $A \in \mathbb{Z}$.

Thus $4^{k+1} + 2$ is divisible by 3 if $4^k + 2$ is divisible by 3.

Hence P_0 is true and P_{k+1} is true whenever P_k is true.

$\therefore$ P_n is true for all $n \in \mathbb{Z}$, $n \geqslant 0$ {Principle of mathematical induction}

6 Use the principle of mathematical induction to prove that:

a $n^3 + 2n$ is divisible by 3 for all positive integers n

b $n(n^2 + 5)$ is divisible by 6 for all integers $n \in \mathbb{Z}^+$

c $6^n - 1$ is divisible by 5 for all integers $n \geqslant 0$

d $7^n - 4^n - 3^n$ is divisible by 12 for all $n \in \mathbb{Z}^+$.

SEQUENCES

Example 5

A sequence is defined by: $u_1 = 1$ and $u_{n+1} = 2u_n + 1$ for all $n \in \mathbb{Z}^+$.
Prove that $u_n = 2^n - 1$ for all $n \in \mathbb{Z}^+$.

P_n is: "if $u_1 = 1$ and $u_{n+1} = 2u_n + 1$ for all $n \in \mathbb{Z}^+$, then $u_n = 2^n - 1$."

Proof: (By the principle of mathematical induction)

(1) If $n = 1$, $u_1 = 2^1 - 1 = 2 - 1 = 1$ which is true and so P_1 is true.

(2) If P_k is true, then $u_k = 2^k - 1$ and $u_{k+1} = 2u_k + 1$

$= 2(2^k - 1) + 1$ {using P_k}

$= 2^{k+1} - 2 + 1$

$= 2^{k+1} - 1$

$\therefore$ P_{k+1} is also true.

Thus, P_1 is true and P_{k+1} is true whenever P_k is true,

so P_n is true for all $n \in \mathbb{Z}^+$ {Principle of mathematical induction}

7 Use the principle of mathematical induction to prove these propositions:

    a If sequence $\{u_n\}$ is defined by:

      $u_1 = 5$ and $u_{n+1} = u_n + 8n + 5$ for all $n \in \mathbb{Z}^+$, then $u_n = 4n^2 + n$.

    b If the first term of a sequence is 1 and subsequent terms are defined by the recursion formula $u_{n+1} = 2 + 3u_n$, then $u_n = 2(3^{n-1}) - 1$.

    c If a sequence is defined by: $u_1 = 2$ and $u_{n+1} = \dfrac{u_n}{2(n+1)}$ for all $n \in \mathbb{Z}^+$,

      then $u_n = \dfrac{2^{2-n}}{n!}$.

    d If a sequence is defined by: $u_1 = 1$ and $u_{n+1} = u_n + (-1)^n(n+1)^2$ for all

      $n \in \mathbb{Z}^+$, then $u_n = \dfrac{(-1)^{n-1}n(n+1)}{2}$.

8 A sequence is defined by $u_1 = 1$ and $u_{n+1} = u_n + (2n+1)$ for all $n \in \mathbb{Z}^+$.
By finding u_n for $n = 2, 3$ and 4, conjecture a formula for u_n in terms of n only.
Prove that your conjecture is true using the principle of mathematical induction.

9 A sequence is defined by $u_1 = \frac{1}{3}$ and $u_{n+1} = u_n + \dfrac{1}{(2n+1)(2n+3)}$ for all $n \in \mathbb{Z}^+$.
By finding u_n for $n = 2, 3$ and 4, conjecture a formula for u_n in terms of n only.
Prove that your conjecture is true using the principle of mathematical induction.

10 $(2 + \sqrt{3})^n = A_n + B_n\sqrt{3}$ for all $n \in \mathbb{Z}^+$, where A_n and B_n are integers.

    a Find A_n and B_n for $n = 1, 2, 3$ and 4.

    b Without using induction, show that $A_{n+1} = 2A_n + 3B_n$ and $B_{n+1} = A_n + 2B_n$.

    c Calculate $(A_n)^2 - 3(B_n)^2$ for $n = 1, 2, 3$ and 4 and hence conjecture a result.

    d Prove that your conjecture is true.

11 Prove that $u_n = \dfrac{2^n - (-1)^n}{3}$ is an odd number for all $n \in \mathbb{Z}^+$.

12 Another form of the principle of mathematical induction is:

> If P_n is a proposition defined for all $n \in \mathbb{Z}^+$, and if
> (1) P_1 and P_2 are true, and
> (2) P_{k+2} is true whenever P_k and P_{k+1} are true,
> then P_n is true for all $n \in \mathbb{Z}^+$.

  Use this form to prove that:

    a If a sequence u_n is defined by $u_1 = 11$, $u_2 = 37$ and $u_{n+2} = 5u_{n+1} - 6u_n$ for all $n \in \mathbb{Z}^+$, then $u_n = 5(3^n) - 2^{n+1}$.

    b If $u_n = (3 + \sqrt{5})^n + (3 - \sqrt{5})^n$ where $n \in \mathbb{Z}^+$, then u_n is a multiple of 2^n.
    Hint: First find a and b such that $u_{n+2} = au_{n+1} + bu_n$

OTHER APPLICATIONS

Proof by the principle of mathematical induction is used in several other areas of mathematics. For example, in establishing truths dealing with:

- **inequalities**
- **geometrical generalisations**
- **differential calculus**
- **products**
- **matrices**
- **complex numbers**.

You will find some proofs with these topics in the appropriate chapters later in the book.

Example 6

Prove that a convex n-sided polygon has $\frac{1}{2}n(n-3)$ diagonals for all $n \geqslant 3$.

P_n is: "A convex n-sided polygon has $\frac{1}{2}n(n-3)$ diagonals for all $n \geqslant 3$".

Proof: (By the principle of mathematical induction)

(1) If $n = 3$ we have a triangle   There are 0 diagonals.

and $\frac{1}{2} \times 0 \times (-3) = 0$

$\therefore$ P_3 is true.

(2) If P_k is true, a convex k-sided polygon has $\frac{1}{2}k(k-3)$ diagonals.

If we label the vertices

$$1, 2, 3, 4, 5, \ ....., \ k-1, \ k$$

and $k+1$ as an additional vertex
then

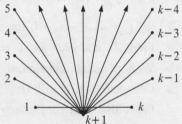

$$P_{k+1} = P_k + \underbrace{k - 2}_{} + 1 \quad \longleftarrow \quad \text{the line from 1 to } k \text{ was once a side and is now a diagonal}$$

the number of diagonals from $k+1$ to the
vertices $2, 3, 4, 5, \ ....., \ k-1$

$\therefore$ $P_{k+1} = \frac{1}{2}k(k-3) + k - 1$

$= \frac{1}{2}k(k-3) + \frac{2}{2}(k-1)$

$= \frac{1}{2}[k^2 - 3k + 2k - 2]$

$= \frac{1}{2}[k^2 - k - 2]$

$= \frac{1}{2}(k+1)(k-2)$

$= \frac{1}{2}(k+1)([k+1] - 3)$

Try it for $k = 3, 4, ...$

Thus P_3 is true and P_{k+1} is true whenever P_k is true.

$\therefore$ P_n is true for all $n \geqslant 3$ {Principle of mathematical induction}

13 Use the principle of mathematical induction to prove the following propositions:

a $\left(1 - \dfrac{1}{2}\right)\left(1 - \dfrac{1}{3}\right)\left(1 - \dfrac{1}{4}\right)\left(1 - \dfrac{1}{5}\right) \dots \left(1 - \dfrac{1}{n+1}\right) = \dfrac{1}{n+1}$, $n \in \mathbb{Z}^+$.

Note: The LHS $\neq \displaystyle\sum_{i=1}^{n}\left(1 - \dfrac{1}{i+1}\right)$ since it is a product not a sum.

b If n straight lines are drawn on a plane such that each line intersects every other line and no three lines have a common point of intersection, then the plane is divided into $\dfrac{n(n+1)}{2} + 1$ regions.

c If n points are placed inside a triangle and non-intersecting lines are drawn connecting the 3 vertices of the triangle and the points within it to partition the triangle into smaller triangles, then the number of triangles resulting is $2n + 1$.

d $\left(1 - \dfrac{1}{2^2}\right)\left(1 - \dfrac{1}{3^2}\right)\left(1 - \dfrac{1}{4^2}\right)\dots\left(1 - \dfrac{1}{n^2}\right) = \dfrac{n+1}{2n}$ for all integers $n \geqslant 2$.

14 Prove the following propositions to be true using the principle of mathematical induction:

a $3^n \geqslant 1 + 2n$ for all $n \in \mathbb{Z}$, $n \geqslant 0$

b $n! \geqslant 2^n$ for all $n \in \mathbb{Z}$, $n \geqslant 4$

c $8^n \geqslant n^3$ for all $n \in \mathbb{Z}^+$

d $(1 - h)^n \leqslant \dfrac{1}{1 + nh}$ for $0 \leqslant h \leqslant 1$ and all $n \in \mathbb{Z}^+$.

INVESTIGATION   **SEQUENCES, SERIES AND INDUCTION**

This investigation involves the principle of mathematical induction as well as concepts from sequences, series, and counting.

What to do:

1 The sequence of numbers $\{u_n\}$ is defined by $u_1 = 1 \times 1!$, $u_2 = 2 \times 2!$, $u_3 = 3 \times 3!$, etc.   What is the nth term of the sequence?

2 Let $S_n = u_1 + u_2 + u_3 + \dots + u_n$. Investigate S_n for several different values of n.

3 Based on your results from **2**, conjecture an expression for S_n.

4 Prove your conjecture to be true using the principle of mathematical induction.

5 Show that u_n can be written as $(n + 1)! - n!$ and devise an alternative direct proof of your conjecture for S_n.

6 Let $C_n = u_n + u_{n+1}$. Write an expression for C_n in factorial notation and simplify it.

7 Let $T_n = C_1 + C_2 + C_3 + \dots + C_n$ and find T_n for $n = 1, 2, 3, 4$ and 5.

8 Conjecture an expression for T_n.

9 Prove your conjecture for T_n by any method.

C   INDIRECT PROOF (EXTENSION)

Some propositions may be proven to be true by using an **indirect proof** such as **proof by contradiction**.

In such proofs we suppose the opposite of the statement to be true and, by using correct argument, hope to obtain a contradiction.

Example 7

Prove that the sum of any positive real number and its reciprocal is at least 2.

Proof: (by contradiction)

Suppose that $x + \dfrac{1}{x} < 2$ for some $x > 0$

$$\therefore \quad x\left(x + \frac{1}{x}\right) < 2x \qquad \text{\{multiplying both sides by } x \text{ where } x > 0\}$$

$$\therefore \quad x^2 + 1 < 2x$$
$$\therefore \quad x^2 - 2x + 1 < 0$$
$$\therefore \quad (x-1)^2 < 0$$

which is a contradiction as no perfect square of a real number can be negative.

So, the supposition is false and its opposite $x + \dfrac{1}{x} \geqslant 2$, $x > 0$ must be true.

Example 8

Prove that the solution of $2^x = 3$ is an irrational number.

Proof: (by contradiction)

Suppose that if $2^x = 3$ then x is rational

$$\therefore \quad 2^{\frac{p}{q}} = 3 \quad \text{for some positive integers } p \text{ and } q, \ q \neq 0$$

$$\therefore \quad (2^{\frac{p}{q}})^q = 3^q$$

$$\therefore \quad 2^p = 3^q$$

which is clearly a contradiction, as the LHS $= 2^p$ is even and the RHS $= 3^q$ is odd.

$\therefore$ the supposition is false and its opposite is true

i.e.,   if $2^x = 3$ then x is irrational.

Reminder: A **rational number** can be written in the form $\dfrac{p}{q}$ where p and q are integers, $q \neq 0$ and p, q have no common factors.

EXERCISE 9C

1   Use proof by contradiction to prove that:

   a   the sum of a positive number and nine times its reciprocal is at least 6

   b   the solution of $3^x = 4$ is an irrational number

   c $\log_2 5$ is irrational.

2   **Challenge:** Prove by contradiction that $\sqrt{2}$ is irrational.

REVIEW SET 9A

Prove the following propositions using the principle of mathematical induction:

1   $\displaystyle\sum_{i=1}^{n}(2i-1) = n^2, \quad n \in \mathbb{Z}^+$.

2   $7^n + 2$ is divisible by 3, $\quad n \in \mathbb{Z}^+$.

3   $\displaystyle\sum_{i=1}^{n} i(i+1)(i+2) = \frac{n(n+1)(n+2)(n+3)}{4}, \quad n \in \mathbb{Z}^+$.

4   $1 + r + r^2 + r^3 + r^4 + \ldots + r^{n-1} = \dfrac{1-r^n}{1-r}, \quad n \in \mathbb{Z}^+$, provided that $r \neq 1$.

5   $5^{2n} - 1$ is divisible by 24, $\quad n \in \mathbb{Z}^+$.

6   $5^n \geqslant 1 + 4n, \quad n \in \mathbb{Z}^+$.

7   If $u_1 = 1$ and $u_{n+1} = 3u_n + 2^n$, then $u_n = 3^n - 2^n, \quad n \in \mathbb{Z}^+$.

REVIEW SET 9B

Prove the following propositions using the principle of mathematical induction:

1   $\displaystyle\sum_{i=1}^{n}(2i-1)^2 = \frac{n(2n+1)(2n-1)}{3} \quad n \in \mathbb{Z}^+, \quad n \geqslant 1$.

2   $3^{2n+2} - 8n - 9$ is divisible by 64 for all positive integers n.

3   $\displaystyle\sum_{i=1}^{n}(2i+1)2^{i-1} = 1 + (2n-1) \times 2^n$ for all positive integers n.

4   $5^n + 3$ is divisible by 4 for all integers $n \geqslant 0$.

5   $\displaystyle\sum_{i=1}^{n} i(i+1)^2 = \frac{n(n+1)(n+2)(3n+5)}{12}$ for all positive integers n.

6   $5^n + 3^n \geqslant 2^{2n+1}, \quad n \in \mathbb{Z}^+$.

7   If $u_1 = 9$ and $u_{n+1} = 2u_n + 3(5^n)$, then $u_n = 2^{n+1} + 5^n, \quad n \in \mathbb{Z}^+$.

REVIEW SET 9C

Prove the following propositions using the principle of mathematical induction:

1 $\displaystyle\sum_{i=1}^{n} i(i+2) = \frac{n(n+1)(2n+7)}{6}, \quad n \in \mathbb{Z}^{+}.$

2 $7^n - 1$ is divisible by 6, $\quad n \in \mathbb{Z}^{+}.$

3 $\displaystyle\sum_{i=1}^{n} (2i-1)^3 = n^2(2n^2 - 1) \quad$ for all positive integers $n \geqslant 1.$

4 $3^n - 1 - 2n$ is divisible by 4 for all non-negative integers $n.$

5 $\displaystyle\sum_{i=1}^{n} \frac{1}{(2i-1)(2i+1)} = \frac{n}{2n+1} \quad$ for all positive integers $n.$

6 If $u_1 = 5$ and $u_{n+1} = 2u_n - 3(-1)^n$, then $u_n = 3(2^n) + (-1)^n, \quad n \in \mathbb{Z}^{+}.$

7 $\sqrt[n]{n!} \leqslant \dfrac{n+1}{2}, \quad n \in \mathbb{Z}^{+}.$

Chapter 10

The unit circle and radian measure

Contents:

Before starting this chapter you should make sure that you have a good understanding of the necessary background knowledge in trigonometry and Pythagoras.

Click on the icon alongside to obtain a printable set of exercises and answers on this background knowledge.

BACKGROUND KNOWLEDGE

OPENING PROBLEM

Consider an equilateral triangle with sides 10 cm long. All its angles are of size $60°$. Altitude AN bisects side BC and the vertical angle BAC.

- Can you see from this figure that $\sin 30° = \frac{1}{2}$?
- Use your calculator to find the values of $\sin 30°$, $\sin 150°$, $\sin 390°$, $\sin 1110°$ and $\sin(-330°)$. What do you notice? Can you explain why this result occurs even though the angles are not between $0°$ and $90°$?

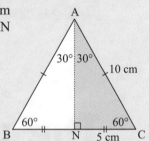

A | RADIAN MEASURE

DEGREE MEASUREMENT OF ANGLES

Recall that one full revolution makes an angle of $360°$ and a straight angle is $180°$. Hence, one **degree**, $1°$, can be defined as $\frac{1}{360}$th of one full revolution. This measure of angle is probably most useful for surveyors and architects, and is the one you have probably used in earlier years.

For greater accuracy we define one **minute**, $1'$, as $\frac{1}{60}$th of one degree and one **second**, $1''$, as $\frac{1}{60}$th of one minute. Obviously a minute and a second are very small angles.

Most graphics calculators have the capacity to convert fractions of angles measured in degrees into minutes and seconds. This is also useful for converting fractions of hours into minutes and seconds for time measurement, as one minute is $\frac{1}{60}$th of one hour, and one second is $\frac{1}{60}$th of one minute.

RADIAN MEASUREMENT OF ANGLES

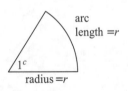

arc length $=r$

radius $=r$

An angle is said to have a measure of 1 **radian** (1^c) if it is subtended at the centre of a circle by an arc equal in length to the radius.

The symbol 'c' is used for radian measure but is usually omitted, whilst the degree symbol is always used when the measure of an angle is given in degrees.

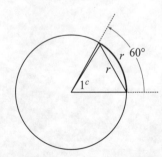

From the diagram to the right, it can be seen that 1^c is slightly smaller than $60°$. In fact, $1^c \approx 57.3°$.

The word "radian" is an abbreviation of "radial angle".

DEGREE-RADIAN CONVERSIONS

If the radius of a circle is r, then an arc of length $2r$ will subtend an angle of 2 radians at the centre. An arc of length πr (half the circumference) will subtend an angle of π radians.

Therefore, π radians $\equiv 180^o$.

So, $1^c = \left(\frac{180}{\pi}\right)^o \approx 57.3^o$ and $1^o = \left(\frac{\pi}{180}\right)^c \approx 0.0175^c$

To convert from degrees to radians, multiply by $\frac{\pi}{180}$.

To convert from radians to degrees, multiply by $\frac{180}{\pi}$.

We can summarise these results in the conversion diagram:

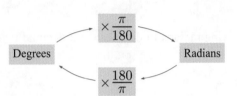

If degrees are used we indicate this with a small ^{o}. To indicate radians, we can use a small ^{c} or else use no symbol at all.

Example 1

Convert 45° to radians in terms of π.

$45^o = \left(45 \times \frac{\pi}{180}\right)$ radians   *or* $180^o = \pi$ radians

$\quad = \frac{\pi}{4}$ radians $\therefore \ \left(\frac{180}{4}\right)^o = \frac{\pi}{4}$ radians

$\qquad\qquad\qquad\qquad\qquad \therefore \quad 45^o = \frac{\pi}{4}$ radians

---

Example 2

Convert 126.5^o to radians.

126.5^o

$= \left(126.5 \times \frac{\pi}{180}\right)$ radians

≈ 2.21 radians   (3 s.f.)

Example 3

Convert $\frac{5\pi}{6}$ to degrees.

$\frac{5\pi}{6}$

$= \left(\frac{5\pi}{6} \times \frac{180}{\pi}\right)^o$

$= 150^o$

Notice that angles in radians are expressed either in terms of π or as decimals.

Example 4

Convert 0.638 radians to degrees.

0.638 radians

$= \left(0.638 \times \frac{180}{\pi}\right)^o$

$\approx 36.6^o$

EXERCISE 10A

1 Convert to radians, in terms of π:

a	90°	**b**	60°	**c**	30°	**d**	18°	**e**	9°
f	135°	**g**	225°	**h**	270°	**i**	360°	**j**	720°
k	315°	**l**	540°	**m**	36°	**n**	80°	**o**	230°

2 Convert to radians (correct to 3 s.f.):

    a 36.7° **b** 137.2° **c** 317.9° **d** 219.6° **e** 396.7°

3 Convert the following radian measure to degrees:

a	$\frac{\pi}{5}$	**b**	$\frac{3\pi}{5}$	**c**	$\frac{3\pi}{4}$	**d**	$\frac{\pi}{18}$	**e**	$\frac{\pi}{9}$
f	$\frac{7\pi}{9}$	**g**	$\frac{\pi}{10}$	**h**	$\frac{3\pi}{20}$	**i**	$\frac{5\pi}{6}$	**j**	$\frac{\pi}{8}$

4 Convert the following radians to degrees (to 2 decimal places):

    a 2 **b** 1.53 **c** 0.867 **d** 3.179 **e** 5.267

5 Copy and complete:

a

Degrees	0	45	90	135	180	225	270	315	360
Radians									

b

Degrees	0	30	60	90	120	150	180	210	240	270	300	330	360
Radians													

B   ARC LENGTH AND SECTOR AREA

ARC LENGTH

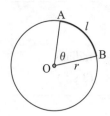

In the diagram, θ is measured in **radians**.

$$\frac{\text{arc length}}{\text{circumference}} = \frac{\theta}{2\pi}$$

$$\therefore \quad \frac{l}{2\pi r} = \frac{\theta}{2\pi}$$

$$\therefore \quad l = \theta r$$

AREA OF SECTOR

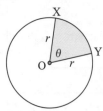

θ is measured in **radians**.

$$\frac{\text{area of minor sector XOY}}{\text{area of circle}} = \frac{\theta}{2\pi}$$

$$\therefore \quad \frac{A}{\pi r^2} = \frac{\theta}{2\pi}$$

$$\therefore \quad A = \tfrac{1}{2}\theta r^2$$

If θ is in **degrees**, $l = \dfrac{\theta}{360} \times 2\pi r$ and $A = \dfrac{\theta}{360} \times \pi r^2$.

Example 5

A sector has radius 12 cm and angle $65°$. Use radians to find its:
a   arc length   **b**   area

a   arc length $= \theta r$

$= \dfrac{65\pi}{180} \times 12$

≈ 13.6 cm

b   area $= \frac{1}{2}\theta r^2$

$= \frac{1}{2} \times \dfrac{65\pi}{180} \times 12^2$

≈ 81.7 cm^2

Example 6

A sector has radius 8.2 cm and arc length 13.3 cm.
Find its angle in radians and degrees.

$l = \theta r$ {θ in radians}

$\therefore \quad \theta = \dfrac{l}{r} = \dfrac{13.3}{8.2} \approx 1.62^c$

and $\theta = \dfrac{13.3}{8.2} \times \dfrac{180}{\pi} \approx 92.9°$

EXERCISE 10B

1 Use radians to find: **i** the arc length   **ii**   the area of a sector of a circle of
   a   radius 9 cm and angle $41.6°$ **b**   radius 4.93 cm and angle $122°$

2 A sector has an angle of $107.9°$ and an arc length of 5.92 m. Find:
   a   its radius   **b**   its area.

3 A sector has an angle of $68.2°$ and an area of 20.8 cm^2. Find:
   a   its radius   **b**   its perimeter.

4 Find the angle of a sector of:
   a   radius 4.3 m and arc length 2.95 m   **b**   radius 10 cm and area 30 cm^2.

5 Find θ (in radians) for each of the following, and hence find the area of each figure:

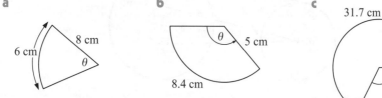

a   6 cm   8 cm θ

b θ 5 cm   8.4 cm

c   31.7 cm   8 cm θ

6 Find the arc length and area of a sector of radius 5 cm and angle 2 radians.

7 If a sector has radius 10 cm and arc length 13 cm, find its area.

8 This cone is made from this sector:

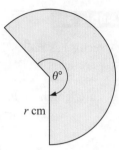

Find correct to 3 significant figures:

- **a** the slant length s cm
- **b** the value of r
- **c** the arc length of the sector
- **d** the sector angle $(\theta°)$

9

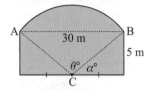

The end wall of a building has the shape illustrated, where the centre of arc AB is at C. Find:

- **a** α to 4 significant figures
- **b** θ to 4 significant figures
- **c** the area of the wall.

10 A **nautical mile** (nmi) is the distance on the Earth's surface that subtends an angle of 1 minute (where 1 minute $= \frac{1}{60}$ degree) of the Great Circle arc measured from the centre of the Earth. A **knot** is a speed of 1 nautical mile per hour.

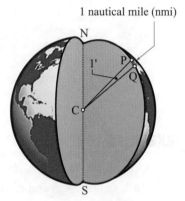

- **a** Given that the radius of the Earth is 6370 km, show that 1 nmi is approximately equal to 1.853 km.
- **b** Calculate how long it would take a plane to fly from Perth to Adelaide (a distance of 2130 km) if the plane can fly at 480 knots.

11

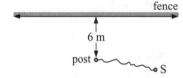

A sheep is tethered to a post which is 6 m from a long fence. The length of rope is 9 m. Find the area which is available for the sheep to feed on.

12 A belt fits tightly around two pulleys of radii 4 cm and 6 cm respectively which have a distance of 20 cm between their centres.

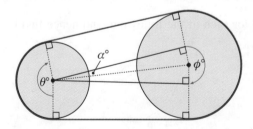

Find, correct to 4 significant figures:

- **a** α
- **b** θ
- **c** ϕ
- **d** the length of the belt

C | THE UNIT CIRCLE AND THE BASIC TRIGONOMETRIC RATIOS

The **unit circle** is the circle with centre (0, 0) and radius 1 unit.

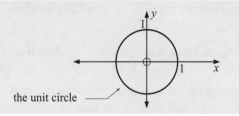

the unit circle

CIRCLES WITH CENTRE (0, 0)

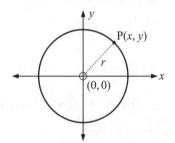

Consider a circle with centre (0, 0) and radius r units, and suppose P(x, y) is any point on this circle.

Since OP $= r$, then

$$\sqrt{(x-0)^2 + (y-0)^2} = r \qquad \text{\{distance formula\}}$$

$$\therefore \quad x^2 + y^2 = r^2$$

So, $x^2 + y^2 = r^2$ is the equation of a circle with centre (0, 0) and radius r.
The equation of the **unit circle** is $x^2 + y^2 = 1$.

ANGLE MEASUREMENT

Suppose P lies anywhere on the unit circle and A is (1, 0).
Let θ be the angle measured from [OA] on the positive x-axis.

> θ is **positive** for anticlockwise rotations and **negative** for clockwise rotations.

For example, $\theta = 210^o$ and $\phi = -150^o$.

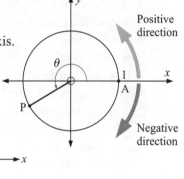

DEFINITION OF SINE, COSINE AND TANGENT

So, as point P moves anywhere on the unit circle,

> $\cos\theta$ is the x-coordinate of P
> $\sin\theta$ is the y-coordinate of P

where θ is the angle made by [OP] with the positive x-axis.

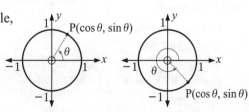

For all points on the unit circle: $-1 \leqslant x \leqslant 1$ and $-1 \leqslant y \leqslant 1$

So, $-1 \leqslant \cos \theta \leqslant 1$ and $-1 \leqslant \sin \theta \leqslant 1$ for all θ.

Also, we have already seen that the equation of the unit circle is $x^2 + y^2 = 1$.

This leads to the identity $\cos^2 \theta + \sin^2 \theta = 1$ for all θ.

The **tangent ratio** is defined as $\tan \theta = \dfrac{\sin \theta}{\cos \theta}$

By considering the first quadrant, we can easily see that the right angled triangle definitions of sine, cosine and tangent are consistent with the unit circle definition, but are restricted to acute angles only. The unit circle definition applies to angles of any value.

From the definition, $\cos \frac{\pi}{2} = 0$ and $\sin \frac{\pi}{2} = 1$

If any integer multiple of 2π is added to θ,   P will still be at $(0, 1)$.

Therefore, $\cos \left(\frac{\pi}{2} + 2k\pi \right) = 0$ and $\sin \left(\frac{\pi}{2} + 2k\pi \right) = 1$, $k \in \mathbb{Z}$.

More generally, adding integer multiples of 2π to any value of θ will not change the position of P.

So for all $k \in \mathbb{Z}$ and angles θ, $\cos (\theta + 2k\pi) = \cos \theta$ and $\sin (\theta + 2k\pi) = \sin \theta$.

This **periodic** feature is an important property of the trigonometric functions.

Example 7

Use the unit circle to show that $\cos \left(\frac{\pi}{2} + \theta \right) = -\sin \theta$.

Consider point B(a, b) on the unit circle such that [OB] makes an angle of θ with the positive x-axis.   Thus $a = \cos \theta$ and $b = \sin \theta$.

Now consider point P on the unit circle such that [OP] makes an angle of $\left(\frac{\pi}{2} + \theta \right)$ with the positive x-axis.

Now   OB $=$ OP $= 1$ unit   and $\widehat{\text{BOP}} = \frac{\pi}{2}$
so P is obtained from B by an anticlockwise rotation of $\frac{\pi}{2}$ or 90° about the origin.

$\therefore$ from transformation geometry, P has coordinates $(-b, a)$ or $(-\sin \theta, \cos \theta)$.

But the coordinates of P are
$(\cos(\frac{\pi}{2} + \theta), \sin(\frac{\pi}{2} + \theta))$.

$\therefore$ $\cos(\frac{\pi}{2} + \theta) = -\sin \theta$

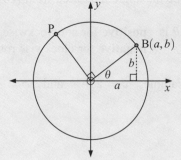

Example 8

Use a unit circle diagram to find the values of $\cos(-270^\circ)$ and $\sin(-270^\circ)$.

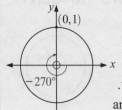

$\therefore$ $\cos(-270^\circ) = 0$ {the x-coordinate}
and $\sin(-270^\circ) = 1$ {the y-coordinate}

Example 9

Find the possible values of $\cos\theta$ for $\sin\theta = \frac{2}{3}$.   Illustrate.

$$\cos^2\theta + \sin^2\theta = 1$$
$$\therefore\ \cos^2\theta + \left(\tfrac{2}{3}\right)^2 = 1$$
$$\therefore\ \cos^2\theta = \tfrac{5}{9}$$
$$\therefore\ \cos\theta = \pm\tfrac{\sqrt{5}}{3}$$

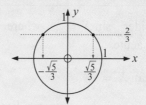

Helpful hint:

We have seen previously how the quadrants of the Cartesian Plane are labelled in anticlockwise order from 1st to 4th.

We can also use a letter to show which trigonometric ratios are positive in each quadrant.

You might like to remember them using

   All Silly Turtles Crawl.

Example 10

If $\sin\theta = -\frac{3}{4}$ and $\pi < \theta < \frac{3\pi}{2}$,   find $\cos\theta$ without using a calculator.

Since $\pi < \theta < \frac{3\pi}{2}$,

θ is a quad. 3 angle and $\therefore$ $\cos\theta$ is *negative*.

Now $\cos^2\theta + \sin^2\theta = 1$

$$\therefore\ \cos^2\theta + \tfrac{9}{16} = 1$$
$$\therefore\ \cos^2\theta = \tfrac{7}{16}$$
$$\therefore\ \cos\theta = \pm\tfrac{\sqrt{7}}{4}$$

and since $\cos\theta$ is negative, $\cos\theta = -\frac{\sqrt{7}}{4}$.

or we can use a **working angle** α in quadrant 1, where α is the acute angle symmetric with θ.

In this case $\sin\alpha = \frac{3}{4}$

$$\text{so}\ n^2 = 4^2 - 3^2 = 7 \quad\{\text{Pythagoras}\}$$
$$\therefore\ n = \sqrt{7}\ \text{and so}\ \cos\alpha = \tfrac{\sqrt{7}}{4}$$

But θ is in quad 3 where $\cos\theta$ is negative

so $\cos\theta = -\frac{\sqrt{7}}{4}$.

Example 11

If $\sin x = -\frac{1}{3}$ and $\pi < x < \frac{3\pi}{2}$, find the value of $\tan x$, without finding x.

Consider $\sin X = \frac{1}{3}$ where X is acute.

So

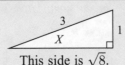

This side is $\sqrt{8}$.   {Pythagoras}

$\therefore \tan X = \frac{1}{\sqrt{8}}$

$\therefore \tan x = \frac{1}{\sqrt{8}}$ {since x lies in quad. 3 where $\tan x > 0$}

Example 12

If $\tan x = \frac{3}{4}$ and $\pi < x < \frac{3\pi}{2}$, find $\sin x$ and $\cos x$.

x is in quadrant 3 $\therefore$ $\sin x < 0$ and $\cos x < 0$.

Consider $\tan X = \frac{3}{4}$ where X is acute.

$\therefore \sin X = \frac{3}{5}$ and $\cos X = \frac{4}{5}$

$\therefore \sin x = -\frac{3}{5}$ and $\cos x = -\frac{4}{5}$

EXERCISE 10C.1

1 Sketch the graph of the curve with equation:

   a $x^2 + y^2 = 1$ **b** $x^2 + y^2 = 4$ **c** $x^2 + y^2 = 1, \ y \geqslant 0$

2 For each angle illustrated:

   i write down the actual coordinates of points A, B and C in terms of sine or cosine

   ii use your calculator to give the coordinates of A, B and C correct to 3 significant figures.

a

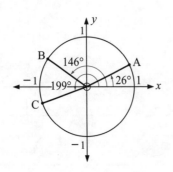

b

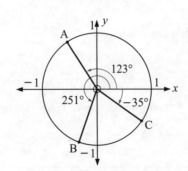

3 With the aid of a unit circle, complete the following table:

θ (degrees)	$0°$	$90°$	$180°$	$270°$	$360°$	$450°$
θ (radians)						
sine						
cosine						
tangent						

4 Use a unit circle to show the following:

    a $\sin(\pi + \theta) = -\sin\theta$ **b** $\sin\left(\frac{3\pi}{2} + \theta\right) = -\cos\theta$

5 Without using your calculator find:

    a $\sin 137°$ if $\sin 43° \approx 0.6820$ **b** $\sin 59°$ if $\sin 121° \approx 0.8572$

    c $\cos 143°$ if $\cos 37° \approx 0.7986$ **d** $\cos 24°$ if $\cos 156° \approx -0.9135$

    e $\sin 115°$ if $\sin 65° \approx 0.9063$ **f** $\cos 132°$ if $\cos 48° \approx 0.6691$

6 Find the possible exact values of $\cos\theta$ for:

    a $\sin\theta = \frac{1}{2}$ **b** $\sin\theta = -\frac{1}{3}$ **c** $\sin\theta = 0$ **d** $\sin\theta = -1$

7 Find the possible exact values of $\sin\theta$ for:

    a $\cos\theta = \frac{4}{5}$ **b** $\cos\theta = -\frac{3}{4}$ **c** $\cos\theta = 1$ **d** $\cos\theta = 0$

8 The diagram alongside shows the 4 quadrants. They are numbered anticlockwise.

    a Copy and complete:

Quadrant	Degree measure	Radian measure	$\cos\theta$	$\sin\theta$	$\tan\theta$
1	$0 < \theta < 90$	$0 < \theta < \frac{\pi}{2}$	positive	positive	
2					
3					
4					

    b In which quadrants are the following true?

         i $\cos\theta$ is positive

         ii $\cos\theta$ is negative

         iii $\cos\theta$ and $\sin\theta$ are both negative

         iv $\cos\theta$ is negative and $\sin\theta$ is positive

Remember:

2nd S / 1st A

3rd T / 4th C

All Silly Turtles Crawl

9 Without using a calculator, find:

    a $\sin\theta$ if $\cos\theta = \frac{2}{3}$, $0 < \theta < \frac{\pi}{2}$ **b** $\cos\theta$ if $\sin\theta = \frac{2}{5}$, $\frac{\pi}{2} < \theta < \pi$

    c $\cos\theta$ if $\sin\theta = -\frac{3}{5}$, $\frac{3\pi}{2} < \theta < 2\pi$ **d** $\sin\theta$ if $\cos\theta = -\frac{5}{13}$, $\pi < \theta < \frac{3\pi}{2}$

10 **a** If $\sin x = \frac{1}{3}$ and $\frac{\pi}{2} < x < \pi$, find $\tan x$ in radical (surd) form.

    b If $\cos x = \frac{1}{5}$ and $\frac{3\pi}{2} < x < 2\pi$, find $\tan x$ in radical (surd) form.

    c If $\sin x = -\frac{1}{\sqrt{3}}$ and $\pi < x < \frac{3\pi}{2}$, find $\tan x$ in radical (surd) form.

    d If $\cos x = -\frac{3}{4}$ and $\frac{\pi}{2} < x < \pi$, find $\tan x$ in radical (surd) form.

11 Find $\sin x$ and $\cos x$ given that:

    a $\tan x = \frac{2}{3}$ and $0 < x < \frac{\pi}{2}$ **b** $\tan x = -\frac{4}{3}$ and $\frac{\pi}{2} < x < \pi$

    c $\tan x = \frac{\sqrt{5}}{3}$ and $\pi < x < \frac{3\pi}{2}$ **d** $\tan x = -\frac{12}{5}$ and $\frac{3\pi}{2} < x < 2\pi$

INVESTIGATION 1   NEGATIVE AND COMPLEMENTARY ANGLE FORMULAE

The purpose of this investigation is to discover relationships (if they exist) between:
- $\cos(-\theta)$, $\sin(-\theta)$, $\cos\theta$ and $\sin\theta$
- $\cos(\frac{\pi}{2} - \theta)$, $\sin(\frac{\pi}{2} - \theta)$, $\cos\theta$ and $\sin\theta$

Note: $-\theta$ is the **negative** of θ and $\frac{\pi}{2} - \theta$ is the **complement** of θ.

What to do:

1 Copy and complete, adding angles of your choice to the table:

θ	$\sin\theta$	$\cos\theta$	$\sin(-\theta)$	$\cos(-\theta)$	$\sin(\frac{\pi}{2} - \theta)$	$\cos(\frac{\pi}{2} - \theta)$
2.67						
0.642						
$\frac{\pi}{6}$						

2 From your table in **1** make a prediction on how to simplify $\sin(-\theta)$, $\cos(-\theta)$, $\sin(\frac{\pi}{2} - \theta)$ and $\cos(\frac{\pi}{2} - \theta)$.

NEGATIVE ANGLE FORMULAE

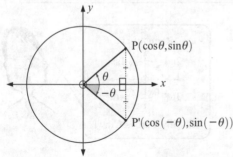

GRAPHING
PACKAGE

P and P′ have the same x-coordinate, but their y-coordinates are negatives.

Hence $\cos(-\theta) = \cos\theta$

and $\sin(-\theta) = -\sin\theta$

$$\therefore \quad \tan(-\theta) = \frac{\sin(-\theta)}{\cos(-\theta)} = \frac{-\sin\theta}{\cos\theta}$$

$$\therefore \quad \tan(-\theta) = -\tan\theta$$

So, $\cos(-\theta) = \cos\theta$

$\sin(-\theta) = -\sin\theta$

$\tan(-\theta) = -\tan\theta$

COMPLEMENTARY ANGLE FORMULAE

Consider P' on the unit circle which corresponds to the angle $\frac{\pi}{2} - \theta$.

$\therefore$ P' is $(\cos(\frac{\pi}{2} - \theta),\ \sin(\frac{\pi}{2} - \theta))$ ...... (1)

But P' is the image of P under a reflection in the line $y = x$.

$\therefore$ P' is $(\sin\theta,\ \cos\theta)$ ...... (2)

GRAPHING PACKAGE

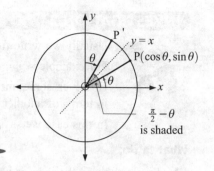

$\frac{\pi}{2} - \theta$ is shaded

Comparing (1) and (2) gives

$\cos(\frac{\pi}{2} - \theta) = \sin\theta$ and $\sin(\frac{\pi}{2} - \theta) = \cos\theta$.

$$\boxed{\begin{aligned}\cos(\tfrac{\pi}{2} - \theta) &= \sin\theta \\ \sin(\tfrac{\pi}{2} - \theta) &= \cos\theta\end{aligned}}$$

Example 13

Simplify:

a $2\sin(-\theta) + 3\sin\theta$

b $2\cos\theta + \cos(-\theta)$

a $2\sin(-\theta) + 3\sin\theta$
$= -2\sin\theta + 3\sin\theta$
$= \sin\theta$

b $2\cos\theta + \cos(-\theta)$
$= 2\cos\theta + \cos\theta$
$= 3\cos\theta$

Example 14

Simplify:

$3\sin\left(\frac{\pi}{2} - \theta\right) + 2\cos\theta$

$3\sin(\frac{\pi}{2} - \theta) + 2\cos\theta$
$= 3\cos\theta + 2\cos\theta$
$= 5\cos\theta$

EXERCISE 10C.2

1 Simplify:

a $\sin\theta + \sin(-\theta)$

b $\tan(-\theta) - \tan\theta$

c $2\cos\theta + \cos(-\theta)$

d $3\sin\theta - \sin(-\theta)$

e $\cos^2(-\alpha)$

f $\sin^2(-\alpha)$

g $\cos(-\alpha)\cos\alpha - \sin(-\alpha)\sin\alpha$

2 Simplify:

a $2\sin\theta - \cos(90° - \theta)$

b $\sin(-\theta) - \cos(90° - \theta)$

c $\sin(90° - \theta) - \cos\theta$

d $3\cos(-\theta) - 4\sin(\frac{\pi}{2} - \theta)$

e $3\cos\theta + \sin(\frac{\pi}{2} - \theta)$

f $\cos(\frac{\pi}{2} - \theta) + 4\sin\theta$

3 Explain why $\sin(\theta - \phi) = -\sin(\phi - \theta)$, $\cos(\theta - \phi) = \cos(\phi - \theta)$.

4 Simplify:

a $\dfrac{\sin\theta}{\cos\theta}$

b $\dfrac{\sin(-\theta)}{\cos(-\theta)}$

c $\dfrac{\sin(\frac{\pi}{2} - \theta)}{\cos\theta}$

d $\dfrac{-\sin(-\theta)}{\cos\theta}$

e $\dfrac{\cos(\frac{\pi}{2} - \theta)}{\sin(\frac{\pi}{2} - \theta)}$

f $\dfrac{\cos(\frac{\pi}{2} - \theta)}{\cos\theta}$

INVESTIGATION 2   PARAMETRIC EQUATIONS

Usually we write functions in the form $y = f(x)$.

For example: $y = 3x + 7$, $y = x^2 - 6x + 8$, $y = \sin x$

However, sometimes it is useful to express **both** x and y in terms of another variable, t say, called the **parameter**.

In this case we say we have **parametric equations**.

GRAPHING PACKAGE

What to do:

1   Either click on the icon or use your graphics calculator (with the same scale on both axes) to plot $\{(x, y): \quad x = \cos t, \quad y = \sin t, \quad 0^o \leqslant t \leqslant 360^o\}$

   Note: Your calculator will need to be set to degrees.

2   Describe the resulting graph.

3   What is the equation of this graph? (There are two possible answers.)

4   If using a graphics calculator, use the *trace* key to move along the curve. What do you notice?

MULTIPLES OF $\frac{\pi}{6}$ AND $\frac{\pi}{4}$

The following diagrams may be helpful when finding exact trigonometric ratios.

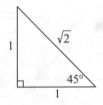

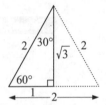

MULTIPLES OF $\frac{\pi}{4}$

Consider $\theta = \frac{\pi}{4} = 45^o$:

Triangle OBP is isosceles as angle OPB measures 45° also.

$\therefore$ OB = BP = a,   say

and $a^2 + a^2 = 1^2$ {Pythagoras}

$\therefore$ $2a^2 = 1$

$\therefore$ $a^2 = \frac{1}{2}$

$\therefore$ $a = \frac{1}{\sqrt{2}}$ as $a > 0$

Hence,   P is $\left(\frac{1}{\sqrt{2}}, \frac{1}{\sqrt{2}}\right)$ where $\frac{1}{\sqrt{2}} \approx 0.7$.

Consequently we can find the coordinates corresponding to angles of $\frac{3\pi}{4}$, $\frac{5\pi}{4}$ and $\frac{7\pi}{4}$ using suitable rotations and reflections.

So, we have:

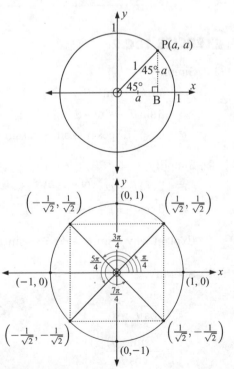

MULTIPLES OF $\frac{\pi}{6}$

Consider $\theta = \frac{\pi}{3} = 60^\circ$:

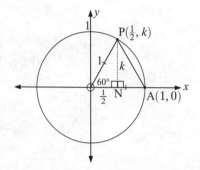

Triangle OAP is isosceles with vertical angle 60°. The remaining angles are therefore 60° and so triangle AOP is equilateral. The altitude [PN] bisects base [OA],

$$\therefore \quad ON = \tfrac{1}{2}$$

If P is $(\tfrac{1}{2}, k)$, then $(\tfrac{1}{2})^2 + k^2 = 1$

$$\therefore \quad k^2 = \tfrac{3}{4}$$

$$\therefore \quad k = \tfrac{\sqrt{3}}{2} \quad \{\text{as } k > 0\}$$

$$\therefore \quad \text{P is } (\tfrac{1}{2}, \tfrac{\sqrt{3}}{2}) \quad \text{where} \quad \tfrac{\sqrt{3}}{2} \approx 0.9$$

Consequently, we can find the coordinates of all points on the unit circle corresponding to multiples of $\frac{\pi}{6}$ using rotations and reflections.

So we have:

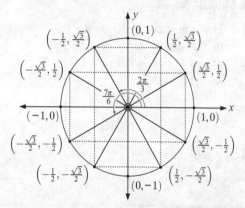

Summary:

- If θ is a **multiple of $\frac{\pi}{2}$**, the coordinates of the points on the unit circle involve 0 and ± 1.

- If θ is a **multiple of $\frac{\pi}{4}$**, (but not a multiple of $\frac{\pi}{2}$), the coordinates involve $\pm\frac{1}{\sqrt{2}}$.

- If θ is a **multiple of $\frac{\pi}{6}$**, (but not a multiple of $\frac{\pi}{2}$), the coordinates involve $\pm\frac{1}{2}$ and $\pm\frac{\sqrt{3}}{2}$.

You should not try to memorise the coordinates on the above circles for every multiple of $\frac{\pi}{6}$ and $\frac{\pi}{4}$, but rather use the summary to work out the correct result.

For example: Consider $225^\circ = \frac{5\pi}{4}$

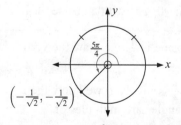

$\frac{5\pi}{4}$ is in quad 3, so signs are both negative and both have $\frac{1}{\sqrt{2}}$ size.

Consider $300^\circ = \frac{5\pi}{3}$

i.e.,   a multiple of $\frac{\pi}{6}$

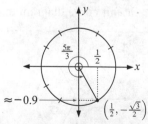

$\frac{5\pi}{4}$ is in quad 4, so signs are $(+, -)$ and from the diagram the x-value is $\frac{1}{2}$.

Example 15

Use a unit circle to find the exact values of $\sin \alpha$, $\cos \alpha$ and $\tan \alpha$ for $\alpha = \frac{3\pi}{4}$.

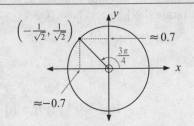

$\therefore \quad \cos\left(\frac{3\pi}{4}\right) = -\frac{1}{\sqrt{2}}, \quad \sin\left(\frac{3\pi}{4}\right) = \frac{1}{\sqrt{2}}$

$\tan\left(\frac{3\pi}{4}\right) = -1$

Example 16

Use a unit circle diagram to find the exact values of $\sin A$, $\cos A$ and $\tan A$ for $A = \frac{4\pi}{3}$.

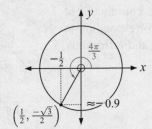

$\therefore \quad \cos\left(\frac{4\pi}{3}\right) = -\frac{1}{2}$

and $\sin\left(\frac{4\pi}{3}\right) = -\frac{\sqrt{3}}{2}$

$\therefore \quad \tan\left(\frac{4\pi}{3}\right) = \frac{-\frac{\sqrt{3}}{2}}{-\frac{1}{2}}$

$\therefore \quad \tan\left(\frac{4\pi}{3}\right) = \sqrt{3}$

Example 17

Without using a calculator, find the value of $8\sin\left(\frac{\pi}{3}\right)\cos\left(\frac{5\pi}{6}\right)$.

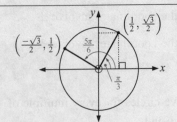

$\sin\left(\frac{\pi}{3}\right) = \frac{\sqrt{3}}{2}$ and $\cos\left(\frac{5\pi}{6}\right) = -\frac{\sqrt{3}}{2}$

$\therefore \quad 8\sin\left(\frac{\pi}{3}\right)\cos\left(\frac{5\pi}{6}\right) = 8\left(\frac{\sqrt{3}}{2}\right)\left(-\frac{\sqrt{3}}{2}\right)$

$= 2(-3)$

$= -6$

Example 18

Use a unit circle diagram to find all angles in $[0, 2\pi]$ with a cosine of $\frac{1}{2}$.

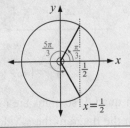

As the cosine is $\frac{1}{2}$, we draw the vertical line $x = \frac{1}{2}$.

Because $\frac{1}{2}$ is involved we know the required angles are multiples of $\frac{\pi}{6}$.

They are $\frac{\pi}{3}$ and $\frac{5\pi}{3}$.

EXERCISE 10C.3

1 Use a unit circle diagram to find $\sin\theta$, $\cos\theta$ and $\tan\theta$ for θ equal to:

   a $\frac{\pi}{4}$ b $\frac{5\pi}{4}$ c $\frac{7\pi}{4}$ d π e $\frac{-3\pi}{4}$

2 Use a unit circle diagram to find $\sin\beta$, $\cos\beta$ and $\tan\beta$ for β equal to:

   a $\frac{\pi}{6}$ b $\frac{2\pi}{3}$ c $\frac{7\pi}{6}$ d $\frac{5\pi}{3}$ e $\frac{11\pi}{6}$

3 Without using a calculator, evaluate:

   a $\sin^2 60^o$ b $\sin 30^o \cos 60^o$ c $4\sin 60^o \cos 30^o$

   d $1 - \cos^2\left(\frac{\pi}{6}\right)$ e $\sin^2\left(\frac{2\pi}{3}\right) - 1$ f $\cos^2\left(\frac{\pi}{4}\right) - \sin\left(\frac{7\pi}{6}\right)$

   g $\sin\left(\frac{3\pi}{4}\right) - \cos\left(\frac{5\pi}{4}\right)$ h $1 - 2\sin^2\left(\frac{7\pi}{6}\right)$ i $\cos^2\left(\frac{5\pi}{6}\right) - \sin^2\left(\frac{5\pi}{6}\right)$

   j $\tan^2\left(\frac{\pi}{3}\right) - 2\sin^2\left(\frac{\pi}{4}\right)$ k $2\tan\left(-\frac{5\pi}{4}\right) - \sin\left(\frac{3\pi}{2}\right)$ l $\dfrac{2\tan 150^o}{1 - \tan^2 150^o}$

Check all answers using your calculator.

4 Use a unit circle diagram to find all angles between 0° and 360° with:

   a a sine of $\frac{1}{2}$ b a sine of $\frac{\sqrt{3}}{2}$ c a cosine of $\frac{1}{\sqrt{2}}$

   d a cosine of $-\frac{1}{2}$ e a cosine of $-\frac{1}{\sqrt{2}}$ f a sine of $-\frac{\sqrt{3}}{2}$

5 Use a unit circle diagram to find all angles between 0 and 2π which have:

   a a tangent of 1 b a tangent of -1 c a tangent of $\sqrt{3}$

   d a tangent of 0 e a tangent of $\frac{1}{\sqrt{3}}$ f a tangent of $-\sqrt{3}$

6 Use a unit circle diagram to find all angles between 0 and 4π with:

   a a cosine of $\frac{\sqrt{3}}{2}$ b a sine of $-\frac{1}{2}$ c a sine of -1

7 Find θ in radians if $0 \leqslant \theta \leqslant 2\pi$ and:

   a $\cos\theta = \frac{1}{2}$ b $\sin\theta = \frac{\sqrt{3}}{2}$ c $\cos\theta = -1$ d $\sin\theta = 1$

   e $\cos\theta = -\frac{1}{\sqrt{2}}$ f $\sin^2\theta = 1$ g $\cos^2\theta = 1$ h $\cos^2\theta = \frac{1}{2}$

   i $\tan\theta = -\frac{1}{\sqrt{3}}$ j $\tan^2\theta = 3$

D   AREAS OF TRIANGLES

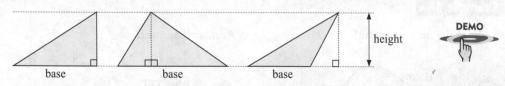

If we know the base and height measurements of a triangle we can calculate the area using

area $= \frac{1}{2}$ **base** $\times$ **height**.

However, cases arise where we do not know the height but we can still calculate the area.

These cases are:

- knowing two sides and the **included angle** between them

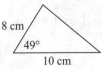

For example:

- knowing all three sides

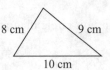

USING THE INCLUDED ANGLE

If triangle ABC has angles of size A, B and C, the sides opposite these angles are labelled a, b and c respectively.

Using trigonometry, we can develop an alternative formula that does not depend on a perpendicular height.

Any triangle that is not right angled must be either acute or obtuse. We will consider both cases:

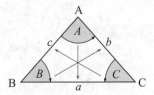

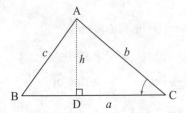

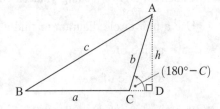

In both triangles a perpendicular is constructed from A to D on [BC] (extended if necessary).

$$\sin C = \frac{h}{b} \qquad\qquad \sin(180^\circ - C) = \frac{h}{b}$$

$$\therefore \quad h = b\sin C \qquad\qquad \therefore \quad h = b\sin(180^\circ - C)$$

$$\text{but} \quad \sin(180^\circ - C) = \sin C$$

$$\therefore \quad h = b\sin C$$

So, area $= \frac{1}{2}ah$ gives $\boxed{\text{area} = \frac{1}{2}ab\sin C}$.

Using different altitudes we can show that the area is also $\frac{1}{2}bc\sin A$ or $\frac{1}{2}ac\sin B$.

Summary:

Given the lengths of two sides of a triangle and the included angle between them, the area of the triangle is

a half of the product of two sides and the sine of the included angle.

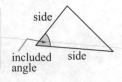

Example 19	
Find the area of triangle ABC: 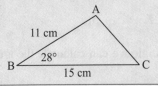	Area $= \frac{1}{2}ac\sin B$ $= \frac{1}{2} \times 15 \times 11 \times \sin 28^\circ$ ≈ 38.7 cm^2

Example 20

A triangle has sides of length 10 cm and 11 cm and an area of 50 cm^2.
Show that the included angle may have two possible sizes.

If the included angle measures θ^o, then $\quad \frac{1}{2} \times 10 \times 11 \times \sin\theta = 50$

$$\therefore \quad \sin\theta = \frac{50}{55}$$

Now $\quad \arcsin\left(\frac{50}{55}\right) \approx 65.4$

$$\therefore \quad \theta \approx 65.4 \quad \text{or} \quad 180 - 65.4$$
$$\text{i.e.,} \quad \theta \approx 65.4 \quad \text{or} \quad 114.6$$

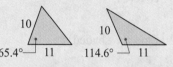

So, the two different possible angles are 65.4^o and 114.6^o.

EXERCISE 10D

1 Find the area of:

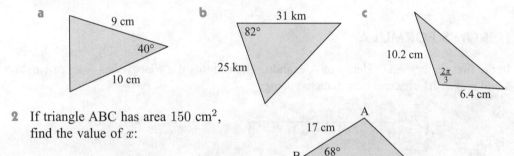

a 9 cm, 40°, 10 cm

b 31 km, 82°, 25 km

c 10.2 cm, $\frac{2\pi}{3}$, 6.4 cm

2 If triangle ABC has area 150 cm^2, find the value of x:

A, 17 cm, B, 68°, x cm, C

3 A parallelogram has two adjacent sides of length 4 cm and 6 cm respectively. If the included angle measures 52°, find the area of the parallelogram.

4 A rhombus has sides of length 12 cm and an angle of 72°. Find its area.

5 Find the area of a regular hexagon with sides of length 12 cm.

6 A rhombus has an area of 50 cm^2 and an internal angle of size 63°. Find the length of its sides.

7 A regular pentagonal garden plot has centre of symmetry O and an area of 338 m^2. Find the distance OA.

8 Find the possible values of the included angle of a triangle with:
   a sides 5 cm and 8 cm, and area 15 cm^2
   b sides 45 km and 53 km, and area 800 km^2.

9 The Australian 50 cent coin has the shape of a regular dodecagon (12 sides).

Eight of these 50 cent coins will fit exactly on an Australian $10 note as shown. What fraction of the $10 note is *not* covered?

10 Find the shaded area in:

a

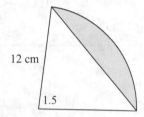

12 cm

1.5

b

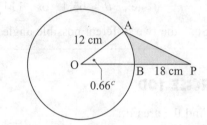

12 cm

O

0.66^c

A

B   18 cm   P

HERON'S FORMULA

In the first century A.D., Heron of Alexandria showed that if a triangle has sides of length a, b and c, then its area can be calculated using

$$A = \sqrt{s(s-a)(s-b)(s-c)} \quad \text{where} \quad s = \frac{a+b+c}{2}.$$

11 **a** Find the area of the right angled triangle with sides 3 cm, 4 cm and 5 cm:
   i   without using Heron's formula   **ii**   using Heron's formula.
   b Find the area of a triangle with sides of length:
   i   6 cm, 8 cm and 12 cm   **ii**   7.2 cm, 8.9 cm and 9.7 cm.

REVIEW SET 10A

1 Determine the area of:

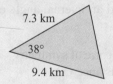

7.3 km

38°

9.4 km

2 Determine the area of:
   a a sector of angle 80° and radius 13 cm
   b a triangle with sides 11 cm, 9 cm and included angle 65°.

3 Find the coordinates of the points M, N and P on the unit circle.

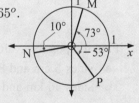

4 Find the angle [OA] makes with the positive x-axis if the x-coordinate of the point A on the unit circle is -0.222.

5 Find the acute angles that would have the same:

    a sine as $\frac{2\pi}{3}$ **b** sine as 165° **c** cosine as 276°

6 Find the obtuse angles which have the same:

    a sine as 47° **b** sine as $\frac{\pi}{15}$ **c** cosine as 186°

7 Without using your calculator, find:

    a $\sin 159^o$ if $\sin 21^o \approx 0.358$ **b** $\cos 92^o$ if $\cos 88^o \approx 0.035$

    c $\cos 75^o$ if $\cos 105^o \approx -0.259$ **d** $\sin 227^o$ if $\sin 47^o \approx 0.731$

8 Use a unit circle diagram to find:

    a $\cos 360^o$ and $\sin 360^o$ **b** $\cos(-\pi)$ and $\sin(-\pi)$

9 Explain how to use the unit circle to find θ when $\cos \theta = -\sin \theta$.

10 If $\sin 74^o \approx 0.961$, find without using a calculator the value of:

    a $\sin 106^o$ **b** $\sin 254^o$ **c** $\sin 286^o$ **d** $\sin 646^o$

11 Without a calculator, evaluate: **a** $\tan^2\left(\frac{2\pi}{3}\right)$ **b** $\cos\left(\frac{3\pi}{4}\right) - \sin\left(\frac{3\pi}{4}\right)$

12 If $\sin x = -\frac{1}{4}$ and $\pi < x < \frac{3\pi}{2}$, find $\tan x$ in radical (surd) form.

REVIEW SET 10B

1 Convert these to radians in terms of π: **a** 120° **b** 225° **c** 150° **d** 540°

2 Convert to radians (to 4 sig. figs.): **a** 71° **b** 124.6^o **c** -142° **d** -25.3^o

3 Convert these radian measure to degrees: **a** $\frac{2\pi}{5}$ **b** $\frac{5\pi}{4}$ **c** $\frac{7\pi}{9}$ **d** $\frac{11\pi}{6}$

4 Convert these radian measure to degrees (to 2 decimal places):

    a 3 **b** 1.46 **c** 0.435 **d** -5.271

5 Find the perimeter and area of a sector of radius 11 cm and angle 63°.

6 Find the radius and area of a sector of perimeter 36 cm with an angle of $\frac{2\pi}{3}$.

7 A triangle has sides of length 7 cm and 13 cm and its area is 42 cm^2. Find the size of its included angle.

8 Anke and Lucas are considering buying a block of land. The land agent supplies them with the given accurate sketch. Find the area of the property, giving your answer in:

    a m^2 **b** hectares.

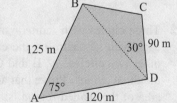

9 If $\cos 42^o \approx 0.743$, without using a calculator, find the value of:

    a $\cos 138^o$ **b** $\cos 222^o$ **c** $\cos 318^o$ **d** $\cos(-222^o)$

10 If $\cos \theta = \frac{3}{4}$ find the possible values of $\sin \theta$.

11 Without a calculator evaluate:

   a $2\sin\left(\frac{\pi}{3}\right)\cos\left(\frac{\pi}{3}\right)$ **b** $\tan^2\left(\frac{\pi}{4}\right) - 1$ **c** $\cos^2\left(\frac{\pi}{6}\right) - \sin^2\left(\frac{\pi}{6}\right)$

12 Given $\tan x = -\frac{3}{2}$ and $\frac{3\pi}{2} < x < 2\pi$,   find: **a** $\sin x$ **b** $\cos x$

REVIEW SET 10C

1 Use your calculator to determine the coordinates of the point on the unit circle corresponding to an angle of: **a** 320° **b** 163°

2 Illustrate the regions where $\sin\theta$ and $\cos\theta$ have the same sign.

3 Use a unit circle diagram to find exact values for $\sin\theta$ and $\cos\theta$ for θ equal to:

   a $\frac{2\pi}{3}$ **b** $\frac{8\pi}{3}$

4 Use a unit circle diagram to find:

   a $\cos\left(\frac{3\pi}{2}\right)$ and $\sin\left(\frac{3\pi}{2}\right)$ **b** $\cos\left(-\frac{\pi}{2}\right)$ and $\sin\left(-\frac{\pi}{2}\right)$

5 If $\cos\theta = -\frac{3}{4}$, $\frac{\pi}{2} < \theta < \pi$ find: **a** $\sin\theta$ **b** $\tan\theta$

6 Use a unit circle diagram to find all angles between 0° and 360° which have:

   a   a cosine of $-\frac{\sqrt{3}}{2}$ **b**   a sine of $\frac{1}{\sqrt{2}}$ **c**   a tangent of $-\sqrt{3}$

7 Find θ in radians if: **a** $\cos\theta = -1$ **b** $\sin^2\theta = \frac{3}{4}$

8 Without using a calculator, evaluate:

   a $\tan^2 60^o - \sin^2 45^o$ **b** $\cos^2\left(\frac{\pi}{4}\right) + \sin\left(\frac{\pi}{2}\right)$ **c** $\cos\left(\frac{5\pi}{3}\right) - \tan\left(\frac{5\pi}{4}\right)$

9 Simplify: **a** $\cos\left(\frac{\pi}{2} - \theta\right) - \sin\theta$ **b** $\cos\theta\tan\theta$

10 Find the value of x if the area is 80 cm^2. Hence, find the length of [AC].

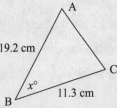

11 Determine the yellow shaded area:

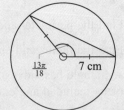

12 Three circles with radius r are drawn as shown, each with its centre on the circumference of the other two circles. A, B and C are the centres of the three circles. Prove that an expression for the area of the shaded region is:

$$A = \frac{r^2}{2}(\pi - \sqrt{3})$$

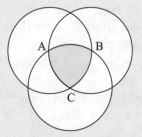

Chapter 11

Non-right angled triangle trigonometry

A | THE COSINE RULE

The **cosine rule** involves the sides and angles of a triangle.

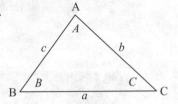

In any $\triangle ABC$:

$$a^2 = b^2 + c^2 - 2bc \cos A$$
$$or \quad b^2 = a^2 + c^2 - 2ac \cos B$$
$$or \quad c^2 = a^2 + b^2 - 2ab \cos C$$

We will develop the first formula for both an acute and an obtuse triangle.

Proof:

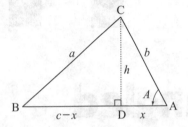
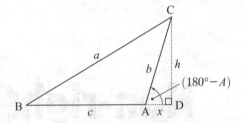

In both triangles drop a perpendicular from C to meet [AB] (extended if necessary) at D.

Let $AD = x$ and let $CD = h$.

Apply the theorem of Pythagoras in $\triangle BCD$:

$$a^2 = h^2 + (c - x)^2 \qquad\qquad a^2 = h^2 + (c + x)^2$$
$$\therefore \quad a^2 = h^2 + c^2 - 2cx + x^2 \qquad\qquad \therefore \quad a^2 = h^2 + c^2 + 2cx + x^2$$

In both cases, applying Pythagoras to $\triangle ADC$ gives $h^2 + x^2 = b^2$

$\therefore$ $h^2 = b^2 - x^2$, and we substitute this into the equations above.

$$\therefore \quad a^2 = b^2 + c^2 - 2cx \qquad\qquad \therefore \quad a^2 = b^2 + c^2 + 2cx$$

In ADC: $\quad \cos A = \dfrac{x}{b}$ $\qquad\qquad\qquad \cos(180^o - A) = \dfrac{x}{b}$

$\therefore \quad b \cos A = x$ $\qquad\qquad\qquad \therefore \quad b \cos(180^o - A) = x$

$\therefore \quad a^2 = b^2 + c^2 - 2bc \cos A \qquad$ But $\cos(180^o - A) = -\cos A$

$$\therefore \quad -b \cos A = x$$
$$\therefore \quad a^2 = b^2 + c^2 - 2bc \cos A$$

The other variations of the cosine rule could be developed by rearranging the vertices of $\triangle ABC$.

Note that if $A = 90^o$ then $\cos A = 0$ and $a^2 = b^2 + c^2 - 2bc \cos A$ reduces to $a^2 = b^2 + c^2$, which is the Pythagorean Rule.

The **cosine rule** can be used to solve triangles given:

- **two sides** and an **included angle**
- **three sides**.

If we are given **two sides** and a **non-included angle**, then when we try to find the third side we will end up with a quadratic equation. This is an *ambiguous* case where there may be two plausible solutions.

Example 1	
Find, correct to 2 decimal places, the length of [BC]. 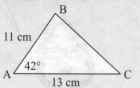	By the cosine rule: $$BC^2 = 11^2 + 13^2 - 2 \times 11 \times 13 \times \cos 42°$$ $$\therefore \quad BC \approx \sqrt{(11^2 + 13^2 - 2 \times 11 \times 13 \times \cos 42°)}$$ $$\therefore \quad BC \approx 8.801$$ $$\therefore \quad BC \text{ is } 8.80 \text{ cm in length.}$$

Rearrangement of the original cosine rule formulae can be used for finding angles if we know all three sides. The formulae for finding the angles are:

$$\cos A = \frac{b^2 + c^2 - a^2}{2bc} \qquad \cos B = \frac{c^2 + a^2 - b^2}{2ca} \qquad \cos C = \frac{a^2 + b^2 - c^2}{2ab}$$

Example 2

In triangle ABC, if AB = 7 cm, BC = 8 cm and CA = 5 cm, find the measure of angle BCA.

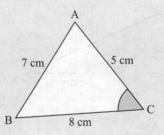

By the cosine rule:
$$\cos C = \frac{(5^2 + 8^2 - 7^2)}{(2 \times 5 \times 8)}$$
$$\therefore \quad C = \cos^{-1}\left(\frac{5^2 + 8^2 - 7^2}{2 \times 5 \times 8}\right)$$
$$\therefore \quad C = 60°$$

So, angle BCA measures 60°.

EXERCISE 11A

1 Find the length of the remaining side in the given triangle:

a 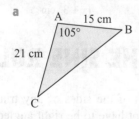   **b** 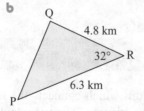   **c**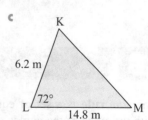

2 Find the measure of all angles of:

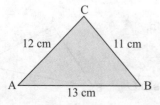

3 Find the measure of obtuse angle PQR.

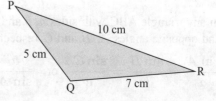

4 Find:

    a the smallest angle of a triangle with sides 11 cm, 13 cm and 17 cm

    b the largest angle of a triangle with sides 4 cm, 7 cm and 9 cm.

The smallest angle is opposite the shortest side.

5 Find:

    a $\cos \theta$ but not θ

    b the value of x.

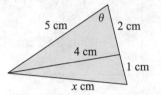

6 Find the exact value of x in each of the following diagrams:

    a
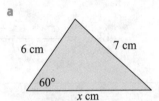

    b
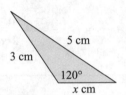

    c
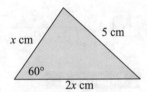

7 Find x in each of the following diagrams:

    a
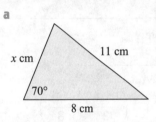

    b
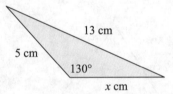

8 In the diagram alongside, $\cos \theta = -\frac{1}{5}$.

    a Find x.

    b Hence find the exact value of the area of the triangle.

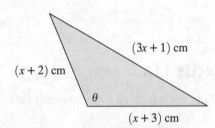

B   THE SINE RULE

The **sine rule** is a set of equations which connects the lengths of the sides of any triangle with the sines of the angles of the triangle. The triangle does not have to be right angled for the sine rule to be used.

In any triangle ABC with sides a, b and c units in length, and opposite angles A, B and C respectively,

$$\frac{\sin A}{a} = \frac{\sin B}{b} = \frac{\sin C}{c} \quad \text{or} \quad \frac{a}{\sin A} = \frac{b}{\sin B} = \frac{c}{\sin C}.$$

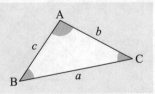

Proof: The area of any triangle ABC is given by $\frac{1}{2}bc\sin A = \frac{1}{2}ac\sin B = \frac{1}{2}ab\sin C$.

Dividing each expression by $\frac{1}{2}abc$ gives $\dfrac{\sin A}{a} = \dfrac{\sin B}{b} = \dfrac{\sin C}{c}$.

The sine rule is used to solve problems involving triangles given either:

* **two angles** and **one side**
* **two sides** and a **non-included** angle.

FINDING SIDES

Example 3	
Find the length of [AC] correct to two decimal places. 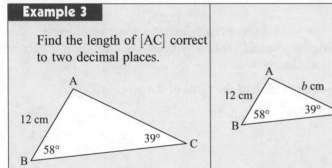	By the sine rule: $$\frac{b}{\sin 58^o} = \frac{12}{\sin 39^o}$$ $$\therefore \quad b = \frac{12 \times \sin 58^o}{\sin 39^o}$$ $$\therefore \quad b \approx 16.17074$$ $\therefore$ AC is about 16.17 cm long.

EXERCISE 11B.1

1   Find the value of x:

a
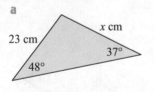

b
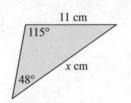

c
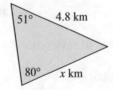

2   In triangle ABC find:

a a if $A = 63^o$, $B = 49^o$ and $b = 18$ cm
b b if $A = 82^o$, $C = 25^o$ and $c = 34$ cm
c c if $B = 21^o$, $C = 48^o$ and $a = 6.4$ cm

FINDING ANGLES

The problem of finding angles using the sine rule is more complicated because there may be two possible answers. We call this situation the **ambiguous case**.

INVESTIGATION	THE AMBIGUOUS CASE

   You will need a blank sheet of paper, a ruler, a protractor and a compass for the tasks that follow. In each task you will be required to construct triangles from given information. You could also do this using a computer package such as "The Geometer's Sketchpad".

Task 1:   Draw AB = 10 cm. At A construct an angle of 30°. Using B as centre, draw an arc of a circle of radius 6 cm. Let the arc intersect the ray from A at C. How many different positions may C have and therefore how many different triangles ABC may be constructed?

Task 2:   As before, draw AB = 10 cm and construct a 30° angle at A. This time draw an arc of radius 5 cm centred at B. How many different triangles are possible?

Task 3:   Repeat, but this time draw an arc of radius 3 cm centred at B. How many different triangles are possible?

Task 4:   Repeat with an arc of radius 12 cm from B. How many triangles are possible now?

You should have discovered that when you are given two sides and a non-included angle there are a number of different possibilities. You could get two triangles, one triangle or it may be impossible to draw any triangles from the given data.

Now consider the calculations involved in each of the cases of the investigation.

Task 1:   Given: $c = 10$ cm, $a = 6$ cm, $A = 30°$

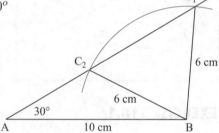

Finding C: $\dfrac{\sin C}{c} = \dfrac{\sin A}{a}$

$\therefore \quad \sin C = \dfrac{c \sin A}{a}$

$\therefore \quad \sin C = \dfrac{10 \times \sin 30°}{6} \approx 0.8333$

Because $\sin \theta = \sin(180° - \theta)$ there are two possible angles:

$C = 56.44°$ or $180° - 56.44° = 123.56°$

Task 2:   Given: $c = 10$ cm, $a = 5$ cm, $A = 30°$

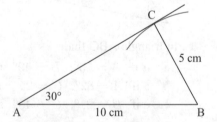

Finding C $\dfrac{\sin C}{c} = \dfrac{\sin A}{a}$

$\therefore \quad \sin C = \dfrac{c \sin A}{a}$

$\therefore \quad \sin C = \dfrac{10 \times \sin 30°}{5} = 1$

There is only one possible solution for C in the range from $0°$ to $180°$ and that is $C = 90°$. Only one triangle is therefore possible. Complete the solution of the triangle yourself.

Task 3:   Given: $c = 10$ cm, $a = 3$ cm, $A = 30°$

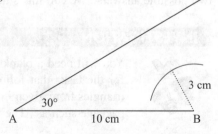

Finding C: $\dfrac{\sin C}{c} = \dfrac{\sin A}{a}$

$\therefore \quad \sin C = \dfrac{c \sin A}{a}$

$\therefore \quad \sin C = \dfrac{10 \times \sin 30°}{3} \approx 1.6667$

There is no angle that has a sine ratio > 1. Therefore there is *no solution* for this given data, and no possible triangle can be drawn.

Task 4:   Given: $c = 10$ cm, $a = 12$ cm, $A = 30^o$

Finding C:

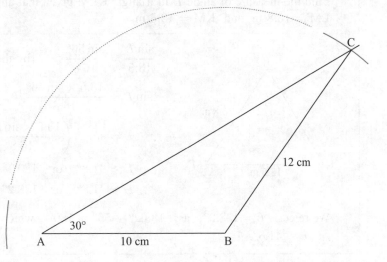

$$\frac{\sin C}{c} = \frac{\sin A}{a}$$

$\therefore$ $\sin C = \dfrac{c \sin A}{a}$

$\therefore$ $\sin C = \dfrac{10 \times \sin 30^o}{12}$

$\therefore$ $\sin C = 0.4167$

Two angles have a sine ratio of 0.4167:

$C \approx 24.62^o$ *or*
   $180^o - 24.62^o$

$C \approx 24.62^o$ *or* 155.38^o

However, in this case only one of these two angles is valid. If $A = 30^o$ then C cannot possibly equal 155.38^o because $30^o + 155.38^o > 180^o$.

Therefore, there is only one possible solution, $C \approx 24.62^o$. Once again, you may wish to carry on and complete the solution.

Conclusion: Each situation using the sine rule with two sides and a non-included angle must be examined very carefully.

Example 4

Find the measure of angle C in triangle ABC if AC is 7 cm, AB is 11 cm and angle B measures 25°.

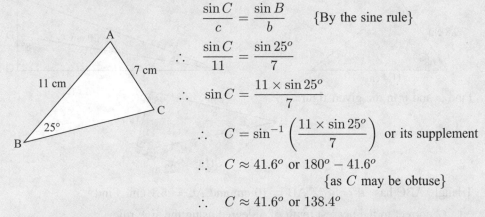

$$\frac{\sin C}{c} = \frac{\sin B}{b} \qquad \{\text{By the sine rule}\}$$

$\therefore$ $\dfrac{\sin C}{11} = \dfrac{\sin 25^o}{7}$

$\therefore$ $\sin C = \dfrac{11 \times \sin 25^o}{7}$

$\therefore$ $C = \sin^{-1}\left(\dfrac{11 \times \sin 25^o}{7}\right)$ or its supplement

$\therefore$ $C \approx 41.6^o$ or $180^o - 41.6^o$
                   $\{\text{as } C \text{ may be obtuse}\}$

$\therefore$ $C \approx 41.6^o$ or 138.4^o

$\therefore$ C measures 41.6^o if angle C is acute, or 138.4^o if angle C is obtuse.

In this example there is insufficient information to determine the actual shape of the triangle.

Sometimes there is information in the question which enables us to **reject** one of the answers.

Example 5

Find the measure of angle L in triangle KLM given that angle LKM measures $56°$, LM = 16.8 m and KM = 13.5 m.

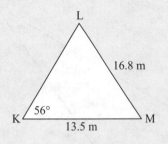

$$\frac{\sin L}{13.5} = \frac{\sin 56°}{16.8} \quad \text{\{by the sine rule\}}$$

$$\therefore \quad \sin L = \frac{13.5 \times \sin 56°}{16.8}$$

$$\therefore \quad L = \sin^{-1}\left(\frac{13.5 \times \sin 56°}{16.8}\right) \quad \text{or its supplement}$$

$$\therefore \quad L \approx 41.8° \quad \text{or} \quad 180° - 41.8°$$

$$\therefore \quad L \approx 41.8° \quad \text{or} \quad 138.2°$$

We reject $L = 138.2°$ as $138.2° + 56° > 180°$ which is impossible.
$\therefore \quad L \approx 41.8°$.

EXERCISE 11B.2

1   Triangle ABC has angle $B = 40°$, $b = 8$ cm   and $c = 11$ cm. Find the two possible values for angle C.

2   In triangle ABC, find the measure of:
   a   angle A if $a = 14.6$ cm, $b = 17.4$ cm and $A\widehat{B}C = 65°$
   b   angle B if $b = 43.8$ cm, $c = 31.4$ cm and $A\widehat{C}B = 43°$
   c   angle C if $a = 6.5$ km, $c = 4.8$ km and $B\widehat{A}C = 71°$.

3   Is it possible to have a triangle with measurements as shown? Explain!

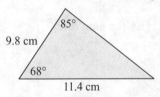

4   Find the magnitude of the angle ABC and hence the length BD.

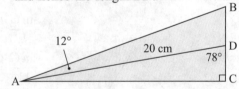

5   Find x and y in the given figure.

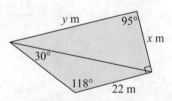

6   Triangle ABC has $\widehat{A} = 58°$, AB = 10 cm and AC = 5.1 cm. Find:
   a $\widehat{C}$ correct to the nearest tenth of a degree using the sine rule
   b $\widehat{C}$ correct to the nearest tenth of a degree using the cosine rule.
   c   Copy and complete: "When faced with using either the sine rule or the cosine rule it is better to use the .... as it avoids ...."

7 In triangle ABC, $\widehat{ABC} = 30°$,   AC = 9 cm   and   AB = 7 cm.   Find the area of the triangle.

8 In the diagram alongside, find the exact value of x. Express your answer in the form $a + b\sqrt{2}$ where $a, b \in \mathbb{Q}$.

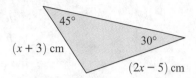

$45°$
$30°$
$(x + 3)$ cm
$(2x - 5)$ cm

C   USING THE SINE AND COSINE RULES

If we are given a problem involving a triangle, we must first decide which rule to use.

If the triangle is right angled then the trigonometric ratios or Pythagoras' Theorem can be used. For some problems we can add an extra line or two to the diagram to create a right angled triangle.

However, if we do not have a right angled triangle and we have to choose between the sine and cosine rules, the following checklist may be helpful:

Use the **cosine rule** when given:
- three sides
- two sides and an included angle.

Use the **sine rule** when given:
- one side and two angles
- two sides and a non-included angle, but beware of the *ambiguous case* which can occur when the smaller of the two given sides is opposite the given angle.

Example 6

The angles of elevation to the top of a mountain are measured from two beacons A and B at sea.

These angles are as shown on the diagram.

If the beacons are 1473 m apart, how high is the mountain?

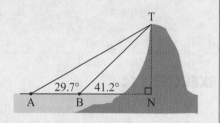

$29.7°$ $41.2°$
A   B   N

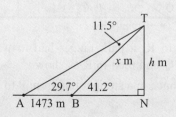

$11.5°$ T
x m h m
$29.7°$ $41.2°$
A 1473 m B   N

$\widehat{ATB} = 41.2° - 29.7°$ {exterior angle of $\triangle$}
$= 11.5°$

We find x in $\triangle ABT$ using the sine rule:

$$\frac{x}{\sin 29.7°} = \frac{1473}{\sin 11.5°}$$

$$\therefore \quad x = \frac{1473}{\sin 11.5°} \times \sin 29.7°$$

$$\approx 3660.62$$

Now, in $\triangle BNT$, $\sin 41.2^o = \dfrac{h}{x} \approx \dfrac{h}{3660.62}$

$\therefore \quad h \approx \sin 41.2^o \times 3660.62$

$\therefore \quad h \approx 2410$

So, the mountain is about 2410 m high.

Example 7

Find the measure of angle RPV.

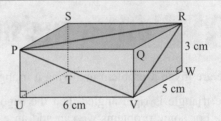

In $\triangle RVW$, $RV = \sqrt{5^2 + 3^2} = \sqrt{34}$ cm.   {Pythagoras}

In $\triangle PUV$, $PV = \sqrt{6^2 + 3^2} = \sqrt{45}$ cm.   {Pythagoras}

In $\triangle PQR$, $PR = \sqrt{6^2 + 5^2} = \sqrt{61}$ cm.   {Pythagoras}

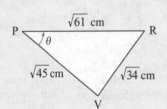

$$\cos \theta = \frac{(\sqrt{61})^2 + (\sqrt{45})^2 - (\sqrt{34})^2}{2\sqrt{61}\sqrt{45}}$$

$$= \frac{61 + 45 - 34}{2\sqrt{61}\sqrt{45}}$$

$$= \frac{72}{2\sqrt{61}\sqrt{45}}$$

$$\therefore \quad \theta = \cos^{-1}\left(\frac{36}{\sqrt{61}\sqrt{45}}\right) \approx 46.6^o$$

$\therefore$ angle RPV measures about 46.6^o.

EXERCISE 11C

1 Rodrigo wishes to determine the height of a flagpole. He takes a sighting of the top of the flagpole from point P. He then moves further away from the flagpole by 20 metres to point Q and takes a second sighting. The information is shown in the diagram alongside. How high is the flagpole?

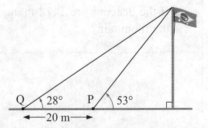

2

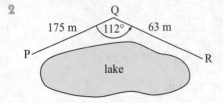

To get from P to R, a park ranger had to walk along a path to Q and then to R as shown.

What is the distance in a straight line from P to R?

3 A golfer played his tee shot a distance of 220 m to a point A. He then played a 165 m six iron to the green. If the distance from tee to green is 340 m, determine the number of degrees the golfer was off line with his tee shot.

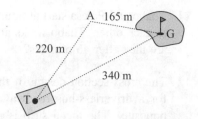

4

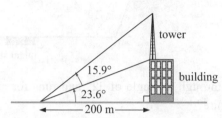

A Communications Tower is constructed on top of a building as shown. Find the height of the tower.

5 A football goal is 5 metres wide. When a player is 26 metres from one goal post and 23 metres from the other, he shoots for goal. What is the angle of view of the goals that the player sees?

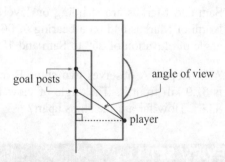

6 A tower 42 metres high stands on top of a hill. From a point some distance from the base of the hill, the angle of elevation to the top of the tower is $13.2°$ and the angle of elevation to the bottom of the tower is $8.3°$. Find the height of the hill.

7 From the foot of a building I have to look upwards at an angle of $22°$ to sight the top of a tree. From the top of the building, 150 metres above ground level, I have to look down at an angle of $50°$ below the horizontal to sight the tree top.
   a How high is the tree?   b How far from the building is this tree?

8

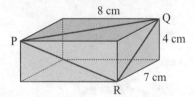

Find the measure of angle PQR in the rectangular box shown.

9 Two observation posts are 12 km apart at A and B. A third observation post C is located such that angle CAB is $42°$ and angle CBA is $67°$. Find the distance of C from both A and B.

10 Stan and Olga are considering buying a sheep farm. A surveyor has supplied them with the given accurate sketch. Find the area of the property, giving your answer in:
   a km^2 b hectares.

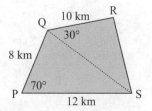

11 Thabo and Palesa start at point A. They each walk in a straight line at an angle of $120°$ to each other. Thabo walks at 6 km h^{-1} and Palesa walks at 8 km h^{-1}. How far apart are they after 45 minutes?

12 The cross-section design of the kerbing for a driverless-bus roadway is shown opposite. The metal strip is inlaid into the concrete and is used to control the direction and speed of the bus. Find the width of the metal strip.

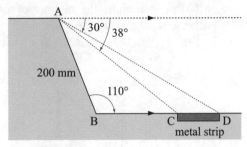

13 An orienteer runs for $4\frac{1}{2}$ km, then turns through an angle of $32°$ and runs for another 6 km. How far is she from her starting point?

14 Sam and Markus are standing on level ground 100 metres apart. A large tree is due North of Markus and on a bearing of $065°$ from Sam. The top of the tree appears at an angle of elevation of $25°$ to Sam and $15°$ to Markus. Find the height of the tree.

15 A helicopter A observes two ships B and C. B is 23.8 km from the helicopter and C is 31.9 km from it. The angle of view from the helicopter to B and C (angle BAC) is $83.6°$. How far are the ships apart?

REVIEW SET 11A

1 Determine the value of x:

a

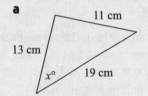

b

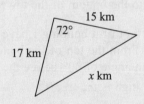

2 Find the value of x:

a

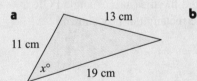

b

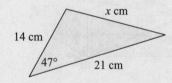

3 Find the unknown side and angles:

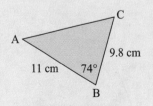

4 Find the area of quadrilateral ABCD:

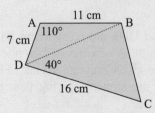

5   A vertical tree is growing on the side of a hill with slope of $10°$ to the horizontal. From a point 50 m downhill from the tree, the angle of elevation to the top of the tree is $18°$. Find the height of the tree.

6   From point A, the angle of elevation to the top of a tall building is $20°$. On walking 80 m towards the building the angle of elevation is now $23°$. How tall is the building?

7   Peter, Sue and Alix are sea-kayaking. Peter is 430 m from Sue on a bearing of $113°$ while Alix is on a bearing of $203°$ and a distance 310 m from Sue. Find the distance and bearing of Peter from Alix.

8   A family in Germany drives at 140 km h^{-1} for 45 minutes on a bearing of $032°$ and then 180 km h^{-1} for 40 minutes on a bearing $317°$. Find the distance and bearing of the car from its starting point.

9   You are given details of a triangle such that you could use either the cosine rule or the sine rule to find an unknown. Which rule should you use? Explain your answer.

10   Kady was asked to draw the illustrated triangle exactly.

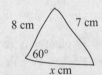

    a   Use the cosine rule to find x.

    b   What should Kady's response be?

11   Soil contractor Frank was given the following dimensions over the telephone:

The triangular garden plot ABC has angle CAB measuring $44°$, [AC] is 8 m long and [BC] is 6 m long. Soil to a depth of 10 cm is required.

    a   Explain why Frank needs extra information from his client.

    b   What is the maximum volume of soil needed if his client is unable to supply the necessary information?

REVIEW SET 11B

1   Find the measure of angle EDG:

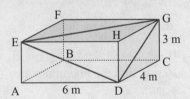

2   Hikers Andrew and Brett take separate trails from their starting point P to get to their destination at D. They walk at an angle of $40°$ apart from each other as shown, and camp overnight at positions A and B respectively. How far does Brett have to walk the next day to reach the destination?

3   Consider the kite ABCD alongside:

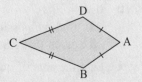

    a   Use the cosine rule to show that $A\hat{D}C = A\hat{B}C$.

    b   Use the sine rule to show that $D\hat{A}C = B\hat{A}C$.

4 A boat sailing from A to B travels in a straight line until the captain realises he is off course. The boat is turned through an angle of $60°$, then travels another 10 km to B. The trip would have been 4 km shorter if the boat had gone straight from A to B. How far did the boat travel?

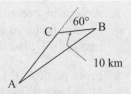

5 At 1 pm, runner A runs at 14 km h^{-1} on a bearing of $25°$, while runner B starting at the same point as A runs at 12 km h^{-1} on a bearing of $97°$.

    a At what time will A and B be 20 km apart?

    b What will be the bearing of B from A at this time?

6 Triangle ABC has [AB] of length 5 m, [AC] of length d m, [BC] of length x m, and angle ABC measures $20°$.

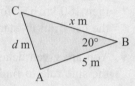

    a Find an expression for d^2 in terms of x.

    b By using the fact that, for $d > 0$, d is minimised when d^2 is minimised, find the exact value of x which minimises d.

    c Hence, show that d is minimised when $B\widehat{C}A$ is a right angle.

7 **a** Explain why $\cos(180° - \theta) = -\cos\theta$.

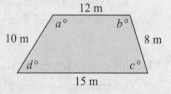

    b For the given quadrilateral:

        i Show that $300\cos d° - 192\cos b° = 117$.

        ii If $b + d = 180$, find the values of b and d.

        iii Hence, find the values of a and c.

8 **a** For the quadratic function $y = -x^2 + 12x - 20$, find the maximum or minimum value and the corresponding value of x.

    b In triangle ABC, $AB = y$, $BC = x$, $AC = 8$, and the perimeter of the triangle is 20.

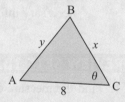

        i Write y in terms of x.

        ii Use the cosine rule to write y^2 in terms of x and $\cos\theta$.

        iii Hence show that $\cos\theta = \dfrac{3x - 10}{2x}$.

    c If the area of the triangle is A, show that $A^2 = 20(-x^2 + 12x - 20)$.

    d Hence, find the maximum area of the triangle and the triangle's shape when this occurs.

9 The given figure shows quadrilateral PQRS which has been divided into two triangles by the diagonal [QS]. $PQ = 3$, $QR = 7$, $PS = 6$, $Q\widehat{P}S = \phi$ and $Q\widehat{R}S = 32°$.

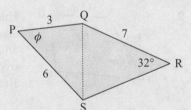

    a Find QS in terms of $\cos\phi$.

    b If $\phi = 50°$:

        i find the possible values of $R\widehat{S}Q$

        ii given that $R\widehat{S}Q$ is acute, find the perimeter of the quadrilateral.

    c Find the area of quadrilateral PQRS if $\phi = 50°$.

Chapter 12

Advanced trigonometry

Contents:

INTRODUCTION

Periodic phenomena occur all the time in the physical world. For example, in:

- seasonal variations in our climate
- variations in average maximum and minimum monthly temperatures
- the number of daylight hours at a particular location
- variations in the depth of water in a harbour due to tidal movement
- the phases of the moon
- animal populations.

These phenomena illustrate variable behaviour which is repeated over time. The repetition may be called **periodic**, **oscillatory** or **cyclic** in different situations.

In this topic we will consider how trigonometric functions can be used to model periodic phenomena. We will then extend our knowledge of the trigonometric functions by considering formulae that connect them.

OPENING PROBLEM

A Ferris wheel rotates at a constant speed. The wheel's radius is 10 m and the bottom of the wheel is 2 m above ground level. From a point in front of the wheel, Andrew is watching a green light on the perimeter of the wheel. Andrew notices that the green light moves in a circle. He estimates how high the light is above ground level at two second intervals and draws a scatterplot of his results.

- What does his scatterplot look like?
- Could a known function be used to model the data?
- How could this function be used to find the light's position at any point in time?
- How could this function be used to find the times when the light is at its maximum and minimum heights?
- What part of the function would indicate the time interval over which one complete cycle occurs?

Click on the icon to visit a simulation of the Ferris wheel.

You will be able to view the light on the Ferris wheel:

- from a position in front of the wheel
- from a side-on position
- from above the wheel.

DEMO

Observe the graph of height above (or below) the wheel's axis as the wheel rotates at a constant rate.

A | OBSERVING PERIODIC BEHAVIOUR

Consider the table below which shows the mean monthly maximum temperature (^{o}C) for Cape Town, South Africa.

Month	Jan	Feb	Mar	Apr	May	Jun	Jul	Aug	Sep	Oct	Nov	Dec
Temp	28	27	$25\frac{1}{2}$	22	$18\frac{1}{2}$	16	15	16	18	$21\frac{1}{2}$	24	26

The data is graphed alongside using a scatterplot, assigning January = 1, February = 2 etc., for the 12 months of the year.

Note: The points are not joined as interpolation has no meaning here.

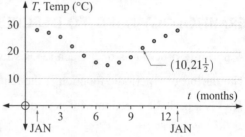

The temperature shows a variation from an average of 28°C in January through a range of values across the months and the cycle will repeat itself for the next 12 months.

It is worthwhile noting that later we will be able to establish a function which approximately fits this set of points.

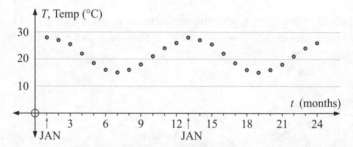

HISTORICAL NOTE

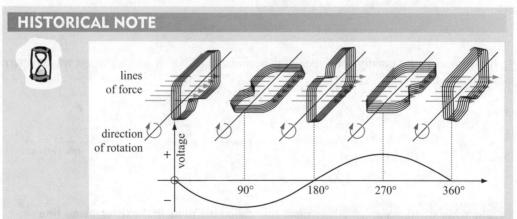

In 1831 **Michael Faraday** discovered that an electric current was generated by rotating a coil of wire in a magnetic field. The electric current produced showed a voltage which varied between positive and negative values as the coil rotated through 360°.

Graphs with this basic shape where the cycle is repeated over and over are called **sine waves**.

GATHERING PERIODIC DATA

Data on a number of periodic phenomena can be found online or in other publications. For example:

- Maximum and minimum monthly temperatures can be found at
  http://www.bom.gov.au/silo/
- Tidal details can be obtained from daily newspapers or
  http://tidesandcurrents.noaa.gov   or   http://www.bom.gov.au/oceanography

TERMINOLOGY USED TO DESCRIBE PERIODICITY

A **periodic function** is one which repeats itself over and over in a horizontal direction.

The **period** of a periodic function is the length of one repetition or cycle.

$f(x)$ is a periodic function with period $p \Leftrightarrow f(x + p) = f(x)$ for all x, and p is the smallest positive value for this to be true.

Use a **graphing package** to examine the function: $f : x \mapsto x - [x]$

where $[x]$ is "the largest integer less than or equal to x".

Is $f(x)$ periodic?   What is its period?

GRAPHING PACKAGE

A **cycloid** is another example of a periodic function. It is the curve traced out by a point on a circle as the circle moves along a flat surface. However, the cycloid function cannot be written as $y = \ldots\ldots$ or $f(x) = \ldots\ldots$

DEMO

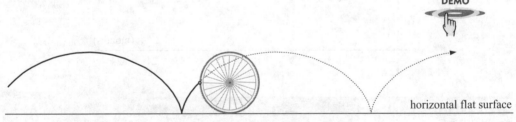

horizontal flat surface

In this course we are mainly concerned with periodic phenomena which show a wave pattern when graphed.

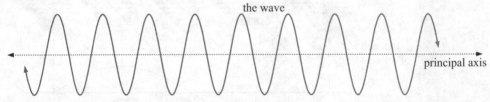

the wave

principal axis

The wave oscillates about a horizontal line called the **principal axis** or **mean line**.

A **maximum point** occurs at the top of a crest and a **minimum point** at the bottom of a trough.

The **amplitude** is the distance between a maximum (or minimum) point and the principal axis.

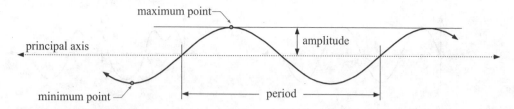

EXERCISE 12A

1 For each set of data below, draw a scatterplot and decide whether or not the data exhibits approximately periodic behaviour.

a

x	0	1	2	3	4	5	6	7	8	9	10	11	12
y	0	1	1.4	1	0	−1	−1.4	−1	0	1	1.4	1	0

b

x	0	1	2	3	4
y	4	1	0	1	4

c

x	0	0.5	1.0	1.5	2.0	2.5	3.0	3.5
y	0	1.9	3.5	4.5	4.7	4.3	3.4	2.4

d

x	0	2	3	4	5	6	7	8	9	10	12
y	0	4.7	3.4	1.7	2.1	5.2	8.9	10.9	10.2	8.4	10.4

2 The following tabled values show the height above the ground of a point on a bicycle wheel as the bicycle is wheeled along a flat surface.

Distance travelled (cm)	0	20	40	60	80	100	120	140	160	180	200
Height above ground (cm)	0	6	23	42	57	64	59	43	23	7	1

Distance travelled (cm)	220	240	260	280	300	320	340	360	380	400
Height above ground (cm)	5	27	40	55	63	60	44	24	9	3

  a Plot the graph of height against distance.
  b Is the data periodic? If so, estimate:
    i the equation of the principal axis   **ii** the maximum value
    iii the period   **iv** the amplitude.
  c Is it reasonable to fit a curve to this data, or should we leave it as discrete points?

3 Which of these graphs show periodic behaviour?

a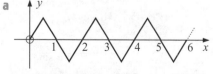

b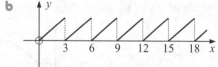

c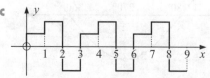

d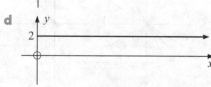

e
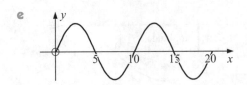

f
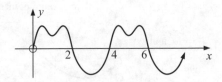

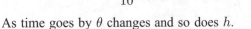

THE SINE FUNCTION

In previous studies of trigonometry we have only considered right angled triangles, or static situations where an angle θ is fixed. However, when an object moves in a circle, the situation is dynamic with the angle between the radius OP and the horizontal axis continually changing.

Consider again the **Opening Problem** in which a Ferris wheel of radius 10 m revolves at constant speed.

The height of P, the point representing the green light on the wheel relative to the principal axis O, can be determined using right angled triangle trigonometry.

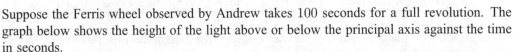

$$\text{As} \quad \sin \theta = \frac{h}{10}, \quad \text{then} \quad h = 10 \sin \theta.$$

As time goes by θ changes and so does h.

So, h is a function of θ, but more importantly h is a function of time t.

Suppose the Ferris wheel observed by Andrew takes 100 seconds for a full revolution. The graph below shows the height of the light above or below the principal axis against the time in seconds.

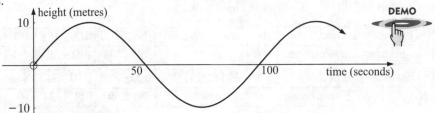

DEMO

We observe that the amplitude is 10 metres and the period is 100 seconds.

The family of sine curves can have different amplitudes and different periods. We will examine such families in this section.

THE BASIC SINE CURVE

If we project the values of $\sin \theta$ from the unit circle to the set of axes on the right we obtain the graph of $y = \sin x$.

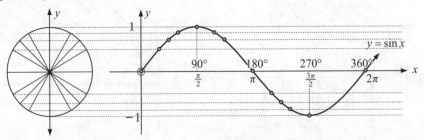

The wave of course can be continued beyond $0 \leqslant x \leqslant 2\pi$.

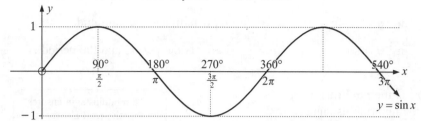

We expect the *period* to be 2π, since the Ferris wheel repeats its positioning after one full revolution.

The *maximum* value is 1 and the *minimum* is -1 as $-1 \leqslant y \leqslant 1$ on the unit circle. The *amplitude* is 1.

Use your **graphics calculator** or **graphing package** to obtain the graph of $y = \sin x$ to check these features.

When patterns of variation can be identified and quantified in terms of a formula or equation, predictions may be made about behaviour in the future. Examples of this include tidal movement which can be predicted many months ahead, and the date of a future full moon.

INVESTIGATION 1   **THE FAMILY** $y = A\sin x$

What to do:

1 Use technology to graph on the same set of axes:

   a $y = \sin x$ and $y = 2\sin x$

   b $y = \sin x$ and $y = 0.5\sin x$

   c $y = \sin x$ and $y = -\sin x$ $(A = -1)$

   If using a graphics calculator, make sure that the mode is set in **radians** and that your viewing window is appropriate.

2 For each of $y = \sin x$, $y = 2\sin x$, $y = 0.5\sin x$, $y = -\sin x$ record the maximum and minimum values and state the period and amplitude.

3 How does A affect the function $y = A\sin x$?

4 State the amplitude of:

   a $y = 3\sin x$ **b** $y = \sqrt{7}\sin x$ **c** $y = -2\sin x$

INVESTIGATION 2   **THE FAMILY** $y = \sin Bx, \quad B > 0$

What to do:

1 Use technology to graph on the same set of axes:
      a $y = \sin x$ and $y = \sin 2x$ **b** $y = \sin x$ and $y = \sin(\frac{1}{2}x)$

2 For each of $y = \sin x$, $y = \sin 2x$, $y = \sin(\frac{1}{2}x)$ record the maximum and minimum values and state the period and amplitude.

3 How does B affect the function $y = \sin Bx$?

4 State the period of:

   a $y = \sin 3x$ **b** $y = \sin(\frac{1}{3}x)$ **c** $y = \sin(1.2x)$ **d** $y = \sin Bx$

From the previous investigations you should have observed that:

- in $y = A \sin x$, $\quad |A|$ determines the amplitude
- in $y = \sin Bx$, $\quad B > 0$, $\quad B$ affects the period and the period is $\dfrac{2\pi}{B}$.

Recall $|x|$ is the **modulus** of x, or size of x ignoring its sign.

The modulus sign ensures that the final answer is non-negative. This must be so for amplitudes.

Example 1

Without using technology sketch the graphs of:
a $y = 2 \sin x$ b $y = -2 \sin x$ for $0 \leqslant x \leqslant 2\pi$.

a   The amplitude is 2 and the period is 2π.

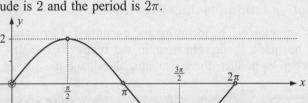

We place the 5 points as shown and fit the sine wave to them.

b   The amplitude is 2, the period is 2π, and it is the reflection of $y = 2 \sin x$ in the x-axis.

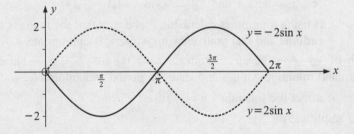

Example 2

Without using technology sketch the graph of $y = \sin 2x$, $\quad 0 \leqslant x \leqslant 2\pi$.

The period is $\dfrac{2\pi}{2} = \pi$.

So, for example, the maximum values are π units apart.

As $\sin 2x$ has half the period of $\sin x$, the first maximum is at $\frac{\pi}{4}$ not $\frac{\pi}{2}$.

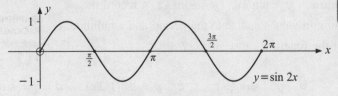

EXERCISE 12B.1

1 Without using technology sketch the graphs of the following for $0 \leqslant x \leqslant 2\pi$:

a $y = 3 \sin x$
b $y = -3 \sin x$
c $y = \frac{3}{2} \sin x$
d $y = -\frac{3}{2} \sin x$

2 Without using technology sketch the graphs of the following for $0 \leqslant x \leqslant 3\pi$:

a $y = \sin 3x$
b $y = \sin\left(\frac{x}{2}\right)$
c $y = \sin(-2x)$

3 State the period of:

a $y = \sin 4x$
b $y = \sin(-4x)$
c $y = \sin\left(\frac{x}{3}\right)$
d $y = \sin(0.6x)$

4 Find B given that the function $y = \sin Bx$, $B > 0$ has period:

a 5π
b $\frac{2\pi}{3}$
c 12π
d 4
e 100

5 Use a **graphics calculator** or **graphing package** to help you graph, for $0° \leqslant x \leqslant 720°$:

a $y = 2 \sin x + \sin 2x$
b $y = \sin x + \sin 2x + \sin 3x$
c $y = \dfrac{1}{\sin x}$

6 Use a **graphing package** or **graphics calculator** to graph:

GRAPHING PACKAGE

a $f(x) = \sin x + \dfrac{\sin 3x}{3} + \dfrac{\sin 5x}{5}$

b $f(x) = \sin x + \dfrac{\sin 3x}{3} + \dfrac{\sin 5x}{5} + \dfrac{\sin 7x}{7} + \dfrac{\sin 9x}{9} + \dfrac{\sin 11x}{11}$

Predict the graph of $f(x) = \sin x + \dfrac{\sin 3x}{3} + \dfrac{\sin 5x}{5} + \dfrac{\sin 7x}{7} + \ldots\ldots + \dfrac{\sin 1001x}{1001}$

INVESTIGATION 3   THE FAMILIES $y = \sin(x - C)$ AND $y = \sin x + D$

What to do:

1 Use technology to graph on the same set of axes:

GRAPHING PACKAGE

a $y = \sin x$ and $y = \sin(x - 2)$

b $y = \sin x$ and $y = \sin(x + 2)$

c $y = \sin x$ and $y = \sin\left(x - \frac{\pi}{3}\right)$

2 For each of $y = \sin x$, $y = \sin(x - 2)$, $y = \sin(x + 2)$, $y = \sin\left(x - \frac{\pi}{3}\right)$ record the maximum and minimum values and state the period and amplitude.

3 What transformation moves $y = \sin x$ to $y = \sin(x - C)$?

4 Use technology to graph on the same set of axes:

a $y = \sin x$ and $y = \sin x + 3$
b $y = \sin x$ and $y = \sin x - 2$

5 For each of $y = \sin x$, $y = \sin x + 3$ and $y = \sin x - 2$ record the maximum and minimum values and state the period and amplitude.

6 What transformation moves $y = \sin x$ to $y = \sin x + D$?

7 What transformation moves $y = \sin x$ to $y = \sin(x - C) + D$?

From **Investigation 3** we observe that:

- $y = \sin(x - C)$ is a **horizontal translation** of $y = \sin x$ through C units.
- $y = \sin x + D$ is a **vertical translation** of $y = \sin x$ through D units.
- $y = \sin(x - C) + D$ is a **translation** of $y = \sin x$ through vector $\begin{bmatrix} C \\ D \end{bmatrix}$.

Example 3

On the same set of axes graph for $0 \leqslant x \leqslant 4\pi$:

a $y = \sin x$ and $y = \sin(x - 1)$ **b** $y = \sin x$ and $y = \sin x - 1$

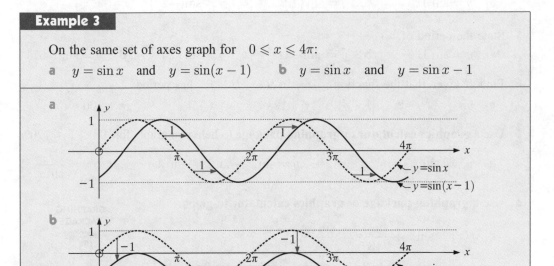

THE GENERAL SINE FUNCTION

$$y = A \sin B(x - C) + D \quad \text{is called the \textbf{general sine function}.}$$

affects **amplitude**   affects **period**   affects **horizontal translation**   affects **vertical translation**

The **principal axis** of the general sine function is $y = D$.

The **period** of the general sine function is $\dfrac{2\pi}{B}$.

Consider $y = 2 \sin 3 (x - \frac{\pi}{4}) + 1$.   It is a translation of $y = 2 \sin 3x$ under $\begin{bmatrix} \frac{\pi}{4} \\ 1 \end{bmatrix}$.

So, starting with $y = \sin x$ we would:

- double the amplitude to produce $y = 2 \sin x$,   then
- divide the period by 3 to produce $y = 2 \sin 3x$,   then
- translate by $\begin{bmatrix} \frac{\pi}{4} \\ 1 \end{bmatrix}$ to produce $y = 2 \sin 3 \left(x - \frac{\pi}{4}\right) + 1$.

EXERCISE 12B.2

1 Draw sketch graphs of:

  a $y = \sin x - 2$ **b** $y = \sin(x - 2)$ **c** $y = \sin(x + 2)$

  d $y = \sin x + 2$ **e** $y = \sin(x + \frac{\pi}{4})$ **f** $y = \sin(x - \frac{\pi}{6}) + 1$

2 Check your answers to **1** using technology.

GRAPHING PACKAGE

3 State the period of:

  a $y = \sin 5t$ **b** $y = \sin\left(\frac{t}{4}\right)$ **c** $y = \sin(-2t)$

4 Find B in $y = \sin Bx$ if $B > 0$ and the period is:

  a 3π **b** $\frac{\pi}{10}$ **c** 100π **d** 50

5 State the transformation(s) which maps:

  a $y = \sin x$ onto $y = \sin x - 1$ **b** $y = \sin x$ onto $y = \sin(x - \frac{\pi}{4})$

  c $y = \sin x$ onto $y = 2\sin x$ **d** $y = \sin x$ onto $y = \sin 4x$

  e $y = \sin x$ onto $y = \frac{1}{2}\sin x$ **f** $y = \sin x$ onto $y = \sin\left(\frac{x}{4}\right)$

  g $y = \sin x$ onto $y = -\sin x$ **h** $y = \sin x$ onto $y = -3 + \sin(x + 2)$

  i $y = \sin x$ onto $y = 2\sin 3x$ **j** $y = \sin x$ onto $y = \sin(x - \frac{\pi}{3}) + 2$

C   MODELLING USING SINE FUNCTIONS

Sine functions can be useful for modelling certain biological and physical phenomena in nature which are approximately periodic.

MEAN MONTHLY TEMPERATURE

Consider again the mean monthly maximum temperature (°C) for Cape Town:

Month	Jan	Feb	Mar	Apr	May	Jun	Jul	Aug	Sep	Oct	Nov	Dec
Temp	28	27	$25\frac{1}{2}$	22	$18\frac{1}{2}$	16	15	16	18	$21\frac{1}{2}$	24	26

The graph over a two year period is shown below:

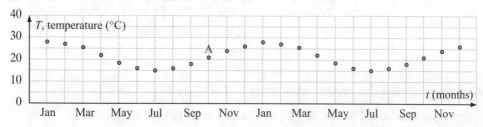

We attempt to model this data using the general sine function $y = A \sin B(x - C) + D$,

$$\text{or in this case} \quad T = A \sin B(t - C) + D.$$

The period is 12 months, so $\dfrac{2\pi}{B} = 12$ and $\therefore \quad B = \frac{\pi}{6}$.

The amplitude $= \dfrac{\text{max} - \text{min}}{2} \approx \dfrac{28 - 15}{2} \approx 6.5$, so $A \approx 6.5$.

The principal axis is midway between max. and min., so $D \approx \dfrac{28 + 15}{2} \approx 21.5$.

So, the model is $T \approx 6.5 \sin \frac{\pi}{6}(t - C) + 21.5$ for some constant C.

We notice that point A on the original graph lies on the principle axis and is a point at which we are starting a new period. $\therefore$ since A is at $(10, 21.5)$, $C = 10$.

The model is therefore $T \approx 6.5 \sin \frac{\pi}{6}(t - 10) + 21.5$ and we can superimpose it on the original data as follows.

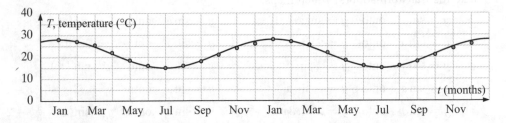

TIDAL MODELS

The tides at Juneau, Alaska were recorded over a two day period. The results are shown in the table opposite:

Day 1	high tide	1.18 pm
	low tide	6.46 am, 7.13 pm
Day 2	high tide	1.31 am, 2.09 pm
	low tide	7.30 am, 7.57 pm

Suppose high tide corresponds to height 1 and low tide to height -1.

Plotting these times with t being the time after midnight before the first low tide, we get:

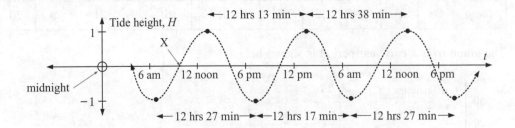

We attempt to model this periodic data using $H = A \sin B(t - C) + D$.

The principal axis is $H = 0$, so $D = 0$. The amplitude is 1, so $A = 1$.

The graph shows that the 'average' period is about 12 hours 24 min $\approx$ 12.4 hours.

But the period is $\dfrac{2\pi}{B}$. $\therefore$ $\dfrac{2\pi}{B} \approx 12.4$ and so $B \approx \dfrac{2\pi}{12.4} \approx 0.507$.

The model is now $H \approx \sin 0.507(t - C)$ for some constant C.

We find point X which is midway between the *first minimum* and the *following maximum*,

$\therefore$ $C \approx \dfrac{6.77 + 13.3}{2} \approx 10.0$.

So, the model is $H \approx \sin 0.507(t - 10.04)$.

Below is our original graph of seven plotted points and our model which attempts to fit them.

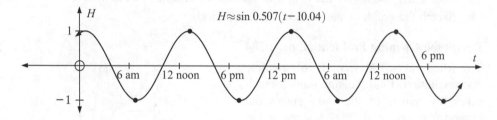

Use your **graphics calculator** to check this result.

Times must be given in hours after midnight,

i.e., $(6.77, -1)$, $(13.3, 1)$, $(19.22, -1)$,   etc.

MODELLING

EXERCISE 12C

1   Below is a table which shows the mean monthly maximum temperatures ($^\circ$C) for a city in Greece.

Month	Jan	Feb	Mar	Apr	May	Jun	July	Aug	Sept	Oct	Nov	Dec
Temperature ($^\circ$C)	15	14	15	18	21	25	27	26	24	20	18	16

    a   Use a sine function of the form $T \approx A \sin B(t - C) + D$ to model the data. Find good estimates of the constants A, B, C and D without using technology. Use   Jan $\equiv$ 1, Feb $\equiv$ 2, etc.

    b   Use technology to check your answer to **a**. How well does your model fit?

2   The data in the table shows the mean monthly temperatures for Christchurch.

Month	Jan	Feb	Mar	Apr	May	Jun	July	Aug	Sept	Oct	Nov	Dec
Temperature ($^\circ$C)	15	16	$14\frac{1}{2}$	12	10	$7\frac{1}{2}$	7	$7\frac{1}{2}$	$8\frac{1}{2}$	$10\frac{1}{2}$	$12\frac{1}{2}$	14

    a   Find a sine model for this data in the form $T \approx A \sin B(t - C) + D$.   Assume Jan $\equiv$ 1, Feb $\equiv$ 2, etc. Do not use technology.

    b   Use technology to check your answer to **a**.

3 At the Mawson base in Antarctica, the mean monthly temperatures for the last 30 years are as follows:

Month	Jan	Feb	Mar	Apr	May	Jun	July	Aug	Sept	Oct	Nov	Dec
Temperature (°C)	0	−4	−10	−15	−16	−17	−18	−19	−17	−13	−6	−1

Find a sine model for this data using your calculator. Use Jan ≡ 1, Feb ≡ 2, etc. How appropriate is the model?

4 Some of the largest tides in the world are observed in Canada's Bay of Fundy. The difference between high and low tides is 14 metres and the average time difference between high tides is about 12.4 hours.

   a Find a sine model for the height of the tide H in terms of the time t.

   b Sketch the graph of the model over one period.

5 Revisit the **Opening Problem** on page **284**.

The wheel takes 100 seconds to complete one revolution. Find the sine model which gives the height of the light above the ground at any point in time. Assume that at time $t = 0$, the light is at its lowest point.

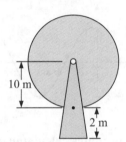

D | THE COSINE FUNCTION

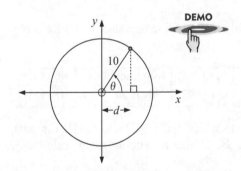

DEMO

We return to the Ferris wheel to see the cosine function being generated.

Click on the icon to inspect a simulation of the view from above the wheel.

The graph being generated over time is a **cosine function**.

This is no surprise as $\cos \theta = \dfrac{d}{10}$

and so $d = 10 \cos \theta$.

Now view the relationship between the sine and cosine functions.

Notice that the functions are identical in shape, but the cosine function is $\frac{\pi}{2}$ units left of the sine function under a horizontal translation.

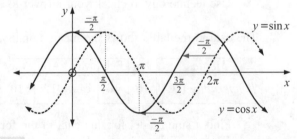

This suggests that $\boxed{\cos x = \sin \left(x + \frac{\pi}{2} \right)}.$

Use your graphing package or graphics calculator to check this by graphing $y = \cos x$ and $y = \sin \left(x + \frac{\pi}{2} \right)$.

GRAPHING PACKAGE

Example 4

On the same set of axes graph $y = \cos x$ and $y = \cos\left(x - \frac{\pi}{3}\right)$.

$y = \cos\left(x - \frac{\pi}{3}\right)$ comes from $y = \cos x$ under a horizontal translation through $\frac{\pi}{3}$.

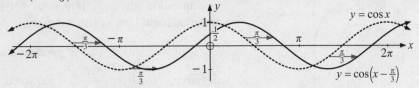

EXERCISE 12D

1 Given the graph of $y = \cos x$, sketch the graphs of:

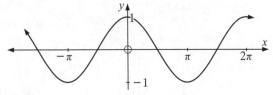

a	$y = \cos x + 2$	**b**	$y = \cos x - 1$
d	$y = \cos(x + \frac{\pi}{6})$	**e**	$y = \frac{2}{3}\cos x$
g	$y = -\cos x$	**h**	$y = \cos(x - \frac{\pi}{6}) + 1$
j	$y = \cos 2x$	**k**	$y = \cos\left(\frac{x}{2}\right)$

c $y = \cos(x - \frac{\pi}{4})$
f $y = \frac{3}{2}\cos x$
i $y = \cos(x + \frac{\pi}{4}) - 1$
l $y = 3\cos 2x$

2 Without graphing them, state the periods of:

a $y = \cos 3x$ **b** $y = \cos\left(\frac{x}{3}\right)$ **c** $y = \cos\left(\frac{\pi}{50}x\right)$

3 The general cosine function is $y = A\cos B(x - C) + D$.
State the geometrical significance of A, B, C and D.

4 For the following graphs, find the cosine function representing them:

a
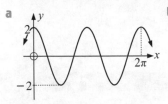

b
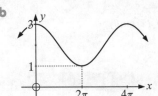

c
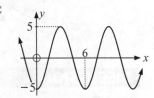

E   THE TANGENT FUNCTION

Consider the unit circle diagram given.

$P(\cos\theta, \sin\theta)$ is a point which is free to move around the circle.

In the first quadrant we extend [OP] to meet the tangent at A(1, 0) so the intersection occurs at Q. As P moves, so does Q.

The position of Q relative to A is defined as the **tangent function**.

Notice that Δs ONP and OAQ are equiangular and therefore similar.

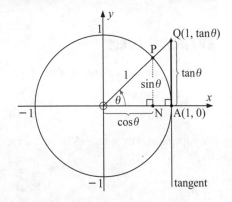

Consequently $\dfrac{AQ}{OA} = \dfrac{NP}{ON}$ i.e., $\dfrac{AQ}{1} = \dfrac{\sin\theta}{\cos\theta}$ which suggests that $\boxed{\tan\theta = \dfrac{\sin\theta}{\cos\theta}.}$

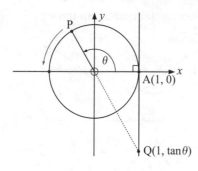

The question arises: "If P does not lie in the first quadrant, how is $\tan\theta$ defined?"

For θ obtuse, since $\sin\theta$ is positive and $\cos\theta$ is negative, $\tan\theta = \dfrac{\sin\theta}{\cos\theta}$ is negative.

As before, [PO] is extended to meet the tangent at A at Q$(1, \tan\theta)$.

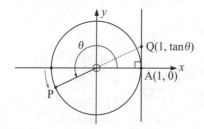

For θ in quadrant 3, $\sin\theta$ and $\cos\theta$ are both negative and so $\tan\theta$ is positive. This is clearly demonstrated as Q is back above the x-axis.

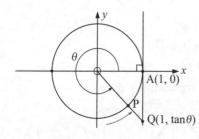

For θ in quadrant 4, $\sin\theta$ is negative and $\cos\theta$ is positive. So, $\tan\theta$ is negative.

DISCUSSION

- What is $\tan\theta$ when P is at $(0, 1)$?
- What is $\tan\theta$ when P is at $(0, -1)$?

EXERCISE 12E.1

1 Use your calculator to find the value of:

   a $\tan 0^o$ **b** $\tan 15^o$ **c** $\tan 20^o$ **d** $\tan 25^o$

   e $\tan 35^o$ **f** $\tan 45^o$ **g** $\tan 50^o$ **h** $\tan 55^o$

2 Explain why $\tan 45^o = 1$ exactly.

THE GRAPH OF $y = \tan x$

The graph of $y = \tan x$ is

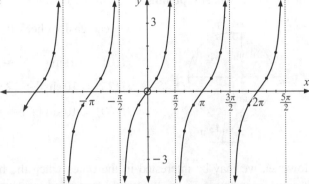

DISCUSSION

- Is the tangent function periodic? If so, what is its period?
- For what values of x does the graph not exist? What physical characteristics are shown near these values? Explain why these values must occur when $\cos x = 0$.
- Discuss how to find the x-intercepts of $y = \tan x$.
- What must $\tan(x - \pi)$ simplify to?
- How many solutions does the equation $\tan x = 2$ have?

EXERCISE 12E.2

1 **a** Use a transformation approach to *sketch* the graphs of these functions, $x \in [0, 3\pi]$:

     i $y = \tan(x - \frac{\pi}{2})$ **ii** $y = -\tan x$ **iii** $y = \tan 2x$

   b Use technology to check your answers to **a**.
     Look in particular for: • asymptotes   • x-axis intercepts.

               GRAPHING PACKAGE

2 Use the graphing package to graph, on the same set of axes:

   a $y = \tan x$ and $y = \tan(x - 1)$ **b** $y = \tan x$ and $y = -\tan x$

   c $y = \tan x$ and $y = \tan\left(\frac{x}{2}\right)$

Describe the transformation which moves the first curve to the second in each case.

               GRAPHING PACKAGE

3 What is the period of:

   a $y = \tan x$ **b** $y = \tan 2x$ **c** $y = \tan nx$?

F   TRIGONOMETRIC EQUATIONS

Linear equations such as $2x + 3 = 11$ have exactly one solution. Quadratic equations of the form $ax^2 + bx + c = 0$, $a \neq 0$ have at most two real solutions.

Trigonometric equations generally have infinitely many solutions unless a restrictive domain such as $0 \leqslant x \leqslant 3\pi$ is given.

We will examine solving trigonometric equations using:

     • preprepared graphs   • technology   • algebraic methods.

For the Ferris wheel **Opening Problem** the model is $H = 10\sin\frac{\pi}{50}(t - 25) + 12$.

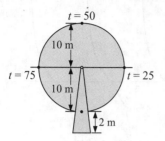

We can easily check this by substituting $t = 0, 25, 50, 75$

$$H(0) = 10\sin\left(-\frac{\pi}{2}\right) + 12 = -10 + 12 = 2 \quad \checkmark$$

$$H(25) = 10\sin 0 + 12 = 12 \quad \checkmark$$

$$H(50) = 10\sin\left(\frac{\pi}{2}\right) + 12 = 22 \quad \checkmark$$

etc.

However, we may be interested in the times when the light is some other height above the ground, for example 16 m. We would then need to solve the equation

$$10\sin\frac{\pi}{50}(t - 25) + 12 = 16 \quad \text{which is called a \textbf{sine equation}.}$$

GRAPHICAL SOLUTION OF TRIGONOMETRIC EQUATIONS

Sometimes simple sine or cosine graphs are available on grid paper. In such cases we can estimate solutions straight from the graph.

For example, we could use a graph to find approximate solutions for trigonometric equations such as $\cos\theta = 0.4$ for $0 \leqslant \theta \leqslant 10$ radians.

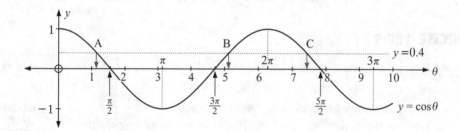

$y = 0.4$ meets $y = \cos\theta$ at A, B and C and hence $\theta \approx 1.2, 5.1$ or 7.4.

So, the solutions of $\cos\theta = 0.4$ for $0 \leqslant \theta \leqslant 10$ radians are $1.2, 5.1$ and 7.4.

EXERCISE 12F.1

1

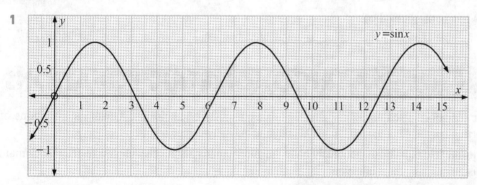

Use the graph of $y = \sin x$ to find, correct to 1 decimal place, the solutions of:

   a $\sin x = 0.3$ for $0 \leqslant x \leqslant 15$ **b** $\sin x = -0.4$ for $5 \leqslant x \leqslant 15$

2

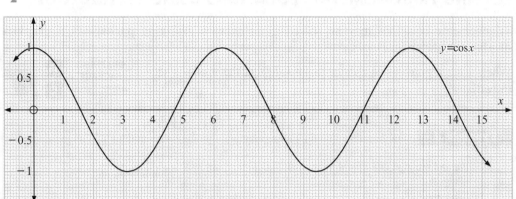

Use the graph of $y = \cos x$ to find, to 1 decimal place, approximate solutions of:

a $\cos x = 0.4, \;\; x \in [0, 10]$
b $\cos x = -0.3, \;\; x \in [4, 12]$

3

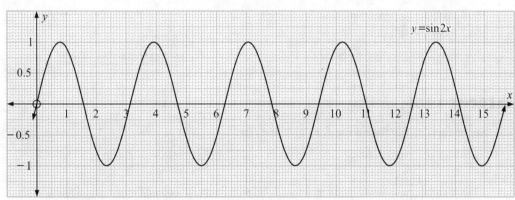

Use the graph of $y = \sin 2x$ to find, correct to 1 decimal place, the solutions of:

a $\sin 2x = 0.7, \;\; x \in [0, 16]$
b $\sin 2x = -0.3, \;\; x \in [0, 16]$

4   The graph of $y = \tan x$ is illustrated.

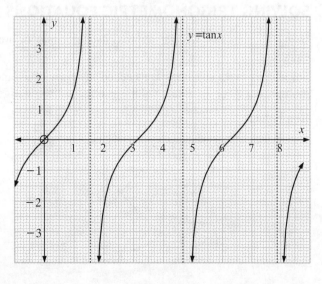

   a   Use the graph to find estimates of:

       i $\tan 1$ ii $\tan 2.3$

   b   Check your answers with a calculator.

   c   Find, correct to 1 decimal place, the solutions of:

       i $\tan x = 2$ for $0 \leqslant x \leqslant 8$

       ii $\tan x = -1.4$ for $2 \leqslant x \leqslant 7$

SOLVING TRIGONOMETRIC EQUATIONS USING TECHNOLOGY

Trigonometric equations may be solved using either a **graphing package** or a **graphics display calculator** (gdc).

When using a graphics calculator make sure that the **mode** is set to **radians**.

Example 5

Solve $2\sin x - \cos x = 4 - x$ for $0 \leqslant x \leqslant 2\pi$.

We need to use **window** settings just larger than the domain.

In this case, $X\text{min} = -\frac{\pi}{6}$ $X\text{max} = \frac{13\pi}{6}$ $X\text{scale} = \frac{\pi}{6}$

The grid facility on the gdc can also be helpful, particularly when a sketch is required.

Using the appropriate function on the gdc gives the following solutions:

$x = 1.82,\ 3.28,\ 5.81$ (3 s.f.)

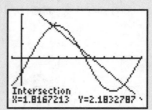

EXERCISE 12F.2

1   Solve each of the following for $0 \leqslant x \leqslant 2\pi$:

   a $\sin(x + 2) = 0.0652$

   b $\sin^2 x + \sin x - 1 = 0$

   c $x \tan\left(\dfrac{x^2}{10}\right) = x^2 - 6x + 1$

   d $2\sin(2x)\cos x = \ln x$

2   Solve for x, $-2 \leqslant x \leqslant 6$: $\cos(x - 1) + \sin(x + 1) = 6x + 5x^2 - x^3$

SOLVING TRIGONOMETRIC EQUATIONS ALGEBRAICALLY

Using a calculator we get approximate decimal or **numerical** solutions to trigonometric equations.

Sometimes exact solutions are needed in terms of π, and these arise when the solutions are multiples of $\frac{\pi}{6}$ or $\frac{\pi}{4}$. Exact solutions obtained using algebra are called **analytical** solutions.

Reminder:

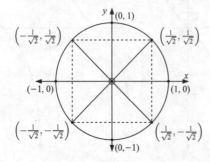

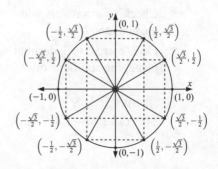

Example 6

Use the unit circle to find the exact solutions of x, $0 \leqslant x \leqslant 3\pi$ for:

a $\sin x = -\frac{1}{2}$ **b** $\sin 2x = -\frac{1}{2}$ **c** $\sin\left(x - \frac{\pi}{6}\right) = -\frac{1}{2}$

a $\sin x = -\frac{1}{2}$,   so from the unit circle

$$x = \left.\begin{array}{c} \frac{7\pi}{6} \\ \frac{11\pi}{6} \end{array}\right\} + k2\pi, \quad k \text{ an integer}$$

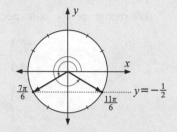

$$\therefore \quad x = \underset{\underset{k=0}{\uparrow}}{\frac{7\pi}{6}}, \quad \underset{\underset{k=0}{\uparrow}}{\frac{11\pi}{6}}, \quad \underset{\underset{k=1}{\uparrow}}{\cancel{\frac{19\pi}{6}}} \text{ is too big}$$

Substituting $k = 1, 2, 3, \dots$ gives answers outside the required domain.
Likewise $k = -1, -2, \dots$ gives answers outside the required domain.

$\therefore$ there are *two solutions*: $x = \frac{7\pi}{6}$ or $\frac{11\pi}{6}$.

b $\sin 2x = -\frac{1}{2}$ is solved in exactly the same way:

$$2x = \left.\begin{array}{c} \frac{7\pi}{6} \\ \frac{11\pi}{6} \end{array}\right\} + k2\pi, \quad k \text{ an integer}$$

$$\therefore \quad x = \left.\begin{array}{c} \frac{7\pi}{12} \\ \frac{11\pi}{12} \end{array}\right\} + k\pi \quad \{\text{divide each term by 2}\}$$

$$\therefore \quad x = \frac{7\pi}{12}, \frac{11\pi}{12}, \frac{19\pi}{12}, \frac{23\pi}{12}, \frac{31\pi}{12}, \frac{35\pi}{12} \quad \{\text{obtained by letting } k = 0, 1, 2\}$$

c $\sin\left(x - \frac{\pi}{6}\right) = -\frac{1}{2}$ is also solved in the same way:

$$x - \frac{\pi}{6} = \left.\begin{array}{c} \frac{7\pi}{6} \\ \frac{11\pi}{6} \end{array}\right\} + k2\pi$$

$$\therefore \quad x = \left.\begin{array}{c} \frac{8\pi}{6} \\ 2\pi \end{array}\right\} + k2\pi \quad \{\text{adding } \frac{\pi}{6} \text{ to both sides}\}$$

$$\therefore \quad x = \underset{\underset{k=0}{\uparrow}}{\frac{4\pi}{3}}, \quad \underset{\underset{k=0}{\uparrow}}{2\pi}, \quad \underset{\underset{k=1}{\uparrow}}{\cancel{\frac{10\pi}{3}}} \text{ is too big}, \quad \underset{\underset{k=-1}{\uparrow}}{0}$$

Don't forget to try $k = -1, -2$, etc. as sometimes we get solutions from them.

So, $x = 0$, $\frac{4\pi}{3}$ or 2π which is *three solutions*.

Example 7

Find exact solutions of $\sqrt{2}\cos\left(x - \frac{3\pi}{4}\right) + 1 = 0$ for $x \in [0, 6\pi]$.

Rearranging $\sqrt{2}\cos\left(x - \frac{3\pi}{4}\right) + 1 = 0$, we find $\cos\left(x - \frac{3\pi}{4}\right) = -\frac{1}{\sqrt{2}}$

We recognise $\frac{1}{\sqrt{2}}$ as a special fraction (for multiples of $\frac{\pi}{4}$)

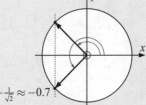

$$\therefore \quad x - \frac{3\pi}{4} = \left.\begin{array}{c}\frac{3\pi}{4} \\ \frac{5\pi}{4}\end{array}\right\} + k2\pi, \quad k \text{ an integer}$$

$$\therefore \quad x = \left.\begin{array}{c}\frac{3\pi}{2} \\ 2\pi\end{array}\right\} + k2\pi$$

$-\frac{1}{\sqrt{2}} \approx -0.7$

If $k = -1$, $x = -\frac{\pi}{2}$ or 0.   If $k = 0$, $x = \frac{3\pi}{2}$ or 2π.

If $k = 1$, $x = \frac{7\pi}{2}$ or 4π.   If $k = 2$, $x = \frac{11\pi}{2}$ or 6π.

If $k = 3$, the answers are greater than 6π.

So, the solutions are: $x = 0, \frac{3\pi}{2}, 2\pi, \frac{7\pi}{2}, 4\pi, \frac{11\pi}{2}$ or 6π.

Since the tangent function is periodic with period π we see that $\tan(x + \pi) = \tan x$ for all values of x. This means that equal tan values are π units apart.

Example 8

Find exact solutions of $\tan\left(2x - \frac{\pi}{3}\right) = 1$ for $x \in [-\pi, \pi]$

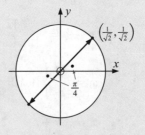

$2x - \frac{\pi}{3} = \frac{\pi}{4} + k\pi$ {since $\tan\frac{\pi}{4} = 1$}

$\therefore \quad 2x = \frac{7\pi}{12} + k\pi$

$\therefore \quad x = \frac{7\pi}{24} + k\frac{\pi}{2}$

$\therefore \quad x = -\frac{17\pi}{24}, \quad -\frac{5\pi}{24}, \quad \frac{7\pi}{24}, \quad \frac{19\pi}{24}$

$\qquad\qquad\quad \uparrow \qquad\quad \uparrow \qquad\quad \uparrow \qquad\quad \uparrow$

$\qquad\quad k = -2 \quad k = -1 \quad k = 0 \quad k = 1$

Example 9

Find the exact solutions of $\sqrt{3}\sin x = \cos x$ for $0 \leqslant x \leqslant 2\pi$.

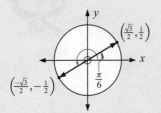

$\sqrt{3}\sin x = \cos x$

$\therefore \quad \dfrac{\sin x}{\cos x} = \dfrac{1}{\sqrt{3}}$ {dividing both sides by $\sqrt{3}\cos x$}

$\therefore \quad \tan x = \dfrac{1}{\sqrt{3}}$

$\therefore \quad x = \dfrac{\pi}{6}$ or $\dfrac{7\pi}{6}$

EXERCISE 12F.3

1 List the possible solutions for x if k is an integer and:

    a $x = \frac{\pi}{6} + k2\pi, \quad 0 \leqslant x \leqslant 6\pi$
    b $x = -\frac{\pi}{3} + k2\pi, \quad -2\pi \leqslant x \leqslant 2\pi$

    c $x = -\frac{\pi}{2} + k\pi, \quad -4\pi \leqslant x \leqslant 4\pi$
    d $x = \frac{5\pi}{6} + k\left(\frac{\pi}{2}\right), \quad 0 \leqslant x \leqslant 4\pi$

2 Find the exact solutions of:

    a $\cos x = -\frac{1}{2}, \quad x \in [0, 5\pi]$
    b $2\sin x - 1 = 0, \quad -2\pi \leqslant x \leqslant 2\pi$

    c $2\cos x + \sqrt{3} = 0, \quad 0 \leqslant x \leqslant 3\pi$
    d $\cos\left(x - \frac{2\pi}{3}\right) = \frac{1}{2}, \quad x \in [-2\pi, 2\pi]$

    e $2\sin\left(x + \frac{\pi}{3}\right) = 1, \quad x \in [-3\pi, 3\pi]$
    f $\sqrt{2}\sin\left(x - \frac{\pi}{4}\right) + 1 = 0, \quad x \in [0, 3\pi]$

3 Find the exact solutions of $\tan X = \sqrt{3}$ in terms of π only. Hence solve the equations:

    a $\tan\left(x - \frac{\pi}{6}\right) = \sqrt{3}$
    b $\tan 4x = \sqrt{3}$
    c $\tan^2 x = 3$

4 Find the zeros of:

    a $y = \sin 2x$ between 0 and π (inclusive)

    b $y = \sin(x - \frac{\pi}{4})$ between 0 and 3π (inclusive)

5   **a**   Use your graphics calculator to sketch the graphs of $y = \sin x$ and $y = \cos x$ on the same set of axes on the domain $x \in [0, 2\pi]$.

    b   Find the x values of the points of intersection of the two graphs.

    c   Confirm that these values are the solutions of $\sin x = \cos x$ on $x \in [0, 2\pi]$.

6 Find the exact solutions to these equations for $0 \leqslant x \leqslant 2\pi$:

    a $\sin x = -\cos x$
    b $\sin(3x) = \cos(3x)$
    c $\sin(2x) = \sqrt{3}\cos(2x)$

7 Check your answers to question **6** using a graphics calculator.
Find the points of intersection of the appropriate graphs.

G   USING TRIGONOMETRIC MODELS

Example 10

The height $h(t)$ metres of the tide above mean sea level on January 24th at Cape Town is modelled approximately by $h(t) = 3\sin\left(\frac{\pi t}{6}\right)$ where t is the number of hours after midnight.

    a   Graph $y = h(t)$ for $0 \leqslant t \leqslant 24$.

    b   When is high tide and what is the maximum height?

    c   What is the height at 2 pm?

    d   If a ship can cross the harbour provided the tide is at least 2 m above mean sea level, when is crossing possible on January 24?

a $h(t) = 3\sin\left(\frac{\pi t}{6}\right)$ has period $= \dfrac{2\pi}{\frac{\pi}{6}} = 2\pi \times \frac{6}{\pi} = 12$ hours   and $h(0) = 0$

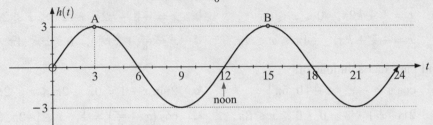

b   High tide is at 3 am and 3 pm. The maximum height is 3 m above the mean as seen at points A and B.

c   At 2 pm, $t = 14$ and $h(14) = 3\sin\left(\frac{14\pi}{6}\right) \approx 2.60$ (3 sig figs)
So the tide is 2.6 m above the mean.

d

We need to solve $h(t) = 2$ i.e., $3\sin\left(\frac{\pi t}{6}\right) = 2$.

Using a graphics calculator with $Y_1 = 3\sin\left(\frac{\pi X}{6}\right)$ and $Y_2 = 2$

we obtain $t_1 = 1.39$, $t_2 = 4.61$, $t_3 = 13.39$, $t_4 = 16.61$

or   you could **trace** across the graph to find these values.

Now   1.39 hours $= 1$ hour 23 minutes, etc.

$\therefore$ can cross between   1:23 am and 4:37 am   or   1:23 pm and 4:37 pm.

EXERCISE 12G

1   The population of grasshoppers after t weeks where $0 \leqslant t \leqslant 12$ is estimated by
$P(t) = 7500 + 3000\sin\left(\frac{\pi t}{8}\right)$.

   a   What is: **i**   the initial estimate **ii**   the estimate after 5 weeks?
   b   What is the greatest population size over this interval and when does it occur?
   c   When is the population **i**   9000   **ii**   6000?
   d   During what time interval(s) does the population size exceed 10 000?

2   The model for the height of a light on a Ferris wheel is $H(t) = 20 - 19\sin\left(\frac{2\pi t}{3}\right)$,
where H is the height in metres above the ground, and t is in minutes.

   a   Where is the light at time $t = 0$?
   b   At what time is the light at its lowest in the first revolution of the wheel?
   c   How long does the wheel take to complete one revolution?
   d   Sketch the graph of the function $H(t)$ over one revolution.

3 The population of water buffalo is given by

$P(t) = 400 + 250 \sin\left(\frac{\pi t}{2}\right)$ where t is the number of

years since the first estimate was made.

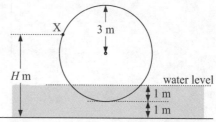

  a What was the initial estimate?
  b What was the population size after:
    i 6 months   **ii** two years?
  c Find $P(1)$. What is the significance of this value?
  d Find the smallest population size and when it first occurs.
  e Find the first time when the herd exceeded 500.

4 A paint spot X lies on the outer rim of the wheel of a paddle-steamer. The wheel has radius 3 m and as it rotates at a constant rate, X is seen entering the water every 4 seconds. H is the distance of X above the bottom of the boat. At time $t = 0$, X is at its highest point.

  a Find a cosine model for H in the form $H(t) = A\cos B(t - C) + D$.
  b At what time does X first enter the water?

5 Over a 28 day period, the cost per litre of petrol was modelled by
$C(t) = 9.2\sin\frac{\pi}{7}(t - 4) + 107.8$ cents L^{-1}.

  a True or false?
    i "The cost per litre oscillates about 107.8 cents with maximum price \$1.17."
    ii "Every 14 days, the cycle repeats itself."
  b What was the cost of petrol at day 7?
  c On what days was the petrol priced at \$1.10 per litre?
  d What was the minimum cost per litre and when did it occur?

H ▮ RECIPROCAL TRIGONOMETRIC FUNCTIONS

We define the reciprocal trigonometric functions cosec x, secant x and cotangent x as:

$$\csc x = \frac{1}{\sin x}, \qquad \sec x = \frac{1}{\cos x} \quad \text{and} \quad \cot x = \frac{1}{\tan x} = \frac{\cos x}{\sin x}$$

Note the important identities: $\tan^2 x + 1 = \sec^2 x$ and $1 + \cot^2 x = \csc^2 x$

Proof: Start with $\sin^2 x + \cos^2 x = 1$

$$\therefore \quad \frac{\sin^2 x}{\cos^2 x} + \frac{\cos^2 x}{\cos^2 x} = \frac{1}{\cos^2 x} \quad \text{\{dividing each term by } \cos^2 x\text{\}}$$

$$\therefore \quad \tan^2 x + 1 = \sec^2 x$$

To prove the second identity we instead divide each term by $\sin^2 x$.

Example 11

Use sketching techniques from **Chapter 5** to sketch the graph

of $y = \dfrac{1}{\sin x} = \csc x$ from

the graph of $y = \sin x$ for $x \in [-2\pi, 2\pi]$.

Check your answer using your calculator.

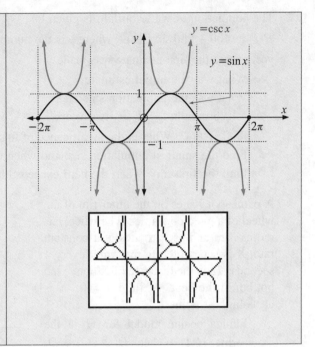

EXERCISE 12H

1 Without using a calculator, find $\csc x$, $\sec x$ and $\cot x$ for:

    a $\sin x = \frac{3}{5}$, $0 \leqslant x \leqslant \frac{\pi}{2}$ **b** $\cos x = \frac{2}{3}$, $\frac{3\pi}{2} < x < 2\pi$

2 Without using a calculator, find:

    a $\csc\left(\frac{\pi}{3}\right)$ **b** $\cot\left(\frac{2\pi}{3}\right)$ **c** $\sec\left(\frac{5\pi}{6}\right)$ **d** $\cot(\pi)$

3 Find the other *five* trigonometric ratios if:

    a $\cos x = \frac{3}{4}$ and $\frac{3\pi}{2} < x < 2\pi$ **b** $\sin x = -\frac{2}{3}$ and $\pi < x < \frac{3\pi}{2}$

    c $\sec x = 2\frac{1}{2}$ and $0 < x < \frac{\pi}{2}$ **d** $\csc x = 2$ and $\frac{\pi}{2} < x < \pi$

    e $\tan \beta = \frac{1}{2}$ and $\pi < \beta < \frac{3\pi}{2}$ **f** $\cot \theta = \frac{4}{3}$ and $\pi < \theta < \frac{3\pi}{2}$

4 Simplify:

    a $\tan x \cot x$ **b** $\sin x \csc x$ **c** $\csc x \cot x$

    d $\sin x \cot x$ **e** $\dfrac{\cot x}{\csc x}$ **f** $\dfrac{2\sin x \cot x + 3\cos x}{\cot x}$

5 Use technology to help sketch graphs on $[-2\pi, 2\pi]$ of: **a** $y = \sec x$ **b** $y = \cot x$

6 Solve for x when $x \in [0, 2\pi]$:

    a $\sec x = 2$ **b** $\csc x = -\sqrt{2}$ **c** $\cot x = 4$

    d $\sec 2x = \frac{1}{3}$ **e** $\csc 3x = -\frac{2}{3}$ **f** $\cot\left(2x - \frac{\pi}{4}\right) + 3 = 0$

TRIGONOMETRIC RELATIONSHIPS

There are a vast number of trigonometric relationships. However, we only need to remember a few because we can obtain the rest by rearrangement or substitution.

SIMPLIFYING TRIGONOMETRIC EXPRESSIONS

For any given angle θ, $\sin\theta$ and $\cos\theta$ are real numbers, so the algebra of trigonometry is identical to the algebra of real numbers.

Consequently, expressions like $2\sin\theta + 3\sin\theta$ compare with $2x + 3x$ when we wish to do simplification. So, $2\sin\theta + 3\sin\theta = 5\sin\theta$.

To simplify complicated trigonometric expressions, we often use the Pythagorean identities:

$$\sin^2\theta + \cos^2\theta = 1$$
$$\tan^2\theta + 1 = \sec^2\theta$$
$$1 + \cot^2\theta = \csc^2\theta$$

Notice that we can also use the rearrangements:

$$\sin^2\theta = 1 - \cos^2\theta \qquad \tan^2\theta = \sec^2\theta - 1$$
$$\cos^2\theta = 1 - \sin^2\theta \qquad \cot^2\theta = \csc^2\theta - 1$$

EXERCISE 12I

1 Factorise:

  a $1 - \sin^2\theta$ **b** $3\tan^2\alpha - 2\tan\alpha$ **c** $\sec^2\beta - \csc^2\beta$

  d $2\cot^2 x - 3\cot x + 1$ **e** $2\sin^2 x + 7\sin x\cos x + 3\cos^2 x$

2 Simplify:

  a $3\sin^2\theta + 3\cos^2\theta$ **b** $1 - \sec^2\beta$

  c $4 - 4\cos^2\theta$ **d** $2\cos^2\alpha - 2$

  e $\dfrac{\tan^2\theta(\cot^2\theta + 1)}{\tan^2\theta + 1}$ **f** $\cos^2\alpha(\sec^2\alpha - 1)$

  g $(2\sin\theta + 3\cos\theta)^2 + (3\sin\theta - 2\cos\theta)^2$ **h** $(1 + \csc\theta)(\sin\theta - \sin^2\theta)$

  i $\sec A - \sin A\tan A - \cos A$ **j** $1 - \dfrac{\cos^2\theta}{1 + \sin\theta}$

  k $\dfrac{1 + \cot\theta}{\csc\theta} - \dfrac{\sec\theta}{\tan\theta + \cot\theta}$ **l** $\dfrac{\cos^2\beta - \sin^2\beta}{\cos\beta - \sin\beta}$

  m $\dfrac{\tan^2\theta}{\sec\theta - 1}$

3 Prove:

  a $\sec A - \cos A = \tan A\sin A$ **b** $\dfrac{\cos\theta}{1 - \sin\theta} = \sec\theta + \tan\theta$

  c $\dfrac{\cos\alpha}{1 - \tan\alpha} + \dfrac{\sin\alpha}{1 - \cot\alpha} = \sin\alpha + \cos\alpha$ **d** $\dfrac{\sin\theta}{1 + \cos\theta} + \dfrac{1 + \cos\theta}{\sin\theta} = 2\csc\theta$

J   COMPOUND ANGLE FORMULAE

INVESTIGATION 4   COMPOUND ANGLE FORMULAE

What to do:

1 Copy and complete for angles A and B in radians or degrees:

A	B	$\cos A$	$\cos B$	$\cos(A-B)$	$\cos A - \cos B$	$\cos A \cos B + \sin A \sin B$
47°	24°					
138°	49°					
3^c	2^c					
⋮	⋮		Make sure you include some angles of your choosing.			

2 What do you suspect from the results of this table?

3 Make another table with columns A, B, $\sin A$, $\sin B$, $\sin(A+B)$,
$\sin A + \sin B$, $\sin A \cos B + \cos A \sin B$ and complete it for four sets of angles of
your choosing. What is your conclusion?

If A and B are **any** two angles then:

$$\cos(A \pm B) = \cos A \cos B \mp \sin A \sin B$$
$$\sin(A \pm B) = \sin A \cos B \pm \cos A \sin B$$
$$\tan(A \pm B) = \frac{\tan A \pm \tan B}{1 \mp \tan A \tan B}$$

These are known as the **compound angle formulae**. There are many ways of establishing
them, but many are unsatisfactory as the arguments limit the angles A and B to being acute.

Proof:

Consider   P$(\cos A, \sin A)$ and   Q$(\cos B, \sin B)$
as any two points on the unit circle, as shown.

Angle POQ is $A - B$.

Using the distance formula:

$$PQ = \sqrt{(\cos A - \cos B)^2 + (\sin A - \sin B)^2}$$
$$\therefore \ (PQ)^2 = \cos^2 A - 2\cos A \cos B + \cos^2 B + \sin^2 A - 2\sin A \sin B + \sin^2 B$$
$$= (\cos^2 A + \sin^2 A) + (\cos^2 B + \sin^2 B) - 2(\cos A \cos B + \sin A \sin B)$$
$$= 2 - 2(\cos A \cos B + \sin A \sin B) \ \ ...... \ (1)$$

But, by the *cosine rule* in $\triangle$POQ,
$$(PQ)^2 = 1^2 + 1^2 - 2(1)(1)\cos(A - B)$$
$$= 2 - 2\cos(A - B) \ \ ...... \ (2)$$
$$\therefore \ \cos(A - B) = \cos A \cos B + \sin A \sin B \quad \{\text{comparing (1) and (2)}\}$$

From this formula the other formulae can be established:
$$\cos(A + B) = \cos(A - (-B))$$
$$= \cos A \cos(-B) + \sin A \sin(-B)$$
$$= \cos A \cos B + \sin A(-\sin B) \quad \{\cos(-\theta) = \cos\theta \ \text{ and } \ \sin(-\theta) = -\sin\theta\}$$
$$= \cos A \cos B - \sin A \sin B$$

Also $\sin(A - B)$
$$= \cos(\tfrac{\pi}{2} - (A - B))$$
$$= \cos((\tfrac{\pi}{2} - A) + B)$$
$$= \cos(\tfrac{\pi}{2} - A)\cos B - \sin(\tfrac{\pi}{2} - A)\sin B$$
$$= \sin A \cos B - \cos A \sin B$$

$\sin(A + B)$
$$= \sin(A - (-B))$$
$$= \sin A \cos(-B) - \cos A \sin(-B)$$
$$= \sin A \cos B - \cos A(-\sin B)$$
$$= \sin A \cos B + \cos A \sin B$$

$\tan(A + B)$
$$= \frac{\sin(A + B)}{\cos(A + B)}$$
$$= \frac{\sin A \cos B + \cos A \sin B}{\cos A \cos B - \sin A \sin B}$$
$$= \frac{\dfrac{\sin A \cos B}{\cos A \cos B} + \dfrac{\cos A \sin B}{\cos A \cos B}}{\dfrac{\cos A \cos B}{\cos A \cos B} - \dfrac{\sin A \sin B}{\cos A \cos B}}$$
$$= \frac{\tan A + \tan B}{1 - \tan A \tan B}$$

$\tan(A - B)$
$$= \tan(A + (-B))$$
$$= \frac{\tan A + \tan(-B)}{1 - \tan A \tan(-B)}$$
$$= \frac{\tan A - \tan B}{1 + \tan A \tan B}$$
$$\{\tan(-B) = -\tan B\}$$

Example 12

Expand and simplify $\sin(270^o + \alpha)$.

$$\sin(270^o + \alpha)$$
$$= \sin 270^o \cos \alpha + \cos 270^o \sin \alpha$$
$$= -1 \times \cos \alpha + 0 \times \sin \alpha$$
$$= -\cos \alpha$$

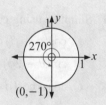

Example 13

Simplify:
$\cos 3\theta \cos \theta - \sin 3\theta \sin \theta$

$$\cos 3\theta \cos \theta - \sin 3\theta \sin \theta$$
$$= \cos(3\theta + \theta) \quad \{\text{compound formula in reverse}\}$$
$$= \cos 4\theta$$

Example 14

Without using your calculator, show that $\sin 75^o = \frac{\sqrt{6}+\sqrt{2}}{4}$.

$$\sin 75^o = \sin(45^o + 30^o)$$
$$= \sin 45^o \cos 30^o + \cos 45^o \sin 30^o$$
$$= (\tfrac{1}{\sqrt{2}})(\tfrac{\sqrt{3}}{2}) + (\tfrac{1}{\sqrt{2}})(\tfrac{1}{2})$$
$$= \left(\frac{\sqrt{3}+1}{2\sqrt{2}}\right) \frac{\sqrt{2}}{\sqrt{2}}$$
$$= \frac{\sqrt{6}+\sqrt{2}}{4}$$

EXERCISE 12J

1 Expand and simplify:

    a $\sin(90° + \theta)$ **b** $\cos(90° + \theta)$ **c** $\sin(180° - \alpha)$

    d $\cos(\pi + \alpha)$ **e** $\sin(2\pi - A)$ **f** $\cos(\frac{3\pi}{2} - \theta)$

    g $\tan\left(\frac{\pi}{4} + \theta\right)$ **h** $\tan\left(\theta - \frac{3\pi}{4}\right)$ **i** $\tan(\pi + \theta)$

2 Expand, then simplify and write your answer in the form $A\sin\theta + B\cos\theta$:

    a $\sin(\theta + \frac{\pi}{3})$ **b** $\cos(\frac{2\pi}{3} - \theta)$ **c** $\cos(\theta + \frac{\pi}{4})$ **d** $\sin(\frac{\pi}{6} - \theta)$

3 Simplify using appropriate compound formulae in reverse:

    a $\cos 2\theta \cos \theta + \sin 2\theta \sin \theta$ **b** $\sin 2A \cos A + \cos 2A \sin A$

    c $\cos A \sin B - \sin A \cos B$ **d** $\sin \alpha \sin \beta + \cos \alpha \cos \beta$

    e $\sin \phi \sin \theta - \cos \phi \cos \theta$ **f** $2\sin \alpha \cos \beta - 2\cos \alpha \sin \beta$

    g $\dfrac{\tan 2\theta - \tan \theta}{1 + \tan 2\theta \tan \theta}$ **h** $\dfrac{\tan 2A + \tan A}{1 - \tan 2A \tan A}$

4 Prove:

    a $\dfrac{\sin 2\theta}{1 + \cos 2\theta} - \tan \theta = 0$ **b** $\csc 2\theta = \tan \theta + \cot 2\theta$ **c** $\dfrac{\sin 2\theta}{\sin \theta} - \dfrac{\cos 2\theta}{\cos \theta} = \sec \theta$

5 Simplify using compound formulae:

    a $\cos(\alpha + \beta) \cos(\alpha - \beta) - \sin(\alpha + \beta) \sin(\alpha - \beta)$

    b $\sin(\theta - 2\phi) \cos(\theta + \phi) - \cos(\theta - 2\phi) \sin(\theta + \phi)$

    c $\cos \alpha \cos(\beta - \alpha) - \sin \alpha \sin(\beta - \alpha)$

6 Without using your calculator, show that the following are true:

    a $\cos 75° = \frac{\sqrt{6} - \sqrt{2}}{4}$ **b** $\sin 105° = \frac{\sqrt{6} + \sqrt{2}}{4}$ **c** $\cos\left(\frac{13\pi}{12}\right) = \frac{-\sqrt{6} - \sqrt{2}}{4}$

7 Find the exact value of each of the following: **a** $\tan\left(\frac{5\pi}{12}\right)$ **b** $\tan 105°$

8 If $\tan A = \frac{2}{3}$ and $\tan B = -\frac{1}{5}$,   find the exact value of $\tan(A + B)$.

9 If $\tan A = \frac{3}{4}$,   evaluate $\tan\left(A + \frac{\pi}{4}\right)$.

10 Simplify each of the following:

    a $\tan\left(A + \frac{\pi}{4}\right) \tan\left(A - \frac{\pi}{4}\right)$ **b** $\dfrac{\tan(A + B) + \tan(A - B)}{1 - \tan(A + B) \tan(A - B)}$

11 Simplify, giving your answer as an exact value: $\dfrac{\tan 80° - \tan 20°}{1 + \tan 80° \tan 20°}$

12 If $\tan(A + B) = \frac{3}{5}$ and $\tan B = \frac{2}{3}$,   find the exact value of $\tan A$.

13 Find $\tan A$ if $\tan(A - B) \tan(A + B) = 1$.

14 Find the exact value of $\tan \alpha$ in the diagram:

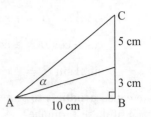

15 Find the exact value of the tangent of the acute angle between two lines if their gradients are $\frac{1}{2}$ and $\frac{2}{3}$.

16 Express $\tan(A + B + C)$ in terms of $\tan A$, $\tan B$ and $\tan C$.

Hence show that, if A, B and C are the angles of a triangle,

$$\tan A + \tan B + \tan C = \tan A \tan B \tan C.$$

17 Show that

a $\sqrt{2} \cos \left(\theta + \frac{\pi}{4}\right) = \cos \theta - \sin \theta$.

b $2 \cos \left(\theta - \frac{\pi}{3}\right) = \cos \theta + \sqrt{3} \sin \theta$.

c $\cos(\alpha + \beta) - \cos(\alpha - \beta) = -2 \sin \alpha \sin \beta$.

d $\cos(\alpha + \beta) \cos(\alpha - \beta) = \cos^2 \alpha - \sin^2 \beta$.

18 Prove that, in the given figure, $\alpha + \beta = \frac{\pi}{4}$.

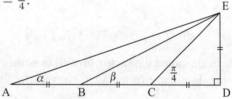

19 **a** Show that: $\sin(A + B) + \sin(A - B) = 2 \sin A \cos B$

b From **a** we notice that $\sin A \cos B = \frac{1}{2} \sin(A + B) + \frac{1}{2} \sin(A - B)$ and this formula enables us to convert a product into a sum. Use the formula to write the following as sums:

i $\sin 3\theta \cos \theta$ **ii** $\sin 6\alpha \cos \alpha$ **iii** $2 \sin 5\beta \cos \beta$

iv $4 \cos \theta \sin 4\theta$ **v** $6 \cos 4\alpha \sin 3\alpha$ **vi** $\frac{1}{3} \cos 5A \sin 3A$

20 **a** Show that $\cos(A + B) + \cos(A - B) = 2 \cos A \cos B$

b From **a** we notice that $\cos A \cos B = \frac{1}{2} \cos (A + B) + \frac{1}{2} \cos (A - B)$.

Use this formula to convert the following to a *sum* of cosines:

i $\cos 4\theta \cos \theta$ **ii** $\cos 7\alpha \cos \alpha$ **iii** $2 \cos 3\beta \cos \beta$

iv $6 \cos x \cos 7x$ **v** $3 \cos P \cos 4P$ **vi** $\frac{1}{4} \cos 4x \cos 2x$

21 **a** Show that $\cos(A - B) - \cos(A + B) = 2 \sin A \sin B$.

b From **a** we notice that $\sin A \sin B = \frac{1}{2} \cos(A - B) - \frac{1}{2} \cos(A + B)$.

Use this formula to convert the following to a *difference* of cosines:

i $\sin 3\theta \sin \theta$ **ii** $\sin 6\alpha \sin \alpha$ **iii** $2 \sin 5\beta \sin \beta$

iv $4 \sin \theta \sin 4\theta$ **v** $10 \sin 2A \sin 8A$ **vi** $\frac{1}{5} \sin 3M \sin 7M$

22

$$\sin A \cos B = \tfrac{1}{2}\sin(A+B) + \tfrac{1}{2}\sin(A-B) \quad \text{...... (1)}$$

$$\cos A \cos B = \tfrac{1}{2}\cos(A+B) + \tfrac{1}{2}\cos(A-B) \quad \text{...... (2)}$$

$$\sin A \sin B = \tfrac{1}{2}\cos(A-B) - \tfrac{1}{2}\cos(A+B) \quad \text{...... (3)}$$

are called **products to sums formulae**.   What formulae result if we replace B by A in each of these formulae?

23 Suppose $A + B = S$ and $A - B = D$.

　a Show that $A = \frac{S+D}{2}$ and $B = \frac{S-D}{2}$.

　b For the substitution $A + B = S$ and $A - B = D$,   show that equation (1) in
　　　question **22** becomes $\sin S + \sin D = 2\sin\left(\frac{S+D}{2}\right)\cos\left(\frac{S-D}{2}\right) \quad \text{...... (4)}$

　c In (4) replace D by $(-D)$ and show that $\sin S - \sin D = 2\cos\left(\frac{S+D}{2}\right)\sin\left(\frac{S-D}{2}\right)$.

　d What results when the substitution $A = \frac{S+D}{2}$ and $B = \frac{S-D}{2}$ is made into
　　　(2) of question **22**?

　e What results when the substitution $A = \frac{S+D}{2}$ and $B = \frac{S-D}{2}$ is made into
　　　(3) of question **22**?

24 From question **23** we obtain the formulae:

$$\sin S + \sin D = 2\sin\left(\tfrac{S+D}{2}\right)\cos\left(\tfrac{S-D}{2}\right) \qquad \cos S + \cos D = 2\cos\left(\tfrac{S+D}{2}\right)\cos\left(\tfrac{S-D}{2}\right)$$

$$\sin S - \sin D = 2\cos\left(\tfrac{S+D}{2}\right)\sin\left(\tfrac{S-D}{2}\right) \qquad \cos S - \cos D = -2\sin\left(\tfrac{S+D}{2}\right)\sin\left(\tfrac{S-D}{2}\right)$$

These are called the **factor formulae** as they convert sums and differences into factorised forms. Use these formulae to convert the following to products:

　a $\sin 5x + \sin x$　　　　　**b** $\cos 8A + \cos 2A$　　　　　**c** $\cos 3\alpha - \cos \alpha$

　d $\sin 5\theta - \sin 3\theta$　　　　　**e** $\cos 7\alpha - \cos \alpha$　　　　　**f** $\sin 3\alpha + \sin 7\alpha$

　g $\cos 2B - \cos 4B$　　　　　**h** $\sin(x+h) - \sin x$　　　　　**i** $\cos(x+h) - \cos x$

K   DOUBLE ANGLE FORMULAE

By replacing B by A in each of the addition compound angle formulae (on **page 310**), we obtain the **double angle formulae**.

Replacing B by A in the formula $\sin(A+B) = \sin A \cos B + \cos A \sin B$

we obtain $\sin(A+A) = \sin A \cos A + \cos A \sin A$

$$\therefore \quad \sin 2A = 2\sin A \cos A$$

Replacing B by A in the formula $\cos(A+B) = \cos A \cos B - \sin A \sin B$

we obtain $\cos(A+A) = \cos A \cos A - \sin A \sin A$

$$\therefore \quad \cos 2A = \cos^2 A - \sin^2 A$$

Two other forms of this formula can be obtained by respectively replacing $\cos^2 A$ by $1 - \sin^2 A$ and $\sin^2 A$ by $1 - \cos^2 A$.

We obtain $\cos 2A = (1 - \sin^2 A) - \sin^2 A = 1 - 2\sin^2 A$

and $\cos 2A = \cos^2 A - (1 - \cos^2 A) = 2\cos^2 A - 1$

Replacing B by A in the formula $\tan(A + B) = \dfrac{\tan A + \tan B}{1 - \tan A \tan B}$,

we obtain $\tan(A + A) = \dfrac{\tan A + \tan A}{1 - \tan A \tan A}$

$\therefore \quad \tan 2A = \dfrac{2\tan A}{1 - \tan^2 A}$

The **double angle formulae** are:

$$\sin 2A = 2\sin A \cos A$$

$$\cos 2A = \cos^2 A - \sin^2 A$$

$$= 1 - 2\sin^2 A$$

$$= 2\cos^2 A - 1$$

$$\tan 2A = \dfrac{2\tan A}{1 - \tan^2 A}$$

GRAPHING
PACKAGE

Example 15

Given that $\sin \alpha = \frac{3}{5}$ and $\cos \alpha = -\frac{4}{5}$ find:

a $\sin 2\alpha$ b $\cos 2\alpha$

a $\sin 2\alpha$
$= 2\sin \alpha \cos \alpha$
$= 2(\frac{3}{5})(-\frac{4}{5})$
$= -\frac{24}{25}$

b $\cos 2\alpha$
$= \cos^2 \alpha - \sin^2 \alpha$
$= (-\frac{4}{5})^2 - (\frac{3}{5})^2$
$= \frac{7}{25}$

Example 16

Given that $\sin \alpha = -\frac{5}{13}$ and $\cos \alpha = \frac{12}{13}$, find $\tan 2\alpha$.

$\tan \alpha = \dfrac{\sin \alpha}{\cos \alpha} = -\frac{5}{12}$

$\therefore \quad \tan 2\alpha = \dfrac{2\tan \alpha}{1 - \tan^2 \alpha} = \dfrac{2\left(-\frac{5}{12}\right)}{1 - \left(-\frac{5}{12}\right)^2} = \dfrac{-\frac{5}{6}}{1 - \frac{25}{144}} = \dfrac{-120}{144 - 25} = -\frac{120}{119}$

Example 17

If α is acute and $\cos 2\alpha = \frac{3}{4}$ find the values of **a** $\cos \alpha$ **b** $\sin \alpha$.

a
$$\cos 2\alpha = 2\cos^2 \alpha - 1$$
$$\therefore \quad \frac{3}{4} = 2\cos^2 \alpha - 1$$
$$\therefore \quad \cos^2 \alpha = \frac{7}{8}$$
$$\therefore \quad \cos \alpha = \pm \frac{\sqrt{7}}{2\sqrt{2}}$$
$$\therefore \quad \cos \alpha = \frac{\sqrt{7}}{2\sqrt{2}}$$
{as α is acute, $\cos \alpha > 0$}

b
$$\sin \alpha = \sqrt{1 - \cos^2 \alpha}$$
{as α is acute, $\sin \alpha > 0$}
$$\therefore \quad \sin \alpha = \sqrt{1 - \frac{7}{8}}$$
$$\therefore \quad \sin \alpha = \sqrt{\frac{1}{8}}$$
$$\therefore \quad \sin \alpha = \frac{1}{2\sqrt{2}}$$

Example 18

Use an appropriate 'double angle formula' to simplify:
a $3\sin\theta\cos\theta$ **b** $4\cos^2 2B - 2$

a $3\sin\theta\cos\theta$

$= \frac{3}{2}(2\sin\theta\cos\theta)$

$= \frac{3}{2}\sin 2\theta$

b $4\cos^2 2B - 2$

$= 2(2\cos^2 2B - 1)$

$= 2\cos 2(2B)$

$= 2\cos 4B$

EXERCISE 12K

1 If $\sin A = \frac{4}{5}$ and $\cos A = \frac{3}{5}$ find the values of: **a** $\sin 2A$ **b** $\cos 2A$

2 **a** If $\cos A = \frac{1}{3}$, find $\cos 2A$.   **b** If $\sin \phi = -\frac{2}{3}$, find $\cos 2\phi$.

3 **a** If $\sin \alpha = -\frac{2}{3}$ where $\pi < \alpha < \frac{3\pi}{2}$ find the value of $\cos \alpha$ and hence the value of $\sin 2\alpha$.

b If $\cos \beta = \frac{2}{5}$ where $\frac{3\pi}{2} < \beta < 2\pi$, find the value of $\sin \beta$ and hence the value of $\sin 2\beta$.

4 If α is acute and $\cos 2\alpha = -\frac{7}{9}$, find without a calculator: **a** $\cos \alpha$ **b** $\sin \alpha$

5 Find the exact value of $\tan A$ if $\tan 2A = \frac{21}{20}$ and A is obtuse.

6 Find the exact value of $\tan A$ if $\tan 2A = -\frac{12}{5}$ and A is acute.

7 Find the exact value of $\tan\left(\frac{\pi}{8}\right)$.

8 If $\sin A = -\frac{1}{3}$, $\pi \leqslant A \leqslant \frac{3\pi}{2}$ and $\cos B = \frac{1}{\sqrt{5}}$, $0 \leqslant B \leqslant \frac{\pi}{2}$, find
a $\tan(A + B)$ **b** $\tan 2A$.

9 Find the exact value of $\left[\cos\left(\frac{\pi}{12}\right) + \sin\left(\frac{\pi}{12}\right)\right]^2$.

10 Use an appropriate 'double angle' formula to simplify:

   a $2\sin\alpha\cos\alpha$ **b** $4\cos\alpha\sin\alpha$ **c** $\sin\alpha\cos\alpha$

   d $2\cos^2\beta - 1$ **e** $1 - 2\cos^2\phi$ **f** $1 - 2\sin^2 N$

   g $2\sin^2 M - 1$ **h** $\cos^2\alpha - \sin^2\alpha$ **i** $\sin^2\alpha - \cos^2\alpha$

   j $2\sin 2A\cos 2A$ **k** $2\cos 3\alpha\sin 3\alpha$ **l** $2\cos^2 4\theta - 1$

   m $1 - 2\cos^2 3\beta$ **n** $1 - 2\sin^2 5\alpha$ **o** $2\sin^2 3D - 1$

   p $\cos^2 2A - \sin^2 2A$ **q** $\cos^2(\frac{\alpha}{2}) - \sin^2(\frac{\alpha}{2})$ **r** $2\sin^2 3P - 2\cos^2 3P$

11 Show that:

GRAPHING
PACKAGE

   a $(\sin\theta + \cos\theta)^2 = 1 + \sin 2\theta$ **b** $\cos^4\theta - \sin^4\theta = \cos 2\theta$

12 Find the exact value of $\cos A$ in the diagram:

   a   **b**

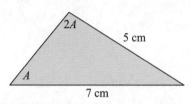
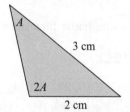

13 Find the domain and range of:

   a $x \mapsto \tan x$ **b** $x \mapsto \sec 2x$ **c** $x \mapsto \cot(3x)$

14 Prove that: **a** $\sin^2\theta = \frac{1}{2} - \frac{1}{2}\cos 2\theta$ **b** $\cos^2\theta = \frac{1}{2} + \frac{1}{2}\cos 2\theta$

15 Prove the identities:

   a $\dfrac{\sin 2\theta}{1 - \cos 2\theta} = \cot\theta$ **b** $\dfrac{\sin\theta + \sin 2\theta}{1 + \cos\theta + \cos 2\theta} = \tan\theta$

16 If $\sqrt{3}\sin x + \cos x = k\sin(x + b)$ for $k > 0$ and $0 < b < 2\pi$, find k and b.

17 Use the identity $\sin A - \sin B = 2\cos\frac{1}{2}(A + B)\sin\frac{1}{2}(A - B)$ to show that if $\sin A = \sin B$, then either $A = B + k2\pi$ or $A + B = \pi + k2\pi$, for some $k \in \mathbb{Z}$.

18 **a**   Prove that $\cos 3\theta = 4\cos^3\theta - 3\cos\theta$ by replacing 3θ by $(2\theta + \theta)$.

    b   Hence, solve the equation $8\cos^3\theta - 6\cos\theta + 1 = 0$ for $\theta \in [-\pi, \pi]$.

19 **a**   Write $\sin 3\theta$ in the form $a\sin^3\theta + b\sin\theta$ where $a, b \in \mathbb{Z}$.

    b   Hence, solve the equation $\sin 3\theta = \sin\theta$ for $\theta \in [0, 3\pi]$.

20 Use the basic definition of periodicity to show algebraically that the period of $f(x) = \sin(nx)$ is $\dfrac{2\pi}{n}$, for all $n > 0$.

21 **a**   Write $2\cos x - 5\sin x$ in the form $k\cos(x + b)$ for $k > 0$, $0 < b < 2\pi$.

    b   Use **a** to solve the equation $2\cos x - 5\sin x = -2$ for $0 \leqslant x \leqslant \pi$.

    c   Given that $t = \tan(\frac{x}{2})$, prove that $\sin x = \dfrac{2t}{1 + t^2}$ and $\cos x = \dfrac{1 - t^2}{1 + t^2}$.

    d   Solve $2\cos x - 5\sin x = -2$ for $0 \leqslant x \leqslant \pi$ using **c**.

L   TRIGONOMETRIC EQUATIONS IN QUADRATIC FORM

Sometimes we may be given trigonometric equations in quadratic form.

For example, $2 \sin^2 x + \sin x = 0$ and $2 \cos^2 x + \cos x - 1 = 0$ are clearly quadratic equations where the variables are $\sin x$ and $\cos x$ respectively.

These equations can be factorised and then solved:

$$2 \sin^2 x + \sin x = 0 \qquad \text{and} \qquad 2 \cos^2 x + \cos x + 1 = 0$$
$$\therefore \quad \sin x (2 \sin x + 1) = 0 \qquad \qquad \therefore \quad (2 \cos x - 1)(\cos x + 1) = 0$$
$$\therefore \quad \sin x = 0 \text{ or } -\tfrac{1}{2} \qquad \qquad \therefore \quad \cos x = \tfrac{1}{2} \text{ or } -1$$
$$\text{etc.} \qquad\qquad\qquad\qquad\qquad\qquad \text{etc.}$$

The use of the **quadratic formula** is often necessary.

EXERCISE 12L

1 Solve for $x \in [0, \, 2\pi]$ giving your answers as **exact** values:

 a $2 \sin^2 x + \sin x = 0$ **b** $2 \cos^2 x = \cos x$ **c** $2 \cos^2 x + \cos x - 1 = 0$

 d $2 \sin^2 x + 3 \sin x + 1 = 0$ **e** $\sin^2 x = 2 - \cos x$ **f** $3 \tan x = \cot x$

 g $\sin 4x = \sin 2x$ **h** $\sin x + \cos x = \sqrt{2}$

2 Solve for $x \in [-\pi, \, \pi]$ giving your answers as **exact** values:

 a $2 \sin x + \csc x = 3$ **b** $\sin 2x + \cos x - 2 \sin x - 1 = 0$

 c $\tan^4 x - 2 \tan^2 x - 3 = 0$

3 Solve for $x \in [0, \, 2\pi]$:

 a $2 \cos^2 x = \sin x$ **b** $\cos 2x + 5 \sin x = 0$ **c** $2 \tan^2 x + 3 \sec^2 x = 7$

M   TRIGONOMETRIC SERIES AND PRODUCTS

EXERCISE 12M

1 **a** Simplify $1 + \sin x + \sin^2 x + \sin^3 x + \sin^4 x + \dots + \sin^{n-1} x$.

 b What is the sum of the infinite series $1 + \sin x + \sin^2 x + \sin^3 x + \dots$?

 c If the series in **b** has sum $\frac{2}{3}$, find x such that $x \in [0, \, 2\pi]$.

2 We know that $2 \sin x \cos x = \sin 2x$.

 a Show that:

   i $2 \sin x (\cos x + \cos 3x) = \sin 4x$ **ii** $2 \sin x (\cos x + \cos 3x + \cos 5x) = \sin 6x$

 b What do you suspect the following would simplify to?

   i $2 \sin x (\cos x + \cos 3x + \cos 5x + \cos 7x)$

   ii $\cos x + \cos 3x + \cos 5x + \dots + \cos 19x$ (i.e.,   10 terms)

 c Write down the possible generalisation of **b ii** to n terms.

3 From $\sin 2x = 2\sin x \cos x$ we observe that $\sin x \cos x = \dfrac{\sin 2x}{2} = \dfrac{\sin(2^1 x)}{2^1}$

  a Prove that:

  i $\sin x \cos x \cos 2x = \dfrac{\sin(2^2 x)}{2^2}$ **ii** $\sin x \cos x \cos 2x \cos 4x = \dfrac{\sin(2^3 x)}{2^3}$

  b If the pattern observed in **a** continues, what would:

  i $\sin x \cos x \cos 2x \cos 4x \cos 8x$

  ii $\sin x \cos x \cos 2x .... \cos 32x$ simplify to?

  c What is the generalisation of the results in **a** and **b**?

4 **a** Use the principle of mathematical induction to prove that:

  $$\cos\theta + \cos 3\theta + \cos 5\theta + ... + \cos(2n-1)\theta = \dfrac{\sin 2n\theta}{2\sin\theta}, \quad n \in \mathbb{Z}^+.$$

  b What does $\cos\theta + \cos 3\theta + \cos 5\theta + ... + \cos 31\theta$ simplify to?

5 Use the principle of mathematical induction to prove that:
  $$\sin\theta + \sin 3\theta + \sin 5\theta + ... + \sin(2n-1)\theta = \dfrac{1-\cos 2n\theta}{2\sin\theta}$$
  for all positive integers n, and hence find the value of
  $\sin\frac{\pi}{7} + \sin\frac{3\pi}{7} + \sin\frac{5\pi}{7} + \sin\pi + \sin\frac{9\pi}{7} + \sin\frac{11\pi}{7} + \sin\frac{13\pi}{7}$.

6 Use the principle of mathematical induction to prove that:
  $$\cos x \times \cos 2x \times \cos 4x \times \cos 8x....... \cos(2^{n-1}x) = \dfrac{\sin(2^n x)}{2^n \times \sin x} \quad \text{for all } n \in \mathbb{Z}^+.$$

7 Use the principle of mathematical induction to prove that:
  $$\cos^2\theta + \cos^2 2\theta + \cos^2 3\theta + \cos^2 4\theta....... \cos^2(n\theta) = \tfrac{1}{2}\left[n + \dfrac{\cos(n+1)\theta\,\sin n\theta}{\sin\theta}\right]$$
  for all $n \in \mathbb{Z}^+$.

REVIEW SET 12A

1 Without using technology draw the graph of $y = 4\sin x$ for $0 \leqslant x \leqslant 2\pi$.

2 Without using technology draw the graph of $y = \sin 3x$ for $0 \leqslant x \leqslant 2\pi$.

3 State the period of: **a** $y = 4\sin\left(\frac{x}{3}\right)$ **b** $y = -2\tan 4x$

4 Without using technology draw a sketch graph of $y = \sin\left(x - \frac{\pi}{3}\right) + 2$.

5 The table below gives the mean monthly maximum temperature ($^\circ$C) for Perth Airport in Western Australia.

Month	Jan	Feb	Mar	Apr	May	Jun	Jul	Aug	Sep	Oct	Nov	Dec
Temp	31.5	31.8	29.5	25.4	21.5	18.8	17.7	18.3	20.1	22.4	25.5	28.8

  a A sine function of the form $T \approx A\sin B(t-C)+D$ is used to model the data. Find good estimates of the constants A, B, C and D without using technology. Use Jan $\equiv 1$, Feb $\equiv 2$, etc.

  b Check your answer to **a** using your technology. How well does your model fit?

6 Use technology to solve for $x \in [0, 8]$:

    a $\sin x = 0.382$ **b** $\tan \left(\frac{x}{2}\right) = -0.458$

7 Use technology to solve for $x \in [0, 8]$:

    a $\sin(x - 2.4) = 0.754$ **b** $\sin \left(x + \frac{\pi}{3}\right) = 0.6049$

8 Solve algebraically in terms of π:

    a $2 \sin x = -1$ for $x \in [0, 4\pi]$ **b** $\sqrt{2} \sin x - 1 = 0$ for $x \in [-2\pi, 2\pi]$

9 Solve algebraically in terms of π:

    a $2 \sin 3x + \sqrt{3} = 0$ for $x \in [0, 2\pi]$ **b** $\sec^2 x = \tan x + 1$ for $x \in [0, 2\pi]$

10 An ecologist studying a species of water beetle estimates the population of a colony over an eight week period. If t is the number of weeks after the initial estimate is made, then the population can be modelled by $P(t) = 5 + 2 \sin \left(\frac{\pi t}{3}\right)$ where $0 \leqslant t \leqslant 8$.

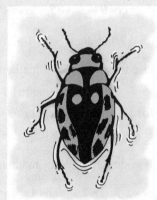

    a What was the initial population?

    b What were the smallest and largest populations?

    c During what time interval(s) did the population exceed 6000?

REVIEW SET 12B

1 Solve algebraically, giving answers in terms of π:

    a $\sin^2 x - \sin x - 2 = 0$ **b** $4 \sin^2 x = 1$

2 **a** On the same set of axes, sketch $y = \cos x$ and $y = \cos x - 3$.

    b On the same set of axes, sketch $y = \cos x$ and $y = \cos \left(x - \frac{\pi}{4}\right)$.

    c On the same set of axes, sketch $y = \cos x$ and $y = 3 \cos 2x$.

    d On the same set of axes, sketch $y = \cos x$ and $y = 2 \cos \left(x - \frac{\pi}{3}\right) + 3$.

3 In an industrial city, the amount of pollution in the air becomes greater during the working week when factories are operating, and lessens over the weekend. The number of milligrams of pollutants in a cubic metre of air is given by

$$P(t) = 40 + 12 \sin \frac{2\pi}{7} \left(t - \frac{37}{12}\right)$$

where t is the number of days after midnight on Saturday night.

    a What is the minimum level of pollution?

    b At what time during the week does this minimum level occur?

4 Find the cosine function represented in the following graphs:

a 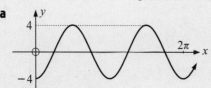   **b**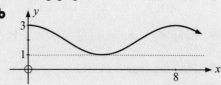

5 Use technology to solve:

    a $\cos x = 0.4379$ for $0 \leqslant x \leqslant 10$ **b** $\cos(x - 2.4) = -0.6014$ for $0 \leqslant x \leqslant 6$

6 Find the exact value of: **a** $\cos(165^{o})$ **b** $\tan\left(\frac{\pi}{12}\right)$

7 Find the exact solutions of:

    a $\tan\left(x - \frac{\pi}{3}\right) = \frac{1}{\sqrt{3}}$, $x \in [0, 4\pi]$ **b** $\cos\left(x + \frac{2\pi}{3}\right) = \frac{1}{2}$, $x \in [-2\pi, 2\pi]$

8 Find the exact solutions of:

    a $\sqrt{2}\cos\left(x + \frac{\pi}{4}\right) - 1 = 0$, $x \in [0, 4\pi]$ **b** $\tan 2x - \sqrt{3} = 0$, $x \in [0, 2\pi]$

9 Simplify: **a** $\cos^3\theta + \sin^2\theta\cos\theta$ **b** $\dfrac{\cos^2\theta - 1}{\sin\theta}$ **c** $5 - 5\sin^2\theta$

    d $\dfrac{\sin^2\theta - 1}{\cos\theta}$ **e** $\cos^2\theta\,(\tan\theta + 1)^2 - 1$

10 Expand and simplify if possible: **a** $(2\sin\alpha - 1)^2$ **b** $(\cos\alpha - \sin\alpha)^2$

REVIEW SET 12C

1 Simplify:

    a $\dfrac{1 - \cos^2\theta}{1 + \cos\theta}$ **b** $\dfrac{\sin\alpha - \cos\alpha}{\sin^2\alpha - \cos^2\alpha}$ **c** $\dfrac{4\sin^2\alpha - 4}{8\cos\alpha}$

2 Show that:

    a $\dfrac{\cos\theta}{1 + \sin\theta} + \dfrac{1 + \sin\theta}{\cos\theta} = 2\sec\theta$ **b** $\left(1 + \dfrac{1}{\cos\theta}\right)(\cos\theta - \cos^2\theta) = \sin^2\theta$.

3 If $\sin A = \frac{5}{13}$ and $\cos A = \frac{12}{13}$ find the values of: **a** $\sin 2A$ **b** $\cos 2A$

4 If $\sin\alpha = -\frac{3}{4}$, $\alpha \in [\pi, \frac{3\pi}{2}]$ find the value of $\cos\alpha$ and hence the value of $\sin 2\alpha$.

5 If $\cos x = -\frac{3}{4}$ and $\pi < x < \frac{3\pi}{2}$ find the exact value of $\sin\left(\frac{x}{2}\right)$.

6 **a** Solve algebraically:

      i $\tan x = 4$ **ii** $\tan\left(\frac{x}{4}\right) = 4$ **iii** $\tan(x - 1.5) = 4$

  b Find the exact solutions in terms of π only for:

      i $\tan\left(x + \frac{\pi}{6}\right) = -\sqrt{3}$ **ii** $\tan 2x = -\sqrt{3}$ **iii** $\tan^2 x - 3 = 0$

  c Use technology to solve $3\tan(x - 1.2) = -2$.

7 If $\tan\theta = -\frac{2}{3}$, $\frac{\pi}{2} < \theta < \pi$, find $\sin\theta$ and $\cos\theta$ without using a calculator.

8 Show that $\dfrac{\sin 2\alpha - \sin \alpha}{\cos 2\alpha - \cos \alpha + 1}$ simplifies to $\tan \alpha$.

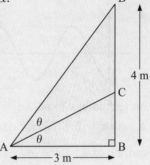

9 Simplify: **a** $\cos\left(\frac{3\pi}{2} - \theta\right)$ **b** $\sin\left(\theta + \frac{\pi}{2}\right)$

10 Find the length of BC:

REVIEW SET 12D

1 Show, in the simplest possible way, that:

a $\sqrt{2}\cos\left(\theta + \frac{\pi}{4}\right) = \cos\theta - \sin\theta$

b $\cos\alpha \cos(\beta - \alpha) - \sin\alpha \sin(\beta - \alpha) = \cos\beta$

2 If $\sin x = \frac{3}{4}$ for $x \in \left[\frac{\pi}{2}, \pi\right]$, find without using a calculator the exact values of:

a $\cos x$ **b** $\sin 2x$ **c** $\cos 2x$ **d** $\tan 2x$

3 Show that $\sin\left(\frac{\pi}{8}\right) = \frac{1}{2}\sqrt{2 - \sqrt{2}}$ using a suitable double angle formula.

4 If α and β are the other angles of a right angled triangle, show that $\sin 2\alpha = \sin 2\beta$.

5 Prove that: **a** $(\sin\theta + \cos\theta)^2 = 1 + \sin 2\theta$ **b** $\csc 2x + \cot 2x = \cot x$

6 Solve for x in $[0, 2\pi]$:   **a** $2\cos 2x + 1 = 0$ **b** $\sin 2x = -\sqrt{3}\cos 2x$

7 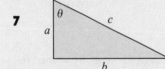   Prove that: **a** $\sin 2\theta = \dfrac{2ab}{c^2}$

   b $\cos 2\theta = \dfrac{a^2 - b^2}{c^2}$

8 If $\tan 2\alpha = \frac{4}{3}$ for $\alpha \in \left]0, \frac{\pi}{2}\right[$, find $\sin\alpha$ without using a calculator.

9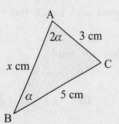

Without using a calculator:

a Show that $\cos\alpha = \frac{5}{6}$.

b Show that x is a solution of $3x^2 - 25x + 48 = 0$.

c Find x by solving the equation in **b**.

10 From ground level, a shooter is aiming at targets on a vertical brick wall. At the current angle of elevation of his rifle, he will hit a target 20 m above ground level. If he doubles the angle of elevation of the rifle, he will hit a target 45 m above ground level. How far is the shooter from the wall?

Chapter 13

Matrices

Contents:

Matrices are rectangular arrays of numbers which are used to organise information of a numeric nature. They are used in a wide array of fields extending far beyond mathematics, including:

- **Solving systems of equations** in business, physics, engineering, etc.
- **Linear programming** where we may wish to optimise a linear expression subject to linear constraints. For example, optimising profits of a business.
- **Business inventories** involving stock control, cost, revenue and profit calculations. Matrices form the basis of business computer software.
- **Markov chains** for predicting long term probabilities such as in weather.
- **Strategies in games** where we wish to maximise our chance of winning.
- **Economic modelling** where the input from various suppliers is needed to help a business be successful.
- **Graph (network) theory** used to determine routes for trucks and airlines to minimise distance travelled and therefore costs.
- **Assignment problems** to direct resources in industrial situations in the most cost effective way.
- **Forestry and fisheries management** where we need to select an appropriate sustainable harvesting policy.
- **Cubic spline interpolation** used to construct curves and fonts. Each font is stored in matrix form in the memory of a computer.
- **Computer graphics**, **flight simulation**, **Computer Aided Tomography** (CAT scanning) and **Magnetic Resonance Imaging** (MRI), **Fractals**, **Chaos**, **Genetics**, **Cryptography** (coding, code breaking, computer confidentiality), etc.

A   MATRIX STRUCTURE

A **matrix** is a rectangular array of numbers arranged in **rows** and **columns**.

In general the numbers within a matrix represent specific quantities. You have been using matrices for many years without realising it.

For example:

	Won	Lost	Drew	Points
Arsenal	24	2	4	76
Liverpool	23	3	4	73
Chelsea	21	4	5	68
Leeds	20	5	5	65
⋮				

Ingredients	Amount
sugar	1 tspn
flour	1 cup
milk	200 mL
salt	1 pinch

Consider these two items of information:

Shopping list

Bread	2 loaves
Juice	1 carton
Eggs	6
Cheese	1

Furniture inventory			
	chairs	tables	beds
Flat	6	1	2
Unit	9	2	3
House	10	3	4

We can write these tables as matrices by extracting the numbers and placing them in square or round brackets:

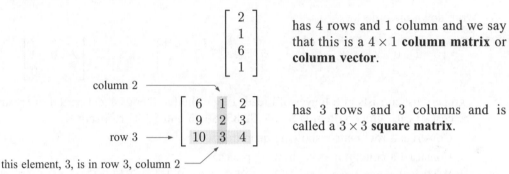

$$\begin{array}{c} \text{number} \\ \begin{array}{c} \text{B} \\ \text{J} \\ \text{E} \\ \text{C} \end{array} \begin{bmatrix} 2 \\ 1 \\ 6 \\ 1 \end{bmatrix} \end{array} \quad \text{and} \quad \begin{array}{c} \\ \text{F} \\ \text{U} \\ \text{H} \end{array} \begin{array}{ccc} \text{C} & \text{T} & \text{B} \\ \begin{bmatrix} 6 & 1 & 2 \\ 9 & 2 & 3 \\ 10 & 3 & 4 \end{bmatrix} \end{array} \quad \text{or simply} \quad \begin{bmatrix} 2 \\ 1 \\ 6 \\ 1 \end{bmatrix} \quad \text{and} \quad \begin{bmatrix} 6 & 1 & 2 \\ 9 & 2 & 3 \\ 10 & 3 & 4 \end{bmatrix}$$

Notice how the organisation of the data is maintained in matrix form.

$$\begin{bmatrix} 2 \\ 1 \\ 6 \\ 1 \end{bmatrix}$$

has 4 rows and 1 column and we say that this is a 4×1 **column matrix** or **column vector**.

column 2

row 3 $\longrightarrow$

$$\begin{bmatrix} 6 & 1 & 2 \\ 9 & 2 & 3 \\ 10 & 3 & 4 \end{bmatrix}$$

has 3 rows and 3 columns and is called a 3×3 **square matrix**.

this element, 3, is in row 3, column 2

$$\begin{bmatrix} 3 & 0 & -1 & 2 \end{bmatrix}$$

has 1 row and 4 columns and is called a 1×4 **row matrix** or **row vector**.

Note:
- An $m \times n$ matrix has m rows and n columns.

  rows columns

- $m \times n$ specifies the **order** of a matrix.

In business, a matrix can be used to represent numbers of items to be purchased, prices of items to be purchased, and so on.

Example 1

Lisa goes shopping at store A to buy 2 loaves of bread at $2.65 each, 3 litres of milk at $1.55 per litre, and one 500 g tub of butter at $2.35.

a Represent the quantities purchased in a row matrix **Q** and the costs in a column matrix **A**.

b Lisa goes to a different supermarket (store B) and finds that the prices for the same items are $2.25 for bread, $1.50 for milk, and $2.20 for butter.
Write the costs for both stores in a single costs matrix **C**.

a The quantities matrix is $\mathbf{Q} = \begin{bmatrix} 2 & 3 & 1 \end{bmatrix}$

   bread milk butter

The costs matrix is $\mathbf{A} = \begin{bmatrix} 2.65 \\ 1.55 \\ 2.35 \end{bmatrix} \begin{matrix} \leftarrow \text{bread} \\ \leftarrow \text{milk} \\ \leftarrow \text{butter} \end{matrix}$

b   We write the costs for each store in separate columns.

The new costs matrix is $C = \begin{bmatrix} 2.65 & 2.25 \\ 1.55 & 1.50 \\ 2.35 & 2.20 \end{bmatrix}$ $\begin{array}{l} \longleftarrow \text{ bread} \\ \longleftarrow \text{ milk} \\ \longleftarrow \text{ butter} \end{array}$

$\begin{array}{cc} \uparrow & \uparrow \\ \text{store A} & \text{store B} \end{array}$

EXERCISE 13A

1   Write down the order of:

   a $\begin{bmatrix} 5 & 1 & 0 & 2 \end{bmatrix}$ **b** $\begin{bmatrix} 2 \\ 7 \end{bmatrix}$ **c** $\begin{bmatrix} 2 & -1 \\ 1 & 3 \end{bmatrix}$ **d** $\begin{bmatrix} 1 & 2 & 3 \\ 2 & 0 & 4 \\ 5 & 1 & 0 \end{bmatrix}$

2   A grocery list consists of 2 loaves of bread, 1 kg of butter, 6 eggs and 1 carton of cream. The cost of each grocery item is $1.95, $2.35, $0.15 and $0.95 respectively.

   a   Construct a row matrix showing quantities.

   b   Construct a column matrix showing prices.

   c   What is the significance of $(2 \times 1.95) + (1 \times 2.35) + (6 \times 0.15) + (1 \times 0.95)$?

3   Big Bart's Baked Beans factory produces cans of baked beans in 3 sizes: 200 g, 300 g and 500 g. In February they produced respectively:

1000, 1500 and 1250 cans of each in week 1;   1500, 1000 and 1000 of each in week 2; 800, 2300 and 1300 cans of each in week 3;   1200 cans of each in week 4.

Construct a matrix to show February's production levels.

4   Over a long weekend holiday, a baker produced the following food items: On Friday he baked 40 dozen pies, 50 dozen pasties, 55 dozen rolls and 40 dozen buns. On Saturday, 25 dozen pies, 65 dozen pasties, 30 dozen buns and 44 dozen rolls were made. On Sunday 40 dozen pasties, 40 dozen rolls, 35 dozen of each of pies and buns were made. On Monday the totals were 40 dozen pasties, 50 dozen buns and 35 dozen of each of pies and rolls. Represent this information as a matrix.

B   MATRIX OPERATIONS AND DEFINITIONS

MATRIX NOTATION

Consider a matrix **A** which has order $m \times n$.

We can write $\mathbf{A} = (a_{ij})$ where $i = 1, 2, 3, ..., m$

$j = 1, 2, 3, ..., n$

and a_{ij} is the element in the ith row, jth column.

For example, a_{23} is the number in row 2 and column 3 of matrix **A**.

EQUALITY

Two matrices are **equal** if they have exactly the same shape (order) *and* the elements in corresponding positions are equal.

For example, if $\begin{bmatrix} a & b \\ c & d \end{bmatrix} = \begin{bmatrix} w & x \\ y & z \end{bmatrix}$ then $a = w,\ b = x,\ c = y$ and $d = z$.

We can write: $\mathbf{A} = \mathbf{B} \iff (a_{ij}) = (b_{ij})$ for all i, j.

MATRIX ADDITION

Thao has three stores (A, B and C). Her stock levels for dresses, skirts and blouses are given by the matrix:

$$
\begin{array}{ccc}
 & \text{Store} & \\
\text{A} & \text{B} & \text{C}
\end{array}
$$

$$
\begin{bmatrix} 23 & 41 & 68 \\ 28 & 39 & 79 \\ 46 & 17 & 62 \end{bmatrix}
\begin{array}{l} \text{dresses} \\ \text{skirts} \\ \text{blouses} \end{array}
$$

Some newly ordered stock has just arrived. For each store 20 dresses, 30 skirts and 50 blouses must be added to stock levels. Her stock order is given by the matrix:

$$
\begin{bmatrix} 20 & 20 & 20 \\ 30 & 30 & 30 \\ 50 & 50 & 50 \end{bmatrix}
$$

Clearly the new levels are shown as:

$$
\begin{bmatrix} 23 + 20 & 41 + 20 & 68 + 20 \\ 28 + 30 & 39 + 30 & 79 + 30 \\ 46 + 50 & 17 + 50 & 62 + 50 \end{bmatrix}
$$

or $\begin{bmatrix} 23 & 41 & 68 \\ 28 & 39 & 79 \\ 46 & 17 & 62 \end{bmatrix} + \begin{bmatrix} 20 & 20 & 20 \\ 30 & 30 & 30 \\ 50 & 50 & 50 \end{bmatrix} = \begin{bmatrix} 43 & 61 & 88 \\ 58 & 69 & 109 \\ 96 & 67 & 112 \end{bmatrix}$

So,   to **add** two matrices they must be of the **same order** and then we **add corresponding elements**.

MATRIX SUBTRACTION

If Thao's stock levels were $\begin{bmatrix} 29 & 51 & 19 \\ 31 & 28 & 32 \\ 40 & 17 & 29 \end{bmatrix}$ and her sales matrix for the week was $\begin{bmatrix} 15 & 12 & 6 \\ 20 & 16 & 19 \\ 19 & 8 & 14 \end{bmatrix}$ what are the current stock levels?

What Thao has left is her original stock levels less what she has sold. Clearly, we need to subtract corresponding elements:

$$
\begin{bmatrix} 29 & 51 & 19 \\ 31 & 28 & 32 \\ 40 & 17 & 29 \end{bmatrix} - \begin{bmatrix} 15 & 12 & 6 \\ 20 & 16 & 19 \\ 19 & 8 & 14 \end{bmatrix} = \begin{bmatrix} 14 & 39 & 13 \\ 11 & 12 & 13 \\ 21 & 9 & 15 \end{bmatrix}
$$

So,   to **subtract** matrices they must be of the **same order** and then we **subtract corresponding elements**.

Summary:

- $A \pm B = (a_{ij}) \pm (b_{ij}) = (a_{ij} \pm b_{ij})$

- We can only add or subtract matrices of the same order.

- We add or subtract corresponding elements.

- The result of addition or subtraction is another matrix of same order.

Example 2

If $A = \begin{bmatrix} 1 & 2 & 3 \\ 6 & 5 & 4 \end{bmatrix}$, $B = \begin{bmatrix} 2 & 1 & 6 \\ 0 & 3 & 5 \end{bmatrix}$ and $C = \begin{bmatrix} 3 & 1 \\ 2 & 4 \end{bmatrix}$ find:

a $A + B$

b $A + C$

a $A + B = \begin{bmatrix} 1 & 2 & 3 \\ 6 & 5 & 4 \end{bmatrix} + \begin{bmatrix} 2 & 1 & 6 \\ 0 & 3 & 5 \end{bmatrix}$

$= \begin{bmatrix} 1+2 & 2+1 & 3+6 \\ 6+0 & 5+3 & 4+5 \end{bmatrix}$

$= \begin{bmatrix} 3 & 3 & 9 \\ 6 & 8 & 9 \end{bmatrix}$

b $A + C$ cannot be found as A and C are not the same sized matrices i.e., they have different orders.

Example 3

If $A = \begin{bmatrix} 3 & 4 & 8 \\ 2 & 1 & 0 \\ 1 & 4 & 7 \end{bmatrix}$

and $B = \begin{bmatrix} 2 & 0 & 6 \\ 3 & 0 & 4 \\ 5 & 2 & 3 \end{bmatrix}$

find $A - B$.

$A - B = \begin{bmatrix} 3 & 4 & 8 \\ 2 & 1 & 0 \\ 1 & 4 & 7 \end{bmatrix} - \begin{bmatrix} 2 & 0 & 6 \\ 3 & 0 & 4 \\ 5 & 2 & 3 \end{bmatrix}$

$= \begin{bmatrix} 3-2 & 4-0 & 8-6 \\ 2-3 & 1-0 & 0-4 \\ 1-5 & 4-2 & 7-3 \end{bmatrix}$

$= \begin{bmatrix} 1 & 4 & 2 \\ -1 & 1 & -4 \\ -4 & 2 & 4 \end{bmatrix}$

EXERCISE 13B.1

1 If $A = \begin{bmatrix} 3 & 4 \\ 5 & 2 \end{bmatrix}$, $B = \begin{bmatrix} 6 & -3 \\ -2 & 1 \end{bmatrix}$ and $C = \begin{bmatrix} -3 & 7 \\ -4 & -2 \end{bmatrix}$, find:

a $A + B$

b $A + B + C$

c $B + C$

d $C + B - A$

2 If $P = \begin{bmatrix} 3 & 5 & -11 \\ 10 & 2 & 6 \\ -2 & -1 & 7 \end{bmatrix}$ and $Q = \begin{bmatrix} 17 & -4 & 3 \\ -2 & 8 & -8 \\ 3 & -4 & 11 \end{bmatrix}$, find:

a $P + Q$

b $P - Q$

c $Q - P$

3 A restaurant served 85 men, 92 women and 52 children on Friday night. On Saturday night they served 102 men, 137 women and 49 children.

    a Express this information in *two* column matrices.

    b Use the matrices to find the totals of men, women and children served over the Friday-Saturday period.

4 On Monday David bought shares in five companies and on Friday he sold them. The details are:

	Cost price per share	Selling price per share
A	$1.72	$1.79
B	$27.85	$28.75
C	$0.92	$1.33
D	$2.53	$2.25
E	$3.56	$3.51

    a Write down David's column matrix for:

       i cost price   **ii** selling price

    b What matrix operation is needed to find David's profit or loss matrix?

    c Find David's profit or loss matrix.

5 In November, Lou E Gee sold 23 fridges, 17 stoves and 31 microwave ovens. His partner Rose A Lee sold 19 fridges, 29 stoves and 24 microwave ovens.

In December, Lou's sales were: 18 fridges, 7 stoves and 36 microwaves while Rose's sales were: 25 fridges, 13 stoves and 19 microwaves.

    a Write their sales for November as a 3×2 matrix.

    b Write their sales for December as a 3×2 matrix.

    c Write their total sales for November and December as a 3×2 matrix.

6 Find x and y if: **a** $\begin{bmatrix} x & x^2 \\ 3 & -1 \end{bmatrix} = \begin{bmatrix} y & 4 \\ 3 & y+1 \end{bmatrix}$ **b** $\begin{bmatrix} x & y \\ y & x \end{bmatrix} = \begin{bmatrix} -y & x \\ x & -y \end{bmatrix}$

7 **a** If $A = \begin{bmatrix} 2 & 1 \\ 3 & -1 \end{bmatrix}$ and $B = \begin{bmatrix} -1 & 2 \\ 2 & 3 \end{bmatrix}$ find $A + B$ and $B + A$.

    b Explain why $A + B = B + A$ for all 2×2 matrices A and B.

8 **a** For $A = \begin{bmatrix} -1 & 0 \\ 1 & 5 \end{bmatrix}$, $B = \begin{bmatrix} 3 & 4 \\ -1 & -2 \end{bmatrix}$ and $C = \begin{bmatrix} 4 & -1 \\ -1 & 3 \end{bmatrix}$ find

    $(A + B) + C$ and $A + (B + C)$.

    b Prove that, if A, B and C are any 2×2 matrices then
$(A + B) + C = A + (B + C)$.

    Hint: Let $A = \begin{bmatrix} a & b \\ c & d \end{bmatrix}$, $B = \begin{bmatrix} p & q \\ r & s \end{bmatrix}$ and $C = \begin{bmatrix} w & x \\ y & z \end{bmatrix}$.

MULTIPLES OF MATRICES

In the pantry there are 6 cans of peaches, 4 cans of apricots and 8 cans of pears.

This information could be represented by the column vector $C = \begin{bmatrix} 6 \\ 4 \\ 8 \end{bmatrix}$.

Doubling these cans in the pantry we would have $\begin{bmatrix} 12 \\ 8 \\ 16 \end{bmatrix}$ which is $\mathbf{C} + \mathbf{C}$ or $2\mathbf{C}$.

Notice that to get $2\mathbf{C}$ from $\mathbf{C}$ we simply multiply all matrix elements by 2.

Likewise, trebling the fruit cans in the pantry gives: $3\mathbf{C} = \begin{bmatrix} 3 \times 6 \\ 3 \times 4 \\ 3 \times 8 \end{bmatrix} = \begin{bmatrix} 18 \\ 12 \\ 24 \end{bmatrix}$ and halving them gives: $\frac{1}{2}\mathbf{C} = \begin{bmatrix} \frac{1}{2} \times 6 \\ \frac{1}{2} \times 4 \\ \frac{1}{2} \times 8 \end{bmatrix} = \begin{bmatrix} 3 \\ 2 \\ 4 \end{bmatrix}$

If $\mathbf{A} = (a_{ij})$ is of order $m \times n$ and k is a scalar, then $k\mathbf{A} = (ka_{ij})$.

So, to find $k\mathbf{A}$, we multiply each element in $\mathbf{A}$ by k.

The result is another matrix of order $m \times n$.

Note: The notation we use is capital letters for matrices and lower-case letters for scalars.

Example 4

If $\mathbf{A}$ is $\begin{bmatrix} 1 & 2 & 5 \\ 2 & 0 & 1 \end{bmatrix}$

find a $3\mathbf{A}$ b $\frac{1}{2}\mathbf{A}$

a $3\mathbf{A} = 3\begin{bmatrix} 1 & 2 & 5 \\ 2 & 0 & 1 \end{bmatrix}$

$= \begin{bmatrix} 3 & 6 & 15 \\ 6 & 0 & 3 \end{bmatrix}$

b $\frac{1}{2}\mathbf{A} = \frac{1}{2}\begin{bmatrix} 1 & 2 & 5 \\ 2 & 0 & 1 \end{bmatrix}$

$= \begin{bmatrix} \frac{1}{2} & 1 & 2\frac{1}{2} \\ 1 & 0 & \frac{1}{2} \end{bmatrix}$

EXERCISE 13B.2

1 If $\mathbf{B} = \begin{bmatrix} 6 & 12 \\ 24 & 6 \end{bmatrix}$ find: a $2\mathbf{B}$ b $\frac{1}{3}\mathbf{B}$ c $\frac{1}{12}\mathbf{B}$ d $-\frac{1}{2}\mathbf{B}$

2 If $\mathbf{A} = \begin{bmatrix} 2 & 3 & 5 \\ 1 & 6 & 4 \end{bmatrix}$ and $\mathbf{B} = \begin{bmatrix} 1 & 2 & 1 \\ 1 & 2 & 3 \end{bmatrix}$ find:

   a $\mathbf{A} + \mathbf{B}$ b $\mathbf{A} - \mathbf{B}$ c $2\mathbf{A} + \mathbf{B}$ d $3\mathbf{A} - \mathbf{B}$

3 Isabelle sells clothing made by four different companies which we will call A, B, C and D. Her usual monthly order is:

	A	B	C	D
skirt	30	40	40	60
dress	50	40	30	75
evening	40	40	50	50
suit	10	20	20	15

Find her order, to the nearest whole number, if:
   a she increases her total order by 15%
   b she decreases her total order by 15%.

4 During weekdays a video store finds that its average hirings are: 75 movies (DVD), 27 movies (VHS) and 102 video/computer games. On the weekends the average figures are: 43 VHS movies, 136 DVD movies and 129 games.

    a Represent the data using *two* column matrices.

    b Find the sum of the matrices in **a**.

    c What does the sum matrix in **b** represent?

$$\begin{bmatrix} \\ \\ \\ \end{bmatrix} \begin{matrix} \longleftarrow \text{DVD} \\ \longleftarrow \text{VHS} \\ \longleftarrow \text{games} \end{matrix}$$

5 A builder builds a block of 12 identical flats. Each flat is to contain 1 table, 4 chairs, 2 beds and 1 wardrobe.

If $\mathbf{F} = \begin{bmatrix} 1 \\ 4 \\ 2 \\ 1 \end{bmatrix}$ is the matrix representing the furniture in one flat, what, in terms of **F**, is the matrix representing the furniture in **all** flats?

ZERO OR NULL MATRIX

For real numbers, it is true that $a + 0 = 0 + a = a$ for all values of a.

So, is there a matrix **O** such that $\mathbf{A} + \mathbf{O} = \mathbf{O} + \mathbf{A} = \mathbf{A}$ for any matrix **A**?

Simple examples like: $\begin{bmatrix} 2 & 3 \\ 4 & -1 \end{bmatrix} + \begin{bmatrix} 0 & 0 \\ 0 & 0 \end{bmatrix} = \begin{bmatrix} 2 & 3 \\ 4 & -1 \end{bmatrix}$ suggest that **O** consists of all zeros.

> A **zero matrix** is a matrix in which all elements are zero.

For example, the 2×2 zero matrix is $\begin{bmatrix} 0 & 0 \\ 0 & 0 \end{bmatrix}$; the 2×3 zero matrix is $\begin{bmatrix} 0 & 0 & 0 \\ 0 & 0 & 0 \end{bmatrix}$.

Zero matrices have the property that:

> If **A** is a matrix of any order and **O** is the corresponding **zero matrix**, then $\mathbf{A} + \mathbf{O} = \mathbf{O} + \mathbf{A} = \mathbf{A}$.

NEGATIVE MATRICES

> The **negative** matrix **A**, denoted $-\mathbf{A}$ is actually $-1\mathbf{A}$.

So, if $\mathbf{A} = \begin{bmatrix} 3 & -1 \\ 2 & 4 \end{bmatrix}$,   then $-\mathbf{A} = \begin{bmatrix} -1 \times 3 & -1 \times -1 \\ -1 \times 2 & -1 \times 4 \end{bmatrix} = \begin{bmatrix} -3 & 1 \\ -2 & -4 \end{bmatrix}$

Thus $-\mathbf{A}$ is obtained from **A** by reversing the sign of each element of **A**.

The addition of a matrix and its negative always produces a zero matrix. For example:

$$\begin{bmatrix} 3 & -1 \\ 2 & 4 \end{bmatrix} + \begin{bmatrix} -3 & 1 \\ -2 & -4 \end{bmatrix} = \begin{bmatrix} 0 & 0 \\ 0 & 0 \end{bmatrix}$$

Thus, in general, $\mathbf{A} + (-\mathbf{A}) = (-\mathbf{A}) + \mathbf{A} = \mathbf{O}$.

MATRIX ALGEBRA

Compare our discoveries about matrices so far with ordinary algebra.

We will assume that **A** and **B** are matrices of the same order.

Ordinary algebra	Matrix algebra
• If a and b are real numbers then $a + b$ is also a real number.	• If **A** and **B** are matrices then **A**+**B** is a matrix of the same order.
• $a + b = b + a$	• $\mathbf{A} + \mathbf{B} = \mathbf{B} + \mathbf{A}$
• $(a + b) + c = a + (b + c)$	• $(\mathbf{A} + \mathbf{B}) + \mathbf{C} = \mathbf{A} + (\mathbf{B} + \mathbf{C})$
• $a + 0 = 0 + a = a$	• $\mathbf{A} + \mathbf{O} = \mathbf{O} + \mathbf{A} = \mathbf{A}$
• $a + (-a) = (-a) + a = 0$	• $\mathbf{A} + (-\mathbf{A}) = (-\mathbf{A}) + \mathbf{A} = \mathbf{O}$
• a half of a is $\dfrac{a}{2}$	• a half of **A** is $\frac{1}{2}\mathbf{A}$ $\left(\text{not } \dfrac{\mathbf{A}}{2}\right)$

Example 5

Explain why it is true that:

a if $\mathbf{X} + \mathbf{A} = \mathbf{B}$ then $\mathbf{X} = \mathbf{B} - \mathbf{A}$ **b** if $3\mathbf{X} = \mathbf{A}$ then $\mathbf{X} = \frac{1}{3}\mathbf{A}$

a   If $\mathbf{X} + \mathbf{A} = \mathbf{B}$

then $\mathbf{X} + \mathbf{A} + (-\mathbf{A}) = \mathbf{B} + (-\mathbf{A})$

$\therefore \ \mathbf{X} + \mathbf{O} = \mathbf{B} - \mathbf{A}$

$\therefore \ \mathbf{X} = \mathbf{B} - \mathbf{A}$

b   If $3\mathbf{X} = \mathbf{A}$

then $\frac{1}{3}(3\mathbf{X}) = \frac{1}{3}\mathbf{A}$

$\therefore \ 1\mathbf{X} = \frac{1}{3}\mathbf{A}$

$\therefore \ \mathbf{X} = \frac{1}{3}\mathbf{A}$

EXERCISE 13B.3

1 Simplify:

  a $\mathbf{A} + 2\mathbf{A}$ **b** $3\mathbf{B} - 3\mathbf{B}$ **c** $\mathbf{C} - 2\mathbf{C}$

  d $-\mathbf{B} + \mathbf{B}$ **e** $2(\mathbf{A} + \mathbf{B})$ **f** $-(\mathbf{A} + \mathbf{B})$

  g $-(2\mathbf{A} - \mathbf{C})$ **h** $3\mathbf{A} - (\mathbf{B} - \mathbf{A})$ **i** $\mathbf{A} + 2\mathbf{B} - (\mathbf{A} - \mathbf{B})$

2 Find **X** in terms of **A**, **B** and **C** if:

  a $\mathbf{X} + \mathbf{B} = \mathbf{A}$ **b** $\mathbf{B} + \mathbf{X} = \mathbf{C}$ **c** $4\mathbf{B} + \mathbf{X} = 2\mathbf{C}$

  d $2\mathbf{X} = \mathbf{A}$ **e** $3\mathbf{X} = \mathbf{B}$ **f** $\mathbf{A} - \mathbf{X} = \mathbf{B}$

  g $\frac{1}{2}\mathbf{X} = \mathbf{C}$ **h** $2(\mathbf{X} + \mathbf{A}) = \mathbf{B}$ **i** $\mathbf{A} - 4\mathbf{X} = \mathbf{C}$

3 **a** If $\mathbf{M} = \begin{bmatrix} 1 & 2 \\ 3 & 6 \end{bmatrix}$, find **X** if $\frac{1}{3}\mathbf{X} = \mathbf{M}$.

  b If $\mathbf{N} = \begin{bmatrix} 2 & -1 \\ 3 & 5 \end{bmatrix}$, find **X** if $4\mathbf{X} = \mathbf{N}$.

  c If $\mathbf{A} = \begin{bmatrix} 1 & 0 \\ -1 & 2 \end{bmatrix}$ and $\mathbf{B} = \begin{bmatrix} 1 & 4 \\ -1 & 1 \end{bmatrix}$, find **X** if $\mathbf{A} - 2\mathbf{X} = 3\mathbf{B}$.

MATRIX MULTIPLICATION

Suppose you go to a shop and purchase 3 soft drink cans, 4 chocolate bars and 2 icecreams. We can represent this by the quantities matrix $\mathbf{A} = \begin{bmatrix} 3 & 4 & 2 \end{bmatrix}$.

If the prices are:

soft drink cans	chocolate bars	ice creams
$1.30	$0.90	$1.20

then we can represent these using the costs matrix $\mathbf{B} = \begin{bmatrix} 1.30 \\ 0.90 \\ 1.20 \end{bmatrix}$.

We can find the total cost of the items by multiplying the number of each item by its respective cost, and then adding the results. The total cost is thus

$$3 \times \$1.30 + 4 \times \$0.90 + 2 \times \$1.20 = \$9.90$$

We can also determine the total cost by the **matrix multiplication**:

$$\mathbf{AB} = \begin{bmatrix} 3 & 4 & 2 \end{bmatrix} \begin{bmatrix} 1.30 \\ 0.90 \\ 1.20 \end{bmatrix}$$

$$= (3 \times 1.30) + (4 \times 0.90) + (2 \times 1.20)$$

$$= 9.90$$

Notice that we write the **row matrix** first and the **column matrix** second.

In general,

$$\begin{bmatrix} a & b & c \end{bmatrix} \begin{bmatrix} p \\ q \\ r \end{bmatrix} = ap + bq + cr.$$

EXERCISE 13B.4

1 Determine:

a $\begin{bmatrix} 3 & -1 \end{bmatrix} \begin{bmatrix} 5 \\ 4 \end{bmatrix}$ b $\begin{bmatrix} 1 & 3 & 2 \end{bmatrix} \begin{bmatrix} 5 \\ 1 \\ 7 \end{bmatrix}$ c $\begin{bmatrix} 6 & -1 & 2 & 3 \end{bmatrix} \begin{bmatrix} 1 \\ 0 \\ -1 \\ 4 \end{bmatrix}$

2 Show that the sum of w, x, y and z is given by $\begin{bmatrix} w & x & y & z \end{bmatrix} \begin{bmatrix} 1 \\ 1 \\ 1 \\ 1 \end{bmatrix}$.

Represent the average of w, x, y and z in the same way.

3 Lucy buys 4 shirts, 3 skirts and 2 blouses costing $27, $35 and $39 respectively.

a Write down a quantities matrix $\mathbf{Q}$ and a price matrix $\mathbf{P}$.

b Show how to use $\mathbf{P}$ and $\mathbf{Q}$ to determine the total cost.

4 In the interschool public speaking competition a first place is awarded 10 points, second place 6 points, third place 3 points and fourth place 1 point. One school won 3 first places, 2 seconds, 4 thirds and 2 fourths.

a Write down this information in terms of points matrix $\mathbf{P}$ and a numbers matrix $\mathbf{N}$.

b Show how to use $\mathbf{P}$ and $\mathbf{N}$ to find the total number of points awarded to the school.

MORE COMPLICATED MULTIPLICATIONS

Consider again **Example 1** on page **325** where Lisa needed 2 loaves of bread, 3 litres of milk and 1 tub of butter.

We represented this by the quantities matrix $\mathbf{Q} = \begin{bmatrix} 2 & 3 & 1 \end{bmatrix}$.

The prices for each store were summarised in the costs matrix $\mathbf{C} = \begin{bmatrix} 2.65 & 2.25 \\ 1.55 & 1.50 \\ 2.35 & 2.20 \end{bmatrix}$.

To find the *total cost* of the items in each store, Lisa needs to multiply the number of items by their respective cost.

In Store A a loaf of bread is \$2.65, a litre of milk is \$1.55 and a tub of butter is \$2.35, so the total cost is
$$2 \times \$2.65 + 3 \times \$1.55 + 1 \times \$2.35 = \$12.30$$

In Store B a loaf of bread is \$2.25, a litre of milk is \$1.50 and a tub of butter is \$2.20, so the total cost is
$$2 \times \$2.25 + 3 \times \$1.50 + 1 \times \$2.20 = \$11.20$$

To do this using matrices notice that:

$$\mathbf{QC} = \begin{bmatrix} 2 & 3 & 1 \end{bmatrix} \times \begin{bmatrix} 2.65 & 2.25 \\ 1.55 & 1.50 \\ 2.35 & 2.20 \end{bmatrix} = \begin{bmatrix} 12.30 & 11.20 \end{bmatrix}$$

orders: 1×3 ← the same → 3×2 1×2
                └──── resultant matrix ────┘

Now suppose Lisa's friend Olu needs 1 loaf of bread, 2 litres of milk and 2 tubs of butter.

The quantities matrix for both Lisa and Olu would be $\begin{bmatrix} 2 & 3 & 1 \\ 1 & 2 & 2 \end{bmatrix}$ ← Lisa ← Olu

bread   milk   butter

Lisa's *total cost* at   Store A is \$12.30 and at store B is \$11.20

Olu's *total cost* at   Store A is $1 \times \$2.65 + 2 \times \$1.55 + 2 \times \$2.35 = \$10.45$

Store B is $1 \times \$2.25 + 2 \times \$1.50 + 2 \times \$2.20 = \$9.65$

So, using matrices we require that

$$\begin{bmatrix} 2 & 3 & 1 \\ 1 & 2 & 2 \end{bmatrix} \times \begin{bmatrix} 2.65 & 2.25 \\ 1.55 & 1.50 \\ 2.35 & 2.20 \end{bmatrix} = \begin{bmatrix} 12.30 & 11.20 \\ 10.45 & 9.65 \end{bmatrix}$$

row 1 × column 1   row 1 × column 2   row 2 × column 1   row 2 × column 2

2×3 ← the same → 3×2 2×2
└──── resultant matrix ────┘

Having observed the usefulness of multiplying matrices in the contextual examples above, we are now in a position to define matrix multiplication more formally.

The **product** of an $m \times n$ matrix $\mathbf{A}$ with an $n \times p$ matrix $\mathbf{B}$, is the $m \times p$ matrix $\mathbf{AB}$ in which the element in the rth row and cth column is the sum of the products of the elements in the rth row of $\mathbf{A}$ with the corresponding elements in the cth column of $\mathbf{B}$.

If $\mathbf{C} = \mathbf{AB}$ then $(c_{ij}) = \sum_{r=1}^{n} a_{ir} b_{rj} = a_{i1}b_{1j} + a_{i2}b_{2j} + \ldots\ldots + a_{in}b_{nj}$

for each pair i and j with $1 \leqslant i \leqslant m$ and $1 \leqslant j \leqslant p$.

Note: The product $\mathbf{AB}$ exists *only* if the number of columns of $\mathbf{A}$ equals the number of rows of $\mathbf{B}$.

For example:

If $\mathbf{A} = \begin{bmatrix} a & b \\ c & d \end{bmatrix}$ and $\mathbf{B} = \begin{bmatrix} p & q \\ r & s \end{bmatrix}$, then $\mathbf{AB} = \begin{bmatrix} ap+br & aq+bs \\ cp+dr & cq+ds \end{bmatrix}$.

If $\underset{2 \times 3}{\mathbf{C} = \begin{bmatrix} a & b & c \\ d & e & f \end{bmatrix}}$ and $\underset{3 \times 1}{\mathbf{D} = \begin{bmatrix} x \\ y \\ z \end{bmatrix}}$, then $\underset{2 \times 1}{\mathbf{CD} = \begin{bmatrix} ax+by+cz \\ dx+ey+fz \end{bmatrix}}$.

To get the matrix $\mathbf{AB}$ you multiply **rows by columns**. To get the element in the 5th row and 3rd column of $\mathbf{AB}$ (if it exists) multiply the 5th row of $\mathbf{A}$ by the 3rd column of $\mathbf{B}$.

Example 6

If $\mathbf{A} = \begin{bmatrix} 1 & 3 & 5 \end{bmatrix}$, $\mathbf{B} = \begin{bmatrix} 1 & 3 & 5 \\ 2 & 1 & 3 \end{bmatrix}$, and $\mathbf{C} = \begin{bmatrix} 1 & 0 \\ 2 & 3 \\ 1 & 4 \end{bmatrix}$ find: **a** $\mathbf{AC}$ **b** $\mathbf{BC}$

a $\mathbf{A}$ is 1×3 and $\mathbf{C}$ is 3×2 $\therefore$ $\mathbf{AC}$ is 1×2

$\mathbf{AC} = \begin{bmatrix} 1 & 3 & 5 \end{bmatrix} \begin{bmatrix} 1 & 0 \\ 2 & 3 \\ 1 & 4 \end{bmatrix}$

$= \begin{bmatrix} 1 \times 1 + 3 \times 2 + 5 \times 1 & 1 \times 0 + 3 \times 3 + 5 \times 4 \end{bmatrix}$

$= \begin{bmatrix} 12 & 29 \end{bmatrix}$

b $\mathbf{B}$ is 2×3 and $\mathbf{C}$ is 3×2 $\therefore$ $\mathbf{BC}$ is 2×2

$\mathbf{BC} = \begin{bmatrix} 1 & 3 & 5 \\ 2 & 1 & 3 \end{bmatrix} \begin{bmatrix} 1 & 0 \\ 2 & 3 \\ 1 & 4 \end{bmatrix}$

$= \begin{bmatrix} 1 \times 1 + 3 \times 2 + 5 \times 1 & 1 \times 0 + 3 \times 3 + 5 \times 4 \\ 2 \times 1 + 1 \times 2 + 3 \times 1 & 2 \times 0 + 1 \times 3 + 3 \times 4 \end{bmatrix}$

$= \begin{bmatrix} 12 & 29 \\ 7 & 15 \end{bmatrix}$

EXERCISE 13B.5

1 Explain why **AB** cannot be found for $\mathbf{A} = \begin{bmatrix} 4 & 2 & 1 \end{bmatrix}$ and $\mathbf{B} = \begin{bmatrix} 1 & 2 & 1 \\ 0 & 1 & 0 \end{bmatrix}$.

2 If **A** is $2 \times n$ and **B** is $m \times 3$:

   a When can we find **AB**?   **b** If **AB** can be found, what is its order?

   c Why can **BA** never be found?

3 **a** For $\mathbf{A} = \begin{bmatrix} 2 & 1 \\ 3 & 4 \end{bmatrix}$ and $\mathbf{B} = \begin{bmatrix} 5 & 6 \end{bmatrix}$ find **i** **AB**   **ii** **BA**.

   b For $\mathbf{A} = \begin{bmatrix} 2 & 0 & 3 \end{bmatrix}$ and $\mathbf{B} = \begin{bmatrix} 1 \\ 4 \\ 2 \end{bmatrix}$ find **i** **AB**   **ii** **BA**.

4 Find: **a** $\begin{bmatrix} 1 & 2 & 1 \end{bmatrix} \begin{bmatrix} 2 & 3 & 1 \\ 0 & 1 & 0 \\ 1 & 0 & 2 \end{bmatrix}$ **b** $\begin{bmatrix} 1 & 0 & -1 \\ -1 & 1 & 0 \\ 0 & -1 & 1 \end{bmatrix} \begin{bmatrix} 2 \\ 3 \\ 4 \end{bmatrix}$

5

At a fair, tickets for the Ferris wheel are $12.50 per adult and $9.50 per child. On the first day of the fair, 2375 adults and 5156 children ride this wheel. On the second day the figures are 2502 adults and 3612 children.

   a Write the costs matrix **C** as a 2×1 matrix and the numbers matrix **N** as a 2×2 matrix.

   b Find **NC** and interpret the resulting matrix.

   c Find the total income for the two days.

6 You and your friend each go to your local hardware stores A and B to price items you wish to purchase. You want to buy 1 hammer, 1 screwdriver and 2 cans of white paint and your friend wants 1 hammer, 2 screwdrivers and 3 cans of white paint. The prices of these goods are:

	Hammer	Screwdriver	Can of paint
Store A	€7	€3	€19
Store B	€6	€2	€22

   a Write the requirements matrix **R** as a 3×2 matrix.

   b Write the prices matrix **P** as a 2×3 matrix.

   c Find **PR**.

   d What are your costs at store A and your friend's costs at store B?

   e Should you buy from store A or store B?

USING TECHNOLOGY FOR MATRIX OPERATIONS

Click on the appropriate icon to obtain **graphics calculator** instructions on how to perform operations with matrices.

Alternatively, click on the **Matrix Operations** icon to obtain computer software for these tasks.

MATRIX OPERATIONS

EXERCISE 13B.6

1 Use technology to find:

a $\begin{bmatrix} 13 & 12 & 4 \\ 11 & 12 & 8 \\ 7 & 9 & 7 \end{bmatrix} + \begin{bmatrix} 3 & 6 & 11 \\ 2 & 9 & 8 \\ 3 & 13 & 17 \end{bmatrix}$

b $\begin{bmatrix} 13 & 12 & 4 \\ 11 & 12 & 8 \\ 7 & 9 & 7 \end{bmatrix} - \begin{bmatrix} 3 & 6 & 11 \\ 2 & 9 & 8 \\ 3 & 13 & 17 \end{bmatrix}$

c $22 \begin{bmatrix} 1 & 0 & 6 & 8 & 9 \\ 2 & 7 & 4 & 5 & 0 \\ 8 & 2 & 4 & 4 & 6 \end{bmatrix}$

d $\begin{bmatrix} 2 & 6 & 0 & 7 \\ 3 & 2 & 8 & 6 \\ 1 & 4 & 0 & 2 \\ 3 & 0 & 1 & 8 \end{bmatrix} \begin{bmatrix} 4 \\ 5 \\ 6 \\ 11 \end{bmatrix}$

Use technology to assist in solving the following problems:

2 For their holiday, Lars and Simke are planning to spend time at a popular tourist resort. They will need accommodation at one of the local motels and they are not certain how long they will stay. Their initial planning is for three nights and includes three breakfasts and two dinners. They have gathered prices from three different motels.

The Bay View has rooms at $125 per night. A full breakfast costs $22 per person (and therefore $44 for them both). An evening meal for two usually costs $75 including drinks.

By contrast, 'The Terrace' has rooms at $150 per night, breakfast at $40 per double and dinner costs on average $80.

Things seem to be a little better at the Staunton Star Motel. Accommodation is $140 per night, full breakfast (for two) is $40, while an evening meal for two usually costs $65.

a Write down a 'numbers' matrix as a 1×3 row matrix.

b Write down a 'prices' matrix in 3×3 form.

c Use matrix multiplication to establish total prices for each venue.

d Instead of the couple staying three nights, the alternative is to spend just two nights. In that event Lars and Simke decide on having breakfast just once and one evening meal before moving on. Recalculate prices for each venue.

e Now remake the 'numbers' matrix (2×3) so that it includes both scenarios. Calculate the product with the 'prices' matrix to check your answers to c and d.

3 A bus company runs four tours. Tour A costs $125, Tour B costs $315, Tour C costs $405, and Tour D costs $375. The numbers of clients they had over the summer period are shown in the table below.

	Tour A	Tour B	Tour C	Tour D
November	50	42	18	65
December	65	37	25	82
January	120	29	23	75
February	42	36	19	72

Use the information and matrix methods to find the total income for the tour company.

4 The Oregon Motel has three types of suites for guests.

Standard suites cost $125 per night. They have 20 suites.

Deluxe suites cost $195 per night. They have 15 suites.

Executive suites cost $225 per night. They have 5 suites.

The rooms which are occupied also have a maintenance cost:

Standard suites cost $85 per day to maintain.

Deluxe suites cost $120 per day to maintain.

Executive suites cost $130 per day to maintain.

The hotel has confirmed room bookings for the next week:

	M	T	W	Th	F	S	Su
Standard	15	12	13	11	14	16	8
Deluxe	4	3	6	2	0	4	7
Executive	3	1	4	4	3	2	0

a The profit per day is given by

(income from room) × (bookings per day)

− (maintenance cost per room) × (bookings per day)

Create the matrices required to show how the profit per week can be found.

b How would the results alter if the hotel maintained (cleaned) all rooms every day? Show calculations.

c Produce a profit per room matrix and show how **a** could be done with a single matrix product.

PROPERTIES OF MATRIX MULTIPLICATION

In the following exercise we should discover the properties of 2×2 matrix multiplication which are like those of ordinary number multiplication, and those which are not.

EXERCISE 13B.7

1 For ordinary arithmetic $2 \times 3 = 3 \times 2$ and in algebra $ab = ba$.

For matrices, does **AB** always equal **BA**?

Hint: Try $\mathbf{A} = \begin{bmatrix} 1 & 0 \\ 1 & 2 \end{bmatrix}$ and $\mathbf{B} = \begin{bmatrix} -1 & 1 \\ 0 & 3 \end{bmatrix}$.

2 If $\mathbf{A} = \begin{bmatrix} a & b \\ c & d \end{bmatrix}$ and $\mathbf{O} = \begin{bmatrix} 0 & 0 \\ 0 & 0 \end{bmatrix}$ find **AO** and **OA**.

3 For all real numbers a, b and c it is true that $a(b + c) = ab + ac$. This is known as the **distributive law**.

a Use any three 2×2 matrices **A**, **B** and **C** to verify that $\mathbf{A}(\mathbf{B} + \mathbf{C}) = \mathbf{AB} + \mathbf{AC}$.

b Now let $\mathbf{A} = \begin{bmatrix} a & b \\ c & d \end{bmatrix}$, $\mathbf{B} = \begin{bmatrix} p & q \\ r & s \end{bmatrix}$ and $\mathbf{C} = \begin{bmatrix} w & x \\ y & z \end{bmatrix}$.

Prove that in general, $\mathbf{A}(\mathbf{B} + \mathbf{C}) = \mathbf{AB} + \mathbf{AC}$.

c Use the matrices you 'made up' in **a** to verify that $(\mathbf{AB})\mathbf{C} = \mathbf{A}(\mathbf{BC})$.

d Prove that $(\mathbf{AB})\mathbf{C} = \mathbf{A}(\mathbf{BC})$.

4 **a** If $\begin{bmatrix} a & b \\ c & d \end{bmatrix} \begin{bmatrix} w & x \\ y & z \end{bmatrix} = \begin{bmatrix} a & b \\ c & d \end{bmatrix}$ i.e., $\mathbf{AX} = \mathbf{A}$,

show that $w = z = 1$ and $x = y = 0$ is a solution.

b For any real number a, it is true that $a \times 1 = 1 \times a = a$.

Is there a matrix $\mathbf{I}$ such that $\mathbf{AI} = \mathbf{IA} = \mathbf{A}$ for all 2×2 matrices $\mathbf{A}$?

5 Suppose $\mathbf{A}^2 = \mathbf{AA}$ or $\mathbf{A} \times \mathbf{A}$ and that $\mathbf{A}^3 = \mathbf{AAA}$.

a Find $\mathbf{A}^2$ if $\mathbf{A} = \begin{bmatrix} 2 & 1 \\ 3 & -2 \end{bmatrix}$
b Find $\mathbf{A}^3$ if $\mathbf{A} = \begin{bmatrix} 5 & -1 \\ 2 & 4 \end{bmatrix}$.

6 **a** If $\mathbf{A} = \begin{bmatrix} 1 & 2 \\ 3 & 4 \\ 5 & 6 \end{bmatrix}$ try to find $\mathbf{A}^2$.

b When can $\mathbf{A}^2$ be found, i.e., under what conditions can we square a matrix?

7 Show that if $\mathbf{I} = \begin{bmatrix} 1 & 0 \\ 0 & 1 \end{bmatrix}$ then $\mathbf{I}^2 = \mathbf{I}$ and $\mathbf{I}^3 = \mathbf{I}$.

$\mathbf{I} = \begin{bmatrix} 1 & 0 \\ 0 & 1 \end{bmatrix}$ is called the **identity matrix**.

You should have discovered from the above exercise that:

Ordinary algebra	Matrix algebra
• If a and b are real numbers then so is ab.	• If $\mathbf{A}$ and $\mathbf{B}$ are matrices that can be multiplied then $\mathbf{AB}$ is also a matrix. {closure}
• $ab = ba$ for all a, b	• In general $\mathbf{AB} \neq \mathbf{BA}$. {non-commutative}
• $a0 = 0a = 0$ for all a	• If $\mathbf{O}$ is a zero matrix then $\mathbf{AO} = \mathbf{OA} = \mathbf{O}$ for all $\mathbf{A}$.
• $a(b + c) = ab + ac$	• $\mathbf{A}(\mathbf{B} + \mathbf{C}) = \mathbf{AB} + \mathbf{AC}$ {distributive law}
• $a \times 1 = 1 \times a = a$	• If $\mathbf{I}$ is the **identity matrix** $\begin{bmatrix} 1 & 0 \\ 0 & 1 \end{bmatrix}$ then $\mathbf{AI} = \mathbf{IA} = \mathbf{A}$ for all 2×2 matrices $\mathbf{A}$. {identity law}
• a^n exists for all $a \geqslant 0$ and $n \in \mathbb{R}$.	• $\mathbf{A}^n$ exists provided $\mathbf{A}$ is square and $n \in \mathbb{Z}^+$.

Note: In general, $\mathbf{A}(k\mathbf{B}) = k(\mathbf{AB}) \neq k\mathbf{BA}$. We can change the order in which we multiply by a scalar, but in general we cannot reverse the order in which we multiply matrices.

Example 7

Expand and simplify where possible: a $(\mathbf{A} + 2\mathbf{I})^2$ b $(\mathbf{A} - \mathbf{B})^2$

a $(\mathbf{A} + 2\mathbf{I})^2$
$= (\mathbf{A} + 2\mathbf{I})(\mathbf{A} + 2\mathbf{I})$ $\{\mathbf{X}^2 = \mathbf{XX}$ by definition$\}$
$= (\mathbf{A} + 2\mathbf{I})\mathbf{A} + (\mathbf{A} + 2\mathbf{I})2\mathbf{I}$ $\{\mathbf{B}(\mathbf{C} + \mathbf{D}) = \mathbf{BC} + \mathbf{BD}\}$
$= \mathbf{A}^2 + 2\mathbf{IA} + 2\mathbf{AI} + 4\mathbf{I}^2$ $\{\mathbf{B}(\mathbf{C} + \mathbf{D}) = \mathbf{BC} + \mathbf{BD}$ again, twice$\}$
$= \mathbf{A}^2 + 2\mathbf{A} + 2\mathbf{A} + 4\mathbf{I}$ $\{\mathbf{AI} = \mathbf{IA} = \mathbf{A}$ and $\mathbf{I}^2 = \mathbf{I}\}$
$= \mathbf{A}^2 + 4\mathbf{A} + 4\mathbf{I}$

b $(\mathbf{A} - \mathbf{B})^2$
$= (\mathbf{A} - \mathbf{B})(\mathbf{A} - \mathbf{B})$ $\{\mathbf{X}^2 = \mathbf{XX}$ by definition$\}$
$= (\mathbf{A} - \mathbf{B})\mathbf{A} - (\mathbf{A} - \mathbf{B})\mathbf{B}$ $\{\mathbf{C}(\mathbf{D} - \mathbf{E}) = \mathbf{CD} - \mathbf{CE}$ twice$\}$
$= \mathbf{A}^2 - \mathbf{BA} - \mathbf{AB} + \mathbf{B}^2$

Note: b cannot be simplified further since, in general, $\mathbf{AB} \neq \mathbf{BA}$.

Example 8

If $\mathbf{A}^2 = 2\mathbf{A} + 3\mathbf{I}$,   find $\mathbf{A}^3$ and $\mathbf{A}^4$ in the form $k\mathbf{A} + l\mathbf{I}$ where k and l are scalars.

$\mathbf{A}^3 = \mathbf{A} \times \mathbf{A}^2$ $\mathbf{A}^4 = \mathbf{A} \times \mathbf{A}^3$
$= \mathbf{A}(2\mathbf{A} + 3\mathbf{I})$ $= \mathbf{A}(7\mathbf{A} + 6\mathbf{I})$
$= 2\mathbf{A}^2 + 3\mathbf{AI}$ $= 7\mathbf{A}^2 + 6\mathbf{AI}$
$= 2(2\mathbf{A} + 3\mathbf{I}) + 3\mathbf{AI}$ $= 7(2\mathbf{A} + 3\mathbf{I}) + 6\mathbf{A}$
$= 7\mathbf{A} + 6\mathbf{I}$ $= 20\mathbf{A} + 21\mathbf{I}$

Example 9

Find constants a and b such that $\mathbf{A}^2 = a\mathbf{A} + b\mathbf{I}$ for $\mathbf{A}$ equal to $\begin{bmatrix} 1 & 2 \\ 3 & 4 \end{bmatrix}$.

Since $\mathbf{A}^2 = a\mathbf{A} + b\mathbf{I}$, $\begin{bmatrix} 1 & 2 \\ 3 & 4 \end{bmatrix}\begin{bmatrix} 1 & 2 \\ 3 & 4 \end{bmatrix} = a\begin{bmatrix} 1 & 2 \\ 3 & 4 \end{bmatrix} + b\begin{bmatrix} 1 & 0 \\ 0 & 1 \end{bmatrix}$

$\therefore \begin{bmatrix} 1+6 & 2+8 \\ 3+12 & 6+16 \end{bmatrix} = \begin{bmatrix} a & 2a \\ 3a & 4a \end{bmatrix} + \begin{bmatrix} b & 0 \\ 0 & b \end{bmatrix}$

$\therefore \begin{bmatrix} 7 & 10 \\ 15 & 22 \end{bmatrix} = \begin{bmatrix} a+b & 2a \\ 3a & 4a+b \end{bmatrix}$

Thus $a + b = 7$ and $2a = 10$
$\therefore \quad a = 5$ and $b = 2$

Checking for consistency: $3a = 3(5) = 15$ ✓ $4a + b = 4(5) + (2) = 22$ ✓

EXERCISE 13B.8

1   Given that all matrices are 2×2 and $\mathbf{I}$ is the identity matrix, expand and simplify:

    a $\mathbf{A}(\mathbf{A} + \mathbf{I})$ b $(\mathbf{B} + 2\mathbf{I})\mathbf{B}$ c $\mathbf{A}(\mathbf{A}^2 - 2\mathbf{A} + \mathbf{I})$

    d $\mathbf{A}(\mathbf{A}^2 + \mathbf{A} - 2\mathbf{I})$ e $(\mathbf{A} + \mathbf{B})(\mathbf{C} + \mathbf{D})$ f $(\mathbf{A} + \mathbf{B})^2$

    g $(\mathbf{A} + \mathbf{B})(\mathbf{A} - \mathbf{B})$ h $(\mathbf{A} + \mathbf{I})^2$ i $(3\mathbf{I} - \mathbf{B})^2$

2   a   If $\mathbf{A}^2 = 2\mathbf{A} - \mathbf{I}$, find $\mathbf{A}^3$ and $\mathbf{A}^4$ in the linear form $k\mathbf{A} + l\mathbf{I}$ where k and l are scalars.

    b   If $\mathbf{B}^2 = 2\mathbf{I} - \mathbf{B}$, find $\mathbf{B}^3$, $\mathbf{B}^4$ and $\mathbf{B}^5$ in linear form.

    c   If $\mathbf{C}^2 = 4\mathbf{C} - 3\mathbf{I}$, find $\mathbf{C}^3$ and $\mathbf{C}^5$ in linear form.

3   a   If $\mathbf{A}^2 = \mathbf{I}$, simplify:

       i $\mathbf{A}(\mathbf{A} + 2\mathbf{I})$ ii $(\mathbf{A} - \mathbf{I})^2$ iii $\mathbf{A}(\mathbf{A} + 3\mathbf{I})^2$

    b   If $\mathbf{A}^3 = \mathbf{I}$, simplify $\mathbf{A}^2(\mathbf{A} + \mathbf{I})^2$.

    c   If $\mathbf{A}^2 = \mathbf{O}$, simplify:

       i $\mathbf{A}(2\mathbf{A} - 3\mathbf{I})$ ii $\mathbf{A}(\mathbf{A} + 2\mathbf{I})(\mathbf{A} - \mathbf{I})$ iii $\mathbf{A}(\mathbf{A} + \mathbf{I})^3$

4   The result "if $ab = 0$ then $a = 0$ or $b = 0$" for real numbers does not have an equivalent result for matrices.

    a   If $\mathbf{A} = \begin{bmatrix} 1 & 0 \\ 0 & 0 \end{bmatrix}$ and $\mathbf{B} = \begin{bmatrix} 0 & 0 \\ 0 & 1 \end{bmatrix}$ find $\mathbf{AB}$.

    This example provides us with evidence that
    "If $\mathbf{AB} = \mathbf{O}$ then $\mathbf{A} = \mathbf{O}$ or $\mathbf{B} = \mathbf{O}$" is a false statement.

    b   If $\mathbf{A} = \begin{bmatrix} \frac{1}{2} & \frac{1}{2} \\ \frac{1}{2} & \frac{1}{2} \end{bmatrix}$ determine $\mathbf{A}^2$.

    c   Comment on the following argument for a 2×2 matrix $\mathbf{A}$:

       It is known that $\mathbf{A}^2 = \mathbf{A}$,   so $\mathbf{A}^2 - \mathbf{A} = \mathbf{O}$

$$\therefore \quad \mathbf{A}(\mathbf{A} - \mathbf{I}) = \mathbf{O}$$
$$\therefore \quad \mathbf{A} = \mathbf{O} \text{ or } \mathbf{A} - \mathbf{I} = \mathbf{O}$$
$$\therefore \quad \mathbf{A} = \mathbf{O} \text{ or } \mathbf{I}$$

    d   Find **all** 2×2 matrices $\mathbf{A}$ for which $\mathbf{A}^2 = \mathbf{A}$. **Hint:** Let $\mathbf{A} = \begin{bmatrix} a & b \\ c & d \end{bmatrix}$.

5   Give **one** example which shows that "if $\mathbf{A}^2 = \mathbf{O}$ then $\mathbf{A} = \mathbf{O}$" is a *false* statement.

6   Find constants a and b such that $\mathbf{A}^2 = a\mathbf{A} + b\mathbf{I}$ for $\mathbf{A}$ equal to:

    a $\begin{bmatrix} 1 & 2 \\ -1 & 2 \end{bmatrix}$ b $\begin{bmatrix} 3 & 1 \\ 2 & -2 \end{bmatrix}$

7   If $\mathbf{A} = \begin{bmatrix} 1 & 2 \\ -1 & -3 \end{bmatrix}$, find constants p and q such that $\mathbf{A}^2 = p\mathbf{A} + q\mathbf{I}$.

    a   Hence, write $\mathbf{A}^3$ in the linear form $r\mathbf{A} + s\mathbf{I}$ where r and s are scalars.

    b   Write $\mathbf{A}^4$ in linear form.

C   THE INVERSE OF A 2×2 MATRIX

We can solve $\begin{cases} 2x + 3y = 4 \\ 5x + 4y = 17 \end{cases}$ algebraically to get $x = 5$, $y = -2$.

Notice that this system can be written as a matrix equation $\begin{bmatrix} 2 & 3 \\ 5 & 4 \end{bmatrix} \begin{bmatrix} x \\ y \end{bmatrix} = \begin{bmatrix} 4 \\ 17 \end{bmatrix}$.

The solution $x = 5$, $y = -2$ is easily checked as

$$\begin{bmatrix} 2 & 3 \\ 5 & 4 \end{bmatrix} \begin{bmatrix} 5 \\ -2 \end{bmatrix} = \begin{bmatrix} 2(5) + 3(-2) \\ 5(5) + 4(-2) \end{bmatrix} = \begin{bmatrix} 4 \\ 17 \end{bmatrix} \checkmark$$

In general, a system of linear equations can be written in the form $\mathbf{AX} = \mathbf{B}$ where $\mathbf{A}$ is the matrix of coefficients, $\mathbf{X}$ is the unknown column matrix, and $\mathbf{B}$ is the column matrix of constants.

The question arises: If $\mathbf{AX} = \mathbf{B}$, how can we find $\mathbf{X}$ using matrices?

To answer this question, suppose there exists a matrix $\mathbf{C}$ such that $\mathbf{CA} = \mathbf{I}$.

If we *premultiply* each side of $\mathbf{AX} = \mathbf{B}$ by $\mathbf{C}$ we get

$$\mathbf{C(AX)} = \mathbf{CB}$$
$$\therefore \quad \mathbf{(CA)X} = \mathbf{CB}$$
$$\therefore \quad \mathbf{IX} = \mathbf{CB}$$
$$\text{and so} \quad \mathbf{X} = \mathbf{CB}$$

Premultiply means multiply on the left of each side.

If $\mathbf{C}$ exists such that $\mathbf{CA} = \mathbf{I}$ then $\mathbf{C}$ is said to be the **multiplicative inverse** of $\mathbf{A}$, and we denote $\mathbf{C}$ by $\mathbf{A}^{-1}$.

The **multiplicative inverse** of $\mathbf{A}$, denoted $\mathbf{A}^{-1}$, satisfies $\mathbf{A}^{-1}\mathbf{A} = \mathbf{A}\mathbf{A}^{-1} = \mathbf{I}$.

Suppose $\mathbf{A} = \begin{bmatrix} a & b \\ c & d \end{bmatrix}$ and $\mathbf{A}^{-1} = \begin{bmatrix} w & x \\ y & z \end{bmatrix}$

so $\mathbf{AA}^{-1} = \begin{bmatrix} a & b \\ c & d \end{bmatrix} \begin{bmatrix} w & x \\ y & z \end{bmatrix} = \mathbf{I}$

$\therefore \begin{bmatrix} aw + by & ax + bz \\ cw + dy & cx + dz \end{bmatrix} = \begin{bmatrix} 1 & 0 \\ 0 & 1 \end{bmatrix}$

$\therefore \begin{cases} aw + by = 1 & \text{...... (1)} \\ cw + dy = 0 & \text{...... (2)} \end{cases}$ and $\begin{cases} ax + bz = 0 & \text{...... (3)} \\ cx + dz = 1 & \text{...... (4)} \end{cases}$

Solving (1) and (2) simultaneously for w and y gives: $w = \dfrac{d}{ad - bc}$ and $y = \dfrac{-c}{ad - bc}$.

Solving (3) and (4) simultaneously for x and z gives: $x = \dfrac{-b}{ad - bc}$ and $z = \dfrac{a}{ad - bc}$.

So, if $\mathbf{A} = \begin{bmatrix} a & b \\ c & d \end{bmatrix}$ then $\mathbf{A}^{-1} = \dfrac{1}{ad - bc} \begin{bmatrix} d & -b \\ -c & a \end{bmatrix}$.

If $ad - bc \neq 0$ then $\mathbf{A}^{-1}$ exists and we say that $\mathbf{A}$ is **invertible** or **non-singular**.

If $ad - bc = 0$ then $\mathbf{A}^{-1}$ does not exist and we say that $\mathbf{A}$ is **singular**.

If $\mathbf{A} = \begin{bmatrix} a & b \\ c & d \end{bmatrix}$, the value $ad - bc$ is called the **determinant** of $\mathbf{A}$, denoted $|\mathbf{A}|$ or $\det\mathbf{A}$.

If $|\mathbf{A}| = 0$ then $\mathbf{A}^{-1}$ does not exist and $\mathbf{A}$ is **singular**.

If $|\mathbf{A}| \neq 0$ then $\mathbf{A}$ is **invertible** and $\mathbf{A}^{-1} = \dfrac{1}{|\mathbf{A}|} \begin{bmatrix} d & -b \\ -c & a \end{bmatrix}$.

EXERCISE 13C.1

1 **a** Find $\begin{bmatrix} 5 & 6 \\ 2 & 3 \end{bmatrix} \begin{bmatrix} 3 & -6 \\ -2 & 5 \end{bmatrix}$ and hence find the inverse of $\begin{bmatrix} 5 & 6 \\ 2 & 3 \end{bmatrix}$.

   b Find $\begin{bmatrix} 3 & -4 \\ 1 & 2 \end{bmatrix} \begin{bmatrix} 2 & 4 \\ -1 & 3 \end{bmatrix}$ and hence find the inverse of $\begin{bmatrix} 3 & -4 \\ 1 & 2 \end{bmatrix}$.

2 Find $|\mathbf{A}|$ for $\mathbf{A}$ equal to:

   a $\begin{bmatrix} 3 & 7 \\ 2 & 4 \end{bmatrix}$ **b** $\begin{bmatrix} -1 & 3 \\ 1 & -2 \end{bmatrix}$ **c** $\begin{bmatrix} 0 & 0 \\ 0 & 0 \end{bmatrix}$ **d** $\begin{bmatrix} 1 & 0 \\ 0 & 1 \end{bmatrix}$

3 Find $\det\mathbf{B}$ for $\mathbf{B}$ equal to:

   a $\begin{bmatrix} 3 & -2 \\ 7 & 4 \end{bmatrix}$ **b** $\begin{bmatrix} 3 & 0 \\ 0 & 2 \end{bmatrix}$ **c** $\begin{bmatrix} 0 & 1 \\ 1 & 0 \end{bmatrix}$ **d** $\begin{bmatrix} a & -a \\ 1 & a \end{bmatrix}$

4 For $\mathbf{A} = \begin{bmatrix} 2 & -1 \\ -1 & -1 \end{bmatrix}$ find: **a** $|\mathbf{A}|$ **b** $|\mathbf{A}|^2$ **c** $|2\mathbf{A}|$

5 Prove that if $\mathbf{A}$ is any 2×2 matrix and k is a constant, then $|k\mathbf{A}| = k^2 |\mathbf{A}|$.

6 By letting $\mathbf{A} = \begin{bmatrix} a & b \\ c & d \end{bmatrix}$ and $\mathbf{B} = \begin{bmatrix} w & x \\ y & z \end{bmatrix}$

   a find $|\mathbf{A}|$ and $|\mathbf{B}|$ **b** find $\mathbf{AB}$ and $|\mathbf{AB}|$.
   c Hence show that $|\mathbf{AB}| = |\mathbf{A}||\mathbf{B}|$ for all 2×2 matrices $\mathbf{A}$ and $\mathbf{B}$.

7 $\mathbf{A} = \begin{bmatrix} 1 & 2 \\ 3 & 4 \end{bmatrix}$ and $\mathbf{B} = \begin{bmatrix} -1 & 2 \\ 0 & 1 \end{bmatrix}$.

   a Using the results of **5** and **6** above and the calculated values of $|\mathbf{A}|$ and $|\mathbf{B}|$, find:
   i $|\mathbf{A}|$ **ii** $|2\mathbf{A}|$ **iii** $|-\mathbf{A}|$ **iv** $|-3\mathbf{B}|$ **v** $|\mathbf{AB}|$
   b Check your answers without using the results of **5** and **6** above.

8 Find, if it exists, the inverse matrix of:

   a $\begin{bmatrix} 2 & 4 \\ -1 & 5 \end{bmatrix}$ **b** $\begin{bmatrix} 1 & 0 \\ 1 & -1 \end{bmatrix}$ **c** $\begin{bmatrix} 2 & 4 \\ 1 & 2 \end{bmatrix}$ **d** $\begin{bmatrix} 1 & 0 \\ 0 & 1 \end{bmatrix}$

   e $\begin{bmatrix} 3 & 5 \\ -6 & -10 \end{bmatrix}$ **f** $\begin{bmatrix} -1 & 2 \\ 4 & 7 \end{bmatrix}$ **g** $\begin{bmatrix} 3 & 4 \\ -1 & 2 \end{bmatrix}$ **h** $\begin{bmatrix} -1 & -1 \\ 2 & 3 \end{bmatrix}$

9   **a**   If $\mathbf{A} = \begin{bmatrix} 1 & 0 & 2 \\ -1 & 1 & 3 \end{bmatrix}$ and $\mathbf{B} = \begin{bmatrix} -1 & 2 \\ -4 & 6 \\ 1 & -1 \end{bmatrix}$,   find $\mathbf{AB}$.

   b   Does your result in **a** imply that **A** and **B** are inverses?   **Hint:**   Find $\mathbf{BA}$.

   The above example illustrates that only square matrices can have inverses.   Why?

SOLVING A PAIR OF LINEAR EQUATIONS

We have already seen how a system of linear equations can be written in matrix form. We can solve the system using an inverse matrix if such an inverse exists.

If two lines are **parallel** then the resulting matrix will be singular and no inverse exists. This indicates that either the lines are **coincident** and there are infinitely many solutions, or the lines never meet and there are no solutions.

If the lines are not parallel then the resulting matrix will be invertible. We premultiply by the inverse to find the unique solution which is the point of intersection.

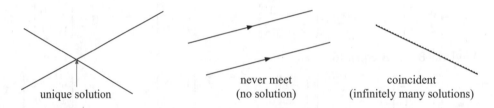

| unique solution | never meet (no solution) | coincident (infinitely many solutions) |

Example 10

a   If $\mathbf{A} = \begin{bmatrix} 2 & 1 \\ 3 & 4 \end{bmatrix}$ find $|\mathbf{A}|$.   **b**   Does $\begin{cases} 2x + y = 4 \\ 3x + 4y = -1 \end{cases}$ have a unique solution?

a $|\mathbf{A}| = 2(4) - 1(3)$
          $= 8 - 3$
          $= 5$

b   The system in matrix form is: $\begin{bmatrix} 2 & 1 \\ 3 & 4 \end{bmatrix} \begin{bmatrix} x \\ y \end{bmatrix} = \begin{bmatrix} 4 \\ -1 \end{bmatrix}$

Now as $|\mathbf{A}| = 5 \neq 0$, $\mathbf{A}^{-1}$ exists and there is a unique solution.

Example 11

If $\mathbf{A} = \begin{bmatrix} 2 & 3 \\ 5 & 4 \end{bmatrix}$,   find $\mathbf{A}^{-1}$ and hence solve $\begin{cases} 2x + 3y = 4 \\ 5x + 4y = 17 \end{cases}$.

> Notice that we **premultiply** with the inverse matrix on both sides.

In matrix form the system is: $\begin{bmatrix} 2 & 3 \\ 5 & 4 \end{bmatrix} \begin{bmatrix} x \\ y \end{bmatrix} = \begin{bmatrix} 4 \\ 17 \end{bmatrix}$

i.e., $\mathbf{AX} = \mathbf{B}$ where $|\mathbf{A}| = 8 - 15 = -7$

Now $\mathbf{A}^{-1}\mathbf{AX} = \mathbf{A}^{-1}\mathbf{B}$

$$\therefore \quad \mathbf{IX} = \frac{1}{-7} \begin{bmatrix} 4 & -3 \\ -5 & 2 \end{bmatrix} \begin{bmatrix} 4 \\ 17 \end{bmatrix}$$

$$\therefore \quad \mathbf{X} = \frac{1}{-7} \begin{bmatrix} -35 \\ 14 \end{bmatrix} = \begin{bmatrix} 5 \\ -2 \end{bmatrix} \quad \text{and so} \quad x = 5, \ y = -2$$

Check this answer!

Example 12

Find $\mathbf{A}^{-1}$ when $\mathbf{A} = \begin{bmatrix} 4 & k \\ 2 & -1 \end{bmatrix}$ and state k when $\mathbf{A}^{-1}$ exists.

If $|\mathbf{A}| = 0$, the matrix $\mathbf{A}$ is singular and is not invertible.

$$\mathbf{A}^{-1} = \frac{1}{-4 - 2k} \begin{bmatrix} -1 & -k \\ -2 & 4 \end{bmatrix} = \begin{bmatrix} \dfrac{1}{2k+4} & \dfrac{k}{2k+4} \\ \dfrac{2}{2k+4} & \dfrac{-4}{2k+4} \end{bmatrix}$$

So $\mathbf{A}^{-1}$ exists provided that $2k + 4 \neq 0$, i.e., $k \neq -2$.

EXERCISE 13C.2

1 Convert into matrix equations:

a $\quad 3x - y = 8$
$\quad\ \ 2x + 3y = 6$

b $\quad 4x - 3y = 11$
$\quad\ \ 3x + 2y = -5$

c $\quad 3a - b = 6$
$\quad\ \ 2a + 7b = -4$

2 Use matrix algebra to solve the system:

a $\quad 2x - y = 6$
$\quad\ \ x + 3y = 14$

b $\quad 5x - 4y = 5$
$\quad\ \ 2x + 3y = -13$

c $\quad x - 2y = 7$
$\quad\ \ 5x + 3y = -2$

d $\quad 3x + 5y = 4$
$\quad\ \ 2x - y = 11$

e $\quad 4x - 7y = 8$
$\quad\ \ 3x - 5y = 0$

f $\quad 7x + 11y = 18$
$\quad\ \ 11x - 7y = -11$

3 a Show that if $\mathbf{AX} = \mathbf{B}$ then $\mathbf{X} = \mathbf{A}^{-1}\mathbf{B}$ whereas if $\mathbf{XA} = \mathbf{B}$ then $\mathbf{X} = \mathbf{BA}^{-1}$.

b Find $\mathbf{X}$ if:

i $\mathbf{X} \begin{bmatrix} 1 & 2 \\ 5 & -1 \end{bmatrix} = \begin{bmatrix} 14 & -5 \\ 22 & 0 \end{bmatrix}$

ii $\begin{bmatrix} 1 & 3 \\ 2 & -1 \end{bmatrix} \mathbf{X} = \begin{bmatrix} 1 & -3 \\ 4 & 2 \end{bmatrix}$

4 For a $\mathbf{A} = \begin{bmatrix} k & 1 \\ -6 & 2 \end{bmatrix}$ b $\mathbf{A} = \begin{bmatrix} 3 & -1 \\ 0 & k \end{bmatrix}$ c $\mathbf{A} = \begin{bmatrix} k+1 & 2 \\ 1 & k \end{bmatrix}$

i find the values of k for which the matrix $\mathbf{A}$ is singular

ii find $\mathbf{A}^{-1}$ when $\mathbf{A}$ is non-singular.

5 a Consider the system $\begin{cases} 2x - 3y = 8 \\ 4x - y = 11 \end{cases}$

i Write the equations in the form $\mathbf{AX} = \mathbf{B}$ and find $|\mathbf{A}|$.

ii Does the system have a unique solution? If so, find it.

b Consider the system $\begin{cases} 2x + ky = 8 \\ 4x - y = 11 \end{cases}$

i Write the system in the form $\mathbf{AX} = \mathbf{B}$ and find $|\mathbf{A}|$.

ii For what value(s) of k does the system have a unique solution? Find the unique solution.

iii Find k when the system does not have a unique solution. How many solutions does it have in this case?

FURTHER MATRIX ALGEBRA

The following exercise requires matrix algebra with inverse matrices. Be careful that you use multiplication correctly. In particular, remember that:

- We can only perform matrix multiplication if the orders of the matrices allow it.
- If we *pre*multiply on one side then we must *pre*multiply on the other. This is important because, in general, $\mathbf{AB} \neq \mathbf{BA}$. The same applies if we *post*multiply.

Example 13

If $\mathbf{A}^2 = 2\mathbf{A} + 3\mathbf{I}$, find $\mathbf{A}^{-1}$ in linear form $r\mathbf{A} + s\mathbf{I}$, where r and s are scalars.

$$\mathbf{A}^2 = 2\mathbf{A} + 3\mathbf{I}$$
$$\therefore \quad \mathbf{A}^{-1}\mathbf{A}^2 = \mathbf{A}^{-1}(2\mathbf{A} + 3\mathbf{I}) \qquad \{\text{premultiply both sides by } \mathbf{A}^{-1}\}$$
$$\therefore \quad \mathbf{A}^{-1}\mathbf{A}\mathbf{A} = 2\mathbf{A}^{-1}\mathbf{A} + 3\mathbf{A}^{-1}\mathbf{I}$$
$$\therefore \quad \mathbf{I}\mathbf{A} = 2\mathbf{I} + 3\mathbf{A}^{-1}$$
$$\therefore \quad \mathbf{A} - 2\mathbf{I} = 3\mathbf{A}^{-1}$$
$$\therefore \quad \mathbf{A}^{-1} = \tfrac{1}{3}(\mathbf{A} - 2\mathbf{I}) \qquad \text{i.e., } \quad \mathbf{A}^{-1} = \tfrac{1}{3}\mathbf{A} - \tfrac{2}{3}\mathbf{I}$$

EXERCISE 13C.3

1 Given $\mathbf{A} = \begin{bmatrix} 2 & 1 \\ 0 & 1 \end{bmatrix}$, $\mathbf{B} = \begin{bmatrix} 1 & 2 \\ -1 & 0 \end{bmatrix}$ and $\mathbf{C} = \begin{bmatrix} 0 & 3 \\ 1 & 2 \end{bmatrix}$, find $\mathbf{X}$ if $\mathbf{AXB} = \mathbf{C}$.

2 If a matrix $\mathbf{A}$ is its own inverse, then $\mathbf{A} = \mathbf{A}^{-1}$.

For example, if $\mathbf{A} = \begin{bmatrix} 0 & -1 \\ -1 & 0 \end{bmatrix}$ then $\mathbf{A}^{-1} = \dfrac{1}{-1}\begin{bmatrix} 0 & 1 \\ 1 & 0 \end{bmatrix} = \begin{bmatrix} 0 & -1 \\ -1 & 0 \end{bmatrix} = \mathbf{A}$.

a Show that, if $\mathbf{A} = \mathbf{A}^{-1}$, then $\mathbf{A}^2 = \mathbf{I}$.

b If $\begin{bmatrix} a & b \\ b & a \end{bmatrix}$ is its own inverse, show that there are exactly 4 matrices of this form.

3 **a** If $A = \begin{bmatrix} 1 & 2 \\ -1 & 0 \end{bmatrix}$ find A^{-1} and $(A^{-1})^{-1}$.

    b If **A** is any square matrix which has inverse A^{-1}, simplify $(A^{-1})^{-1}(A^{-1})$ and $(A^{-1})(A^{-1})^{-1}$ by replacing A^{-1} by **B**.

    c What can be deduced from **b**?

4 **a** If $A = \begin{bmatrix} 1 & 1 \\ 2 & -1 \end{bmatrix}$ and $B = \begin{bmatrix} 0 & 1 \\ 2 & -3 \end{bmatrix}$ find in simplest form:

       i A^{-1} **ii** B^{-1} **iii** $(AB)^{-1}$

       iv $(BA)^{-1}$ **v** $A^{-1}B^{-1}$ **vi** $B^{-1}A^{-1}$

    b Choose any two invertible matrices and repeat question **a**.

    c What do the results of **a** and **b** suggest?

    d Simplify $(AB)(B^{-1}A^{-1})$ and $(B^{-1}A^{-1})(AB)$ given that A^{-1} and B^{-1} exist. Conclusion?

5 If k is a non-zero number and A^{-1} exists, simplify $(kA)(\frac{1}{k}A^{-1})$ and $(\frac{1}{k}A^{-1})(kA)$. What conclusion follows from your results?

6 Suppose **X**, **Y** and **Z** are 2×1 matrices and **A**, **B** are 2×2 matrices. If $X = AY$ and $Y = BZ$ where **A** and **B** are invertible, find:

    a **X** in terms of **Z**   **b** **Z** in terms of **X**.

7 If $A = \begin{bmatrix} 3 & 2 \\ -2 & -1 \end{bmatrix}$, write A^2 in the form $pA + qI$ where p and q are scalars.

Hence write A^{-1} in the form $rA + sI$ where r and s are scalars.

8 Find A^{-1} in linear form given that

    a $A^2 = 4A - I$ **b** $5A = I - A^2$ **c** $2I = 3A^2 - 4A$

9 It is known that $AB = A$ and $BA = B$ where the matrices **A** and **B** are not necessarily invertible. Prove that $A^2 = A$. (**Note:** From $AB = A$, you cannot deduce that $B = I$. Why?)

10 Under what condition is it true that   "if $AB = AC$ then $B = C$"?

11 If $X = P^{-1}AP$ and $A^3 = I$, prove that $X^3 = I$.

12 If $aA^2 + bA + cI = O$ and $X = P^{-1}AP$, prove that $aX^2 + bX + cI = O$.

Summary: During this exercise you should have discovered that:

- $(A^{-1})^{-1} = A$
- $(AB)^{-1} = B^{-1}A^{-1}$

D 3×3 AND LARGER MATRICES

The principles of determinants and inverses are equally applicable to 3×3 and other larger square matrices.

THE DETERMINANT OF A 3×3 MATRIX

The **determinant** of $\mathbf{A} = \begin{bmatrix} a_1 & b_1 & c_1 \\ a_2 & b_2 & c_2 \\ a_3 & b_3 & c_3 \end{bmatrix}$ is defined as

$$|\mathbf{A}| = \begin{vmatrix} a_1 & b_1 & c_1 \\ a_2 & b_2 & c_2 \\ a_3 & b_3 & c_3 \end{vmatrix} = a_1 \begin{vmatrix} b_2 & c_2 \\ b_3 & c_3 \end{vmatrix} - b_1 \begin{vmatrix} a_2 & c_2 \\ a_3 & c_3 \end{vmatrix} + c_1 \begin{vmatrix} a_2 & b_2 \\ a_3 & b_3 \end{vmatrix}$$

Example 14

Find $|\mathbf{A}|$ for

$$\mathbf{A} = \begin{bmatrix} 1 & 2 & 4 \\ 2 & 0 & 1 \\ 3 & -1 & 2 \end{bmatrix}$$

$|\mathbf{A}| = 1 \begin{vmatrix} 0 & 1 \\ -1 & 2 \end{vmatrix} - 2 \begin{vmatrix} 2 & 1 \\ 3 & 2 \end{vmatrix} + 4 \begin{vmatrix} 2 & 0 \\ 3 & -1 \end{vmatrix}$

same
same
same

$= 1(0 - -1) - 2(4 - 3) + 4(-2 - 0)$

$= 1 - 2 - 8$

$= -9$

Just like 2×2 systems, a 3×3 system of linear equations in matrix form $\mathbf{AX} = \mathbf{B}$ will have a **unique solution** if $|\mathbf{A}| \neq 0$.

MATRIX
OPERATIONS

Remember that you can use your graphics calculator or matrix software to find the value of a determinant.

EXERCISE 13D.1

1 Evaluate:

a $\begin{vmatrix} 2 & 3 & 0 \\ -1 & 2 & 1 \\ 2 & 0 & 5 \end{vmatrix}$

b $\begin{vmatrix} -1 & 2 & -3 \\ 1 & 0 & 0 \\ -1 & 2 & 1 \end{vmatrix}$

c $\begin{vmatrix} 2 & 1 & 3 \\ -1 & 1 & 2 \\ 2 & 1 & 3 \end{vmatrix}$

d $\begin{vmatrix} 1 & 0 & 0 \\ 0 & 2 & 0 \\ 0 & 0 & 3 \end{vmatrix}$

e $\begin{vmatrix} 0 & 0 & 2 \\ 0 & 1 & 0 \\ 3 & 0 & 0 \end{vmatrix}$

f $\begin{vmatrix} 4 & 1 & 3 \\ -1 & 0 & 2 \\ -1 & 1 & 1 \end{vmatrix}$

2 a Find the values of x for which the matrix $\begin{bmatrix} x & 2 & 9 \\ 3 & 1 & 2 \\ -1 & 0 & x \end{bmatrix}$ is singular.

b What does your answer to **a** mean?

3 Evaluate:

a $\begin{vmatrix} a & 0 & 0 \\ 0 & b & 0 \\ 0 & 0 & c \end{vmatrix}$

b $\begin{vmatrix} 0 & x & y \\ -x & 0 & z \\ -y & -z & 0 \end{vmatrix}$

c $\begin{vmatrix} a & b & c \\ b & c & a \\ c & a & b \end{vmatrix}$

4 For what values of k does
$$\begin{cases} x + 2y - 3z = 5 \\ 2x - y - z = 8 \\ kx + y + 2z = 14 \end{cases}$$
have a unique solution?

5 For what values of k does
$$\begin{cases} 2x - y - 4z = 8 \\ 3x - ky + z = 1 \\ 5x - y + kz = -2 \end{cases}$$
have a unique solution?

6 Find k given that:

a $\begin{vmatrix} 1 & k & 3 \\ k & 1 & -1 \\ 3 & 4 & 2 \end{vmatrix} = 7$

b $\begin{vmatrix} k & 2 & 1 \\ 2 & k & 2 \\ 1 & 2 & k \end{vmatrix} = 0$

7 Use technology to find the determinant and inverse of:

a $\begin{bmatrix} 1 & 2 & 3 & 1 \\ 2 & 0 & 1 & 2 \\ 3 & 1 & 4 & 0 \\ 1 & 2 & 0 & 5 \end{bmatrix}$

b $\begin{bmatrix} 1 & 2 & 3 & 4 & 6 \\ 2 & 3 & 4 & 5 & 0 \\ 1 & 2 & 0 & 1 & 4 \\ 2 & 1 & 0 & 1 & 5 \\ 3 & 0 & 1 & 2 & 1 \end{bmatrix}$

8 If Jan bought one orange, two apples, a pear, a cabbage and a lettuce the total cost would be $6.30. Two oranges, one apple, two pears, one cabbage and one lettuce would cost a total of $6.70. One orange, two apples, three pears, one cabbage and one lettuce would cost a total of $7.70. Two oranges, two apples, one pear, one cabbage and three lettuces would cost a total of $9.80. Three oranges, three apples, five pears, two cabbages and two lettuces would cost a total of $10.90.

a Write this information in the form $\mathbf{AX} = \mathbf{B}$ where $\mathbf{A}$ is the quantities matrix, $\mathbf{X}$ is the cost per item column matrix, and $\mathbf{B}$ is the total costs column matrix.

b Explain why $\mathbf{X}$ cannot be found from the given information.

c If the last lot of information is deleted and in its place "three oranges, one apple, two pears, two cabbages and one lettuce cost a total of $9.20" is substituted, can the system be solved now, and if so, what is the solution?

THE INVERSE OF A 3×3 MATRIX

There is no simple rule for finding the inverse of a 3×3 matrix like there is for a 2×2 matrix. Hence we use technology.

MATRIX OPERATIONS

For example, if $\mathbf{A} = \begin{bmatrix} 1 & 2 & 4 \\ 2 & 0 & 1 \\ 3 & -1 & 2 \end{bmatrix}$ what is $\mathbf{A}^{-1}$?

We obtain $\mathbf{A}^{-1} = \begin{bmatrix} -0.111 & 0.888 & -0.222 \\ 0.111 & 1.111 & -0.777 \\ 0.222 & -0.777 & 0.444 \end{bmatrix}$ which converts to $\begin{bmatrix} -\frac{1}{9} & \frac{8}{9} & -\frac{2}{9} \\ \frac{1}{9} & \frac{10}{9} & -\frac{7}{9} \\ \frac{2}{9} & -\frac{7}{9} & \frac{4}{9} \end{bmatrix}$.

EXERCISE 13D.2

1   Find
$\begin{bmatrix} 2 & 0 & 3 \\ 1 & 5 & 2 \\ 1 & -3 & 1 \end{bmatrix} \begin{bmatrix} -11 & 9 & 15 \\ -1 & 1 & 1 \\ 8 & -6 & -10 \end{bmatrix}$
and hence the inverse of
$\begin{bmatrix} 2 & 0 & 3 \\ 1 & 5 & 2 \\ 1 & -3 & 1 \end{bmatrix}$.

2   Use technology to find $\mathbf{A}^{-1}$ for:
   a $\mathbf{A} = \begin{bmatrix} 3 & 2 & 3 \\ 1 & -1 & 2 \\ 2 & 1 & 3 \end{bmatrix}$
   b $\mathbf{A} = \begin{bmatrix} 2 & 0 & 3 \\ 1 & 5 & 2 \\ 1 & -3 & 1 \end{bmatrix}$

3   Find $\mathbf{B}^{-1}$ for:
   a $\mathbf{B} = \begin{bmatrix} 13 & 43 & -11 \\ 16 & 9 & 27 \\ -8 & 31 & -13 \end{bmatrix}$
   b $\mathbf{B} = \begin{bmatrix} 1.61 & 4.32 & 6.18 \\ 0.37 & 6.02 & 9.41 \\ 7.12 & 5.31 & 2.88 \end{bmatrix}$

4   Check that your answers to **2** and **3** are correct.

Note:
- In general, we can only find the determinants of square matrices i.e., for 2×2, 3×3, 4×4, ... etc matrices.
- If $\mathbf{A}$ is square and $|\mathbf{A}| \neq 0$, then $\mathbf{A}^{-1}$ exists and $\mathbf{A}$ is called an **invertible** or **non-singular** matrix.
- If $\mathbf{A}$ is square and $|\mathbf{A}| = 0$, then $\mathbf{A}^{-1}$ does not exist and $\mathbf{A}$ is called a **singular** matrix.
- $\det(\mathbf{AB}) = \det\mathbf{A} \det\mathbf{B}$ or $|\mathbf{AB}| = |\mathbf{A}||\mathbf{B}|$ for all square matrices $\mathbf{A}$, $\mathbf{B}$ of equal size.

E   SOLVING SYSTEMS OF LINEAR EQUATIONS

Example 15

Solve the system
$\begin{aligned} x - y - z &= 2 \\ x + y + 3z &= 7 \\ 9x - y - 3z &= -1 \end{aligned}$
using matrix methods and a graphics calculator.

In matrix form $\mathbf{AX} = \mathbf{B}$ the system is:
$\begin{bmatrix} 1 & -1 & -1 \\ 1 & 1 & 3 \\ 9 & -1 & -3 \end{bmatrix} \begin{bmatrix} x \\ y \\ z \end{bmatrix} = \begin{bmatrix} 2 \\ 7 \\ -1 \end{bmatrix}$

We enter $\mathbf{A}$ and $\mathbf{B}$ into our GDC and calculate $[\mathbf{A}]^{-1}[\mathbf{B}]$.

$\therefore \begin{bmatrix} x \\ y \\ z \end{bmatrix} = \begin{bmatrix} 1 & -1 & -1 \\ 1 & 1 & 3 \\ 9 & -1 & -3 \end{bmatrix}^{-1} \begin{bmatrix} 2 \\ 7 \\ -1 \end{bmatrix} = \begin{bmatrix} 0.6 \\ -5.3 \\ 3.9 \end{bmatrix}$

```
[A]⁻¹[B]
        [[.6  ]
         [-5.3]
         [3.9 ]]
■
```

So, $x = 0.6$, $y = -5.3$, $z = 3.9$

Example 16

Rent-a-car has three different makes of vehicles, P, Q and R, for hire. These cars are located at yards A and B on either side of a city. Some cars are out (being rented). In total they have 150 cars. At yard A they have 20% of P, 40% of Q and 30% of R which is 46 cars in total. At yard B they have 40% of P, 20% of Q and 50% of R which is 54 cars in total. How many of each car type does Rent-a-car have?

Suppose Rent-a-car has x of P, y of Q and z of R.

Then as it has 150 cars in total, $x + y + z = 150$ ...... (1)

But yard A has 20% of P + 40% of Q + 30% of R and this is 46.

$$\therefore \quad \tfrac{2}{10}x + \tfrac{4}{10}y + \tfrac{3}{10}z = 46$$

$$\therefore \quad 2x + 4y + 3z = 460 \quad \text{...... (2)}$$

Yard B has 40% of P + 20% of Q + 50% of R and this is 54.

$$\therefore \quad \tfrac{4}{10}x + \tfrac{2}{10}y + \tfrac{5}{10}z = 54$$

$$\therefore \quad 4x + 2y + 5z = 540 \quad \text{...... (3)}$$

We need to solve the system:
$$x + y + z = 150$$
$$2x + 4y + 3z = 460$$
$$4x + 2y + 5z = 540$$

```
[A]⁻¹[B]
          [[45]
           [55]
           [50]]
```

i.e., $\begin{bmatrix} 1 & 1 & 1 \\ 2 & 4 & 3 \\ 4 & 2 & 5 \end{bmatrix} \begin{bmatrix} x \\ y \\ z \end{bmatrix} = \begin{bmatrix} 150 \\ 460 \\ 540 \end{bmatrix}$

So, $\begin{bmatrix} x \\ y \\ z \end{bmatrix} = \begin{bmatrix} 1 & 1 & 1 \\ 2 & 4 & 3 \\ 4 & 2 & 5 \end{bmatrix}^{-1} \begin{bmatrix} 150 \\ 460 \\ 540 \end{bmatrix} = \begin{bmatrix} 45 \\ 55 \\ 50 \end{bmatrix}$ {using tech}

Thus, Rent-a-car has 45 of P, 55 of Q and 50 of R.

A 3×3 system of linear equations in the form $\mathbf{AX} = \mathbf{B}$ has a unique solution if $|\mathbf{A}| \neq 0$.

EXERCISE 13E

1 Write as a matrix equation:

a
$$x - y - z = 2$$
$$x + y + 3z = 7$$
$$9x - y - 3z = -1$$

b
$$2x + y - z = 3$$
$$y + 2z = 6$$
$$x - y + z = 13$$

c
$$a + b - c = 7$$
$$a - b + c = 6$$
$$2a + b - 3c = -2$$

2 For $\mathbf{A} = \begin{bmatrix} 2 & 1 & -1 \\ -1 & 2 & 1 \\ 0 & 6 & 1 \end{bmatrix}$ and $\mathbf{B} = \begin{bmatrix} 4 & 7 & -3 \\ -1 & -2 & 1 \\ 6 & 12 & -5 \end{bmatrix}$,

calculate $\mathbf{AB}$ and hence solve the system of equations
$$4a + 7b - 3c = -8$$
$$-a - 2b + c = 3$$
$$6a + 12b - 5c = -15.$$

3 For $\mathbf{M} = \begin{bmatrix} 5 & 3 & -7 \\ -1 & -3 & 3 \\ -3 & -1 & 5 \end{bmatrix}$ and $\mathbf{N} = \begin{bmatrix} 3 & 2 & 3 \\ 1 & -1 & 2 \\ 2 & 1 & 3 \end{bmatrix}$,

calculate $\mathbf{MN}$ and hence solve the system $3u + 2v + 3w = 18$
$$u - v + 2w = 6$$
$$2u + v + 3w = 16.$$

4 Use matrix methods and technology to solve:

a $3x + 2y - z = 14$
  $x - y + 2z = -8$
  $2x + 3y - z = 13$

b $x - y - 2z = 4$
  $5x + y + 2z = -6$
  $3x - 4y - z = 17$

c $x + 3y - z = 15$
  $2x + y + z = 7$
  $x - y - 2z = 0$

5 Use your graphics calculator to solve:

a $x + y + z = 6$
  $2x + 4y + z = 5$
  $2x + 3y + z = 6$

b $x + 4y + 11z = 7$
  $x + 6y + 17z = 9$
  $x + 4y + 8z = 4$

c $2x - y + 3z = 17$
  $2x - 2y - 5z = 4$
  $3x + 2y + 2z = 10$

d $x + 2y - z = 23$
  $x - y + 3z = -23$
  $7x + y - 4z = 62$

e $10x - y + 4z = -9$
  $7x + 3y - 5z = 89$
  $13x - 17y + 23z = -309$

f $1.3x + 2.7y - 3.1z = 8.2$
  $2.8x - 0.9y + 5.6z = 17.3$
  $6.1x + 1.4y - 3.2z = -0.6$

6 Westwood School bought two footballs, one baseball and three basketballs for a total cost of \$90. Sequoia School bought three footballs, two baseballs and a basketball for \$81. Lamar School bought five footballs and two basketballs for \$104.

a State clearly what the variables x, y and z must represent if this situation is to be described by the set of equations: $2x + y + 3z = 90$, $3x + 2y + z = 81$, $5x + 2z = 104$.

b If Kato International School needs 4 footballs and 5 baseballs, and wishes to order as many basketballs as they can afford, how many basketballs will they be able to purchase if there is a total of \$315 to be spent?

7 Managers, clerks and labourers are paid according to an industry award.
Xenon employs 2 managers, 3 clerks and 8 labourers with a total salary bill of €352 000.
Xanda employs 1 manager, 5 clerks and 4 labourers with a total salary bill of €274 000.
Xylon employs 1 manager, 2 clerks and 11 labourers with a total salary bill of €351 000.

a If x, y and z represent the salaries (in thousands of euros) for managers, clerks and labourers respectively, show that the above information can be represented by a system of three equations.

b Solve the above system of equations.

c Determine the total salary bill for Xulu company which employs 3 managers, 8 clerks and 37 labourers.

8 A mixed nut company uses cashews, macadamias and Brazil nuts to make three gourmet mixes. The table alongside indicates the weight in hundreds of grams of each kind of nut required to make a kilogram of mix.

	Mix A	Mix B	Mix C
Cashews	5	2	6
Macas.	3	4	1
Brazils	2	4	3

If 1 kg of mix A costs $12.50 to produce, 1 kg of mix B costs $12.40 and 1 kg of mix C costs $11.70, determine the cost per kilogram of each of the different kinds of nuts.

Hence, find the cost per kilogram to produce a mix containing 400 grams of cashews, 200 grams of macadamias and 400 grams of Brazil nuts.

9 Klondike High has 76 students in total in classes P, Q and R. There are p students in P, q in Q and r in R.

One-third of P, one-third of Q and two-fifths of R study Chemistry.

One-half of P, two-thirds of Q and one-fifth of R study Mathematics.

One-quarter of P, one-third of Q and three-fifths of R study Geography.

Given that 27 students study Chemistry, 35 study Mathematics and 30 study Geography:

a find a system of equations which contains this information, making sure that the coefficients of p, q and r are integers.

b Solve for p, q and r.

10 Susan and James opened a new business in 2001. Their annual profit was £160 000 in 2004, £198 000 in 2005 and £240 000 in 2006. Based on the information from these three years they believe that their annual profit could be predicted by the model

$$P(t) = at + b + \frac{c}{t+4} \quad \text{pounds}$$

where t is the number of years after 2004, i.e., $t = 0$ gives the 2004 profit.

a Determine the values of a, b and c which fit the profits for 2004, 2005 and 2006.

b If the profit in 2003 was £130 000, does this profit fit the model in **a**?

c Susan and James believe their profit will continue to grow according to this model. Predict their profit in 2007 and 2009.

The system of equations in each of the examples above could be represented as $\mathbf{AX} = \mathbf{B}$ where we are looking for matrix $\mathbf{X}$. In every case above we could find $\mathbf{X}$ by pre-multiplying each side by $\mathbf{A}^{-1}$ to get $\mathbf{X} = \mathbf{A}^{-1}\mathbf{B}$.

This pre-supposes that $\mathbf{A}$ is non-singular which may not be the case. Hence, in the next section we will investigate another technique for solving the system of equations that will still work if $\mathbf{A}$ is singular, i.e., $\det\mathbf{A} = 0$ and $\mathbf{A}^{-1}$ does not exist.

INVESTIGATION   USING MATRICES IN CRYPTOGRAPHY

Cryptography is the study of encoding and decoding messages.

Cryptography was first developed for the military to send secret messages. However, today it is used to maintain privacy when information is being transmitted via public communication services such as the internet.

Messages are sent in **code** or **cipher** form. The method of converting text to ciphertext is called **enciphering** and the reverse process is called **deciphering**.

The operations of matrix addition and multiplication can be used to create codes and the coded messages are transmitted. Decoding using additive or multiplicative inverses is required by the receiver in order to read the message.

PRINTABLE INVESTIGATION

Click on the icon for a printable investigation on cryptography.

F   SOLVING SYSTEMS USING ROW OPERATIONS

The system of equations $\begin{cases} 2x + y = -1 \\ x - 3y = 17 \end{cases}$ is called a 2×2 system, because there are **2 equations** in **2 unknowns**.

In the method of 'elimination' used to solve these equations, we observe that the following operations produce equations with the same solutions as the original pair.

- The equations can be interchanged without affecting the solutions.

   For example, $\begin{cases} 2x + y = -1 \\ x - 3y = 17 \end{cases}$ has the same solutions as $\begin{cases} x - 3y = 17 \\ 2x + y = -1 \end{cases}$.

- An equation can be replaced by a non-zero multiple of itself.

   For example, $2x + y = -1$ could be replaced by $-6x - 3y = 3$
   (obtained by multiplying each term by -3).

- Any equation can be replaced by a multiple of itself plus (or minus) a multiple of another equation.

   For example, suppose we replace the second equation by "twice the second equation minus the first equation". In this case:

   $\begin{cases} 2x + y = -1 \\ x - 3y = 17 \end{cases}$ becomes $\begin{cases} 2x + y = -1 \\ -7y = 35 \end{cases}$ using: $\begin{array}{r} 2x - 6y = 34 \\ -\ (2x + y = -1) \\ \hline -7y = 35 \end{array}$

We can use these principles to develop **row operations** for matrices.

AUGMENTED MATRICES

We will now solve systems of equations using row operations on an **augmented matrix**.

Instead of writing $\begin{cases} 2x + y = -1 \\ x - 3y = 17 \end{cases}$ we detach the coefficients and write the system in

augmented matrix form $\left[\begin{array}{cc|c} 2 & 1 & -1 \\ 1 & -3 & 17 \end{array} \right]$.

In this form we can use **elementary row operations** equivalent to the three legitimate operations with equations. We can hence:

- interchange rows
- replace any row by a non-zero multiple of itself
- replace any row by itself plus (or minus) a multiple of another row.

Interchanging rows is equivalent to writing the equations in a different order. It is often desirable to have 1 in the *top left hand corner*.

We can do this by swapping rows 1 and 2. We can write this as $R_1 \leftrightarrow R_2$.

So, $\begin{bmatrix} 2 & 1 & | & -1 \\ 1 & -3 & | & 17 \end{bmatrix}$ becomes $\begin{bmatrix} 1 & -3 & | & 17 \\ 2 & 1 & | & -1 \end{bmatrix}$.

We now attempt to eliminate one of the variables in the second equation by obtaining a 0 in its place. To do this we replace R_2 by $R_2 - 2R_1$, i.e., row 2 by (row 2 $- 2 \times$ row 1).

So, $\begin{bmatrix} 1 & -3 & | & 17 \\ 2 & 1 & | & -1 \end{bmatrix}$ becomes $\begin{bmatrix} 1 & -3 & | & 17 \\ 0 & 7 & | & -35 \end{bmatrix}$

$$
\begin{array}{rrrl}
2 & 1 & -1 & \longleftarrow R_2 \\
-2 & 6 & -34 & \longleftarrow -2R_1 \\
\hline
0 & 7 & -35 & \text{adding}
\end{array}
$$

The second row of the matrix is now really $7y = -35$ and so $y = -5$.

Substituting $y = -5$ into the first equation, $x - 3(-5) = 17$ and so $x = 2$.

So, the solution is $x = 2$, $y = -5$.

This process of solving a system using elementary row operations is known as **row reduction**.

When we have rewritten the augmented matrix so there are all zeros in the bottom left hand corner, the system is said to be in **echelon form**.

We may not see the benefit of this method right now but we will certainly appreciate it when solving 3×3 or higher order systems.

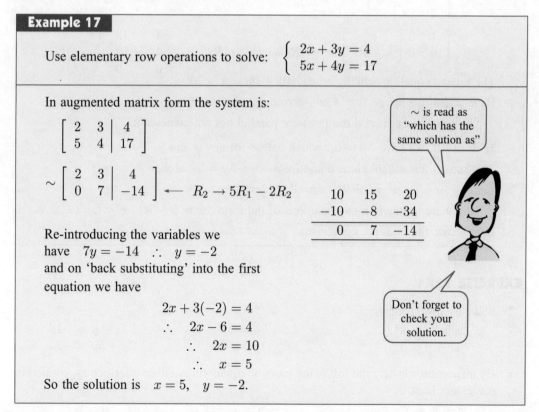

Example 17

Use elementary row operations to solve: $\begin{cases} 2x + 3y = 4 \\ 5x + 4y = 17 \end{cases}$

In augmented matrix form the system is:

$$\begin{bmatrix} 2 & 3 & | & 4 \\ 5 & 4 & | & 17 \end{bmatrix}$$

$\sim \begin{bmatrix} 2 & 3 & | & 4 \\ 0 & 7 & | & -14 \end{bmatrix} \longleftarrow R_2 \to 5R_1 - 2R_2$

$\sim$ is read as "which has the same solution as"

$$
\begin{array}{rrr}
10 & 15 & 20 \\
-10 & -8 & -34 \\
\hline
0 & 7 & -14
\end{array}
$$

Re-introducing the variables we have $7y = -14$ $\therefore$ $y = -2$

and on 'back substituting' into the first equation we have

$$2x + 3(-2) = 4$$
$$\therefore \quad 2x - 6 = 4$$
$$\therefore \quad 2x = 10$$
$$\therefore \quad x = 5$$

Don't forget to check your solution.

So the solution is $x = 5$, $y = -2$.

Reminder: In two dimensional geometry $ax + by = c$ where a, b and c are constants, are the equations of straight lines. If we are given two such equations then there are three different cases which could occur:

intersecting lines   **parallel lines**   **coincident lines**

e.g. $2x + 3y = 1$ e.g. $2x + 3y = 1$ e.g. $2x + 3y = 1$
       $x - 2y = 8$ $2x + 3y = 7$ $4x + 6y = 2$

one point of intersection   no points of intersection   infinitely many points of
$\therefore$ a **unique solution** $\therefore$ **no solution**   intersection
                                                                   $\therefore$ **infinitely many solutions**

Example 18

Find all solutions to $\left\{ \begin{array}{ll} x + 3y = 5 & \text{where } k \text{ is a constant, by using} \\ 4x + 12y = k & \text{elementary row operations.} \end{array} \right.$

In augmented matrix form, the system is:

$$\left[\begin{array}{cc|c} 1 & 3 & 5 \\ 4 & 12 & k \end{array} \right]$$

$$\sim \left[\begin{array}{cc|c} 1 & 3 & 5 \\ 0 & 0 & k - 20 \end{array} \right] \longleftarrow R_2 \to R_2 - 4R_1$$

$$\begin{array}{rrr} 4 & 12 & k \\ -4 & -12 & -20 \\ \hline 0 & 0 & k - 20 \end{array}$$

The second equation actually reads $0x + 0y = k - 20$

If $k \neq 20$ we have $0 = $ a non-zero number, which is absurd

$\therefore$ no solution exists and the lines are parallel but not coincident.

If $k = 20$ we have $0 = 0$, which is true for any x and y.

This means that all solutions come from $x + 3y = 5$ alone.

Letting $y = t$, $x = 5 - 3t$ for all values of t

$\therefore$ there are infinitely many solutions of the form $x = 5 - 3t$, $y = t$, $t \in \mathbb{R}$.

In this case the lines are coincident.

EXERCISE 13F.1

1 Solve by row reduction:

    a $x - 2y = 8$ **b** $4x + 5y = 21$ **c** $3x + y = -10$
        $4x + y = 5$ $5x - 3y = -20$ $2x + 5y = -24$

2 By inspection, classify the following pairs of equations as either intersecting, parallel or
coincident lines:

    a $x - 3y = 2$ **b** $x + y = 7$ **c** $4x - y = 8$
        $3x + y = 8$ $3x + 3y = 1$ $y = 2$

    d $x - 2y = 4$ **e** $5x - 11y = 2$ **f** $3x - 4y = 5$
        $2x - 4y = 8$ $6x + y = 8$ $-3x + 4y = 2$

3 Consider the equation pair $\begin{cases} x + 2y = 3 \\ 2x + 4y = 6 \end{cases}$.

   a Explain why there are infinitely many solutions, giving geometric evidence.
   b Explain why the second equation can be ignored when finding all solutions.
   c Give all solutions in the form:

   i $x = t, \quad y = $ ......   **ii** $y = s, \quad x = $ ......

4 **a** Use elementary row operations on the system $\begin{cases} 2x + 3y = 5 \\ 2x + 3y = 11 \end{cases}$ to show that it
   reduces to $\begin{bmatrix} 2 & 3 & | & 5 \\ 0 & 0 & | & 6 \end{bmatrix}$.   What does the second row indicate? What is the
   geometrical significance of your result?

   b Use elementary row operations on the system $\begin{cases} 2x + 3y = 5 \\ 4x + 6y = 10 \end{cases}$ to show that it
   reduces to $\begin{bmatrix} 2 & 3 & | & 5 \\ 0 & 0 & | & 0 \end{bmatrix}$.   Explain this result geometrically.

5 **a** By using augmented matrices show that $\begin{cases} 3x - y = 2 \\ 6x - 2y = 4 \end{cases}$ has infinitely many
   solutions of the form $x = t, \; y = 3t - 2$.

   b Discuss the solutions to $\begin{cases} 3x - y = 2 \\ 6x - 2y = k \end{cases}$ where k can take any real value.

6 Consider $\begin{cases} 3x - y = 8 \\ 6x - 2y = k \end{cases}$ where k is any real number.

   a Use elementary row operations to reduce the system to: $\begin{bmatrix} 3 & -1 & | & 8 \\ 0 & 0 & | & .... \end{bmatrix}$
   b For what value of k is there infinitely many solutions?
   c What form do the infinite number of solutions have?
   d When does the system have no solutions?

7 Consider $\begin{cases} 4x + 8y = 1 \\ 2x - ay = 11 \end{cases}$

   a Use elementary row operations to reduce the system to: $\begin{bmatrix} 4 & 8 & | & 1 \\ 0 & .... & | & .... \end{bmatrix}$

   b For what values of a does the system have a unique solution?

   c Show that the unique solution is $x = \dfrac{a + 88}{4a + 16}, \; y = \dfrac{-21}{2a + 8}$ for these a values.

   d What is the solution in all other cases?

8 Use elementary row operations to find the values of m when the system $\begin{cases} mx + 2y = 6 \\ 2x + my = 6 \end{cases}$
   has a unique solution.

   a Find the unique solution.   **b** Discuss the solutions in the other *two* cases.

USING A GRAPHICS CALCULATOR

Click on the appropriate icon to obtain instructions on how to enter an
augmented matrix. You can then obtain the **reduced row-echelon
form** which has row reduction performed so that there are 0s in the
bottom left corner and in the higher rows wherever possible.

For the example $\begin{cases} 2x + y = -1 \\ x - 3y = 17 \end{cases}$ the reduced row-echelon form is $\begin{bmatrix} 1 & 0 & 2 \\ 0 & 1 & -5 \end{bmatrix}$.

Consequently $x = 2$ and $y = -5$.

Try solving other 2×2 systems using your calculator:

a $\begin{cases} 3x + 5y = 4 \\ 6x - y = -11 \end{cases}$ b $\begin{cases} 0.83x + 1.72y = 13.76 \\ 1.65x - 2.77y = 3.49 \end{cases}$

USING ROW OPERATIONS TO SOLVE A 3×3 SYSTEM

A general 3×3 system in variables x, y and z has the form $\begin{cases} a_1x + b_1y + c_1z = d_1 \\ a_2x + b_2y + c_2z = d_2 \\ a_3x + b_3y + c_3z = d_3 \end{cases}$

where the coefficients of x, y and z are constants.

$\begin{bmatrix} a_1 & b_1 & c_1 & d_1 \\ a_2 & b_2 & c_2 & d_2 \\ a_3 & b_3 & c_3 & d_3 \end{bmatrix}$ is the system's **augmented matrix form** which we need to reduce to **echelon form**: $\begin{bmatrix} a & b & c & d \\ 0 & e & f & g \\ 0 & 0 & h & i \end{bmatrix}$ using **elementary row operations**.

Notice the creation of a **triangle of zeros** in the **bottom left hand corner**.

In this form we can easily solve the system because the last row is really $hz = i$.

- If $h \neq 0$ (i may or may not be 0) we can determine z uniquely using $z = \dfrac{i}{h}$, and likewise y and x from the other two rows. Thus we arrive at a **unique solution**.
- If $h = 0$ and $i \neq 0$, the last row reads $0 \times z = i$ where $i \neq 0$ which is absurd. Hence, there is **no solution** and we say that the system is **inconsistent**.
- If $h = 0$ and $i = 0$, the last row is all zeros. Consequently, there are **infinitely many** solutions of the form $x = p + kt$, $y = q + lt$ and $z = t$ where $t \in \mathbb{R}$.

Note:
- The **parametric representation** of infinite solutions in terms of the parameter t is not unique.

  This particular form assumes you are eliminating x and y to get z from Row 3. It may be easier to eliminate, for example, x and z to get y.

- A geometric interpretation of the different cases for three equations in three unknowns will be given later in **Chapter 16**.

Example 19

Solve the system: $\begin{cases} x + 3y - z = 15 \\ 2x + y + z = 7 \\ x - y - 2z = 0. \end{cases}$

In augmented matrix form, the system is

$\begin{bmatrix} 1 & 3 & -1 & 15 \\ 2 & 1 & 1 & 7 \\ 1 & -1 & -2 & 0 \end{bmatrix}$

$$\sim \begin{bmatrix} 1 & 3 & -1 & 15 \\ 0 & -5 & 3 & -23 \\ 0 & -4 & -1 & -15 \end{bmatrix}$$

$R_2 \rightarrow R_2 - 2R_1$

$$\begin{array}{rrrr} 2 & 1 & 1 & 7 \\ -2 & -6 & 2 & -30 \\ \hline 0 & -5 & 3 & -23 \end{array}$$

$$\sim \begin{bmatrix} 1 & 3 & -1 & 15 \\ 0 & -5 & 3 & -23 \\ 0 & 0 & -17 & 17 \end{bmatrix}$$

$R_3 \rightarrow R_3 - R_1$

$$\begin{array}{rrrr} 1 & -1 & -2 & 0 \\ -1 & -3 & 1 & -15 \\ \hline 0 & -4 & -1 & -15 \end{array}$$

$R_3 \rightarrow 5R_3 - 4R_2$

$$\begin{array}{rrrr} 0 & -20 & -5 & -75 \\ 0 & 20 & -12 & 92 \\ \hline 0 & 0 & -17 & 17 \end{array}$$

The last row gives $-17z = 17$

$$\therefore \quad z = -1$$

Using the final row 2 $-5y + 3z = -23$

we get $-5y - 3 = -23$

$$\therefore \quad -5y = -20$$

$$\therefore \quad y = 4$$

Using the final row 1 $x + 3y - z = 15$

we get $x + 12 + 1 = 15$

$$\therefore \quad x = 2$$

Thus we have a unique solution $x = 2, \ y = 4, \ z = -1$.

A typical graphics calculator solution:

```
rref([A])
    [[1 0 0 2 ]
     [0 1 0 4 ]
     [0 0 1 -1]]
```

Remember: You can use matrix algebra to find unique solutions:

$$\begin{bmatrix} x \\ y \\ z \end{bmatrix} = \begin{bmatrix} 1 & 3 & -1 \\ 2 & 1 & 1 \\ 1 & -1 & -2 \end{bmatrix}^{-1} \begin{bmatrix} 15 \\ 7 \\ 0 \end{bmatrix} = \begin{bmatrix} 2 \\ 4 \\ -1 \end{bmatrix}.$$

CASES WITH NON-UNIQUE SOLUTIONS

As with 2×2 systems of linear equations, 3×3 systems may have a **unique solution** where a single value of each variable satisfies all three equations simultaneously. Alternatively, it could have **no solutions** or **infinitely many solutions**.

We will now consider examples which show each of these situations.

Example 20

Solve the system: $\begin{cases} x + 2y + z = 3 \\ 2x - y + z = 8 \\ 3x - 4y + z = 18 \end{cases}$

In augmented matrix form, the system is:

$$\begin{bmatrix} 1 & 2 & 1 & 3 \\ 2 & -1 & 1 & 8 \\ 3 & -4 & 1 & 18 \end{bmatrix}$$

$R_2 \rightarrow R_2 - 2R_1$

$$\begin{array}{rrrr} 2 & -1 & 1 & 8 \\ -2 & -4 & -2 & -6 \\ \hline 0 & -5 & -1 & 2 \end{array}$$

$$\sim \begin{bmatrix} 1 & 2 & 1 & | & 3 \\ 0 & -5 & -1 & | & 2 \\ 0 & -10 & -2 & | & 9 \end{bmatrix} \begin{array}{l} \\ \leftarrow R_2 \to R_2 - 2R_1 \\ \leftarrow R_3 \to R_3 - 3R_1 \end{array}$$

$$\begin{array}{rrrr} 3 & -4 & 1 & 18 \\ -3 & -6 & -3 & -9 \\ \hline 0 & -10 & -2 & 9 \end{array}$$

$$\sim \begin{bmatrix} 1 & 2 & 1 & | & 3 \\ 0 & -5 & -1 & | & 2 \\ 0 & 0 & 0 & | & 5 \end{bmatrix} \begin{array}{l} \\ \\ \leftarrow R_3 \to R_3 - 2R_2 \end{array}$$

$$\begin{array}{rrrr} 0 & -10 & -2 & 9 \\ 0 & 10 & 2 & -4 \\ \hline 0 & 0 & 0 & 5 \end{array}$$

The last equation is really

$0x + 0y + 0z = 5$ i.e., $0 = 5$,   which is absurd,

$\therefore$ the system has no solution.

Use a **graphics calculator** to confirm there is no solution.

```
rref([A])
      [[1 0 .6 0]
       [0 1 .2 0]
       [0 0 0  1]]
```

Example 21

Solve the system: $\begin{cases} 2x - y + z = 5 \\ x + y - z = 2 \\ 3x - 3y + 3z = 8 \end{cases}$

In augmented matrix form, the system is:

$$\begin{bmatrix} 1 & 1 & -1 & | & 2 \\ 2 & -1 & 1 & | & 5 \\ 3 & -3 & 3 & | & 8 \end{bmatrix} \begin{array}{l} \\ \end{array}$$ Notice the swapping $R_1 \leftrightarrow R_2$.

$$\begin{array}{rrrr} 2 & -1 & 1 & 5 \\ -2 & -2 & 2 & -4 \\ \hline 0 & -3 & 3 & 1 \end{array}$$

$$\sim \begin{bmatrix} 1 & 1 & -1 & | & 2 \\ 0 & -3 & 3 & | & 1 \\ 0 & -6 & 6 & | & 2 \end{bmatrix} \begin{array}{l} \\ \leftarrow R_2 \to R_2 - 2R_1 \\ \leftarrow R_3 \to R_3 - 3R_1 \end{array}$$

$$\begin{array}{rrrr} 3 & -3 & 3 & 8 \\ -3 & -3 & 3 & -6 \\ \hline 0 & -6 & 6 & 2 \end{array}$$

$$\sim \begin{bmatrix} 1 & 1 & -1 & | & 2 \\ 0 & -3 & 3 & | & 1 \\ 0 & 0 & 0 & | & 0 \end{bmatrix} \begin{array}{l} \\ \\ \leftarrow R_3 \to R_3 - 2R_2 \end{array}$$

$$\begin{array}{rrrr} 0 & -6 & 6 & 2 \\ 0 & 6 & -6 & -2 \\ \hline 0 & 0 & 0 & 0 \end{array}$$

The row of zeros indicates infinitely many solutions.

If we let $z = t$ in row 2,

$$-3y + 3t = 1$$
$$\therefore \quad -3y = 1 - 3t$$
$$\therefore \quad y = \frac{1 - 3t}{-3} = -\tfrac{1}{3} + t$$

```
rref([A])▶Frac
      [[1 0 0   7/3 ]
       [0 1 -1 -1/3]
       [0 0 0   0   ]]
```

Thus in equation 1, $x + (-\tfrac{1}{3} + t) - t = 2$

$$\therefore \quad x - \tfrac{1}{3} = 2 \quad \text{and so} \quad x = \tfrac{7}{3}$$

$\therefore$ the solutions have the form: $x = \tfrac{7}{3}, \quad y = -\tfrac{1}{3} + t, \quad z = t, \quad$ where $t \in \mathbb{R}$.

Example 22

Consider the system $\begin{cases} x - 2y - z = -1 \\ 2x + y + 3z = 13 \\ x + 8y + 9z = a \end{cases}$ where a takes all real values.

a Use elementary row operations to reduce the system to echelon form.

b When does the system have no solutions?

c When does the system have infinitely many solutions? What are the solutions?

a In augmented matrix form, the system is:

$$\left[\begin{array}{ccc|c} 1 & -2 & -1 & -1 \\ 2 & 1 & 3 & 13 \\ 1 & 8 & 9 & a \end{array}\right]$$

$$\begin{array}{cccc} 2 & 1 & 3 & 13 \\ -2 & 4 & 2 & 2 \\ \hline 0 & 5 & 5 & 15 \end{array}$$

$$\sim \left[\begin{array}{ccc|c} 1 & -2 & -1 & -1 \\ 0 & 5 & 5 & 15 \\ 0 & 10 & 10 & a+1 \end{array}\right] \begin{array}{l} \\ \leftarrow R_2 \to R_2 - 2R_1 \\ \leftarrow R_3 \to R_3 - R_1 \end{array}$$

$$\begin{array}{cccc} 1 & 8 & 9 & a \\ -1 & 2 & 1 & 1 \\ \hline 0 & 10 & 10 & a+1 \end{array}$$

$$\sim \left[\begin{array}{ccc|c} 1 & -2 & -1 & -1 \\ 0 & 5 & 5 & 15 \\ 0 & 0 & 0 & a-29 \end{array}\right] \begin{array}{l} \\ \\ \leftarrow R_3 \to R_3 - 2R_2 \end{array}$$

$$\begin{array}{cccc} 0 & 10 & 10 & a+1 \\ 0 & -10 & -10 & -30 \\ \hline 0 & 0 & 0 & a-29 \end{array}$$

b Now if $a \neq 29$, we have an inconsistent system as zero = non-zero, and $\therefore$ no solutions.

c If $a = 29$, the last row is all zeros indicating infinitely many solutions.

Letting $z = t$, in equation 2 gives $\qquad 5y + 5t = 15$

$$\therefore \quad y = 3 - t$$

Using the first equation, $\qquad x - 2y - z = -1$

gives $\quad x - 2(3 - t) - t = -1$

$$\therefore \quad x - 6 + 2t - t = -1$$

$$\therefore \quad x = 5 - t$$

Thus we have infinitely many solutions, in the form:

$$x = 5 - t, \quad y = 3 - t, \quad z = t, \quad \text{where} \quad t \in \mathbb{R}.$$

EXERCISE 13F.2

1 Solve the following systems using row reduction:

a $\begin{aligned} x - 2y + 5z &= 1 \\ 2x - 4y + 8z &= 2 \\ -3x + 6y + 7z &= -3 \end{aligned}$
  b $\begin{aligned} x + 4y + 11z &= 7 \\ x + 6y + 17z &= 9 \\ x + 4y + 8z &= 4 \end{aligned}$

c $\begin{aligned} 2x - y + 3z &= 17 \\ 2x - 2y - 5z &= 4 \\ 3x + 2y + 2z &= 10 \end{aligned}$
  d $\begin{aligned} 2x + 3y + 4z &= 1 \\ 5x + 6y + 7z &= 2 \\ 8x + 9y + 10z &= 4 \end{aligned}$

Use technology to check your answers to **b** and **c**.

2 Without using technology, solve using row operations on the augmented matrix:

a
$$x + y + z = 6$$
$$2x + 4y + z = 5$$
$$2x + 3y + z = 6$$

b
$$x + 2y - z = 4$$
$$3x + 2y + z = 7$$
$$5x + 2y + 3z = 11$$

c
$$2x + 4y + z = 1$$
$$3x + 5y = 1$$
$$5x + 13y + 7z = 4$$

3 Write the system of equations
$$x + 2y + z = 3$$
$$2x - y + 4z = 1$$
$$x + 7y - z = k \quad \text{in augmented matrix form.}$$

a Use elementary row operations to reduce the system to echelon form as shown:

b Show that the system has either no solutions or infinitely many solutions and write down these solutions.

$$\begin{bmatrix} \bullet & \bullet & \bullet & | & \bullet \\ 0 & \bullet & \bullet & | & \bullet \\ 0 & 0 & \bullet & | & \bullet \end{bmatrix}$$

c Why does the system not have a unique solution?

4 Consider the system of equations
$$x + 2y - 2z = 5$$
$$x - y + 3z = -1$$
$$x - 7y + kz = -k.$$

a Reduce the system to echelon form.

b Show that for one value of k the system has infinitely many solutions and find the solutions in this case.

c Show that a unique solution exists for all other k. Find this solution.

5 A system of equations is
$$x + 3y + 3z = a - 1$$
$$2x - y + z = 7$$
$$3x - 5y + az = 16.$$

a Reduce the system to echelon form using elementary row operations.

b Show that if $a = -1$ the system has infinitely many solutions, and find their form.

c If $a \neq -1$, find the unique solution in terms of a.

6 Reduce the system of equations:
$$2x + y - z = 3$$
$$mx - 2y + z = 1$$
$$x + 2y + mz = -1$$
to a form in which the solutions may be determined for all real values of m.

a Show that the system has no solutions for one value of m $(m = m_1,$ say$)$.

b Show that there are infinitely many solutions for another value of m $(m = m_2,$ say$)$.

c For what values of m does the system have a unique solution?

Show that the unique solution is $x = \dfrac{7}{m + 5}$, $y = \dfrac{3(m - 2)}{m + 5}$, $z = \dfrac{-7}{m + 5}$.

7 Consider the system of equations
$$x + 3y + kz = 2$$
$$kx - 2y + 3z = k$$
$$4x - 3y + 10z = 5.$$

a Write the system in augmented matrix form and reduce it by elementary row operations to the form:

$$\begin{bmatrix} 1 & 3 & k & | & 2 \\ 0 & \bullet & \bullet & | & \bullet \\ 0 & 0 & \bullet & | & \bullet \end{bmatrix}$$

b Show that for one value of k the system has infinitely many solutions and find the form of these solutions.

c For what value(s) of k does the system have no solutions?

d For what values of k does the system have a unique solution? (There is no need to find the unique solution.)

NOT ENOUGH OR TOO MANY EQUATIONS

$$\begin{cases} x+y+2z=2 \\ 2x+y-z=4 \end{cases}$$ is an example of a 2×3 system of two linear equations in three unknowns which has infinitely many solutions.

It requires a further equation if a unique solution is to be obtained.   We call this an **underspecified system**.

If $\mathbf{AX} = \mathbf{B}$ where $\mathbf{A}$ is $m \times n$, $m < n$, the system is **underspecified**.

If $\mathbf{AX} = \mathbf{B}$ where $\mathbf{A}$ is $m \times n$, $m > n$, the system is **overspecified** and any solutions must fit *all* of the equations. You need to check they do.

Example 23

a   Solve: $\begin{cases} x+y+2z=2 \\ 2x+y-z=4 \end{cases}$

b   What can be deduced if the following equation is added to the system:

   i $3x-y-4z=18$ **ii** $3x+y-4z=18$?

a   The augmented matrix is:

$$\begin{bmatrix} 1 & 1 & 2 & | & 2 \\ 2 & 1 & -1 & | & 4 \end{bmatrix}$$

$$\sim \begin{bmatrix} 1 & 1 & 2 & | & 2 \\ 0 & -1 & -5 & | & 0 \end{bmatrix} \quad R_2 \to R_2 - 2R_1$$

$$\begin{array}{rrrr} 2 & 1 & -1 & 4 \\ -2 & -2 & -4 & -4 \\ \hline 0 & -1 & -5 & 0 \end{array}$$

So, $-y-5z=0$ and if $z=t$, $y=-5t$

and as $x+y+2z=2$,

$$x-5t+2t=2$$

$\therefore$ $x = 2 + 3t$. So, $x = 2 + 3t$, $y = -5t$, $z = t$ for all $t \in \mathbb{R}$.

b   **i**   If in addition $3x-y-4z=18$

then $3(2+3t)-(-5t)-4t=18$

$\therefore$ $6+9t+5t-4t=18$

$\therefore$ $10t=12$

$\therefore$ $t=1.2$

When $t=1.2$, $x=5.6$, $y=-6$, $z=1.2$ is a unique solution.

ii   If in addition $3x+y-4z=18$

then $3(2+3t)+(-5t)-4t=18$

$\therefore$ $6=18$ which is absurd, so no solution exists.

Note: Underspecified systems may also have no solutions.
This will be evident by any inconsistency.

EXERCISE 13F.3

1 Solve the systems:

    a $2x + y + z = 5$
          $x - y + z = 3$

    b $3x + y + 2z = 10$
          $x - 2y + z = -4$

    c $x + 2y + z = 5$
          $2x + 4y + 2z = 16$

2 Solve $\begin{cases} x - 3y + z = 0 \\ 2x + y - 2z = 0 \end{cases}$ and hence solve the system $\begin{cases} x - 3y + z = 0 \\ 2x + y - 2z = 0 \\ 3x - y + z = 18. \end{cases}$

3 Solve $\begin{cases} 2x + 3y + z = 0 \\ x - y + 2z = 0 \end{cases}$ and hence solve $\begin{cases} 2x + 3y + z = 0 \\ x - y + 2z = 0 \\ ax + y - z = 0 \end{cases}$ for all $a \in \mathbb{R}$.

4 An economist producing x thousand items attempts to model a profit function as a quadratic model $P(x) = ax^2 + bx + c$ thousand dollars. She knows that when producing 1000 items the profit is \$8000, and when producing 4000 items the profit is \$17 000.

    a Using the supplied information show that $\begin{cases} a + b + c = 8 \\ 16a + 4b + c = 17 \end{cases}$

    b Show that $a = t$, $b = 3 - 5t$, $c = 5 + 4t$ represents the possible solutions for the system.

    c If she discovers that the profit for producing 2500 items is \$19 750, find the actual profit function.

    d What is the maximum profit to be made and what level of production is needed to achieve it?

G   INDUCTION WITH MATRICES

Example 24

Let the matrix $\mathbf{B} = \begin{bmatrix} 2 & 0 \\ -1 & 1 \end{bmatrix}$.

    a Find $\mathbf{B}^2$, $\mathbf{B}^3$ and $\mathbf{B}^4$.

    b   **i** Give a proposition (conjecture) for $\mathbf{B}^n$, $n \in \mathbb{Z}^+$.

          ii Prove your proposition is true using mathematical induction.

---

    a $\mathbf{B}^2 = \begin{bmatrix} 2 & 0 \\ -1 & 1 \end{bmatrix}^2 = \begin{bmatrix} 4 & 0 \\ -3 & 1 \end{bmatrix}$. Also $\mathbf{B}^3 = \begin{bmatrix} 8 & 0 \\ -7 & 1 \end{bmatrix}$ and $\mathbf{B}^4 = \begin{bmatrix} 16 & 0 \\ -15 & 1 \end{bmatrix}$.

    b   **i** P_n is that "if $\mathbf{B} = \begin{bmatrix} 2 & 0 \\ -1 & 1 \end{bmatrix}$ then $\mathbf{B}^n = \begin{bmatrix} 2^n & 0 \\ 1 - 2^n & 1 \end{bmatrix}$" for all $n \in \mathbb{Z}^+$.

          ii For $n = 1$, $\mathbf{B}^1 = \begin{bmatrix} 2^1 & 0 \\ 1 - 2^1 & 1 \end{bmatrix} = \begin{bmatrix} 2 & 0 \\ -1 & 1 \end{bmatrix}$

                $\therefore$ P_1 is true.

Assume that P_k is true for some $k \in \mathbb{Z}^+$, so $\mathbf{B}^k = \begin{bmatrix} 2^k & 0 \\ 1 - 2^k & 1 \end{bmatrix}$.

Now $\mathbf{B}^{k+1} = \mathbf{B}\,\mathbf{B}^k$

$$= \begin{bmatrix} 2 & 0 \\ -1 & 1 \end{bmatrix} \begin{bmatrix} 2^k & 0 \\ 1 - 2^k & 1 \end{bmatrix} \quad \{\text{by assumption}\}$$

$$= \begin{bmatrix} 2(2^k) & 0 \\ -2^k + 1 - 2^k & 1 \end{bmatrix}$$

$$= \begin{bmatrix} 2^{k+1} & 0 \\ 1 - 2(2^k) & 1 \end{bmatrix}$$

$$= \begin{bmatrix} 2^{k+1} & 0 \\ 1 - 2^{k+1} & 1 \end{bmatrix} \quad \text{as required.}$$

So, P_1 is true and P_{n+1} is true whenever P_n is true.

$\therefore \ \mathbf{B}^n = \begin{bmatrix} 2^n & 0 \\ 1 - 2^n & 1 \end{bmatrix}$ for all $n \in \mathbb{Z}^+$ by mathematical induction.

EXERCISE 13G

1 Let $\mathbf{M} = \begin{bmatrix} 1 & 2 \\ 0 & 1 \end{bmatrix}$.

    a Find $\mathbf{M}^2$, $\mathbf{M}^3$ and $\mathbf{M}^4$.   b State a proposition for $\mathbf{M}^n$.

    c Prove your conjecture is true using mathematical induction.

2 a Given $\mathbf{A} = \begin{bmatrix} 1 & 2 \\ 0 & 3 \end{bmatrix}$, find $\mathbf{A}^2$, $\mathbf{A}^3$, $\mathbf{A}^4$ and $\mathbf{A}^5$.

    b Conjecture a value for $\mathbf{A}^n$ in terms of n where $n \in \mathbb{Z}^+$.

    c Use mathematical induction to prove your conjecture is true.

    d Is the result true when $n = -1$?

3 Let the matrix $\mathbf{P} = \begin{bmatrix} 2 & 1 \\ -1 & 0 \end{bmatrix}$.

    a Find $\mathbf{P}^2$, $\mathbf{P}^3$ and $\mathbf{P}^4$.

    b Give a proposition (conjecture) for $\mathbf{P}^n$ where $n \in \mathbb{Z}^+$.

    c Prove your proposition is true using mathematical induction.

4 For the sequence $1, 1, 2, 3, 5, 8, 13, \ldots$ where $u_1 = u_2 = 1$ and $u_{n+2} = u_n + u_{n+1}$,

$n \in \mathbb{Z}^+$, and the matrix $\mathbf{A} = \begin{bmatrix} 1 & 1 \\ 1 & 0 \end{bmatrix}$, prove by the principle of mathematical

induction that $\mathbf{A}^{n+1} = \begin{bmatrix} u_{n+2} & u_{n+1} \\ u_{n+1} & u_n \end{bmatrix}$ for all integers $n \geqslant 1$.

REVIEW SET 13A

1 If $A = \begin{bmatrix} 3 & 2 \\ 0 & -1 \end{bmatrix}$ and $B = \begin{bmatrix} 1 & 0 \\ -2 & 4 \end{bmatrix}$ find:

   a $A + B$ **b** $3A$ **c** $-2B$ **d** $A - B$

   e $B - 2A$ **f** $3A - 2B$ **g** AB **h** BA

   i A^{-1} **j** A^2 **k** ABA **l** $(AB)^{-1}$

2 Find a, b, c and d if:

   a $\begin{bmatrix} a & b-2 \\ c & d \end{bmatrix} = \begin{bmatrix} -a & 3 \\ 2-c & -4 \end{bmatrix}$ **b** $\begin{bmatrix} 3 & 2a \\ b & -2 \end{bmatrix} + \begin{bmatrix} b & -a \\ c & d \end{bmatrix} = \begin{bmatrix} a & 2 \\ 2 & 6 \end{bmatrix}$

3 Make Y the subject of:

   a $B - Y = A$ **b** $2Y + C = D$ **c** $AY = B$

   d $YB = C$ **e** $C - AY = B$ **f** $AY^{-1} = B$

4 Solve using an inverse matrix:

   a $\begin{aligned} 3x - 4y &= 2 \\ 5x + 2y &= -1 \end{aligned}$ **b** $\begin{aligned} 4x - y &= 5 \\ 2x + 3y &= 9 \end{aligned}$ Why is this possible?

   c $X \begin{bmatrix} 3 & 4 \\ 1 & 1 \end{bmatrix} = \begin{bmatrix} 5 & 4 \\ 0 & -2 \end{bmatrix}$ **d** $\begin{bmatrix} 2 & 0 \\ -1 & 1 \end{bmatrix} X = \begin{bmatrix} -1 \\ 2 \end{bmatrix}$

   e $\begin{bmatrix} 1 & 1 \\ 1 & -2 \end{bmatrix} X = \begin{bmatrix} 5 \\ 4 \end{bmatrix}$ **f** $\begin{bmatrix} 1 & 1 \\ -1 & 1 \end{bmatrix} X \begin{bmatrix} 2 & 1 \\ 1 & -1 \end{bmatrix} = \begin{bmatrix} 5 & 1 \\ 0 & 3 \end{bmatrix}$

5 If A is $\begin{bmatrix} 1 & 2 & 3 \end{bmatrix}$ and B is $\begin{bmatrix} 2 & 4 \\ 0 & 1 \\ 3 & 2 \end{bmatrix}$ find, if possible:

   a $2B$ **b** $\frac{1}{2}B$ **c** AB **d** BA

6 For $P = \begin{bmatrix} 1 & 2 \\ 1 & 0 \\ 2 & 3 \end{bmatrix}$ and $Q = \begin{bmatrix} 3 & 0 \\ 1 & 4 \\ 1 & 1 \end{bmatrix}$ find:

   a $P + Q$ **b** $Q - P$ **c** $\frac{3}{2}P - Q$

7 When does the system $\begin{aligned} x + 4y &= 2 \\ kx + 3y &= -6 \end{aligned}$ have a unique solution?

   Comment on the solutions for the non-unique cases.

8 Solve the system $\begin{aligned} 3x - y + 2z &= 3 \\ 2x + 3y - z &= -3 \\ x - 2y + 3z &= 2. \end{aligned}$

9 The two points $(-2, 4)$ and $(1, 3)$ lie on a circle $x^2 + y^2 + ax + by + c = 0$.

   a Find two equations in a, b and c and solve the system of equations.

   b Explain why infinitely many solutions are obtained in **a**.

   c If $(2, 2)$ is also on the circle, find the equation of the circle.

10 $2x + 3y - 4z = 13$
$\quad x - y + 3z = -1$ Solve the system using elementary row operations, and
$\ 3x + 7y - 11z = k$ describe the solution set as k takes all real values.

11 Solve the system: $3x + y - z = 0$, $x + y + 2z = 0$.

REVIEW SET 13B

1 Determine the 2×2 matrix which when multiplied by $\begin{bmatrix} 1 & 0 \\ 1 & 1 \end{bmatrix}$ gives an answer

of $\begin{bmatrix} 1 & 0 \\ 1 & 1 \end{bmatrix}$. **Hint:** Let the matrix be $\begin{bmatrix} a & b \\ c & d \end{bmatrix}$.

2 $A = \begin{bmatrix} 4 & 3 & 2 \end{bmatrix}$, $B = \begin{bmatrix} 1 \\ 2 \\ 0 \end{bmatrix}$ and $C = \begin{bmatrix} 1 & 2 & 3 \\ 3 & 2 & 1 \\ 1 & 2 & 3 \end{bmatrix}$. Find, if possible:

    a AB   **b** BA   **c** AC   **d** CA   **e** CB

3 Find, if they exist, the inverse matrices of each of the following:

    a $\begin{bmatrix} 6 & 8 \\ 5 & 7 \end{bmatrix}$ **b** $\begin{bmatrix} 4 & -3 \\ 8 & -6 \end{bmatrix}$ **c** $\begin{bmatrix} 11 & 5 \\ -6 & -3 \end{bmatrix}$

4   **a** If $A = 2A^{-1}$, show that $A^2 = 2I$.

    b If $A = 2A^{-1}$, simplify $(A - I)(A + 3I)$ giving your answer in the form
$rA + sI$ where r and s are real numbers.

5 A café sells two types of cola drinks. The drinks each come in three sizes: small, medium and large. At the beginning and end of the day the stock in the fridge was counted. The results are shown below:

Start of the day: *End of the day:*

	Brand C	Brand P
small	42	54
medium	36	27
large	34	30

	Brand C	Brand P
small	27	31
medium	28	15
large	28	22

The profit matrix is: $\begin{matrix} \text{small} & \text{medium} & \text{large} \\ \begin{bmatrix} \$0.75 & \$0.55 & \$1.20 \end{bmatrix} \end{matrix}$

Use matrix methods to calculate the profit made for the day from the sale of these drinks.

6 If $A = \begin{bmatrix} 1 & 2 & 3 \\ 2 & 5 & 7 \\ -2 & -4 & -5 \end{bmatrix}$ and $B = \begin{bmatrix} 3 & -2 & -1 \\ -4 & 1 & -1 \\ 2 & 0 & 1 \end{bmatrix}$, find AB and BA and

hence find A^{-1} in terms of **B**.

7 Solve the system of equations: $\begin{cases} 2x + y + z = 8 \\ 4x - 7y + 3z = 10 \\ 3x - 2y - z = 1. \end{cases}$

8 Solve the system: $\begin{aligned} x + 2y - 3z &= 3 \\ 6x + 3y + 2z &= 4. \end{aligned}$

9 **a** Show that the system $\begin{cases} 2x - 3y = 9 \\ mx - 7y = n \end{cases}$ has an augmented matrix after

elementary row operations of $\begin{bmatrix} 2 & -3 & | & 9 \\ 14 - 3m & 0 & | & 63 - 3n \end{bmatrix}$.

   b Under what conditions does the system have a unique solution?

REVIEW SET 13C

1 When does the system $\begin{aligned} kx + 3y &= -6 \\ x + (k+2)y &= 2 \end{aligned}$ have a unique solution?

Comment on the solutions for the non-unique cases.

2 Find x if $\begin{vmatrix} x & 2 & 0 \\ 2 & x+1 & -2 \\ 0 & -2 & x+2 \end{vmatrix} = 0$, given that x is real.

3 If $A = \begin{bmatrix} -2 & 3 \\ 4 & -1 \end{bmatrix}$, $B = \begin{bmatrix} -7 & 9 \\ 9 & -3 \end{bmatrix}$, $C = \begin{bmatrix} -1 & 0 & 3 \\ 0 & 2 & 1 \end{bmatrix}$, evaluate if possible:

   a $2A - 2B$ **b** AC **c** CB **d** D, given that $DA = B$.

4 Find X if $AX = B$, $A = \begin{bmatrix} 2 & -1 \\ 3 & 4 \end{bmatrix}$ and $B = \begin{bmatrix} 3 & 5 & 1 \\ -1 & 13 & 18 \end{bmatrix}$.

5 Write $5A^2 - 6A = 3I$ in the form $AB = I$ and hence find A^{-1} in terms of A and I.

6 **a** If A and B are square matrices, under what conditions are the following true?
   i If $AB = B$ then $A = I$ **ii** $(A + B)^2 = A^2 + 2AB + B^2$

   b If $M = \begin{bmatrix} k & 2 \\ 2 & k \end{bmatrix}\begin{bmatrix} k-1 & -2 \\ -3 & k \end{bmatrix}$ has an inverse M^{-1}, what values can k have?

7 Find the values of t for which the system of equations $\begin{cases} x - y - 2z = -3 \\ tx + y - z = 3t \\ x + 3y + tz = 13 \end{cases}$ does not have a unique solution for x, y and z.

   Show that no solution exists for one of these values of t, and find the solution set for the other values of t.

8 A rock was thrown from the top of a cliff such that its distance above sea level was given by $s(t) = at^2 + bt + c$, where t is the time in seconds after the rock was released. After 1 second the rock was 63 m above sea level, after 2 seconds 72 m, and after 7 seconds 27 m.

   a Find a, b and c and hence an expression for $s(t)$.
   b Find the height of the cliff.
   c Find the time taken for the rock to reach sea level.

REVIEW SET 13D

1 Solve the system:
$$3x - y + 2z = 8$$
$$2x + 3y - z = -3$$
$$x - 2y + 3z = 9$$

2 Prove that $\begin{vmatrix} a+b & c & c \\ a & b+c & a \\ b & b & c+a \end{vmatrix} = 4abc$.

3 If $\mathbf{A}^2 = 5\mathbf{A} + 2\mathbf{I}$, find $\mathbf{A}^3$, $\mathbf{A}^4$, $\mathbf{A}^5$ and $\mathbf{A}^6$ in the form $r\mathbf{A} + s\mathbf{I}$.

4 The cost of producing x hundred bottles of correcting fluid per day is given by the function $C(x) = ax^3 + bx^2 + cx + d$ dollars where a, b, c and d are constants.

  a If it costs $80 before any bottles are produced, find d.

  b It costs $100 to produce 100 bottles, $148 to produce 200 bottles and $376 to produce 400 bottles per day. Determine a, b and c.

5 If $\mathbf{A} = \begin{bmatrix} 1 & -3 \\ 2 & 1 \end{bmatrix}$, $\mathbf{B} = \begin{bmatrix} -1 & 2 \\ 3 & 1 \end{bmatrix}$, $\mathbf{C} = \begin{bmatrix} -12 & -11 \\ -10 & -1 \end{bmatrix}$, find $\mathbf{X}$ if $\mathbf{AXB} = \mathbf{C}$.

6 Find the solution set of the following:

  a $2x + y - z = 9$ **b** $2x + y - z = 3$
        $3x + 2y + 5z = 19$ $3x + 2y + z = 1$
        $x + y - 3z = 1$ $x - 3y = 5$

7 Solve the system of equations $\begin{cases} kx + 2y = 1 \\ 2x + ky = -2 \end{cases}$ as k takes all real values.

8 Solve the system $\begin{cases} 2x - 3y + z = 10 \\ 4x - 6y + kz = m \end{cases}$ for all possible values of k and m.

9 Consider the system of equations
$$x + 5y - 6z = 2$$
$$kx + y - z = 3$$
$$5x - ky + 3z = 7 \quad \text{as } k \text{ takes all real values.}$$

  a Write the system in augmented matrix form. Show using elementary row operations that it reduces to:
$$\begin{bmatrix} 1 & 5 & -6 & 2 \\ 0 & 1-5k & 6k-1 & 3-2k \\ 0 & 0 & (k-2)(3k-2) & -(k-2)(k+18) \end{bmatrix}$$

  b For what values of k does the system have a unique solution?

  c For what value of k does the system have infinitely many solutions? Find the solutions.

  d For what value of k is the system inconsistent? How many solutions does the system have in this case?

REVIEW SET 13E

1 Hung, Quan and Ariel bought tickets for three separate performances. The table below shows the number of tickets bought by each person:

	Opera	Play	Concert
Hung	3	2	5
Quan	2	3	1
Ariel	1	5	4

a If the total cost for Hung was €267, for Quan €145 and for Ariel €230, represent this information in the form of three equations.

b Find the cost per ticket for each of the performances.

c Determine how much it would cost Phuong to purchase 4 opera, 1 play and 2 concert tickets.

2 Solve the system of equations:
$$\begin{aligned} 2x + y + z &= 8 \\ 4x - 7y + 3z &= 10 \\ 3x - 2y - z &= 1 \end{aligned}$$

3 If $\mathbf{A} = \begin{bmatrix} -3 & 2 & 2 \\ 1 & -1 & 0 \end{bmatrix}$, $\mathbf{B} = \begin{bmatrix} 2 & 4 \\ -3 & 1 \\ 1 & 2 \end{bmatrix}$ and $\mathbf{C} = \begin{bmatrix} -2 & 5 \\ 1 & 3 \end{bmatrix}$ find, if possible:

a $3\mathbf{A}$ **b** $\mathbf{AB}$ **c** $\mathbf{BA}$ **d** $\mathbf{AC}$ **e** $\mathbf{BC}$

4 If $\mathbf{A} = \begin{bmatrix} 1 & 2 & 1 \\ 2 & 4 & 6 \\ 3 & 1 & 2 \end{bmatrix}$ and $\mathbf{B} = \begin{bmatrix} -1 & 2 & -3 \\ 2 & -1 & 4 \\ 3 & 4 & 1 \end{bmatrix}$ show by calculation that

$\det(\mathbf{AB}) = \det\mathbf{A} \times \det\mathbf{B} = 80$.

5 A matrix $\mathbf{A}$ has the property that $\mathbf{A}^2 = \mathbf{A} - \mathbf{I}$.

Find expressions for $\mathbf{A}^n$ for $n = 3, 4, ..., 8$ in terms of $\mathbf{A}$ and $\mathbf{I}$. Hence:

a deduce simple expressions for $\mathbf{A}^{6n+3}$ and $\mathbf{A}^{6n+5}$

b express $\mathbf{A}^{-1}$ in terms of $\mathbf{A}$ and $\mathbf{I}$.

c Prove your result for $\mathbf{A}^{6n+5}$ is true by mathematical induction.

6 **a** Find the values of a and b for which the matrix $\begin{bmatrix} 2 & 1 & 1 \\ 1 & 1 & 1 \\ 2 & 2 & 1 \end{bmatrix}$ has an inverse

of the form $\begin{bmatrix} a & b & 0 \\ b & 0 & a \\ 0 & 2 & b \end{bmatrix}$.

b Use your answer to **a** above to solve the system of equations:
$$\begin{aligned} 2x + y + z &= 1 \\ x + y + z &= 6 \\ 2x + 2y + z &= 5 \end{aligned}$$

Chapter 14

Vectors in 2 and 3 dimensions

Contents:

A VECTORS

 An aeroplane in calm conditions is flying due east. A cold wind suddenly blows in from the south west. The aeroplane, cruising at 800 km h^{-1}, is blown slightly off course by the 35 km h^{-1} wind.

- What effect does the wind have on the speed and direction of the aeroplane?
- How can we accurately determine the new speed and direction using mathematics?
- How much of the force of the wind operates in the direction of the aeroplane? How does this affect fuel consumption and the time of the flight?

VECTORS AND SCALARS

To solve questions like those in the **Opening Problem**, we need to examine the **size** or **magnitude** of the quantities under consideration as well as the **direction** in which they are acting.

For example, the effect of the wind on an aeroplane would be different if the wind was blowing from behind the plane rather than against it.

Consider the problem of forces acting at a point.

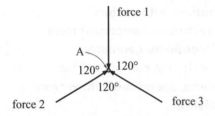

If three equal forces act on point A and they are from directions 120° apart then clearly A would not move.

For example, imagine three people 120° apart around a statue, pushing with equal force.

Now suppose three forces act on the point A as shown. What is the resultant force acting on A? In what direction would A move under these three forces?

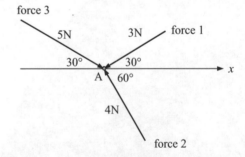

To handle these situations we need to consider quantities called **vectors** which have both size (magnitude) and direction.

> Quantities which have only magnitude are called **scalars**.
>
> Quantities which have both size (magnitude) and direction are called **vectors**.

Velocity is a vector since it describes speed (a scalar) in a particular direction.

Other examples of vector quantities are:
- acceleration
- force
- displacement
- momentum
- weight

DIRECTED LINE SEGMENT REPRESENTATION

Consider a car that is travelling at 80 km h^{-1} in a NE direction.

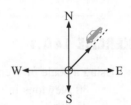

One good way of representing this is to use an arrow on a scale diagram.

Scale: 1 cm represents 40 km h^{-1}

The **length of the arrow** represents the size (magnitude) of the quantity and the **arrowhead** shows the direction of travel.

Consider the vector represented by the line segment from O to A.

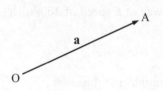

- This **vector** could be represented by

  $\overrightarrow{OA}$ or **a** or $\tilde{a}$ or $\overrightarrow{a}$

  ↑   ↑

  bold used   used by
  in text books   students

- The **magnitude (length)** could be represented by

  $|\overrightarrow{OA}|$ or OA or $|\mathbf{a}|$ or $|\tilde{a}|$ or $|\overrightarrow{a}|$

For

we say that $\overrightarrow{AB}$ is the vector which **emanates** from A and **terminates** at B,

and that $\overrightarrow{AB}$ is the **position vector** of B relative to A.

Example 1	
On a scale diagram, sketch the vector which represents "a force of 20 m s^{-1} in a southerly direction".	*Scale:* 1 cm $\equiv$ 10 m s^{-1} 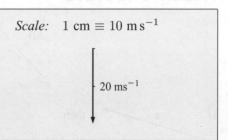

Example 2

Draw a scaled arrow diagram representing "a force of 40 Newtons on a bearing 115°".

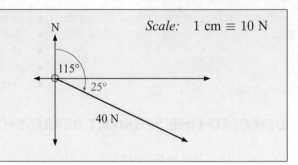

EXERCISE 14A.1

1   Using a scale of 1 cm represents 10 units, sketch a vector to represent:
   a   30 Newtons in a SE direction
   b   25 m s^{-1} in a northerly direction
   c   a displacement of 35 m in the direction 070°
   d   an aeroplane taking off at an angle of 10° to the runway with a speed of 50 m s^{-1}.

2   If  represents a velocity of 50 m s^{-1} due east, draw a directed line segment representing a velocity of:
   a   100 m s^{-1} due west   b   75 m s^{-1} north east.

3   Draw a scaled arrow diagram representing the following vectors:
   a   a force of 30 Newtons in the NW direction
   b   a velocity of 40 m s^{-1} in the direction 146°
   c   a displacement of 25 km in the direction S32^{o}E
   d   an aeroplane taking off at an angle of 8° to the runway at a speed of 150 km h^{-1}.

VECTOR EQUALITY

Two vectors are **equal** if they have the same magnitude and direction.

So, if arrows are used to represent vectors, then equal vectors are **parallel** and **equal in length**.

The arrows that represent them are translations of one another.

As we can draw a vector with given magnitude and direction from *any* point, we consider vectors to be **free**. They are sometimes referred to as **free vectors**.

NEGATIVE VECTORS

Notice that $\overrightarrow{AB}$ and $\overrightarrow{BA}$ have the same length but have opposite directions.

We say that $\overrightarrow{BA}$ is the negative of $\overrightarrow{AB}$ and write $\overrightarrow{BA} = -\overrightarrow{AB}$.

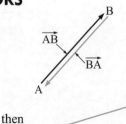

If   **a** then

since **a** and $-$**a** must be parallel and equal in length, but opposite in direction.

Example 3

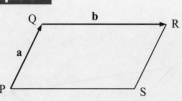

PQRS is a parallelogram in which
$\overrightarrow{PQ} = \mathbf{a}$ and $\overrightarrow{QR} = \mathbf{b}$.
Find vector expressions for:

a $\overrightarrow{QP}$ b $\overrightarrow{RQ}$ c $\overrightarrow{SR}$ d $\overrightarrow{SP}$

a $\overrightarrow{QP} = -\mathbf{a}$ {the negative vector of $\overrightarrow{PQ}$}

b $\overrightarrow{RQ} = -\mathbf{b}$ {the negative vector of $\overrightarrow{QR}$}

c $\overrightarrow{SR} = \mathbf{a}$ {parallel to and the same length as $\overrightarrow{PQ}$}

d $\overrightarrow{SP} = -\mathbf{b}$ {parallel to and the same length as $\overrightarrow{RQ}$}

EXERCISE 14A.2

1 State the vectors which are:
   a equal in magnitude   b parallel
   c in the same direction   d equal
   e negatives of one another.

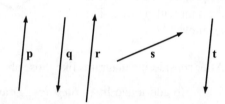

2 The figure alongside consists of 2 equilateral triangles. A, B and C lie on a straight line. $\overrightarrow{AB} = \mathbf{p}$, $\overrightarrow{AE} = \mathbf{q}$ and $\overrightarrow{DC} = \mathbf{r}$.
   Which of the following statements is true?

   a $\overrightarrow{EB} = \mathbf{r}$ b $|\mathbf{p}| = |\mathbf{q}|$ c $\overrightarrow{BC} = \mathbf{r}$
   d $\overrightarrow{DB} = \mathbf{q}$ e $\overrightarrow{ED} = \mathbf{p}$ f $\mathbf{p} = \mathbf{q}$

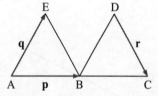

DISCUSSION

Could we have a zero vector?
What would its length be?
What would its direction be?

B   OPERATIONS WITH VECTORS

We have already been operating with vectors without realising it.

Bearing problems are an example of this. The vectors in these cases are **displacements**.

A typical problem could be:

A runner runs in an easterly direction for 4 km and then in a southerly direction for 2 km.

How far is she from her starting point and in what direction?

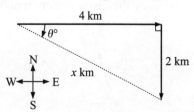

Trigonometry and Pythagoras' theorem are used to answer such problems as we need to find θ and x.

VECTOR ADDITION

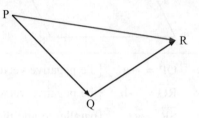

Suppose we have three towns P, Q and R.

A trip from P to Q followed by a trip from Q to R is equivalent to a trip from P to R.

This can be expressed in a vector form as the sum $\overrightarrow{PQ} + \overrightarrow{QR} = \overrightarrow{PR}$.

This triangular diagram could take all sorts of shapes, but in each case the sum will be true. For example:

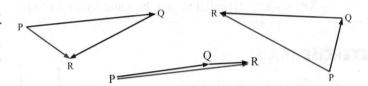

After considering diagrams like those above, we can now define vector addition geometrically:

> To add **a** and **b**:   *Step 1:*   Draw **a**.
> *Step 2:*   At the arrowhead end of **a**, draw **b**.
> *Step 3:*   Join the beginning of **a** to the arrowhead end of **b**. This is vector **a + b**.

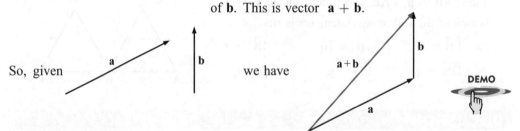

So, given   **a**   **b**   we have   **a+b**   **b**   **a**

DEMO

Example 4	
Given **a** and **b** as shown, construct **a + b**.	

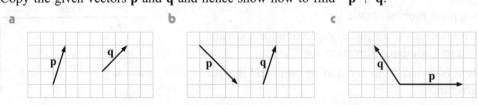

EXERCISE 14B.1

1   Copy the given vectors **p** and **q** and hence show how to find   **p + q**:

a   b   c

d 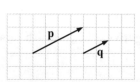 **e** 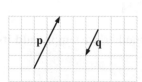 **f**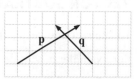

Example 5

Find a single vector which is equal to:

a $\overrightarrow{BC} + \overrightarrow{CA}$

b $\overrightarrow{BA} + \overrightarrow{AE} + \overrightarrow{EC}$

c $\overrightarrow{AB} + \overrightarrow{BC} + \overrightarrow{CA}$

d $\overrightarrow{AB} + \overrightarrow{BC} + \overrightarrow{CD} + \overrightarrow{DE}$

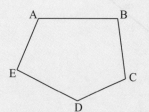

a $\overrightarrow{BC} + \overrightarrow{CA} = \overrightarrow{BA}$ {as shown}

b $\overrightarrow{BA} + \overrightarrow{AE} + \overrightarrow{EC} = \overrightarrow{BC}$

c $\overrightarrow{AB} + \overrightarrow{BC} + \overrightarrow{CA} = \overrightarrow{AA}$

d $\overrightarrow{AB} + \overrightarrow{BC} + \overrightarrow{CD} + \overrightarrow{DE} = \overrightarrow{AE}$

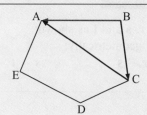

---

2 Find a single vector which is equal to:

   a $\overrightarrow{AB} + \overrightarrow{BC}$ **b** $\overrightarrow{BC} + \overrightarrow{CD}$ **c** $\overrightarrow{AB} + \overrightarrow{BC} + \overrightarrow{CD}$ **d** $\overrightarrow{AC} + \overrightarrow{CB} + \overrightarrow{BD}$

3 a Use vector diagrams to find **i** $\mathbf{p} + \mathbf{q}$ **ii** $\mathbf{q} + \mathbf{p}$ given that:

    p is   and **q** is

  b For any two vectors **p** and **q**, is $\mathbf{p} + \mathbf{q} = \mathbf{q} + \mathbf{p}$?

4 Consider: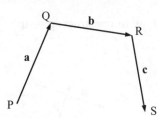

One way of finding $\overrightarrow{PS}$ is:

$$\overrightarrow{PS} = \overrightarrow{PR} + \overrightarrow{RS}$$
$$= (\mathbf{a} + \mathbf{b}) + \mathbf{c}.$$

Use the diagram to show that
$(\mathbf{a} + \mathbf{b}) + \mathbf{c} = \mathbf{a} + (\mathbf{b} + \mathbf{c})$.

THE ZERO VECTOR

Having defined vector addition, we are now able to state that:

> The **zero vector 0** is a vector of length 0.
>
> For any vector **a**: $\mathbf{a} + \mathbf{0} = \mathbf{0} + \mathbf{a} = \mathbf{a}$
> $\mathbf{a} + (-\mathbf{a}) = (-\mathbf{a}) + \mathbf{a} = \mathbf{0}$.

When we write the zero vector by hand, we usually write $\overrightarrow{0}$.

VECTOR SUBTRACTION

To subtract one vector from another, we simply **add its negative**,   i.e., $\mathbf{a} - \mathbf{b} = \mathbf{a} + (-\mathbf{b})$.

For example:

for   and   then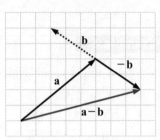

Example 6

For **r**, **s** and **t** as shown find geometrically:

   a $\mathbf{r} - \mathbf{s}$ **b** $\mathbf{s} - \mathbf{t} - \mathbf{r}$

a 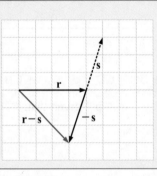   **b**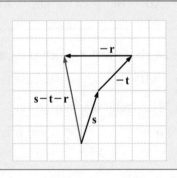

EXERCISE 14B.2

1   For the following vectors **p** and **q**, show how to construct $\mathbf{p} - \mathbf{q}$:

   a   **b**   **c**   **d**

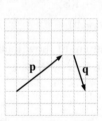 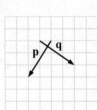 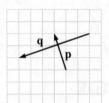 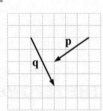

2   For the following vectors:

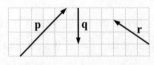

show how to construct: **a** $\mathbf{p} + \mathbf{q} - \mathbf{r}$ **b** $\mathbf{p} - \mathbf{q} - \mathbf{r}$ **c** $\mathbf{r} - \mathbf{q} - \mathbf{p}$

Example 7

For points A, B, C and D, simplify the following vector expressions:

a $\overrightarrow{AB} - \overrightarrow{CB}$

b $\overrightarrow{AC} - \overrightarrow{BC} - \overrightarrow{DB}$

a $\overrightarrow{AB} - \overrightarrow{CB}$
$= \overrightarrow{AB} + \overrightarrow{BC}$ {as $\overrightarrow{BC} = -\overrightarrow{CB}$}
$= \overrightarrow{AC}$

b $\overrightarrow{AC} - \overrightarrow{BC} - \overrightarrow{DB}$
$= \overrightarrow{AC} + \overrightarrow{CB} + \overrightarrow{BD}$
$= \overrightarrow{AD}$

Example 8

Construct vector equations for:

a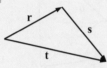
b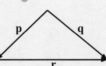
c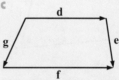

a $t = r + s$

b $r = -p + q$

c $f = -g + d + e$

We select any vector for the LHS and then take another path from its starting point to its finishing point.

Example 9

Find, in terms of **r**, **s** and **t**:

a $\overrightarrow{RS}$ b $\overrightarrow{SR}$ c $\overrightarrow{ST}$

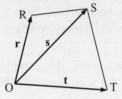

a $\overrightarrow{RS}$
$= \overrightarrow{RO} + \overrightarrow{OS}$
$= -\overrightarrow{OR} + \overrightarrow{OS}$
$= -r + s$
$= s - r$

b $\overrightarrow{SR}$
$= \overrightarrow{SO} + \overrightarrow{OR}$
$= -\overrightarrow{OS} + \overrightarrow{OR}$
$= -s + r$
$= r - s$

c $\overrightarrow{ST}$
$= \overrightarrow{SO} + \overrightarrow{OT}$
$= -\overrightarrow{OS} + \overrightarrow{OT}$
$= -s + t$
$= t - s$

3 For points A, B, C and D, simplify the following vector expressions:

a $\overrightarrow{AC} + \overrightarrow{CB}$

b $\overrightarrow{AD} - \overrightarrow{BD}$

c $\overrightarrow{AC} + \overrightarrow{CA}$

d $\overrightarrow{AB} + \overrightarrow{BC} + \overrightarrow{CD}$

e $\overrightarrow{BA} - \overrightarrow{CA} + \overrightarrow{CB}$

f $\overrightarrow{AB} - \overrightarrow{CB} - \overrightarrow{DC}$

4 Construct vector equations for:

a 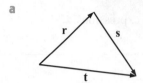　　b 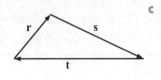　　c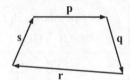

d 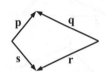　　e 　　f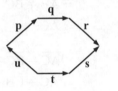

5　**a**　Find, in terms of **r**, **s** and **t**:

　　i $\overrightarrow{OB}$　**ii** $\overrightarrow{CA}$　**iii** $\overrightarrow{OC}$

　　b　Find, in terms of **p**, **q** and **r**:

　　i $\overrightarrow{AD}$　**ii** $\overrightarrow{BC}$　**iii** $\overrightarrow{AC}$

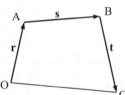　　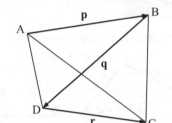

AN APPLICATION OF VECTOR SUBTRACTION

Vector subtraction is used to solve problems involving displacement, velocity and force.

Consider the following velocity application:

An aeroplane needs to fly due east from one city to another at a speed of 400 km h^{-1}. However, a 50 km h^{-1} wind blows constantly from the north-east.

In what direction must the aeroplane head to compensate for the wind, and how does the wind affect its speed?

On this occasion we are given:

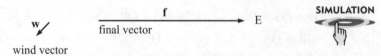

SIMULATION

We also know that the aeroplane will have to head a little north of its final destination so the north-easterly wind will blow it back to the correct direction.

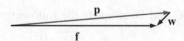

In order to move in the **f** direction, the aeroplane must actually head in the **p** direction.

Notice that $\mathbf{p} + \mathbf{w} = \mathbf{f}$

$\therefore \quad \mathbf{p} + \mathbf{w} + (-\mathbf{w}) = \mathbf{f} + (-\mathbf{w})$

$\therefore \quad \mathbf{p} + \mathbf{0} = \mathbf{f} - \mathbf{w}$

$\therefore \quad \mathbf{p} = \mathbf{f} - \mathbf{w}$

By the cosine rule,

$$x^2 = 50^2 + 400^2 - 2 \times 50 \times 400 \cos 135^o$$

$$\therefore \quad x \approx 437$$

By the sine rule, $\dfrac{\sin \theta}{50} = \dfrac{\sin 135^o}{436.8}$

$$\therefore \quad \theta \approx 4.64$$

Consequently, the aeroplane must head 4.64^o north of east. It needs to fly so that its speed in still air would be 437 km h^{-1}. The wind slows the aeroplane down to 400 km h^{-1}.

EXERCISE 14B.3

1   A boat needs to travel south at a speed of 20 km h^{-1}. However a constant current of 6 km h^{-1} is flowing from the south-east. Use vector subtraction to find:

   a   the equivalent speed in still water for the boat to achieve the actual speed of 20 km h^{-1}

   b   the direction in which the boat must head to compensate for the current.

2   As part of an endurance race, Stephanie needs to swim from X to Y across a wide river.

   Stephanie swims at 1.8 m s^{-1} in still water.

   If the river flows with a consistent current of 0.3 m s^{-1} as shown, find:

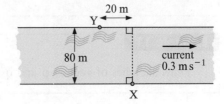

   a   the distance from X to Y

   b   the direction in which Stephanie should head

   c   the time Stephanie will take to cross the river.

SCALAR MULTIPLICATION

A **scalar** is a non-vector quantity. It has a size but no direction.

We can multiply vectors by scalars such as 2 and -3. If $\mathbf{a}$ is a vector, what do $2\mathbf{a}$ and $-3\mathbf{a}$ mean?

We define $2\mathbf{a} = \mathbf{a} + \mathbf{a}$ and $3\mathbf{a} = \mathbf{a} + \mathbf{a} + \mathbf{a}$

so $-3\mathbf{a} = 3(-\mathbf{a}) = (-\mathbf{a}) + (-\mathbf{a}) + (-\mathbf{a})$.

If **a** is   then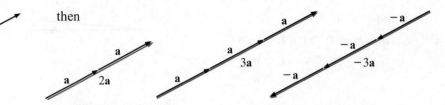

So,   2**a** is in the same direction as **a** but is twice as long as **a**

3**a** is in the same direction as **a** but is three times longer than **a**

−3**a** has the opposite direction to **a** and is three times longer than **a**.

In general: If **a** is a vector and k is a scalar, then:

k**a** is also a vector and we are performing **scalar multiplication**.

If $k > 0$, k**a** and **a** have the same direction.

If $k < 0$, k**a** and **a** have opposite directions.

Example 10

Given vectors and

show how to find   **a**   2**r** + **s**   **b**   **r** − 3**s**   geometrically.

a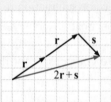

b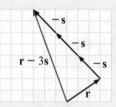

Example 11

Draw sketches of vectors **p** and **q** if **a** **p** = 3**q**   **b** **p** = $-\frac{1}{2}$**q**.

Let **q** be   **a** 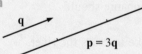   **b**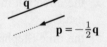

EXERCISE 14B.4

1 Given vectors   and   , show how to find geometrically:

a   −**r**   **b**   2**s**   **c** $\frac{1}{2}$**r**   **d** $-\frac{3}{2}$**s**

e   2**r** − **s**   **f**   2**r** + 3**s**   **g** $\frac{1}{2}$**r** + 2**s**   **h** $\frac{1}{2}$(**r** + 3**s**)

2 Draw sketches of **p** and **q** if:

a **p** = **q**   **b** **p** = −**q**   **c** **p** = 2**q**   **d** **p** = $\frac{1}{3}$**q**   **e** **p** = −3**q**

3   **a**   Copy this diagram and on it mark the points:

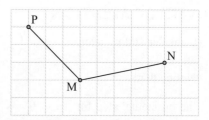

     i   X such that $\overrightarrow{MX} = \overrightarrow{MN} + \overrightarrow{MP}$

     ii   Y such that $\overrightarrow{MY} = \overrightarrow{MN} - \overrightarrow{MP}$

     iii   Z such that $\overrightarrow{PZ} = 2\overrightarrow{PM}$

  b   What type of figure is MNYZ?

C   2-D VECTORS IN COMPONENT FORM

So far we have examined vectors from their geometric representation.

We have used arrows where:

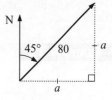

- the **length** of the arrow represents size or magnitude
- the **arrowhead** indicates direction.

Consider a car travelling at 80 km h^{-1} in a NE direction.

The velocity vector could be represented using the x and y steps which are necessary to go from the start to the finish.

In this case the **column vector** $\begin{pmatrix} 56.6 \\ 56.6 \end{pmatrix}$ gives the x and y steps.

$$a^2 + a^2 = 80^2$$
$$\therefore \ 2a^2 = 6400$$
$$\therefore \ a^2 = 3200$$
$$\therefore \ a \approx 56.6$$

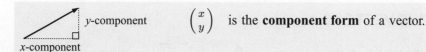

$\begin{pmatrix} x \\ y \end{pmatrix}$ is the **component form** of a vector.

For example,   given $\begin{pmatrix} 2 \\ 3 \end{pmatrix}$ we could draw

2 is the horizontal step and
3 is the vertical step.

EXERCISE 14C.1

1   Draw arrow diagrams to represent the vectors:

  a $\begin{pmatrix} 3 \\ 4 \end{pmatrix}$
      b $\begin{pmatrix} 2 \\ 0 \end{pmatrix}$
      c $\begin{pmatrix} 2 \\ -5 \end{pmatrix}$
      d $\begin{pmatrix} -1 \\ -3 \end{pmatrix}$

2   Write the illustrated vectors in component form:

  a

  b

  c

  d

  e

  f

VECTOR ADDITION

Consider adding vectors $\mathbf{a} = \begin{pmatrix} a_1 \\ a_2 \end{pmatrix}$ and $\mathbf{b} = \begin{pmatrix} b_1 \\ b_2 \end{pmatrix}$.

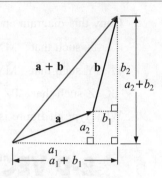

Notice that:

the horizontal step for $\mathbf{a} + \mathbf{b}$ is $a_1 + b_1$

the vertical step for $\mathbf{a} + \mathbf{b}$ is $a_2 + b_2$.

So, if $\mathbf{a} = \begin{pmatrix} a_1 \\ a_2 \end{pmatrix}$ and $\mathbf{b} = \begin{pmatrix} b_1 \\ b_2 \end{pmatrix}$ then $\mathbf{a} + \mathbf{b} = \begin{pmatrix} a_1 + b_1 \\ a_2 + b_2 \end{pmatrix}$.

Example 12	
If $\mathbf{a} = \begin{pmatrix} 1 \\ -3 \end{pmatrix}$ and $\mathbf{b} = \begin{pmatrix} 4 \\ 7 \end{pmatrix}$ find $\mathbf{a} + \mathbf{b}$. Check graphically.	$\begin{aligned} \mathbf{a} + \mathbf{b} &= \begin{pmatrix} 1 \\ -3 \end{pmatrix} + \begin{pmatrix} 4 \\ 7 \end{pmatrix} \\ &= \begin{pmatrix} 1+4 \\ -3+7 \end{pmatrix} \\ &= \begin{pmatrix} 5 \\ 4 \end{pmatrix} \end{aligned}$ *Graphical check:* 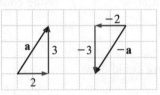

NEGATIVE VECTORS

Consider the vector $\mathbf{a} = \begin{pmatrix} 2 \\ 3 \end{pmatrix}$.

Notice that $-\mathbf{a} = \begin{pmatrix} -2 \\ -3 \end{pmatrix}$.

In general, if $\mathbf{a} = \begin{pmatrix} a_1 \\ a_2 \end{pmatrix}$ then $-\mathbf{a} = \begin{pmatrix} -a_1 \\ -a_2 \end{pmatrix}$.

ZERO VECTOR

The zero vector is $\mathbf{0} = \begin{pmatrix} 0 \\ 0 \end{pmatrix}$.

For any vector $\mathbf{a}$: $\qquad \mathbf{a} + \mathbf{0} = \mathbf{0} + \mathbf{a} = \mathbf{a}$

$\qquad\qquad\qquad\qquad \mathbf{a} + (-\mathbf{a}) = (-\mathbf{a}) + \mathbf{a} = \mathbf{0}$.

VECTOR SUBTRACTION

To subtract one vector from another, we simply **add its negative**, i.e., $\mathbf{a} - \mathbf{b} = \mathbf{a} + (-\mathbf{b})$.

Notice that, if $\mathbf{a} = \begin{pmatrix} a_1 \\ a_2 \end{pmatrix}$ and $\mathbf{b} = \begin{pmatrix} b_1 \\ b_2 \end{pmatrix}$

then $\mathbf{a} - \mathbf{b} = \mathbf{a} + (-\mathbf{b}) = \begin{pmatrix} a_1 \\ a_2 \end{pmatrix} + \begin{pmatrix} -b_1 \\ -b_2 \end{pmatrix} = \begin{pmatrix} a_1 - b_1 \\ a_2 - b_2 \end{pmatrix}$

If $\mathbf{a} = \begin{pmatrix} a_1 \\ a_2 \end{pmatrix}$ and $\mathbf{b} = \begin{pmatrix} b_1 \\ b_2 \end{pmatrix}$ then $\mathbf{a} - \mathbf{b} = \begin{pmatrix} a_1 - b_1 \\ a_2 - b_2 \end{pmatrix}$.

Example 13

Given $\mathbf{p} = \begin{pmatrix} 3 \\ -2 \end{pmatrix}$,

$\mathbf{q} = \begin{pmatrix} 1 \\ 4 \end{pmatrix}$

and $\mathbf{r} = \begin{pmatrix} -2 \\ -5 \end{pmatrix}$ find:

a $\mathbf{q} - \mathbf{p}$
b $\mathbf{p} - \mathbf{q} - \mathbf{r}$

a $\mathbf{q} - \mathbf{p}$

$= \begin{pmatrix} 1 \\ 4 \end{pmatrix} - \begin{pmatrix} 3 \\ -2 \end{pmatrix}$

$= \begin{pmatrix} 1-3 \\ 4+2 \end{pmatrix}$

$= \begin{pmatrix} -2 \\ 6 \end{pmatrix}$

b $\mathbf{p} - \mathbf{q} - \mathbf{r}$

$= \begin{pmatrix} 3 \\ -2 \end{pmatrix} - \begin{pmatrix} 1 \\ 4 \end{pmatrix} - \begin{pmatrix} -2 \\ -5 \end{pmatrix}$

$= \begin{pmatrix} 3-1+2 \\ -2-4+5 \end{pmatrix}$

$= \begin{pmatrix} 4 \\ -1 \end{pmatrix}$

VECTORS BETWEEN TWO POINTS

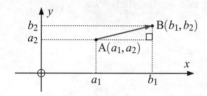

The position vector of $B(b_1, b_2)$ relative to $A(a_1, a_2)$ is: $\overrightarrow{AB} = \begin{pmatrix} b_1 - a_1 \\ b_2 - a_2 \end{pmatrix}$.

Notice that this result could be found using:

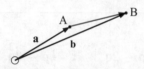

$\overrightarrow{AB} = \overrightarrow{AO} + \overrightarrow{OB} = \mathbf{b} - \mathbf{a}$

$\therefore \quad \overrightarrow{AB} = \begin{pmatrix} b_1 \\ b_2 \end{pmatrix} - \begin{pmatrix} a_1 \\ a_2 \end{pmatrix} = \begin{pmatrix} b_1 - a_1 \\ b_2 - a_2 \end{pmatrix}$.

EXERCISE 14C.2

1 If $\mathbf{a} = \begin{pmatrix} -3 \\ 2 \end{pmatrix}$ $\mathbf{b} = \begin{pmatrix} 1 \\ 4 \end{pmatrix}$, $\mathbf{c} = \begin{pmatrix} -2 \\ -5 \end{pmatrix}$ find:

a $\mathbf{a} + \mathbf{b}$ **b** $\mathbf{b} + \mathbf{a}$ **c** $\mathbf{b} + \mathbf{c}$ **d** $\mathbf{c} + \mathbf{b}$
e $\mathbf{a} + \mathbf{c}$ **f** $\mathbf{c} + \mathbf{a}$ **g** $\mathbf{a} + \mathbf{a}$ **h** $\mathbf{b} + \mathbf{a} + \mathbf{c}$

2 Given $\mathbf{p} = \begin{pmatrix} -4 \\ 2 \end{pmatrix}$, $\mathbf{q} = \begin{pmatrix} -1 \\ -5 \end{pmatrix}$ and $\mathbf{r} = \begin{pmatrix} 3 \\ -2 \end{pmatrix}$ find:

a $\mathbf{p} - \mathbf{q}$ **b** $\mathbf{q} - \mathbf{r}$ **c** $\mathbf{p} + \mathbf{q} - \mathbf{r}$
d $\mathbf{p} - \mathbf{q} - \mathbf{r}$ **e** $\mathbf{q} - \mathbf{r} - \mathbf{p}$ **f** $\mathbf{r} + \mathbf{q} - \mathbf{p}$

3 **a** Given $\overrightarrow{BA} = \begin{pmatrix} 2 \\ -3 \end{pmatrix}$ and $\overrightarrow{BC} = \begin{pmatrix} -3 \\ 1 \end{pmatrix}$ find $\overrightarrow{AC}$.

b If $\overrightarrow{AB} = \begin{pmatrix} -1 \\ 3 \end{pmatrix}$ and $\overrightarrow{CA} = \begin{pmatrix} 2 \\ -1 \end{pmatrix}$, find $\overrightarrow{CB}$.

c If $\overrightarrow{PQ} = \begin{pmatrix} -1 \\ 4 \end{pmatrix}$, $\overrightarrow{RQ} = \begin{pmatrix} 2 \\ 1 \end{pmatrix}$ and $\overrightarrow{RS} = \begin{pmatrix} -3 \\ 2 \end{pmatrix}$, find $\overrightarrow{SP}$.

4 Find $\overrightarrow{AB}$ given:

a $A(2, 3)$ and $B(4, 7)$ **b** $A(3, -1)$ and $B(1, 4)$ **c** $A(-2, 7)$ and $B(1, 4)$
d $B(3, 0)$ and $A(2, 5)$ **e** $B(6, -1)$ and $A(0, 4)$ **f** $B(0, 0)$ and $A(-1, -3)$.

SCALAR MULTIPLICATION

Recall the geometric approach for scalar multiplication.

For example:

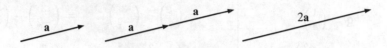

Consider $\mathbf{a} = \begin{pmatrix} 1 \\ 3 \end{pmatrix}$. $2\mathbf{a} = \mathbf{a} + \mathbf{a} = \begin{pmatrix} 1 \\ 3 \end{pmatrix} + \begin{pmatrix} 1 \\ 3 \end{pmatrix} = \begin{pmatrix} 2 \\ 6 \end{pmatrix}$ and

$$3\mathbf{a} = \mathbf{a} + \mathbf{a} + \mathbf{a} = \begin{pmatrix} 1 \\ 3 \end{pmatrix} + \begin{pmatrix} 1 \\ 3 \end{pmatrix} + \begin{pmatrix} 1 \\ 3 \end{pmatrix} = \begin{pmatrix} 3 \\ 9 \end{pmatrix}$$

Examples like these suggest the following definition for **scalar multiplication**:   If k is a scalar, then $k\mathbf{a} = \begin{pmatrix} ka_1 \\ ka_2 \end{pmatrix}$.

Notice that:
- $(-1)\mathbf{a} = \begin{pmatrix} (-1)\,a_1 \\ (-1)\,a_2 \end{pmatrix} = \begin{pmatrix} -a_1 \\ -a_2 \end{pmatrix} = -\mathbf{a}$

- $(0)\mathbf{a} = \begin{pmatrix} (0)\,a_1 \\ (0)\,a_2 \end{pmatrix} = \begin{pmatrix} 0 \\ 0 \end{pmatrix} = \mathbf{0}$

Example 14

For $\mathbf{p} = \begin{pmatrix} 4 \\ 1 \end{pmatrix}$, $\mathbf{q} = \begin{pmatrix} 2 \\ -3 \end{pmatrix}$ find: **a** $3\mathbf{q}$ **b** $\mathbf{p} + 2\mathbf{q}$ **c** $\tfrac{1}{2}\mathbf{p} - 3\mathbf{q}$

a $3\mathbf{q}$

$= 3\begin{pmatrix} 2 \\ -3 \end{pmatrix}$

$= \begin{pmatrix} 6 \\ -9 \end{pmatrix}$

b $\mathbf{p} + 2\mathbf{q}$

$= \begin{pmatrix} 4 \\ 1 \end{pmatrix} + 2\begin{pmatrix} 2 \\ -3 \end{pmatrix}$

$= \begin{pmatrix} 4 + 2(2) \\ 1 + 2(-3) \end{pmatrix}$

$= \begin{pmatrix} 8 \\ -5 \end{pmatrix}$

c $\tfrac{1}{2}\mathbf{p} - 3\mathbf{q}$

$= \tfrac{1}{2}\begin{pmatrix} 4 \\ 1 \end{pmatrix} - 3\begin{pmatrix} 2 \\ -3 \end{pmatrix}$

$= \begin{pmatrix} \tfrac{1}{2}(4) - 3(2) \\ \tfrac{1}{2}(1) - 3(-3) \end{pmatrix}$

$= \begin{pmatrix} -4 \\ 9\tfrac{1}{2} \end{pmatrix}$

EXERCISE 14C.3

1 For $\mathbf{p} = \begin{pmatrix} 1 \\ 5 \end{pmatrix}$, $\mathbf{q} = \begin{pmatrix} -2 \\ 4 \end{pmatrix}$ and $\mathbf{r} = \begin{pmatrix} -3 \\ -1 \end{pmatrix}$ find:

a $-3\mathbf{p}$ **b** $\tfrac{1}{2}\mathbf{q}$.   **c** $2\mathbf{p} + \mathbf{q}$ **d** $\mathbf{p} - 2\mathbf{q}$

e $\mathbf{p} - \tfrac{1}{2}\mathbf{r}$ **f** $2\mathbf{p} + 3\mathbf{r}$ **g** $2\mathbf{q} - 3\mathbf{r}$ **h** $2\mathbf{p} - \mathbf{q} + \tfrac{1}{3}\mathbf{r}$

2 If $\mathbf{p} = \begin{pmatrix} 1 \\ 1 \end{pmatrix}$ and $\mathbf{q} = \begin{pmatrix} 2 \\ -1 \end{pmatrix}$ find by diagram and then comment on the results:

a $\mathbf{p} + \mathbf{p} + \mathbf{q} + \mathbf{q} + \mathbf{q}$ **b** $\mathbf{p} + \mathbf{q} + \mathbf{p} + \mathbf{q} + \mathbf{q}$ **c** $\mathbf{q} + \mathbf{p} + \mathbf{q} + \mathbf{p} + \mathbf{q}$

LENGTH OF A VECTOR

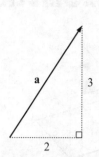

Consider vector $\mathbf{a} = \begin{pmatrix} 2 \\ 3 \end{pmatrix}$ as illustrated.

Recall that $|\mathbf{a}|$ represents the length of $\mathbf{a}$.

By Pythagoras, $|\mathbf{a}|^2 = 2^2 + 3^2 = 4 + 9 = 13$

$\therefore \ |\mathbf{a}| = \sqrt{13}$ units $\{$since $|\mathbf{a}| > 0\}$

In general, if $\mathbf{a} = \begin{pmatrix} a_1 \\ a_2 \end{pmatrix}$, then $|\mathbf{a}| = \sqrt{a_1{}^2 + a_2{}^2}$.

Example 15

If $\mathbf{p} = \begin{pmatrix} 3 \\ -5 \end{pmatrix}$ and $\mathbf{q} = \begin{pmatrix} -1 \\ -2 \end{pmatrix}$ find: **a** $|\mathbf{p}|$ **b** $|\mathbf{q}|$ **c** $|\mathbf{p} - 2\mathbf{q}|$

a $\mathbf{p} = \begin{pmatrix} 3 \\ -5 \end{pmatrix} \ \therefore \ |\mathbf{p}| = \sqrt{9 + 25}$
$= \sqrt{34}$ units

b $\mathbf{q} = \begin{pmatrix} -1 \\ -2 \end{pmatrix} \ \therefore \ |\mathbf{q}| = \sqrt{1 + 4}$
$= \sqrt{5}$ units

c $\mathbf{p} - 2\mathbf{q} = \begin{pmatrix} 3 \\ -5 \end{pmatrix} - 2\begin{pmatrix} -1 \\ -2 \end{pmatrix} = \begin{pmatrix} 5 \\ -1 \end{pmatrix}$
$\therefore \ |\mathbf{p} - 2\mathbf{q}| = \sqrt{5^2 + (-1)^2}$
$= \sqrt{26}$ units

EXERCISE 14C.4

1 For $\mathbf{r} = \begin{pmatrix} 2 \\ 3 \end{pmatrix}$ and $\mathbf{s} = \begin{pmatrix} -1 \\ 4 \end{pmatrix}$ find:

  a $|\mathbf{r}|$ **b** $|\mathbf{s}|$ **c** $|\mathbf{r} + \mathbf{s}|$ **d** $|\mathbf{r} - \mathbf{s}|$ **e** $|\mathbf{s} - 2\mathbf{r}|$

2 If $\mathbf{p} = \begin{pmatrix} 1 \\ 3 \end{pmatrix}$ and $\mathbf{q} = \begin{pmatrix} -2 \\ 4 \end{pmatrix}$ find:

  a $|\mathbf{p}|$ **b** $|2\mathbf{p}|$ **c** $|-2\mathbf{p}|$ **d** $|3\mathbf{p}|$ **e** $|-3\mathbf{p}|$

  f $|\mathbf{q}|$ **g** $|4\mathbf{q}|$ **h** $|-4\mathbf{q}|$ **i** $|\frac{1}{2}\mathbf{q}|$ **j** $|-\frac{1}{2}\mathbf{q}|$

3 From your answers in **2**, you should have noticed that $|k\mathbf{a}| = |k||\mathbf{a}|$

So, (the length of $k\mathbf{a}$) = (the modulus of k) $\times$ (the length of $\mathbf{a}$).

By letting $\mathbf{a} = \begin{pmatrix} a_1 \\ a_2 \end{pmatrix}$, prove that $|k\mathbf{a}| = |k||\mathbf{a}|$.

4 The length of the vector between A and B is denoted $\left|\overrightarrow{AB}\right|$ or simply AB.

Given A(2, −1), B(3, 5), C(−1, 4) and D(−4, −3), find:

  a $\overrightarrow{AB}$ and AB   **b** $\overrightarrow{BA}$ and BA   **c** $\overrightarrow{BC}$ and BC

  d $\overrightarrow{DC}$ and DC   **e** $\overrightarrow{CA}$ and CA   **f** $\overrightarrow{DA}$ and DA.

D   3-D COORDINATE GEOMETRY

To specify points in **3-dimensional space** we need a point of reference, O, called the **origin**.

Through O we draw 3 **mutually perpendicular** lines and call them the X, Y and Z-axes. We often think of the YZ-plane as the plane of the page, with the X-axis coming directly out of the page. However, we cannot of course draw this.

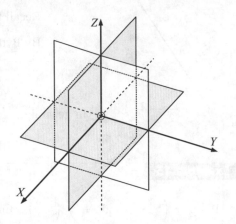

Once the positive directions of the X and Y-axes are determined, convention requires the positive Z-axis is given by the **right hand rule**. (See page **411**.)

In the diagram alongside the **coordinate planes** divide space into 8 regions, each pair of planes intersecting on the axes.

The **positive direction** of each axis is a solid line whereas the **negative direction** is 'dashed'.

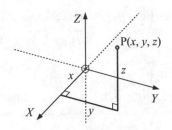

> Any point P in space can be specified by an **ordered triple** of numbers $(x,\ y,\ z)$ where x, y and z are the **steps** in the X, Y and Z directions from the origin O, to P.
>
> The **position vector** of P is $\overrightarrow{OP} = \begin{pmatrix} x \\ y \\ z \end{pmatrix}$.

To help us visualise the 3-D position of a point on our 2-D paper, it is useful to complete a rectangular prism or box with the origin O as one vertex, the axes as sides adjacent to it, and P being the vertex opposite O.

3-D POINT PLOTTER

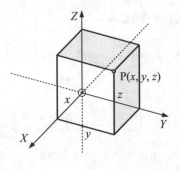

Example 16

Illustrate the points: **a** A(0, 2, 0)   **b** B(3, 0, 2)   **c** C(−1, 2, 3)

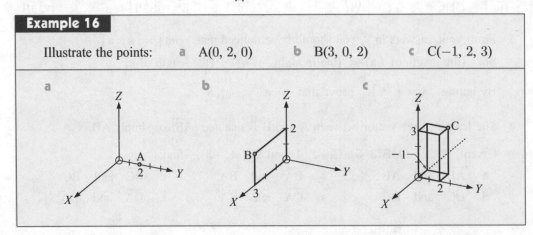

DISTANCE AND MIDPOINTS

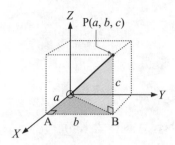

Triangle OAB is right angled at A

$$\therefore \quad OB^2 = a^2 + b^2 \quad \text{...... (1)} \quad \text{\{Pythagoras\}}$$

Triangle OBP is right angled at B

$$\therefore \quad OP^2 = OB^2 + c^2 \qquad \text{\{Pythagoras\}}$$

$$\therefore \quad OP^2 = a^2 + b^2 + c^2 \qquad \text{\{from (1)\}}$$

$$\therefore \quad OP = \sqrt{a^2 + b^2 + c^2}$$

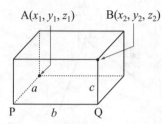

For two general points $A(x_1, y_1, z_1)$
and $B(x_2, y_2, z_2)$

  a, the x-step from A to B $= x_2 - x_1 = \Delta x$

  b, the y-step from A to B $= y_2 - y_1 = \Delta y$

  c, the z-step from A to B $= z_2 - z_1 = \Delta z$

So, $AB = \sqrt{(x_2 - x_1)^2 + (y_2 - y_1)^2 + (z_2 - z_1)^2}$

A simple extension from 2-D to 3-D geometry also gives

the **midpoint** of [AB] is $\left(\dfrac{x_1 + x_2}{2}, \ \dfrac{y_1 + y_2}{2}, \ \dfrac{z_1 + z_2}{2} \right)$.

Note: As with the 2-D case, a proof of this rule can be made using similar triangles.

Example 17

If $A(-1, 2, 4)$ and $B(1, 0, -1)$ are two points in space, find:
a the distance from A to B   **b** the coordinates of the midpoint of [AB].

a AB	**b** The midpoint is
$= \sqrt{(1 - -1)^2 + (0 - 2)^2 + (-1 - 4)^2}$	$\left(\dfrac{-1 + 1}{2}, \dfrac{2 + 0}{2}, \dfrac{4 + (-1)}{2} \right)$
$= \sqrt{4 + 4 + 25}$	
$= \sqrt{33}$ units	which is $(0, 1, \frac{3}{2})$.

EXERCISE 14D

1 Illustrate P and find its distance from the origin O if P is:

  a $(0, 0, -3)$ **b** $(0, -1, 2)$ **c** $(3, 1, 4)$ **d** $(-1, -2, 3)$

2 For each of the following:

   i find the distance AB   **ii** find the midpoint of [AB]

  a $A(-1, 2, 3)$ and $B(0, -1, 1)$ **b** $A(0, 0, 0)$ and $B(2, -1, 3)$

  c $A(3, -1, -1)$ and $B(-1, 0, 1)$ **d** $A(2, 0, -3)$ and $B(0, 1, 0)$

3 Show that P(0, 4, 4), Q(2, 6, 5) and R(1, 4, 3) are vertices of an isosceles triangle.

4 Determine the nature of triangle ABC using distances:

    a   A(2, −1, 7), B(3, 1, 4) and C(5, 4, 5)

    b   A(0, 0, 3), B(2, 8, 1) and C(−9, 6, 18)

    c   A(5, 6, −2), B(6, 12, 9) and C(2, 4, 2)

    d   A(1, 0, −3), B(2, 2, 0) and C(4, 6, 6).

5 A sphere has centre C(−1, 2, 4) and diameter [AB] where A is (−2, 1, 3).
Find the coordinates of B and the radius of the circle.

6 **a** State the coordinates of any point on the Y-axis.

    b Use **a** and the diagram opposite to find the coordinates of two points on the Y-axis which are $\sqrt{14}$ units from B(−1, −1, 2).

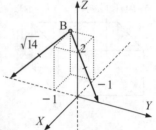

E   3-D VECTORS IN COMPONENT FORM

Consider a point $P(x_1, y_1, z_1)$.

The x, y and z-steps from the origin to P are x_1, y_1 and z_1 respectively.

So, $\overrightarrow{OP} = \begin{pmatrix} x_1 \\ y_1 \\ z_1 \end{pmatrix}$ is the vector which emanates from O

and terminates at P.

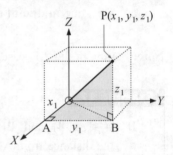

In general,   if $A(x_1, y_1, z_1)$ and $B(x_2, y_2, z_2)$ are two points in space then:

$$\overrightarrow{AB} = \begin{pmatrix} x_2 - x_1 \\ y_2 - y_1 \\ z_2 - z_1 \end{pmatrix} \begin{matrix} \leftarrow x\text{-step} \\ \leftarrow y\text{-step} \\ \leftarrow z\text{-step} \end{matrix} \quad \text{and} \quad |\overrightarrow{AB}| = \sqrt{(x_2 - x_1)^2 + (y_2 - y_1)^2 + (z_2 - z_1)^2}$$

$\overrightarrow{AB}$ is called 'vector AB' or the '**position vector of B relative to A**'.

$\overrightarrow{OP}$, the position vector of P relative to O, is called the **position vector of the point P** in both 2-D and 3-D. Its usefulness is marked by the fact that its components are exactly the same as the coordinates of the point P.

Example 18

If A is (3, −1, 2) and B is (1, 0, −2) find: **a** $\overrightarrow{OA}$ **b** $\overrightarrow{AB}$

a $\overrightarrow{OA} = \begin{pmatrix} 3 - 0 \\ -1 - 0 \\ 2 - 0 \end{pmatrix} = \begin{pmatrix} 3 \\ -1 \\ 2 \end{pmatrix}$ **b** $\overrightarrow{AB} = \begin{pmatrix} 1 - 3 \\ 0 - (-1) \\ -2 - 2 \end{pmatrix} = \begin{pmatrix} -2 \\ 1 \\ -4 \end{pmatrix}$

Example 19

If P is $(-3, 1, 2)$ and Q is $(1, -1, 3)$, find $|\overrightarrow{PQ}|$.

$$\overrightarrow{PQ} = \begin{pmatrix} 1-(-3) \\ -1-1 \\ 3-2 \end{pmatrix} = \begin{pmatrix} 4 \\ -2 \\ 1 \end{pmatrix} \qquad \therefore \quad |\overrightarrow{PQ}| = \sqrt{4^2 + (-2)^2 + 1^2}$$
$$= \sqrt{21} \text{ units}$$

Example 20

If A is $(-1, 3, 2)$ and B is $(2, 1, -4)$, find:

a   the position vector of A from B   b   the distance between A and B.

a   The position vector of A from B is $\overrightarrow{BA} = \begin{pmatrix} -1-2 \\ 3-1 \\ 2-(-4) \end{pmatrix} = \begin{pmatrix} -3 \\ 2 \\ 6 \end{pmatrix}$

b $AB = |\overrightarrow{BA}|$
$= \sqrt{9 + 4 + 36}$
$= 7$ units

$|\overrightarrow{AB}| = |\overrightarrow{BA}|$ is the distance between A and B.

EXERCISE 14E.1

1   Consider the point T$(3, -1, 4)$.
   a   Draw a diagram to locate the position of T in space.
   b   Find $\overrightarrow{OT}$.   c   How far is it from O to T?

2   Given A$(-3, 1, 2)$ and B$(1, 0, -1)$ find:
   a $\overrightarrow{AB}$ and $\overrightarrow{BA}$ b   the length of $\overrightarrow{AB}$ and $\overrightarrow{BA}$.

3   Given A$(3, 1, 0)$ and B$(-1, 1, 2)$ find $\overrightarrow{OA}$, $\overrightarrow{OB}$, and $\overrightarrow{AB}$.

4   Given M$(4, -2, -1)$ and N$(-1, 2, 0)$ find:
   a   the position vector of M from N   b   the position vector of N from M
   c   the distance between M and N.

5   For A$(-1, 2, 5)$, B$(2, 0, 3)$ and C$(-3, 1, 0)$ find the position vector of:
   a   A from O and the distance from O to A
   b   C from A and the distance from A to C
   c   B from C and the distance from C to B.

6   Find the distance from Q$(3, 1, -2)$ to:
   a   the Y-axis   b   the origin   c   the YOZ plane.

GEOMETRIC REPRESENTATION

As for 2-D vectors, 3-D vectors are represented by **directed line segments** or **arrows**.

Consider the vector represented by the directed line segment from O to A.

- This **vector** could be represented by

$$\overrightarrow{OA} \quad \text{or} \quad \mathbf{a} \quad \text{or} \quad \underset{\sim}{a} \text{ or } \overrightarrow{a}$$

                   ↑   ↑

           bold used   used by
       in text books   students

- The **magnitude** could be represented by $|\overrightarrow{OA}|$, OA, $|\mathbf{a}|$, $|\underset{\sim}{a}|$ or $|\overrightarrow{a}|$.

If $\mathbf{a} = \begin{pmatrix} a_1 \\ a_2 \\ a_3 \end{pmatrix}$ then $|\mathbf{a}| = \sqrt{a_1^2 + a_2^2 + a_3^2}$.

VECTOR EQUALITY

Two vectors are **equal** if they have the same magnitude and direction.

So, if arrows are used to represent vectors, then equal vectors are **parallel** and **equal in length**.

This means that equal vector arrows are translations of one another, but in space (free vectors).

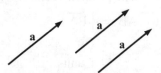

If $\mathbf{a} = \begin{pmatrix} a_1 \\ a_2 \\ a_3 \end{pmatrix}$ and $\mathbf{b} = \begin{pmatrix} b_1 \\ b_2 \\ b_3 \end{pmatrix}$, then $\mathbf{a} = \mathbf{b} \iff a_1 = b_1, \ a_2 = b_2, \ a_3 = b_3.$

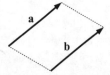

$\mathbf{a} = \mathbf{b}$ implies that vector $\mathbf{a}$ is parallel to vector $\mathbf{b}$, and $|\mathbf{a}| = |\mathbf{b}|$.

Consequently, $\mathbf{a}$ and $\mathbf{b}$ are opposite sides of a parallelogram and lie in the same plane.

DISCUSSION

- Do any three points in space define a plane? What about four points? Illustrate.
- What simple tests on four points in space enable us to deduce that the points are vertices of a parallelogram? Consider using vectors and not using vectors.

Example 21

Find a, b, and c if $\begin{pmatrix} a - 3 \\ b - 2 \\ c - 1 \end{pmatrix} = \begin{pmatrix} 1 - a \\ -b \\ -3 - c \end{pmatrix}$.

Equating components, $\quad a - 3 = 1 - a, \quad b - 2 = -b \quad$ and $\quad c - 1 = -3 - c$

$\qquad\qquad\qquad\therefore \quad 2a = 4, \qquad\qquad 2b = 2 \qquad$ and $\qquad 2c = -2$

$\qquad\qquad\qquad\therefore \quad a = 2, \qquad\qquad b = 1 \qquad$ and $\qquad c = -1$

Example 22

ABCD is a parallelogram. A is $(-1, 2, 1)$, B is $(2, 0, -1)$ and D is $(3, 1, 4)$.
Find the coordinates of C.

First we sketch the points as shown:

Let C be (a, b, c).

Now [AB] is parallel to [DC] and has the same length, so $\overrightarrow{DC} = \overrightarrow{AB}$

$$\therefore \quad \begin{pmatrix} a-3 \\ b-1 \\ c-4 \end{pmatrix} = \begin{pmatrix} 3 \\ -2 \\ -2 \end{pmatrix}$$

$\therefore \quad a-3 = 3, \quad b-1 = -2, \quad c-4 = -2$

$\therefore \quad a = 6, \qquad b = -1, \qquad c = 2 \qquad$ So, C is $(6, -1, 2)$.

Check: midpoint of [DB] is   midpoint of [AC] is

$\left(\dfrac{3+2}{2}, \dfrac{1+0}{2}, \dfrac{4+-1}{2} \right)$ or $\left(\dfrac{5}{2}, \dfrac{1}{2}, \dfrac{3}{2} \right)$ $\left(\dfrac{-1+6}{2}, \dfrac{2+-1}{2}, \dfrac{1+2}{2} \right)$ or $\left(\dfrac{5}{2}, \dfrac{1}{2}, \dfrac{3}{2} \right)$

What property of a parallelogram are we checking?

EXERCISE 14E.2

1 Find a, b and c if: **a** $\begin{pmatrix} a-4 \\ b-3 \\ c+2 \end{pmatrix} = \begin{pmatrix} 1 \\ 3 \\ -4 \end{pmatrix}$ **b** $\begin{pmatrix} a-5 \\ b-2 \\ c+3 \end{pmatrix} = \begin{pmatrix} 3-a \\ 2-b \\ 5-c \end{pmatrix}$

2 Find scalars a, b and c if:

a $2\begin{pmatrix} 1 \\ 0 \\ 3a \end{pmatrix} = \begin{pmatrix} b \\ c-1 \\ 2 \end{pmatrix}$ **b** $\begin{pmatrix} 2 \\ a \\ 3 \end{pmatrix} = \begin{pmatrix} b \\ a^2 \\ a+b \end{pmatrix}$ **c** $a\begin{pmatrix} 1 \\ 1 \\ 0 \end{pmatrix} + b\begin{pmatrix} 2 \\ 0 \\ -1 \end{pmatrix} + c\begin{pmatrix} 0 \\ 1 \\ 1 \end{pmatrix} = \begin{pmatrix} -1 \\ 3 \\ 3 \end{pmatrix}$

3 A$(-1, 3, 4)$, B$(2, 5, -1)$, C$(-1, 2, -2)$ and D (r, s, t) are four points in space. Find r, s and t if: **a** $\overrightarrow{AC} = \overrightarrow{BD}$ **b** $\overrightarrow{AB} = \overrightarrow{DC}$

4 A quadrilateral has vertices A$(1, 2, 3)$, B$(3, -3, 2)$, C$(7, -4, 5)$ and D$(5, 1, 6)$.
  a Find $\overrightarrow{AB}$ and $\overrightarrow{DC}$.   **b** What can be deduced about the quadrilateral ABCD?

5 PQRS is a parallelogram. P is $(-1, 2, 3)$, Q$(1, -2, 5)$ and R$(0, 4, -1)$.
  a Use vectors to find the coordinates of S.
  b Use midpoints of diagonals to check your answer.

F   ALGEBRAIC OPERATIONS WITH VECTORS

The rules for algebra with vectors readily extend from 2-D to 3-D:

If $\mathbf{a} = \begin{pmatrix} a_1 \\ a_2 \\ a_3 \end{pmatrix}$ and $\mathbf{b} = \begin{pmatrix} b_1 \\ b_2 \\ b_3 \end{pmatrix}$ then $\mathbf{a} + \mathbf{b} = \begin{pmatrix} a_1 + b_1 \\ a_2 + b_2 \\ a_3 + b_3 \end{pmatrix}$, $\mathbf{a} - \mathbf{b} = \begin{pmatrix} a_1 - b_1 \\ a_2 - b_2 \\ a_3 - b_3 \end{pmatrix}$

and $\quad k\mathbf{a} = \begin{pmatrix} ka_1 \\ ka_2 \\ ka_3 \end{pmatrix}$ for some scalar k.

SOME PROPERTIES OF VECTORS

- $\quad \mathbf{a} + \mathbf{b} = \mathbf{b} + \mathbf{a}$
- $\quad (\mathbf{a} + \mathbf{b}) + \mathbf{c} = \mathbf{a} + (\mathbf{b} + \mathbf{c})$
- $\quad \mathbf{a} + \mathbf{0} = \mathbf{0} + \mathbf{a} = \mathbf{a}$
- $\quad \mathbf{a} + (-\mathbf{a}) = (-\mathbf{a}) + \mathbf{a} = \mathbf{0}$

- $\quad |k\mathbf{a}| = |k|\,|\mathbf{a}|$ where $k\mathbf{a}$ is parallel to $\mathbf{a}$

length of $k\mathbf{a}$ · · · · · · length of $\mathbf{a}$

modulus of k

The rules for solving vector equations are similar to those for solving real number equations. However, there is no such thing as dividing a vector by a scalar. Instead, we multiply by reciprocals.

For example,   if $2\mathbf{x} = \mathbf{a}$ then $\mathbf{x} = \frac{1}{2}\mathbf{a}$ and *not* $\dfrac{\mathbf{a}}{2}$.

$\dfrac{\mathbf{a}}{2}$ has no meaning in vector algebra.

Two useful rules are:
- if $\mathbf{x} + \mathbf{a} = \mathbf{b}$ then $\mathbf{x} = \mathbf{b} - \mathbf{a}$
- if $k\mathbf{x} = \mathbf{a}$ then $\mathbf{x} = \frac{1}{k}\mathbf{a}$ $(k \neq 0)$

To establish these notice that:

if $\mathbf{x} + \mathbf{a} = \mathbf{b}$

then $\mathbf{x} + \mathbf{a} + (-\mathbf{a}) = \mathbf{b} + (-\mathbf{a})$

$\therefore \quad \mathbf{x} + \mathbf{0} = \mathbf{b} - \mathbf{a}$

$\therefore \quad \mathbf{x} = \mathbf{b} - \mathbf{a}$

and if $k\mathbf{x} = \mathbf{a}$

then $\frac{1}{k}(k\mathbf{x}) = \frac{1}{k}\mathbf{a}$

$\therefore \quad 1\mathbf{x} = \frac{1}{k}\mathbf{a}$

$\therefore \quad \mathbf{x} = \frac{1}{k}\mathbf{a}$

Another useful property is that:

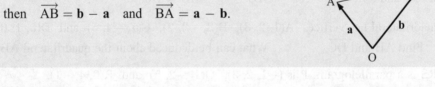

if $\overrightarrow{OA} = \mathbf{a}$ and $\overrightarrow{OB} = \mathbf{b}$ where O is the origin

then $\overrightarrow{AB} = \mathbf{b} - \mathbf{a}$ and $\overrightarrow{BA} = \mathbf{a} - \mathbf{b}$.

Example 23

Solve for $\mathbf{x}$:

a $3\mathbf{x} - \mathbf{r} = \mathbf{s}$

b $\mathbf{c} - 2\mathbf{x} = \mathbf{d}$

a $3\mathbf{x} - \mathbf{r} = \mathbf{s}$

$\therefore \quad 3\mathbf{x} = \mathbf{s} + \mathbf{r}$

$\therefore \quad \mathbf{x} = \frac{1}{3}(\mathbf{s} + \mathbf{r})$

b $\mathbf{c} - 2\mathbf{x} = \mathbf{d}$

$\therefore \quad \mathbf{c} - \mathbf{d} = 2\mathbf{x}$

$\therefore \quad \frac{1}{2}(\mathbf{c} - \mathbf{d}) = \mathbf{x}$

Example 24

If $\mathbf{a} = \begin{pmatrix} -1 \\ 3 \\ 2 \end{pmatrix}$,   find $|2\mathbf{a}|$.

$|2\mathbf{a}| = 2|\mathbf{a}|$

$= 2\sqrt{(-1)^2 + 3^2 + 2^2}$

$= 2\sqrt{1 + 9 + 4}$

$= 2\sqrt{14}$ units

EXERCISE 14F.1

1 Solve the following vector equations for **x**:

   a $2\mathbf{x} = \mathbf{q}$ **b** $\frac{1}{2}\mathbf{x} = \mathbf{n}$ **c** $-3\mathbf{x} = \mathbf{p}$

   d $\mathbf{q} + 2\mathbf{x} = \mathbf{r}$ **e** $4\mathbf{s} - 5\mathbf{x} = \mathbf{t}$ **f** $4\mathbf{m} - \frac{1}{3}\mathbf{x} = \mathbf{n}$

2 If $\mathbf{r} = \begin{pmatrix} -2 \\ 3 \end{pmatrix}$ and $\mathbf{s} = \begin{pmatrix} 1 \\ 2 \end{pmatrix}$,   find **y** if:

   a $2\mathbf{y} = \mathbf{r}$ **b** $\frac{1}{2}\mathbf{y} = \mathbf{s}$ **c** $\mathbf{r} + 2\mathbf{y} = \mathbf{s}$ **d** $3\mathbf{s} - 4\mathbf{y} = \mathbf{r}$

3 Show by equating components, that if $\mathbf{x} = \begin{pmatrix} x_1 \\ x_2 \end{pmatrix}$, $\mathbf{a} = \begin{pmatrix} a_1 \\ a_2 \end{pmatrix}$ and $k\mathbf{x} = \mathbf{a}$,   then
$\mathbf{x} = \frac{1}{k}\mathbf{a}$.

4 Find B if C is the centre of a circle with diameter [AB]:

   a   A is $(3, -2)$ and $C(1, 4)$ **b**   A is $(0, 5)$ and $C(-1, -2)$

   c   A is $(-1, -4)$ and $C(3, 0)$

5

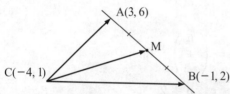

Find:

   a   the coordinates of M

   b   vectors $\overrightarrow{CA}$, $\overrightarrow{CM}$ and $\overrightarrow{CB}$.

   c   Verify that $\overrightarrow{CM} = \frac{1}{2}\overrightarrow{CA} + \frac{1}{2}\overrightarrow{CB}$.

6 If $\mathbf{a} = \begin{pmatrix} -1 \\ 2 \\ 3 \end{pmatrix}$ and $\mathbf{b} = \begin{pmatrix} 2 \\ -2 \\ 1 \end{pmatrix}$ find **x** if: **a** $2\mathbf{a} + \mathbf{x} = \mathbf{b}$ **b** $3\mathbf{x} - \mathbf{a} = 2\mathbf{b}$

                                                      c $2\mathbf{b} - 2\mathbf{x} = -\mathbf{a}$

7 If $\overrightarrow{OA} = \begin{pmatrix} -2 \\ -1 \\ 1 \end{pmatrix}$ and $\overrightarrow{OB} = \begin{pmatrix} 1 \\ 3 \\ -1 \end{pmatrix}$ find $\overrightarrow{AB}$ and hence the distance from A to B.

8 The position vectors of A, B, C and D from O are $\begin{pmatrix} 2 \\ 1 \\ -2 \end{pmatrix}$, $\begin{pmatrix} 0 \\ 3 \\ -4 \end{pmatrix}$, $\begin{pmatrix} 1 \\ -2 \\ 1 \end{pmatrix}$ and
$\begin{pmatrix} -2 \\ -3 \\ 2 \end{pmatrix}$ respectively. Deduce that $\overrightarrow{BD} = 2\overrightarrow{AC}$.

9 Find the coordinates of C, D and E.

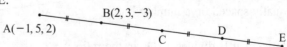

10 Use vectors to find whether or not ABCD is a parallelogram:

   a $A(3, -1)$, $B(4, 2)$, $C(-1, 4)$ and $D(-2, 1)$

   b $A(5, 0, 3)$, $B(-1, 2, 4)$, $C(4, -3, 6)$ and $D(10, -5, 5)$

   c $A(2, -3, 2)$, $B(1, 4, -1)$, $C(-2, 6, -2)$ and $D(-1, -1, 2)$.

11 Use vector methods to find the remaining vertex of:

a

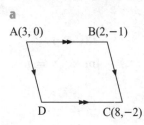

b

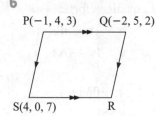

c

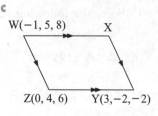

12

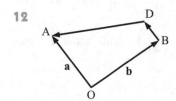

In the given figure BD is parallel to OA and half its length. Find, in terms of **a** and **b**, vector expressions for:

a $\overrightarrow{BD}$	**b** $\overrightarrow{AB}$	**c** $\overrightarrow{BA}$
d $\overrightarrow{OD}$	**e** $\overrightarrow{AD}$	**f** $\overrightarrow{DA}$

13 If $\overrightarrow{AB} = \begin{pmatrix} -1 \\ 3 \\ 2 \end{pmatrix}$, $\overrightarrow{AC} = \begin{pmatrix} 2 \\ -1 \\ 4 \end{pmatrix}$ and $\overrightarrow{BD} = \begin{pmatrix} 0 \\ 2 \\ -3 \end{pmatrix}$ find:

    a $\overrightarrow{AD}$ **b** $\overrightarrow{CB}$ **c** $\overrightarrow{CD}$

14 For $\mathbf{a} = \begin{pmatrix} 2 \\ -1 \\ 1 \end{pmatrix}$, $\mathbf{b} = \begin{pmatrix} 1 \\ 2 \\ -3 \end{pmatrix}$ and $\mathbf{c} = \begin{pmatrix} 0 \\ 1 \\ -3 \end{pmatrix}$, find:

a $\mathbf{a} + \mathbf{b}$	**b** $\mathbf{a} - \mathbf{b}$	**c** $\mathbf{b} + 2\mathbf{c}$	**d** $\mathbf{a} - 3\mathbf{c}$
e $\mathbf{a} + \mathbf{b} + \mathbf{c}$	**f** $\mathbf{c} - \frac{1}{2}\mathbf{a}$	**g** $\mathbf{a} - \mathbf{b} - \mathbf{c}$	**h** $2\mathbf{b} - \mathbf{c} + \mathbf{a}$

15 If $\mathbf{a} = \begin{pmatrix} -1 \\ 1 \\ 3 \end{pmatrix}$, $\mathbf{b} = \begin{pmatrix} 1 \\ -3 \\ 2 \end{pmatrix}$ and $\mathbf{c} = \begin{pmatrix} -2 \\ 2 \\ 4 \end{pmatrix}$ find: **a** $|\mathbf{a}|$ **b** $|\mathbf{b}|$ **c** $|\mathbf{b} + \mathbf{c}|$

                                               d $|\mathbf{a} - \mathbf{c}|$ **e** $|\mathbf{a}|\mathbf{b}$ **f** $\dfrac{1}{|\mathbf{a}|}\mathbf{a}$

16 Find scalars r and s such that:

    a $r\begin{pmatrix} 1 \\ -1 \end{pmatrix} + s\begin{pmatrix} 2 \\ 5 \end{pmatrix} = \begin{pmatrix} -8 \\ -27 \end{pmatrix}$ **b** $r\begin{pmatrix} 2 \\ -3 \\ 1 \end{pmatrix} + s\begin{pmatrix} 1 \\ 7 \\ 2 \end{pmatrix} = \begin{pmatrix} 7 \\ -19 \\ 2 \end{pmatrix}$

THE DIVISION OF A LINE SEGMENT

Consider these points which are equally spaced on a number line:

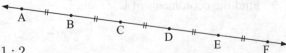

Notice that B divides [AD] in the ratio $1 : 2$.

But in what ratio does B divide [DA] and F divide [AD]?

Because confusion can arise we adopt the following convention to interpret the ratio of the division of a line segment:

> X divides [AB] in the ratio $a : b$ means $\overrightarrow{AX} : \overrightarrow{XB} = a : b$

So, to find the ratio in which B divides [DA], we find $\overrightarrow{DB} : \overrightarrow{BA}$. This is clearly $2 : 1$.

Notice that both $\overrightarrow{DB}$ and $\overrightarrow{BA}$ have the same direction. B lies in between A and D, so this is **internal division**.

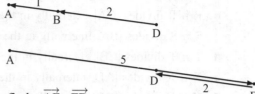

To find the ratio in which F divides [AD], we find $\overrightarrow{AF} : \overrightarrow{FD}$. This is $5 : -2$ or $-5 : 2$.

The minus sign indicates that these two vectors are opposite in direction.

F is outside the interval [AD], so this is **external division**.

We say that F divides [AD] *externally* in the ratio $5 : 2$.

Example 25

If A is $(-1, 4, 7)$ and B is $(3, 0, 5)$ find:
a P if P divides [AB] in the ratio $3 : 1$
b Q if Q divides [BA] externally in the ratio $3 : 1$.

a $\overrightarrow{AP} : \overrightarrow{PB} = 3 : 1$

$\therefore \ \overrightarrow{AP} = \tfrac{3}{4} \overrightarrow{AB}$

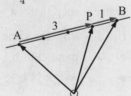

$\overrightarrow{OP} = \overrightarrow{OA} + \overrightarrow{AP}$

$= \overrightarrow{OA} + \tfrac{3}{4} \overrightarrow{AB}$

$= \begin{pmatrix} -1 \\ 4 \\ 7 \end{pmatrix} + \tfrac{3}{4} \begin{pmatrix} 4 \\ -4 \\ -2 \end{pmatrix}$

$= \begin{pmatrix} 2 \\ 1 \\ 5\tfrac{1}{2} \end{pmatrix}$ $\quad \therefore$ P is $(2, 1, 5\tfrac{1}{2})$.

b Since Q divides [BA] *externally* in the ratio $3 : 1$, we need to use a minus sign.

$\overrightarrow{BQ} : \overrightarrow{QA} = -3 : 1$

$\therefore \ \overrightarrow{AQ} = \tfrac{1}{2} \overrightarrow{BA}$

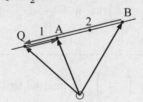

$\overrightarrow{OQ} = \overrightarrow{OA} + \overrightarrow{AQ}$

$= \overrightarrow{OA} + \tfrac{1}{2} \overrightarrow{BA}$

$= \begin{pmatrix} -1 \\ 4 \\ 7 \end{pmatrix} + \tfrac{1}{2} \begin{pmatrix} -4 \\ 4 \\ 2 \end{pmatrix}$

$= \begin{pmatrix} -3 \\ 6 \\ 8 \end{pmatrix}$ $\quad \therefore$ Q is $(-3, 6, 8)$.

EXERCISE 14F.2

1

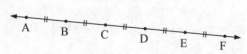

The points A to F are equally spaced on a number line. Find the ratio in which:

a B divides [AC] **b** C divides [BF]
c C divides [FB] **d** D divides [EA]
e C divides [AB] **f** F divides [DA].

2 For A(3, 1, 1), B(−1, 2, 0), C(1, −1, 4) and D(3, −2, 4) find:

    a Q if Q divides [BC] internally in the ratio 1 : 2

    b R if R divides [CA] externally in the ratio 3 : 4

    c S if S divides [BA] internally in the ratio 3 : 1

    d T if T divides [CB] externally in the ratio 2 : 5

    e X if X divides [AD] internally in the ratio 2 : 7

    f Y if Y divides [DB] externally in the ratio 5 : 3.

3

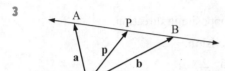

P lies on the line passing through points A and B. Find the position vector **p** of point P if:

    a P divides [AB] internally in the ratio 3 : 5

    b P divides [AB] externally in the ratio 2 : 7

    c P divides [AB] in the ratio $m : n$.

G   PARALLELISM

If two non-zero vectors are **parallel**, then one is a scalar multiple of the other and vice versa.

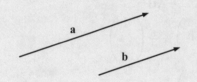

Note:
- If **a** is parallel to **b**, then there exists a scalar k such that $\mathbf{a} = k\mathbf{b}$.
- If $\mathbf{a} = k\mathbf{b}$ for some scalar k, then
  - **a** is parallel to **b**, and
  - $|\mathbf{a}| = |k||\mathbf{b}|$.

Notice that $\mathbf{a} = \begin{pmatrix} 2 \\ 6 \\ -4 \end{pmatrix}$ is parallel to $\mathbf{b} = \begin{pmatrix} 1 \\ 3 \\ -2 \end{pmatrix}$ and $\mathbf{c} = \begin{pmatrix} 4 \\ 12 \\ -8 \end{pmatrix}$ as $\mathbf{a} = 2\mathbf{b}$ and $\mathbf{a} = \tfrac{1}{2}\mathbf{c}$.

$\mathbf{a} = \begin{pmatrix} 2 \\ 6 \\ -4 \end{pmatrix}$ is also parallel to $\mathbf{d} = \begin{pmatrix} -3 \\ -9 \\ 6 \end{pmatrix}$ as $\mathbf{a} = -\tfrac{2}{3}\mathbf{d}$.

Example 26

Find r and s given that $\mathbf{a} = \begin{pmatrix} 2 \\ -1 \\ r \end{pmatrix}$ is parallel to $\mathbf{b} = \begin{pmatrix} s \\ 2 \\ -3 \end{pmatrix}$.

Since **a** and **b** are parallel, then $\mathbf{a} = k\mathbf{b}$ for some scalar k

$\therefore \begin{pmatrix} 2 \\ -1 \\ r \end{pmatrix} = k \begin{pmatrix} s \\ 2 \\ -3 \end{pmatrix}$ $\therefore$ $2 = ks$, $-1 = 2k$ and $r = -3k$

Consequently, $k = -\tfrac{1}{2}$ and $\therefore$ $2 = -\tfrac{1}{2}s$ and $r = -3\left(-\tfrac{1}{2}\right)$

$\therefore$ $r = \tfrac{3}{2}$ and $s = -4$

Three or more points are said to be **collinear** if they lie on the same straight line.

A, B and C are **collinear** if $\overrightarrow{AB} = k\overrightarrow{BC}$ for some scalar k.

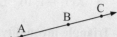

Example 27

Prove that A(-1, 2, 3), B(4, 0, -1) and C(14, -4, -9) are collinear and hence find the ratio in which B divides [CA].

$$\overrightarrow{AB} = \begin{pmatrix} 5 \\ -2 \\ -4 \end{pmatrix} \quad \overrightarrow{BC} = \begin{pmatrix} 10 \\ -4 \\ -8 \end{pmatrix} = 2\begin{pmatrix} 5 \\ -2 \\ -4 \end{pmatrix} \quad \therefore \ \overrightarrow{BC} = 2\overrightarrow{AB}$$

$\therefore$ [BC] is parallel to [AB] and since B is common to both, A, B and C are collinear.

To find the ratio in which B divides [CA], we find

$$\overrightarrow{CB} : \overrightarrow{BA} = -2\begin{pmatrix} 5 \\ -2 \\ -4 \end{pmatrix} : -\begin{pmatrix} 5 \\ -2 \\ -4 \end{pmatrix} = 2 : 1$$

$\therefore$ B divides [CA] internally in the ratio 2 : 1.

EXERCISE 14G

1 $\mathbf{a} = \begin{pmatrix} 2 \\ -1 \\ 3 \end{pmatrix}$ and $\mathbf{b} = \begin{pmatrix} -6 \\ r \\ s \end{pmatrix}$ are parallel. Find r and s.

2 Find scalars a and b given that $\begin{pmatrix} 3 \\ -1 \\ 2 \end{pmatrix}$ and $\begin{pmatrix} a \\ 2 \\ b \end{pmatrix}$ are parallel.

3 **a** Find a vector of length 1 unit which is parallel to $\mathbf{a} = \begin{pmatrix} 2 \\ -1 \\ -2 \end{pmatrix}$.
   Hint: Let the vector be $k\mathbf{a}$.

   b Find a vector of length 2 units which is parallel to $\mathbf{b} = \begin{pmatrix} -2 \\ -1 \\ 2 \end{pmatrix}$.

4 What can be deduced from the following?

   a $\overrightarrow{AB} = 3\overrightarrow{CD}$ **b** $\overrightarrow{RS} = -\frac{1}{2}\overrightarrow{KL}$ **c** $\overrightarrow{AB} = 2\overrightarrow{BC}$ **d** $\overrightarrow{BC} = \frac{1}{3}\overrightarrow{AC}$

5 The position vectors of P, Q, R and S from O are $\begin{pmatrix} 3 \\ 2 \\ -1 \end{pmatrix}$, $\begin{pmatrix} 1 \\ 4 \\ -3 \end{pmatrix}$, $\begin{pmatrix} 2 \\ -1 \\ 2 \end{pmatrix}$ and $\begin{pmatrix} -1 \\ -2 \\ 3 \end{pmatrix}$ respectively.

   a Deduce that [PR] and [QS] are parallel.
   b What is the relationship between the lengths of [PR] and [QS]?

6 **a** Prove that A(-2, 1, 4), B(4, 3, 0) and C(19, 8, -10) are collinear and hence find the ratio in which A divides [CB].

   b Prove that P(2, 1, 1), Q(5, -5, -2) and R(-1, 7, 4) are collinear and hence find the ratio in which Q divides [PR].

7   **a**   A(2, −3, 4), B(11, −9, 7) and C(−13, a, b) are collinear. Find a and b.

      b   K(1, −1, 0), L(4, −3, 7) and M(a, 2, b) are collinear. Find a and b.

8   **Triangle inequality**

In any triangle, the sum of any two sides must always be greater
than the third side. This is based on the well known result:
"the shortest distance between two points is a straight line".

Prove that $|\mathbf{a} + \mathbf{b}| \leqslant |\mathbf{a}| + |\mathbf{b}|$ using a geometrical argument.

Hint: Consider   •   **a** is not parallel to **b** and use the triangle inequality

                 •   **a** and **b** parallel   •   any other cases.

H   UNIT VECTORS

A **unit vector** is any vector which has a length of one unit.

For example: • $\begin{pmatrix} 1 \\ 0 \\ 0 \end{pmatrix}$ is a unit vector as its length is $\sqrt{1^2 + 0^2 + 0^2} = 1$

           • $\begin{pmatrix} \frac{1}{\sqrt{2}} \\ 0 \\ -\frac{1}{\sqrt{2}} \end{pmatrix}$ is a unit vector as its length is $\sqrt{\left(\frac{1}{\sqrt{2}}\right)^2 + 0^2 + \left(-\frac{1}{\sqrt{2}}\right)^2} = 1$

$\mathbf{i} = \begin{pmatrix} 1 \\ 0 \\ 0 \end{pmatrix}$, $\mathbf{j} = \begin{pmatrix} 0 \\ 1 \\ 0 \end{pmatrix}$ and $\mathbf{k} = \begin{pmatrix} 0 \\ 0 \\ 1 \end{pmatrix}$ are special unit vectors in the directions of the positive X, Y and Z-axes respectively.

Notice that $\mathbf{a} = \begin{pmatrix} a_1 \\ a_2 \\ a_3 \end{pmatrix}$ $\Leftrightarrow$ $\mathbf{a} = \underbrace{a_1\mathbf{i} + a_2\mathbf{j} + a_3\mathbf{k}}$.

                     ↑   ↑

           component form   unit vector form

Thus, $\mathbf{a} = \begin{pmatrix} 2 \\ 3 \\ -5 \end{pmatrix}$ can be written as $\mathbf{a} = 2\mathbf{i} + 3\mathbf{j} - 5\mathbf{k}$ and vice versa.

We call **i**, **j** and **k** the **base** vectors as any vector can be written as a linear combination of
the vectors **i**, **j** and **k**.

Example 28	
Find the length of the 2-D vector $2\mathbf{i} - 5\mathbf{j}$.	As $2\mathbf{i} - 5\mathbf{j} = \begin{pmatrix} 2 \\ -5 \end{pmatrix}$, its length is $\sqrt{2^2 + (-5)^2}$ $= \sqrt{29}$ units

Example 29

Find a vector **b** of length 7 in the opposite direction to the vector $\mathbf{a} = \begin{pmatrix} 2 \\ -1 \\ 1 \end{pmatrix}$.

The unit vector in the direction of **a** is $\dfrac{1}{\sqrt{4+1+1}} \begin{pmatrix} 2 \\ -1 \\ 1 \end{pmatrix} = \dfrac{1}{\sqrt{6}} \begin{pmatrix} 2 \\ -1 \\ 1 \end{pmatrix}$.

We now multiply this unit vector by -7. The negative reverses the direction and the 7 gives the required length.

Thus $\mathbf{b} = -\dfrac{7}{\sqrt{6}} \begin{pmatrix} 2 \\ -1 \\ 1 \end{pmatrix}$.   Check that $|\mathbf{b}| = 7$.

EXERCISE 14H

1 Express the following vectors in component form and find their length:

     a $\mathbf{i} - \mathbf{j} + \mathbf{k}$ **b** $3\mathbf{i} - \mathbf{j} + \mathbf{k}$ **c** $\mathbf{i} - 5\mathbf{k}$ **d** $\frac{1}{2}(\mathbf{j} + \mathbf{k})$

2 Find k for the unit vectors:

     a $\begin{pmatrix} 0 \\ k \end{pmatrix}$ **b** $\begin{pmatrix} k \\ 0 \end{pmatrix}$ **c** $\begin{pmatrix} k \\ 1 \end{pmatrix}$ **d** $\begin{pmatrix} -\frac{1}{2} \\ k \\ \frac{1}{4} \end{pmatrix}$ **e** $\begin{pmatrix} k \\ \frac{2}{3} \\ -\frac{1}{3} \end{pmatrix}$

3 Find the lengths of the vectors:

     a $3\mathbf{i} + 4\mathbf{j}$ **b** $2\mathbf{i} - \mathbf{j} + \mathbf{k}$ **c** $\mathbf{i} + 2\mathbf{j} - 2\mathbf{k}$ **d** $-2.36\mathbf{i} + 5.65\mathbf{j}$

4 Find the unit vector in the direction of: **a** $\mathbf{i} + 2\mathbf{j}$ **b** $2\mathbf{i} - 3\mathbf{k}$ **c** $-2\mathbf{i} - 5\mathbf{j} - 2\mathbf{k}$

5 Find a vector **b** if:

     a it has the same direction as $\begin{pmatrix} 2 \\ -1 \end{pmatrix}$ and has length 3 units

     b it has the opposite direction to $\begin{pmatrix} -1 \\ -4 \end{pmatrix}$ and has length 2 units

     c it has the same direction as $\begin{pmatrix} -1 \\ 4 \\ 1 \end{pmatrix}$ and has length 6 units

     d it has the opposite direction to $\begin{pmatrix} -1 \\ -2 \\ -2 \end{pmatrix}$ and has length 5 units

Note: • A vector **b** of length k in the same direction as **a** is $\mathbf{b} = \dfrac{k}{|\mathbf{a}|}\mathbf{a}$

           • A vector **b** of length k in the opposite direction to **a** is $\mathbf{b} = -\dfrac{k}{|\mathbf{a}|}\mathbf{a}$

           • A vector **b** of length k which is parallel to **a** could be $\mathbf{b} = \pm\dfrac{k}{|\mathbf{a}|}\mathbf{a}$

I   THE SCALAR PRODUCT OF TWO VECTORS

We have learned how to add, subtract and multiply vectors by a scalar. These operations have all been demonstrated to have practical uses. For example, **scalar multiplication** is used in the concept of **parallelism** and finding **unit vectors**.

VECTOR PRODUCTS

For ordinary numbers numbers a and b we can write the product of a and b as ab or $a \times b$. There is only one interpretation for this product, and so we have developed power notation as a shorthand. $a^2 = a \times a$, $a^3 = a \times a \times a$, and so on.

However, there are *two* different types of product involving two vectors. These are:

- The **scalar product** of 2 vectors, which results in a **scalar** answer and has the notation   **a • b**   (read "a dot b").

- The **vector product** of 2 vectors, which results in a **vector** answer and has the notation   **a × b**   (read "a cross b").

Consequently, for vector **a**, $\mathbf{a}^2$ or $(\mathbf{a})^2$ has no meaning, as it not clear which of the vector products we mean.

So, we should **never** write $\mathbf{a}^n$ or $(\mathbf{a})^n$.

SCALAR DOT PRODUCT

The **scalar product** of two vectors is also known as the **dot product** or **inner product**.

Definition: If $\mathbf{a} = \begin{pmatrix} a_1 \\ a_2 \\ a_3 \end{pmatrix}$ and $\mathbf{b} = \begin{pmatrix} b_1 \\ b_2 \\ b_3 \end{pmatrix}$, the **scalar product** of **a** and **b**

is defined as $\mathbf{a} \bullet \mathbf{b} = a_1 b_1 + a_2 b_2 + a_3 b_3$.

ANGLE BETWEEN VECTORS

Consider vectors: $\mathbf{a} = \begin{pmatrix} a_1 \\ a_2 \\ a_3 \end{pmatrix}$ and $\mathbf{b} = \begin{pmatrix} b_1 \\ b_2 \\ b_3 \end{pmatrix}$

We translate one of the vectors so that they both emanate from the same point.

This vector is $-\mathbf{a} + \mathbf{b} = \mathbf{b} - \mathbf{a}$ and has length $|\mathbf{b} - \mathbf{a}|$.

Using the cosine rule, $|\mathbf{b} - \mathbf{a}|^2 = |\mathbf{a}|^2 + |\mathbf{b}|^2 - 2|\mathbf{a}||\mathbf{b}|\cos\theta$

But $\mathbf{b} - \mathbf{a} = \begin{pmatrix} b_1 \\ b_2 \\ b_3 \end{pmatrix} - \begin{pmatrix} a_1 \\ a_2 \\ a_3 \end{pmatrix} = \begin{pmatrix} b_1 - a_1 \\ b_2 - a_2 \\ b_3 - a_3 \end{pmatrix}$

$\therefore \ (b_1 - a_1)^2 + (b_2 - a_2)^2 + (b_3 - a_3)^2 = a_1{}^2 + a_2{}^2 + a_3{}^2 + b_1{}^2 + b_2{}^2 + b_3{}^2 - 2\,|\mathbf{a}|\,|\mathbf{b}|\cos\theta$

which simplifies to $\ a_1 b_1 + a_2 b_2 + a_3 b_3 = |\mathbf{a}|\,|\mathbf{b}|\cos\theta$

$$\therefore \quad \mathbf{a} \bullet \mathbf{b} = |\mathbf{a}|\,|\mathbf{b}|\cos\theta$$

So, $\qquad \cos\theta = \dfrac{\mathbf{a} \bullet \mathbf{b}}{|\mathbf{a}|\,|\mathbf{b}|} \qquad$ can be used to find the angle between two vectors $\mathbf{a}$ and $\mathbf{b}$.

ALGEBRAIC PROPERTIES OF THE SCALAR PRODUCT

The scalar product has the following algebraic properties for both 2-D and 3-D vectors:

- $\mathbf{a} \bullet \mathbf{b} = \mathbf{b} \bullet \mathbf{a} \qquad$ and $\qquad \mathbf{a} \bullet \mathbf{a} = |\mathbf{a}|^2$
- $\mathbf{a} \bullet (\mathbf{b} + \mathbf{c}) = \mathbf{a} \bullet \mathbf{b} + \mathbf{a} \bullet \mathbf{c}$
- $(\mathbf{a} + \mathbf{b}) \bullet (\mathbf{c} + \mathbf{d}) = \mathbf{a} \bullet \mathbf{c} + \mathbf{a} \bullet \mathbf{d} + \mathbf{b} \bullet \mathbf{c} + \mathbf{b} \bullet \mathbf{d}$

These properties are proven in general by using vectors such as: $\qquad \mathbf{a} = \begin{pmatrix} a_1 \\ a_2 \\ a_3 \end{pmatrix} \ $ and $ \ \mathbf{b} = \begin{pmatrix} b_1 \\ b_2 \\ b_3 \end{pmatrix}$.

Be careful not to confuse the **scalar product**, which is the product of two vectors to give a scalar answer, with **scalar multiplication**, which is the product of a scalar and a vector to give a parallel vector. They are quite different.

GEOMETRIC PROPERTIES OF THE SCALAR PRODUCT

- If θ is the angle between vectors $\mathbf{a}$ and $\mathbf{b}$ then: $\ \mathbf{a} \bullet \mathbf{b} = |\mathbf{a}|\,|\mathbf{b}|\cos\theta$

  So, if θ is acute, $\ \cos\theta > 0 \ $ and $\ \therefore \ \mathbf{a} \bullet \mathbf{b} > 0$

  if θ is obtuse, $\ \cos\theta < 0 \ $ and $\ \therefore \ \mathbf{a} \bullet \mathbf{b} < 0$.
- For non-zero vectors $\mathbf{a}$ and $\mathbf{b}$: $\ \mathbf{a} \bullet \mathbf{b} = 0 \ \Leftrightarrow \ \mathbf{a}$ and $\mathbf{b}$ are **perpendicular**.
- $\mathbf{a} \bullet \mathbf{b} = \pm |\mathbf{a}|\,|\mathbf{b}| \ \Leftrightarrow \ \mathbf{a}$ and $\mathbf{b}$ are non-zero **parallel vectors**

Two vectors form two angles θ and α as in the diagram drawn. The angle between two vectors is always taken as the smaller angle, so we take θ to be the angle between the two vectors with $0 \leqslant \theta \leqslant 180^{\circ}$.

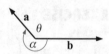

Example 30

If $\ \mathbf{p} = \begin{pmatrix} 2 \\ 3 \\ -1 \end{pmatrix} \ $ and $ \ \mathbf{q} = \begin{pmatrix} -1 \\ 0 \\ 2 \end{pmatrix}$, find: **a** $\ \mathbf{p} \bullet \mathbf{q}$ **b**   the angle between $\mathbf{p}$ and $\mathbf{q}$.

a $\mathbf{p} \bullet \mathbf{q}$

$= \begin{pmatrix} 2 \\ 3 \\ -1 \end{pmatrix} \bullet \begin{pmatrix} -1 \\ 0 \\ 2 \end{pmatrix}$

$= 2(-1) + 3(0) + (-1)2$

$= -2 + 0 - 2$

$= -4$

b $\cos\theta = \dfrac{\mathbf{p} \bullet \mathbf{q}}{|\mathbf{p}|\,|\mathbf{q}|}$

$ = \dfrac{-4}{\sqrt{4+9+1}\,\sqrt{1+0+4}}$

$ = \dfrac{-4}{\sqrt{70}}$

$\therefore \quad \theta = \arccos\left(\dfrac{-4}{\sqrt{70}}\right) \approx 119^{\circ}$

Example 31

Find t such that

$\mathbf{a} = \begin{pmatrix} -1 \\ 5 \end{pmatrix}$ and

$\mathbf{b} = \begin{pmatrix} 2 \\ t \end{pmatrix}$

are perpendicular.

Since $\mathbf{a}$ and $\mathbf{b}$ are perpendicular, $\mathbf{a} \bullet \mathbf{b} = 0$

$\therefore \begin{pmatrix} -1 \\ 5 \end{pmatrix} \bullet \begin{pmatrix} 2 \\ t \end{pmatrix} = 0$

$\therefore (-1)(2) + 5t = 0$

$\therefore -2 + 5t = 0$

$\therefore 5t = 2$ and so $t = \frac{2}{5}$

If two vectors are perpendicular then their scalar product is **zero**.

Example 32

Find the measure of the angle between the lines $2x + y = 5$ and $3x - 2y = 8$.

$2x + y = 5$ has slope $-\frac{2}{1}$ and $\therefore$ direction vector $\begin{pmatrix} 1 \\ -2 \end{pmatrix}$ which we call $\mathbf{a}$.

$3x - 2y = 8$ has slope $\frac{3}{2}$ and $\therefore$ direction vector $\begin{pmatrix} 2 \\ 3 \end{pmatrix}$ which we call $\mathbf{b}$.

If the angle between the lines is θ, then

$$\cos\theta = \frac{\mathbf{a} \bullet \mathbf{b}}{|\mathbf{a}||\mathbf{b}|} = \frac{(1 \times 2) + (-2 \times 3)}{\sqrt{1+4}\sqrt{4+9}} = \frac{-4}{\sqrt{5}\sqrt{13}}$$

$$\therefore \theta = \arccos\left(\frac{-4}{\sqrt{65}}\right) \approx 119.7°$$

If a line has slope $\frac{b}{a}$, it has direction vector $\begin{pmatrix} a \\ b \end{pmatrix}$.

When finding the angle between two lines we choose the acute angle, in this case $180° - \theta$

$\therefore$ the angle is about $60.3°$.

EXERCISE 14I

1 For $\mathbf{p} = \begin{pmatrix} 3 \\ 2 \end{pmatrix}$, $\mathbf{q} = \begin{pmatrix} -1 \\ 5 \end{pmatrix}$ and $\mathbf{r} = \begin{pmatrix} -2 \\ 4 \end{pmatrix}$, find:

a $\mathbf{q} \bullet \mathbf{p}$ **b** $\mathbf{q} \bullet \mathbf{r}$ **c** $\mathbf{q} \bullet (\mathbf{p} + \mathbf{r})$ **d** $3\mathbf{r} \bullet \mathbf{q}$

e $2\mathbf{p} \bullet 2\mathbf{p}$ **f** $\mathbf{i} \bullet \mathbf{p}$ **g** $\mathbf{q} \bullet \mathbf{j}$ **h** $\mathbf{i} \bullet \mathbf{i}$

2 For $\mathbf{a} = \begin{pmatrix} 2 \\ 1 \\ 3 \end{pmatrix}$, $\mathbf{b} = \begin{pmatrix} -1 \\ 1 \\ 1 \end{pmatrix}$ and $\mathbf{c} = \begin{pmatrix} 0 \\ -1 \\ 1 \end{pmatrix}$ find:

a $\mathbf{a} \bullet \mathbf{b}$ **b** $\mathbf{b} \bullet \mathbf{a}$ **c** $|\mathbf{a}|^2$

d $\mathbf{a} \bullet \mathbf{a}$ **e** $\mathbf{a} \bullet (\mathbf{b} + \mathbf{c})$ **f** $\mathbf{a} \bullet \mathbf{b} + \mathbf{a} \bullet \mathbf{c}$

3 If $\mathbf{p} = \begin{pmatrix} 3 \\ -1 \\ 2 \end{pmatrix}$ and $\mathbf{q} = \begin{pmatrix} -2 \\ 1 \\ 3 \end{pmatrix}$, find: **a** $\mathbf{p} \bullet \mathbf{q}$ **b** the angle between $\mathbf{p}$ and $\mathbf{q}$.

4 Find: **a** $(\mathbf{i} + \mathbf{j} - \mathbf{k}) \bullet (2\mathbf{j} + \mathbf{k})$ **b** $\mathbf{i} \bullet \mathbf{i}$ **c** $\mathbf{i} \bullet \mathbf{j}$

5 Using $\mathbf{a} = \begin{pmatrix} a_1 \\ a_2 \\ a_3 \end{pmatrix}$, $\mathbf{b} = \begin{pmatrix} b_1 \\ b_2 \\ b_3 \end{pmatrix}$ and $\mathbf{c} = \begin{pmatrix} c_1 \\ c_2 \\ c_3 \end{pmatrix}$ prove that

$\mathbf{a} \bullet (\mathbf{b} + \mathbf{c}) = \mathbf{a} \bullet \mathbf{b} + \mathbf{a} \bullet \mathbf{c}$.

Hence, prove that $(\mathbf{a} + \mathbf{b}) \bullet (\mathbf{c} + \mathbf{d}) = \mathbf{a} \bullet \mathbf{c} + \mathbf{a} \bullet \mathbf{d} + \mathbf{b} \bullet \mathbf{c} + \mathbf{b} \bullet \mathbf{d}$.

6 Find t given that these vectors are perpendicular:

  a $\mathbf{p} = \begin{pmatrix} 3 \\ t \end{pmatrix}$ and $\mathbf{q} = \begin{pmatrix} -2 \\ 1 \end{pmatrix}$ **b** $\mathbf{r} = \begin{pmatrix} t \\ t+2 \end{pmatrix}$ and $\mathbf{s} = \begin{pmatrix} 3 \\ -4 \end{pmatrix}$

  c $\mathbf{a} = \begin{pmatrix} t \\ t+2 \end{pmatrix}$ and $\mathbf{b} = \begin{pmatrix} 2-3t \\ t \end{pmatrix}$ **d** $\mathbf{a} = \begin{pmatrix} 3 \\ -1 \\ t \end{pmatrix}$ and $\mathbf{b} = \begin{pmatrix} 2t \\ -3 \\ -4 \end{pmatrix}$

7 For question **6** find, where possible, the value(s) of t for which the given vectors are *parallel*. Explain why in some cases the vectors can never be parallel.

8 Show that $\mathbf{a} = \begin{pmatrix} 3 \\ 1 \\ 2 \end{pmatrix}$, $\mathbf{b} = \begin{pmatrix} -1 \\ 1 \\ 1 \end{pmatrix}$ and $\mathbf{c} = \begin{pmatrix} 1 \\ 5 \\ -4 \end{pmatrix}$ are mutually perpendicular.

9   **a** Show that $\begin{pmatrix} 1 \\ 1 \\ 5 \end{pmatrix}$ and $\begin{pmatrix} 2 \\ 3 \\ -1 \end{pmatrix}$ are perpendicular.

  b Find t if $\begin{pmatrix} 3 \\ t \\ -2 \end{pmatrix}$ is perpendicular to $\begin{pmatrix} 1-t \\ -3 \\ 4 \end{pmatrix}$.

10 Consider triangle ABC in which A is $(5, 1, 2)$, $B(6, -1, 0)$ and $C(3, 2, 0)$. Using scalar product only, show that the triangle is right angled.

11 $A(2, 4, 2)$, $B(-1, 2, 3)$, $C(-3, 3, 6)$ and $D(0, 5, 5)$ are vertices of a quadrilateral.

  a Prove that ABCD is a parallelogram.

  b Find $|\overrightarrow{AB}|$ and $|\overrightarrow{BC}|$. What can be said about ABCD?

  c Find $\overrightarrow{AC} \bullet \overrightarrow{BD}$. What property of figure ABCD has been found to be valid?

12 Find the measure of the angle between the lines:

  a $x - y = 3$ and $3x + 2y = 11$ **b** $y = x + 2$ and $y = 1 - 3x$

  c $y + x = 7$ and $x - 3y + 2 = 0$ **d** $y = 2 - x$ and $x - 2y = 7$

13 Find $\mathbf{p} \bullet \mathbf{q}$ if: **a** $|\mathbf{p}| = 2$, $|\mathbf{q}| = 5$, $\theta = 60°$ **b** $|\mathbf{p}| = 6$, $|\mathbf{q}| = 3$, $\theta = 120°$

Example 33

Find the form of all vectors which are perpendicular to $\begin{pmatrix} 3 \\ 4 \end{pmatrix}$.

$\begin{pmatrix} 3 \\ 4 \end{pmatrix} \bullet \begin{pmatrix} -4 \\ 3 \end{pmatrix} = -12 + 12 = 0$

So, $\begin{pmatrix} -4 \\ 3 \end{pmatrix}$ is one such vector

$\therefore$ required vectors have form $k\begin{pmatrix} -4 \\ 3 \end{pmatrix}$, $k \neq 0$.

14 Find the form of all vectors which are perpendicular to:

  a $\begin{pmatrix} 5 \\ 2 \end{pmatrix}$ **b** $\begin{pmatrix} -1 \\ -2 \end{pmatrix}$ **c** $\begin{pmatrix} 3 \\ -1 \end{pmatrix}$ **d** $\begin{pmatrix} -4 \\ 3 \end{pmatrix}$ **e** $\begin{pmatrix} 2 \\ 0 \end{pmatrix}$

15 Find the angle ABC of triangle ABC for A(3, 0, 1), B(−3, 1, 2) and C(−2, 1, −1).

  Hint: To find the angle at B, use $\overrightarrow{BA}$ and $\overrightarrow{BC}$.

  What angle is found if $\overrightarrow{BA}$ and $\overrightarrow{CB}$ are used?

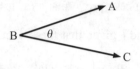

Example 34

Use vector methods to determine the measure of angle ABC.

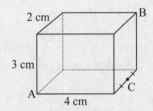

> Notice that vectors used must both be away from B (or towards B). If this is not done you will be finding the exterior angle at B.

Placing the coordinate axes as illustrated,

A is (2, 0, 0), B is (0, 4, 3) and C is (1, 4, 0)

$$\therefore \ \overrightarrow{BA} \text{ is } \begin{pmatrix} 2 \\ -4 \\ -3 \end{pmatrix} \text{ and } \overrightarrow{BC} \text{ is } \begin{pmatrix} 1 \\ 0 \\ -3 \end{pmatrix}$$

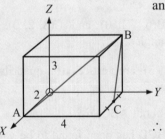

and $\cos A\widehat{B}C = \dfrac{\overrightarrow{BA} \cdot \overrightarrow{BC}}{|\overrightarrow{BA}| \ |\overrightarrow{BC}|}$

$$= \frac{2(1) + (-4)(0) + (-3)(-3)}{\sqrt{4+16+9} \sqrt{1+0+9}}$$

$$= \tfrac{11}{\sqrt{290}}$$

$$\therefore \ A\widehat{B}C = \arccos\left(\tfrac{11}{\sqrt{290}}\right) \approx 49.8^{o}$$

---

16 For the cube alongside with sides of length 2 cm, find using vector methods:

  a the measure of angle ABS

  b the measure of angle RBP

  c the measure of angle PBS.

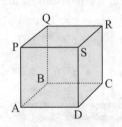

17 KL, LM and LX are 8, 5 and 3 units long respectively. P is the midpoint of KL. Find, using vector methods:

  a the measure of angle YNX

  b the measure of angle YNP.

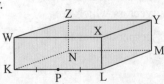

18 For the tetrahedron ABCD:

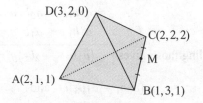

   a find the coordinates of M

   b find the measure of angle DMA.

19 **a** Find t if $2\mathbf{i} + t\mathbf{j} + (t-2)\mathbf{k}$ and $t\mathbf{i} + 3\mathbf{j} + t\mathbf{k}$ are perpendicular.

   b Find r, s and t if $\mathbf{a} = \begin{pmatrix} 1 \\ 2 \\ 3 \end{pmatrix}$, $\mathbf{b} = \begin{pmatrix} 2 \\ 2 \\ r \end{pmatrix}$ and $\mathbf{c} = \begin{pmatrix} s \\ t \\ 1 \end{pmatrix}$ are mutually perpendicular.

20 Find the angle made by:

   a the X-axis and $\begin{pmatrix} 1 \\ 2 \\ 3 \end{pmatrix}$ **b** a line parallel to the Y-axis and $\begin{pmatrix} -1 \\ 1 \\ 3 \end{pmatrix}$.

21 Find three vectors $\mathbf{a}$, $\mathbf{b}$ and $\mathbf{c}$ such that $\mathbf{a} \neq \mathbf{0}$ and $\mathbf{a} \bullet \mathbf{b} = \mathbf{a} \bullet \mathbf{c}$ but $\mathbf{b} \neq \mathbf{c}$.

22 Show, using $|\mathbf{x}|^2 = \mathbf{x} \bullet \mathbf{x}$, that:

   a $|\mathbf{a} + \mathbf{b}|^2 + |\mathbf{a} - \mathbf{b}|^2 = 2|\mathbf{a}|^2 + 2|\mathbf{b}|^2$ **b** $|\mathbf{a} + \mathbf{b}|^2 - |\mathbf{a} - \mathbf{b}|^2 = 4\mathbf{a} \bullet \mathbf{b}$

23 **a** and **b** are the position vectors of two distinct points A and B, neither of which is the origin. Show that if $|\mathbf{a} + \mathbf{b}| = |\mathbf{a} - \mathbf{b}|$ then $\mathbf{a}$ is perpendicular to $\mathbf{b}$ using:

   a a vector algebraic method   **b** a geometric argument.

24 If $|\mathbf{a}| = 3$ and $|\mathbf{b}| = 4$, find $(\mathbf{a} + \mathbf{b}) \bullet (\mathbf{a} - \mathbf{b})$.

25 Explain why $\mathbf{a} \bullet \mathbf{b} \bullet \mathbf{c}$ is meaningless.

J   THE VECTOR PRODUCT OF TWO VECTORS

We have now seen how the scalar product of two vectors results in a **scalar**.

The second form of product between two vectors is the **vector product** or **vector cross product**, and this results in a **vector**.

The **vector product** arises when we attempt to find a vector which is *perpendicular to two other known vectors*. Following is such an attempt:

Suppose $\mathbf{x} = \begin{pmatrix} x \\ y \\ z \end{pmatrix}$ is perpendicular to both $\mathbf{a} = \begin{pmatrix} a_1 \\ a_2 \\ a_3 \end{pmatrix}$ and $\mathbf{b} = \begin{pmatrix} b_1 \\ b_2 \\ b_3 \end{pmatrix}$

$$\therefore \quad \begin{cases} a_1 x + a_2 y + a_3 z = 0 \\ b_1 x + b_2 y + b_3 z = 0 \end{cases} \quad \text{\{as dot products are zero\}}$$

$$\therefore \quad \begin{cases} a_1 x + a_2 y = -a_3 z \quad \text{...... (1)} \\ b_1 x + b_2 y = -b_3 z \quad \text{...... (2)} \end{cases}$$

We will now try to solve these two equations to get expressions for x and y in terms of z.

To eliminate x, we multiply (1) by $-b_1$ and (2) by a_1

$$-a_1b_1x - a_2b_1y = a_3b_1z$$
$$a_1b_1x + a_1b_2y = -a_1b_3z$$

Adding these gives $\quad \overline{(a_1b_2 - a_2b_1)y = (a_3b_1 - a_1b_3)z} \quad$ and so $\quad \dfrac{y}{z} = \dfrac{a_3b_1 - a_1b_3}{a_1b_2 - a_2b_1}$

$\therefore \quad y = (a_3b_1 - a_1b_3)t \quad$ and $\quad z = (a_1b_2 - a_2b_1)t \quad$ for any non-zero t.

Substituting into (1), $\qquad a_1x = -a_3(a_1b_2 - a_2b_1)t - a_2(a_3b_1 - a_1b_3)t$

$\qquad \therefore \quad a_1x = (-a_1a_3b_2 + a_2a_3b_1 - a_2a_3b_1 + a_1a_2b_3)t$

$\qquad \therefore \quad a_1x = a_1(a_2b_3 - a_3b_2)t$

$\qquad \therefore \quad x = (a_2b_3 - a_3b_2)t$

So, the simplest vector perpendicular to both **a** and **b** is obtained by letting $t = 1$.

In this case this gives $\quad \mathbf{x} = \begin{pmatrix} a_2b_3 - a_3b_2 \\ a_3b_1 - a_1b_3 \\ a_1b_2 - a_2b_1 \end{pmatrix}$.

We call this vector the **cross product** of **a** and **b**, and it is written as $\mathbf{a} \times \mathbf{b}$.

$$\mathbf{a} \times \mathbf{b} = \begin{pmatrix} a_2b_3 - a_3b_2 \\ a_3b_1 - a_1b_3 \\ a_1b_2 - a_2b_1 \end{pmatrix} = \begin{vmatrix} a_2 & a_3 \\ b_2 & b_3 \end{vmatrix} \mathbf{i} - \begin{vmatrix} a_1 & a_3 \\ b_1 & b_3 \end{vmatrix} \mathbf{j} + \begin{vmatrix} a_1 & a_2 \\ b_1 & b_2 \end{vmatrix} \mathbf{k}.$$

Notice also that: $\quad \mathbf{a} \times \mathbf{b} = \begin{vmatrix} \mathbf{i} & \mathbf{j} & \mathbf{k} \\ a_1 & a_2 & a_3 \\ b_1 & b_2 & b_3 \end{vmatrix} \longleftarrow$ This form is known as a **3 × 3 determinant**.

> After finding $\mathbf{a} \times \mathbf{b}$, check that your answer is perpendicular to both **a** and **b**.

Example 35

If $\mathbf{a} = \begin{pmatrix} 2 \\ 3 \\ -1 \end{pmatrix}$

and $\mathbf{b} = \begin{pmatrix} -1 \\ 2 \\ 4 \end{pmatrix}$,

find $\mathbf{a} \times \mathbf{b}$.

$\mathbf{a} \times \mathbf{b}$

$= \begin{vmatrix} \mathbf{i} & \mathbf{j} & \mathbf{k} \\ 2 & 3 & -1 \\ -1 & 2 & 4 \end{vmatrix}$

$= \begin{vmatrix} 3 & -1 \\ 2 & 4 \end{vmatrix} \mathbf{i} - \begin{vmatrix} 2 & -1 \\ -1 & 4 \end{vmatrix} \mathbf{j} + \begin{vmatrix} 2 & 3 \\ -1 & 2 \end{vmatrix} \mathbf{k}$

$= 14\mathbf{i} - 7\mathbf{j} + 7\mathbf{k}$

Example 36

For $\mathbf{a} = \begin{pmatrix} 2 \\ 1 \\ -1 \end{pmatrix}$, $\mathbf{b} = \begin{pmatrix} 1 \\ 2 \\ 3 \end{pmatrix}$ and $\mathbf{c} = \begin{pmatrix} 2 \\ 0 \\ 4 \end{pmatrix}$ find: **a** $\mathbf{b} \times \mathbf{c}$
b $\mathbf{a} \bullet (\mathbf{b} \times \mathbf{c})$

a $\quad \mathbf{b} \times \mathbf{c}$

$= \begin{vmatrix} \mathbf{i} & \mathbf{j} & \mathbf{k} \\ 1 & 2 & 3 \\ 2 & 0 & 4 \end{vmatrix}$

$= \begin{vmatrix} 2 & 3 \\ 0 & 4 \end{vmatrix} \mathbf{i} - \begin{vmatrix} 1 & 3 \\ 2 & 4 \end{vmatrix} \mathbf{j} + \begin{vmatrix} 1 & 2 \\ 2 & 0 \end{vmatrix} \mathbf{k}$

$= 8\mathbf{i} + 2\mathbf{j} - 4\mathbf{k}$

b $\quad \mathbf{a} \bullet (\mathbf{b} \times \mathbf{c})$

$= \begin{pmatrix} 2 \\ 1 \\ -1 \end{pmatrix} \bullet \begin{pmatrix} 8 \\ 2 \\ -4 \end{pmatrix}$

$= 16 + 2 + 4$

$= 22$

Example 37

Find *all* vectors perpendicular to both $\mathbf{a} = \begin{pmatrix} 1 \\ 2 \\ -1 \end{pmatrix}$ and $\mathbf{b} = \begin{pmatrix} 1 \\ 0 \\ -3 \end{pmatrix}$

$$\mathbf{a} \times \mathbf{b} = \begin{vmatrix} \mathbf{i} & \mathbf{j} & \mathbf{k} \\ 1 & 2 & -1 \\ 1 & 0 & -3 \end{vmatrix} = \begin{vmatrix} 2 & -1 \\ 0 & -3 \end{vmatrix} \mathbf{i} - \begin{vmatrix} 1 & -1 \\ 1 & -3 \end{vmatrix} \mathbf{j} + \begin{vmatrix} 1 & 2 \\ 1 & 0 \end{vmatrix} \mathbf{k}$$

$$= -6\mathbf{i} + 2\mathbf{j} - 2\mathbf{k} \quad \text{which is} \quad -2(3\mathbf{i} - \mathbf{j} + \mathbf{k})$$

$\therefore$ the vectors have form $k(3\mathbf{i} - \mathbf{j} + \mathbf{k})$, where k is any non-zero real number.

Example 38

Find a direction vector which is perpendicular to the plane passing through the points A(1, −1, 2), B(3, 1, 0) and C(−1, 2, −3).

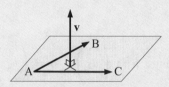

$$\overrightarrow{AB} = \begin{pmatrix} 2 \\ 2 \\ -2 \end{pmatrix}, \quad \overrightarrow{AC} = \begin{pmatrix} -2 \\ 3 \\ -5 \end{pmatrix}$$

The vector **v** must be perpendicular to both $\overrightarrow{AB}$ and $\overrightarrow{AC}$.

$$\text{Thus} \quad \mathbf{v} = \begin{vmatrix} \mathbf{i} & \mathbf{j} & \mathbf{k} \\ 2 & 2 & -2 \\ -2 & 3 & -5 \end{vmatrix} = \begin{vmatrix} 2 & -2 \\ 3 & -5 \end{vmatrix} \mathbf{i} - \begin{vmatrix} 2 & -2 \\ -2 & -5 \end{vmatrix} \mathbf{j} + \begin{vmatrix} 2 & 2 \\ -2 & 3 \end{vmatrix} \mathbf{k}$$

$$= -4\mathbf{i} + 14\mathbf{j} + 10\mathbf{k} \quad \text{which is} \quad -2(2\mathbf{i} - 7\mathbf{j} - 5\mathbf{k})$$

Thus any non-zero multiple of $(2\mathbf{i} - 7\mathbf{j} - 5\mathbf{k})$ will do.

EXERCISE 14J.1

1 Calculate:

  a $\begin{pmatrix} 2 \\ -3 \\ 1 \end{pmatrix} \times \begin{pmatrix} 1 \\ 4 \\ -2 \end{pmatrix}$
  b $\begin{pmatrix} -1 \\ 0 \\ 2 \end{pmatrix} \times \begin{pmatrix} 3 \\ -1 \\ -2 \end{pmatrix}$
  c $(\mathbf{i} + \mathbf{j} - 2\mathbf{k}) \times (\mathbf{i} - \mathbf{k})$
  d $(2\mathbf{i} - \mathbf{k}) \times (\mathbf{j} + 3\mathbf{k})$

2 Given $\mathbf{a} = \begin{pmatrix} 1 \\ 2 \\ 3 \end{pmatrix}$ and $\mathbf{b} = \begin{pmatrix} -1 \\ 3 \\ -1 \end{pmatrix}$, find $\mathbf{a} \times \mathbf{b}$ and hence determine $\mathbf{a} \bullet (\mathbf{a} \times \mathbf{b})$

and $\mathbf{b} \bullet (\mathbf{a} \times \mathbf{b})$. What has been verified from these results?

3 If **i**, **j** and **k** are the unit vectors parallel to the coordinate axes:

  a find $\mathbf{i} \times \mathbf{i}$, $\mathbf{j} \times \mathbf{j}$, and $\mathbf{k} \times \mathbf{k}$

  b find $\mathbf{i} \times \mathbf{j}$ and $\mathbf{j} \times \mathbf{i}$, $\mathbf{j} \times \mathbf{k}$ and $\mathbf{k} \times \mathbf{j}$, and $\mathbf{i} \times \mathbf{k}$ and $\mathbf{k} \times \mathbf{i}$.

What do you suspect $\mathbf{a} \times \mathbf{a}$ equals for any vector **a**?

What do you suspect is the relationship between $\mathbf{a} \times \mathbf{b}$ and $\mathbf{b} \times \mathbf{a}$?

4 Using $\mathbf{a} = \begin{pmatrix} a_1 \\ a_2 \\ a_3 \end{pmatrix}$ and $\mathbf{b} = \begin{pmatrix} b_1 \\ b_2 \\ b_3 \end{pmatrix}$, prove that:

  a $\mathbf{a} \times \mathbf{a} = \mathbf{0}$ for all space vectors $\mathbf{a}$

  b $\mathbf{a} \times \mathbf{b} = -\mathbf{b} \times \mathbf{a}$ for all space vectors $\mathbf{a}$ and $\mathbf{b}$.

5 For $\mathbf{a} = \begin{pmatrix} 1 \\ 3 \\ 2 \end{pmatrix}$, $\mathbf{b} = \begin{pmatrix} 2 \\ -1 \\ 1 \end{pmatrix}$ and $\mathbf{c} = \begin{pmatrix} 0 \\ 1 \\ -2 \end{pmatrix}$ find:

  a $\mathbf{b} \times \mathbf{c}$ **b** $\mathbf{a} \bullet (\mathbf{b} \times \mathbf{c})$ **c** $\begin{vmatrix} 1 & 3 & 2 \\ 2 & -1 & 1 \\ 0 & 1 & -2 \end{vmatrix}$

Explain why the answers to **b** and **c** are the same.

6 Repeat **5** for vectors of your choosing.

7 If $\mathbf{a} = \mathbf{i} + 2\mathbf{k}$, $\mathbf{b} = -\mathbf{j} + \mathbf{k}$ and $\mathbf{c} = 2\mathbf{i} - \mathbf{k}$, determine:

  a $\mathbf{a} \times \mathbf{b}$ **b** $\mathbf{a} \times \mathbf{c}$ **c** $(\mathbf{a} \times \mathbf{b}) + (\mathbf{a} \times \mathbf{c})$ **d** $\mathbf{a} \times (\mathbf{b} + \mathbf{c})$

8 What do you suspect to be true from **7**?

Check with vectors $\mathbf{a}$, $\mathbf{b}$ and $\mathbf{c}$ of your choosing.

9 Prove that $\mathbf{a} \times (\mathbf{b} + \mathbf{c}) = \mathbf{a} \times \mathbf{b} + \mathbf{a} \times \mathbf{c}$ using $\mathbf{a} = \begin{pmatrix} a_1 \\ a_2 \\ a_3 \end{pmatrix}$, $\mathbf{b} = \begin{pmatrix} b_1 \\ b_2 \\ b_3 \end{pmatrix}$ and $\mathbf{c} = \begin{pmatrix} c_1 \\ c_2 \\ c_3 \end{pmatrix}$.

10 Use $\mathbf{a} \times (\mathbf{b} + \mathbf{c}) = (\mathbf{a} \times \mathbf{b}) + (\mathbf{a} \times \mathbf{c})$ to prove that

$(\mathbf{a} + \mathbf{b}) \times (\mathbf{c} + \mathbf{d}) = (\mathbf{a} \times \mathbf{c}) + (\mathbf{a} \times \mathbf{d}) + (\mathbf{b} \times \mathbf{c}) + (\mathbf{b} \times \mathbf{d})$.

Notice that the order of the vectors must be maintained as $\mathbf{x} \times \mathbf{y} = -\mathbf{y} \times \mathbf{x}$.

11 Use the properties found in **4** and **9** to simplify:

  a $\mathbf{a} \times (\mathbf{a} + \mathbf{b})$ **b** $(\mathbf{a} + \mathbf{b}) \times (\mathbf{a} + \mathbf{b})$

  c $(\mathbf{a} + \mathbf{b}) \times (\mathbf{a} - \mathbf{b})$ **d** $2\mathbf{a} \bullet (\mathbf{a} \times \mathbf{b})$

12 Find *all* vectors perpendicular to both:

  a $\begin{pmatrix} 2 \\ -1 \\ 3 \end{pmatrix}$ and $\begin{pmatrix} 1 \\ 1 \\ 1 \end{pmatrix}$ **b** $\begin{pmatrix} -1 \\ 3 \\ 4 \end{pmatrix}$ and $\begin{pmatrix} 5 \\ 0 \\ 2 \end{pmatrix}$

  c $\mathbf{i} + \mathbf{j}$ and $\mathbf{i} - \mathbf{j} - \mathbf{k}$ **d** $\mathbf{i} - \mathbf{j} - \mathbf{k}$ and $2\mathbf{i} + 2\mathbf{j} - 3\mathbf{k}$

13 Find all vectors perpendicular to both $\mathbf{a} = \begin{pmatrix} 2 \\ 3 \\ -1 \end{pmatrix}$ and $\mathbf{b} = \begin{pmatrix} 1 \\ -2 \\ 2 \end{pmatrix}$.

Hence find a vector of length 5 units which is perpendicular to both $\mathbf{a}$ and $\mathbf{b}$.

14 Find a direction vector which is perpendicular to the plane passing through the points:

  a A(1, 3, 2), B(0, 2, −5) and C(3, 1, −4)

  b P(2, 0, −1), Q(0, 1, 3) and R(1, −1, 1).

In the above exercise you should have observed the following **properties** of **vector cross products**:

> ▶ $\mathbf{a} \times \mathbf{b}$ is a vector which is perpendicular to both $\mathbf{a}$ and $\mathbf{b}$.
>
> ▶ $\mathbf{a} \times \mathbf{a} = \mathbf{0}$ for all space vectors $\mathbf{a}$.
>
> ▶ $\mathbf{a} \times \mathbf{b} = -\mathbf{b} \times \mathbf{a}$ for all space vectors $\mathbf{a}$ and $\mathbf{b}$,
>   i.e., $\mathbf{a} \times \mathbf{b}$ and $\mathbf{b} \times \mathbf{a}$ have the same length but opposite direction.
>
> ▶ $\mathbf{a} \bullet (\mathbf{b} \times \mathbf{c}) = \begin{vmatrix} a_1 & a_2 & a_3 \\ b_1 & b_2 & b_3 \\ c_1 & c_2 & c_3 \end{vmatrix}$ and is called the **scalar triple product**.
>
> ▶ $\mathbf{a} \times (\mathbf{b} + \mathbf{c}) = (\mathbf{a} \times \mathbf{b}) + (\mathbf{a} \times \mathbf{c})$ and hence
> $(\mathbf{a} + \mathbf{b}) \times (\mathbf{c} + \mathbf{d}) = (\mathbf{a} \times \mathbf{c}) + (\mathbf{a} \times \mathbf{d}) + (\mathbf{b} \times \mathbf{c}) + (\mathbf{b} \times \mathbf{d})$.

DIRECTION OF $\mathbf{a} \times \mathbf{b}$

We have already observed that as $\mathbf{a} \times \mathbf{b} = -\mathbf{b} \times \mathbf{a}$
then $\mathbf{a} \times \mathbf{b}$ and $\mathbf{b} \times \mathbf{a}$ are oppositely directed.

However, what is the direction of each?

Consider $\mathbf{i} \times \mathbf{j}$ and $\mathbf{j} \times \mathbf{i}$. In the last Exercise,
we saw that $\mathbf{i} \times \mathbf{j} = \mathbf{k}$ and $\mathbf{j} \times \mathbf{i} = -\mathbf{k}$.

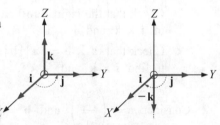

In general, the **direction** of $\mathbf{x} \times \mathbf{y}$ is determined by the **right hand rule**:

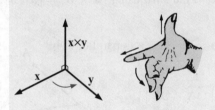

To determine the direction of $\mathbf{x} \times \mathbf{y}$ use your **right hand**. If your fingers turn from $\mathbf{x}$ to $\mathbf{y}$ then your thumb points in the direction of $\mathbf{x} \times \mathbf{y}$.

THE LENGTH OF $\mathbf{a} \times \mathbf{b}$

As $\mathbf{a} \times \mathbf{b} = \begin{pmatrix} a_2 b_3 - a_3 b_2 \\ a_3 b_1 - a_1 b_3 \\ a_1 b_2 - a_2 b_1 \end{pmatrix}$, $|\mathbf{a} \times \mathbf{b}| = \sqrt{(a_2 b_3 - a_3 b_2)^2 + (a_3 b_1 - a_1 b_3)^2 + (a_1 b_2 - a_2 b_1)^2}$

However, another very useful form of the length of $\mathbf{a} \times \mathbf{b}$ exists. This is:

$$|\mathbf{a} \times \mathbf{b}| = |\mathbf{a}||\mathbf{b}|\sin\theta \quad \text{where } \theta \text{ is the angle between } \mathbf{a} \text{ and } \mathbf{b}.$$

Proof: We start with $|\mathbf{a}|^2 |\mathbf{b}|^2 \sin^2\theta$
$$= |\mathbf{a}|^2 |\mathbf{b}|^2 (1 - \cos^2\theta)$$
$$= |\mathbf{a}|^2 |\mathbf{b}|^2 - |\mathbf{a}|^2 |\mathbf{b}|^2 \cos^2\theta$$
$$= |\mathbf{a}|^2 |\mathbf{b}|^2 - (\mathbf{a} \bullet \mathbf{b})^2$$

$$= (a_1{}^2 + a_2{}^2 + a_3{}^2)(b_1{}^2 + b_2{}^2 + b_3{}^2) - (a_1b_1 + a_2b_2 + a_3b_3)^2$$

which on expanding and then factorising gives

$$= (a_2b_3 - a_3b_2)^2 + (a_3b_1 - a_1b_3)^2 + (a_1b_2 - a_2b_1)^2$$

$$= |\mathbf{a} \times \mathbf{b}|^2$$

and so $|\mathbf{a} \times \mathbf{b}| = |\mathbf{a}||\mathbf{b}|\sin\theta$ $\{$as $\sin\theta > 0\}$

Immediate consequences are:

- If $\mathbf{u}$ is a **unit vector** in the direction of $\mathbf{a} \times \mathbf{b}$ then $\mathbf{a} \times \mathbf{b} = |\mathbf{a}||\mathbf{b}|\sin\theta\,\mathbf{u}$
  In some texts this is the **geometric definition** of $\mathbf{a} \times \mathbf{b}$.
- If $\mathbf{a}$ and $\mathbf{b}$ are non-zero vectors, then $\mathbf{a} \times \mathbf{b} = \mathbf{0} \iff \mathbf{a}$ is parallel to $\mathbf{b}$.

EXERCISE 14J.2

1 **a** Find $\mathbf{i} \times \mathbf{k}$ and $\mathbf{k} \times \mathbf{i}$ using the original definition of $\mathbf{a} \times \mathbf{b}$.

   b Check that the **right-hand rule** correctly gives the direction of $\mathbf{i} \times \mathbf{k}$ and $\mathbf{k} \times \mathbf{i}$.

   c Check that $\mathbf{a} \times \mathbf{b} = |\mathbf{a}||\mathbf{b}|\sin\theta\,\mathbf{u}$ could be used to find $\mathbf{i} \times \mathbf{k}$ and $\mathbf{k} \times \mathbf{i}$.

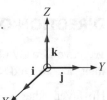

2 Consider $\mathbf{a} = \begin{pmatrix} 2 \\ -1 \\ 3 \end{pmatrix}$ and $\mathbf{b} = \begin{pmatrix} 1 \\ 0 \\ -1 \end{pmatrix}$.

   a Find $\mathbf{a} \bullet \mathbf{b}$ and $\mathbf{a} \times \mathbf{b}$.   **b** Find $\cos\theta$ using $\mathbf{a} \bullet \mathbf{b} = |\mathbf{a}||\mathbf{b}|\cos\theta$.

   c Find $\sin\theta$ using $\sin^2\theta + \cos^2\theta = 1$.   **d** Find $\sin\theta$ using $|\mathbf{a} \times \mathbf{b}| = |\mathbf{a}||\mathbf{b}|\sin\theta$.

3 Prove the property:

   "If $\mathbf{a}$ and $\mathbf{b}$ are non-zero vectors then $\mathbf{a} \times \mathbf{b} = \mathbf{0} \iff \mathbf{a}$ is parallel to $\mathbf{b}$."

4 O is the origin. Find:

   a $\overrightarrow{OA}$ and $\overrightarrow{OB}$ **b** $\overrightarrow{OA} \times \overrightarrow{OB}$ and $|\overrightarrow{OA} \times \overrightarrow{OB}|$.

   c Explain why the area of triangle OAB is $\frac{1}{2}|\overrightarrow{OA} \times \overrightarrow{OB}|$.

5 A, B and C are 3 distinct points with non-zero position vectors $\mathbf{a}$, $\mathbf{b}$ and $\mathbf{c}$ respectively.

   a If $\mathbf{a} \times \mathbf{c} = \mathbf{b} \times \mathbf{c}$, what can be deduced about $\overrightarrow{OC}$ and $\overrightarrow{AB}$?

   b If $\mathbf{a} + \mathbf{b} + \mathbf{c} = \mathbf{0}$, what relationship exists between $\mathbf{a} \times \mathbf{b}$ and $\mathbf{b} \times \mathbf{c}$?

   c If $\mathbf{c} \neq \mathbf{0}$ and $\mathbf{b} \times \mathbf{c} = \mathbf{c} \times \mathbf{a}$, prove that $\mathbf{a} + \mathbf{b} = k\mathbf{c}$ for some scalar k.

AREAS AND VOLUMES

TRIANGLES

If a triangle has defining vectors $\mathbf{a}$ and $\mathbf{b}$ then its area is $\frac{1}{2}|\mathbf{a} \times \mathbf{b}|$ units^2.

Proof: Area $= \frac{1}{2} \times$ product of two sides $\times$ sine of included angle $= \frac{1}{2}|\mathbf{a}||\mathbf{b}|\sin\theta$

$$= \frac{1}{2}|\mathbf{a} \times \mathbf{b}|$$

Example 39

Find the area of $\triangle ABC$ given $A(-1, 2, 3)$, $B(2, 1, 4)$ and $C(0, 5, -1)$.

$$\overrightarrow{AB} \times \overrightarrow{AC} = \begin{vmatrix} \mathbf{i} & \mathbf{j} & \mathbf{k} \\ 3 & -1 & 1 \\ 1 & 3 & -4 \end{vmatrix}$$

$$= \begin{vmatrix} -1 & 1 \\ 3 & -4 \end{vmatrix} \mathbf{i} - \begin{vmatrix} 3 & 1 \\ 1 & -4 \end{vmatrix} \mathbf{j} + \begin{vmatrix} 3 & -1 \\ 1 & 3 \end{vmatrix} \mathbf{k}$$

$$= \mathbf{i} + 13\mathbf{j} + 10\mathbf{k}$$

$$\therefore \quad \text{area} = \tfrac{1}{2} \mid \overrightarrow{AB} \times \overrightarrow{AC} \mid = \tfrac{1}{2}\sqrt{1 + 169 + 100}$$

$$= \tfrac{1}{2}\sqrt{270} \text{ units}^2$$

PARALLELOGRAMS

If a parallelogram has defining vectors $\mathbf{a}$ and $\mathbf{b}$ then its area is $\mid \mathbf{a} \times \mathbf{b} \mid$ units^2.

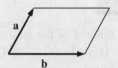

The proof follows directly from that of a triangle as the parallelogram consists of two congruent triangles with defining vectors $\mathbf{a}$ and $\mathbf{b}$.

PARALLELEPIPED (EXTENSION)

If a parallelepiped has defining vectors $\mathbf{a}$, $\mathbf{b}$ and $\mathbf{c}$ then its volume is

$$\underbrace{\mid \mathbf{a} \bullet (\mathbf{b} \times \mathbf{c}) \mid}_{\text{modulus}} = \underbrace{\begin{Vmatrix} a_1 & a_2 & a_3 \\ b_1 & b_2 & b_3 \\ c_1 & c_2 & c_3 \end{Vmatrix}}_{\text{modulus}} \overset{\text{determinant}}{} \text{units}^3.$$

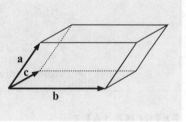

Proof:

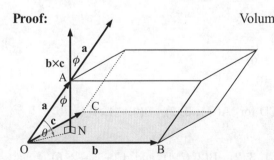

Volume $= (\text{area of base}) \times (\text{perp. height})$

$= \mid \mathbf{b} \times \mathbf{c} \mid \times \text{AN}$

$= \mid \mathbf{b} \times \mathbf{c} \mid \times \mid \mathbf{a} \mid \sin \theta \quad \{\text{as } \sin \theta = \dfrac{\text{AN}}{\mid \mathbf{a} \mid}\}$

$= \mid \mathbf{a} \mid \mid \mathbf{b} \times \mathbf{c} \mid \sin \theta$

$= \mid \mathbf{a} \mid \mid \mathbf{b} \times \mathbf{c} \mid \cos \phi$

where ϕ is the angle between $\mathbf{a}$ and $\mathbf{b} \times \mathbf{c}$

$= \mid \mathbf{a} \bullet (\mathbf{b} \times \mathbf{c}) \mid \quad$ as $\cos \phi > 0$.

TETRAHEDRON (EXTENSION)

If a tetrahedron has defining vectors **a**, **b** and **c** then its volume is

$$\frac{1}{6}|\mathbf{a} \bullet (\mathbf{b} \times \mathbf{c})| = \frac{1}{6}\left\| \begin{matrix} a_1 & a_2 & a_3 \\ b_1 & b_2 & b_3 \\ c_1 & c_2 & c_3 \end{matrix} \right\| \quad \text{units}^3.$$

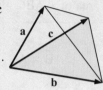

Proof:

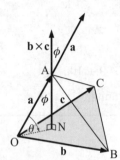

Volume $= \frac{1}{3}$(area of base) × (perp. height)

$= \frac{1}{3} \times \frac{1}{2}|\mathbf{b} \times \mathbf{c}| \times$ AN

$= \frac{1}{6}|\mathbf{b} \times \mathbf{c}||\mathbf{a}|\sin\theta \quad \{\text{as} \quad \sin\theta = \dfrac{\text{AN}}{|\mathbf{a}|}\}$

$= \frac{1}{6}|\mathbf{a}||\mathbf{b} \times \mathbf{c}|\cos\phi$

where ϕ is the angle between **a** and **b** × **c**

$= \frac{1}{6}|\mathbf{a} \bullet (\mathbf{b} \times \mathbf{c})| \quad \text{as} \quad \cos\phi > 0.$

Example 40

Find the volume of the tetrahedron with vertices P(0, 0, 1), Q(2, 3, 0), R(−1, 2, 1) and S(1, −2, 4).

$\overrightarrow{PQ} = \begin{pmatrix} 2 \\ 3 \\ -1 \end{pmatrix}$, $\overrightarrow{PR} = \begin{pmatrix} -1 \\ 2 \\ 0 \end{pmatrix}$, $\overrightarrow{PS} = \begin{pmatrix} 1 \\ -2 \\ 3 \end{pmatrix}$ are the defining vectors from P

$\therefore$ volume $= \frac{1}{6}\left\| \begin{matrix} 2 & 3 & -1 \\ -1 & 2 & 0 \\ 1 & -2 & 3 \end{matrix} \right\|$

$= \frac{1}{6}\left| 2 \begin{vmatrix} 2 & 0 \\ -2 & 3 \end{vmatrix} - 3 \begin{vmatrix} -1 & 0 \\ 1 & 3 \end{vmatrix} - 1 \begin{vmatrix} -1 & 2 \\ 1 & -2 \end{vmatrix} \right|$

$= \frac{1}{6}|12 + 9 - 0|$

$= 3\frac{1}{2} \quad \text{units}^3$

EXERCISE 14J.3

1   Calculate the area of triangle ABC for:

   a   A(2, 1, 1), B(4, 3, 0), C(1, 3, −2)

   b   A(0, 0, 0), B(−1, 2, 3) and C(1, 2, 6)

   c   A(1, 3, 2), B(2, −1, 0) and C(1, 10, 6)

2   Calculate the area of parallelogram ABCD for A(−1, 2, 2), B(2, −1, 4) and C(0, 1, 0).

3   ABCD is a parallelogram where A is (−1, 3, 2), B(2, 0, 4) and C(−1, −2, 5). Find the   **a**   coordinates of D   **b**   area of ABCD.

4 ABCD is a tetrahedron with A(1, −1, 0), B(2, 1, −1), C(0, 1, −3) and
D(−1, 1, 2). Find the:

    a volume of the tetrahedron   **b** total surface area of the tetrahedron.

5 A(3, 0, 0), B(0, 1, 0) and C(1, 2, 3) are the vertices of a parallelepiped which are
adjacent to another vertex at O(0, 0, 0). Find the:

    a coordinates of the other four vertices   **b** measure of $\angle ABC$

    c volume of the parallelepiped.

6 If A(−1, 1, 2), B(2, 0, 1) and C(k, 2, −1) are three points in space, find k if the
area of triangle ABC is $\sqrt{88}$ units^2.

7 A, B and C are three points with position vectors **a**, **b** and **c** respectively. Find a formula
for S, the total surface area of the tetrahedron OABC.

8 Three distinct points A, B and C have position vectors **a**, **b** and **c** respectively. Prove
that A, B and C are collinear $\Leftrightarrow$ $(\mathbf{b} - \mathbf{a}) \times (\mathbf{c} - \mathbf{b}) = \mathbf{0}$.

TEST FOR COPLANAR POINTS

Four points in space are either coplanar or form the vertices of a tetrahedron. If they are
coplanar, the volume of the tetrahedron is zero. So:

> If four points A, B, C and D have position vectors **a**, **b**, **c** and **d** respectively
> then A, B, C and D are coplanar $\Leftrightarrow$ $(\mathbf{b} - \mathbf{a}) \bullet (\mathbf{c} - \mathbf{a}) \times (\mathbf{d} - \mathbf{a}) = 0$.

Example 41

Are the points A(1, 2, −4), B(3, 2, 0), C(2, 5, 1) and D(5, −3, −1) coplanar?

$$\mathbf{b} - \mathbf{a} = \overrightarrow{AB} = \begin{pmatrix} 3-1 \\ 2-2 \\ 0--4 \end{pmatrix} = \begin{pmatrix} 2 \\ 0 \\ 4 \end{pmatrix} \qquad \mathbf{c} - \mathbf{a} = \overrightarrow{AC} = \begin{pmatrix} 2-1 \\ 5-2 \\ 1--4 \end{pmatrix} = \begin{pmatrix} 1 \\ 3 \\ 5 \end{pmatrix}$$

$$\mathbf{d} - \mathbf{a} = \overrightarrow{AD} = \begin{pmatrix} 5-1 \\ -3-2 \\ -1--4 \end{pmatrix} = \begin{pmatrix} 4 \\ -5 \\ 3 \end{pmatrix}$$

$$\text{and} \quad (\mathbf{b} - \mathbf{a}) \bullet (\mathbf{c} - \mathbf{a}) \times (\mathbf{d} - \mathbf{a}) = \begin{vmatrix} 2 & 0 & 4 \\ 1 & 3 & 5 \\ 4 & -5 & 3 \end{vmatrix}$$

$$= 2(9 + 25) + 4(-5 - 12)$$
$$= 0$$

$\therefore$ A, B, C and D are coplanar.

9 Are these points coplanar?

    a A(1, 1, 2), B(2, 4, 0), C(3, 1, 1) and D(4, 0, 1)

    b P(2, 0, 5), Q(0, −1, 4), R(2, 1, 0), S(1, 1, 1)

10 Find k given that A(2, 1, 3), B(4, 0, 1), C(0, k, 2), D(1, 2, −1) are coplanar.

REVIEW SET 14A (Mainly 2-D)

1 Using a scale of 1 cm represents 10 units, sketch a vector to represent:

   a an aeroplane taking off at an angle of $8°$ to the runway with a speed of 60 m s^{-1}

   b a displacement of 45 m in a direction of $060°$.

2 Copy the given vectors and find geometrically:

   a $x + y$ **b** $y - 2x$

3 Find a single vector which is equal to: **a** $\overrightarrow{PR} + \overrightarrow{RQ}$ **b** $\overrightarrow{PS} + \overrightarrow{SQ} + \overrightarrow{QR}$

4 Dino walks for 9 km in the direction $246°$ and then for 6 km in the direction $096°$. Find his displacement from his starting point.

5 Simplify   **a** $\overrightarrow{AB} - \overrightarrow{CB}$ **b** $\overrightarrow{AB} + \overrightarrow{BC} - \overrightarrow{DC}$.

6 What geometrical facts can be deduced from the equations:

   a $\overrightarrow{AB} = \frac{1}{2}\overrightarrow{CD}$ **b** $\overrightarrow{AB} = 2\overrightarrow{AC}$?

7 Construct vector   **a**   **b**
equations for:

8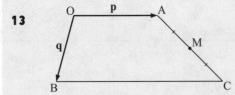

In the figure alongside $\overrightarrow{OP} = \mathbf{p}$, $\overrightarrow{OR} = \mathbf{r}$ and $\overrightarrow{RQ} = \mathbf{q}$.

If M and N are midpoints of the sides as shown, find in terms of $\mathbf{p}$, $\mathbf{q}$ and $\mathbf{r}$:

   a $\overrightarrow{OQ}$ **b** $\overrightarrow{PQ}$ **c** $\overrightarrow{ON}$ **d** $\overrightarrow{MN}$

9 Draw arrow diagrams to represent: **a** $\begin{pmatrix} 4 \\ 3 \end{pmatrix}$ **b** $\begin{pmatrix} 3 \\ -5 \end{pmatrix}$ **c** $\begin{pmatrix} 0 \\ -4 \end{pmatrix}$

10 If $\mathbf{p} = \begin{pmatrix} -3 \\ 1 \end{pmatrix}$, $\mathbf{q} = \begin{pmatrix} 2 \\ -4 \end{pmatrix}$ and $\mathbf{r} = \begin{pmatrix} 1 \\ 3 \end{pmatrix}$ find:

   a $2\mathbf{p} + \mathbf{q}$ **b** $\mathbf{q} - 3\mathbf{r}$ **c** $\mathbf{p} - \mathbf{q} + \mathbf{r}$

11 If $\overrightarrow{PQ} = \begin{pmatrix} -4 \\ 1 \end{pmatrix}$, $\overrightarrow{RQ} = \begin{pmatrix} -1 \\ 2 \end{pmatrix}$ and $\overrightarrow{RS} = \begin{pmatrix} 2 \\ -3 \end{pmatrix}$, find $\overrightarrow{SP}$.

12 If $\mathbf{r} = \begin{pmatrix} 4 \\ 1 \end{pmatrix}$ and $\mathbf{s} = \begin{pmatrix} -3 \\ 2 \end{pmatrix}$ find: **a** $|\mathbf{r}|$ **b** $|\mathbf{s}|$ **c** $|\mathbf{r} + \mathbf{s}|$ **d** $|2\mathbf{s} - \mathbf{r}|$

13

BC is parallel to OA and is twice its length. Find, in terms of $\mathbf{p}$ and $\mathbf{q}$, vector expressions for   **a** $\overrightarrow{AC}$ **b** $\overrightarrow{OM}$.

14 If $\mathbf{p} = \begin{pmatrix} -3 \\ 1 \end{pmatrix}$, $\mathbf{q} = \begin{pmatrix} 2 \\ -4 \end{pmatrix}$ and $\mathbf{r} = \begin{pmatrix} 3 \\ 2 \end{pmatrix}$, find $\mathbf{x}$ if: **a** $\mathbf{p} - 3\mathbf{x} = \mathbf{0}$

                                                    b $2\mathbf{q} - \mathbf{x} = \mathbf{r}$

15 Use vectors to show that WYZX is a parallelogram if X is $(-2, 5)$, Y$(3, 4)$, W$(-3, -1)$, and Z$(4, 10)$.

16 Find scalars r and s such that $r \begin{pmatrix} -2 \\ 1 \end{pmatrix} + s \begin{pmatrix} 3 \\ -4 \end{pmatrix} = \begin{pmatrix} 13 \\ -24 \end{pmatrix}$.

17 [AB] and [CD] are diameters of a circle centre O. If $\overrightarrow{OC} = \mathbf{q}$ and $\overrightarrow{OB} = \mathbf{r}$, find:

   a $\overrightarrow{DB}$ in terms of $\mathbf{q}$ and $\mathbf{r}$ **b** $\overrightarrow{AC}$ in terms of $\mathbf{q}$ and $\mathbf{r}$.

  What can be deduced about [DB] and [AC]?

REVIEW SET 14B (Mainly 3-D)

1 Given P$(2, -5, 6)$ and Q$(-1, 7, 9)$, find:

   a the position vector of Q from P   **b** the distance from P to Q

   c the distance from P to the x-axis.

2 For $\mathbf{m} = \begin{pmatrix} 6 \\ -3 \\ 1 \end{pmatrix}$, $\mathbf{n} = \begin{pmatrix} 2 \\ 3 \\ -4 \end{pmatrix}$ and $\mathbf{p} = \begin{pmatrix} -1 \\ 3 \\ 6 \end{pmatrix}$, find:

   a $\mathbf{m} - \mathbf{n} + \mathbf{p}$ **b** $2\mathbf{n} - 3\mathbf{p}$ **c** $|\mathbf{m} + \mathbf{p}|$

3 If $\overrightarrow{AB} = \begin{pmatrix} 2 \\ -7 \\ 4 \end{pmatrix}$ and $\overrightarrow{AC} = \begin{pmatrix} -6 \\ 1 \\ -3 \end{pmatrix}$, find $\overrightarrow{CB}$.

4 Find m and n if $\begin{pmatrix} 3 \\ m \\ n \end{pmatrix}$ and $\begin{pmatrix} -12 \\ -20 \\ 2 \end{pmatrix}$ are parallel vectors.

5 Prove that P$(-6, 8, 2)$, Q$(4, 6, 8)$ and R$(19, 3, 17)$ are collinear. Hence find the ratio in which Q divides [PR].

6 Find t if $\begin{pmatrix} -4 \\ t+2 \\ t \end{pmatrix}$ and $\begin{pmatrix} t \\ 1+t \\ -3 \end{pmatrix}$ are perpendicular vectors.

7 Determine the angle between $\begin{pmatrix} 2 \\ -4 \\ 3 \end{pmatrix}$ and $\begin{pmatrix} -1 \\ 1 \\ 3 \end{pmatrix}$.

8 Find the measure of angle GAC in the rectangular box alongside. Use vector methods.

5 cm, 4 cm, 8 cm (box with vertices E, H, F, G, D, C, A, B)

9 For P$(2, 3, -1)$ and Q$(-4, 4, 2)$ find:

   a $\overrightarrow{PQ}$ **b** the distance between P and Q   **c** the midpoint of [PQ].

10 For $\mathbf{p} = \begin{pmatrix} -1 \\ 2 \\ 1 \end{pmatrix}$, $\mathbf{q} = \begin{pmatrix} 3 \\ -1 \\ 4 \end{pmatrix}$ and $\mathbf{r} = \begin{pmatrix} 1 \\ 1 \\ 2 \end{pmatrix}$ find:

   a $\mathbf{p} \bullet \mathbf{q}$ **b** $\mathbf{p} + 2\mathbf{q} - \mathbf{r}$ **c** the angle between $\mathbf{p}$ and $\mathbf{r}$.

11 Find all angles of the triangle with vertices K$(3, 1, 4)$, L$(-2, 1, 3)$ and M$(4, 1, 3)$.

12 Find the angle between $\begin{pmatrix} 3 \\ 1 \\ -2 \end{pmatrix}$ and $\begin{pmatrix} 2 \\ 5 \\ 1 \end{pmatrix}$.

13 If A(4, 2, −1), B(−1, 5, 2), C(3, −3, c) are vertices of triangle ABC which is right angled at B, find the possible values of c.

14 Explain why:

    a $\mathbf{a} \bullet \mathbf{b} \bullet \mathbf{c}$ is meaningless   **b** you do not need brackets for $\mathbf{a} \bullet \mathbf{b} \times \mathbf{c}$.

15 Find k if the following are unit vectors: **a** $\begin{pmatrix} \frac{4}{7} \\ \frac{1}{k} \end{pmatrix}$ **b** $\begin{pmatrix} k \\ k \end{pmatrix}$

REVIEW SET 14C (Mainly 2-D)

1 If $\mathbf{p} = \begin{pmatrix} 3 \\ -2 \end{pmatrix}$, $\mathbf{q} = \begin{pmatrix} -1 \\ 5 \end{pmatrix}$ and $\mathbf{r} = \begin{pmatrix} -3 \\ 4 \end{pmatrix}$ find: **a** $\mathbf{p} \bullet \mathbf{q}$ **b** $\mathbf{q} \bullet (\mathbf{p} - \mathbf{r})$

2 Using $\mathbf{p} = \begin{pmatrix} 3 \\ -2 \end{pmatrix}$, $\mathbf{q} = \begin{pmatrix} -2 \\ 5 \end{pmatrix}$ and $\mathbf{r} = \begin{pmatrix} 1 \\ -3 \end{pmatrix}$ verify that:

  $\mathbf{p} \bullet (\mathbf{q} - \mathbf{r}) = \mathbf{p} \bullet \mathbf{q} - \mathbf{p} \bullet \mathbf{r}$.

3 Determine the value of t if $\begin{pmatrix} 3 \\ 3 - 2t \end{pmatrix}$ and $\begin{pmatrix} t^2 + t \\ -2 \end{pmatrix}$ are perpendicular.

4 Given A(2, 3), B(−1, 4) and C(3, k), find k if $\widehat{BAC}$ is a right angle.

5 Find all vectors which are perpendicular to the vector $\begin{pmatrix} -4 \\ 5 \end{pmatrix}$.

6 Find the measure of all angles of triangle KLM for K(−2, 1), L(3, 2) and M(1, −3).

7 Find the angle between the two lines with equations $4x - 5y = 11$ and $2x + 3y = 7$.

8 In this question you may **not** assume any diagonal properties of parallelograms.

  OABC is a parallelogram with $\overrightarrow{OA} = \mathbf{p}$ and $\overrightarrow{OC} = \mathbf{q}$. M is the midpoint of AC.

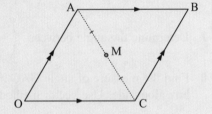

  a Find in terms of $\mathbf{p}$ and $\mathbf{q}$:

    i $\overrightarrow{OB}$ **ii** $\overrightarrow{OM}$

  b Show using **a** only that O, M and B are collinear and M is the midpoint of OB.

9 AP and BQ are altitudes of triangle ABC.

  Let $\overrightarrow{OA} = \mathbf{p}$, $\overrightarrow{OB} = \mathbf{q}$ and $\overrightarrow{OC} = \mathbf{r}$.

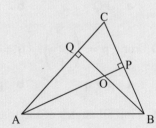

  a Find vector expressions for $\overrightarrow{AC}$ and $\overrightarrow{BC}$ in terms of $\mathbf{p}$, $\mathbf{q}$ and $\mathbf{r}$.

  b Deduce that $\mathbf{q} \bullet \mathbf{r} = \mathbf{p} \bullet \mathbf{q} = \mathbf{p} \bullet \mathbf{r}$.

  c Hence prove that OC is perpendicular to AB.

10 If $\mathbf{a} = \begin{pmatrix} 2 \\ -3 \\ 1 \end{pmatrix}$ and $\mathbf{b} = \begin{pmatrix} -1 \\ 2 \\ 3 \end{pmatrix}$, find: **a** $2\mathbf{a} - 3\mathbf{b}$

   b $\mathbf{x}$ if $\mathbf{a} - 3\mathbf{x} = \mathbf{b}$.

11 If $\overrightarrow{OA} = \mathbf{a}$, $\overrightarrow{OB} = \mathbf{b}$, $|\mathbf{a}| = 3$, $|\mathbf{b}| = \sqrt{7}$ and $\mathbf{a} \times \mathbf{b} = \mathbf{i} + 2\mathbf{j} - 3\mathbf{k}$ find:

   a $\mathbf{a} \bullet \mathbf{b}$ **b** the area of triangle OAB

   c the volume of tetrahedron OABC if C is the point $(1, -1, 2)$.

REVIEW SET 14D (Mainly 3-D)

1 If $\mathbf{a} = 3\mathbf{i} - \mathbf{j} + 2\mathbf{k}$ and $\mathbf{b} = \mathbf{i} - 2\mathbf{k}$ find:

   a $3\mathbf{a} - 2\mathbf{b}$ **b** $|\mathbf{a}|$

2 If k is a scalar and $\mathbf{a}$ is any 3-dimensional vector, prove that $|k\mathbf{a}| = |k||\mathbf{a}|$.

3 $P(-1, 2, 3)$ and $Q(4, 0, -1)$ are two points in space. Find:

   a $\overrightarrow{PQ}$ **b** the angle that $\overrightarrow{PQ}$ makes with the X-axis

   c the coordinates of R if R divides QP in the ratio $2 : 1$.

4 The triangle with vertices $P(-1, 2, 1)$, $Q(0, 1, 4)$ and $R(a, -1, -2)$ has an area of $\sqrt{118}$ units^2. Find a.

5 M is $(-1, 3, 4)$ and N is $(2, 0, 1)$. Find:

   a the coordinates of *two* points on MN such that their distance from N is $\sqrt{3}$ units

   b a vector in the direction of $\overrightarrow{MN}$ with length 2 units.

6 Show that $A(1, -3, 2)$, $B(2, 0, 1)$ and $C(-1, -9, 4)$ are collinear and hence find the ratio in which C divides BA.

7 Find the coordinates of the point which divides the line segment joining $A(-2, 3, 5)$ to $B(3, -1, 1)$ externally in the ratio $2 : 5$.

8 Find the volume of tetrahedron ABCD given $A(3, 1, 2)$, $B(-1, 2, 1)$, $C(-2, 0, 3)$ and $D(4, 3, -1)$.

9 S divides AB externally in the ratio $3 : 5$ and T divides CS internally in the ratio $1 : 2$. If A, B and C have position vectors $\mathbf{a}$, $\mathbf{b}$ and $\mathbf{c}$ respectively, find $\mathbf{t} = \overrightarrow{OT}$.

10 Find a unit vector parallel to $\mathbf{i} + r\mathbf{j} + 2\mathbf{k}$ and perpendicular to $2\mathbf{i} + 2\mathbf{j} - \mathbf{k}$.

11 Given $|\mathbf{u}| = 3$ and $|\mathbf{v}| = 5$ and $\mathbf{u} \times \mathbf{v} = \begin{pmatrix} 1 \\ -3 \\ -4 \end{pmatrix}$ find the possible values of $\mathbf{u} \bullet \mathbf{v}$.

12 If $\mathbf{v} = \mathbf{i} + 2\mathbf{j} - 3\mathbf{k}$, $\mathbf{u} = 2\mathbf{i} + 2\mathbf{j} + 3\mathbf{k}$, and $\mathbf{w} = \mathbf{i} + (2-t)\mathbf{j} + (t+1)\mathbf{k}$, find the value of t such that $\mathbf{u}$, $\mathbf{v}$ and $\mathbf{w}$ are coplanar.

13 Determine the measure of angle QDM given that M is the midpoint of [PS] of the rectangular prism.

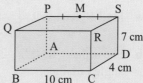

REVIEW SET 14E

1 Show that $A(-2, -1, 3)$, $B(4, 0, -1)$ and $C(-2, 1, -4)$ are vertices of an isosceles triangle.

2 Find scalars r, s and t if $2 \begin{pmatrix} s-1 \\ r+1 \\ t \end{pmatrix} = \begin{pmatrix} 4s \\ 3r \\ r \end{pmatrix} + \begin{pmatrix} r \\ -1 \\ s \end{pmatrix}$.

3 Find two points on the Z-axis which are 6 units from $P(-4, 2, 5)$.

4 If $\mathbf{a} = \begin{pmatrix} -1 \\ 3 \\ -2 \end{pmatrix}$ and $\mathbf{b} = \begin{pmatrix} 5 \\ -1 \\ 4 \end{pmatrix}$, find $\mathbf{x}$ if: **a** $\mathbf{a} - \mathbf{x} = 2\mathbf{b}$ **b** $\mathbf{b} - 2\mathbf{x} = -\mathbf{a}$

5 Find a and b if $J(-4, 1, 3)$, $K(2, -2, 0)$ and $L(a, b, 2)$ are collinear.

6 Given $\mathbf{p} = 2\mathbf{i} - \mathbf{j} + 4\mathbf{k}$ and $\mathbf{q} = -\mathbf{i} - 4\mathbf{j} + 2\mathbf{k}$, find:

    a $|\mathbf{p} \bullet \mathbf{q}|$ **b** the angle between $\mathbf{p}$ and $\mathbf{q}$.

7 **a** Find r and s if $\begin{pmatrix} r \\ 4 \\ 3 \end{pmatrix}$ and $\begin{pmatrix} -5 \\ 10 \\ s \end{pmatrix}$ are parallel.

    b Find a vector of length 4 units which is parallel to $3\mathbf{i} - 2\mathbf{j} + \mathbf{k}$.

8 **a** Find k given that $\begin{pmatrix} k \\ \frac{1}{\sqrt{2}} \\ -k \end{pmatrix}$ is a unit vector.

    b Find the vector which is 5 units long and has the opposite direction to $\begin{pmatrix} 3 \\ 2 \\ -1 \end{pmatrix}$.

9 If $\mathbf{u} = \begin{pmatrix} -4 \\ 2 \\ 1 \end{pmatrix}$ and $\mathbf{v} = \begin{pmatrix} -1 \\ 3 \\ -2 \end{pmatrix}$, find:

    a $\mathbf{u} \bullet \mathbf{v}$ **b** the angle between $\mathbf{u}$ and $\mathbf{v}$

10 For the given tetrahedron, find the measure of angle DMC.

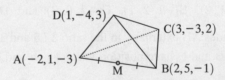

11 Consider the points $A(0, 1, 1)$, $B(-2, 2, 3)$, $C(1, -1, 2)$ and $D(-1, 3, k)$.

    a Find a vector of length 10 units which is perpendicular to the plane defined by points A, B and C.

    b Find the area of triangle ABC. **c** If point D lies on plane ABC, find k.

12 **a** Find t given that $\begin{pmatrix} 2-t \\ 3 \\ t \end{pmatrix}$ and $\begin{pmatrix} t \\ 4 \\ t+1 \end{pmatrix}$ are perpendicular.

    b Show that $K(4, 3, -1)$, $L(-3, 4, 2)$ and $M(2, 1, -2)$ are vertices of a right angled triangle.

Chapter 15

Complex numbers

Contents:

A   COMPLEX NUMBERS AS 2-D VECTORS

Recall from **Chapter 7** that a complex number can be written in Cartesian form as $z = a + bi$ where $a = \mathcal{R}e(z)$ and $b = \mathcal{I}m(z)$ are both real numbers.

Hence, there exists a one-to-one relationship between any complex number $a + bi$ and any point (a, b) in the Cartesian Plane.

When we view points in a plane as complex numbers, we refer to the plane as the **complex plane** or the **Argand plane**.

The x-axis is called the **real axis** and the y-axis is called the **imaginary axis**.

All **real** numbers with $b = 0$ lie on the real axis, and all **purely imaginary** numbers with $a = 0$ lie on the imaginary axis. The origin $(0, 0)$ lies on both axes and it corresponds to $z = 0$, a real number.

Complex numbers that are neither real nor pure imaginary (a and b both $\neq 0$) lie in one of the four quadrants.

Now recall from **Chapter 14** that any point P in the Cartesian plane corresponds uniquely to a vector. The position vector of the point P is $\overrightarrow{OP}$. We know that vectors have magnitude and direction, so we can in turn attribute a magnitude and direction to complex numbers.

We can apply the vector operations of addition, subtraction, and scalar multiplication to give the correct answers for these operations with complex numbers.

Note: For those studying the option "sets, relations and groups" this means there is an **isomorphic relationship** between complex numbers and 2-D vectors under the **binary** operation of $+$.

$$\begin{pmatrix} a \\ b \end{pmatrix} + \begin{pmatrix} c \\ d \end{pmatrix} = \begin{pmatrix} a + c \\ b + d \end{pmatrix} \qquad \text{for vectors}$$

and $(a + bi) + (c + di) = (a + c) + (b + d)i$ for complex numbers

so $\begin{pmatrix} a + c \\ b + d \end{pmatrix} \equiv (a + c) + (b + d)i$

> The **plane of complex numbers** (also called the **complex plane** or **Argand plane**), has a horizontal **real axis** and a vertical **imaginary axis**.

When we illustrate complex numbers on the Argand plane, we call it an **Argand diagram**.

For example:

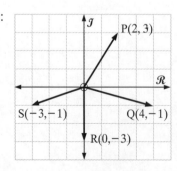

$\overrightarrow{OP} = \begin{pmatrix} 2 \\ 3 \end{pmatrix}$ represents $2 + 3i$

$\overrightarrow{OQ} = \begin{pmatrix} 4 \\ -1 \end{pmatrix}$ represents $4 - i$

$\overrightarrow{OR} = \begin{pmatrix} 0 \\ -3 \end{pmatrix}$ represents $-3i$

$\overrightarrow{OS} = \begin{pmatrix} -3 \\ -1 \end{pmatrix}$ represents $-3 - i$

$\mathcal{R}$ is the real axis, $\mathcal{I}$ is the imaginary axis.

In general,

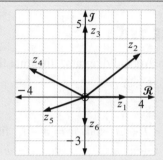

$\overrightarrow{OP} = \begin{pmatrix} x \\ y \end{pmatrix}$ represents $x + yi$

Example 1

Illustrate the positions of:

$z_1 = 3$, $z_2 = 4 + 3i$,

$z_3 = 5i$, $z_4 = -4 + 2i$,

$z_5 = -3 - i$ and $z_6 = -2i$

in the complex plane.

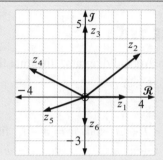

Example 2

If $z_1 = 3 + i$ and $z_2 = 1 - 4i$ find algebraically and vectorially:

a $z_1 + z_2$ **b** $z_1 - z_2$

a $z_1 + z_2$
$= 3 + i + 1 - 4i$
$= 4 - 3i$

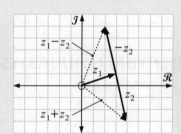

b $z_1 - z_2$
$= 3 + i - (1 - 4i)$
$= 3 + i - 1 + 4i$
$= 2 + 5i$

Reminder:

Draw z_1 first and at its arrow end draw z_2.

$z_1 + z_2$ goes from the start of z_1 to the end of z_2.

Example 3

If $z = 1 + 2i$ and $w = 3 - i$,   find both algebraically and vectorially:

a $2z + w$ **b** $z - 2w$

a $2z + w$
$= 2(1 + 2i) + 3 - i$
$= 2 + 4i + 3 - i$
$= 5 + 3i$

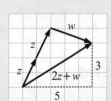

b $z - 2w$
$= 1 + 2i - 2(3 - i)$
$= 1 + 2i - 6 + 2i$
$= -5 + 4i$

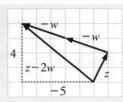

EXERCISE 15A.1

1 On an Argand diagram, illustrate the complex numbers:

    a $z_1 = 5$ **b** $z_2 = -1 + 2i$ **c** $z_3 = -6 - 2i$

    d $z_4 = -6i$ **e** $z_5 = 2 - i$ **f** $z_6 = 4i$

2 If $z = 1 + 2i$ and $w = 3 - i$, find both algebraically and vectorially:

    a $z + w$ **b** $z - w$ **c** $2z - w$ **d** $w - 3z$

3 If $z_1 = 4 - i$ and $z_2 = 2 + 3i$, find both algebraically and vectorially:

    a $z_1 + 1$ **b** $z_1 + 2i$ **c** $z_2 + \frac{1}{2}z_1$ **d** $\dfrac{z_1 + 4}{2}$

4 If z is any complex number, explain with illustration how to find geometrically:

    a $3z$ **b** $-2z$ **c** z^* **d** $3i - z$

    e $2 - z$ **f** $z^* + i$ **g** $\dfrac{z + 2}{3}$ **h** $\dfrac{z - 4}{2}$

REPRESENTING CONJUGATES

If $z = x + iy$, then $z^* = x - iy$.

This means that if $\overrightarrow{OP} = \begin{pmatrix} x \\ y \end{pmatrix}$ represents z, then $\overrightarrow{OQ} = \begin{pmatrix} x \\ -y \end{pmatrix}$ represents z^*.

For example:

    $\overrightarrow{OP_1}$ represents $2 + 4i$ and

    $\overrightarrow{OQ_1}$ represents $2 - 4i$

    $\overrightarrow{OP_3}$ represents $-3i$ and

    $\overrightarrow{OQ_3}$ represents $3i$ etc.

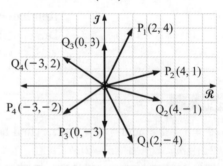

It is clear that:

If z is $\overrightarrow{OP}$, its conjugate z^* is $\overrightarrow{OQ}$ where $\overrightarrow{OQ}$ is a reflection of $\overrightarrow{OP}$ in the real axis.

EXERCISE 15A.2

1 Show on an Argand diagram:

    a $z = 3 + 2i$ and its conjugate $z^* = 3 - 2i$

    b $z = -2 + 5i$ and its conjugate $z^* = -2 - 5i$

2 If $z = 2 - i$ we can add $z + z^*$ as shown in the diagram.

We notice that $z + z^*$ is 4 which is real.

Explain, by illustration, that $z + z^*$ is always real.

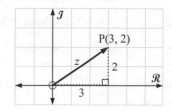

3 Explain, by illustration, that $z - z^*$ is always purely imaginary or zero. What distinguishes these two cases?

4 If z is real, what is z^*?

5 Given that $(a + i)(3 + bi) = 40 - 74i$ find the values of a and b where a and $b \in \mathbb{Z}$.

B   MODULUS, ARGUMENT, POLAR FORM

MODULUS

The **modulus** of the complex number $z = a + bi$ is the length of the corresponding vector $\begin{pmatrix} a \\ b \end{pmatrix}$.

We denote the modulus of z by $|z|$.

> The **modulus** of the complex number $z = a + bi$ is the real number $|z| = \sqrt{a^2 + b^2}$.

Notice that if $z = a + bi$ then $|z|$ gives the distance of the point (a, b) from the origin. This is consistent with the definition in **Chapter 1** of $|x|$ for $x \in \mathbb{R}$. We stated there that $|x|$ is the distance of real number x from the origin O.

Consider the complex number $z = 3 + 2i$.

The distance from O to P is its modulus, $|z|$.

So, $|z| = \sqrt{3^2 + 2^2}$ {Pythagoras}

Example 4

Find $|z|$ for z equal to:

a $3 + 2i$ **b** $3 - 2i$ **c** $-3 - 2i$

a $|z|$
$= \sqrt{3^2 + 2^2}$
$= \sqrt{13}$

b $|z|$
$= \sqrt{3^2 + (-2)^2}$
$= \sqrt{9 + 4}$
$= \sqrt{13}$

c $|z|$
$= \sqrt{(-3)^2 + (-2)^2}$
$= \sqrt{9 + 4}$
$= \sqrt{13}$

Example 5

Prove that $|z_1 z_2| = |z_1| |z_2|$ for all complex numbers z_1 and z_2.

Let $z_1 = a + bi$ and $z_2 = c + di$ where a, b, c and d are real

$\therefore \quad z_1 z_2 = (a + bi)(c + di) = [ac - bd] + i[ad + bc]$

Thus $|z_1 z_2| = \sqrt{(ac - bd)^2 + (ad + bc)^2}$

$\qquad = \sqrt{a^2 c^2 - 2abcd + b^2 d^2 + a^2 d^2 + 2abcd + b^2 c^2}$

$\qquad = \sqrt{a^2(c^2 + d^2) + b^2(c^2 + d^2)}$

$\qquad = \sqrt{(c^2 + d^2)(a^2 + b^2)}$

$\qquad = \sqrt{a^2 + b^2} \times \sqrt{c^2 + d^2}$

$\qquad = |z_1| |z_2|$

EXERCISE 15B.1

1 Find $|z|$ for z equal to:

   a $3 - 4i$ b $5 + 12i$ c $-8 + 2i$ d $3i$ e -4

2 If $z = 2 + i$ and $w = -1 + 3i$ find:

   a $|z|$ b $|z^*|$ c $|z^*|^2$ d zz^*

   e $|zw|$ f $|z||w|$ g $\left|\dfrac{z}{w}\right|$ h $\dfrac{|z|}{|w|}$

   i $|z^2|$ j $|z|^2$ k $|z^3|$ l $|z|^3$

3 From **2**, suggest *five* possible rules for modulus.

4 If $z = a + bi$ is a complex number, show that: a $|z^*| = |z|$ b $|z|^2 = zz^*$

5 If $z = \cos\theta + i\sin\theta$, find $|z|$.

6 Simplify $\left|\dfrac{z}{w}\right| \times |w|$ using the result of **Example 5** and use it to show that

$\left|\dfrac{z}{w}\right| = \dfrac{|z|}{|w|}$ provided $w \neq 0$.

7   a   Use the result $|z_1 z_2| = |z_1||z_2|$ to show that:

      i $|z_1 z_2 z_3| = |z_1||z_2||z_3|$ and that $|z^3| = |z|^3$

      ii $|z_1 z_2 z_3 z_4| = |z_1||z_2||z_3||z_4|$ and that $|z^4| = |z|^4$.

   b   What is the generalisation of the results in **a**?

   c   Use the Principle of mathematical induction to prove your conjecture in **b**.

   d   Hence prove that $|z^n| = |z|^n$ for all $n \in \mathbb{Z}^+$.

   e   Use the result of **d** to find $|z^{20}|$ for $z = 1 - i\sqrt{3}$.

8 Given $|z| = 3$, use the rules $|zw| = |z||w|$ and $\left|\dfrac{z}{w}\right| = \dfrac{|z|}{|w|}$ to find:

   a $|2z|$ **b** $|-3z|$ **c** $|(1+2i)z|$

   d $|iz|$ **e** $\left|\dfrac{1}{z}\right|$ **f** $\left|\dfrac{2i}{z^2}\right|$

9 **a** If $w = \dfrac{z+1}{z-1}$ where $z = a + bi$, find w in the form $X + Yi$ when X and Y involve a and b.

   b If $w = \dfrac{z+1}{z-1}$ and $|z| = 1$, find $\mathcal{R}e(w)$.

SUMMARY OF MODULUS DISCOVERIES

- $|z^*| = |z|$
- $|z|^2 = zz^*$
- $|z_1 z_2| = |z_1||z_2|$ and $\left|\dfrac{z_1}{z_2}\right| = \dfrac{|z_1|}{|z_2|}$ provided $z_2 \neq 0$
- $|z_1 z_2 z_3 \,....\, z_n| = |z_1||z_2||z_3|\,.....\,|z_n|$ and $|z^n| = |z|^n$ for $n \in \mathbb{Z}^+$.

Example 6

Find $|z|$ given that $5|z-1| = |z-25|$ where z is a complex number.

$$5|z-1| = |z-25|$$
$$\therefore \quad 25|z-1|^2 = |z-25|^2$$
$$25(z-1)(z-1)^* = (z-25)(z-25)^* \quad \{\text{as } zz^* = |z|^2\}$$
$$\therefore \quad 25(z-1)(z^*-1) = (z-25)(z^*-25) \quad \{\text{as } (z \pm w)^* = z^* \pm w^*\}$$
$$\therefore \quad 25zz^* - 25z - 25z^* + 25 = zz^* - 25z - 25z^* + 625$$
$$\therefore \quad 24zz^* = 600$$
$$\therefore \quad zz^* = 25$$
$$\therefore \quad |z|^2 = 25$$
$$\therefore \quad |z| = 5 \quad \{\text{as } |z| > 0\}$$

10 Find $|z|$ for the complex number z if $|z+9| = 3|z+1|$.

11 Find $|z|$ for the complex number z if $\left|\dfrac{z+4}{z+1}\right| = 2$.

12 If $|z+w| = |z-w|$ deduce that $\dfrac{z}{z^*} = -\dfrac{w}{w^*}$

DISTANCE IN THE NUMBER PLANE

Suppose P_1 and P_2 are two points in the complex plane which correspond to the complex numbers z_1 and z_2.

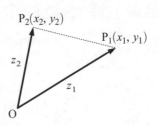

Now
$$\begin{aligned}
|z_1 - z_2| &= |(x_1 + y_1 i) - (x_2 + y_2 i)| \\
&= |(x_1 - x_2) + (y_1 - y_2)i| \\
&= \sqrt{(x_1 - x_2)^2 + (y_1 - y_2)^2}
\end{aligned}$$
which we recognise as the distance between P_1 and P_2.

Alternatively:

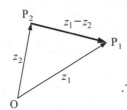

$$\begin{aligned}
\overrightarrow{P_2 P_1} &= \overrightarrow{P_2 O} + \overrightarrow{O P_1} \\
&= -z_2 + z_1 \\
&= z_1 - z_2
\end{aligned}$$

$$\therefore \quad |z_1 - z_2| = \left|\overrightarrow{P_2 P_1}\right| = \text{distance between } P_1 \text{ and } P_2.$$

Thus,

> $|z_1 - z_2|$ is the distance between points P_1 and P_2, where $z_1 \equiv \overrightarrow{O P_1}$ and $z_2 \equiv \overrightarrow{O P_2}$.

Note: The point corresponding to $z_1 - z_2$ can be found by drawing a vector equal to $\overrightarrow{P_2 P_1}$ emanating (starting) from the origin. Can you explain why?

CONNECTION TO COORDINATE GEOMETRY

There is a clear connection between complex numbers, vector geometry and coordinate geometry.

For example:

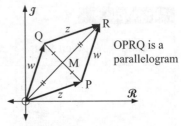

OPRQ is a parallelogram

Notice that $\overrightarrow{OR} \equiv w + z$ and $\overrightarrow{OM} \equiv \dfrac{w + z}{2}$

as the diagonals of the parallelogram bisect each other.

$\overrightarrow{OR}$ and $\overrightarrow{PQ}$ give the diagonals of the parallelogram formed by w and z.

Example 7

P(2, 3) and Q(6, 1) are two points on the Cartesian plane. Use complex numbers to find: **a** distance PQ   **b** the midpoint of PQ.

a   If $z = 2 + 3i$ and $w = 6 + i$

then $z - w = 2 + 3i - 6 - i$
$$= -4 + 2i$$

$\therefore \quad |z - w| = \sqrt{(-4)^2 + 2^2} = \sqrt{20}$

$\therefore \quad$ PQ $= \sqrt{20}$ units

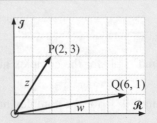

b $\dfrac{z + w}{2} = \dfrac{2 + 3i + 6 + i}{2} = 4 + 2i$ $\therefore$ the midpoint of PQ is (4, 2).

Example 8

What transformation moves z to iz?

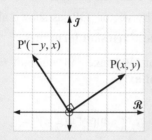

If $z = x + iy$

then $iz = i(x + iy)$
$$= xi + i^2y$$
$$= -y + xi$$

We notice that $|z| = \sqrt{x^2 + y^2}$

and $|iz| = \sqrt{(-y)^2 + x^2}$
$$= \sqrt{x^2 + y^2}$$

$\therefore$ OP$'$ = OP

So, $(x, y) \rightarrow (-y, x)$ under an anti-clockwise rotation of $\frac{\pi}{2}$ about O.

The transformation found in **Example 8** can be found more easily later. (See **Example 12**.)

EXERCISE 15B.2

1 Use complex numbers to find: **i** distance AB **ii** the midpoint of AB for

    a A(3, 6) and B(−1, 2)   **b** A(−4, 7) and B(1, −3)

2 OPQR is a parallelogram as shown. $\overrightarrow{OP}$ represents z and $\overrightarrow{OR}$ represents w where z and w are complex numbers.

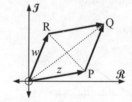

    a In terms of z and w, what are:

        i $\overrightarrow{OQ}$ **ii** $\overrightarrow{PR}$?

    b Explain from triangle OPQ, why $|z + w| \leqslant |z| + |w|$.
        It is important to discuss when the equality case occurs.

    c Explain from triangle OPR, why $|z - w| \geqslant |w| - |z|$.
        Once again discuss when the equality case occurs.

3 What transformation moves:

    a z to z^* **b** z to $-z$ **c** z to $-z^*$ **d** z to $-iz$?

4 Find the complex number z that satisfies the equation $\dfrac{50}{z^*} - \dfrac{10}{z} = 2 + 9i$ given $|z| = 2\sqrt{10}$.

ARGUMENT

The direction of the vector $\begin{pmatrix} a \\ b \end{pmatrix}$ can be described by its angle from the positive real axis.

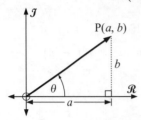

Suppose the complex number $z = a + bi$ is represented by vector $\overrightarrow{OP}$ as shown alongside. $a + bi$ is the **Cartesian form** of z.

Suppose that $\overrightarrow{OP}$ makes an angle of θ with the **positive real axis**.

The angle θ is called the **argument** of z, or simply $\arg z$.

$\arg z = \theta$ has infinitely many possibilities   i.e., $z \mapsto \arg z = \theta$ is one-to-many and is not a function. Can you explain why?

To avoid the infinite number of possibilities for θ, we may choose to use $\theta \in \,]-\pi,\, \pi]$ which covers one full revolution and guarantees that $z \mapsto \arg z = \theta$ is a function.

Note:
- Real numbers have argument of 0 *or* π.
- Pure imaginary numbers have argument of $\frac{\pi}{2}$ *or* $-\frac{\pi}{2}$.

POLAR FORM

The **polar form** representation of a complex number is an alternative to Cartesian form, and has many useful applications.

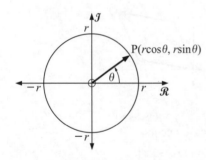

Any point P which lies on a circle with centre $O(0,\, 0)$ and radius r, has Cartesian coordinates $(r \cos \theta,\, r \sin \theta)$.

So, $z = r \cos \theta + ir \sin \theta = r(\cos \theta + i \sin \theta)$

But $r = |z|$ and if we define

$$\text{cis } \theta = \cos \theta + i \sin \theta$$

then $z = |z| \text{ cis } \theta$.

Consequently:

Any complex number z has **Cartesian form** $z = x + yi$ or **polar form** $z = |z| \text{ cis } \theta$ where $|z|$ is the **modulus** of z, θ is the **argument** of z, and $\text{cis } \theta = \cos \theta + i \sin \theta$.

We will soon see that polar form is extremely powerful for dealing with multiplication and division of complex numbers, as well as quickly finding powers and roots of numbers (see **De Moivre's theorem**).

A useful identity is:

If $z = |z| \text{ cis } \theta$, then $z^* = |z| \text{ cis } (-\theta)$.

EULER FORM

z can also be written in **Euler form** as $\quad z = re^{i\theta}\quad$ where $\quad r = |z|\quad$ and $\quad \theta = \arg z.$

In other words, $\qquad$ **cis $\theta = e^{i\theta}$.** $\qquad$ We will derive this identity in **Chapter 27**.

For example, consider the complex number $\quad z = 1 + i.$

$\quad |z| = \sqrt{2}\quad$ and $\quad \theta = \frac{\pi}{4},$

$\quad \therefore\quad 1 + i = \sqrt{2}\,\text{cis}\left(\frac{\pi}{4}\right) = \sqrt{2}e^{i\frac{\pi}{4}}$

So, $\quad \sqrt{2}\,\text{cis}\left(\frac{\pi}{4}\right)\quad$ is the polar form of $\ 1 + i$

$\qquad$ and $\ \sqrt{2}e^{i\frac{\pi}{4}}\ $ is the Euler form of $\ 1 + i.$

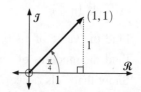

Example 9

Write in polar form: $\qquad$ **a** $\ 2i\qquad$ **b** $\ -3\qquad$ **c** $\ 1 - i$

a

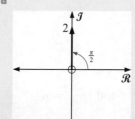

b

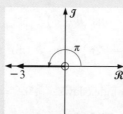

c

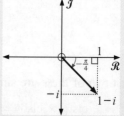

$|2i| = 2$

$\theta = \frac{\pi}{2}$

$\therefore\quad 2i = 2\,\text{cis}\,\frac{\pi}{2}$

$|-3| = 3$

$\theta = \pi$

$\therefore\quad -3 = 3\,\text{cis}\,\pi$

$|1 - i| = \sqrt{1 + 1} = \sqrt{2}$

$\theta = -\frac{\pi}{4}$

$\therefore\quad 1 - i = \sqrt{2}\,\text{cis}\left(-\frac{\pi}{4}\right)$

Example 10

Convert $\ \sqrt{3}\,\text{cis}\left(\frac{5\pi}{6}\right)$
to Cartesian form.

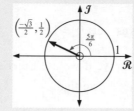

$\sqrt{3}\,\text{cis}\left(\frac{5\pi}{6}\right)$

$= \sqrt{3}\left[\cos\left(\frac{5\pi}{6}\right) + i\sin\left(\frac{5\pi}{6}\right)\right]$

$= \sqrt{3}\left[-\frac{\sqrt{3}}{2} + i \times \frac{1}{2}\right]$

$= -\frac{3}{2} + \frac{\sqrt{3}}{2}i$

EXERCISE 15B.3

1 Find the modulus and argument of the following complex numbers and hence write them in polar form:

$\quad$ **a** $\ 4\qquad\qquad$ **b** $\ 2i\qquad\qquad$ **c** $\ -6\qquad\qquad$ **d** $\ -3i$

$\quad$ **e** $\ 1 + i\qquad$ **f** $\ 2 - 2i\qquad$ **g** $\ -\sqrt{3} + i\qquad$ **h** $\ 2\sqrt{3} + 2i$

2   What complex number cannot be written in polar form? Why?

3   Convert $k + ki$ to polar form.   (Careful! You must consider $k > 0$, $k = 0$, $k < 0$.)

4   Convert to Cartesian form without using a calculator:

    a $2 \operatorname{cis} \left(\frac{\pi}{2}\right)$
    b $8 \operatorname{cis} \left(\frac{\pi}{4}\right)$
    c $4 \operatorname{cis} \left(\frac{\pi}{6}\right)$

    d $\sqrt{2} \operatorname{cis} \left(-\frac{\pi}{4}\right)$
    e $\sqrt{3} \operatorname{cis} \left(\frac{2\pi}{3}\right)$
    f $5 \operatorname{cis} \pi$

5   **a**   Find the value of $\operatorname{cis} 0$.

    b   Find the modulus of $\operatorname{cis} \theta$, i.e., $|\operatorname{cis} \theta|$.

    c   Show that $\operatorname{cis} \alpha \operatorname{cis} \beta = \operatorname{cis} (\alpha + \beta)$.

MULTIPLYING AND DIVIDING IN POLAR FORM

$\operatorname{cis} \theta$ has three useful properties. These are:

> - $\operatorname{cis} \theta \times \operatorname{cis} \phi = \operatorname{cis} (\theta + \phi)$
>
> - $\dfrac{\operatorname{cis} \theta}{\operatorname{cis} \phi} = \operatorname{cis} (\theta - \phi)$
>
> - $\operatorname{cis} (\theta + k2\pi) = \operatorname{cis} \theta$ for all $k \in \mathbb{Z}$.

The first two of these are similar to index laws: $a^\theta a^\phi = a^{\theta + \phi}$ and $\dfrac{a^\theta}{a^\phi} = a^{\theta - \phi}$.

Proof:
- $\operatorname{cis} \theta \times \operatorname{cis} \phi = (\cos \theta + i \sin \theta)(\cos \phi + i \sin \phi)$

$$= [\cos \theta \cos \phi - \sin \theta \sin \phi] + i[\sin \theta \cos \phi + \cos \theta \sin \phi]$$
$$= \cos(\theta + \phi) + i \sin(\theta + \phi)   \text{\{compound angle identities\}}$$
$$= \operatorname{cis} (\theta + \phi)$$

- $\dfrac{\operatorname{cis} \theta}{\operatorname{cis} \phi} = \dfrac{\operatorname{cis} \theta}{\operatorname{cis} \phi} \times \dfrac{\operatorname{cis} (-\phi)}{\operatorname{cis} (-\phi)}$

    $= \dfrac{\operatorname{cis} (\theta - \phi)}{\operatorname{cis} 0}$

    $= \operatorname{cis} (\theta - \phi)$ \{as $\operatorname{cis} 0 = 1$\}

- $\operatorname{cis} (\theta + k2\pi) = \operatorname{cis} \theta \times \operatorname{cis} (k2\pi)$

    $= \operatorname{cis} \theta \times 1$

    $= \operatorname{cis} \theta$

The above results are even easier to prove if we use Euler's form.

Using $\operatorname{cis} \theta = e^{i\theta}$ and $\operatorname{cis} \phi = e^{i\phi}$,   we find:

- $\operatorname{cis} \theta \operatorname{cis} \phi = e^{i\theta} e^{i\phi}$

    $= e^{i(\theta + \phi)}$

    $= \operatorname{cis} (\theta + \phi)$

- $\dfrac{\operatorname{cis} \theta}{\operatorname{cis} \phi} = \dfrac{e^{i\theta}}{e^{i\phi}}$

    $= e^{i\theta - i\phi}$

    $= e^{i(\theta - \phi)}$

    $= \operatorname{cis} (\theta - \phi)$

Example 11

Use the properties of cis to simplify: **a** $\text{cis}\left(\frac{\pi}{5}\right)\text{cis}\left(\frac{3\pi}{10}\right)$ **b** $\dfrac{\text{cis}\left(\frac{\pi}{5}\right)}{\text{cis}\left(\frac{7\pi}{10}\right)}$

a $\text{cis}\left(\frac{\pi}{5}\right)\text{cis}\left(\frac{3\pi}{10}\right)$

$= \text{cis}\left(\frac{\pi}{5} + \frac{3\pi}{10}\right)$

$= \text{cis}\left(\frac{5\pi}{10}\right)$

$= \text{cis}\,\frac{\pi}{2}$

$= \cos\frac{\pi}{2} + i\sin\frac{\pi}{2}$

$= 0 + i(1)$

$= i$

b $\dfrac{\text{cis}\left(\frac{\pi}{5}\right)}{\text{cis}\left(\frac{7\pi}{10}\right)}$

$= \text{cis}\left(\frac{\pi}{5} - \frac{7\pi}{10}\right)$

$= \text{cis}\left(-\frac{\pi}{2}\right)$

$= \cos\left(-\frac{\pi}{2}\right) + i\sin\left(-\frac{\pi}{2}\right)$

$= 0 + i(-1)$

$= -i$

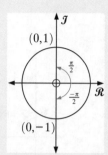

Example 12

What transformation moves z to iz?

(see **Example 8** earlier)

Let $z = r\,\text{cis}\,\theta$ and use $i = 1\,\text{cis}\,\frac{\pi}{2}$.

$\therefore\quad iz = r\,\text{cis}\,\theta \times \text{cis}\,\frac{\pi}{2}$

$= r\,\text{cis}\left(\theta + \frac{\pi}{2}\right)$

So, z has been rotated anti-clockwise by $\frac{\pi}{2}$ about O.

Example 13

Simplify $\text{cis}\left(\frac{107\pi}{6}\right)$.

$\frac{107\pi}{6} = 17\frac{5}{6}\pi = 18\pi - \frac{\pi}{6}$

$\therefore\quad \text{cis}\left(\frac{107\pi}{6}\right) = \text{cis}\left(18\pi - \frac{\pi}{6}\right)$

$= \text{cis}\left(-\frac{\pi}{6}\right)$ $\{\text{cis}\,(\theta + k2\pi) = \text{cis}\,\theta\}$

$= \frac{\sqrt{3}}{2} - \frac{1}{2}i$

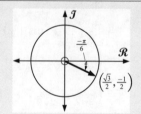

Example 14

a Write $z = 1 + \sqrt{3}i$ in polar form and then multiply it by $2\,\text{cis}\left(\frac{\pi}{6}\right)$.

b Illustrate what has happened on an Argand diagram.

c What transformations have taken place when multiplying by $2\,\text{cis}\left(\frac{\pi}{6}\right)$?

a

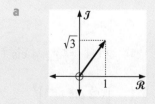

If $z = 1 + \sqrt{3}i$, then $|z| = \sqrt{1^2 + (\sqrt{3})^2}$

$= 2$

$\therefore\quad z = 2\left(\frac{1}{2} + \frac{\sqrt{3}}{2}i\right)$

$\therefore\quad z = 2\left(\cos\left(\frac{\pi}{3}\right) + i\sin\left(\frac{\pi}{3}\right)\right)$

$\therefore\quad z = 2\,\text{cis}\left(\frac{\pi}{3}\right)$

$$(1 + \sqrt{3}i) \times 2 \text{ cis } \tfrac{\pi}{6} = 2 \text{ cis } \left(\tfrac{\pi}{3}\right) \times 2 \text{ cis } \left(\tfrac{\pi}{6}\right)$$
$$= 4 \text{ cis } \left(\tfrac{\pi}{3} + \tfrac{\pi}{6}\right)$$
$$= 4 \text{ cis } \left(\tfrac{\pi}{2}\right)$$
$$= 4(0 + 1i)$$
$$= 4i$$

b

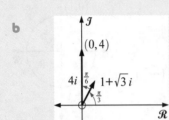

c When z was multiplied by $2 \text{ cis } \left(\tfrac{\pi}{6}\right)$ its modulus (length) was doubled and it was rotated through $\tfrac{\pi}{6}$.

If a complex number z is multiplied by $r \text{ cis } \theta$ then its modulus is *multiplied* by r and its argument is *increased* by θ.

Example 15

Use complex numbers to write $\cos\left(\tfrac{7\pi}{12}\right)$ and $\sin\left(\tfrac{7\pi}{12}\right)$ in simplest surd form.

$$\cos\left(\tfrac{7\pi}{12}\right) + i\sin\left(\tfrac{7\pi}{12}\right)$$
$$= \text{cis }\left(\tfrac{7\pi}{12}\right)$$
$$= \text{cis }\left(\tfrac{3\pi}{12} + \tfrac{4\pi}{12}\right)$$
$$= \text{cis }\left(\tfrac{\pi}{4}\right) \times \text{cis }\left(\tfrac{\pi}{3}\right) \quad \{\text{cis }(\theta + \phi) = \text{cis }\theta \times \text{cis }\phi\}$$
$$= \left(\tfrac{1}{\sqrt{2}} + \tfrac{1}{\sqrt{2}}i\right)\left(\tfrac{1}{2} + \tfrac{\sqrt{3}}{2}i\right)$$
$$= \left(\tfrac{1}{2\sqrt{2}} - \tfrac{\sqrt{3}}{2\sqrt{2}}\right) + i\left(\tfrac{\sqrt{3}}{2\sqrt{2}} + \tfrac{1}{2\sqrt{2}}\right)$$

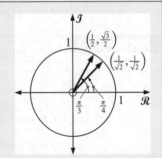

Equating real parts: $\cos \tfrac{7\pi}{12} = \left(\tfrac{1 - \sqrt{3}}{2\sqrt{2}}\right) \times \tfrac{\sqrt{2}}{\sqrt{2}} = \tfrac{\sqrt{2} - \sqrt{6}}{4}$

Equating imaginary parts: $\sin \tfrac{7\pi}{12} = \tfrac{\sqrt{3} + 1}{2\sqrt{2}} = \tfrac{\sqrt{6} + \sqrt{2}}{4}$

EXERCISE 15B.4

1 Use the properties of cis to simplify:

a $\text{cis }\theta \text{ cis } 2\theta$

b $\dfrac{\text{cis } 3\theta}{\text{cis }\theta}$

c $[\text{cis }\theta]^3$

d $\text{cis }\left(\tfrac{\pi}{18}\right) \text{ cis }\left(\tfrac{\pi}{9}\right)$

e $2 \text{ cis }\left(\tfrac{\pi}{12}\right) \text{ cis }\left(\tfrac{\pi}{6}\right)$

f $2 \text{ cis }\left(\tfrac{2\pi}{5}\right) \times 4 \text{ cis }\left(\tfrac{8\pi}{5}\right)$

g $\dfrac{4 \text{ cis }\left(\tfrac{\pi}{12}\right)}{2 \text{ cis }\left(\tfrac{7\pi}{12}\right)}$

h $\dfrac{\sqrt{32} \text{ cis }\left(\tfrac{\pi}{8}\right)}{\sqrt{2} \text{ cis }\left(-\tfrac{7\pi}{8}\right)}$

i $\left[\sqrt{2} \text{ cis }\left(\tfrac{\pi}{8}\right)\right]^4$

2 Use the property   cis $(\theta + k2\pi) = $ cis θ to evaluate:

    a   cis 17π **b**   cis (-37π) **c**   cis $\left(\frac{91\pi}{3}\right)$

3 If $z = 2$ cis θ:

    a   What is $|z|$ and arg z?

    b   Write z^* in polar form.

    c   Write $-z$ in polar form.   **Note:** -2 cis θ is not in polar form as the coefficient
                                                   of cis θ is a length and so must be positive.

    d   Write $-z^*$ in polar form.

4   **a**   Write i in polar form.

    b $z = r$ cis θ is any complex number. Write iz in polar form.

    c   Explain why iz is the anti-clockwise rotation of z about O through $\frac{\pi}{2}$ radians.

    d   What transformation maps z onto $-iz$? Give reasoning in polar form.

5 Write in polar form: **a** $\cos\theta - i\sin\theta$ **b** $\sin\theta - i\cos\theta$

Use **a** above to complete this sentence:

If $z = r$ cis θ then $z^* = $ .....   in polar form.

6 Use complex number methods to find, in simplest surd form:

    a $\cos\left(\frac{\pi}{12}\right)$ and $\sin\left(\frac{\pi}{12}\right)$ **b** $\cos\left(\frac{11\pi}{12}\right)$ and $\sin\left(\frac{11\pi}{12}\right)$

PROPERTIES OF ARGUMENT

The basic properties of
argument are:

- $\arg(zw) = \arg z + \arg w$ • $\arg\left(\dfrac{z}{w}\right) = \arg z - \arg w$
- $\arg\left(z^n\right) = n\arg z$

Notice that they are *identical to the laws of logarithms*, with arg replaced by log or ln.
Properties of modulus and argument can be proved jointly using polar form.

Example 16

Use polar form to establish that $|zw| = |z||w|$ and $\arg(zw) = \arg z + \arg w$.

Let $z = |z|$ cis θ and $w = |w|$ cis ϕ.

    Now $zw = |z|$ cis $\theta \times |w|$ cis ϕ

                $= \underbrace{|z||w|}_{\text{non-negative}}$ cis $(\theta + \phi)$ {property of cis}

    $\therefore$ $|zw| = |z||w|$ {the non-negative number multiplied by cis (.....)}

and $\arg(zw) = \theta + \phi = \arg z + \arg w$.

Example 17

If $z = \sqrt{2} \text{ cis } \theta$, find the modulus and argument of: **a** $2z$ **b** iz **c** $(1-i)z$

a $2z = 2\sqrt{2} \text{ cis } \theta$ $\therefore$ $|2z| = 2\sqrt{2}$ and $\arg(2z) = \theta$

b $i = \text{cis } \frac{\pi}{2}$

$\therefore$ $iz = \text{cis } \frac{\pi}{2} \times \sqrt{2} \text{ cis } \theta$

$= \sqrt{2} \text{ cis } \left(\frac{\pi}{2} + \theta\right)$ So, $|iz| = \sqrt{2}$ and $\arg(iz) = \frac{\pi}{2} + \theta$

c

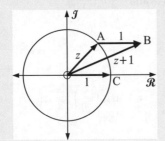

$1 - i = \sqrt{2} \text{ cis } \left(-\frac{\pi}{4}\right)$

$\therefore$ $(1-i)z = \sqrt{2} \text{ cis } \left(-\frac{\pi}{4}\right) \times \sqrt{2} \text{ cis } \theta$

$= 2 \text{ cis } \left(-\frac{\pi}{4} + \theta\right)$

$\therefore$ $|(1-i)z| = 2$ and $\arg((1-i)z) = \theta - \frac{\pi}{4}$

Example 18

Suppose $z = \text{cis } \phi$ where ϕ is acute. Find the modulus and argument of $z + 1$.

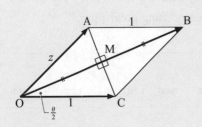

$|z| = 1$

$\therefore$ z lies on the unit circle

$z + 1$ is $\overrightarrow{OB}$ {found vectorially}

OABC is a rhombus

$\therefore$ $\arg(z+1) = \frac{\theta}{2}$

{diagonals bisect the angles of the rhombus}

Also $\cos\left(\frac{\theta}{2}\right) = \dfrac{\text{OM}}{1}$

$\therefore$ $\text{OM} = \cos\left(\frac{\theta}{2}\right)$

$\therefore$ $\text{OB} = 2\cos\left(\frac{\theta}{2}\right)$

$\therefore$ $|z+1| = 2\cos\left(\frac{\theta}{2}\right)$

EXERCISE 15B.5

1 Use polar form to establish:

$$\left|\frac{z}{w}\right| = \frac{|z|}{|w|} \quad \text{and} \quad \arg\left(\frac{z}{w}\right) = \arg z - \arg w, \quad \text{provided}\quad w \neq 0.$$

2 Suppose $z = 3 \text{ cis } \theta$. Determine the modulus and argument of:

   a $-z$ **b** z^* **c** iz **d** $(1+i)z$

3 **a** If $z = \text{cis } \phi$ where ϕ is acute, determine the modulus and argument of $z - 1$.

    b Using **a**, write $z - 1$ in polar form.

    c Hence write $(z - 1)^*$ in polar form.

4 ABC is an equilateral triangle. Suppose z_1 represents $\overrightarrow{OA}$, z_2 represents $\overrightarrow{OB}$ and z_3 represents $\overrightarrow{OC}$.

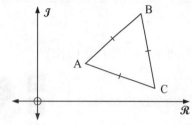

    a Explain what vectors represent $z_2 - z_1$ and $z_3 - z_2$.

    b Find $\left| \dfrac{z_2 - z_1}{z_3 - z_2} \right|$.

    c Determine $\arg\left(\dfrac{z_2 - z_1}{z_3 - z_2} \right)$.

    d Use **b** and **c** to find the value of $\left(\dfrac{z_2 - z_1}{z_3 - z_2} \right)^3$.

5 Given that $z = a - i$ where a is real, find the exact value of a if $\arg z = -\frac{5\pi}{6}$.

6 **a** Use $e^{i\theta} = \cos\theta + i\sin\theta$ to find the values of $e^{i\pi}$ and $e^{\frac{i\pi}{2}}$.

    b Prove that $\text{cis } \theta \text{ cis } \phi = \text{cis }(\theta + \phi)$ and $\dfrac{\text{cis } \theta}{\text{cis } \phi} = \text{cis }(\theta - \phi)$.

    c If $z = \text{cis } \theta$, find the argument of **i** $\sqrt{z}$ **ii** iz **iii** $-iz^2$ **iv** $\dfrac{i}{z}$

FURTHER CONVERSION BETWEEN CARTESIAN AND POLAR FORMS

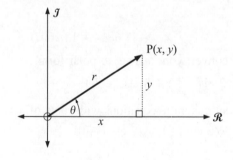

If $z = \underbrace{x + iy}_{\text{Cartesian form}} = \underbrace{r \text{ cis } \theta}_{\text{Polar form}}$ then:

$$r = \sqrt{x^2 + y^2}, \qquad \tan\theta = \frac{y}{x},$$

$$\cos\theta = \frac{x}{\sqrt{x^2 + y^2}}, \qquad \sin\theta = \frac{y}{\sqrt{x^2 + y^2}}$$

POLAR TO CARTESIAN

$z = 2 \text{ cis }\left(\frac{\pi}{8}\right)$

$= 2\left(\cos\frac{\pi}{8} + i\sin\frac{\pi}{8}\right)$

$\approx 1.85 + 0.765i$

```
2*(cos(π/8)+i*si
n(π/8))
   1.84776+.76537i
```

CARTESIAN TO POLAR

$z = -3 + i$ has $r = \sqrt{(-3)^2 + 1^2} = \sqrt{10}$ and $\cos\theta = \dfrac{-3}{\sqrt{10}}, \quad \sin\theta = \dfrac{1}{\sqrt{10}}$

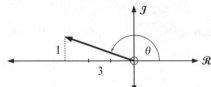

$$\therefore \quad \theta = \pi - \sin^{-1}\left(\tfrac{1}{\sqrt{10}}\right) \quad \{\text{quadrant 2}\}$$

$$(or \quad \cos^{-1}\left(\tfrac{-3}{\sqrt{10}}\right))$$

$\therefore \quad -3 + i \approx \sqrt{10} \text{ cis } (2.82)$

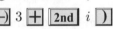

Alternatively (TI-83):

MATH CPX takes us to the complex number menu.

Pressing 5 brings up **abs(** for calculating the **modulus** (absolute value).

To find the modulus of $-3 + i$, press (−) 3 **+** **2nd** i **)** **ENTER**

MATH CPX then 4 brings up **angle(** for calculating the **argument**. To find the argument of $-3 + i$, press

(−) 3 **+** **2nd** i **)** **ENTER**

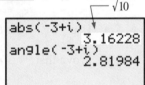

EXERCISE 15B.6

1 Use your calculator to convert to Cartesian form:

    a $\sqrt{3}$ cis (2.5187) **b** $\sqrt{11}$ cis $\left(-\tfrac{3\pi}{8}\right)$ **c** $2.836\,49$ cis $(-2.684\,32)$

2 Use your calculator to convert to polar form:

    a $3 - 4i$ **b** $-5 - 12i$ **c** $-11.6814 + 13.2697i$

3 Add the following using $a + bi$ surd form and convert your answer to polar form:

    a 3 cis $\left(\tfrac{\pi}{4}\right) +$ cis $\left(\tfrac{-3\pi}{4}\right)$ **b** 2 cis $\left(\tfrac{2\pi}{3}\right) + 5$ cis $\left(\tfrac{-2\pi}{3}\right)$

4 Use the sum and product of roots to find the real quadratic equations with roots of:

    a 2 cis $\left(\tfrac{2\pi}{3}\right)$, 2 cis $\left(\tfrac{4\pi}{3}\right)$ **b** $\sqrt{2}$ cis $\left(\tfrac{\pi}{4}\right)$, $\sqrt{2}$ cis $\left(\tfrac{-\pi}{4}\right)$

C   DE MOIVRE'S THEOREM

Polar form enables us to easily calculate powers of complex numbers.

Notice that if $z = |z|$ cis θ

then $z^2 = |z|$ cis $\theta \times |z|$ cis θ and $z^3 = z^2 z$

$\quad\quad\quad\quad = |z|^2$ cis $(\theta + \theta)$ $= |z|^2$ cis $2\theta \times |z|$ cis θ

$\quad\quad\quad\quad = |z|^2$ cis 2θ $= |z|^3$ cis $(2\theta + \theta)$

$\quad\quad\quad\quad\quad\quad\quad\quad\quad\quad\quad\quad\quad\quad\quad\quad\quad = |z|^3$ cis 3θ

The generalisation of this process is De Moivre's Theorem: $(|z| \operatorname{cis} \theta)^n = |z|^n \operatorname{cis} n\theta$

Proof for $n \in \mathbb{Z}^+$:   (using mathematical induction)

P_n is: $(|z| \operatorname{cis} \theta)^n = |z|^n \operatorname{cis} n\theta$

  (1) If $n = 1$,   then $(|z| \operatorname{cis} \theta)^1 = |z| \operatorname{cis} \theta$ $\therefore$ P_1 is true.

  (2) If P_k is true, then $(|z| \operatorname{cis} \theta)^k = |z|^k \operatorname{cis} k\theta$

$$\begin{aligned} \text{Thus}\quad (|z| \operatorname{cis} \theta)^{k+1} &= (|z| \operatorname{cis} \theta)^k \times |z| \operatorname{cis} \theta && \{\text{index law}\} \\ &= |z|^k \operatorname{cis} k\theta \times |z| \operatorname{cis} \theta && \{\text{using } P_k\} \\ &= |z|^{k+1} \operatorname{cis}(k\theta + \theta) && \{\text{index law and cis property}\} \\ &= |z|^{k+1} \operatorname{cis}(k+1)\theta \end{aligned}$$

Thus P_{k+1} is true whenever P_k is true and P_1 is true.

  $\therefore$ P_n is true   {Principle of mathematical induction}

We observe also that $\operatorname{cis}(-n\theta) = \operatorname{cis}(0 - n\theta) = \dfrac{\operatorname{cis} 0}{\operatorname{cis} n\theta}$ $\left\{\text{as } \dfrac{\operatorname{cis}\theta}{\operatorname{cis}\phi} = \operatorname{cis}(\theta - \phi)\right\}$

$$\begin{aligned} \therefore\quad \operatorname{cis}(-n\theta) &= \frac{1}{\operatorname{cis} n\theta} && \{\text{as } \operatorname{cis} 0 = 1\} \\ &= \frac{1}{[\operatorname{cis}\theta]^n} && \{\text{for } n \text{ a positive integer}\} \\ &= [\operatorname{cis}\theta]^{-n} && \text{so the theorem is true for all } n \in \mathbb{Z} \end{aligned}$$

Also $[\operatorname{cis}\left(\frac{\theta}{n}\right)]^n = \operatorname{cis}\left(n\left(\frac{\theta}{n}\right)\right) = \operatorname{cis}\theta$ and so $[\operatorname{cis}\theta]^{\frac{1}{n}} = \operatorname{cis}\left(\frac{\theta}{n}\right)$

So, De Moivre's theorem seems to hold for any integer n and for $\frac{1}{n}$.

DE MOIVRE'S THEOREM

$$(|z| \operatorname{\textbf{cis}} \theta)^n = |z|^n \operatorname{\textbf{cis}} n\theta \quad \text{for all rational } n.$$

Example 19

Find the exact value of $(\sqrt{3} + i)^8$ using De Moivre's theorem.
Check your answer by calculator.

$\sqrt{3} + i$ has modulus $\sqrt{(\sqrt{3})^2 + 1^2} = \sqrt{4} = 2$

$\therefore$ $\sqrt{3} + i = 2\left(\frac{\sqrt{3}}{2} + \frac{1}{2}i\right)$

$\qquad\qquad = 2 \operatorname{cis} \frac{\pi}{6}$

$$\therefore \quad (\sqrt{3}+i)^8 = \left(2 \text{ cis } \tfrac{\pi}{6}\right)^8$$
$$= 2^8 \text{ cis }\left(\tfrac{8\pi}{6}\right)$$
$$= 2^8 \text{ cis }\left(\tfrac{4\pi}{3}\right)$$
$$= 2^8 \left(-\tfrac{1}{2} - \tfrac{\sqrt{3}}{2}i\right)$$
$$= -128 - 128\sqrt{3}i$$

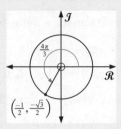

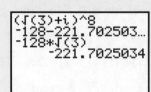

Example 20

By considering $\cos 2\theta + i \sin 2\theta$, deduce the double angle formulae for $\cos 2\theta$ and $\sin 2\theta$.

Now $\quad \cos 2\theta + i \sin 2\theta$
$$= \text{cis } 2\theta$$
$$= [\text{cis } \theta]^2 \qquad \{\text{De Moivre's theorem}\}$$
$$= [\cos \theta + i \sin \theta]^2$$
$$= [\cos^2 \theta - \sin^2 \theta] + i[2 \sin \theta \cos \theta]$$

Equating imaginary parts, $\quad \sin 2\theta = 2 \sin \theta \cos \theta$
Equating real parts, $\qquad \cos 2\theta = \cos^2 \theta - \sin^2 \theta$

EXERCISE 15C

1 Use De Moivre's theorem to simplify:

    a $\left(\sqrt{2} \text{ cis } \tfrac{\pi}{5}\right)^{10}$
    b $\left(\text{cis } \tfrac{\pi}{12}\right)^{36}$
    c $\left(\sqrt{2} \text{ cis } \tfrac{\pi}{8}\right)^{12}$

    d $\sqrt{5 \text{ cis } \tfrac{\pi}{7}}$
    e $\sqrt[3]{8 \text{ cis } \tfrac{\pi}{2}}$
    f $\left(8 \text{ cis } \tfrac{\pi}{5}\right)^{\frac{5}{3}}$

2 Use De Moivre's theorem to find the exact value of:

    a $(1+i)^{15}$
    b $(1-i\sqrt{3})^{11}$
    c $(\sqrt{2} - i\sqrt{2})^{-19}$

    d $(-1+i)^{-11}$
    e $(\sqrt{3}-i)^{\frac{1}{2}}$
    f $(2+2i\sqrt{3})^{-\frac{5}{2}}$

3 Use your calculator to check the answers to **2**.

4   **a** Suppose $z = |z| \text{ cis } \theta$ where $-\pi < \theta \leqslant \pi$.
      Use De Moivre's theorem to find $\sqrt{z}$ in terms of $|z|$ and θ.

    b What restrictions apply to $\phi = \arg(\sqrt{z})$?

    c True or false? "$\sqrt{z}$ has a non-negative real part."

5 Use De Moivre's theorem to explain why $|z^n| = |z|^n$ and $\arg(z^n) = n \arg z$.

6 Show that $\cos \theta - i \sin \theta = \text{cis }(-\theta)$. Hence, simplify $(\cos \theta - i \sin \theta)^{-3}$.

7 Write $z = 1 + i$ in polar form and hence write z^n in polar form. Find all values of n for which: **a** z^n is real   **b** z^n is purely imaginary.

8 If $|z| = 2$ and $\arg z = \theta$, determine the modulus and argument of:

    a z^3 **b** iz^2 **c** $\dfrac{1}{z}$ **d** $-\dfrac{i}{z^2}$

9 If $z = \operatorname{cis}\theta$, prove that $\dfrac{z^2 - 1}{z^2 + 1} = i\tan\theta$.

10 **a** Use complex number methods to deduce that:

         i $\cos 3\theta = 4\cos^3\theta - 3\cos\theta$ **ii** $\sin 3\theta = 3\sin\theta - 4\sin^3\theta$

    b Hence, find $\tan 3\theta$ in terms of $\tan\theta$ only.

    c Using **a** and **b** above, solve the equations:

         i $4x^3 - 3x = -\dfrac{1}{\sqrt{2}}$ **ii** $x^3 - 3\sqrt{3}x^2 - 3x + \sqrt{3} = 0$.

11 Points A, B and C form an isosceles triangle with a right angle at B. Let the points A, B and C be represented by the complex numbers z_1, z_2, and z_3 respectively.

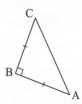

    a Show that $(z_1 - z_2)^2 = -(z_3 - z_2)^2$.

    b If ABCD forms a square, what complex number represents the point D? Give your answer in terms of z_1, z_2 and z_3.

12 Find a formula for   **a** $\cos 4\theta$ in terms of $\cos\theta$

                        b $\sin 4\theta$ in terms of $\cos\theta$ and $\sin\theta$

13 **a** If $z = \operatorname{cis}\theta$ prove that $z^n + \dfrac{1}{z^n} = 2\cos n\theta$.

    b Hence, explain why $z + \dfrac{1}{z} = 2\cos\theta$.

    c Use the binomial theorem to expand $\left(z + \dfrac{1}{z}\right)^3$, and simplify your result.

    d By using **a**, **b** and **c** above show that $\cos^3\theta = \frac{1}{4}\cos 3\theta + \frac{3}{4}\cos\theta$.

    e Hence show the exact value of $\cos^3\left(\frac{13\pi}{12}\right)$ is $\dfrac{-5\sqrt{2} - 3\sqrt{6}}{16}$.   **Hint:** $\frac{13\pi}{12} = \frac{3\pi}{4} + \frac{\pi}{3}$

14 Show that if $z = \operatorname{cis}\theta$ then $z^n - \dfrac{1}{z^n} = 2i\sin n\theta$ and hence

that $\sin^3\theta = \frac{3}{4}\sin\theta - \frac{1}{4}\sin 3\theta$.

15 Use the results of **13** and **14** to prove that $\sin^3\theta\cos^3\theta = \frac{1}{32}(3\sin 2\theta - \sin 6\theta)$.

D   ROOTS OF COMPLEX NUMBERS

SOLVING $z^n = c$

We will examine solutions of equations of the form $z^n = c$ where n is a positive integer and c is a complex number.

Definition: The **nth roots of complex number c** are the n solutions of $z^n = c$.

For example,   the 4th roots of $2i$ are the four solutions of $z^4 = 2i$.

The roots may be found by factorisation, but this is sometimes difficult. It is therefore desirable to have an alternative method such as the **nth roots method** presented in the following example.

Example 21

Find the four 4th roots of 1 by: a   factorisation   b   the 'nth roots method'.

We need to find the 4 solutions of $z^4 = 1$.

a   By factorisation, $z^4 = 1$
$\qquad \therefore \quad z^4 - 1 = 0$
$\qquad \therefore \quad (z^2 + 1)(z^2 - 1) = 0$
$\quad (z + i)(z - i)(z + 1)(z - 1) = 0$
$\qquad \therefore \quad z = \pm i$ or ± 1

b   By the 'nth roots method',
$\qquad z^4 = 1$
$\qquad \therefore \quad z^4 = 1 \operatorname{cis} (0 + k2\pi)$ {polar form}
$\qquad \therefore \quad z = [\operatorname{cis} (k2\pi)]^{\frac{1}{4}}$
$\qquad \therefore \quad z = \operatorname{cis} \left(\frac{k2\pi}{4}\right)$ {De Moivre}
$\qquad \therefore \quad z = \operatorname{cis} \left(\frac{k\pi}{2}\right)$
$\qquad \therefore \quad z = \operatorname{cis} 0, \ \operatorname{cis} \frac{\pi}{2}, \ \operatorname{cis} \pi, \ \operatorname{cis} \frac{3\pi}{2}$
$\qquad \qquad$ {letting $k = 0, 1, 2, 3$}
$\qquad \therefore \quad z = 1, \ i, \ -1, \ -i$

Note:
- The factorisation method is fine provided the polynomial factorises easily. This is not usually the case.
- The substitution of $k = 0, 1, 2, 3$ to find the 4 roots could be done using any 4 consecutive integers for k.   Why?

EXERCISE 15D.1

1 Find the three cube roots of 1 using: a   factorisation   b   the 'nth roots method'.

2 Solve for z: a $z^3 = -8i$ b $z^3 = -27i$

3 Find the three cube roots of -1, and display them on an Argand diagram.

4 Solve for z: a $z^4 = 16$ b $z^4 = -16$

5 Find the four fourth roots of $-i$, and display them on an Argand diagram.

6 Solve the following and display the roots on an Argand diagram:

   a $z^3 = 2 + 2i$ b $z^3 = -2 + 2i$ c $z^2 = \frac{1}{2} + \frac{\sqrt{3}}{2}i$

   d $z^4 = \sqrt{3} + i$ e $z^5 = -4 - 4i$ f $z^3 = -2\sqrt{3} - 2i$

Example 22

Find the fourth roots of -4 in the form $a + bi$ and then factorise $z^4 + 4$ into linear factors. Hence, write $z^4 + 4$ as a product of real quadratic factors.

The fourth roots of -4 are solutions of

$z^4 = -4$

$\therefore \quad z^4 = 4 \operatorname{cis}(\pi + k2\pi)$

$\therefore \quad z = [4 \operatorname{cis}(\pi + k2\pi)]^{\frac{1}{4}}$

$\therefore \quad z = 4^{\frac{1}{4}} \operatorname{cis}\left(\dfrac{\pi + k2\pi}{4}\right)$

$\therefore \quad z = 2^{\frac{1}{2}} \operatorname{cis} \frac{\pi}{4}, \quad 2^{\frac{1}{2}} \operatorname{cis} \frac{3\pi}{4}, \quad 2^{\frac{1}{2}} \operatorname{cis} \frac{5\pi}{4}, \quad 2^{\frac{1}{2}} \operatorname{cis} \frac{7\pi}{4}$ {letting $k = 0, 1, 2, 3$}

$\therefore \quad z = \sqrt{2}\left(\frac{1}{\sqrt{2}} + \frac{1}{\sqrt{2}}i\right), \sqrt{2}\left(-\frac{1}{\sqrt{2}} + \frac{1}{\sqrt{2}}i\right), \sqrt{2}\left(-\frac{1}{\sqrt{2}} - \frac{1}{\sqrt{2}}i\right), \sqrt{2}\left(\frac{1}{\sqrt{2}} - \frac{1}{\sqrt{2}}i\right)$

$\therefore \quad z = 1 + i, \quad -1 + i, \quad -1 - i, \quad 1 - i$

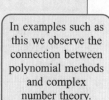

Roots $1 \pm i$ have sum $= 2$ and product $= (1 + i)(1 - i) = 2$ and $\therefore$ come from the quadratic factor $z^2 - 2z + 2$.

Roots $-1 \pm i$ have sum $= -2$ and product $= (-1 + i)(-1 - i) = 2$ and $\therefore$ come from the quadratic factor $z^2 + 2z + 2$.

Thus $z^4 + 4 = (z^2 - 2z + 2)(z^2 + 2z + 2)$

> In examples such as this we observe the connection between polynomial methods and complex number theory.

7 Find the four solutions of $z^4 + 1 = 0$ giving each in the form $a + bi$, and display them on an Argand diagram. Hence write $z^4 + 1$ as the product of two real quadratic factors.

8 Consider $z = \dfrac{\left(\frac{\sqrt{3}}{2} - \frac{1}{2}i\right)^2}{\left(\cos \frac{\pi}{10} - i\sin \frac{\pi}{10}\right)^5 \left(\cos \frac{\pi}{30} + i\sin \frac{\pi}{30}\right)^{25}}$

    a Using polar form and De Moivre's theorem, find the *modulus* and *argument* of z.

    b Hence show that z is a cube root of 1.

    c By simplifying and without using a calculator, show that $(1 - 2z)(2z^2 - 1)$ is a real number.

9   **a** Write $-16i$ in polar form.

    b The fourth root of $-16i$ which lies in the second quadrant is denoted by z. Express z exactly in:

      i polar form   **ii** Cartesian form.

SUMMARY OF SOLUTIONS OF $z^n = c$ (*n*th roots of *c*)

- There are **exactly** n nth roots of c.
- If $c \in \mathbb{R}$, the complex roots must occur in conjugate pairs.
- If $c \notin \mathbb{R}$, the complex roots do not all occur in conjugate pairs.
- The roots of z^n will all have the same modulus which is $|c|^{\frac{1}{n}}$.

  Thus on an Argand diagram, the roots will all be the same distance from the origin and hence lie on a circle radius $|c|^{\frac{1}{n}}$.

- The roots on the circle $r = |c|^{\frac{1}{n}}$ will be equally spaced around the circle.

  If you join all the points you will get a geometric shape that is a regular polygon.

  For example, $n = 3$ (equilateral $\triangle$), $n = 4$ (square)

  $\qquad\qquad n = 5$ (regular pentagon)

  $\qquad\qquad n = 6$ (regular hexagon) etc.

THE nth ROOTS OF UNITY

The **nth roots of unity** are the solutions of $z^n = 1$.

Example 23

Find the three cube roots of unity and display them on an Argand diagram. If w is the root with smallest positive argument, show that the roots are 1, w and w^2 and that $1 + w + w^2 = 0$.

The cube roots of unity are the solutions of $z^3 = 1$.

But $1 = \text{cis } 0 = \text{cis } (0 + k2\pi)$ for all $k \in \mathbb{Z}$

$\therefore \quad z^3 = \text{cis } (k2\pi)$

$\therefore \quad z = [\text{cis } (k2\pi)]^{\frac{1}{3}}$

$\therefore \quad z = \text{cis } \left(\frac{k2\pi}{3}\right) \qquad$ {De Moivre's theorem}

$\therefore \quad z = \text{cis } 0, \text{cis } \left(\frac{2\pi}{3}\right), \text{cis } \left(\frac{4\pi}{3}\right) \qquad$ {letting $k = 0, 1, 2$}

$\therefore \quad z = 1, \quad -\frac{1}{2} + \frac{\sqrt{3}}{2}i, \quad -\frac{1}{2} - \frac{\sqrt{3}}{2}i$

$w = \text{cis } \left(\frac{2\pi}{3}\right)$ and $w^2 = [\text{cis } \left(\frac{2\pi}{3}\right)]^2 = \text{cis } \left(\frac{4\pi}{3}\right)$

$\therefore$ the roots are 1, w and w^2 where $w = \text{cis } \left(\frac{2\pi}{3}\right)$

and $1 + w + w^2 = 1 + \left(-\frac{1}{2} + \frac{\sqrt{3}}{2}i\right) + \left(-\frac{1}{2} - \frac{\sqrt{3}}{2}i\right) = 0$

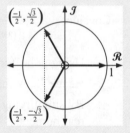

EXERCISE 15D.2

1 In **Example 23** we showed that the cube roots of 1 are 1, w, w^2 where $w = \text{cis } \left(\frac{2\pi}{3}\right)$.

   a Use this fact to solve the following equations, giving your answers in terms of w:

   i $(z + 3)^3 = 1$ **ii** $(z - 1)^3 = 8$ **iii** $(2z - 1)^3 = -1$

   b Show by vector addition that $1 + w + w^2 = 0$ if 1, w and w^2 are the cube roots of unity.

2 In **Example 21** we showed that the four fourth roots of unity were 1, i, -1, $-i$.

   a Is it true that the four fourth roots of unity can be written in the form 1, w, w^2, w^3 where $w = \text{cis } \frac{\pi}{2}$?

   b Show that $1 + w + w^2 + w^3 = 0$.

   c Show by vector addition that **b** is true.

3 **a** Find the 5 fifth roots of unity and display them on an Argand diagram.

   b If w is the root with smallest positive argument, show that the roots are 1, w, w^2, w^3 and w^4.

   c Simplify $(1+w+w^2+w^3+w^4)(1-w)$ and hence show that $1+w+w^2+w^3+w^4$ must be zero.

   d Show by vector addition that $1 + w + w^2 + w^3 + w^4 = 0$.

4 If $w = \operatorname{cis}\left(\frac{2\pi}{n}\right)$ is the nth root of unity with the smallest positive argument, show that:

   a the n roots of $z^n = 1$ are $1,\ w,\ w^2,\ w^3,\ \ldots..,\ w^{n-1}$

   b $1 + w + w^2 + w^3 + \ldots\ldots + w^{n-1} = 0$

   Note: The roots of unity lie on the unit circle, equally spaced around the unit circle.

5 Show that for any complex number α, the sum of the n zeros of $z^n = \alpha$ is 0.

E | FURTHER COMPLEX NUMBER PROBLEMS

The following questions combine complex number theory with topics covered in previous chapters.

EXERCISE 15E

1 Solve for z: $z^2 - (2+i)z + (3+i) = 0$

2 Find the Cartesian equation for the locus of $P(x, y)$ if $z = x + iy$ and

   a $z^* = -iz$ **b** $\arg(z - i) = \frac{\pi}{6}$ **c** $|z+3| + |z-3| = 8$

3 Use the binomial expansion of $(1 + i)^{2n}$ to prove that:

$$\binom{2n}{0} - \binom{2n}{2} + \binom{2n}{4} - \binom{2n}{6} + \ldots\ldots + (-1)^n \binom{2n}{2n} = 2^n \cos\left(\frac{n\pi}{2}\right), \quad n \in \mathbb{Z}^+.$$

4 By considering $1 + \operatorname{cis}\theta + \operatorname{cis}2\theta + \operatorname{cis}3\theta + \ldots\ldots + \operatorname{cis}n\theta$ as a geometric series, find $\displaystyle\sum_{r=0}^{n} \cos r\theta$.

5 Prove that $1 + \operatorname{cis}\theta = 2\cos\left(\frac{\theta}{2}\right)\operatorname{cis}\left(\frac{\theta}{2}\right)$ and hence determine the sum of the series $\displaystyle\sum_{r=0}^{n} \binom{n}{r}\cos(r\theta).$

REVIEW SET 15A

1 Find the real and imaginary parts of $(i - \sqrt{3})^5$.

2 If $z = x + yi$ and $P(x, y)$ moves in the complex plane, find the Cartesian equation for: **a** $|z - i| = |z + 1 + i|$ **b** $z^* - iz = 0$

3 Find $|z|$ if z is a complex number and $|z + 16| = 4|z + 1|$.

4 Points A and B are the representations in the complex plane of the numbers $z = 2 - 2i$ and $w = -1 - \sqrt{3}i$ respectively.

   a Given that the origin is O, find the angle AOB in terms of π.

   b Calculate the argument of zw in terms of π.

5 Write in polar form: **a** $-5i$ **b** $2 - 2i\sqrt{3}$ **c** $k - ki$ where $k < 0$

6 Given that $z = (1 + bi)^2$ where b is real and positive, find the exact value of b if $\arg z = \frac{\pi}{3}$.

7   **a** Prove that $\text{cis } \theta \times \text{cis } \phi = \text{cis } (\theta + \phi)$.

   b If $z = 2\sqrt{2}\,\text{cis } \alpha$, write $(1 - i)z$ in polar form. Hence find $\arg[(1 - i)z]$.

8 $z_1 \equiv \overrightarrow{OA}$ and $z_2 \equiv \overrightarrow{OB}$ represent two sides of a right angled isosceles triangle OAB.

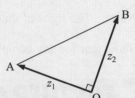

   a Determine the modulus and argument of $\dfrac{z_1^{\,2}}{z_2^{\,2}}$.

   b Hence, deduce that $z_1^{\,2} + z_2^{\,2} = 0$.

9 Let $z = \sqrt[4]{a}\left(\cos \frac{\pi}{6} + i \sin \frac{\pi}{6}\right)$ and $w = \sqrt[4]{b}\left(\cos \frac{\pi}{4} - i \sin \frac{\pi}{4}\right)$.

Find in terms of a and b the exact values of the real and imaginary parts of $\left(\dfrac{z}{w}\right)^4$.

10   **a** List the five fifth roots of 1 in terms of w where $w = \text{cis}\left(\frac{2\pi}{5}\right)$.

   b Display the roots in **a** on an Argand diagram.

   c By considering the factorisation of $z^5 - 1$ in *two different ways*, show that:
$$z^4 + z^3 + z^2 + z + 1 = (z - w)(z - w^2)(z - w^3)(z - w^4).$$

   d Hence, find the value of $(2 - w)(2 - w^2)(2 - w^3)(2 - w^4)$.

11 Find the cube roots of $-8i$, giving your answers in the form $a + bi$ where a and b do not involve trigonometric ratios.

REVIEW SET 15B

1 Let $z_1 = \cos \frac{\pi}{6} + i \sin \frac{\pi}{6}$ and $z_2 = \cos \frac{\pi}{4} + i \sin \frac{\pi}{4}$.

Express $\left(\dfrac{z_1}{z_2}\right)^3$ in the form $z = a + bi$.

2 If $z = 4 + i$ and $w = 2 - 3i$, find:

   a $2w^* - iz$ **b** $|w - z^*|$ **c** $|z^{10}|$ **d** $\arg(w - z)$

3 Find rationals a and b such that $\dfrac{2 - 3i}{2a + bi} = 3 + 2i$.

4 If $z = x + yi$ and P(x, y) moves in the complex plane, find the Cartesian equation for the curve:

   a $\arg(z - i) = \frac{\pi}{2}$ **b** $\left|\dfrac{z + 2}{z - 2}\right| = 2$

5 Write $2 - 2\sqrt{3}i$ in polar form. Hence find all values of n for which $(2 - 2\sqrt{3}i)^n$ is real.

6 Determine the cube roots of -27.

7 If $z = 4 \operatorname{cis} \theta$, find the modulus and argument of:

    a z^3 **b** $\dfrac{1}{z}$ **c** iz^*

8 Prove the following:

    a $\arg(z^n) = n \arg z$ for all complex numbers z and rational n.

    b $\left(\dfrac{z}{w}\right)^* = \dfrac{z^*}{w^*}$ for all z and for all $w \neq 0$.

9 Find n such that each of the following can be written in the form $[\operatorname{cis} \theta]^n$:

    a $\cos 3\theta + i \sin 3\theta$ **b** $\dfrac{1}{\cos 2\theta + i \sin 2\theta}$ **c** $\cos \theta - i \sin \theta$

10 Determine the fifth roots of $2 + 2i$.

11 If $z + \dfrac{1}{z}$ is real, prove that either $|z| = 1$ or z is real.

12 If $z = \operatorname{cis} \theta$, prove that:

    a $|z| = 1$ **b** $z^* = \dfrac{1}{z}$ **c** $\sin^4 \theta = \tfrac{1}{8}(\cos 4\theta - 4 \cos 2\theta + 3)$

13 If w is the root of $z^5 = 1$ with smallest positive argument, find real quadratic equations with roots of:

    a w and w^4 **b** $w + w^4$ and $w^2 + w^3$

14 If $|z + w| = |z - w|$ prove that $\arg z$ and $\arg w$ differ by $\frac{\pi}{2}$.

15 The complex number z is a root of the equation $|z| = |z + 4|$.

    a Show that the real part of z is -2.

    b Let v and w be two possible values of z such that $|z| = 4$.

        i On an Argand diagram, sketch the points that represent v and w, given that v is in the 2nd quadrant.

        ii Show that $\arg v = \frac{2\pi}{3}$.

        iii Find $\arg w$ where $-\pi < \arg w \leqslant \pi$.

    c **i** Find $\arg\left(\dfrac{v^m w}{i}\right)$ in terms of m and π.

        ii Hence find a value of m for which $\dfrac{v^m w}{i}$ is a real number.

REVIEW SET 15C

1 What single transformation maps z onto: **a** z^* **b** $-z$ **c** iz?

2 z and w are non-real complex numbers with the property that both $z + w$ and zw are real. Prove that $z^* = w$.

3 If $(x + iy)^n = X + Yi$ where n is a positive integer, show that
$X^2 + Y^2 = (x^2 + y^2)^n$.

4 Prove that $|z - w|^2 + |z + w|^2 = 2 \left(|z|^2 + |w|^2 \right)$.

5 $z^5 = 1$ has roots 1, α, α^2, α^3 and α^4 where $\alpha = \operatorname{cis} \left(\frac{2\pi}{5} \right)$.

   a Prove that $1 + \alpha + \alpha^2 + \alpha^3 + \alpha^4 = 0$.

   b Solve the equation $\left(\dfrac{z+2}{z-1} \right)^5 = 1$ in terms of α.

6 If $z \neq 0$ and $\left| \dfrac{z+1}{z-1} \right| = 1$, prove that z is purely imaginary.

7 If $z = \operatorname{cis} \phi$ and $w = \dfrac{1+z}{1+z^*}$, show that $w = \operatorname{cis} \phi$ also.

8 Write $-1 + i\sqrt{3}$ in polar form and hence find the values of m for which $(-1 + i\sqrt{3})^m$ is real.

9 Prove that $\operatorname{cis} \theta + \operatorname{cis} \phi = 2 \cos \left(\frac{\theta - \phi}{2} \right) \operatorname{cis} \left(\frac{\theta + \phi}{2} \right)$ and hence show that

   $\left(\dfrac{z+1}{z-1} \right)^5 = 1$ has solutions of the form $z = i \cot \left(\frac{n\pi}{5} \right)$ for $n = 1, 2, 3$ and 4.

10 Find the cube roots of $-64i$, giving your answers in the form $a + bi$ where a and b are real.

11 If $z = \operatorname{cis} \theta$, find the modulus and argument of: **a** $(2z)^{-1}$ **b** $1 - z$

12 Illustrate the region defined by $\{z: \ 2 \leqslant |z| \leqslant 5 \ \text{and} \ -\frac{\pi}{4} < \arg z \leqslant \frac{\pi}{2} \}$.
Show clearly all included boundary points.

13 Use polar form to deduce that $\left| \dfrac{1}{z} \right| = \dfrac{1}{|z|}$ for $z \neq 0$ and $\arg \left(\dfrac{1}{z} \right) = -\arg z$.

14 If $z = \operatorname{cis} \alpha$, write $1 + z$ in polar form and hence determine the modulus and argument of $1 + z$.
Hint: $\sin \theta = 2 \sin \left(\frac{\theta}{2} \right) \cos \left(\frac{\theta}{2} \right)$

15 $\Delta P_1 P_2 P_3$ is an equilateral triangle, as illustrated.
O is an origin such that $\overrightarrow{OP_1} \equiv z_1$, $\overrightarrow{OP_2} \equiv z_2$
and $\overrightarrow{OP_3} \equiv z_3$.
Suppose $\arg(z_2 - z_1) = \alpha$.

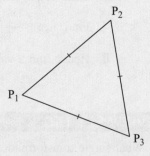

   a Show that $\arg(z_3 - z_2) = \alpha - \frac{2\pi}{3}$.

   b Find the modulus and argument of $\dfrac{z_2 - z_1}{z_3 - z_2}$.

16 Two of the zeros of $P(z) = z^3 + az^2 + bz + c$ where $a, b, c \in \mathbb{R}$, are $z = -3$ and $z = 3 + i$. Find the values of a, b and c.

17 State the five fifth roots of unity and hence solve:

   a $(2z - 1)^5 = 32$ **b** $z^5 + 5z^4 + 10z^3 + 10z^2 + 5z = 0$ **c** $(z+1)^5 = (z-1)^5$

Chapter **16**

Lines and planes in space

Contents:

INTRODUCTION

Suppose the vector $\begin{pmatrix} 1 \\ 0 \end{pmatrix}$ represents a displacement of 1 km due East and

$\begin{pmatrix} 0 \\ 1 \end{pmatrix}$ represents a displacement of 1 km due North.

The diagram shows the path of a yacht relative to a yacht club which is situated at (0, 0). At 12:00 noon the yacht is at the point A(2, 20).

The yacht is travelling in the direction $\begin{pmatrix} 4 \\ -3 \end{pmatrix}$ with a constant speed of 5 km h^{-1}.

Since $\left| \begin{pmatrix} 4 \\ -3 \end{pmatrix} \right| = 5$ we can see that $\begin{pmatrix} 4 \\ -3 \end{pmatrix}$ gives both the direction and speed of travel.

So, $\begin{pmatrix} 4 \\ -3 \end{pmatrix}$ is called the **velocity vector** of the yacht.

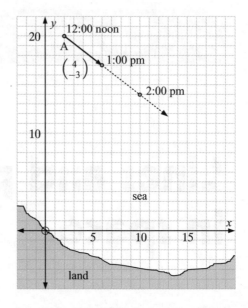

In order to define the position of the yacht at any time t hours after 12 noon, we can use the **parametric equations** $x = 2 + 4t$ and $y = 20 - 3t$ where t is called the **parameter**.

Note: If $t = 0$, $x = 2$ and $y = 20$, so the yacht is at (2, 20).
    If $t = 1$, $x = 6$ and $y = 17$, so the yacht is at (6, 17).
    If $t = 2$, $x = 10$ and $y = 14$, so the yacht is at (10, 14).

We can find a **vector equation** for the yacht's path as follows:

Suppose the yacht is at R(x, y) at time t hours after 12:00 noon.

$$\therefore \quad \overrightarrow{OR} = \overrightarrow{OA} + \overrightarrow{AR}$$

$$\therefore \quad \mathbf{r} = \begin{pmatrix} 2 \\ 20 \end{pmatrix} + t \begin{pmatrix} 4 \\ -3 \end{pmatrix} \quad \text{for } t \geqslant 0$$

$$\therefore \quad \begin{pmatrix} x \\ y \end{pmatrix} = \begin{pmatrix} 2 \\ 20 \end{pmatrix} + t \begin{pmatrix} 4 \\ -3 \end{pmatrix}$$

which is the **vector equation** of the yacht's path.

Notice how the parametric equations are easily found from the vector equation:

If $\begin{pmatrix} x \\ y \end{pmatrix} = \begin{pmatrix} 2 \\ 20 \end{pmatrix} + t \begin{pmatrix} 4 \\ -3 \end{pmatrix}$ then $x = 2 + 4t$ and $y = 20 - 3t$.

We can also find the **Cartesian equation** of the yacht's path:

As $\quad x = 2 + 4t, \quad 4t = x - 2 \quad$ and so $\quad t = \dfrac{x-2}{4}$.

Substituting into $\quad y = 20 - 3t \quad$ gives $\quad y = 20 - 3\left(\dfrac{x-2}{4}\right)$

$$\therefore \quad 4y = 80 - 3(x - 2)$$
$$\therefore \quad 4y = 80 - 3x + 6$$
$$\therefore \quad 3x + 4y = 86 \quad \text{where} \quad x \geqslant 2 \quad \text{because} \quad t \geqslant 0.$$

A | LINES IN 2-D AND 3-D

In both 2-D and 3-D geometry we can determine the **equation of a line** by its **direction** and a **fixed point** through which it passes.

Suppose a line passes through a fixed point A such that $\overrightarrow{OA} = \mathbf{a}$, and its direction is given by vector $\mathbf{b}$ (i.e., the line is parallel to $\mathbf{b}$).

Let any point R be on the line so that $\overrightarrow{OR} = \mathbf{r}$.

By vector addition, $\overrightarrow{OR} = \overrightarrow{OA} + \overrightarrow{AR}$.

Since $\overrightarrow{AR} \parallel \mathbf{b}, \quad \overrightarrow{AR} = t\mathbf{b} \quad$ for some $t \in \mathbb{R}$

$$\therefore \quad \mathbf{r} = \mathbf{a} + t\mathbf{b}$$

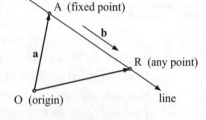

So, $\quad\quad\quad \mathbf{r} = \mathbf{a} + t\mathbf{b}, \quad t \in \mathbb{R} \quad$ is the **vector equation** of the line.

LINES IN 2-D

- In 2-D we are dealing with a **line in a plane**.

- $\begin{pmatrix} x \\ y \end{pmatrix} = \begin{pmatrix} a_1 \\ a_2 \end{pmatrix} + t \begin{pmatrix} b_1 \\ b_2 \end{pmatrix}$ is the **vector equation** of the line

  where $\quad$ R(x, y) is any point on the line

  $\quad\quad\quad$ A(a_1, a_2) is the known (fixed) point on the line

  $\quad\quad\quad \mathbf{b} = \begin{pmatrix} b_1 \\ b_2 \end{pmatrix}$ is the **direction vector** of the line.

  Note: $\mathbf{b} = \begin{pmatrix} b_1 \\ b_2 \end{pmatrix}$ also enables us to calculate the slope of the line, $\quad m = \dfrac{b_2}{b_1} \left(\dfrac{\text{rise}}{\text{run}}\right)$

- $\left.\begin{aligned} x &= a_1 + b_1 t \\ y &= a_2 + b_2 t \end{aligned}\right\}, \; t \in \mathbb{R},$ $\quad$ are the **parametric equations** of the line

  $\quad\quad\quad\quad\quad\quad\quad\quad\quad\quad\quad\quad\quad\quad$ where t is called the **parameter**.

  With these equations each point on the line corresponds to exactly one value of t, so every point has a one-to-one correspondence with a real number.

- We can convert these equations into Cartesian form by equating t values.

  Using $\quad t = \dfrac{x - a_1}{b_1} = \dfrac{y - a_2}{b_2} \quad$ we obtain $\quad b_2 x - b_1 y = b_2 a_1 - b_1 a_2$

  $\quad\quad\quad\quad\quad\quad\quad\quad\quad\quad\quad\quad\quad\quad$ which is the **Cartesian equation** of the line.

Example 1

Find   **a**   the vector   **b**   the parametric   **c**   the Cartesian equation

of the line passing through the point $(1, 5)$ with direction $\begin{pmatrix} 3 \\ 2 \end{pmatrix}$.

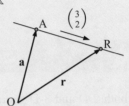

a $\mathbf{a} = \overrightarrow{OA} = \begin{pmatrix} 1 \\ 5 \end{pmatrix}$ and $\mathbf{b} = \begin{pmatrix} 3 \\ 2 \end{pmatrix}$

But $\mathbf{r} = \mathbf{a} + t\mathbf{b}$ $\therefore$ $\begin{pmatrix} x \\ y \end{pmatrix} = \begin{pmatrix} 1 \\ 5 \end{pmatrix} + t \begin{pmatrix} 3 \\ 2 \end{pmatrix}, \quad t \in \mathbb{R}$

b   From **a**, $x = 1 + 3t$ and $y = 5 + 2t, \quad t \in \mathbb{R}$

c   Now $t = \dfrac{x - 1}{3} = \dfrac{y - 5}{2}$

$\therefore \quad 2x - 2 = 3y - 15$

$\therefore \quad 2x - 3y = -13 \qquad$ {general form}

Example 2

A particle at $P(x(t), y(t))$ moves such that $x(t) = 2 - 3t$ and $y(t) = 2t + 4$,
$t \geqslant 0$.   The distance units are metres and t is in seconds.

a   Find the initial position of P.

b   Illustrate the motion showing points where $t = 0, 1, 2$ and 3.

c   Find the speed of P.

a $x(0) = 2, \quad y(0) = 4 \qquad \therefore$ the initial position of P is $(2, 4)$

b $x(1) = -1, \quad y(1) = 6$
$x(2) = -4, \quad y(2) = 8$
$x(3) = -7, \quad y(3) = 10$

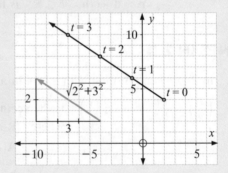

c   Every second P moves with
x-step -3 and y-step 2,
which is a distance of $\sqrt{13}$ m.

$\therefore$ the speed is constant and
is $\sqrt{13}$ m s^{-1}.

EXERCISE 16A.1

1   Find   **i**   the vector equation   **ii**   the parametric equations of the line:

   a   passing through $(3, -4)$ with direction $\begin{pmatrix} 1 \\ 4 \end{pmatrix}$

   b   passing through $(5, 2)$ with direction $\begin{pmatrix} -8 \\ 2 \end{pmatrix}$

   c   cutting the x-axis at -6 with direction $3\mathbf{i} + 7\mathbf{j}$

   d   with direction $-2\mathbf{i} + \mathbf{j}$ that passes through $(-1, 11)$.

2 Find the parametric equations of the line passing through $(-1, 4)$ with direction vector $\begin{pmatrix} 2 \\ -1 \end{pmatrix}$ and parameter λ. Find the points on the line when $\lambda = 0, 1, 3, -1, -4$.

3 **a** Does $(3, -2)$ lie on the line with parametric equations $x = t + 2, \quad y = 1 - 3t$? Does $(0, 6)$ lie on this line?

 b $(k, 4)$ lies on the line with parametric equations $x = 1 - 2t, \quad y = 1 + t$. Find k.

4 A particle at $P(x(t), y(t))$ moves such that $x(t) = 1 + 2t$ and $y(t) = 2 - 5t$, $t \geqslant 0$. The distances are in centimetres and t is in seconds.

 a Find the initial position of P.

 b Illustrate the initial part of the motion of P where $t = 0, 1, 2, 3$.

 c Find the speed of P.

LINES IN 3-D

- In 3-D we are dealing with a **line in space**.

- $\begin{pmatrix} x \\ y \\ z \end{pmatrix} = \begin{pmatrix} a_1 \\ a_2 \\ a_3 \end{pmatrix} + \lambda \begin{pmatrix} b_1 \\ b_2 \\ b_3 \end{pmatrix}$ is the **vector equation** of the line

    where $R(x, y, z)$ is any point on the line

     $A(a_1, a_2, a_3)$ is the known (fixed) point on the line

     $\mathbf{b} = \begin{pmatrix} b_1 \\ b_2 \\ b_3 \end{pmatrix}$ is the **direction vector** of the line.

    Note: We do not talk about the **slope** of a line in 3-D.

     We describe its direction only by its **direction vector**.

- $\left. \begin{array}{l} x = a_1 + \lambda b_1 \\ y = a_2 + \lambda b_2 \\ z = a_3 + \lambda b_3 \end{array} \right\}$ are the **parametric equations** of the line

     where $\lambda \in \mathbb{R}$ is called the **parameter**.

    Every point on the line corresponds to exactly one value of λ.

- $\dfrac{x - a_1}{b_1} = \dfrac{y - a_2}{b_2} = \dfrac{z - a_3}{b_3} \; (= \lambda)$ are the **Cartesian equations** of the line.

Example 3

Find the vector equation and the parametric equations of the line through $(1, -2, 3)$ in the direction $4\mathbf{i} + 5\mathbf{j} - 6\mathbf{k}$.

The vector equation is $\begin{pmatrix} x \\ y \\ z \end{pmatrix} = \begin{pmatrix} 1 \\ -2 \\ 3 \end{pmatrix} + \lambda \begin{pmatrix} 4 \\ 5 \\ -6 \end{pmatrix}$, $\lambda \in \mathbb{R}$.

The parametric equations are: $x = 1 + 4\lambda, \; y = -2 + 5\lambda, \; z = 3 - 6\lambda, \; \lambda \in \mathbb{R}$.

Example 4

Find the parametric equations of the line through A(2, −1, 4) and B(−1, 0, 2).

We require a direction vector for the line, either $\overrightarrow{AB}$ or $\overrightarrow{BA}$.

$$\overrightarrow{AB} = \begin{pmatrix} -1-2 \\ 0--1 \\ 2-4 \end{pmatrix} = \begin{pmatrix} -3 \\ 1 \\ -2 \end{pmatrix}$$

Using the point A, the equations are: $x = 2 - 3\lambda$, $y = -1 + \lambda$, $z = 4 - 2\lambda$, $\lambda \in \mathbb{R}$.

Note: Using the point B, the equations are: $x = -1 - 3\mu$, $y = \mu$, $z = 2 - 2\mu$, $\mu \in \mathbb{R}$.

These sets of equations are actually equivalent, and generate the same set of points. They are related by $\mu = \lambda - 1$.

EXERCISE 16A.2

1 Find the vector equation of the line:

  a parallel to $\begin{pmatrix} 2 \\ 1 \\ 3 \end{pmatrix}$ and through the point (1, 3, −7)

  b through (0, 1, 2) and with direction vector $\mathbf{i} + \mathbf{j} - 2\mathbf{k}$

  c parallel to the X-axis and through the point (−2, 2, 1).

2 Find the parametric equations of the line:

  a parallel to $\begin{pmatrix} -1 \\ 2 \\ 6 \end{pmatrix}$ and through the point (5, 2, −1)

  b parallel to $2\mathbf{i} - \mathbf{j} + 3\mathbf{k}$ and through the point (0, 2, −1)

  c perpendicular to the XOY plane and through (3, 2, −1).

3 Find the parametric equations of the line through:

  a A(1, 2, 1) and B(−1, 3, 2)   **b** C(0, 1, 3) and D(3, 1, −1)

  c E(1, 2, 5) and F(1, −1, 5)   **d** G(0, 1, −1) and H(5, −1, 3)

4 Find the coordinates of the point where the line with parametric equations $x = 1 - \lambda$, $y = 3 + \lambda$ and $z = 3 - 2\lambda$ meets:

  a the XOY plane   **b** the YOZ plane   **c** the XOZ plane.

5 Find points on the line with parametric equations $x = 2 - \lambda$, $y = 3 + 2\lambda$ and $z = 1 + \lambda$ which are $5\sqrt{3}$ units from the point (1, 0, −2).

6 The perpendicular from a point to a line minimises the distance from the point to that line.

Use quadratic theory to find the coordinates of the foot of the perpendicular:

  a from (1, 1, 2) to the line with equations $x = 1 + \lambda$, $y = 2 - \lambda$, $z = 3 + \lambda$

  b from (2, 1, 3) to the line with vector equation $\begin{pmatrix} x \\ y \\ z \end{pmatrix} = \begin{pmatrix} 1 \\ 2 \\ 0 \end{pmatrix} + \mu \begin{pmatrix} 1 \\ -1 \\ 2 \end{pmatrix}$.

THE ANGLE BETWEEN TWO LINES (2-D and 3-D)

In **Chapter 14** we saw that the angle between two vectors
is measured in the range $0^o \leqslant \theta \leqslant 180^o$. We used the
formula $\cos \theta = \dfrac{\mathbf{b_1} \bullet \mathbf{b_2}}{|\mathbf{b_1}||\mathbf{b_2}|}$.

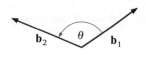

In the case of lines which continue infinitely in both
directions, we agree to talk about the *acute* angle between
them. We therefore use the formula

$$\cos \theta = \frac{|\mathbf{b_1} \bullet \mathbf{b_2}|}{|\mathbf{b_1}||\mathbf{b_2}|}$$

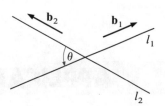

where $\mathbf{b}_1$ and $\mathbf{b}_2$ are the direction vectors of the given lines
l_1 and l_2 respectively.

Example 5

Find the angle between the lines l_1: $x = 2 - 3t$, $y = -1 + t$ and
l_2: $x = 1 + 2s$, $y = -4 + 3s$

$$\mathbf{b_1} = \begin{pmatrix} -3 \\ 1 \end{pmatrix} \qquad \mathbf{b_2} = \begin{pmatrix} 2 \\ 3 \end{pmatrix}$$

$$\therefore \quad \cos \theta = \frac{|-6 + 3|}{\sqrt{10}\sqrt{13}}$$

$$\therefore \quad \cos \theta \approx 0.2631$$

and so $\theta \approx 74.7^o$ (1.30 radians)

Example 6

Find the angle between the lines l_1: $x = 4 - 3\lambda$, $y = -1 + \lambda$, $z = 4 - 2\lambda$

and l_2: $\dfrac{1 - x}{3} = y = \dfrac{2 - z}{2}$

$$\mathbf{b_1} = \begin{pmatrix} -3 \\ 1 \\ -2 \end{pmatrix} \text{ and } \mathbf{b_2} = \begin{pmatrix} -3 \\ 1 \\ -2 \end{pmatrix} \qquad \therefore \quad \cos \theta = \frac{|9 + 1 + 4|}{\sqrt{14}\sqrt{14}}$$

$$\therefore \quad \cos \theta = 1$$

and so $\theta = 0^o$

In fact these lines are coincident, i.e., l_1 and l_2 are the same line.

EXERCISE 16A.3

1 Find the angle between the lines: l_1 passing through $(-6, 3)$ parallel to $\begin{pmatrix} 4 \\ -3 \end{pmatrix}$ and
l_2 cutting the y-axis at $(0, 8)$ with direction $5\mathbf{i} + 4\mathbf{j}$.

2 Find the angle between the lines: $l_1:$ $x = -4 + 12t,$ $y = 3 + 5t$ and
$l_2:$ $x = 3s,$ $y = -6 - 4s$

3 Show that the lines: $x = 2 + 5p,$ $y = 19 - 2p$ and
$x = 3 + 4r,$ $y = 7 + 10r$ are perpendicular.

4 Find the angle between the lines: $\dfrac{x-8}{3} = \dfrac{9-y}{16} = \dfrac{z-10}{7}$ and

$x = 15 + 3\mu,$ $y = 29 + 8\mu,$ $z = 5 - 5\mu$

B   APPLICATIONS OF A LINE IN A PLANE

THE VELOCITY VECTOR OF A MOVING OBJECT

In **Example 2** we considered a particle which moves $\begin{pmatrix} -3 \\ 2 \end{pmatrix}$ every second.

$\begin{pmatrix} -3 \\ 2 \end{pmatrix}$ is called the **velocity vector** of the particle.

Since $\left| \begin{pmatrix} -3 \\ 2 \end{pmatrix} \right| = \sqrt{(-3)^2 + 2^2} = \sqrt{13},$

the **velocity** of the particle is $\sqrt{13}$ metres per second in the direction $\begin{pmatrix} -3 \\ 2 \end{pmatrix}$, and

the **speed** of the particle is $\sqrt{13}$ metres per second.

In general,

if $\begin{pmatrix} a \\ b \end{pmatrix}$ is the **velocity vector** of a moving object, then it is travelling

at a speed of $\left| \begin{pmatrix} a \\ b \end{pmatrix} \right| = \sqrt{a^2 + b^2}$ in the direction $\begin{pmatrix} a \\ b \end{pmatrix}$.

Example 7

$\begin{pmatrix} x \\ y \end{pmatrix} = \begin{pmatrix} 7 \\ 5 \end{pmatrix} + t \begin{pmatrix} 6 \\ -8 \end{pmatrix}$ is the vector equation of the path of an object.

t is the time in seconds, $t \geqslant 0$.   The distance units are metres. Find the:
a   object's initial position   **b**   velocity vector of the object   **c**   object's speed.

a   At $t = 0,$ $\begin{pmatrix} x \\ y \end{pmatrix} = \begin{pmatrix} 7 \\ 5 \end{pmatrix}$ $\therefore$ the object is at $(7, 5)$.

b   The velocity vector is $\begin{pmatrix} 6 \\ -8 \end{pmatrix}$ because the object moves $\begin{pmatrix} 6 \\ -8 \end{pmatrix}$ every second.

c   The speed is $\left| \begin{pmatrix} 6 \\ -8 \end{pmatrix} \right| = \sqrt{36 + 64} = \sqrt{100} = 10 \text{ m s}^{-1}.$

CONSTANT VELOCITY PROBLEMS

Suppose an object moves with constant velocity **b**. If the object is
initially at A (when time $t = 0$) and at time t it is at R, then

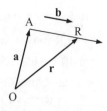

$$\overrightarrow{AR} = t\mathbf{b} \qquad \{\text{distance} = \text{time} \times \text{speed}\}$$

Now $\mathbf{r} = \overrightarrow{OA} + \overrightarrow{AR}$

$\therefore\;\; \mathbf{r} = \mathbf{a} + t\mathbf{b}$

Thus if a body has initial position vector **a**, and moves with constant velocity **b**, its
position at time t is given by

$$\mathbf{r} = \mathbf{a} + t\mathbf{b} \quad \text{for} \quad t \geqslant 0.$$

Example 8

An object is initially at (5, 10) and moves with velocity vector $3\mathbf{i} - \mathbf{j}$. Find:
a   the position of the object at any time t where t is in minutes
b   the position at $t = 3$ **c**   the time when the object is due east of (0, 0).

a

$$\mathbf{r} = \mathbf{a} + t\mathbf{b}$$

$$\therefore\;\; \begin{pmatrix} x \\ y \end{pmatrix} = \begin{pmatrix} 5 \\ 10 \end{pmatrix} + t \begin{pmatrix} 3 \\ -1 \end{pmatrix}, \;\; t \in \mathbb{R}$$

$$\therefore\;\; \begin{pmatrix} x \\ y \end{pmatrix} = \begin{pmatrix} 5 + 3t \\ 10 - t \end{pmatrix}$$

$\therefore$ P is at $(5 + 3t, \, 10 - t)$

b   At $t = 3$, $5 + 3t = 14$ and $10 - t = 7$ $\therefore$ it is at (14, 7).

c   When the object is due east of (0, 0), y must be zero
$\therefore\;\; 10 - t = 0$
$\therefore\;\; t = 10$ The object is due east of (0, 0) after 10 minutes.

THE CLOSEST DISTANCE FROM A POINT TO A LINE

A ship sails through point A in the direction **b**
and continues past a port P. At what time will the
ship R be closest to the port?

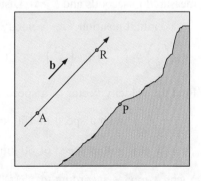

The ship is closest when PR is perpendicular to
AR,

$\therefore\;\; \overrightarrow{PR} \bullet \mathbf{b} = 0$ {the scalar product is zero}

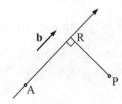

Example 9

If distances are measured in kilometres and a ship R moves in the direction $\begin{pmatrix} 3 \\ 4 \end{pmatrix}$ at a speed of 10 km h^{-1}, find:

a an expression for the position of the ship in terms of t where t is the number of hours after leaving port A

b the time when it is closest to port P(10, 2).

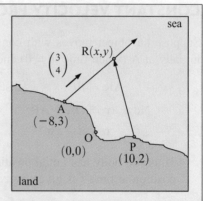

a $\left| \begin{pmatrix} 3 \\ 4 \end{pmatrix} \right| = \sqrt{3^2 + 4^2} = 5$ $\therefore$ since the speed is 10 km h^{-1}, the ship's

velocity vector must be $2 \begin{pmatrix} 3 \\ 4 \end{pmatrix} = \begin{pmatrix} 6 \\ 8 \end{pmatrix}$.

Now $\overrightarrow{OR} = \overrightarrow{OA} + \overrightarrow{AR}$

$\therefore$ $\begin{pmatrix} x \\ y \end{pmatrix} = \begin{pmatrix} -8 \\ 3 \end{pmatrix} + t \begin{pmatrix} 6 \\ 8 \end{pmatrix}$

$\therefore$ R is at $(-8 + 6t, \ 3 + 8t)$

b The ship is closest to P when $\overrightarrow{PR} \perp \begin{pmatrix} 3 \\ 4 \end{pmatrix}$ $\therefore$ $\overrightarrow{PR} \bullet \begin{pmatrix} 3 \\ 4 \end{pmatrix} = 0$

$\therefore$ $\begin{pmatrix} -8 + 6t - 10 \\ 3 + 8t - 2 \end{pmatrix} \bullet \begin{pmatrix} 3 \\ 4 \end{pmatrix} = 0$

$\therefore$ $3(6t - 18) + 4(1 + 8t) = 0$

$\therefore$ $18t - 54 + 4 + 32t = 0$

$\therefore$ $50t - 50 = 0$

$\therefore$ $t = 1$

So, the ship is closest to port P 1 hour after leaving A.

EXERCISE 16B.1

1 Each of the following vector equations represents the path of a moving object. t is measured in seconds and $t \geqslant 0$. Distances are measured in metres. In each case find the:

    i initial position   **ii** velocity vector   **iii** speed of the object.

    a $\begin{pmatrix} x \\ y \end{pmatrix} = \begin{pmatrix} -4 \\ 3 \end{pmatrix} + t \begin{pmatrix} 12 \\ 5 \end{pmatrix}$ **b** $\begin{pmatrix} x \\ y \end{pmatrix} = \begin{pmatrix} 0 \\ -6 \end{pmatrix} + t \begin{pmatrix} 3 \\ -4 \end{pmatrix}$ **c** $\begin{pmatrix} x \\ y \end{pmatrix} = \begin{pmatrix} -2 \\ -7 \end{pmatrix} + t \begin{pmatrix} -6 \\ -4 \end{pmatrix}$

2 Find the velocity vector of a speed boat moving parallel to:

    a $\begin{pmatrix} 4 \\ -3 \end{pmatrix}$ with a speed of 150 km h^{-1} **b** $\begin{pmatrix} 24 \\ 7 \end{pmatrix}$ with a speed of 12.5 km h^{-1}

    c $2\mathbf{i} + \mathbf{j}$ with a speed of 50 km h^{-1} **d** $-3\mathbf{i} + 4\mathbf{j}$ with a speed of 100 km h^{-1}.

3 Yacht A moves according to $x(t) = 4 + t$, $\ y(t) = 5 - 2t$ where the distance units are kilometres and the time units are hours. Yacht B moves according to $x(t) = 1 + 2t$, $y(t) = -8 + t$, $\ t \geqslant 0$.

a Find the initial position of each yacht.   **b** Find the velocity vector of each yacht.

c Show that the speed of each yacht is constant and state the speeds.

d If they start at 6:00 am, find the time when the yachts are closest to each other.

e Prove that the paths of the yachts are at right angles to each other.

4 Submarine P is at $(-5, 4)$ and fires a torpedo with velocity vector $\begin{pmatrix} 3 \\ -1 \end{pmatrix}$ at 1:34 pm.

Submarine Q is at $(15, 7)$ and a minutes later fires a torpedo in the direction $\begin{pmatrix} -4 \\ -3 \end{pmatrix}$. Distances are measured in kilometres and time is in minutes.

a Show that the position of P's torpedo can be written as $P(x_1(t), y_1(t))$ where $x_1(t) = -5 + 3t$ and $y_1(t) = 4 - t$.

b What is the speed of P's torpedo?

c Show that the position of Q's torpedo can be written in the form $x_2(t) = 15 - 4(t - a)$, $y_2(t) = 7 - 3(t - a)$.

d Q's torpedo is successful in knocking out P's torpedo. At what time did Q fire its torpedo and at what time did the explosion occur?

5 Let $\begin{pmatrix} 1 \\ 0 \end{pmatrix}$ represent a 1 km displacement due east

and $\begin{pmatrix} 0 \\ 1 \end{pmatrix}$ represent a 1 km displacement due north.

The control tower of an airport is at $(0, 0)$. Aircraft within 100 km of $(0, 0)$ will become visible on the radar screen at the control tower.

At 12:00 noon an aircraft is 200 km east and 100 km north of the control tower. It is flying parallel to the

vector $\mathbf{b} = \begin{pmatrix} -3 \\ -1 \end{pmatrix}$ with a speed of $40\sqrt{10}$ km h^{-1}.

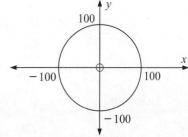

a Write down the velocity vector of the aircraft.

b Write a vector equation for the path of the aircraft using t to represent the time in hours that have elapsed since 12:00 noon.

c Find the position of the aircraft at 1:00 pm.

d Show that the aircraft first becomes visible on the radar screen at 1:00 pm.

e Find the time when the aircraft is closest to the control tower and find the distance between the aircraft and the control tower at this time.

f At what time will the aircraft disappear from the radar screen?

6 Boat A's position is given by
$x(t) = 3 - t$, $y(t) = 2t - 4$ where the distance units are kilometres and the time units are hours.
Boat B's position is given by
$x(t) = 4 - 3t$, $y(t) = 3 - 2t$.

a Find the initial position of each boat.

b Find the velocity vector of each boat.

c What is the angle between the paths of the boats?

d At what time are the boats closest to each other?

GEOMETRIC APPLICATIONS OF $r = a + tb$

Vector equations of two intersecting lines can be **solved simultaneously** to find the point where the lines meet.

Example 10

Line 1 has vector equation $\begin{pmatrix} x \\ y \end{pmatrix} = \begin{pmatrix} -2 \\ 1 \end{pmatrix} + s \begin{pmatrix} 3 \\ 2 \end{pmatrix}$ and

line 2 has vector equation $\begin{pmatrix} x \\ y \end{pmatrix} = \begin{pmatrix} 15 \\ 5 \end{pmatrix} + t \begin{pmatrix} -4 \\ 1 \end{pmatrix}$, where s and t are scalars.

Use vector methods to find where the two lines meet.

The lines meet where $\begin{pmatrix} -2 \\ 1 \end{pmatrix} + s \begin{pmatrix} 3 \\ 2 \end{pmatrix} = \begin{pmatrix} 15 \\ 5 \end{pmatrix} + t \begin{pmatrix} -4 \\ 1 \end{pmatrix}$

$\therefore \quad -2 + 3s = 15 - 4t \qquad$ and $\quad 1 + 2s = 5 + t$

$\therefore \quad 3s + 4t = 17 \quad \text{...... (1)} \qquad$ and $\quad 2s - t = 4 \quad \text{...... (2)}$

$$3s + 4t = 17$$
$$\underline{8s - 4t = 16} \quad \{(2) \text{ is multiplied by } 4\}$$
$$\therefore \quad 11s \qquad = 33$$

So, $s = 3$ and in (2): $\quad 2(3) - t = 4 \quad$ so $\quad t = 2$

Using line 1, $\qquad \begin{pmatrix} x \\ y \end{pmatrix} = \begin{pmatrix} -2 \\ 1 \end{pmatrix} + 3 \begin{pmatrix} 3 \\ 2 \end{pmatrix} = \begin{pmatrix} 7 \\ 7 \end{pmatrix}$

Checking in line 2, $\quad \begin{pmatrix} x \\ y \end{pmatrix} = \begin{pmatrix} 15 \\ 5 \end{pmatrix} + 2 \begin{pmatrix} -4 \\ 1 \end{pmatrix} = \begin{pmatrix} 7 \\ 7 \end{pmatrix} \qquad \therefore$ they meet at $(7, 7)$

EXERCISE 16B.2

1 The triangle formed by the three lines is ABC.

Line 1 (AB) is $\begin{pmatrix} x \\ y \end{pmatrix} = \begin{pmatrix} -1 \\ 6 \end{pmatrix} + r \begin{pmatrix} 3 \\ -2 \end{pmatrix}$, line 2 (AC) is $\begin{pmatrix} x \\ y \end{pmatrix} = \begin{pmatrix} 0 \\ 2 \end{pmatrix} + s \begin{pmatrix} 1 \\ 1 \end{pmatrix}$

and line 3 (BC) is $\begin{pmatrix} x \\ y \end{pmatrix} = \begin{pmatrix} 10 \\ -3 \end{pmatrix} + t \begin{pmatrix} -2 \\ 3 \end{pmatrix}$ where r, s and t are scalars.

  a Draw the three lines accurately on a grid.
  b Hence, find the coordinates of A, B and C.
  c Prove that $\triangle$ABC is isosceles.
  d Use vector methods to *check* your answers to **b**.

2 A parallelogram is defined by four lines as follows:

Line 1 (AB) is $\begin{pmatrix} x \\ y \end{pmatrix} = \begin{pmatrix} -4 \\ 6 \end{pmatrix} + r \begin{pmatrix} 7 \\ 3 \end{pmatrix}$, line 2 (AD) is $\begin{pmatrix} x \\ y \end{pmatrix} = \begin{pmatrix} -4 \\ 6 \end{pmatrix} + s \begin{pmatrix} 1 \\ 2 \end{pmatrix}$,

line 3 (CD) is $\begin{pmatrix} x \\ y \end{pmatrix} = \begin{pmatrix} 22 \\ 25 \end{pmatrix} + t \begin{pmatrix} -7 \\ -3 \end{pmatrix}$, line 4 (CB) is $\begin{pmatrix} x \\ y \end{pmatrix} = \begin{pmatrix} 22 \\ 25 \end{pmatrix} + u \begin{pmatrix} -1 \\ -2 \end{pmatrix}$,

where r, s, t and u are scalars.

    a Draw an accurate sketch of the four lines and the parallelogram formed by them. Label the vertices.

    b From your diagram find the coordinates of A, B, C and D.

    c Use vector methods to confirm your answers to **b**.

3 An isosceles triangle ABC is formed by these lines:

Line 1 (AB) is $\begin{pmatrix} x \\ y \end{pmatrix} = \begin{pmatrix} 0 \\ 2 \end{pmatrix} + r \begin{pmatrix} 2 \\ 1 \end{pmatrix}$, line 2 (BC) is $\begin{pmatrix} x \\ y \end{pmatrix} = \begin{pmatrix} 8 \\ 6 \end{pmatrix} + s \begin{pmatrix} -1 \\ -2 \end{pmatrix}$ and

line 3 (AC) is $\begin{pmatrix} x \\ y \end{pmatrix} = \begin{pmatrix} 0 \\ 5 \end{pmatrix} + t \begin{pmatrix} 1 \\ -1 \end{pmatrix}$ where r, s and t are scalars.

    a Use vector methods to find the coordinates of A, B and C.

    b Which two sides of the triangle are equal in length? Find their lengths.

4 Line QP is $\begin{pmatrix} x \\ y \end{pmatrix} = \begin{pmatrix} 3 \\ -1 \end{pmatrix} + r \begin{pmatrix} 14 \\ 10 \end{pmatrix}$, line QR is $\begin{pmatrix} x \\ y \end{pmatrix} = \begin{pmatrix} 3 \\ -1 \end{pmatrix} + s \begin{pmatrix} 17 \\ -9 \end{pmatrix}$ and

line PR is $\begin{pmatrix} x \\ y \end{pmatrix} = \begin{pmatrix} 0 \\ 18 \end{pmatrix} + t \begin{pmatrix} 5 \\ -7 \end{pmatrix}$ where r, s and t are scalars.

Triangle PQR is formed by these lines.

    a Use vector methods to find the coordinates of P, Q and R.

    b Find vectors $\overrightarrow{PQ}$ and $\overrightarrow{PR}$ and evaluate $\overrightarrow{PQ} \bullet \overrightarrow{PR}$.

    c Hence, find the size of $\angle QPR$.

    d Find the area of $\triangle PQR$.

5 Quadrilateral ABCD is formed by these lines:

Line 1 (AB) is $\begin{pmatrix} x \\ y \end{pmatrix} = \begin{pmatrix} 2 \\ 5 \end{pmatrix} + r \begin{pmatrix} 4 \\ 1 \end{pmatrix}$, line 2 (BC) is $\begin{pmatrix} x \\ y \end{pmatrix} = \begin{pmatrix} 18 \\ 9 \end{pmatrix} + s \begin{pmatrix} -8 \\ 32 \end{pmatrix}$,

line 3 (CD) is $\begin{pmatrix} x \\ y \end{pmatrix} = \begin{pmatrix} 14 \\ 25 \end{pmatrix} + t \begin{pmatrix} -8 \\ -2 \end{pmatrix}$ and line 4 (AD) is $\begin{pmatrix} x \\ y \end{pmatrix} = \begin{pmatrix} 3 \\ 1 \end{pmatrix} + u \begin{pmatrix} -3 \\ 12 \end{pmatrix}$

where r, s, t and u are scalars.

    a Use vector methods to find the coordinates of A, B, C and D.

    b Write down vectors $\overrightarrow{AC}$ and $\overrightarrow{DB}$ and hence find:

        i $|\overrightarrow{AC}|$ **ii** $|\overrightarrow{DB}|$ **iii** $\overrightarrow{AC} \bullet \overrightarrow{DB}$

    c What do the answers to **b** tell you about quadrilateral ABCD?

C   RELATIONSHIP BETWEEN LINES

LINE CLASSIFICATION IN 2 DIMENSIONS

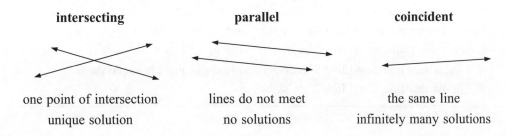

intersecting	parallel	coincident
one point of intersection	lines do not meet	the same line
unique solution	no solutions	infinitely many solutions

LINE CLASSIFICATION IN 3 DIMENSIONS

▶ the lines are **coplanar**, or lie in the same plane:
   - intersecting   • parallel   • coincident

▶ the lines are not coplanar and are hence **skew**

> **Skew lines** are any lines which are neither parallel nor intersecting.

- If the lines are **parallel**, the angle between them is $0°$.

- If the lines are **intersecting**, the angle between them is θ, as shown.

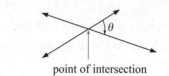

point of intersection

- If the lines are **skew**, there is still an angle that one line makes with the other. If we translate one line to intersect the other, the angle between the original lines is defined as the angle between the intersecting lines, i.e., angle θ.

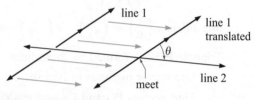

line 1

line 1 translated

line 2

meet

lines 1 and 2 are skew

Example 11

Line 1 has equations $x = -1 + 2s$, $y = 1 - 2s$ and $z = 1 + 4s$.
Line 2 has equations $x = 1 - t$, $y = t$ and $z = 3 - 2t$.
Show that the lines are parallel.

Line 1 is $\begin{pmatrix} x \\ y \\ z \end{pmatrix} = \begin{pmatrix} -1 \\ 1 \\ 1 \end{pmatrix} + s \begin{pmatrix} 2 \\ -2 \\ 4 \end{pmatrix}$ with direction vector $\begin{pmatrix} 2 \\ -2 \\ 4 \end{pmatrix}$.

Likewise, line 2 has direction vector $\begin{pmatrix} -1 \\ 1 \\ -2 \end{pmatrix}$.

Since $\begin{pmatrix} 2 \\ -2 \\ 4 \end{pmatrix} = -2 \begin{pmatrix} -1 \\ 1 \\ -2 \end{pmatrix}$, the lines are parallel.

{If $\mathbf{a} = k\mathbf{b}$ for some scalar k, then $\mathbf{a} \parallel \mathbf{b}$.}

Example 12

Line 1 has equations $x = -1 + 2s$, $y = 1 - 2s$ and $z = 1 + 4s$.
Line 2 has equations $x = 1 - t$, $y = t$ and $z = 3 - 2t$.
Line 3 has equations $x = 1 + 2u$, $y = -1 - u$, $z = 4 + 3u$.

a Show that line 2 and line 3 intersect and find the angle between them.

b Show that line 1 and line 3 are skew.

a Equating x, y and z values in lines 2 and 3 gives

$$1 - t = 1 + 2u \qquad\qquad t = -1 - u \quad \text{and} \quad 3 - 2t = 4 + 3u$$
$$\therefore \;\; t = -2u, \qquad\qquad \therefore \;\; t = -1 - u, \quad \text{and} \quad 3u + 2t = -1 \;\;..... \;(1)$$

Solving these we get $-2u = -1 - u \quad \therefore \quad -u = -1$

$$\therefore \;\; u = 1 \;\; \text{and so} \;\; t = -2$$

Checking in (1): $3u + 2t = 3(1) + 2(-2) = 3 - 4 = -1 \;\checkmark$

$\therefore \;\; u = 1, \;\; t = -2$ satisfies all three equations, a *common solution.*

Using $u = 1$, lines 2 and 3 meet at $(1 + 2(1), -1 - (1), 4 + 3(1))$
i.e., $(3, -2, 7)$.

Direction vectors for lines 2 and 3 are $\mathbf{a} = \begin{pmatrix} -1 \\ 1 \\ -2 \end{pmatrix}$ and $\mathbf{b} = \begin{pmatrix} 2 \\ -1 \\ 3 \end{pmatrix}$
respectively.

Now $\cos\theta = \dfrac{|\mathbf{a} \bullet \mathbf{b}|}{|\mathbf{a}|\,|\mathbf{b}|} = \dfrac{|-2 - 1 - 6|}{\sqrt{1 + 1 + 4}\sqrt{4 + 1 + 9}}$, where θ is the acute

angle between $\mathbf{a}$ and $\mathbf{b}$ $\therefore \;\; \cos\theta = \dfrac{9}{\sqrt{84}}$ and so $\theta \approx 10.89°$

$\therefore$ the angle between lines 2 and 3 is about $10.9°$.

b Equating x, y and z values in lines 1 and 3 gives

$$-1 + 2s = 1 + 2u \qquad\qquad 1 - 2s = -1 - u \quad \text{and} \quad 1 + 4s = 4 + 3u$$
$$\therefore \;\; 2s - 2u = 2, \qquad\qquad \therefore \;\; -2s + u = -2, \quad \text{and} \quad 4s - 3u = 3 \;\;..... \;(1)$$

Solving these we get $\qquad 2s - 2u = 2$
$$\therefore \quad \dfrac{-2s + u = -2}{}$$
$$\therefore \quad -u = 0 \qquad \text{\{adding them\}}$$

$\therefore \;\; u = 0 \;\; \text{and so} \;\; 2s = 2 \;\; \text{i.e.,} \;\; s = 1$

Checking in (1), $4s - 3u = 4(1) - 3(0) = 4 \neq 3$

So, there is no simultaneous solution to all 3 equations.

$\therefore$ the lines cannot meet, and as they are not parallel they must be skew.

Example 13

Discuss the solutions to $\begin{cases} 3x - y = 2 \\ 6x - 2y = k \end{cases}$ for $k \in \mathbb{R}$.

Give a geometric interpretation of the solutions.

In augmented matrix form $\begin{bmatrix} 3 & -1 & | & 2 \\ 6 & -2 & | & k \end{bmatrix} \sim \begin{bmatrix} 3 & -1 & | & 2 \\ 0 & 0 & | & k - 4 \end{bmatrix} \quad R_2 - 2R_1$

<u>If $k - 4 = 0$,</u> the system is consistent, and the lines $3x - y = 2$ and
$\qquad\qquad 6x - 2y = 4$ are coincident.

Let $x = t$, so $y = -2 + 3t$.

There are infinitely many solutions of the form $x = t$, $y = -2 + 3t$, $t \in \mathbb{R}$.

This line has direction vector $\begin{pmatrix} 1 \\ 3 \end{pmatrix}$ or slope 3 and passes through the point $(0, -2)$.

If $k - 4 \neq 0$ i.e., $k \neq 4$ the system is inconsistent. In this case the lines
$3x - y = 2$ and $6x - 2y = k$ are parallel and have no points of intersection.

PERPENDICULAR AND PARALLEL TESTS (for 2-D AND 3-D)

Non-zero vectors $\mathbf{v}$ and $\mathbf{w}$ are
▸ perpendicular if $\mathbf{v} \bullet \mathbf{w} = 0$
▸ parallel if $\mathbf{v} = k\mathbf{w}$ for some scalar k

Proof of perpendicular case:

If $\mathbf{v} \bullet \mathbf{w} = 0$

then $|\mathbf{v}||\mathbf{w}|\cos\theta = 0$

$\therefore \quad \cos\theta = 0 \quad \{\mathbf{v}, \mathbf{w}$ non-zero$\}$

$\therefore \quad \theta = 90^\circ$

EXERCISE 16C

1   Classify the following line pairs as either parallel, intersecting or skew, and in each case find the measure of the acute angle between them:

 a $x = 1 + 2t, \quad y = 2 - t, \quad z = 3 + t$ and $x = -2 + 3s, \quad y = 3 - s, \quad z = 1 + 2s$

 b $x = -1 + 2\lambda, \quad y = 2 - 12\lambda, \quad z = 4 + 12\lambda$
   and $x = 4\mu - 3, \quad y = 3\mu + 2, \quad z = -\mu - 1$

 c $x = 6t, \quad y = 3 + 8t, \quad z = -1 + 2t$ and $x = 2 + 3s, \quad y = 4s, \quad z = 1 + s$

 d $x = 2 - y = z + 2$ and $x = 1 + 3s, \quad y = -2 - 2s, \quad z = 2s + \frac{1}{2}$

 e $x = 1 + \lambda, \quad y = 2 - \lambda, \quad z = 3 + 2\lambda$ and $x = 2 + 3\mu, \quad y = 3 - 2\mu, \quad z = \mu - 5$

 f $x = 1 - 2t, \quad y = 8 + t, \quad z = 5$ and $x = 2 + 4s, \quad y = -1 - 2s, \quad z = 3$

2   Consider the two lines whose equations are $3x - y = 8$ and $6x - 2y = k$ where k is some real number. Discuss the nature of the intersection of these lines for different values of k.

3   Discuss for the different values of a, the geometric solutions of the equations $4x + 8y = 1$ and $2x - ay = 11$.

SHORTEST DISTANCE FROM A POINT TO A LINE (2-D AND 3-D)

The coordinates of any point P on a line can be expressed in terms of the parameter t.

We can hence find the vector $\overrightarrow{AP}$ in terms of t, where A is a point which is not on the line.

The shortest distance d occurs when $\overrightarrow{AP}$ is perpendicular to $\mathbf{b}$, so we find t for which $\overrightarrow{AP} \bullet \mathbf{b} = 0$.

The shortest distance $d = |\overrightarrow{AP}|$ for this value of t.

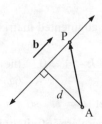

Example 14

Find the shortest distance from P(-1, 2, 3) to the line $\dfrac{x-1}{2} = \dfrac{y+4}{3} = z - 3$.

The equation of the line in parametric form is $x = 1 + 2\lambda, \ y = -4 + 3\lambda, \ z = 3 + \lambda$

$\therefore$ any point A on this line has coordinates $(1 + 2\lambda, \ -4 + 3\lambda, \ 3 + \lambda)$

$\therefore \ \overrightarrow{\text{PA}} = \begin{pmatrix} 2 + 2\lambda \\ -6 + 3\lambda \\ \lambda \end{pmatrix}$ and the direction vector of the line is $\mathbf{b} = \begin{pmatrix} 2 \\ 3 \\ 1 \end{pmatrix}$

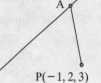

Now for the shortest distance, $\overrightarrow{\text{PA}} \bullet \mathbf{b} = 0$ {perpendicular distance}

$\therefore \quad 4 + 4\lambda - 18 + 9\lambda + \lambda = 0$

$\therefore \quad 14\lambda = 14$ and so $\lambda = 1$

Thus $\overrightarrow{\text{PA}} = \begin{pmatrix} 4 \\ -3 \\ 1 \end{pmatrix}$ and $d = |\,\overrightarrow{\text{PA}}\,| = \sqrt{26}$ units

4 Find the shortest distance from the point $(2, -3)$ to the line $3x - y = 4$.

5 Find the shortest distance from the point $(3, 0, -1)$ to the line with equation
$\mathbf{r} = 2\mathbf{i} - \mathbf{j} + 4\mathbf{k} + \lambda(3\mathbf{i} + 2\mathbf{j} + \mathbf{k})$.

6 Find the shortest distance from $(1, 1, 3)$ to the line $\mathbf{r} = \begin{pmatrix} 1 \\ -1 \\ 2 \end{pmatrix} + \lambda \begin{pmatrix} 2 \\ 3 \\ 1 \end{pmatrix}$.

THE SHORTEST DISTANCE BETWEEN SKEW LINES (EXTENSION)

Example 15

Find the shortest distance between the skew lines $x = t, \ y = 1 - t, \ z = 2 + t$
and $x = 3 - s, \ y = -1 + 2s, \ z = 4 - s$.

The lines have direction vectors $\mathbf{v} = \begin{pmatrix} 1 \\ -1 \\ 1 \end{pmatrix}$ and $\mathbf{w} = \begin{pmatrix} -1 \\ 2 \\ -1 \end{pmatrix}$

so $\mathbf{v} \times \mathbf{w} = \begin{vmatrix} \mathbf{i} & \mathbf{j} & \mathbf{k} \\ 1 & -1 & 1 \\ -1 & 2 & -1 \end{vmatrix} = \begin{vmatrix} -1 & 1 \\ 2 & -1 \end{vmatrix} \mathbf{i} - \begin{vmatrix} 1 & 1 \\ -1 & -1 \end{vmatrix} \mathbf{j} + \begin{vmatrix} 1 & -1 \\ -1 & 2 \end{vmatrix} \mathbf{k} = \begin{pmatrix} -1 \\ 0 \\ 1 \end{pmatrix}$

Let A and B be points on the skew lines.

$\therefore$ A is $(t, 1 - t, 2 + t)$ and B is $(3 - s, -1 + 2s, 4 - s)$ where s and t are scalars.

To find the shortest distance between the two skew lines, we need to find $|\,\overrightarrow{\text{AB}}\,|$

where $\overrightarrow{\text{AB}}$ is parallel to $\mathbf{v} \times \mathbf{w}$, i.e., perpendicular to both skew lines.

As $\overrightarrow{\text{AB}} \parallel \mathbf{v} \times \mathbf{w}$, $\begin{pmatrix} 3 - s - t \\ -1 + 2s - 1 + t \\ 4 - s - 2 - t \end{pmatrix} = k \begin{pmatrix} -1 \\ 0 \\ 1 \end{pmatrix}$ for some scalar k.

$\therefore \quad 3 - s - t = -k, \qquad -2 + 2s + t = 0 \quad \text{and} \quad 2 - s - t = k$

Thus $\quad 2s + t = 2 \quad$ and $\qquad 3 - s - t = -2 + s + t$

$\therefore \quad 2s + t = 2 \quad$ and $\qquad 2s + 2t = 5$

Solving simultaneously, $\quad t = 3 \quad$ and $\quad s = -\frac{1}{2}$

$\therefore \quad \overrightarrow{AB} = \begin{pmatrix} \frac{1}{2} \\ 0 \\ -\frac{1}{2} \end{pmatrix} \quad$ and $\quad |\overrightarrow{AB}| = \sqrt{\frac{1}{4} + 0 + \frac{1}{4}} = \frac{1}{\sqrt{2}}$ units

$\therefore \quad$ the shortest distance is $\frac{1}{\sqrt{2}}$ units.

7 Find the shortest distance between the skew lines:

a $\quad x = 1 + 2t, \quad y = -t, \quad z = 2 + 3t \quad$ and $\quad x = y = z$

b $\quad x = 1 - t, \quad y = 1 + t, \quad z = 3 - t \quad$ and $\quad x = 2 + s, \quad y = 1 - 2s, \quad z = s$

8 Find the shortest distance between the lines given in **Exercise 16C** question **1**.

Note: • To find the distance between parallel lines, find the distance from a point on one line to the other line.

• What is the shortest distance between intersecting/coincident lines?

D   PLANES AND DISTANCES

To find the equation of a plane, we need to know a point on the plane and also its orientation in space.

The orientation of a plane cannot be given by a single parallel vector because infinitely many planes of different orientation are parallel to a single direction vector. We require **two** non-parallel vectors to define the orientation uniquely.

Any point R(x, y, z) on the plane with a known point A(a_1, a_2, a_3) and two non-parallel

vectors $\quad \mathbf{b} = \begin{pmatrix} b_1 \\ b_2 \\ b_3 \end{pmatrix} \quad$ and $\quad \mathbf{c} = \begin{pmatrix} c_1 \\ c_2 \\ c_3 \end{pmatrix} \quad$ must satisfy the vector equation

$\qquad \overrightarrow{AR} = \lambda\mathbf{b} + \mu\mathbf{c} \quad$ for some scalars λ and μ.

$\therefore \quad \overrightarrow{OR} - \overrightarrow{OA} = \lambda\mathbf{b} + \mu\mathbf{c}$

$\therefore \quad \overrightarrow{OR} = \overrightarrow{OA} + \lambda\mathbf{b} + \mu\mathbf{c}$

$\quad \mathbf{r} = \mathbf{a} + \lambda\mathbf{b} + \mu\mathbf{c} \quad$ is the **vector equation of the plane**

where $\quad \mathbf{r}$ is the position vector of any point on the plane,

$\mathbf{a}$ is the position vector of the known point A(a_1, a_2, a_3) on the plane

$\mathbf{b}$ and $\mathbf{c}$ are any two non-parallel vectors that are parallel to the plane

$\lambda, \mu \in \mathbb{R}$ are two independent parameters.

Another way of defining the direction of a plane is to consider the vector cross product of the two vectors **b** and **c** which are parallel to the plane.

The vector $\mathbf{n} = \mathbf{b} \times \mathbf{c}$ is called a **normal vector** to the plane.

n is perpendicular to **b** and **c** and is hence perpendicular to any vector or line in or parallel to the plane. This is because any vector parallel to the plane can be written in the form $\lambda\mathbf{b} + \mu\mathbf{c}$.

Challenge: Show $\mathbf{n} \perp \lambda\mathbf{b} + \mu\mathbf{c}$.

Suppose a plane in space has normal vector $\mathbf{n} = \begin{pmatrix} a \\ b \\ c \end{pmatrix}$

and that it includes the fixed point $A(x_1, y_1, z_1)$.

$R(x, y, z)$ is any other point in the plane.

Now $\overrightarrow{AR}$ is perpendicular to **n**

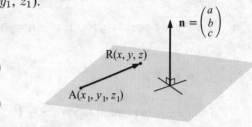

$$\therefore \quad \mathbf{n} \bullet \overrightarrow{AR} = 0$$

$$\therefore \quad \begin{pmatrix} a \\ b \\ c \end{pmatrix} \bullet \begin{pmatrix} x - x_1 \\ y - y_1 \\ z - z_1 \end{pmatrix} = 0$$

$$\therefore \quad a(x - x_1) + b(y - y_1) + c(z - z_1) = 0$$

$$\therefore \quad ax + by + cz = ax_1 + by_1 + cz_1 \quad \text{where the RHS is a constant.}$$

$\mathbf{n} \bullet \overrightarrow{AR} = 0$ is another form of the **vector equation of the plane**. It could also be written as $\mathbf{n} \bullet (\mathbf{r} - \mathbf{a}) = 0$, which implies $\mathbf{r} \bullet \mathbf{n} = \mathbf{a} \bullet \mathbf{n}$.

If a plane has normal vector $\mathbf{n} = \begin{pmatrix} a \\ b \\ c \end{pmatrix}$ and passes through (x_1, y_1, z_1)

then it has equation $ax + by + cz = ax_1 + by_1 + cz_1 = d$, where d is a constant.

This is the **Cartesian equation of the plane**.

Example 16

Find the equation of the plane with normal vector $\begin{pmatrix} 1 \\ 2 \\ 3 \end{pmatrix}$ and containing $(-1, 2, 4)$.

Since $\mathbf{n} = \begin{pmatrix} 1 \\ 2 \\ 3 \end{pmatrix}$ and $(-1, 2, 4)$ lies on the plane, the equation is

$$x + 2y + 3z = (-1) + 2(2) + 3(4)$$
$$\text{i.e., } \quad x + 2y + 3z = 15$$

Example 17

Find the equation of the plane through A$(-1, 2, 0)$, B$(3, 1, 1)$ and C$(1, 0, 3)$:

a   in vector form   **b**   in Cartesian form

a $\overrightarrow{AB} = \begin{pmatrix} 4 \\ -1 \\ 1 \end{pmatrix}$ and $\overrightarrow{CB} = \begin{pmatrix} 2 \\ 1 \\ -2 \end{pmatrix}$

Now $\overrightarrow{AB}$ and $\overrightarrow{CB}$ are two non-parallel vectors both parallel to the plane.

$\therefore \ \mathbf{r} = \begin{pmatrix} x \\ y \\ z \end{pmatrix} = \begin{pmatrix} 1 \\ 0 \\ 3 \end{pmatrix} + \lambda \begin{pmatrix} 4 \\ -1 \\ 1 \end{pmatrix} + \mu \begin{pmatrix} 2 \\ 1 \\ -2 \end{pmatrix}, \ \lambda, \mu \in \mathbb{R}$

using C as the known (fixed) point on the plane.

b   If **n** is the normal vector, then $\mathbf{n} = \overrightarrow{AB} \times \overrightarrow{AC} = \begin{pmatrix} 4 \\ -1 \\ 1 \end{pmatrix} \times \begin{pmatrix} 2 \\ -2 \\ 3 \end{pmatrix}$

$\therefore \ \mathbf{n} = \begin{vmatrix} -1 & 1 \\ -2 & 3 \end{vmatrix} \mathbf{i} - \begin{vmatrix} 4 & 1 \\ 2 & 3 \end{vmatrix} \mathbf{j} + \begin{vmatrix} 4 & -1 \\ 2 & -2 \end{vmatrix} \mathbf{k} = \begin{pmatrix} -1 \\ -10 \\ -6 \end{pmatrix} = - \begin{pmatrix} 1 \\ 10 \\ 6 \end{pmatrix}$

Thus the plane has equation $x + 10y + 6z = (-1) + 10(2) + 6(0)$ {using A}

$\therefore \quad x + 10y + 6z = 19$

Note: Check that all 3 points satisfy this equation.

Example 18

Find the parametric equations of the line through A$(-1, 2, 3)$ and B$(2, 0, -3)$
and hence find where this line meets the plane with equation $x - 2y + 3z = 26$.

$\overrightarrow{AB} = \begin{pmatrix} 3 \\ -2 \\ -6 \end{pmatrix}$ so line AB has parametric equations

$x = -1 + 3t, \quad y = 2 - 2t, \quad z = 3 - 6t$ ..... (*)

This line meets the plane $x - 2y + 3z = 26$ where

$-1 + 3t - 2(2 - 2t) + 3(3 - 6t) = 26$

$\therefore \quad 4 - 11t = 26$

$\therefore \quad -11t = 22$ and so $t = -2$

$\therefore$ it meets the plane at $(-7, 6, 15)$ {substituting $t = -2$ into *}

Example 19

Find the coordinates of the foot of the normal from A$(2, -1, 3)$ to the plane
$x - y + 2z = 27$.   Hence find the shortest distance from A to the plane.

$x - y + 2z = 27$ has normal vector $\begin{pmatrix} 1 \\ -1 \\ 2 \end{pmatrix}$

$\therefore$ the parametric equations of AN are

$x = 2 + t, \quad y = -1 - t, \quad z = 3 + 2t$

and this line meets the plane $x - y + 2z = 27$ where

$$2 + t - (-1 - t) + 2(3 + 2t) = 27$$
$$\therefore \quad 2 + t + 1 + t + 6 + 4t = 27$$
$$\therefore \quad 6t + 9 = 27$$
$$\therefore \quad 6t = 18$$
$$\therefore \quad t = 3 \qquad \qquad \therefore \ \ \text{N is } (5, -4, 9).$$

The shortest distance, $\text{AN} = \sqrt{(5 - 2)^2 + (-4 - -1)^2 + (9 - 3)^2}$
$$= \sqrt{54} \text{ units.}$$

Example 20

Find the coordinates of the foot of the normal N from A$(2, -1, 3)$ to the plane with equation $\mathbf{r} = \mathbf{i} + 3\mathbf{k} + \lambda(4\mathbf{i} - \mathbf{j} + \mathbf{k}) + \mu(2\mathbf{i} + \mathbf{j} - 2\mathbf{k})$, $\lambda, \mu \in \mathbb{R}$.

The normal to the plane has direction vector given by

$$(4\mathbf{i} - \mathbf{j} + \mathbf{k}) \times (2\mathbf{i} + \mathbf{j} - 2\mathbf{k}) = \begin{vmatrix} \mathbf{i} & \mathbf{j} & \mathbf{k} \\ 4 & -1 & 1 \\ 2 & 1 & -2 \end{vmatrix} = \begin{pmatrix} 1 \\ 10 \\ 6 \end{pmatrix}.$$

The equation of the normal through A is $\begin{pmatrix} x \\ y \\ z \end{pmatrix} = \begin{pmatrix} 2 \\ -1 \\ 3 \end{pmatrix} + t \begin{pmatrix} 1 \\ 10 \\ 6 \end{pmatrix}$

so N must have coordinates of the form $(2 + t, \ -1 + 10t, 3 + 6t)$.

But N lies in the plane,   so $\begin{pmatrix} 2 + t \\ -1 + 10t \\ 3 + 6t \end{pmatrix} = \begin{pmatrix} 1 \\ 0 \\ 3 \end{pmatrix} + \lambda \begin{pmatrix} 4 \\ -1 \\ 1 \end{pmatrix} + \mu \begin{pmatrix} 2 \\ 1 \\ -2 \end{pmatrix}$

$$\therefore \ \begin{cases} 2 + t = 1 + 4\lambda + 2\mu \\ -1 + 10t = -\lambda + \mu \\ 3 + 6t = 3 + \lambda - 2\mu \end{cases} \quad \text{and so} \quad \begin{cases} 4\lambda + 2\mu - t = 1 \\ -\lambda + \mu - 10t = -1 \\ \lambda - 2\mu - 6t = 0 \end{cases}$$

Solving simultaneously with technology gives $\lambda = \frac{40}{137}$, $\mu = \frac{-7}{137}$, $t = \frac{9}{137}$

$\therefore \ $ N is the point $\left(2\frac{9}{137}, \ -\frac{47}{137}, 3\frac{54}{137} \right)$

Check by substituting for λ and μ in the equation of the plane.

EXERCISE 16D

1   Find the equation of the plane:

    a   with normal vector $\begin{pmatrix} 2 \\ -1 \\ 3 \end{pmatrix}$ and through $(-1, 2, 4)$

    b   perpendicular to the line connecting   A$(2, 3, 1)$ and   B$(5, 7, 2)$ and through A

    c   perpendicular to the line connecting   A$(1, 4, 2)$ and   B$(4, 1, -4)$ and containing P such that   AP : PB $= 1 : 2$

    d   containing   A$(3, 2, 1)$ and the line $x = 1 + t$, $y = 2 - t$, $z = 3 + 2t$.

2 State the normal vector to the plane with equation:

    a $2x + 3y - z = 8$ **b** $3x - y = 11$ **c** $z = 2$ **d** $x = 0$

3 Find the equation of the:

    a XOZ-plane   **b**   plane perpendicular to the Z-axis and through $(2, -1, 4)$.

4 Find the equation of the plane in   **i**   vector form   **ii**   Cartesian form,   through:

    a   A(0, 2, 6), B(1, 3, 2) and C(−1, 2, 4)   **b**   A(3, 1, 2), B(0, 4, 0) and C(0, 0, 1)

    c   A(2, 0, 3), B(0, −1, 2) and C(4, −3, 0).

5 Find the equations of the following *lines*:

    a   through $(1, -2, 0)$ and normal to the plane $x - 3y + 4z = 8$

    b   through $(3, 4, -1)$ and normal to the plane $x - y - 2z = 11$.

6 Find the parametric equations of the line through A(2, −1, 3) and B(1, 2, 0) and hence find where this line meets the plane with equation $x + 2y - z = 5$.

7 Find the parametric equations of the line through P(1, −2, 4) and Q(2, 0, −1) and hence find where this line meets:

    a   the YOZ-plane   **b**   the plane with equation $y + z = 2$

    c   the line with equations $\dfrac{x-3}{2} = \dfrac{y+2}{3} = \dfrac{z-30}{-1}$.

8 In the following, find the foot of the normal from A to the given plane and hence find the shortest distance from A to the plane:

    a   A(1, 0, 2); $2x + y - 2z + 11 = 0$ **b**   A(2, −1, 3); $x - y + 3z = -10$

    c   A(1, −4, −3); $4x - y - 2z = 8$

9 Find the coordinates of the mirror image of A(3, 1, 2) when reflected in the plane $x + 2y + z = 1$.

10 Does the line through $(3, 4, -1)$ and normal to $x + 4y - z = -2$ intersect any of the coordinate axes?

11 Find the equations of the plane through A(1, 2, 3) and B(0, −1, 2) which is parallel to: **a**   the X-axis   **b**   the Y-axis   **c**   the Z-axis.

12 Show that the lines $x - 1 = \dfrac{y-2}{2} = z + 3$ and $x + 1 = y - 3 = 2z + 5$ are coplanar and find the equation of the plane which contains them.

13 A(1, 2, k) lies on the plane $x + 2y - 2z = 8$.   Find:

    a   the value of k

    b   the coordinates of B such that AB is normal to the plane and 6 units from it.

14 In the following, find the foot of the normal from A to the given plane and hence find the shortest distance from A to the plane:

    a   A(3, 2, 1); $\mathbf{r} = 3\mathbf{i} + \mathbf{j} + 2\mathbf{k} + \lambda(2\mathbf{i} + \mathbf{j} + \mathbf{k}) + \mu(4\mathbf{i} + 2\mathbf{j} - 2\mathbf{k})$

    b   A(1, 0, −2); $\mathbf{r} = \mathbf{i} - \mathbf{j} + \mathbf{k} + \lambda(3\mathbf{i} - \mathbf{j} + 2\mathbf{k}) + \mu(-\mathbf{i} + \mathbf{j} - \mathbf{k})$

15 Q is any point in the plane
$Ax + By + Cz + D = 0$.

d is the distance from P(x_1, y_1, z_1) to the given plane.

a Explain why $d = \dfrac{|\overrightarrow{QP} \bullet \mathbf{n}|}{|\mathbf{n}|}$.

b Hence, show that $d = \dfrac{|Ax_1 + By_1 + Cz_1 + D|}{\sqrt{A^2 + B^2 + C^2}}$.

c Check your answers to question **8** using the formula of **b**.

16 Find the distance from:

a $(0, 0, 0)$ to $x + 2y - z = 10$ **b** $(1, -3, 2)$ to $x + y - z = 2$.

Note: • To find the distance between two parallel planes, find a point on one of the planes and use the method in **Example 20**.

 • To find the distance between a line and a plane, both of which are parallel, find a point on the line and use the method in **Example 20**.

17 Find the distance between the parallel planes:

a $x + y + 2z = 4$ and $2x + 2y + 4z + 11 = 0$
b $ax + by + cz + d_1 = 0$ and $ax + by + cz + d_2 = 0$.

18 Show that the line $x = 2 + t$, $y = -1 + 2t$, $z = -3t$ is parallel to the plane $11x - 4y + z = 0$, and find its distance from the plane.

19 Find the equations of the two planes which are parallel to $2x - y + 2z = 5$ and 2 units from it.

E   ANGLES IN SPACE

THE ANGLE BETWEEN A LINE AND A PLANE

Suppose a line has direction vector $\mathbf{d}$ and a plane has normal vector $\mathbf{n}$. We allow $\mathbf{n}$ to intersect the line making an angle of θ with it. The required acute angle is ϕ and

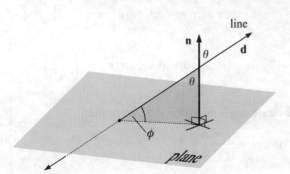

$$\sin \phi = \cos \theta = \frac{|\mathbf{n} \bullet \mathbf{d}|}{|\mathbf{n}| |\mathbf{d}|}$$

$$\therefore \quad \phi = \sin^{-1}\left(\frac{|\mathbf{n} \bullet \mathbf{d}|}{|\mathbf{n}| |\mathbf{d}|}\right)$$

Example 21

Find the angle between the plane $x + 2y - z = 8$ and the line with equations
$x = t$, $y = 1 - t$, $z = 3 + 2t$.

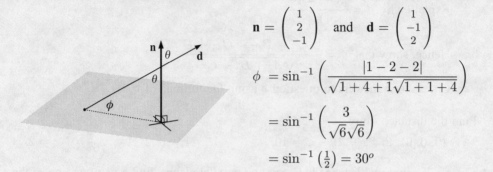

$$\mathbf{n} = \begin{pmatrix} 1 \\ 2 \\ -1 \end{pmatrix} \quad \text{and} \quad \mathbf{d} = \begin{pmatrix} 1 \\ -1 \\ 2 \end{pmatrix}$$

$$\phi = \sin^{-1}\left(\frac{|1 - 2 - 2|}{\sqrt{1 + 4 + 1}\sqrt{1 + 1 + 4}} \right)$$

$$= \sin^{-1}\left(\frac{3}{\sqrt{6}\sqrt{6}} \right)$$

$$= \sin^{-1}\left(\tfrac{1}{2} \right) = 30^{o}$$

THE ANGLE BETWEEN TWO PLANES

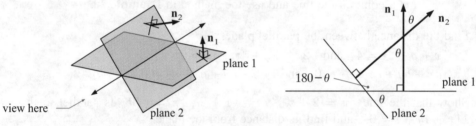

$\cos\theta = \dfrac{|\mathbf{n_1} \bullet \mathbf{n_2}|}{|\mathbf{n_1}||\mathbf{n_2}|}$ is the cosine of the acute angle between two planes.

So,   if two planes have normal vectors $\mathbf{n_1}$ and $\mathbf{n_2}$ and θ is the

acute angle between them then $\theta = \cos^{-1}\left(\dfrac{|\mathbf{n_1} \bullet \mathbf{n_2}|}{|\mathbf{n_1}||\mathbf{n_2}|} \right)$.

Example 22

Find the angle between the planes with equations $x + y - z = 8$ and
$2x - y + 3z = -1$.

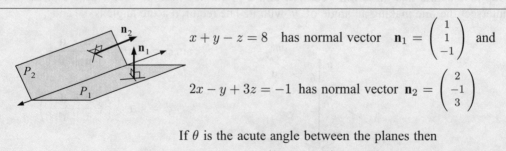

$x + y - z = 8$ has normal vector $\mathbf{n_1} = \begin{pmatrix} 1 \\ 1 \\ -1 \end{pmatrix}$ and

$2x - y + 3z = -1$ has normal vector $\mathbf{n_2} = \begin{pmatrix} 2 \\ -1 \\ 3 \end{pmatrix}$

If θ is the acute angle between the planes then

$$\theta = \cos^{-1}\left(\frac{|\mathbf{n_1} \bullet \mathbf{n_2}|}{|\mathbf{n_1}||\mathbf{n_2}|} \right)$$

$$= \cos^{-1}\left(\frac{|2+-1+-3|}{\sqrt{1+1+1}\sqrt{4+1+9}}\right)$$

$$= \cos^{-1}\left(\frac{2}{\sqrt{42}}\right)$$

$$\approx 72.0^o$$

EXERCISE 16E

1 Find the angle between:

   a the plane $x - y + z = 5$ and the line $\dfrac{x-1}{4} = \dfrac{y+1}{3} = z+2$

   b the plane $2x - y + z = 8$ and the line $x = t+1, \quad y = -1+3t, \quad z = t$

   c the plane $3x + 4y - z = -4$ and the line $x - 4 = 3 - y = 2(z+1)$

   d the plane $\mathbf{r}_p = 2\mathbf{i} - \mathbf{j} + \mathbf{k} + \lambda(3\mathbf{i} - 4\mathbf{j} - \mathbf{k}) + \mu(\mathbf{i} + \mathbf{j} - 2\mathbf{k})$ and
     the line $\mathbf{r}_l = 3\mathbf{i} + 2\mathbf{j} - \mathbf{k} + t(\mathbf{i} - \mathbf{j} + \mathbf{k})$.

2 Find the acute angle between the planes with equations:

   a $2x - y + z = 3$ **b** $x - y + 3z = 2$ **c** $3x - y + z = -11$
      $x + 3y + 2z = 8$ $3x + y - z = -5$ $2x + 4y - z = 2$

   d $\mathbf{r}_1 = 3\mathbf{i} + 2\mathbf{j} - \mathbf{k} - \lambda(\mathbf{i} - \mathbf{j} + \mathbf{k}) + \mu(2\mathbf{i} - 4\mathbf{j} + 3\mathbf{k})$
     and $\mathbf{r}_2 = \mathbf{i} + \mathbf{j} - \mathbf{k} - \lambda(2\mathbf{i} + \mathbf{j} + \mathbf{k}) + \mu(\mathbf{i} + \mathbf{j} + \mathbf{k})$

   e $3x - 4y + z = -2$ and $\mathbf{r} = \begin{pmatrix} 2 \\ -1 \\ 1 \end{pmatrix} + \lambda \begin{pmatrix} 3 \\ -1 \\ 0 \end{pmatrix} + \mu \begin{pmatrix} 2 \\ 1 \\ 1 \end{pmatrix}$

F   THE INTERSECTION OF TWO OR MORE PLANES

- **Two planes** in space could be:

   (1) intersecting   **(2)** parallel   **(3)** coincident

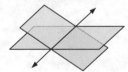   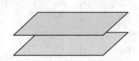   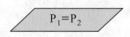

- **Three planes** in space could be:

   (1) all coincident   **(2)** two coincident and   **(3)** two coincident and
                    one intersecting   one parallel

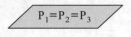   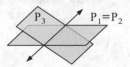   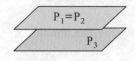

(4) two parallel and
one intersecting

(5) all 3 parallel

(6) all meet at the one
point

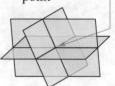

(7) all meet in a
common line

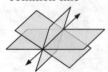

(8) the line of intersection
of any 2 is parallel to
the third plane.

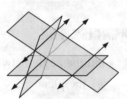

The program Winplot by **Peanuts software** displays these cases.

This work should be linked to **Chapter 13** on matrices. Solutions can be found by using inverse matrices (where there is a unique solution) and/or row operations on the augmented matrix.

The use of row operations on the augmented matrix is essential when the solution is not unique. This is when the matrix of coefficients is singular (determinant = 0) and thus not invertible.

Example 23

a Use elementary row operations to solve the system:
$$x + 3y - z = 0$$
$$3x + 5y - z = 0$$
$$x - 5y + (2 - m)z = 9 - m^2$$

for any real number m. Give geometric interpretations of your results.

b Hence solve $\quad x + 3y - z = 0,\quad$ giving a geometric interpretation.
$$3x + 5y - z = 0$$
$$x - 5y + z = 8$$

---

a Augmented matrix

$$\begin{bmatrix} 1 & 3 & -1 & | & 0 \\ 3 & 5 & -1 & | & 0 \\ 1 & -5 & 2-m & | & 9-m^2 \end{bmatrix}$$

$$\sim \begin{bmatrix} 1 & 3 & -1 & | & 0 \\ 0 & -4 & 2 & | & 0 \\ 0 & -8 & 3-m & | & 9-m^2 \end{bmatrix} \quad \begin{array}{l} R_2 \to R_2 - 3R_1 \\ R_3 \to R_3 - R_1 \end{array}$$

$$\sim \begin{bmatrix} 1 & 3 & -1 & | & 0 \\ 0 & 2 & -1 & | & 0 \\ 0 & 0 & -m-1 & | & 9-m^2 \end{bmatrix} \quad \begin{array}{l} R_2 \to R_2 \times -\tfrac{1}{2} \\ R_3 \to R_3 - 2R_2 \end{array}$$

Case (1) If $m = -1$, the augmented matrix becomes $\begin{bmatrix} 1 & 3 & -1 & | & 0 \\ 0 & 2 & -1 & | & 0 \\ 0 & 0 & 0 & | & 8 \end{bmatrix}$.

The system is inconsistent, so there are no solutions.

∴ the three planes do not have a common point of intersection

The normals are $\quad \mathbf{n}_1 = \begin{pmatrix} 1 \\ 3 \\ -1 \end{pmatrix}, \quad \mathbf{n}_2 = \begin{pmatrix} 3 \\ 5 \\ -1 \end{pmatrix}, \quad \mathbf{n}_3 = \begin{pmatrix} 1 \\ -5 \\ 3 \end{pmatrix}$

None of the planes are parallel.

$\therefore$ the line of intersection of any two is parallel to the third plane. (diag **(8)**)

Case (2) If $m \neq -1$ there is a unique solution. $\quad (-m-1)z = 9 - m^2$

$$\therefore \quad (m+1)z = m^2 - 9$$

$$\therefore \quad z = \frac{m^2 - 9}{m + 1}$$

From row 2, $2y - z = 0 \quad \therefore \quad y = \frac{1}{2}z = \dfrac{m^2 - 9}{2(m+1)}$

From row 1, $x = -3y + z = \dfrac{-3(m^2 - 9)}{2(m+1)} + \dfrac{2(m^2 - 9)}{2(m+1)} = \dfrac{9 - m^2}{2(m+1)}$

The three planes meet at a unique point (diag **(6)**)

$$\left(\frac{9 - m^2}{2(m+1)}, \ \frac{m^2 - 9}{2(m+1)}, \ \frac{m^2 - 9}{m+1} \right) \quad \text{provided} \quad m \neq -1.$$

b Comparing with **a**, $2 - m = 1$ and $9 - m^2 = 8 \quad \therefore \quad m = 1$

$\therefore$ the three planes meet at the point $\left(\frac{8}{4}, \frac{-8}{4}, \frac{-8}{2} \right)$, i.e., $(2, -2, -4)$.

Example 24

a Find the intersection of the planes: $\quad \begin{aligned} x + y + 2z &= 2 \\ 2x + y - z &= 4 \end{aligned}$

b Hence solve: $\quad \begin{aligned} x + y + 2z &= 2 \\ 2x + y - z &= 4 \\ x - y - z &= 5 \end{aligned}$ $\qquad$ Give a geometric interpretation of your result.

---

a The augmented matrix $\quad \begin{bmatrix} 1 & 1 & 2 & | & 2 \\ 2 & 1 & -1 & | & 4 \end{bmatrix} \sim \begin{bmatrix} 1 & 1 & 2 & | & 2 \\ 0 & 1 & 5 & | & 0 \end{bmatrix}$

The system is consistent with infinite solutions.

Let $z = t$ so $y = -5t, \ x = 2 + 3t, \ t \in \mathbb{R}$ are the solutions,

$\therefore$ the two planes meet in the line

$\quad x = 2 + 3t, \quad y = -5t, \quad z = t, \quad t \in \mathbb{R}.$

Note: This line passes through $(2, 0, 0)$ has direction vector $\begin{pmatrix} 3 \\ -5 \\ 1 \end{pmatrix}$.

b The solutions of the first 2 equations are $x = 2 + 3t, \ y = -5t, \ z = t$ {from **a**}

Substitution into the third equation gives $\quad 2 + 3t + 5t - t = 5$

$$\therefore \quad 7t = 3$$

$$\therefore \quad t = \frac{3}{7}$$

$\therefore \quad x = \frac{23}{7}, \quad y = -\frac{15}{7}, \quad z = \frac{3}{7}$

$\therefore$ the three planes meet at the unique point $\left(\frac{23}{7}, \ -\frac{15}{7}, \ \frac{3}{7} \right)$.

EXERCISE 16F

1 **a** How many solutions are possible $a_1x + b_1y + c_1z = d_1$
   when solving simultaneously: $a_2x + b_2y + c_2z = d_2?$

   b Under what conditions will the planes in **a** be: **i** parallel   **ii** coincident?

   c Solve the following using elementary row operations and interpret each system of
   equations geometrically:

   i $x - 3y + 2z = 8$ **ii** $2x + y + z = 5$ **iii** $x + 2y - 3z = 6$
         $3x - 9y + 2z = 4$ $x - y + z = 3$ $3x + 6y - 9z = 18$

2 Discuss the possible solutions of the following systems where k is a real number. Interpret
   the solutions geometrically:

   a $x + 2y - z = 6$ **b** $x - y + 3z = 8$
         $2x + 4y + kz = 12$ $2x - 2y + 6z = k$

3 For the eight possible geometric solutions of three planes in space, comment on the
   possible solutions in each case.

   For example,   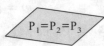   has infinitely many solutions where x, y and z
   are expressed in terms of two parameters s and t.

4 Solve the following systems using elementary row operations and in each case state the
   geometric meaning of your solution:

   a $x + y - z = -5$ **b** $x - y + 2z = 1$ **c** $x + 2y - z = 8$
         $x - y + 2z = 11$ $2x + y - z = 8$ $2x - y - z = 5$
         $4x + y - 5z = -18$ $5x - 2y + 5z = 11$ $3x - 4y - z = 2$

   d $x - y + z = 8$ **e** $x + y - 2z = 1$ **f** $x - y - z = 5$
         $2x - 2y + 2z = 11$ $x - y + z = 4$ $x + y + z = 1$
         $x + 3y - z = -2$ $3x + 3y - 6z = 3$ $5x - y + 2z = 17$

5 Solve the system of equations $x - y + 3z = 1$
                                        $2x - 3y - z = 3$
                                        $3x - 5y - 5z = k$ where k takes all real values.
   State the geometrical meaning of the different solutions.

6 Find all values of m for which $x + 2y + mz = -1$
                                          $2x + y - z = 3$
                                          $mx - 2y + z = 1$ has a unique solution.

   In the cases where there is no unique solution, solve the system. Give geometrical
   meanings to all possible solutions. Illustrate each case.

7 Find if and where the following planes meet:

   $P_1: \mathbf{r}_1 = 2\mathbf{i} - \mathbf{j} + \lambda(3\mathbf{i} + \mathbf{k}) + \mu(\mathbf{i} + \mathbf{j} - \mathbf{k})$ $P_3: \mathbf{r}_3 = \begin{pmatrix} 2 \\ -1 \\ 2 \end{pmatrix} + t\begin{pmatrix} 1 \\ -1 \\ 0 \end{pmatrix} - u\begin{pmatrix} 0 \\ -1 \\ 2 \end{pmatrix}$

   $P_2: \mathbf{r}_2 = 3\mathbf{i} - \mathbf{j} + 3\mathbf{k} + r(2\mathbf{i} - \mathbf{k}) + s(\mathbf{i} + \mathbf{j})$

REVIEW SET 16A (2-D)

1 Find **a** the vector equation   **b** the parametric equations

of the line that passes through $(-6, 3)$ with direction $\begin{pmatrix} 4 \\ -3 \end{pmatrix}$.

2 Find the vector equation of the line which cuts the y-axis at $(0, 8)$ and has direction $5\mathbf{i} + 4\mathbf{j}$.

3 $(-3, m)$ lies on the line with vector equation $\begin{pmatrix} x \\ y \end{pmatrix} = \begin{pmatrix} 18 \\ -2 \end{pmatrix} + t \begin{pmatrix} -7 \\ 4 \end{pmatrix}$. Find m.

4 Find the velocity vector of an object that is moving in the direction $3\mathbf{i} - \mathbf{j}$ with a speed of 20 km h^{-1}.

5 A particle at $P(x(t), y(t))$ moves such that $x(t) = -4 + 8t$ and $y(t) = 3 + 6t$, where $t \geqslant 0$ is the time in seconds. The distance units are metres. Find the:
  a initial position of P
  b position of P after 4 seconds
  c speed of P
  d velocity vector of P.

6 A yacht is sailing at a constant speed of $5\sqrt{10} \text{ km h}^{-1}$ in the direction $-\mathbf{i} - 3\mathbf{j}$. Initially it is at point $(-6, 10)$. A beacon is at $(0, 0)$ at the centre of a tiny atoll.
  a Find in terms of $\mathbf{i}$ and $\mathbf{j}$:
    i the initial position vector of the yacht
    ii the direction vector of the yacht
    iii the position vector of the yacht at any time t hours, $t \geqslant 0$.
  b Find the time when the yacht is closest to the beacon.
  c If there is a reef of radius 8 km around the atoll, will the yacht hit the reef?

7 Submarine X23 is at $(2, 4)$. It fires a torpedo with velocity vector $\begin{pmatrix} 1 \\ -3 \end{pmatrix}$ at exactly 2:17 pm. Submarine Y18 is at $(11, 3)$. It fires a torpedo with velocity vector $\begin{pmatrix} -1 \\ a \end{pmatrix}$ at 2:19 pm to intercept the torpedo from X23.
  a Find $x_1(t)$ and $y_1(t)$ for the torpedo fired from submarine X23.
  b Find $x_2(t)$ and $y_2(t)$ for the torpedo fired from submarine Y18.
  c At what time does the interception occur?
  d What was the direction and speed of the interception torpedo?

8 Trapezoid (trapezium) KLMN is formed by the lines:

line 1 (KL) is $\begin{pmatrix} x \\ y \end{pmatrix} = \begin{pmatrix} 2 \\ 19 \end{pmatrix} + p \begin{pmatrix} 5 \\ -2 \end{pmatrix}$;   line 2 (ML) is $\begin{pmatrix} x \\ y \end{pmatrix} = \begin{pmatrix} 33 \\ -5 \end{pmatrix} + q \begin{pmatrix} -11 \\ 16 \end{pmatrix}$;

line 3 (NK) is $\begin{pmatrix} x \\ y \end{pmatrix} = \begin{pmatrix} 3 \\ 7 \end{pmatrix} + r \begin{pmatrix} 4 \\ 10 \end{pmatrix}$;   line 4 (MN) is $\begin{pmatrix} x \\ y \end{pmatrix} = \begin{pmatrix} 43 \\ -9 \end{pmatrix} + s \begin{pmatrix} -5 \\ 2 \end{pmatrix}$

where p, q, r and s are scalars.
  a Which two lines are parallel? Why?
  b Which lines are perpendicular? Why?
  c Use vector methods to find the coordinates of K, L, M and N.
  d Calculate the area of trapezium KLMN.

REVIEW SET 16B (3-D)

1 Show that A(1, 0, 4), B(3, 1, 12), C(−1, 2, 2) and D(−2, 0, −5) are coplanar.

Find: **a**   the equation of the plane

   b   the coordinates of the nearest point on the plane to E(3, 3, 2).

2 A is (3, 2, −1) and B is (−1, 2, 4).

   a Write down the vector equation of the line through A and B.

   b Find the equation of the plane through B with normal AB.

   c Find *two* points on the line AB which are $2\sqrt{41}$ units from A.

3 P_1 is the plane $2x - y - 2z = 9$ and P_2 is the plane $x + y + 2z = 1$.

l is the line with parametric equations $x = t$, $y = 2t - 1$, $z = 3 - t$.

Find the acute angle: **a**   that l makes with P_1 **b**   between P_1 and P_2.

4 For A(3, −1, 1) and B(0, 2, −1), find the:

   a vector equation of the line passing through A and B

   b the coordinates of P which divides BA in the ratio $2 : 5$.

5 For C(−3, 2, −1) and D(0, 1, −4) find the coordinates of the point(s) where the line passing through C and D meets the plane with equation $2x - y + z = 3$.

6 Given the lines $\dfrac{x - 8}{3} = \dfrac{y + 9}{-16} = \dfrac{z - 10}{7}$ and $x = 15 + 3t$, $y = 29 + 8t$, $z = 5 - 5t$:

   a show that they are skew   **b**   find the acute angle between them

   c find the shortest distance between them.

7 **a** How far is X(−1, 1, 3) from the plane $x - 2y - 2z = 8$?

   b Find the coordinates of the foot of the perpendicular from Q(−1, 2, 3) to the line $2 - x = y - 3 = -\frac{1}{2}z$.

8 P(2, 0, 1), Q(3, 4, −2) and R(−1, 3, 2) are three points in space. Find:

   a $\overrightarrow{PQ}$, $|\overrightarrow{PQ}|$ and $\overrightarrow{QR}$ **b**   the parametric equations of line $\overleftrightarrow{PQ}$.

   c Use **a** to find the vector equation of the plane PQR.

9 Given the point A(−1, 3, 2),   the plane $2x - y + 2z = 8$, and the line defined by $x = 7 - 2t$, $y = -6 + t$, $z = 1 + 5t$,   find:

   a the distance from A to the plane

   b the coordinates of the point on the plane nearest to A

   c the shortest distance from A to the line.

10 **a** Find the equation of the plane through A(−1, 0, 2), B(0, −1, 1) and C(1, 2, −1).

   b Find the equation of the line, in parametric form, which passes through the origin and is normal to the plane in **a**.

   c Find the point where the line in **b** intersects the plane in **a**.

11 Solve the system
$$x - y + z = 5$$
$$2x + y - z = -1$$
$$7x + 2y + kz = -k \quad \text{for any real number } k$$

using elementary row operations. Give geometric interpretations of your results.

12 $\mathbf{p} = \begin{pmatrix} 1 \\ -1 \\ 2 \end{pmatrix}$ and $\mathbf{q} = \begin{pmatrix} 2 \\ 3 \\ -1 \end{pmatrix}$

a Find $\mathbf{p} \times \mathbf{q}$.

b Find m if $\mathbf{p} \times \mathbf{q}$ is perpendicular to the line l with equation
$$\mathbf{r} = \begin{pmatrix} 1 \\ -2 \\ 3 \end{pmatrix} + \lambda \begin{pmatrix} 2 \\ 1 \\ m \end{pmatrix}$$

c Find the equation of the plane P containing l which is perpendicular to $\mathbf{p} \times \mathbf{q}$.

d Find t if the point $A(4, t, 2)$ lies on the plane P.

e If B is the point $(6, -3, 5)$, find the exact value of the sine of the angle between the line AB and the plane P.

REVIEW SET 16C

1 For $A(-1, 2, 3)$, $B(2, 0, -1)$ and $C(-3, 2, -4)$ find:

a the equation of the plane defined by A, B and C

b the measure of angle CAB

c r given that $D(r, 1, -r)$ is a point such that angle BDC is a right angle.

2 a Find where the line through $L(1, 0, 1)$ and $M(-1, 2, -1)$ meets the plane with equation $x - 2y - 3z = 14$.

b Find the shortest distance from L to the plane.

3 Given $A(-1, 2, 3)$, $B(1, 0, -1)$ and $C(1, 3, 0)$, find:

a the normal vector to the plane containing A, B and C

b D, the fourth vertex of parallelogram ACBD

c the coordinates of the foot of the perpendicular from C to the line AB.

4 Show that the line $x - 1 = \dfrac{y + 2}{2} = \dfrac{z - 3}{4}$ is parallel to the plane $6x + 7y - 5z = 8$ and find the distance between them.

5 Consider the lines with equations $\dfrac{x - 3}{2} = y - 4 = \dfrac{z + 1}{-2}$ and $x = -1 + 3t$, $y = 2 + 2t$, $z = 3 - t$.

a Are the lines parallel, intersecting or skew? Justify your answer.

b Determine the cosine of the acute angle between the lines.

6 For $A(2, -1, 3)$ and $B(0, 1, -1)$, find:

a the vector equation of the line through A and B, and hence

b the coordinates of C on AB which is 2 units from A.

7 Find the equation of the plane through A(−1, 2, 3), B(1, 0, −1) and C(0, −1, 5). If X is (3, 2, 4), find the angle that AX makes with this plane.

8 **a** Find all vectors of length 3 units which are normal to the plane $x − y + z = 6$.

   b Find a unit vector parallel to $\mathbf{i} + r\mathbf{j} + 3\mathbf{k}$ and perpendicular to $2\mathbf{i} − \mathbf{j} + 2\mathbf{k}$.

   c The distance from A(−1, 2, 3) to the plane with equation $2x − y + 2z = k$ is 3 units. Find k.

9 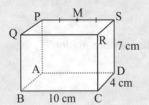   Use vector methods to determine the measure of angle QDM given that M is the midpoint of PS.

10 P(−1, 2, 3) and Q(4, 0, −1) are two points in space. Find:

   a $\overrightarrow{PQ}$ **b** the angle that $\overrightarrow{PQ}$ makes with the X-axis.

11 ABC is a triangle in space. M is the midpoint of side [BC] and O is the origin. P is a point such that $\overrightarrow{OP} = \frac{1}{3}(\overrightarrow{OA} + \overrightarrow{OB} + \overrightarrow{OC})$.

   a Write $\overrightarrow{OM}$ in terms of $\overrightarrow{OB}$ and $\overrightarrow{OC}$.

   b Hence, show that $\overrightarrow{OP} = \frac{1}{3}(\overrightarrow{OA} + 2\overrightarrow{OM})$.

   c Show that P lies on [AM].

   d Find the ratio in which P divides [AM].

12 Lines l_1 and l_2 are given by

$$l_1: \quad \mathbf{r} = \begin{pmatrix} 3 \\ -2 \\ -2 \end{pmatrix} + s \begin{pmatrix} -1 \\ 1 \\ 2 \end{pmatrix} \quad \text{and} \quad l_2: \quad \mathbf{r} = \begin{pmatrix} 3 \\ 0 \\ -1 \end{pmatrix} + t \begin{pmatrix} -1 \\ -1 \\ 1 \end{pmatrix}$$

   a Find the coordinates of A, the point of intersection of the lines.

   b Show that the point B(0, −3, 2) lies on the line l_2.

   c Find the equation of the line BC given that C(3, −2, −2) lies on l_1.

   d Find the equation of the plane containing A, B and C.

   e Find the area of triangle ABC.

   f Show that the point D(9, −4, 2) lies on the normal to the plane passing through C.

   g Find the volume of the pyramid ABCD.

REVIEW SET 16D

1 Given the points A(4, 2, −1), B(2, 1, 5), and C(9, 4, 1):

  a Show that $\overrightarrow{AB}$ is perpendicular to $\overrightarrow{AC}$.

  b Find the equation of the plane containing A, B and C and hence determine the distance from this plane to the point (8, 1, 0).

  c Find the equation of the line through A and B.

  d Determine the distance from D(8, 11, −5) to the line through A and B.

2 The equations of two lines are:
$$l_1: \quad x = 3t - 4, \quad y = t + 2, \quad z = 2t - 1$$
$$l_2: \quad x = \frac{y-5}{2} = \frac{-z-1}{2}.$$

  a Find the point of intersection of l_1 and the plane $2x + y - z = 2$.

  b Find the point of intersection of l_1 and l_2.

  c Find the equation of the plane that contains l_1 and l_2.

3 **a** Show that the plane $2x + y + z = 5$ contains the line
$l_1: x = -2t + 2, \quad y = t, \quad z = 3t + 1, \quad t \in \mathbb{R}$.

  b For what values of k does the plane $x + ky + z = 3$ contain l_1?

  c Without using row operations, find the values of p and q for which the following system of equations has an infinite number of solutions. Clearly explain your reasoning.
$$2x + y + z = 5$$
$$x - y + z = 3$$
$$-2x + py + 2z = q.$$

4 **a** Consider two unit vectors **a** and **b**. Prove that the vector **a** + **b** bisects the angle between vector **a** and vector **b**.

  b Consider the points H(9, 5, −5), J(7, 3, −4) and K(1, 0, 2).
Find the equation of the line l that passes through J and bisects angle HJK.

  c Find the coordinates of the point where l meets HK.

5 $x^2 + y^2 + z^2 = 26$ is the equation of a sphere, centre (0, 0, 0) and radius $\sqrt{26}$ units. Find the point(s) where the line through (3, −1, −2) and (5, 3, −4) meets the sphere.

6 Find the angle between the plane $2x + 2y - z = 3$ and the line $x = t - 1, \ y = -2t + 4, \ z = -t + 3$.

7 Let $\mathbf{r} = 2\mathbf{i} - 2\mathbf{j} - \mathbf{k}$, $\mathbf{s} = 2\mathbf{i} + \mathbf{j} + 2\mathbf{k}$, $\mathbf{t} = \mathbf{i} + 2\mathbf{j} - \mathbf{k}$, be the position vectors of the points R, S and T, respectively. Find the area of the triangle $\triangle RST$.

8 In the figure ABCD is a parallelogram.
X is the midpoint of BC, and Y is on AX such that AY : YX = 2 : 1.

  a Find the coordinates of X and D.

  b Find the coordinates of Y.

  c Show that B, Y and D are collinear.

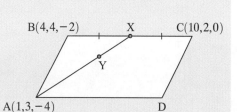

9 Let the vectors **a**, **b** and **c** be $\mathbf{a} = 3\mathbf{i} + 2\mathbf{j} - \mathbf{k}$, $\mathbf{b} = \mathbf{i} + \mathbf{j} - \mathbf{k}$, $\mathbf{c} = 2\mathbf{i} - \mathbf{j} + \mathbf{k}$.

    a Show that $\mathbf{b} \times \mathbf{c} = -3\mathbf{j} - 3\mathbf{k}$.

    b Verify for the given vectors that $\mathbf{a} \times (\mathbf{b} \times \mathbf{c}) = \mathbf{b}\,(\mathbf{a} \bullet \mathbf{c}) - \mathbf{c}\,(\mathbf{a} \bullet \mathbf{b})$.

10 Given the vectors $\mathbf{a} = \begin{pmatrix} 1 \\ 2 \\ -2 \end{pmatrix}$ and $\mathbf{b} = \begin{pmatrix} -t \\ 1+t \\ 2t \end{pmatrix}$, find t if:

    a **a** and **b** are perpendicular   **b** **a** and **b** are parallel.

11 Line 1 has equation $\dfrac{x-8}{3} = \dfrac{y+9}{-16} = \dfrac{z-10}{7}$ and

line 2 has vector equation $\begin{pmatrix} x \\ y \\ z \end{pmatrix} = \begin{pmatrix} 15 \\ 29 \\ 5 \end{pmatrix} + \lambda \begin{pmatrix} 3 \\ 8 \\ -5 \end{pmatrix}$

    a Show that lines 1 and 2 are skew.

    b Line 3 is a translation of line 1 which intersects line 2. Find the equation of the plane containing lines 2 and 3.

    c Use **b** to find the shortest distance between lines 1 and 2.

    d Find the coordinates of the two points where the common perpendicular meets the lines 1 and 2.

Chapter 17

Descriptive statistics

BACKGROUND KNOWLEDGE IN STATISTICS

Before starting this chapter you should make sure that you have a good understanding of the necessary background knowledge.

Click on the icon alongside to obtain a printable set of exercises and answers on this background knowledge.

BACKGROUND
KNOWLEDGE

THE PEA PROBLEM

A farmer wishes to investigate the effect of a new organic fertiliser on his crops of peas. He is hoping to improve the crop yield by using the fertiliser. He divided a small garden into two equal plots and planted many peas in each. Both plots were treated the same except the fertiliser was used on one but not the other.

A random sample of 150 pods was harvested from each plot at the same time, and the number of peas in each pod was counted. The results were:

Without fertiliser

4 6 5 6 5 6 4 6 4 9 5 3 6 8 5 4 6 8 6 5 6 7 4 6 5 2 8 6 5 6 5 5 5 4 4 4 6 7 5 6
7 5 5 6 4 8 5 3 7 5 3 6 4 7 5 6 5 7 5 7 6 7 5 4 7 5 5 5 6 6 5 6 7 5 8 6 8 6 7 6
6 3 7 6 8 3 3 4 4 7 6 5 6 4 5 7 3 7 7 6 7 7 4 6 6 5 6 7 6 3 4 6 6 3 7 6 7 6 8 6
6 6 6 4 7 6 6 5 3 8 6 7 6 8 6 7 6 6 6 8 4 4 8 6 6 2 6 5 7 3

With fertiliser

6 7 7 4 9 5 5 5 8 9 8 9 7 7 5 8 7 6 6 7 9 7 7 7 8 9 3 7 4 8 5 10 8 6 7 6 7 5 6 8
7 9 4 4 9 6 8 5 8 7 7 4 7 8 10 6 10 7 7 7 9 7 7 8 6 8 6 8 7 4 8 6 8 7 3 8 7 6 9 7
6 9 7 6 8 3 9 5 7 6 8 7 9 7 8 4 8 7 7 7 6 6 8 6 3 8 5 8 7 6 7 4 9 6 6 6 8 4 7 8
9 7 7 4 7 5 7 4 7 6 4 6 7 7 6 7 8 7 6 6 7 8 6 7 10 5 13 4 7 11

For you to consider:

- Can you state clearly the problem that the farmer wants to solve?
- How has the farmer tried to make a fair comparison?
- How could the farmer make sure that his selection was at random?
- What is the best way of organising this data?
- What are suitable methods of display?
- Are there any abnormally high or low results and how should they be treated?
- How can we best describe the most typical pod size?
- How can we best describe the spread of possible pod sizes?
- Can a satisfactory conclusion be made?

CONTINUOUS NUMERICAL DATA AND HISTOGRAMS

A **continuous numerical variable** can take any value on part of the number line.

Continuous variables often have to be **measured** so that data can be recorded.

Examples of continuous numerical variables are:

The height of Year 11 students: the variable can take any value from about 140 cm to 200 cm.

The speed of cars on a stretch of highway: the variable can take any value from 0 $km\,h^{-1}$ to the fastest speed that a car can travel, but is most likely to be in the range 60 $km\,h^{-1}$ to 160 $km\,h^{-1}$.

ORGANISATION AND DISPLAY OF CONTINUOUS DATA

When data is recorded for a continuous variable there are likely to be many different values. We organise the data by grouping it into **class intervals**. A special type of graph called a **histogram** is used to display the data.

A histogram is similar to a column graph but, to account for the continuous nature of the variable, a number line is used for the horizontal axis and the 'columns' are joined together.

An example is given alongside. Notice that:

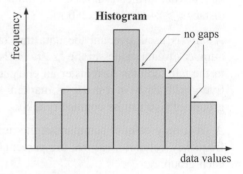

- the **modal class** (the class of values that appears most often) is easy to identify from a histogram
- the class intervals are the same size
- the frequency is represented by the height of the 'columns'.

SUMMARY: COLUMN GRAPHS AND HISTOGRAMS

Column graphs and histograms both have the following features:
- the frequency of occurrence is on the vertical axis
- the range of scores is on the horizontal axis
- column widths are equal and the height varies according to frequency.

Histograms are used for continuous data. They have no gaps between the columns.

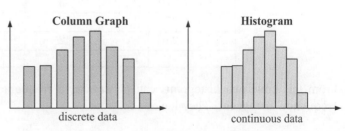

CASE STUDY   DRIVING A GOLF BALL

While Norm Gregory was here for the golf championship, I measured how far he hit 30 drives on the practice fairway. The results are given below in metres:

244.6	245.1	248.0	248.8	250.0
251.1	251.2	253.9	254.5	254.6
255.9	257.0	260.6	262.8	262.9
263.1	263.2	264.3	264.4	265.0
265.5	265.6	266.5	267.4	269.7
270.5	270.7	272.9	275.6	277.5

This type of data must be **grouped** before a histogram can be drawn.

In forming groups, find the lowest and highest values, and then choose a group width so that there are about 6 to 12 groups. In this case the lowest value is 244.6 m and the largest is 277.5 m. This gives a range of approximately 35 m, so a group width of 5 m will give eight groups of equal width.

We will use the following method of grouping. The first group '240 - < 245' includes any data value which is at least 240 m but less than 245 m. Similarly the group '260 - < 265' includes data which is at least 260 m but < 265 m. This technique creates a group for every distance $\geqslant$ 240 m but < 280 m.

A tally is used to count the data that falls in each group. Do not try to determine the number of data values in the '240 - < 245' group first off. Simply place a vertical stroke in the tally column to register an entry as you work through the data from start to finish. Every fifth entry in a group is marked with a diagonal line through the previous four so groups of five can be counted quickly.

A frequency column summarises the number of data values in each group. The relative frequency column measures the percentage of the total number of data values that are in each group.

Norm Gregory's 30 drives

Distance (m)	Tally	Frequency (f)	% Relative Frequency
240 - < 245	|	1	3.3
245 - < 250	|||	3	10.0
250 - < 255	⧸⧸⧸⧸ |	6	20.0
255 - < 260	||	2	6.7
260 - < 265	⧸⧸⧸⧸ ||	7	23.3
265 - < 270	⧸⧸⧸⧸ |	6	20.0
270 - < 275	|||	3	10.0
275 - < 280	||	2	6.7
	Totals	30	100.0

From this table two histograms can be drawn: a **frequency histogram** and a **relative frequency histogram**. They look as follows:

A **frequency histogram** displaying the distribution of 30 of Norm Gregory's drives.

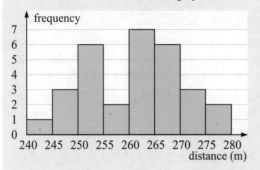

A **relative frequency histogram** displaying the distribution of 30 of Norm Gregory's drives.

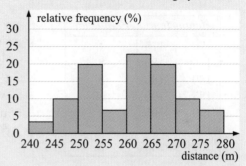

The advantage of the relative frequency histogram is that we can easily compare it with other distributions with different numbers of data values. Using percentages allows for a fair comparison.

Notice how the axes are both labelled and the graphs have titles.

The left edge of each bar is the first possible entry for that group.

Example 1

The weight of parcels sent on a given day from a post office were, in kilograms:

2.1, 3.0, 0.6, 1.5, 1.9, 2.4, 3.2, 4.2, 2.6, 3.1, 1.8, 1.7, 3.9, 2.4, 0.3, 1.5, 1.2

Organise the data using a frequency table and graph the data.

The data is *continuous* since the weight could be any value from 0.1 kg up to 5 kg.

The lowest weight was 0.3 kg and the heaviest was 4.2 kg, so we will use class intervals of 1 kg. The class interval '1 - < 2' includes all weights from 1 kg up to, but not including, 2 kg.

Weight (kg)	Frequency
0 - < 1	2
1 - < 2	6
2 - < 3	4
3 - < 4	4
4 - < 5	1

A histogram is used to graph this continuous data.

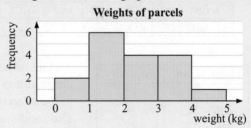

A stemplot could also be used to organise the data:

Note: The modal class is (1 - < 2) kg as this occurred most frequently.

Stem	Leaf
0	3 6
1	2 5 5 7 8 9
2	1 4 4 6
3	0 1 2 9
4	2

Scale: 1 | 2 means 1.2 kg

EXERCISE 17A

1 A frequency table for the heights of a basketball squad is given below.

Height (cm)	Frequency
170 - < 175	1
175 - < 180	8
180 - < 185	9
185 - < 190	11
190 - < 195	9
195 - < 200	3
200 - < 205	3

a Explain why 'height' is a continuous variable.

b Construct a histogram for the data. The axes should be carefully marked and labelled, and you should include a heading for the graph.

c What is the modal class? Explain what this means.

d Describe the distribution of the data.

2 A school has conducted a survey of 60 students to investigate the time it takes for them to travel to school. The following data gives the travel times to the nearest minute:

```
12   15   16    8   10   17   25   34   42   18   24   18   45   33   38
45   40    3   20   12   10   10   27   16   37   45   15   16   26   32
35    8   14   18   15   27   19   32    6   12   14   20   10   16   14
28   31   21   25    8   32   46   14   15   20   18    8   10   25   22
```

a Is travel time a discrete or continuous variable?

b Construct an ordered stemplot for the data using stems 0, 1, 2, ...

c Describe the distribution of the data.

d What is the modal travelling time?

3 For the following data, state whether a histogram or a column graph should be used and draw the appropriate graph.

a The number of matches in 30 match boxes:

Number of matches per box	47	49	50	51	52	53	55
Frequency	1	1	9	12	4	2	1

b The heights of 25 hockey players (to the nearest cm):

Height (cm)	120 - 129	130 - 139	140 - 149	150 - 159	160 - 169
Frequency	1	2	7	14	1

4

Height (mm)	frequency
300 - 324	12
325 - 349	18
350 - 374	42
375 - 399	28
400 - 424	14
425 - 449	6

A plant inspector takes a random sample of six month old seedlings from a nursery and measures their height to the nearest mm.
The results are shown in the table alongside.

a Represent the data on a histogram.

b How many of the seedlings are 400 mm or more?

c What percentage of the seedlings are between 349 and 400 mm?

d The total number of seedlings in the nursery is 1462. Estimate the number of seedlings which measure   i less than 400 mm   ii between 374 and 425 mm.

B   MEASURING THE CENTRE OF DATA

We can get a better understanding of a data set if we can locate the **middle** or **centre** of the data and get an indication of its **spread**. Knowing one of these without the other is often of little use.

There are *three statistics* that are used to measure the **centre** of a data set.

These are: the **mode**, the **mean** and the **median**.

THE MODE

For discrete numerical data, the **mode** is the most frequently occurring value in the data set.

For continuous numerical data, we cannot talk about a mode in this way because no two data values will be *exactly* equal. Instead we talk about a **modal class**, which is the class that occurs most frequently.

THE MEAN

The **mean** of a data set is the statistical name for the arithmetic average.

$$\text{mean} = \frac{\textbf{sum of all data values}}{\textbf{the number of data values}}$$

The mean gives us a single number which indicates a centre of the data set. It is usually not a member of the data set.

For example, a mean test mark of 73% tells us that there are several marks below 73% and several above it. 73% is at the centre, but it does not necessarily mean that one of the students scored 73%.

If we let x be a data value

n be the number of data values in the sample or population

$\overline{x}$ represent the mean of a **sample** and

μ represent the mean of a **population**

then the mean is either: $\mu = \dfrac{\sum x}{n}$ or $\overline{x} = \dfrac{\sum x}{n}$.

'μ' reads 'mu'

THE MEDIAN

The **median** is the *middle value* of an ordered data set.

An ordered data set is obtained by listing the data, usually from smallest to largest.

The median splits the data in halves. Half of the data are less than or equal to the median and half are greater than or equal to it.

For example, if the median mark for a test is 73% then you know that half the class scored less than or equal to 73% and half scored greater than or equal to 73%.

Note: For an **odd number** of data, the median is one of the data.

For an **even number** of data, the median is the average of the two middle values and may not be one of the original data.

Here is a rule for finding the median:

If there are n data values, find $\dfrac{n+1}{2}$. The median is the $\left(\dfrac{n+1}{2}\right)$th data value.

For example:

If $n = 13$, $\dfrac{13+1}{2} = 7$, so the median = 7th ordered data value.

If $n = 14$, $\dfrac{14+1}{2} = 7.5$, so the median = average of 7th and 8th ordered data values.

THE MERITS OF THE MEAN AND MEDIAN AS MEASURES OF CENTRE

The **median** is the only measure of centre that will locate the true centre regardless of the data set's features. It is unaffected by the presence of extreme values. It is called a *resistant* measure of centre.

The **mean** is an accurate measure of centre if the distribution is symmetrical or approximately symmetrical. If it is not, then unbalanced high or low values will *drag* the mean toward them and cause it to be an inaccurate measure of the centre. It is called a *non-resistant* measure of centre because it is influenced by all data values in the set. *If it is considered inaccurate, it should not be used in discussion.*

THE RELATIONSHIP BETWEEN THE MEAN AND THE MEDIAN FOR DIFFERENT DISTRIBUTIONS

For distributions that are **symmetric**, the mean or median will be approximately equal.

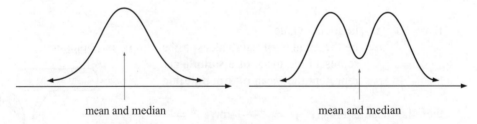

If the data set has symmetry, both the mean and the median should accurately measure the centre of the distribution.

If the data set is not symmetric, it may be positively or negatively skewed:

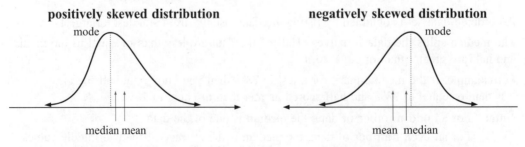

Notice that the mean and median are clearly different for these skewed distributions.

INVESTIGATION   MERITS OF THE MEAN AND MEDIAN

Recall the data gained from Norm Gregory while he was
here for the golf championship. The data was as follows:

244.6	245.1	248.0	248.8	250.0	270.5	251.1	251.2
253.9	254.5	254.6	270.7	255.9	257.0	260.6	262.8
262.9	272.9	263.1	263.2	264.3	264.4	265.0	275.6
265.5	265.6	266.5	267.4	269.7	277.5		

STATISTICS
PACKAGE

What to do:

1 Enter the data as a List into a **graphics calculator** or use the **statistics package**
supplied.

   a Produce a histogram of the data. Set the X values from 240 to 280 with an
increment of 5. Set the Y values from 0 to 30.

   b Comment on the shape of the distribution.

   c Find **i** the median   **ii** the mean

   d Compare the mean and the median. Is the mean an accurate measure of the centre?

2 Since we have continuous numerical data, we have a modal class rather than an
individual mode.

   a What is the modal class?

   b What would the modal class be if our intervals were 2 m starting at 240 m?

3 Now suppose Norm had hit a few very bad drives. Let us say that his three shortest
drives were very short!

   a Change the three shortest drives to 82.1 m, 103.2 m and 111.1 m.

   b Repeat **1 a**, **b**, **c** and **d** but set the X values from 75 to 300 with an increment of
25 for the histogram.

   c Describe the distribution as symmetric, positively skewed, or negatively skewed.
What effect have the changed values had on the mean and median as measures
of the centre of the data?

4 What would have happened if Norm had hit a few really long balls in addition to the
very bad ones? Let us imagine that the longest balls he hit were very long.

   a Change the three longest drives to 403.9 m, 415.5 m and 420.0 m.

   b Repeat **1 a**, **b**, **c** and **d** but set the X values from 50 to 450 with an increment of
50 for the histogram.

   c Describe the distribution as symmetric, positively skewed, or negatively skewed.
What effect have the changed values had on the mean and median as measures
of the centre of the data?

While collecting the data from Norm, I decided to have a hit as well. I hit 30 golf balls
with my driver. The relative frequency
histogram reveals the results below. The
distribution is clearly positively skewed.

The mean would not be a good measure
of the centre of this distribution due to
the few higher scores. Indeed the mean
is 163.66 m compared to the median of
157.50 m.

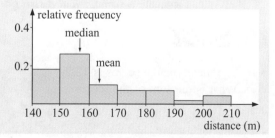

UNGROUPED DATA

Example 2

The number of trucks using a road over a 13-day period is: 4 6 3 2 7 8 3 5 5 7 6 6 4.
For this data set, find: **a** the mean **b** the median **c** the mode.

a   mean $= \dfrac{4 + 6 + 3 + 2 + 7 + 8 + 3 + 5 + 5 + 7 + 6 + 6 + 4}{13}$ ⟵ sum of the data

⟵ 13 data values

$\doteqdot 5.08$ trucks

b   The ordered data set is: 2 3 3 4 4 5 5 6 6 6 7 7 8 $\{$as $n = 13$, $\frac{n+1}{2} = 7\}$
∴ median $= 5$ trucks

c   6 is the score which occurs the most often ∴ mode $= 6$ trucks

For the truck data of **Example 2**, how are the measures of the middle affected if on the 14th day the number of trucks was 7?

We expect the mean to rise as the new data value is greater than the old mean.

In fact,   the new mean $= \dfrac{66 + 7}{14} = \dfrac{73}{14} \approx 5.21$ trucks

The new ordered data set would be: 2 3 3 4 4 5 5 6 6 6 7 7 7 8

two middle scores

∴ median $= \dfrac{5 + 6}{2} = 5.5$ trucks $\{$as $n = 14$, $\frac{n+1}{2} = 7.5\}$

This new data set has two modes. The modes are 6 and 7 trucks and we say that the data set is **bimodal**.

Note: • If a data set has three or more modes, we do not use the mode as a measure of the middle.

• Consider the data: 4 2 5 6 7 4 5 3 5 4 7 6 3 5 8 6 5.
The dot plot of this data is:

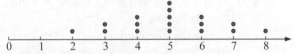

For this data the mean, median and mode are all 5.

Equal values (or approximately equal values) of the mean, mode and median can indicate a *symmetrical distribution* of data.

Example 3

The mean of five scores is 12.2.
What is the sum of the scores?

$\dfrac{\text{sum of scores}}{5} = 12.2$

∴ sum of scores $= 12.2 \times 5 = 61$
The sum of the scores is 61.

EXERCISE 17B.1

1 Find the **i** mean **ii** median **iii** mode   for each of the following data sets:

a 2, 3, 3, 3, 4, 4, 4, 5, 5, 5, 5, 6, 6, 6, 6, 6, 7, 7, 8, 8, 8, 9, 9

b 10, 12, 12, 15, 15, 16, 16, 17, 18, 18, 18, 18, 19, 20, 21

c 22.4, 24.6, 21.8, 26.4, 24.9, 25.0, 23.5, 26.1, 25.3, 29.5, 23.5

2 Consider the following   *Data set A:*   3, 4, 4, 5, 6, 6, 7, 7, 7, 8, 8, 9, 10
two data sets: *Data set B:*   3, 4, 4, 5, 6, 6, 7, 7, 7, 8, 8, 9, 15

a Find the mean for both Data set A and Data set B.

b Find the median of both Data set A and Data set B.

c Explain why the mean of Data set A is less than the mean of Data set B.

d Explain why the median of Data set A is the same as the median of Data set B.

3 The annual salaries of ten $23 000, $46 000, $23 000, $38 000, $24 000,
office workers are: $23 000, $23 000, $38 000, $23 000, $32 000

a Find the mean, median and modal salaries of this group.

b Explain why the mode is an unsatisfactory measure of the middle in this case.

c Is the median a satisfactory measure of the middle of this data set?

4 The following raw data is the daily rainfall (to the nearest millimetre) for the month of July 2007 in the desert:

3, 1, 0, 0, 0, 0, 0, 2, 0, 0, 3, 0, 0, 0, 7, 1, 1, 0, 3, 8, 0, 0, 0, 42, 21, 3, 0, 3, 1, 0, 0

a Find the mean, median and mode for the data.

b Give a reason why the median is not the most suitable measure of centre for this set of data.

c Give a reason why the mode is not the most suitable measure of centre for this set of data.

d Are there any outliers in this data set?

e On some occasions outliers are removed because they must be due to errors in observation and/or calculation. If the outliers in the data set were accurately found, should they be removed before finding the measures of the middle?

5 A basketball team scored 43, 55, 41 and 37 points in their first four matches.

a What is the mean number of points scored for the first four matches?

b What score will the team need to shoot in the next match so that they maintain the same mean score?

c The team scores only 25 points in the fifth match. What is the mean number of points scored for the five matches?

d The team scores 41 points in their sixth and final match. Will this increase or decrease their previous mean score? What is the mean score for all six matches?

6 The mean of 10 scores is 11.6. What is the sum of the scores?

7 While on an outback safari, Bill drove an average of 262 km per day for a period of 12 days. How far did Bill drive in total while on safari?

8 The mean monthly sales for a clothing store are $15 467. Calculate the total sales for the store for the year.

9 Find x if 5, 9, 11, 12, 13, 14, 17 and x have a mean of 12.

10 Find a given that 3, 0, a, a, 4, a, 6, a and 3 have a mean of 4.

11 Over the complete assessment period, Aruna averaged 35 out of a possible 40 marks for her maths tests. However, when checking her files, she could only find 7 of the 8 tests. For these she scored 29, 36, 32, 38, 35, 34 and 39. Determine how many marks out of 40 she scored for the eighth test.

12 A sample of 10 measurements has a mean of 15.7 and a sample of 20 measurements has a mean of 14.3. Find the mean of all 30 measurements.

13 Jana had seven spelling tests, each with twelve words, but she could only find the results of five of them. These were: 9, 5, 7, 9 and 10. She asked her teacher for the other two results and the teacher said that the mode of her scores was 9 and the mean was 8. What are the two missing results, given that Jana knows that her worst result was a 5?

DISCUSSION

Which of the measures of the middle is more affected by the presence of an outlier? Develop at least two examples to show how the measures of the middle can be altered by outliers.

MEASURES OF THE CENTRE FROM OTHER SOURCES

When the same data appears several times we often summarise the data in table form. Consider the data of the given table:

We can find the measures of the centre directly from the table.

Data value (x)	Frequency (f)	Product (fx)
3	1	$1 \times 3 = 3$
4	1	$1 \times 4 = 4$
5	3	$3 \times 5 = 15$
6	7	$7 \times 6 = 42$
7	15	$15 \times 7 = 105$
8	8	$8 \times 8 = 64$
9	5	$5 \times 9 = 45$
Total	$\sum f = 40$	$\sum fx = 278$

The mode

There are 15 of data value 7 which is more than any other data value.

The mode is therefore 7.

The mean

Adding a 'Product' column to the table helps to add all scores.

For example, there are 15 data of value 7 and these add to $7 \times 15 = 105$.

So, the mean $= \dfrac{278}{40} = 6.95$

The median

There are 40 data values, an even number, so there are *two middle* data values.

As the sample size $n = 40$,

$$\frac{n+1}{2} = \frac{41}{2} = 20.5$$

So, the median is the average of the 20th and 21st data values.

In the table, the blue numbers show us accumulated values.

We can see that the 20th and 21st data values (in order) are both 7's,

$$\therefore \quad \text{median} = \frac{7+7}{2} = 7$$

Data Value	Frequency		
3	1	1	one number is 3
4	1	2	two numbers are 4 or less
5	3	5	five numbers are 5 or less
6	7	12	12 numbers are 6 or less
7	15	27	27 numbers are 7 or less
8	8		
9	5		
Total	40		

Notice that we have a skewed distribution even though the mean, median and mode are nearly equal. So, we must be careful if we use measures of the middle to call a distribution symmetric.

Example 4

The table below shows the number of aces served by tennis players in their first sets of a tournament.

Number of aces	1	2	3	4	5	6
Frequency	4	11	18	13	7	2

Determine the mean number of aces for these sets.

No. of aces (x)	Freq. (f)	Product (fx)
1	4	4
2	11	22
3	18	54
4	13	52
5	7	35
6	2	12
Total	$\sum f = 55$	$\sum fx = 179$

$$\overline{x} = \frac{\sum fx}{\sum f}$$

$$= \frac{179}{55}$$

$$\approx 3.25 \text{ aces}$$

Note: $\overline{x} = \dfrac{\sum\limits_{i=1}^{6} f_i x_i}{\sum\limits_{i=1}^{6} f_i}$ has been abbreviated to $\overline{x} = \dfrac{\sum fx}{\sum f}$.

Example 5

In a class of 20 students the results of a spelling test out of 10 are shown in the table.

Calculate the: **a** mean

                      b median

                      c mode.

Score	Number of students
5	1
6	2
7	4
8	7
9	4
10	2
Total	20

a $\sum f = 20$

and $\sum fx = 1 \times 5 + 2 \times 6 + 4 \times 7 + 7 \times 8 + 4 \times 9 + 2 \times 10 = 157$

$\therefore \quad \overline{x} = \dfrac{\sum fx}{\sum f} = \dfrac{157}{20} = 7.85$

b There are 20 scores, so the median is the average of the 10th and 11th.

Score	Number of Students
5	1
6	2
7	4
8	7
9	4
10	2

1st student
2nd and 3rd student
4th, 5th, 6th and 7th student
8th, 9th, **10th, 11th**, 12th, 13th, 14th student

The 10th and 11th students both scored 8
$\therefore$ median = 8.

c Looking down the 'number of students' column, the highest frequency is 7. This corresponds to a score of 8, so the mode = 8.

The publishers acknowledge the late Mr Jim Russell, General Features for the reproduction of this cartoon.

EXERCISE 17B.2

1 The table alongside shows the results when 3 coins were tossed simultaneously 30 times.

Calculate the:

  a mode **b** median

  c mean.

Number of heads	Number of times occurred
0	4
1	12
2	11
3	3
Total	30

2 The following frequency table records the number of phone calls made in a day by 50 fifteen-year-olds.

No. of phone calls	Frequency
0	5
1	8
2	13
3	8
4	6
5	3
6	3
7	2
8	1
11	1

a For this data, find the:
  i mean ii median iii mode.

b Construct a column graph for the data and show the position of the measures of centre (mean, median and mode) on the horizontal axis.

c Describe the distribution of the data.

d Why is the mean larger than the median for this data?

e Which measure of centre would be the most suitable for this data set?

3 A company claims that their match boxes contain, on average, 50 matches per box. On doing a survey, the Consumer Protection Society recorded the following results:

Number in a box	Frequency
47	5
48	4
49	11
50	6
51	3
52	1
Total	30

a For the data calculate the:
  i mode ii median iii mean.

b Do the results of this survey support the company's claim?

c In a court for 'false advertising', the company won their case against the Consumer Protection Society. Suggest why and how they did this.

4 Families at a school in Australia were surveyed. The number of children in each family was recorded. The results of the survey are shown alongside.

Number of children	Frequency
1	5
2	28
3	15
4	8
5	2
6	1
Total	59

a Calculate the:
  i mean ii mode iii median.

b The average Australian family has 2.2 children. How does this school compare to the national average?

c The data set is skewed. Is the skewness positive or negative?

d How has the skewness of the data affected the measures of the centre of the data set?

5 For the data displayed in the following stem-and-leaf plots find the:
  i mean ii median iii mode.

a
Stem	Leaf
5	3 5 6
6	0 1 2 4 6 7 9
7	3 3 6 8
8	4 7
9	1

where 5 | 3 means 53

b
Stem	Leaf
3	7
4	0 4 8 8
5	0 0 1 3 6 7 8 9
6	0 3 6 7 7 7
7	0 6 9
8	1

where 3 | 7 means 3.7

6 Revisit **The Pea Problem** on page **484**.

    a Use a frequency table for the *Without fertiliser* data to find the:

        i mean   **ii** mode   **iii** median number of peas per pod.

    b Use a frequency table for the *With fertiliser* data to find the:

        i mean   **ii** mode   **iii** median number of peas per pod.

    c Which of the measures of the centre is appropriate to use in a report on this data?

    d Has the application of fertiliser significantly improved the number of peas per pod?

7 The selling prices of the last 10 houses sold in a certain district were as follows:

$146 400, $127 600, $211 000, $192 500,
$256 400, $132 400, $148 000, $129 500,
$131 400, $162 500

    a Calculate the mean and median selling prices and comment on the results.

    b Which measure would you use if you were:

        i a vendor wanting to sell your house

        ii looking to buy a house in the district?

8 The table alongside compares the mass at birth of some guinea pigs with their mass when they were two weeks old.

    a What was the mean birth mass?

    b What was the mean mass after two weeks?

    c What was the mean increase over the two weeks?

Guinea Pig	Mass (g) at birth	Mass (g) at 2 weeks
A	75	210
B	70	200
C	80	200
D	70	220
E	74	215
F	60	200
G	55	206
H	83	230

9 15 of 31 measurements are below 10 cm and 12 measurements are above 11 cm. Find the median if the other 4 measurements are 10.1 cm, 10.4 cm, 10.7 cm and 10.9 cm.

10 Two brands of toothpicks claim that their boxes contain an average of 50 toothpicks per box. In a survey the Consumer Protection Society (C.P.S.) recorded the following results:

Brand A

number in a box	46	47	48	49	50	51	52	53	55
frequency	1	1	2	7	10	20	15	3	1

Brand B

number in a box	48	49	50	51	52	53	54
frequency	3	17	30	7	2	1	1

    a Find the average contents of Brands A and B.

    b Would it be fair for the C.P.S. to prosecute the manufacturers of either brand, based on these statistics?

11 Towards the end of season, a netballer had played 14 matches and had an average of 16.5 goals per game. In the final two matches of the season she threw 21 goals and 24 goals. Find the netballer's new average.

12 The mean and median of a set of 9 measurements are both 12. If 7 of the measurements are   7, 9, 11, 13, 14, 17 and 19,   find the other two measurements.

13 In an office of 20 people there are only 4 salary levels paid:

$50 000 (1 person), $42 000 (3 people), $35 000 (6 people), $28 000 (10 people).

   a Calculate: **i** the median salary **ii** the modal salary **iii** the mean salary.

   b Which measure of central tendency might be used by the boss who is against a pay rise for the other employees?

DATA IN CLASSES

When information has been gathered in classes we use the **midpoint** of the class to represent all scores within that interval.

We are assuming that the scores within each class are evenly distributed throughout that interval. The mean calculated will therefore be an **approximation** to the true value.

Example 6

Find the approximate mean of the following *ages of bus drivers* data, to the nearest year:

age (yrs)	21-25	26-30	31-35	36-40	41-45	46-50	51-55
frequency	11	14	32	27	29	17	7

age (yrs)	frequency (f)	midpoint (x)	f x
21-25	11	23	253
26-30	14	28	392
31-35	32	33	1056
36-40	27	38	1026
41-45	29	43	1247
46-50	17	48	816
51-55	7	53	371
Total	$\sum f = 137$		$\sum fx = 5161$

$$\bar{x} = \frac{\sum fx}{\sum f} = \frac{5161}{137} \approx 37.7$$

EXERCISE 17B.3

1 50 students sit a mathematics test and the results are as follows:

Score	0-9	10-19	20-29	30-39	40-49
Frequency	2	5	7	27	9

Find an estimate of the mean score.

2 The table shows the petrol sales in one day by a number of city service stations.

   a How many service stations were involved in the survey?

   b Estimate the total amount of petrol sold for the day by the service stations.

   c Find the approximate mean sales of petrol for the day.

Litres (L)	frequency
2000 to 2999	4
3000 to 3999	4
4000 to 4999	9
5000 to 5999	14
6000 to 6999	23
7000 to 7999	16

3 This histogram illustrates the results of an aptitude test given to a group of people seeking positions in a company.

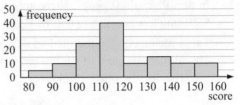

  a How many people sat for the test?

  b Find an estimate of the mean score for the test.

  c What fraction of the people scored less than 100 for the test?

  d If the top 20% of the people are offered positions in the company, estimate the minimum mark required.

C   CUMULATIVE DATA

Sometimes it is useful to know the number of scores that lie above or below a particular value. In such situations we can construct a **cumulative frequency distribution table** and use a graph called an **ogive** or **cumulative frequency polygon** to represent the data.

Example 7

The data shown gives the weights of 120 male footballers.

  a Construct a cumulative frequency distribution table.

  b Represent the data on an ogive.

  c Use your graph to estimate the:

   i median weight

   ii number of men weighing less than 73 kg

   iii number of men weighing more than 92 kg.

Weight (w kg)	frequency
$55 \leqslant w < 60$	2
$60 \leqslant w < 65$	3
$65 \leqslant w < 70$	12
$70 \leqslant w < 75$	14
$75 \leqslant w < 80$	19
$80 \leqslant w < 85$	37
$85 \leqslant w < 90$	22
$90 \leqslant w < 95$	8
$95 \leqslant w < 100$	2
$100 \leqslant w < 105$	1

a

Weight (w kg)	frequency	cumulative frequency
$55 \leqslant w < 60$	2	2
$60 \leqslant w < 65$	3	5
$65 \leqslant w < 70$	12	17
$70 \leqslant w < 75$	14	31
$75 \leqslant w < 80$	19	50
$80 \leqslant w < 85$	37	87
$85 \leqslant w < 90$	22	109
$90 \leqslant w < 95$	8	117
$95 \leqslant w < 100$	2	119
$100 \leqslant w < 105$	1	120

This is $2 + 3$.

This is $2 + 3 + 12$.

This 50 means that there are 50 players who weigh less than 80 kg.

Note: The cumulative frequency gives a *running total* of the number of players up to certain weights.

b   **Ogive of footballers' weights**

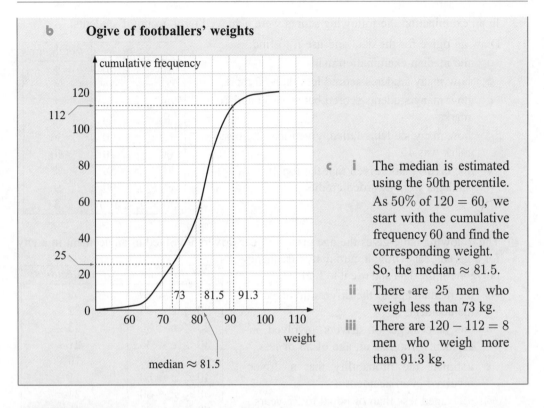

median ≈ 81.5

c **i** The median is estimated using the 50th percentile. As 50% of 120 = 60, we start with the cumulative frequency 60 and find the corresponding weight.
So, the median ≈ 81.5.

ii There are 25 men who weigh less than 73 kg.

iii There are 120 − 112 = 8 men who weigh more than 91.3 kg.

EXERCISE 17C

1 The following frequency distribution was obtained by asking 50 randomly selected people the size of their shoes.

Shoe size	5	$5\frac{1}{2}$	6	$6\frac{1}{2}$	7	$7\frac{1}{2}$	8	$8\frac{1}{2}$	9	$9\frac{1}{2}$	10
frequency	1	1	0	3	5	13	17	7	2	0	1

Draw an ogive for the data and use it to find:

a the median shoe size

b how many people had a shoe size of: **i** $7\frac{1}{2}$ or more   **ii** 8 or less.

2 The following data shows the lengths of 30 trout caught in a lake during a fishing competition. The measurements were taken to the nearest centimetre.

31	38	34	40	24	33	30	36	38	32	35	32	36	27	35
40	34	37	44	38	36	34	33	31	38	35	36	33	33	28

a Construct a cumulative frequency table for trout lengths, x cm, using the intervals: $24 \leqslant x < 27$, $27 \leqslant x < 30$, and so on.

b Draw an ogive for the data.

c Use **b** to find the median length.

d Use the original data to find its median and compare your answer with **c**. Comment!

3   In an examination the following scores were achieved by a group of students:

Draw an ogive for the data and use it to find:

a   the median examination mark

b   how many students scored less than 65 marks

c   how many students scored between 50 and 70 marks

d   how many students failed, given that the pass mark was 45

e   the credit mark, given that the top 16% of students were awarded credits.

Score	frequency
$10 \leqslant x < 20$	2
$20 \leqslant x < 30$	5
$30 \leqslant x < 40$	7
$40 \leqslant x < 50$	21
$50 \leqslant x < 60$	36
$60 \leqslant x < 70$	40
$70 \leqslant x < 80$	27
$80 \leqslant x < 90$	9
$90 \leqslant x < 100$	3

4   The following table gives the age groups of car drivers involved in an accident in a city for a given year. Draw a cumulative frequency polygon for the data and use it to find:

a   the median age of the drivers involved in the accidents

b   the percentage of drivers involved in accidents who had an age of 23 or less.

c   Estimate the probability that a driver involved in an accident is:

   i   aged less than or equal to 27 years

   ii   aged 27 years.

Age (in years)	No. of accidents
$16 \leqslant x < 20$	59
$20 \leqslant x < 25$	82
$25 \leqslant x < 30$	43
$30 \leqslant x < 35$	21
$35 \leqslant x < 40$	19
$40 \leqslant x < 50$	11
$50 \leqslant x < 60$	24
$60 \leqslant x < 80$	41

5   The table below gives the distribution of the life of electric light globes.

Draw an ogive for the data and use it to estimate:

a   the median life of a globe

b   the percentage of globes which had a life of 2700 hours or less

c   the number of globes which had a life between 1500 and 2500 hours.

Life (hours)	Number of globes
$0 \leqslant l < 500$	5
$500 \leqslant l < 1000$	17
$1000 \leqslant l < 2000$	46
$2000 \leqslant l < 3000$	79
$3000 \leqslant l < 4000$	27
$4000 \leqslant l < 5000$	4

D   MEASURING THE SPREAD OF DATA

To accurately describe a distribution we need to measure both its **centre** and its **spread** or **variability**.

The given distributions have the same mean, but clearly they have different spreads. The A distribution has most scores close to the mean whereas the C distribution has the greatest spread.

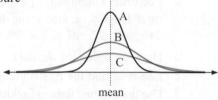

We will examine four different measures of spread: the **range**, the **interquartile range (IQR)**, the **variance** and the **standard deviation**.

THE RANGE

The **range** is the difference between the maximum (largest) and the minimum (smallest) data value.

Example 8

A greengrocer chain considers purchasing apples from two different wholesalers. They take six random samples of 50 apples to examine them for skin blemishes. The counts for the number of blemished apples are:

Wholesaler *"Orchard Road"*:   5   17   15   3   9   11
Wholesaler *"Red Tree"*:   10   13   12   11   12   11

What is the range from each wholesaler?

Orchard Road: Range $= 17 - 3 = 14$ *Red Tree:*   Range $= 13 - 10 = 3$

The **range** is not considered to be a particularly reliable measure of spread as it uses only two data values. It may be influenced by extreme values or outliers.

THE QUARTILES AND THE INTERQUARTILE RANGE

The median divides the ordered data set into two halves and these halves are divided in half again by the **quartiles**.

The middle value of the lower half is called the **lower quartile** or **25th percentile**. One quarter or 25% of the data have values less than or equal to the lower quartile. 75% of the data have values greater than or equal to the lower quartile.

The middle value of the upper half is called the **upper quartile** or **75th percentile**. One quarter or 25% of the data have values greater than or equal to the upper quartile. 75% of the data have values less than or equal to the upper quartile.

The **interquartile range** is the range of the middle half (50%) of the data.

$$\text{interquartile range} = \text{upper quartile} - \text{lower quartile}$$

The data set is thus divided into quarters by the lower quartile (Q_1), the median (Q_2), and the upper quartile (Q_3).

So, the interquartile range, $\mathbf{IQR = Q_3 - Q_1}$.

Example 9

For the data set: 6, 4, 7, 5, 3, 4, 2, 6, 5, 7, 5, 3, 8, 9, 3, 6, 5   find the:
a median   **b** lower quartile   **c** upper quartile   **d** interquartile range

---

The ordered data set is:

   2 3 3 3 4 4 5 5 5 5 6 6 6 7 7 8 9   (17 of them)

a   As $n = 17$, $\dfrac{n+1}{2} = 9$ $\therefore$ the median $=$ 9th score $= 5$

b/c   As the median is a data value we now ignore it and split the remaining data into two

$$\underbrace{2\ 3\ 3\ 3\ 4\ 4\ 5\ 5}_{\text{lower}}\ \underbrace{5\ 6\ 6\ 6\ 7\ 7\ 8\ 9}_{\text{upper}}$$

$Q_1 = $ median of lower half $= \dfrac{3+4}{2} = 3.5$

$Q_3 = $ median of upper half $= \dfrac{6+7}{2} = 6.5$

d   IQR $= Q_3 - Q_1 = 6.5 - 3.5 = 3$

Example 10

For the data set: 11, 6, 7, 8, 13, 10, 8, 7, 5, 2, 9, 4, 4, 5, 8, 2, 3, 6   find:

a the median   b Q_1 c Q_3 d the interquartile range

The ordered data set is:

$$\cancel{2}\ \cancel{2}\ \cancel{3}\ \cancel{4}\ \cancel{4}\ \cancel{5}\ \cancel{5}\ \cancel{6}\ 6\ 7\ \cancel{7}\ \cancel{8}\ \cancel{8}\ \cancel{8}\ \cancel{9}\ \cancel{10}\ \cancel{11}\ \cancel{13}\qquad \text{(18 of them)}$$

a   As $n = 18,\quad \dfrac{n+1}{2} = 9.5$

$\therefore$ median $= \dfrac{\text{9th value} + \text{10th value}}{2} = \dfrac{6+7}{2} = 6.5$

b/c   As the median is not a data value we split the data into two

$$\underbrace{2\ 2\ 3\ 4\ 4\ 5\ 5\ 6\ 6}_{\text{lower}}\quad \underbrace{7\ 7\ 8\ 8\ 8\ 9\ 10\ 11\ 13}_{\text{upper}}$$

$\therefore$ $Q_1 = 4,\quad Q_3 = 8$

d   IQR $= Q_3 - Q_1$
$= 8 - 4$
$= 4$

> **Note:**
> Some computer packages calculate quartiles in a different way to this example.

EXERCISE 17D.1

1 For each of the following data sets, make sure the data is ordered and then find:

   i   the median   ii   the upper and lower quartiles
   iii the range   iv   the interquartile range.

   a   2, 3, 3, 3, 4, 4, 4, 5, 5, 5, 5, 6, 6, 6, 6, 6, 7, 7, 8, 8, 8, 9, 9
   b   10, 12, 15, 12, 24, 18, 19, 18, 18, 15, 16, 20, 21, 17, 18, 16, 22, 14
   c   21.8, 22.4, 23.5, 23.5, 24.6, 24.9, 25, 25.3, 26.1, 26.4, 29.5

2 The times spent (in minutes) by 20 people waiting in a queue at a bank for a teller were:

   3.4 2.1 3.8 2.2 4.5 1.4 0   0   1.6 4.8
   1.5 1.9 0   3.6 5.2 2.7 3.0 0.8 3.8 5.2

   a   Find the median waiting time and the upper and lower quartiles.

b   Find the range and interquartile range of the waiting times.

c   Copy and complete the following statements:

    i   "50% of the waiting times were greater than .... minutes."

    ii   "75% of the waiting times were less than ...... minutes."

    iii   "The minimum waiting time was .... minutes and the maximum waiting time was ..... minutes. The waiting times were spread over ...... minutes."

3

Stem	Leaf
0	3 4 7 9
1	0 3 4 6 7 8
2	0 0 3 5 6 9 9 9
3	1 3 7 8
4	2 3	7 means 37

For the data set given, find:

a   the minimum value   b   the maximum value

c   the median   d   the lower quartile

e   the upper quartile   f   the range

g   the interquartile range.

4   The heights of 20 ten year olds are recorded in the following stem-and-leaf plot:

Stem	Leaf
10	9
11	1 3 4 4 8 9
12	2 2 4 4 6 8 9 9
13	1 2 5 8 8

10 | 9 reads 109 cm

a   Find:

    i   the median height

    ii   the upper and lower quartiles of the data.

b   Copy and complete the following statements:

    i   "Half of the children are no more than ..... cm tall."

    ii   "75% of the children are no more than ..... cm tall."

c   Find the: i   range   ii   interquartile range for the height of the ten year olds.

d   Copy and complete:

"The middle 50% of the children have heights spread over ..... cm."

5   Revisit **The Pea Problem** on page **484**.

a   For the *Without fertiliser* data, find:

    i   the range   ii   the median

    iii   the lower quartile   iv   the upper quartile

    v   the interquartile range.

b   Repeat a for the *With fertiliser* data.

c   Reconsider the questions posed in **The Pea Problem**. Amend your solutions where appropriate.

BOX-AND-WHISKER PLOTS

A **box-and-whisker plot** (or simply a **boxplot**) is a visual display of some of the descriptive statistics of a data set. It shows:

- the minimum value
- the lower quartile (Q_1)
- the median (Q_2)
- the upper quartile (Q_3)
- the maximum value

These five numbers form the **five-number summary** of the data set.

For the data set in **Example 10** on page **504**, the five-number summary and boxplot are:

minimum $= 2$
$Q_1 = 4$
median $= 6.5$
$Q_3 = 8$
maximum $= 13$

The rectangular box represents the 'middle' half of the data set.
The lower whisker represents the 25% of the data with smallest values.
The upper whisker represents the 25% of the data with greatest values.

Example 11

For the data set: 4 5 9 5 1 7 8 7 3 5 6 3 4 3 2 5

a   construct the five-number summary   b   draw a boxplot
c   find the   i   range   ii   interquartile range
d   find the percentage of data values greater than 6.

a   The ordered data set is

1   2   3   3   3   4   4   5 | 5   5   5   6   7   7   8   9   (16 of them)

$Q_1 = 3$ median $= 5$ $Q_3 = 6.5$

So the 5-number summary is: $\begin{cases} \text{minimum} = 1 & Q_1 = 3 \\ \text{median} = 5 & Q_3 = 6.5 \\ \text{maximum} = 9 \end{cases}$

b

c   i   range = maximum − minimum   ii   IQR $= Q_3 - Q_1$
        $= 9 - 1$ $= 6.5 - 3$
        $= 8$ $= 3.5$

d   25% of the data values are greater than 6.

EXERCISE 17D.2

1

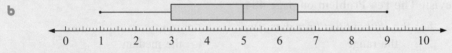

points scored by a basketball team

a   The boxplot given summarises the goals scored by a basketball team. Locate:
    i   the median   ii   the maximum value   iii   the minimum value
    iv   the upper quartile   v   the lower quartile
b   Calculate: i   the range   ii   the interquartile range

2

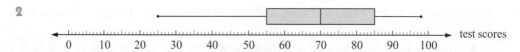

The boxplot above summarises the class results for a test out of 100 marks. Copy and complete the following statements about the test results:

a The highest mark scored for the test was ..... , and the lowest mark was .....

b Half of the class scored a mark greater than or equal to .....

c The top 25% of the class scored at least ..... marks for the test.

d The middle half of the class had scores between ..... and ..... for this test.

e Find the range of the data set.

f Find the interquartile range of the data set.

g Estimate the mean mark for these test scores.

3 For the following data sets:

     i construct a 5-number summary   **ii** draw a boxplot

     iii find the range   **iv** find the interquartile range

a 3, 5, 5, 7, 10, 9, 4, 7, 8, 6, 6, 5, 8, 6

b 3, 7, 0, 1, 4, 6, 8, 8, 8, 9, 7, 5, 6, 8, 7, 8, 8, 2, 9

c

Stem	Leaf
11	7
12	0 3 6 6 8
13	0 1 1 1 3 5 5 7
14	4 7 7 9 9
15	1

11 | 7 represents 117

4 The following side-by-side boxplots compare the time students in years 9 and 12 spend on homework.

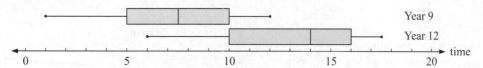

a Copy and complete:

Statistic	Year 9	Year 12
minimum		
Q_1		
median		
Q_3		
maximum		

b Determine the: **i** range **ii** interquartile range   for each group.

c True or false:

    i On average, Year 12 students spend about twice as much time on homework than Year 9 students.

    ii Over 25% of Year 9 students spend less time on homework than all Year 12 students.

5 Enid examines a new variety of bean and does a count on the number of beans in 33 pods. Her results were:

5, 8, 10, 4, 2, 12, 6, 5, 7, 7, 5, 5, 5, 13, 9, 3, 4, 4, 7, 8, 9, 5, 5, 4, 3, 6, 6, 6, 6, 9, 8, 7, 6

   a Find the median, lower quartile and upper quartile of the data set.

   b Find the interquartile range of the data set.

   c Draw a boxplot of the data set.

6 Ranji counts the number of bolts in several boxes and tabulates the data as follows:

Number of bolts	33	34	35	36	37	38	39	40
Frequency	1	5	7	13	12	8	0	1

   a Find the five-number summary for this data set.

   b Find the   **i** range   **ii** IQR   for this data set.

   c Construct a boxplot for the data set.

PERCENTILES

> A **percentile** is the score below which a certain percentage of the data lies.

For example:
- the 85th percentile is the score below which 85% of the data lies.
- If your score in a test is the 95th percentile, then 95% of the class have scored less than you.

Notice that:
- the **lower quartile** (Q_1) is the 25th percentile
- the **median** (Q_2) is the 50th percentile
- the **upper quartile** (Q_3) is the 75th percentile.

One way to display percentiles is to add a separate scale to an ogive. On the graph alongside, the cumulative frequency is read from the axis on the left side, and each value corresponds to a percentage on the right side.

We can use the percentage scale to help find the quartiles.

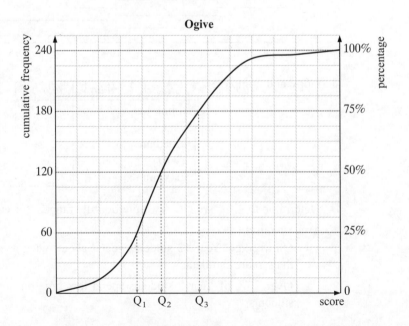

Ogive

7 A botanist has measured the heights of 60 seedlings and has presented her findings on the ogive below.

Heights of seedlings

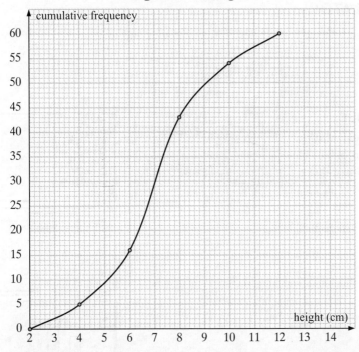

a How many seedlings have heights of 5 cm or less?

b What percentage of seedlings are taller than 8 cm?

c What is the median height?

d What is the interquartile range for the heights?

e Find the 90th percentile for the data and explain what your answer means.

8 The following ogive displays the performance of 80 competitors in a cross-country race.

Cross-country race times

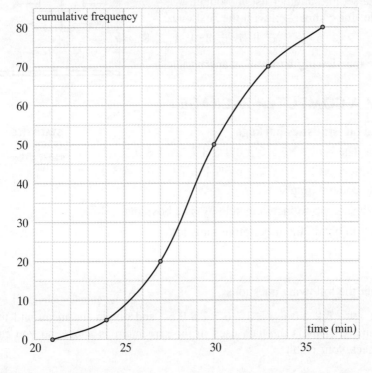

Find:

a the lower quartile time

b the median

c the upper quartile

d the interquartile range

e an estimate of the 40th percentile.

E   STATISTICS USING TECHNOLOGY

GRAPHICS CALCULATOR

A **graphics calculator** can be used to find descriptive statistics and to draw some types of graphs.

Consider the data set: 5 2 3 3 6 4 5 3 7 5 7 1 8 9 5

No matter what brand of calculator you use you should be able to:

- Enter the data as a **list**.
- Enter the **statistics calculation** part of the menu and obtain the descriptive statistics like these shown. $\bar{x}$ is the mean

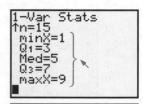

- Obtain a box-and-whisker plot.

- Obtain a vertical barchart if required.

- Enter a second data set into another list and obtain a side-by-side boxplot for comparison with the first one.

    Use the data: 9 6 2 3 5 5 7 5 6 7 6 3 4 4 5 8 4

You will need to change the **viewing window** as appropriate.

STATISTICS FROM A COMPUTER PACKAGE

Click on the icon to load our **statistics package**.

STATISTICS PACKAGE

Enter data set 1:   5 2 3 3 6 4 5 3 7 5 7 1 8 9 5
Enter data set 2:   9 6 2 3 5 5 7 5 6 7 6 3 4 4 5 8 4

Examine the side-by-side column graphs.

Click on the Box-and-Whisker tab to view the side-by-side boxplots.

Click on the Statistics tab to obtain the descriptive statistics.

EXERCISE 17E

Use technology to answer the following questions:

1   a   Enter the data set: 5 2 3 3 6 4 5 3 7 5 7 1 8 9 5   and obtain the mean and the 5-number summary. This is the data used in the screendumps above, so you can use them to check your results.

   b Obtain the boxplot for the data in **a**.

   c Obtain the vertical bar chart for the data in **a**.

   d Enter the data set: 9 6 2 3 5 5 7 5 6 7 6 3 4 4 5 8 4 into a second list. Find the mean and 5-number summary. Create a side-by-side boxplot for both sets of data.

2 Shane and Brett play in the same cricket team and are fierce but friendly rivals when it comes to bowling. During a season the number of wickets taken in each innings by the bowlers were:

Shane: 1 6 2 0 3 4 1 4 2 3 0 3 2 4 3 4 3 3
             3 4 2 4 3 2 3 3 0 5 3 5 3 2 4 3 4 3

Brett: 7 2 4 8 1 3 4 2 3 0 5 3 5 2 3 1 2 0
            4 3 4 0 3 3 0 2 5 1 1 2 2 5 1 4 0 1

   a Is the variable discrete or continuous?

   b Enter the data into a graphics calculator or statistics package.

   c Produce a vertical column graph for each data set.

   d Are there any outliers? Should they be deleted before we start to analyse the data?

   e Describe the shape of each distribution.

   f Compare the measures of the centre of each distribution.

   g Compare the spreads of each distribution.

   h Obtain side-by-side boxplots.

   i What conclusions, if any, can be drawn from the data?

3 A manufacturer of light globes claims that their new design has a 20% longer life than those they are presently selling. Forty of each globe are randomly selected and tested. Here are the results to the nearest hour:

Old type:
   103 96 113 111 126 100 122 110 84 117 103 113 104 104
   111 87 90 121 99 114 105 121 93 109 87 118 75 111
   87 127 117 131 115 116 82 130 113 95 108 112

New type:
   146 131 132 160 128 119 133 117 139 123 109 129 109 131
   191 117 132 107 141 136 146 142 123 144 145 125 164 125
   133 124 153 129 118 130 134 151 145 131 133 135

   a Is the variable discrete or continuous?

   b Enter the data into a graphics calculator or statistics package.

   c Are there any outliers? Should they be deleted before we start to analyse the data?

   d Compare the measures of centre and spread.

   e Obtain side-by-side boxplots.

   f Describe the shape of each distribution.

   g What conclusions, if any, can be drawn from the data?

F   VARIANCE AND STANDARD DEVIATION

The problem with using the range and the IQR as measures of spread or variation is that both of them only use two values in their calculation. Some data sets can therefore have their spread characteristics hidden when the range or IQR are quoted, and so we need a better way of describing variation.

Consider a data set of n values: $x_1, x_2, x_3, x_4, ..., x_n$,   with mean $\overline{x}$.

$x_i - \overline{x}$ measures how far x_i deviates from the mean, so one might suspect that the mean of the deviations $\dfrac{1}{n} \sum\limits_{i=1}^{n} (x_i - \overline{x})$ would give a good measure of variation. However, this value turns out to always be zero.

Instead we adopt the formula $s_n^{\,2} = \dfrac{\sum\limits_{i=1}^{n} (x_i - \overline{x})^2}{n}$ and call it the **variance** of the n data values.

Notice in this formula that:

- $(x_i - \overline{x})^2$ is also a measure of how far x_i deviates from $\overline{x}$. However, the square ensures that each of these is positive, which is why the sum turns out not to be zero.

- If $\sum\limits_{i=1}^{n} (x_i - \overline{x})^2$ is small, it will indicate that most of the data values are close to $\overline{x}$.

- Dividing by n gives an indication of how far, on average, the data is from the mean.

For a data set of n values, $s_n = \sqrt{\dfrac{\sum\limits_{i=1}^{n} (x_i - \overline{x})^2}{n}}$ is called the **standard deviation**.

The square root in the standard deviation is used to correct the units.

For example, if x_i is the weight of a student in kg, s^2 would be in kg^2.

For this reason the standard deviation is more frequently quoted than the variance.

The standard deviation is a **non-resistant** measure of spread.   This is due to its dependence on the mean of the sample and because extreme data values will give large values for $(x - \overline{x})^2$.   It is only a useful measure if the distribution is approximately symmetrical.   However, the standard deviation is particularly useful when the data from which it came is **normally distributed**. This will be discussed later.

The IQR and percentiles are more appropriate tools for measuring spread if the distribution is considerably skewed.

Example 12

Find the means and standard deviations for the apple samples of **Example 8**.
What do these statistics tell us?

Orchard Road

x	$x - \overline{x}$	$(x - \overline{x})^2$
5	−5	25
17	7	49
15	5	25
3	−7	49
9	−1	1
11	1	1
60	*Total*	150

Red Tree

x	$x - \overline{x}$	$(x - \overline{x})^2$
10	−1.5	2.25
13	1.5	2.25
12	0.5	0.25
11	−0.5	0.25
12	0.5	0.25
11	−0.5	0.25
69	*Total*	5.5

$$\therefore \quad \overline{x} = \frac{60}{6} \qquad s = \sqrt{\frac{\sum (x - \overline{x})^2}{n}}$$
$$= 10 \qquad\qquad = \sqrt{\frac{150}{6}}$$
$$= 5$$

$$\therefore \quad \overline{x} = \frac{69}{6} \qquad s = \sqrt{\frac{\sum (x - \overline{x})^2}{n}}$$
$$= 11.5 \qquad\qquad = \sqrt{\frac{5.5}{6}}$$
$$= 0.957$$

The wholesaler *Red Tree* supplied apples with more blemishes but with less
variability (smaller standard deviation) than those supplied by *Orchard Road*.

EXERCISE 17F.1

1 The column graphs show two distributions:

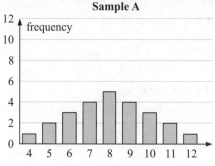

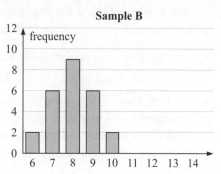

a By looking at the graphs, which distribution appears to have wider spread?

b Find the mean of each sample.

c Find the standard deviation for each sample. Comment on your answers.

2 The number of points scored by Andrew and Brad in the last 8 basketball matches are
tabulated below.

Points by Andrew	23	17	31	25	25	19	28	32
Points by Brad	9	29	41	26	14	44	38	43

a Find the mean and standard deviation for the number of points scored by each
player.

b Which of the two players is more consistent?

3 Two baseball coaches compare the number of runs scored by their teams in their last ten matches:

Rockets	0	10	1	9	11	0	8	5	6	7
Bullets	4	3	4	1	4	11	7	6	12	5

    a Show that each team has the same mean and range of runs scored.

    b Which team's performance do you suspect is more variable over the period?

    c Check your answer to **b** by finding the standard deviation for each distribution.

    d Does the range or the standard deviation give a better indication of variability?

4 A manufacturer of soft drinks employs a statistician for quality control. He needs to check that 375 mL of drink goes into each can. The machine which fills the cans may malfunction or slightly change its delivery due to constant vibration and other factors.

    a Would you expect the standard deviation for the whole production run to be the same for one day as it is for one week? Explain your answer.

    b If samples of 125 cans are taken each day, what measure would be used to:

        i check that an average of 375 mL of drink goes into each can

        ii check the variability of the volume of drink going into each can?

    c What is the significance of a low standard deviation in this case?

5 The weights in kg of seven footballers are: 79, 64, 59, 71, 68, 68 and 74.

    a Find the mean and standard deviation for this group.

    b Surprisingly, each footballer's weight had increased by exactly 10 kg when measured five years later. Find the new mean and standard deviation.

    c Comment on your findings from **a** and **b** in general terms.

6 The weights of ten young turkeys to the nearest 0.1 kg are:

      0.8,   1.1,   1.2,   0.9,   1.2,   1.2,   0.9,   0.7,   1.0,   1.1

    a Find the mean and standard deviation for the turkeys.

    b After being fed a special diet for one month, the weights of the turkeys doubled. Find the new mean and standard deviation.

    c Comment, in general terms, on your findings from **a** and **b**.

7 A sample of 8 integers has a mean of 5 and a variance of 5.25.
The integers are: 1, 3, 5, 7, 4, 5, p, q.   Find p and q given that $p < q$.

8 A sample of 10 integers has a mean of 6 and a variance of 3.2.
The integers are: 3, 9, 5, 5, 6, 4, a, 6, b, 8.   Find a and b given that $a > b$.

9   **a** Prove that $\displaystyle\sum_{i=1}^{n}(x_i - \overline{x})^2 = \sum_{i=1}^{n}(x_i{}^2) - n(\overline{x})^2$.

    b Find the mean of the data set x_1, x_2, ..., x_{25} given that $\displaystyle\sum_{i=1}^{25}x_i{}^2 = 2568.25$ and the standard deviation is 5.2.

10 The following table shows the change in cholesterol levels in 6 volunteers after a two week trial of special diet and exercise.

Volunteer	A	B	C	D	E	F
Change in cholesterol	0.8	0.6	0.7	0.8	0.4	2.8

  a Find the standard deviation of the data.
  b Recalculate the standard deviation with the outlier removed.
  c Discuss the effect of an extreme value on the standard deviation.

SAMPLING FROM A POPULATION

Populations are often huge, and gathering data from every individual is impossible due to time constraints and cost.

Consequently, a **random sample** is taken from the population with the hope that it will truly reflect the characteristics of the population. To ensure this, the sample must be sufficiently large, and be taken in such a way that the results are unbiased.

From the sample we hope to make **inferences** about the population's mean and possibly other key features.

To help distinguish between a sample and the whole population, we use different notation for the mean, variance, and standard deviation. This is shown in the table opposite.

	sample	population
mean	$\overline{x}$	μ
variance	s_n^2	σ^2
standard deviation	s_n	σ

Given statistics from a sample, we can make inferences about the population using the following results which are assumed without proof:

> When a sample of size n is used to draw inference about a population:
> - the mean of the sample $\overline{x}$ is an unbiased estimate of μ
> - $s_{n-1}^2 = \left(\dfrac{n}{n-1}\right)s_n^2$ is an unbiased estimate of the variance σ^2.

Note: Even if s_{n-1}^2 is an unbiased estimate of σ^2, this does not imply that s_{n-1} is an unbiased estimate of σ.

NOTE ON PARAMETERS AND STATISTICS

> A **parameter** is a numerical characteristic of a *population*.
>
> A **statistic** is a numerical characteristic of a *sample*.

Parameter
Population

Sample
Statistic

For example, if we are examining the mean age of people in retirement villages throughout Canada, the mean age found would be a *parameter*. If we take a random sample of 300 people from the population of all retirement village persons, then the mean age would be a *statistic*.

Example 13

A random sample of 48 sheep was taken from a flock of over 2000 sheep.
The sample mean of their weights was 48.6 kg with variance 17.5 kg.
a   Find the standard deviation of the sample.
b   Find an unbiased estimation of the mean weight of sheep in the flock.
c   Find an unbiased estimation of the variance of the population from
which the sample was taken.

a $s_n = \sqrt{\text{variance}} = \sqrt{17.5} \approx 4.18$ kg

b μ is estimated by $\overline{x} = 48.6$ kg

c σ^2 is estimated by $s_{n-1}^2 = \left(\dfrac{n}{n-1}\right)s_n^2 \approx \dfrac{48}{47} \times 17.5 \approx 17.9$ kg^2

EXERCISE 17F.2

1   A random sample of 87 deer from a huge herd had a mean weight of 93.8 kg with a
variance of 45.9 kg.
a   Find the standard deviation of the sample.
b   Find an unbiased estimation of the mean and variance of the entire herd from which
the sample was taken.

2   The weights (in grams) of a random sample of sparrows are as follows:
   87 75 68 69 81 89 73 66 91 77 84 83 77 74 80 76 67
a   Find the mean and standard deviation of the sample.
b   Find unbiased estimates of the mean and variance of the population from which the
sample was taken.

3   Jacko drives down to the beach every morning to go surfing. On 16 randomly chosen
trips he recorded his travel time x_i in minutes.

He finds that $\displaystyle\sum_{i=1}^{16} x_i = 519$ and $\displaystyle\sum_{i=1}^{16} (x_i^2) = 16\,983$.

Calculate unbiased estimates of   a   the mean and   b   the variance   of the driving
times to the beach.

STANDARD DEVIATION FOR GROUPED DATA

For grouped data $s = \sqrt{\dfrac{\sum f(x - \overline{x})^2}{\sum f}}$ where s is the **standard deviation**
x is **any score**, $\overline{x}$ is the **mean**
f is the **frequency** of each score

Example 14

Find the standard deviation of the distribution:

score	1	2	3	4	5
frequency	1	2	4	2	1

x	f	fx	$x - \bar{x}$	$(x - \bar{x})^2$	$f(x - \bar{x})^2$
1	1	1	-2	4	4
2	2	4	-1	1	2
3	4	12	0	0	0
4	2	8	1	1	2
5	1	5	2	4	4
Total	10	30			12

$$\bar{x} = \frac{\sum fx}{\sum f} = \frac{30}{10} = 3$$

$$s = \sqrt{\frac{\sum f(x - \bar{x})^2}{\sum f}}$$

$$= \sqrt{\frac{12}{10}}$$

$$\approx 1.10$$

EXERCISE 17F.3

1 Below is a sample of family sizes taken at random from people in a city.

Number of children, x	0	1	2	3	4	5	6	7
Frequency, f	14	18	13	5	3	2	2	1

  a Find the sample mean and standard deviation.
  b Find unbiased estimates of the mean and variance of the population from which the sample was taken.

2 Below is a random sample of the ages of squash players at the Junior National Squash Championship.

Age	11	12	13	14	15	16	17	18
Frequency	2	1	4	5	6	4	2	1

  a Find the mean and standard deviation of the ages.
  b Find unbiased estimates of the mean and variance of the population from which the sample was taken.

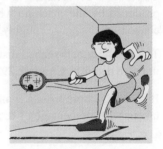

3 The number of toothpicks in a random sample of 48 boxes was counted and the results tabulated.

Number of toothpicks	33	35	36	37	38	39	40
Frequency	1	5	7	13	12	8	2

  a Find the mean and standard deviation of the number of toothpicks in the boxes.
  b Find unbiased estimates of the mean and variance of the population from which the sample was taken.

4 The lengths of 30 randomly selected 12-day old babies were measured to the nearest cm and the following data obtained:

Length (cm)	Frequency
40 - 41	1
42 - 43	1
44 - 45	3
46 - 47	7
48 - 49	11
50 - 51	5
52 - 53	2

   a Find estimates of the mean length and the standard deviation of the lengths.

   b Find unbiased estimates of the mean and variance of the population from which the sample was taken.

5 The weekly wages (in dollars) of 200 randomly selected steel workers are given alongside:

Wage ($)	Number of workers
360 - 369.99	17
370 - 379.99	38
380 - 389.99	47
390 - 399.99	57
400 - 409.99	18
410 - 419.99	10
420 - 429.99	10
430 - 439.99	3

   a Find estimates of the mean and the standard deviation of the wages.

   b Find unbiased estimates of the mean and variance of the population from which the sample was taken.

G THE SIGNIFICANCE OF STANDARD DEVIATION

Consider the volumes of liquid in different cans of a particular brand of soft drink. The distribution of volumes is symmetrical and bell-shaped. This is due to natural variation produced by the machine which has been set to produce a particular volume. Random or chance factors cause roughly the same number of cans to be overfilled as underfilled.

The resulting bell-shaped distribution is called the **normal distribution**. It will be discussed in more detail in **Chapter 29**, but it is worth noting here how it relates to standard deviation.

If a large sample from a typical bell-shaped data distribution is taken, what percentage of the data values would lie between $\overline{x} - s$ and $\overline{x} + s$?

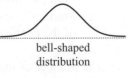
bell-shaped distribution

Click on the icon and try to answer this question.
Repeat the sampling many times.

DEMO

Now try to determine the percentage of data values which would lie between $\overline{x} - 2s$ and $\overline{x} + 2s$, and then between $\overline{x} - 3s$ and $\overline{x} + 3s$.

It can be shown that for any measured variable from any population that is normally distributed, no matter the values of the mean and standard deviation:

- approximately **68%** of the population will measure between **1** standard deviation either side of the mean
- approximately **95%** of the population will measure between **2** standard deviations either side of the mean
- approximately **99.7%** of the population will measure between **3** standard deviations either side of the mean.

Example 15

A sample of 200 cans of peaches was taken from a warehouse and the contents of each can measured for net weight. The sample mean was 486 g with standard deviation 6.2 g. What proportion of the cans might lie within:

a 1 standard deviation from the mean **b** 3 standard deviations from the mean?

a About 68% of the cans would be expected to have contents between
486 ± 6.2 g i.e., 479.8 g and 492.2 g.

b Nearly all of the cans would be expected to have contents between
$486 \pm 3 \times 6.2$ g i.e., 467.4 and 504.6 g.

THE NORMAL CURVE

The smooth curve that models normally distributed data is asymptotic to the horizontal axis, so in theory there are no limits within which all the members of the population will fall.

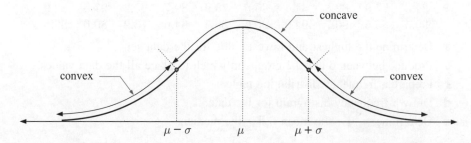

In practice, however, it is rare to find data outside of 3 standard deviations from the mean, and *exceptionally* rare to find data beyond 5 standard deviations from the mean.

Note that the position of 1 standard deviation either side of the mean corresponds to the point where the normal curve changes from a concave to a convex curve.

EXERCISE 17G

1 The mean height of players in a basketball competition is 184 cm. If the standard deviation is 5 cm, what percentage of them are likely to be:

    a taller than 189 cm   **b** taller than 179 cm

    c between 174 cm and 199 cm   **d** over 199 cm tall?

2 The mean average rainfall of Claudona for August is 48 mm with a standard deviation of 6 mm. Over a 20 year period, how many times would you expect there to be less than 42 mm of rainfall during August in Claudona?

3 Two hundred lifesavers competed in a swimming race. The mean time was 10 minutes 30 seconds. The standard deviation was 15 seconds. Find the number of competitors who probably:

    a took longer than 11 minutes   **b** took less than 10 minutes 15 seconds

    c completed the race in a time between 10 min 15 sec and 10 min 45 sec.

4 The weights of babies born at Prince Louis Maternity Hospital last year averaged 3.0 kg with a standard deviation of 200 grams. If there were 545 babies born at this hospital last year, estimate the number that weighed:

    a   less than 3.2 kg   **b**   between 2.8 kg and 3.4 kg.

REVIEW SET 17A

1 The data supplied below is the diameter (in cm) of a number of bacteria colonies as measured by a microbiologist 12 hours after seeding.

    0.4 2.1 3.4 3.9 4.7 3.7 0.8 3.6 4.1 4.9 2.5 3.1 1.5 2.6 4.0
    1.3 3.5 0.9 1.5 4.2 3.5 2.1 3.0 1.7 3.6 2.8 3.7 2.8 3.2 3.3

    a Produce a stemplot for this data.
    b Find the **i** median **ii** range of the data.
    c Comment on the skewness of the data.

2 The data below shows the distance in metres that Thabiso threw a baseball.

    71.2   65.1   68.0   71.1   74.6   68.8   83.2   85.0   74.5   87.4
    84.3   77.0   82.8   84.4   80.6   75.9   89.7   83.2   97.5   82.9
    90.5   85.5   90.7   92.9   95.6   85.5   64.6   73.9   80.0   86.5

    a Determine the highest and lowest value for the data set.
    b Produce between 6 and 12 groups in which to place all the data values.
    c Prepare a frequency distribution table.
    d Draw a frequency histogram for the data.
    e Determine: **i** the mean **ii** the median.

3 $5, 6, 8, a, 3, b$, have a mean of 6 and a variance of 3. Find the values of a and b.

4 For the following distribution of continuous grouped data:

Scores	0 to 9.9	10 to 19.9	20 to 29.9	30 to 39.9	40 to 49.9
Frequency	1	13	27	17	2

    a Construct an ogive.   **b** Find the median of the data.
    c Find the interquartile range.   **d** Find the mean and standard deviation.

5 The back-to-back stemplot alongside represents the times for the 100 metre freestyle recorded by members of a swimming squad.

    a Copy and complete the following table:

Distribution	Girls	Boys
shape		
centre (median)		
spread (range)		

Girls		Boys
	32	1
4	33	0 2 2 7
7 6 3	34	1 3 4 4 8
8 7 4 3 0	35	0 2 4 7 9 9
8 8 3 3	36	7 8 8
7 6 6 6	37	0
6	38	
0	39	
	40	*leaf unit:*
1	41	0.1 sec

    b Discuss the distributions of times for the boys and girls. What conclusion can you make?

6 The given parallel boxplots represent the 100-metre sprint times for the members of two athletics squads.

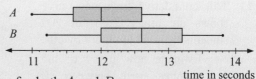

time in seconds

    a Determine the 5 number summaries for both A and B.

    b Determine the **i** range **ii** interquartile range   for each group.

    c Copy and complete:

       i We know the members of squad ...... generally ran faster because ......

      ii We know the times in squad ...... are more varied because ......

7 Katja's golf scores for her last 20 rounds were:

90	106	84	103	112	100	105	81	104	98
107	95	104	108	99	101	106	102	98	101

    a Find the **i** median **ii** lower quartile **iii** upper quartile

    b Find the interquartile range of the data set.

    c Find the mean and standard deviation of her scores.

8 The number of litres of petrol purchased by a random sample of motor vehicle drivers is shown alongside:

Litres	Number of vehicles
15 - < 20	5
20 - < 25	13
25 - < 30	17
30 - < 35	29
35 - < 40	27
40 - < 45	18
45 - < 50	7

    a Find the mean and standard deviation of the number of litres purchased.

    b Find unbiased estimates of the mean and variance for the population this sample comes from.

9 The average height of 17-year old boys was found to be normally distributed with a mean of 179 cm and a standard deviation of 8 cm. Calculate the percentage of 17-year old boys whose heights are:

    a more than 195 cm   **b** between 163 cm and 195 cm

    c between 171 cm and 187 cm.

10 80 senior students needed to run 400 metres in a Physical Education program. Their times were recorded and the results were used to produce the following cumulative frequency graph.

Estimate:

    a the median

    b the interquartile range.

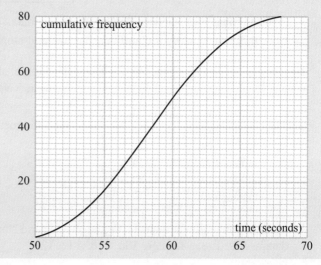

11 This cumulative frequency curve shows the times taken for 200 students to travel to school by bus.

   a Estimate how many of the students spent between 10 and 20 minutes travelling to school.

   b If 30% of the students spent more than m minutes travelling to school, estimate the value of m.

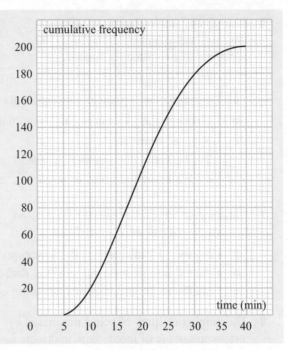

REVIEW SET 17B

1 The winning margin in 100 basketball games was recorded. The results are given alongside:

Draw a histogram to represent this information.

Margin (points)	Frequency
1 - 10	13
11 - 20	35
21 - 30	27
31 - 40	18
41 - 50	7

2 The table alongside shows the number of matches in a sample of boxes.

Number	47	48	49	50	51	52
Frequency	21	29	35	42	18	31

Find the mean and standard deviation for this data.
Does this result justify a claim that the average number of matches per box is 50?

3

No. of customers	Frequency
250 - 299	14
300 - 349	34
350 - 399	68
400 - 449	72
450 - 499	54
500 - 549	23
550 - 599	7

The table alongside shows the number of customers visiting a supermarket on various days.

Find the mean number of customers per day.

4 Find the range, lower quartile, upper quartile and standard deviation for the following data: 120, 118, 132, 127, 135, 116, 122, 128.

5 Draw a box and whisker plot for the following data:

11, 12, 12, 13, 14, 14, 15, 15, 15, 16, 17, 17, 18.

6 A random sample of the weekly supermarket bills for a number of families was observed and recorded in the table given.

a Find the mean bill and the standard deviation of the bills.

b Find unbiased estimates of the mean and variance of the population from which the data was taken.

Bill ($)	No. of families
70 - 79.99	27
80 - 89.99	32
90 - 99.99	48
100 - 109.99	25
110 - 119.99	37
120 - 129.99	21
130 - 139.99	18
140 - 149.99	7

7 The mean and standard deviation of a normal distribution are 150 and 12 respectively. What percentage of values lie between:

a   138 and 162   **b**   126 and 174   **c**   126 and 162   **d**   162 and 174?

8 The middle 68% of a normal distribution lies between 16.2 and 21.4.

a What is the mean and standard deviation of the distribution?

b Over what range of values would you expect the middle 95% of the data to spread?

9

A bottle shop sells on average 2500 bottles per day with a standard deviation of 300 bottles. Assuming that the number of bottles is normally distributed, calculate the percentage of days when:

a   less than 1900 bottles are sold

b   more than 2200 bottles are sold

c   between 2200 and 3100 bottles are sold.

10 Masoumeh measured the width (x_i cm) of 30 randomly selected cockle shells and observed that

$$\sum_{i=1}^{30} x_i = 116.3 \text{ cm} \quad \text{and} \quad \sum_{i=1}^{30} x_i^2 = 452.57 \,.$$

a Calculate:

i the mean width   **ii** the variance of the widths

b Calculate unbiased estimates of the mean and variance of the population from which this sample comes.

11 7, 5, a, 8, 1, a, 4, 6, b have a mean of 5 and a variance of $3\frac{7}{9}$.

a Find the values of a and b given $a, b \in \mathbb{Z}^+$.

b What is the median of the data set?

c Find the interquartile range of the data set.

12 An examination worth 100 marks was given to 800 biology students.

The cumulative frequency graph for the students' results follows:

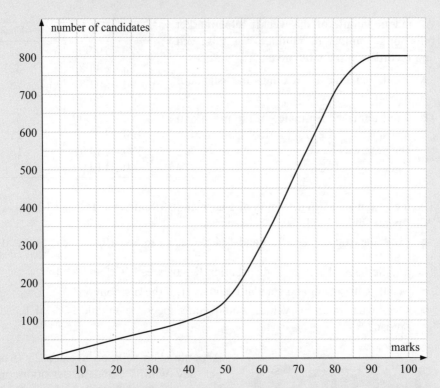

a Find the number of students who scored 45 marks or less for the test.

b Find the median score.

c Between what values do the middle 50% of test results lie?

d Find the interquartile range of the data.

e What percentage of students obtained a mark of 55 or more?

f If a 'distinction' is awarded to the top 10% of students, what score is required to receive this honour?

Chapter 18

Probability

Contents:

In the field of mathematics called **probability theory** we use a mathematical method to describe the **chance** or **likelihood** of an event happening.

This theory has vitally important applications in physical and biological sciences, economics, politics, sport, life insurance, quality control, production planning, and a host of other areas.

We assign to every event a number which lies between 0 and 1 inclusive. We call this number a **probability**.

An **impossible** event which has 0% chance of happening is assigned a probability of 0.

A **certain** event which has 100% chance of happening is assigned a probability of 1.

All other events can be assigned a probability between 0 and 1.

The number line below shows how we could interpret different probabilities:

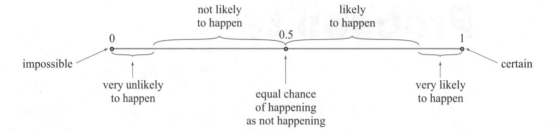

The assigning of probabilities is usually based on either:

- observing the results of an experiment (experimental probability),   or
- using arguments of symmetry (theoretical probability).

HISTORICAL NOTE

The development of modern probability theory began in 1653 when gambler Chevalier de Mere contacted mathematician **Blaise Pascal** with a problem on how to divide the stakes when a gambling game is interrupted during play. Pascal involved **Pierre de Fermat**, a lawyer and amateur mathematician, and together they solved the problem. In the process they laid the foundations upon which the laws of probability were formed.

Blaise Pascal

Pierre de Fermat

In the late 17th century, English mathematicians compiled and analysed mortality tables. These tables showed the number of people who died at different ages. From these tables they could estimate the probability that a person would be alive at a future date. This led to the establishment of the first life-insurance company in 1699.

OPENING PROBLEM

Life Insurance Companies use statistics on **life expectancy** and **death rates** to work out the premiums to charge people who insure with them.

The **life table** shown is from Australia. It shows the number of people out of 100 000 births who survive to different ages, and the expected years of remaining life at each age.

LIFE TABLE					
Male			**Female**		
Age	Number surviving	Expected remaining life	Age	Number surviving	Expected remaining life
0	100 000	73.03	0	100 000	79.46
5	98 809	68.90	5	99 307	75.15
10	98 698	63.97	10	99 125	70.22
15	98 555	59.06	15	98 956	65.27
20	98 052	54.35	20	98 758	60.40
25	97 325	49.74	25	98 516	55.54
30	96 688	45.05	30	98 278	50.67
35	96 080	40.32	35	98 002	45.80
40	95 366	35.60	40	97 615	40.97
45	94 323	30.95	45	96 997	36.22
50	92 709	26.45	50	95 945	31.59
55	89 891	22.20	55	94 285	27.10
60	85 198	18.27	60	91 774	22.76
65	78 123	14.69	65	87 923	18.64
70	67 798	11.52	70	81 924	14.81
75	53 942	8.82	75	72 656	11.36
80	37 532	6.56	80	58 966	8.38
85	20 998	4.79	85	40 842	5.97
90	8416	3.49	90	21 404	4.12
95	2098	2.68	95	7004	3.00
99	482	2.23	99	1953	2.36

Notice that out of 100 000 births, 98 052 males are expected to survive to the age of 20 and at that age the survivors are expected to live a further 54.35 years.

Things to think about:

- Can you use the life table to estimate how many years you can expect to live?

- What is the estimated probability of a new-born boy or girl reaching the age of 15?

- Can the table be used to estimate the probability that:
  - ▶ a 15 year old boy *will* reach the age of 75
  - ▶ a 15 year old girl *will not* reach the age of 75?

- An insurance company sells policies to people to insure them against death over a 30-year period. If the person dies during this period, the beneficiaries receive the agreed payout figure. Why are such policies cheaper to take out for a 20 year old than for a 50 year old?

- How many of your classmates would you expect to be alive and able to attend a 30 year class reunion?

A   EXPERIMENTAL PROBABILITY

In experiments involving chance we use the following terms to describe what we are doing and the results we are obtaining.

- The **number of trials** is the total number of times the experiment is repeated.
- The **outcomes** are the different results possible for one trial of the experiment.
- The **frequency** of a particular outcome is the number of times that this outcome is observed.
- The **relative frequency** of an outcome is the frequency of that outcome expressed as a fraction or percentage of the total number of trials.

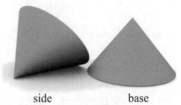

When a small plastic cone was tossed into the air 279 times it fell on its *side* 183 times and on its *base* 96 times.

The relative frequencies of *side* and *base* are
$\frac{183}{279} \approx 0.656$ and $\frac{96}{279} \approx 0.344$ respectively.

side   base

In the absence of any further data, the relative frequency of each event is our best estimate of the probability of each event occurring.

Experimental probability = relative frequency.

We write: Experimental P(side) = 0.656,   Experimental P(base) = 0.344

INVESTIGATION 1   TOSSING DRAWING PINS

If a drawing pin tossed in the air finishes we say it has finished

on its *back*. If it finishes we say it has finished on its *side*.

If two drawing pins are tossed simultaneously the possible results are:

two backs   back and side   two sides

What to do:

1. Obtain two drawing pins of the same shape and size. Toss the pair 80 times and record the outcomes in a table.
2. Obtain relative frequencies (experimental probabilities) for each of the three events.
3. Pool your results with four other people and so obtain experimental probabilities from 400 tosses.
   Note: The others must have pins with the same shape.
4. Which gives the more reliable estimates, your results or the group's? Why?
5. Keep your results as they may be useful later in this chapter.

In some cases, such as in the investigation above, experimentation is the only way of obtaining probabilities.

EXERCISE 18A

1   When a batch of 145 paper clips was dropped onto 6 cm by 6 cm squared paper it was observed that 113 fell completely inside squares and 32 finished up on the grid lines. Find, to 2 decimal places, the estimated probability of a clip falling:

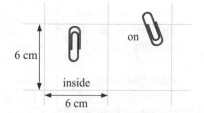

   a   inside a square   b   on a line.

2

Length	Frequency
0 - 19	17
20 - 39	38
40 - 59	19
60+	4

Jose surveyed the length of TV commercials (in seconds). Find to 3 decimal places the estimated probability that a randomly chosen TV commercial will last:

   a   20 to 39 seconds   b   more than a minute
   c   between 20 and 59 seconds (inclusive).

3   Betul records the number of phone calls she receives over a period of consecutive days.

   a   For how many days did the survey last?
   b   Estimate Betul's chance of receiving:
      i   no phone calls on one day
      ii   5 or more phone calls on a day
      iii   less than 3 phone calls on a day.

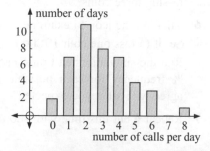

4   Pat does a lot of travelling in her car and she keeps records on how often she fills her car with petrol. The table alongside shows the frequencies of the number of days between refills. Estimate the likelihood that:

   a   there is a four day gap between refills
   b   there is at least a four day gap between refills.

Days between refills	Frequency
1	37
2	81
3	48
4	17
5	6
6	1

INVESTIGATION 2   COIN TOSSING EXPERIMENTS

The coins of most currencies have two distinct faces, usually referred to as "heads" and "tails". When we toss a coin in the air, we expect it to finish on a head or tail with equal likelihood.

In this investigation the coins do not have to be all the same type.

What to do:

1   Toss *one coin* 40 times. Record the number of heads resulting in a table:

Result	Tally	Frequency	Relative frequency
1 head			
0 head			

2 Toss *two coins* 60 times. Record the number of heads resulting in a table.

Result	Tally	Frequency	Relative frequency
2 heads			
1 head			
0 head			

3 Toss *three coins* 80 times. Record the number of heads resulting in a table.

Result	Tally	Frequency	Relative frequency
3 heads			
2 heads			
1 head			
0 head			

4 Share your results to **1**, **2** and **3** with several others. Comment on any similarities and differences.

5 Pool your results and find new relative frequencies for tossing one coin, two coins, tossing three coins.

6 Click on the icon to examine a coin tossing simulation.   **COIN TOSSING**

Set it to toss one coin 10 000 times.

Run the simulation ten times, each time recording the % frequency for each possible result. Comment on these results. Do your results agree with what you expected?

7 Repeat **6** but this time with *two coins* and then with *three coins*.

From the previous investigation you should have observed that, when tossing two coins, there are roughly twice as many 'one head' results as there are 'no heads' or 'two heads'.

The explanation for this is best seen using two different coins where you could get:

two heads   one head   one head   no heads

This shows that we should expect the ratio two heads : one head : no heads to be 1 : 2 : 1.   However, due to chance, there will be variations from this when we look at experimental results.

INVESTIGATION 3   DICE ROLLING EXPERIMENTS

You will need: At least one normal six-sided die with numbers   **WORKSHEET**
1 to 6 on its faces. Several dice would be useful to speed up the experimentation.

What to do:

1 List the possible outcomes for the uppermost face when the die is rolled.

2 Consider the possible outcomes when the die is rolled 60 times.

Copy and complete the following table of your **expected results**:

Outcomes	Expected frequency	Expected rel. frequency
⋮		

3 Roll the die 60 times. Record the results in a table like the one shown:

Outcome	Tally	Frequency	Relative frequency
1			
2			
⋮			
6			
	Total	60	

4 Pool as much data as you can with other students.

- Look at similarities and differences from one set to another.
- Summarise the overall pooled data in one table.

SIMULATION

5 Compare your results with your expectation in **2**.

6 Use the die rolling simulation on the CD to roll the die 10 000 times. Repeat this 10 times. On each occasion, record your results in a table like that in **3**. Do your results further confirm your expected results?

7 The different possible results when a pair of dice is rolled are shown alongside.

There are 36 possible outcomes.

Notice that three of the outcomes, {1, 3}, {2, 2} and {3, 1}, give a sum of 4.

Using the illustration above, copy and complete the table of expected (theoretical) results:

Sum	2	3	4	5	⋯	12
Fraction of total			$\frac{3}{36}$			
Fraction as decimal			0.083			

8 If a pair of dice is rolled 360 times, how many of each result (2, 3, 4, ..., 12) would you expect to get? Extend the table in **7** by adding another row and writing your **expected frequencies** within it.

9 Toss two dice 360 times. Record the *sum of the two numbers* for each toss in a table.

Sum	Tally	Frequency	Rel. Frequency
2			
3			
4			
⋮			
12			
Total		360	1

WORKSHEET

10 Pool as much data as you can with other students and find the overall relative frequency of each sum.

11 Use the two dice simulation on the CD to roll the pair of dice 10 000 times. Repeat this 10 times and on each occasion record your results in a table like that in **9**. Are your results consistent with your expectations?

SIMULATION

SAMPLE SPACE

A **sample space** U is the set of all possible outcomes of an experiment.

There are a variety of ways of representing or illustrating sample spaces.

LISTING OUTCOMES

Example 1

List the sample space of possible outcomes for:

a   tossing a coin

b   rolling a die.

a   When a coin is tossed, there are two possible outcomes.
∴ sample space = {H, T}

b   When a die is rolled, there are 6 possible outcomes.
∴ sample space = {1, 2, 3, 4, 5, 6}

2-DIMENSIONAL GRIDS

When an experiment involves more than one operation we can still use listing to illustrate the sample space. However, a grid can often be more efficient.

Example 2

Illustrate the possible outcomes when 2 coins are tossed by using a 2-dimensional grid.

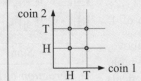

Each of the points on the grid represents one of the possible outcomes:
{HH, HT, TH, TT}

TREE DIAGRAMS

The sample space in **Example 2** could also be represented by a tree diagram. The advantage of tree diagrams is that they can be used when more than two operations are involved.

Example 3

Illustrate, using a tree diagram, the possible outcomes when:

a   tossing two coins

b   drawing two marbles from a bag containing many red, green, and yellow marbles.

a   coin 1   coin 2

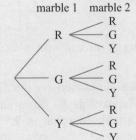

b   marble 1   marble 2

What is the sample space here?

Each "branch" gives a different outcome and the sample space is seen to be {HH, HT, TH, TT}.

EXERCISE 18B

1 List the sample space for the following:
  a twirling a square spinner labelled A, B, C, D
  b the sexes of a 2-child family
  c the order in which 4 blocks A, B, C and D can be lined up
  d the 8 different 3-child families.

2 Illustrate on a 2-dimensional grid the sample space for:

  a rolling a die and tossing a coin simultaneously
  b rolling two dice
  c rolling a die and spinning a spinner with sides A, B, C, D
  d twirling two square spinners: one labelled A, B, C, D and the other 1, 2, 3, 4.

3 Illustrate on a tree diagram the sample space for:
  a tossing a 5-cent and a 10-cent coin simultaneously
  b tossing a coin and twirling an equilateral triangular spinner labelled A, B and C
  c twirling two equilateral triangular spinners labelled 1, 2 and 3 and X, Y and Z
  d drawing two tickets from a hat containing a number of pink, blue and white tickets.

C THEORETICAL PROBABILITY

Consider the **octagonal spinner** alongside.

Since the spinner is symmetrical, when it is spun the arrowed marker could finish with equal likelihood on each of the sections marked 1 to 8.

The likelihood of obtaining a particular number, for example 4, would be:

$$1 \text{ chance in } 8, \qquad \tfrac{1}{8}, \qquad 12\tfrac{1}{2}\% \qquad \text{or} \qquad 0.125.$$

This is a **mathematical** or **theoretical** probability and is based on what we theoretically expect to occur. It is a measure of the chance of that event occurring in any trial of the experiment.

If we are interested in the event of getting a result of *6 or more* from one spin of the octagonal spinner, there are three favourable results (6, 7 or 8) out of the eight possible results. Since each of these is equally likely to occur,   P(6 or more) $= \tfrac{3}{8}$.

> We read $\tfrac{3}{8}$ as '3 chances in 8'.

In general, for an event E containing **equally likely** possible results, the probability of E occurring is

$$P(E) = \frac{\text{the number of members of the event } E}{\text{the total number of possible outcomes}} = \frac{n(E)}{n(U)}.$$

Example 4

A ticket is *randomly selected* from a basket containing 3 green, 4 yellow and 5 blue tickets. Determine the probability of getting:

a   a green ticket   b   a green or yellow ticket

c   an orange ticket   d   a green, yellow or blue ticket

The sample space is $\{G, G, G, Y, Y, Y, Y, B, B, B, B, B\}$

which has $3 + 4 + 5 = 12$ outcomes.

a $P(G)$ b $P(\text{a G or a Y})$ c $P(O)$ d $P(G, Y \text{ or } B)$

$= \frac{3}{12}$ $= \frac{3+4}{12}$ $= \frac{0}{12}$ $= \frac{3+4+5}{12}$

$= \frac{1}{4}$ $= \frac{7}{12}$ $= 0$ $= 1$

In **Example 4** notice that in c an orange result cannot occur. The calculated probability is 0, because the event has *no chance* of occurring.

Also notice in d that a green, yellow or blue result is certain to occur. It is 100% likely so the theoretical probability is 1.

The two events of   *no chance of occurring* with probability 0 and
certain to occur with probability 1 are two extremes.

Consequently, for any event E, $0 \leqslant P(E) \leqslant 1$.

COMPLEMENTARY EVENTS

Example 5

An ordinary 6-sided die is rolled once. Determine the chance of:

a   getting a 6   b   not getting a 6

c   getting a 1 or 2   d   not getting a 1 or 2

The sample space of possible outcomes is $\{1, 2, 3, 4, 5, 6\}$

a $P(6)$ b $P(\text{not a 6})$ c $P(1 \text{ or } 2)$ d $P(\text{not a 1 or 2})$

$= \frac{1}{6}$ $= P(1, 2, 3, 4 \text{ or } 5)$ $= \frac{2}{6}$ $= P(3, 4, 5, \text{ or } 6)$

          $= \frac{5}{6}$ $= \frac{4}{6}$

In **Example 5** notice that $P(6) + P(\text{not getting a 6}) = 1$ and that

$P(1 \text{ or } 2) + P(\text{not getting a 1 or 2}) = 1$.

This is no surprise as *getting a 6* and *not getting a 6* are **complementary events** where one of them **must occur**.

Two events are **complementary** if their probabilities add up to 1.

If E is an event, then E' is the complementary event of E.

$$P(E) + P(E') = 1$$

EXERCISE 18C.1

1 A marble is randomly selected from a box containing 5 green, 3 red and 7 blue marbles. Determine the probability that the marble is:

   a red   **b** green   **c** blue

   d not red   **e** neither green nor blue   **f** green or red

2 A carton of a dozen eggs contains eight brown eggs. The rest are white.

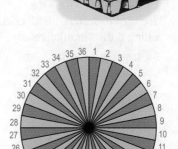

   a How many white eggs are there in the carton?

   b What is the probability that an egg selected at random is: **i** brown **ii** white?

3 A dart board has 36 sectors labelled 1 to 36. Determine the probability that a dart thrown at the centre of the board hits:

   a a multiple of 4

   b a number between 6 and 9 inclusive

   c a number greater than 20

   d 9   **e** a multiple of 13

   f an odd number that is a multiple of 3

   g a multiple of 4 and 6

   h a multiple of 4 or 6.

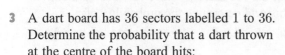

4 What is the probability that a randomly chosen person has his or her next birthday:

   a on a Tuesday   **b** on a weekend   **c** in July   **d** in January or February?

5 List the six different orders in which Antti, Kai and Neda may sit in a row. If the three of them sit randomly in a row, determine the probability that:

   a Antti sits in the middle   **b** Antti sits at the left end

   c Antti sits at the right end   **d** Kai and Neda are seated together

6 **a** List the 8 possible 3-child families according to the gender of the children. For example, GGB means *"the first is a girl, the second is a girl, the third is a boy"*.

   b Assuming that each of these is equally likely to occur, determine the probability that a randomly selected 3-child family consists of:

     i all boys   **ii** all girls

     iii boy then girl then girl   **iv** two girls and a boy

     v a girl for the eldest   **vi** at least one boy.

7 **a** List, in systematic order, the 24 different orders in which four people A, B, C and D may sit in a row.

   b Determine the probability that when the four people sit at random in a row:

     i A sits on one end

     ii B sits on one of the two middle seats

     iii A and B are seated together

     iv A, B and C are seated together, not necessarily in that order.

USING GRIDS TO FIND PROBABILITIES

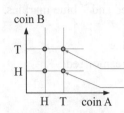

Two-dimensional grids can give us excellent visual displays of sample spaces. We can use them to count favourable outcomes and so calculate probabilities.

This point represents 'a tail from coin A' and 'a tail from coin B'.

This point represents 'a tail from coin A' and 'a head from coin B'.

There are four members of the sample space.

Example 6

Use a two-dimensional grid to illustrate the sample space for tossing a coin and rolling a die simultaneously. From this grid determine the probability of:

a tossing a head   **b** getting a tail and a 5   **c** getting a tail or a 5.

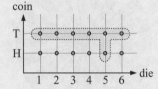

There are 12 members in the sample space.

a $P(head) = \frac{6}{12} = \frac{1}{2}$ **b** $P(tail \text{ and a '5'}) = \frac{1}{12}$

c $P(tail \text{ or a '5'}) = \frac{7}{12}$ {the enclosed points}

EXERCISE 18C.2

1 Draw the grid of the sample space when a 5-cent and a 10-cent coin are tossed simultaneously. Hence determine the probability of getting:

   a two heads   **b** two tails
   c exactly one head   **d** at least one head

2 A coin and a pentagonal spinner with sectors 1, 2, 3, 4 and 5 are tossed and spun respectively.

   a Draw a grid to illustrate the sample space of possible outcomes.

   b How many outcomes are possible?

   c Use your grid to determine the chance of getting:

   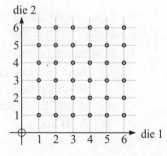

   i a tail and a 3   **ii** a head and an even number
   iii an odd number   **iv** a head or a 5

3 A pair of dice is rolled. The 36 different possible results are illustrated in the 2-dimensional grid.

   Use the grid to determine the probability of getting:

   a two 3's   **b** a 5 and a 6
   c a 5 or a 6   **d** at least one 6
   e exactly one 6   **f** no sixes
   g a sum of 7   **h** a sum greater than 8
   i a sum of 7 or 11   **j** a sum of no more than 8.

DISCUSSION

Read and discuss:

Three children have been experimenting with a coin, tossing it in the air and recording the outcomes. They have done this 10 times and have recorded 10 tails. Before the next toss they make the following statements:

Jack: "It's got to be a head next time!"

Sally: "No, it always has an equal chance of being a head or a tail. The coin cannot remember what the outcomes have been."

Amy: "Actually, I think it will probably be a tail again, because I think the coin must be biased - it might be weighted somehow so that it is more likely to give a tail."

D | COMPOUND EVENTS

Consider the following problem:

Box X contains 2 blue and 2 green balls. Box Y contains 3 red and 1 white ball. A ball is randomly selected from each of the boxes. Determine the probability of getting "a blue ball from X and a red ball from Y".

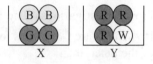

By illustrating the sample space on the two-dimensional grid shown, we can see that 6 of the 16 possibilities are blue from X and red from Y. Each of the outcomes is equally likely, so

$$P(\text{blue from X } \textbf{and} \text{ red from Y}) = \tfrac{6}{16}$$

The question arises,   "Is there a quicker, easier way to find this probability?"

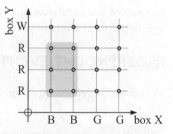

INVESTIGATION 4 | PROBABILITIES OF COMPOUND EVENTS

The purpose of this investigation is to find a rule for calculating $P(A \text{ and } B)$ for two events A and B.

Suppose a coin is tossed and a die is rolled at the same time. The result of the coin toss will be called outcome A, and the result of the die roll will be outcome B.

What to do:

1 Copy and complete, using a 2-dimensional grid if necessary:

	$P(A \text{ and } B)$	$P(A)$	$P(B)$
P(a head and a 4)			
P(a head and an odd number)			
P(a tail and a number larger than 1)			
P(a tail and a number less than 3)			

2 What is the connection between $P(A \text{ and } B)$, $P(A)$, and $P(B)$?

INVESTIGATION 5   REVISITING DRAWING PINS

We cannot find by theoretical argument the probability that a drawing pin will land on its back ⊥ . We can only find this probability by experimentation.

So, when tossing two drawing pins can we use the rule for compound events:

$$P(\text{back } and \text{ back}) = P(\text{back}) \times P(\text{back})?$$

What to do:

1 From **Investigation 1** on page **528**, what is your estimate of P(back *and* back)?

2 **a** Count the number of drawing pins in a full packet. They must be identical to each other and the same ones that you used in **Investigation 1**.

 b Drop the whole packet onto a solid surface and count the number of *backs* and *sides*. Repeat this several times. Pool results with others and finally estimate P(back).

3 Find   P(back) × P(back)   using **2b**.

4 Is   P(back *and* back) ≈ P(back) × P(back)?

From **Investigations 4** and **5**, it seems that:

If A and B are two events for which the occurrence of each one does not affect the occurrence of the other, then $P(A \textbf{ and } B) = P(A) \times P(B)$.

Before we can formalise this as a rule, however, we need to distinguish between **independent** and **dependent** events.

INDEPENDENT EVENTS

Events are independent if the occurrence of each of them does not affect the probability that the others occur.

Consider again the example on the previous page. Suppose we happen to choose a blue ball from box X. This in no way affects the outcome when we choose a ball from box Y. So, the two events "a blue ball from X" and "a red ball from Y" are independent.

> If A and B are **independent events** then $P(A \textbf{ and } B) = P(A) \times P(B)$.

This rule can be extended for any number of independent events.

For example: If A, B and C are all **independent events**, then
$$P(A \textbf{ and } B \textbf{ and } C) = P(A) \times P(B) \times P(C).$$

Example 7

A coin and a die are tossed simultaneously. Determine the probability of getting a head and a 3 without using a grid.

P(a head and a 3) = P(H) × P(3)   {events are clearly physically independent}

$$= \tfrac{1}{2} \times \tfrac{1}{6} = \tfrac{1}{12}$$

EXERCISE 18D.1

1 At a mountain village in Papua New Guinea it rains on average 6 days a week. Determine the probability that it rains on:

    a   any one day   b   two successive days   c   three successive days.

2 A coin is tossed 3 times. Determine the probability of getting the following sequences of results: a   head then head then head   b   tail then head then tail.

3 A school has two photocopiers. On any one day, machine A has an 8% chance of malfunctioning and machine B has a 12% chance of malfunctioning. Determine the probability that on any one day both machines will:

    a   malfunction   b   work effectively.

4 A couple decide that they want 4 children, none of whom will be adopted. They will be disappointed if the children are not born in the order boy, girl, boy, girl. Determine the probability that they will be:

    a   happy with the order of arrival   b   unhappy with the order of arrival.

5 Two marksmen fire at a target simultaneously. Jiri hits the target 70% of the time and Benita hits it 80% of the time. Determine the probability that:

    a   they both hit the target

    b   they both miss the target

    c   Jiri hits it but Benita misses

    d   Benita hits it but Jiri misses.

6  An archer always hits a circular target with each arrow shot, and hits the bullseye on average 2 out of every 5 shots. If 3 arrows are shot at the target, determine the probability that the bullseye is hit:

    a   every time

    b   the first two times, but not on the third shot

    c   on no occasion.

DEPENDENT EVENTS

Suppose a hat contains 5 red and 3 blue tickets. One ticket is randomly chosen, its colour is noted, and it is then put aside. A second ticket is then randomly selected. What is the chance that it is red?

If the first ticket was red,   P(second is red) $= \frac{4}{7}$ 4 reds remaining   7 to choose from

If the first ticket was blue,   P(second is red) $= \frac{5}{7}$ 5 reds remaining   7 to choose from

So, the probability of the second ticket being red **depends** on what colour the first ticket was. We therefore have **dependent events**.

> Two or more events are **dependent** if they are **not independent**.
>
> **Dependent** events are events for which the occurrence of one of the events *does affect* the occurrence of the other event.

For compound events which are dependent, a similar product rule applies as to that for independent events:

> If A and B are dependent events then
>
> $P(A \text{ then } B) = P(A) \times P(B \text{ given that } A \text{ has occurred}).$

Example 8

A box contains 4 red and 2 yellow tickets. Two tickets are randomly selected from the box one by one *without* replacement. Find the probability that:

a   both are red   **b**   the first is red and the second is yellow.

a   P(both red)

= P(first selected is red *and* second is red)

= P(first selected is red) × P(second is red given that the first is red)

= $\frac{4}{6} \times \frac{3}{5}$ ⟵ 3 reds remain out of a total of 5 after a red is drawn first

= $\frac{2}{5}$ ⟵ 4 reds out of a total of 6 tickets

b   P(first is red *and* second is yellow)

= P(first is red) × P(second is yellow given that the first is red)

= $\frac{4}{6} \times \frac{2}{5}$ ⟵ 2 yellows remain out of a total of 5 after a red is drawn first

= $\frac{4}{15}$ ⟵ 4 reds out of a total of 6 tickets

Example 9

A hat contains tickets with numbers 1, 2, 3, ..., 19, 20 printed on them. If 3 tickets are drawn from the hat, without replacement, determine the probability that all are prime numbers.

In each fraction the numerator is the number of outcomes in the event. The denominator is the total number of possible outcomes.

$\{2, 3, 5, 7, 11, 13, 17, 19\}$ are primes.

∴ there are 20 numbers of which 8 are primes.

∴ P(3 primes)

= P(1st drawn is prime *and* 2nd is prime *and* 3rd is prime)

= $\frac{8}{20} \times \frac{7}{19} \times \frac{6}{18}$

⟶ 8 primes out of 20 numbers

⟶ 7 primes out of 19 numbers after a successful first draw

≈ 0.0491   ⟶ 6 primes out of 18 numbers after two successful draws

EXERCISE 18D.2

1   A bin contains 12 identically shaped chocolates of which 8 are strawberry creams. If 3 chocolates are selected simultaneously from the bin, determine the probability that:

a   they are all strawberry creams

b   none of them are strawberry creams.

Drawing three chocolates simultaneously implies there is no replacement.

2   A box contains 7 red and 3 green balls. Two balls are drawn one after another from the box. Determine the probability that:

  a   both are red   **b**   the first is green and the second is red

  c   a green and a red are obtained.

3   A lottery has 100 tickets which are placed in a barrel. Three tickets are drawn at random from the barrel to decide 3 prizes. If John has 3 tickets in the lottery, determine his probability of winning:

  a   first prize   **b**   first and second prize   **c**   all 3 prizes   **d**   none of the prizes.

4   A hat contains 7 names of players in a tennis squad including the captain and the vice captain. If a team of 3 is chosen at random by drawing the names from the hat, determine the probability that it does not:

  a   contain the captain   **b**   contain the captain or the vice captain.

E   USING TREE DIAGRAMS

Tree diagrams can be used to illustrate sample spaces if the alternatives are not too numerous. Once the sample space is illustrated, the tree diagram can be used for determining probabilities.

Consider two archers firing simultaneously at a target.

Li has probability $\frac{3}{4}$ of hitting a target and Yuka has probability $\frac{4}{5}$.

The tree diagram for this information is:

H = hit   M = miss

Li's results	Yuka's results	outcome	probability
	$\frac{4}{5}$ H	H and H	$\frac{3}{4} \times \frac{4}{5} = \frac{12}{20}$
$\frac{3}{4}$ H	$\frac{1}{5}$ M	H and M	$\frac{3}{4} \times \frac{1}{5} = \frac{3}{20}$
$\frac{1}{4}$ M	$\frac{4}{5}$ H	M and H	$\frac{1}{4} \times \frac{4}{5} = \frac{4}{20}$
	$\frac{1}{5}$ M	M and M	$\frac{1}{4} \times \frac{1}{5} = \frac{1}{20}$
		total	1

Notice that:

  • The probabilities for hitting and missing are marked on the branches.
  • There are *four* alternative branches, each showing a particular outcome.
  • All outcomes are represented.
  • The probability of each outcome is obtained by **multiplying** the probabilities along its branch.

Example 10

Carl is not having much luck lately. His car will only start 80% of the time and his motorbike will only start 60% of the time.

  a   Draw a tree diagram to illustrate this situation.

  b   Use the tree diagram to determine the chance that:

    i   both will start   **ii**   Carl has no choice but to use his car.

  a   C = car starts
  M = motorbike starts

car	motorbike	outcome	probability
0.8 C	0.6 M	C and M	$0.8 \times 0.6 = 0.48$
	0.4 M'	C and M'	$0.8 \times 0.4 = 0.32$
0.2 C'	0.6 M	C' and M	$0.2 \times 0.6 = 0.12$
	0.4 M'	C' and M'	$0.2 \times 0.4 = 0.08$
		total	1.00

b i	P(both start)	**ii** P(car starts but motorbike does not)
	= P(C and M)	= P(C and M$'$)
	= 0.8×0.6	= 0.8×0.4
	= 0.48	= 0.32

If there is more than one outcome in an event then we need to **add** the probabilities of these outcomes.

Example 11

Bag A contains 3 red and 2 yellow tickets. Bag B contains 1 red and 4 yellow tickets. A bag is randomly selected by tossing a coin, and one ticket is removed from it. Determine the probability that it is yellow.

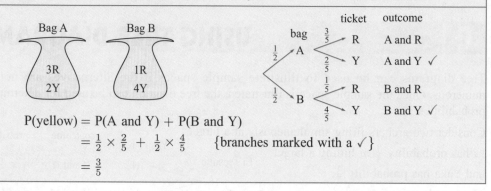

$$P(yellow) = P(A \text{ and } Y) + P(B \text{ and } Y)$$
$$= \tfrac{1}{2} \times \tfrac{2}{5} + \tfrac{1}{2} \times \tfrac{4}{5} \quad \{\text{branches marked with a } \checkmark\}$$
$$= \tfrac{3}{5}$$

EXERCISE 18E

1 Suppose this spinner is spun twice.

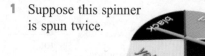

    a Copy and complete the branches on the tree diagram shown.

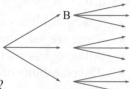

    b What is the probability that black appears on both spins?

    c What is the probability that yellow appears on both spins?

    d What is the probability that different colours appear on the two spins?

    e What is the probability that black appears on either spin?

2 The probability of rain tomorrow is estimated to be $\tfrac{1}{5}$. If it does rain, Mudlark will start favourite with probability $\tfrac{1}{2}$ of winning. If it is fine he only has a 1 in 20 chance of winning. Display the sample space of possible results of the horse race on a tree diagram. Hence determine the probability that Mudlark will win tomorrow.

3 Machine A makes 40% of the bottles produced at a factory. Machine B makes the rest. Machine A spoils 5% of its product, while Machine B spoils only 2%. Determine the probability that the next bottle inspected at this factory is spoiled.

4 Jar A contains 2 white and 3 red discs and Jar B contains 3 white and 1 red disc. A jar is chosen at random by the flip of a coin, and one disc is taken at random from it. Determine the probability that the disc is red.

5   Three bags contain different numbers of blue and red marbles. A bag is selected using a die which has three A faces, two B faces, and one C face.

One marble is then selected randomly from the bag. Determine the probability that it is:

a   blue   **b**   red.

F | # SAMPLING WITH AND WITHOUT REPLACEMENT

Suppose we have a large group of objects. If we select one of the objects at random and inspect it for particular features, then this process is known as **sampling**.

If the object is put back in the group, we call it **sampling with replacement**.

If the object is put to one side, we call it **sampling without replacement**.

Sampling is commonly used in the quality control of industrial processes.

Sometimes the inspection process makes it impossible to return the object to the large group. Such processes include:

- Is a chocolate hard or soft-centred? Bite it or squeeze it to see.
- Does an egg contain one or two yolks? Break it open and see.
- Is the object correctly made? Pull it apart to see.

Consider a box containing 3 red, 2 blue and 1 yellow marble. Suppose we wish to sample two marbles:

- **with replacement** of the first before the second is drawn
- **without replacement** of the first before the second is drawn.

Examine how the tree diagrams differ:

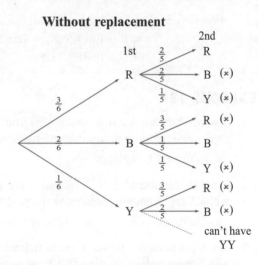

This branch represents a blue marble with the first draw and a red marble with the second draw. We write this as BR.

Notice that:
- with replacement

  $P(\text{two reds}) = \frac{3}{6} \times \frac{3}{6} = \frac{1}{4}$

- without replacement

  $P(\text{two reds}) = \frac{3}{6} \times \frac{2}{5} = \frac{1}{5}$

Example 12

For the example of the box containing 3 red, 2 blue and 1 yellow marble find the probability of getting two different colours:

a if replacement occurs   b if replacement does not occur.

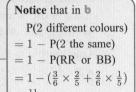

Notice that in b

$P(\text{2 different colours})$
$= 1 - P(\text{2 the same})$
$= 1 - P(\text{RR or BB})$
$= 1 - (\frac{3}{6} \times \frac{2}{5} + \frac{2}{6} \times \frac{1}{5})$
$= \frac{11}{15}$

a   P(two different colours)

$= P(\text{RB or RY or BR or BY or YR or YB})$ {ticked ones}

$= \frac{3}{6} \times \frac{2}{6} + \frac{3}{6} \times \frac{1}{6} + \frac{2}{6} \times \frac{3}{6} + \frac{2}{6} \times \frac{1}{6} + \frac{1}{6} \times \frac{3}{6} + \frac{1}{6} \times \frac{2}{6}$

$= \frac{11}{18}$

b   P(two different colours)

$= P(\text{RB or RY or BR or BY or YR or YB})$ {crossed ones}

$= \frac{3}{6} \times \frac{2}{5} + \frac{3}{6} \times \frac{1}{5} + \frac{2}{6} \times \frac{3}{5} + \frac{2}{6} \times \frac{1}{5} + \frac{1}{6} \times \frac{3}{5} + \frac{1}{6} \times \frac{2}{5}$

$= \frac{11}{15}$

Example 13

A bag contains 5 red and 3 blue marbles. Two marbles are drawn simultaneously from the bag. Determine the probability that at least one is red.

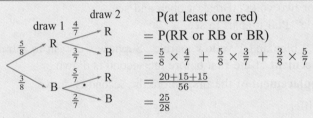

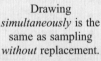

P(at least one red)

$= P(\text{RR or RB or BR})$

$= \frac{5}{8} \times \frac{4}{7} + \frac{5}{8} \times \frac{3}{7} + \frac{3}{8} \times \frac{5}{7}$

$= \frac{20+15+15}{56}$

$= \frac{25}{28}$

Drawing *simultaneously* is the same as sampling *without* replacement.

Alternatively,   P(at least one red)

$= 1 - P(\text{no reds})$ {complementary events}

$= 1 - P(\text{BB})$ etc

EXERCISE 18F

1 Two marbles are drawn in succession from a box containing 2 purple and 5 green marbles. Determine the probability that the two marbles are different colours if:

a the first is replaced   b the first is *not* replaced.

2 5 tickets numbered 1, 2, 3, 4 and 5 are placed in a bag. Two are taken from the bag without replacement. Determine the probability that:

a both are odd   b both are even   c one is odd and the other even.

3 Jar A contains 3 red and 2 green tickets. Jar B contains 3 red and 7 green tickets. A die has 4 faces with A's and 2 faces with B's, and when rolled it is used to select either jar A or jar B. When a jar has been selected, two tickets are randomly selected without replacement from it. Determine the probability that:

a both are green   b they are different in colour.

4 Marie has a bag of sweets which are all identical in shape. The bag contains 6 orange drops and 4 lemon drops. She selects one sweet at random, eats it, and then takes another at random. Determine the probability that:

   a both sweets were orange drops

   b both sweets were lemon drops

   c the first was an orange drop and the second was a lemon drop

   d the first was a lemon drop and the second was an orange drop.

Add your answers to **a**, **b**, **c** and **d**. Explain why the answer must be 1.

5 A bag contains four red and two blue marbles. Three marbles are selected simultaneously. Determine the probablity that:

   a all are red   **b** only two are red   **c** at least two are red.

6 Bag A contains 3 red and 2 white marbles. Bag B contains 4 red and 3 white marbles. One marble is randomly selected from A and its colour noted. If it is red, 2 reds are added to B. If it is white, 2 whites are added to B. A marble is then selected from B. What are the chances that the marble selected from B is white?

7 A man holds two tickets in a 100-ticket lottery in which there are two winning tickets. If no replacement occurs, determine the probability that he will win:

   a both prizes   **b** neither prize   **c** at least one prize.

8 A container holds 3 red balls, 7 white balls, and 2 black balls. A ball is chosen at random from the container and is not replaced. A second ball is then chosen. Find the probability of choosing one white and one black ball in any order.

9 A bag contains 7 yellow and n blue markers.

The probability of choosing 2 yellow markers, without replacement after the first choice, is $\frac{3}{13}$. How many blue markers are there in the bag?

INVESTIGATION 6   **SAMPLING SIMULATION**

 When balls enter the 'sorting' chamber shown they hit a metal rod and may go left or right. This movement continues as the balls fall from one level of rods to the next. The balls finally come to rest in collection chambers at the bottom of the sorter.

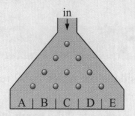

This sorter looks very much like a tree diagram rotated through 90°.

Click on the icon to open the simulation. Notice that the sliding bar will alter the probabilities of balls going to the left or right at each rod.

What to do:

1 To simulate the results of tossing two coins, set the bar to 50% and the sorter to show

SIMULATION

Run the simulation 200 times and repeat this four more times. Record each set of results.

2 A bag contains 7 blue and 3 red marbles. Two marbles are randomly selected from the bag, the first being *replaced* before the second is drawn.

Since   P(blue) $= \frac{7}{10} = 70\%$,   set the bar to 70%.

The sorter should show:

Run the simulation a large number of times. Use the results to estimate the probability of getting: **a**   two blues   **b**   one blue   **c**   no blues.

3 The tree diagram representation of the marble selection in **2** is:

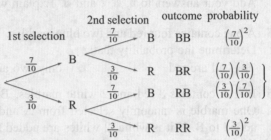

a The tree diagram gives us theoretical probabilities for the different outcomes. Do they agree with the experimental results obtained in **2**?

b Write down the algebraic expansion of $(a+b)^2$.

c Substitute $a = \frac{7}{10}$ and $b = \frac{3}{10}$ in the $(a+b)^2$ expansion. What do you notice?

4 From the bag of 7 blue and 3 red marbles, *three* marbles are randomly selected *with replacement*. Set the sorter to 3 levels and the bar to 70%.

Run the simulation a large number of times to obtain experimental estimates of the probabilities of getting:

a three blues   **b** two blues   **c** one blue   **d** no blues.

5 **a** Use a tree diagram showing 1st selection, 2nd selection and 3rd selection to find theoretical probabilities of getting the results of **4**.

b Show that $(a+b)^3 = a^3 + 3a^2b + 3ab^2 + b^3$ and use this expansion with $a = \frac{7}{10}$ and $b = \frac{3}{10}$ to also check the results of **4** and **5 a**.

6 Consider the sampling simulator with the bar at 50% to explain why many distributions are symmetrical and bell-shaped.

G   BINOMIAL PROBABILITIES

Consider a die which has 2 red faces and 4 black faces. We roll the die three times and record the results.

If R represents "the result is red" and B represents "the result is black", the possible outcomes are as shown alongside:

		BRR	RBB	
		RBR	BRB	
RRR	RRB	BBR	BBB	

Notice that the ratio of possible outcomes is $1:3:3:1$.

One outcome is *all red*.   Three outcomes are *two red and one black*.

Three outcomes are *one red and two black*.   One outcome is *all black*.

Now for each die,   P(R) $= \frac{1}{3}$ and   P(B) $= \frac{2}{3}$.

So, for rolling the die 3 times we have the following events and probabilities:

Event	Outcome	Probabilities	Total Probability
all red	RRR	$\left(\frac{1}{3}\right)\left(\frac{1}{3}\right)\left(\frac{1}{3}\right)$	$\left(\frac{1}{3}\right)^3 = \frac{1}{27}$
2 red and 1 black	BRR	$\left(\frac{2}{3}\right)\left(\frac{1}{3}\right)\left(\frac{1}{3}\right)$	$3\left(\frac{1}{3}\right)^2\left(\frac{2}{3}\right) = \frac{6}{27}$
	RBR	$\left(\frac{1}{3}\right)\left(\frac{2}{3}\right)\left(\frac{1}{3}\right)$	
	RRB	$\left(\frac{1}{3}\right)\left(\frac{1}{3}\right)\left(\frac{2}{3}\right)$	
1 red and 2 black	RBB	$\left(\frac{1}{3}\right)\left(\frac{2}{3}\right)\left(\frac{2}{3}\right)$	$3\left(\frac{1}{3}\right)\left(\frac{2}{3}\right)^2 = \frac{12}{27}$
	BRB	$\left(\frac{2}{3}\right)\left(\frac{1}{3}\right)\left(\frac{2}{3}\right)$	
	BBR	$\left(\frac{2}{3}\right)\left(\frac{2}{3}\right)\left(\frac{1}{3}\right)$	
all black	BBB	$\left(\frac{2}{3}\right)\left(\frac{2}{3}\right)\left(\frac{2}{3}\right)$	$\left(\frac{2}{3}\right)^3 = \frac{8}{27}$

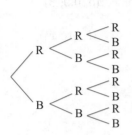

Notice that $\left(\frac{1}{3}\right)^3 + 3\left(\frac{1}{3}\right)^2\left(\frac{2}{3}\right) + 3\left(\frac{1}{3}\right)\left(\frac{2}{3}\right)^2 + \left(\frac{2}{3}\right)^3$ is the binomial expansion for $\left(\frac{1}{3} + \frac{2}{3}\right)^3$.

In general,　If E is an event with probability p of occurring and its complement E' has probability $q = 1 - p$ of occurring, then the **probability generator** for the various outcomes over n **independent trials** is $(p + q)^n$.

For example:

Suppose E is the event of a randomly chosen light globe being faulty, with $P(E) = p = 0.03$ and $P(E') = q = 0.97$.

If four independent samples are taken, the probability generator is $(0.03 + 0.97)^4$

$= (0.03)^4 + 4(0.03)^3(0.97) + 6(0.03)^2(0.97)^2 + 4(0.03)(0.97)^3 + (0.97)^4$

　　4 Es　　　3 Es and 1 E'　　2 Es and 2 E's　　1 E and 3 E's　　4 E's

Notice that　$P(E \text{ occurs } x \text{ times } \textbf{ and } E' \text{ occurs } n - x \text{ times}) = \binom{n}{x} p^x q^{n-x}$.

Example 14

An archer has a 90% chance of hitting the target with each arrow. If 5 arrows are fired, determine the probability generator and hence the chance of hitting the target:

a twice only　　**b** at most 3 times.

Let H be the event of '*hitting the target*', so $P(H) = 0.9$ and $P(H') = 0.1$

The probability generator is $(0.9 + 0.1)^5$

$= (0.9)^5 + 5(0.9)^4(0.1) + 10(0.9)^3(0.1)^2 + 10(0.9)^2(0.1)^3 + 5(0.9)(0.1)^4 + (0.1)^5$

　　5 hits　　4 hits and　　3 hits and　　2 hits and　　1 hit and　　5 misses
　　　　　　　1 miss　　　2 misses　　　3 misses　　　4 misses

Let X be the number of arrows that hit the target.

a　P(hits twice only)　　**b**　P(hits at most 3 times)

$= P(X = 2)$　　　　　　　$= P(X = 0, 1, 2 \text{ or } 3)$

$= 10(0.9)^2(0.1)^3$　　　　$= (0.1)^5 + 5(0.9)(0.1)^4 + 10(0.9)^2(0.1)^3 + 10(0.9)^3(0.1)^2$

$= 0.0081$　　　　　　　　≈ 0.0815

A graphics calculator can be used to find **binomial probabilities**.

For example, to find the probabilities in **Example 14** use:

   a $P(X = 2) = \text{binompdf}(5, 0.9, 2)$ **b** $P(X \leqslant 3) = \text{binomcdf}(5, 0.9, 3)$

                        $\uparrow \;\; \uparrow \;\; \uparrow$ $\uparrow \;\; \uparrow \;\; \uparrow$

                         $n \;\; p \;\; x$ $n \;\; p \;\; x$

Use your calculator to check the answers given above.

EXERCISE 18G

1 **a**   Expand $(p + q)^4$.

    b   If a coin is tossed *four* times, what is the probability of getting 3 heads?

2 **a**   Expand $(p + q)^5$.

    b   If *five* coins are tossed simultaneously, what is the probability of getting:

       i   4 heads and 1 tail in any order   **ii**   2 heads and 3 tails

      iii   4 heads and 1 tail in that order?

3 **a**   Expand $(\frac{2}{3} + \frac{1}{3})^4$.

    b   Four chocolates are randomly taken (with replacement) from a box which contains strawberry creams and almond centres in the ratio $2 : 1$.

        What is the probability of getting:

       i   all strawberry creams   **ii**   two of each type

      iii   at least 2 strawberry creams?

4 **a**   Expand $(\frac{3}{4} + \frac{1}{4})^5$.

    b   In New Zealand in 1946, coins of value two shillings were of two types: normal kiwis and 'flat back' kiwis, in the ratio $3 : 1$. From a batch of 1946 two shilling coins, five were selected at random with replacement. What is the probability that:

       i   two were 'flat backs'   **ii**   at least 3 were 'flat backs'

      iii   at most 3 were normal kiwis?

5   When rifle shooter Huy fires a shot, he hits the target 80% of the time. If Huy fires 4 shots at the target, determine the probability that he has:

    a   2 hits and 2 misses in any order   **b**   at least 2 hits.

6 5% of electric light bulbs are defective at manufacture. If 6 bulbs are tested at random with each one being replaced before the next is chosen, determine the probability that:

    a   two are defective   **b**   at least one is defective.

7   In a multiple choice test there are 10 questions. Each question has 5 choices, one of which is correct. If 70% is the pass mark and Raj (who knows nothing) guesses at each answer, determine the probability that he will pass.

8   Martina beats Jelena in 2 games out of 3 at tennis. What is the probability that Jelena wins a set of tennis 6 games to 4?

    Hint: What is the score after 9 games?

9   How many ordinary dice are needed for there to be a better than an even chance of at least one six when they are thrown together?

H   SETS AND VENN DIAGRAMS

Venn diagrams are a useful way of representing the events in a sample space. These diagrams usually consist of a rectangle which represents the complete sample space or **universal set**, and circles within it which represent particular events.

Venn diagrams can be used to solve certain types of probability questions and also to establish a number of probability laws.

The Venn diagram alongside shows the sample space for rolling a die.

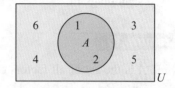

We can write the universal set $U = \{1, 2, 3, 4, 5, 6\}$ since the sample space consists of the numbers from 1 to 6.

The event A is "*a number less than 3*". There are two outcomes which satisfy event A, and we can write $A = \{1, 2\}$.

SET NOTATION

-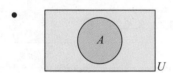

  The **universal set** or **sample space** U is represented by a rectangle.

  An **event** A is usually represented by a circle.

-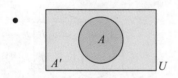

  A' (shaded green) is the **complement** of A (shaded purple).

  It represents the non-occurrence of A.

  Note: $P(A) + P(A') = 1$.

  If $U = \{1, 2, 3, 4, 5, 6, 7\}$ and $A = \{2, 4, 6\}$ then $A' = \{1, 3, 5, 7\}$.

- $x \in A$ reads   'x is in A'   and means that x is an element of the set A.

- $n(A)$ reads 'the number of elements in set A'.

- $A \cup B$ denotes the **union** of sets A and B. This set contains all elements belonging to A **or** B **or both** A and B.

  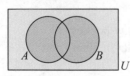

  $A \cup B$ is shaded in purple.

  $A \cup B = \{x \mid x \in A \ \textbf{or} \ x \in B\}$

- $A \cap B$ denotes the **intersection** of sets A and B. This is the set of all elements common to both sets.

  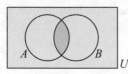

  $A \cap B$ is shaded in purple.

  $A \cap B = \{x \mid x \in A \ \textbf{and} \ x \in B\}$

- **Disjoint sets** are sets which do not have elements in common.

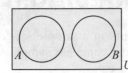

These two sets are disjoint.

$A \cap B = \varnothing$ where $\varnothing$ represents an **empty set**.

A and B are said to be **mutually exclusive**.

Note: We cannot determine whether two or more sets are independent by just looking at a Venn diagram.

Example 15

If A is the set of all factors of 36 and B is the set of all factors of 54, find:
a $A \cup B$ **b** $A \cap B$

$A = \{1, 2, 3, 4, 6, 9, 12, 18, 36\}$ and $B = \{1, 2, 3, 6, 9, 18, 27, 54\}$

a $A \cup B$ = the set of factors of 36 **or** 54
              $= \{1, 2, 3, 4, 6, 9, 12, 18, 27, 36, 54\}$

b $A \cap B$ = the set of factors of both 36 **and** 54 $= \{1, 2, 3, 6, 9, 18\}$

Example 16

On separate Venn diagrams containing two events A and B that intersect, shade the region representing:
a   in A but not in B
b   neither in A nor B.

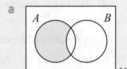

Example 17

If the Venn diagram alongside illustrates the number of people in a sporting club who play tennis (T) and hockey (H), determine the number of people:

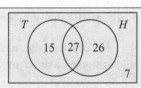

a   in the club
c   who play both sports
e   who play at least one sport.

b   who play hockey
d   who play neither sport

a   Number in the club
        $= 15 + 27 + 26 + 7 = 75$

b   Number who play hockey
        $= 27 + 26 = 53$

c   Number who play both sports $= 27$

d   Number who play neither sport
        $= 7$

e   Number who play at least one sport
        $= 15 + 27 + 26 = 68$

Example 18

The Venn diagram alongside represents the set U of all children in a class. Each dot represents a student. The event E shows all those students with blue eyes.

Determine the probability that a randomly selected child:

a   has blue eyes   b   does not have blue eyes.

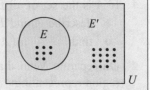

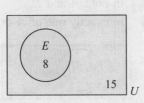

$n(U) = 23, \quad n(E) = 8$

a $P(\text{blue eyes}) = \dfrac{n(E)}{n(U)} = \dfrac{8}{23}$

b $P(\text{not blue eyes}) = \dfrac{n(E')}{n(U)} = \dfrac{15}{23}$

or $P(\text{not blue}) = 1 - P(\text{blue eyes}) = 1 - \dfrac{8}{23} = \dfrac{15}{23}$

Example 19

In a class of 30 students, 19 study Physics, 17 study Chemistry, and 15 study both of these subjects. Display this information on a Venn diagram and hence determine the probability that a randomly selected class member studies:

a   both subjects   b   at least one of the subjects
c   Physics but not Chemistry   d   exactly one of the subjects
e   neither subject   f   Chemistry if it is known that the student studies Physics.

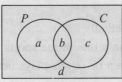

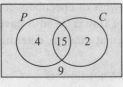

Let P represent the event of 'studying Physics' and C represent the event of 'studying Chemistry'.

Now
$$a + b = 19 \quad \{\text{as 19 study Physics}\}$$
$$b + c = 17 \quad \{\text{as 17 study Chemistry}\}$$
$$b = 15 \quad \{\text{as 15 study both}\}$$
$$a + b + c + d = 30 \quad \{\text{as there are 30 in the class}\}$$
$$\therefore \quad b = 15, \quad a = 4, \quad c = 2, \quad d = 9.$$

a $P(\text{studies both})$
$= \dfrac{15}{30}$ or $\dfrac{1}{2}$

b $P(\text{studies at least one subject})$
$= \dfrac{4+15+2}{30} = \dfrac{7}{10}$

c $P(P \text{ but not } C)$
$= \dfrac{4}{30} = \dfrac{2}{15}$

d $P(\text{studies exactly one})$
$= \dfrac{4+2}{30} = \dfrac{1}{5}$

e $P(\text{studies neither})$
$= \dfrac{9}{30} = \dfrac{3}{10}$

f $P(C \text{ given } P)$
$= \dfrac{15}{15+4} = \dfrac{15}{19}$

EXERCISE 18H.1

1   If A is the set of all factors of 6 and B is the set of all positive even integers < 11:
   a   describe A and B using set notation
   b   find: i $n(A)$ ii $A \cup B$ iii $A \cap B$.

2   On separate Venn diagrams containing two events A and B that intersect, shade the region representing:

   a   in A b   in B c   in both A and B
   d   in A or B e   in B but not in A f   in exactly one of A or B.

3   The Venn diagram alongside illustrates the number of students in a particular class who study Chemistry (C) and History (H). Determine the number of students:

   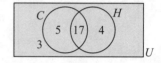

   a   in the class   b   who study both subjects
   c   who study at least one of the subjects   d   who only study Chemistry.

4   In a survey at an alpine resort, people were asked whether they liked skiing (S) or snowboarding (B). Use the Venn diagram to determine the number of people:

   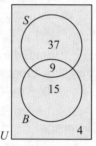

   a   in the survey
   b   who liked both activities
   c   who liked neither activity
   d   who liked exactly one activity.

5   In a class of 40 students, 19 play tennis, 20 play netball, and 8 play neither of these sports. A student is randomly chosen from the class. Determine the probability that the student:
   a   plays tennis   b   does not play netball
   c   plays at least one of the sports   d   plays one and only one of the sports
   e   plays netball but not tennis   f   plays tennis given he or she plays netball.

6   50 married men were asked whether they gave their wife flowers or chocolates for their last birthday. The results were: 31 gave chocolates, 12 gave flowers, and 5 gave both chocolates and flowers. If one of the married men was chosen at random, determine the probability that he gave his wife:
   a   chocolates or flowers   b   chocolates but not flowers
   c   neither chocolates nor flowers
   d   flowers if it is known that he did not give her chocolates.

7   The medical records for a class of 30 children showed that 24 had previously had measles, 12 had previously had measles and mumps, and 26 had previously had at least one of measles or mumps. If one child from the class is selected at random, determine the probability that he or she has had:
   a   mumps   b   mumps but not measles   c   neither mumps nor measles
   d   measles if it is known that the child has had mumps.

8   If A and B are two non-disjoint sets, shade the region of a Venn diagram representing:
   a A' b $A' \cap B$ c $A \cup B'$ d $A' \cap B'$

9 The diagram alongside is the most general case for three events in the same sample space U.

On separate Venn diagram sketches, shade:

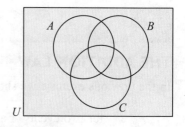

a A	b B'	c $B \cap C$
d $A \cup C$	e $A \cap B \cap C$	f $(A \cup B) \cap C$

USING VENN DIAGRAMS TO VERIFY SET IDENTITIES

Example 20

Verify that $(A \cup B)' = A' \cap B'$.

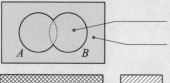

this shaded region is $(A \cup B)$

this shaded region is $(A \cup B)'$

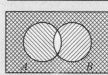

represents A'

represents B'

represents $A' \cap B'$

Thus $(A \cup B)'$ and $A' \cap B'$ are represented by the same regions, verifying that $(A \cup B)' = A' \cap B'$.

EXERCISE 18H.2

1 Verify that:

  a $(A \cap B)' = A' \cup B'$

  b $A \cup (B \cap C) = (A \cup B) \cap (A \cup C)$

  c $A \cap (B \cup C) = (A \cap B) \cup (A \cap C)$

2 Suppose $S = \{x: x$ is a positive integer $< 100\}$.

  Let $A = \{$multiples of 7 in $S\}$ and $B = \{$multiples of 5 in $S\}$.

  a How many elements are there in: i A ii B iii $A \cap B$ iv $A \cup B$?

  b If $n(E)$ represents the number of elements in set E, verify that
  $n(A \cup B) = n(A) + n(B) - n(A \cap B)$.

3

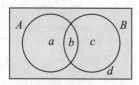

From the Venn diagram, $P(A) = \dfrac{a+b}{a+b+c+d}$.

  a Use the Venn diagram to find:

   i $P(B)$ ii $P(A$ and $B)$ iii $P(A$ or $B)$ iv $P(A) + P(B) - P(A$ and $B)$

  b What is the connection between $P(A$ or $B)$ and $P(A) + P(B) - P(A$ and $B)$?

LAWS OF PROBABILITY

THE ADDITION LAW

In the previous exercise we showed that

$$\text{for two events } A \text{ and } B, \quad P(A \cup B) = P(A) + P(B) - P(A \cap B).$$

This is known as the **addition law of probability**, and can be written as

$$P(\textbf{either } A \textbf{ or } B) = P(A) + P(B) - P(\textbf{both } A \textbf{ and } B).$$

Example 21

If $P(A) = 0.6$, $P(A \cup B) = 0.7$ and $P(A \cap B) = 0.3$, find $P(B)$.

$P(A \cup B) = P(A) + P(B) - P(A \cap B)$
$\therefore \quad 0.7 = 0.6 + P(B) - 0.3$
$\therefore \quad P(B) = 0.4$

or

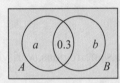

Using a Venn diagram with the probabilities on it,

$a + 0.3 = 0.6$ and $a + b + 0.3 = 0.7$
$\therefore \quad a = 0.3$ $\therefore \quad a + b = 0.4$
                                $\therefore \quad 0.3 + b = 0.4$
$\therefore \quad P(B) = 0.3 + b = 0.4$ $\therefore \quad b = 0.1$

MUTUALLY EXCLUSIVE EVENTS (DISJOINT EVENTS)

If A and B are **mutually exclusive** events then $P(A \cap B) = 0$
and so the addition law becomes $P(A \cup B) = P(A) + P(B)$.

Example 22

A box of chocolates contains 6 with hard centres (H) and 12 with soft centres (S).
a   Are the events H and S mutually exclusive?
b   Find   **i** $P(H)$ **ii** $P(S)$ **iii** $P(H \cap S)$ **iv** $P(H \cup S)$.

a   Chocolates cannot have both a hard and a soft centre.
    $\therefore \quad H$ and S are mutually exclusive.

b   **i** $P(H) = \frac{6}{18}$ **ii** $P(S) = \frac{12}{18}$ **iii** $P(H \cap S)$ **iv** $P(H \cup S)$
          $= \frac{1}{3}$ $= \frac{2}{3}$ $= 0$ $= \frac{18}{18} = 1$

CONDITIONAL PROBABILITY

If we have two events A and B, then

$A \mid B$ is used to represent that 'A occurs knowing that B has occurred'.
$A \mid B$ is often read as 'A given B'.

Example 23

In a class of 25 students, 14 like pizza and 16 like iced coffee. One student likes neither and 6 students like both. One student is randomly selected from the class. What is the probability that the student:

a likes pizza   b likes pizza given that he or she likes iced coffee?

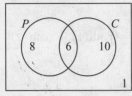

The Venn diagram of the situation is shown.

a $P(\text{pizza}) = \frac{14}{25}$ {of the 25 students, 14 like pizza}

b $P(\text{pizza}\,|\,\text{iced coffee}) = \frac{6}{16}$
{of the 16 who like iced coffee, 6 like pizza}

If A and B are events then

$$P(A\,|\,B) = \frac{P(A \cap B)}{P(B)}.$$

Proof:

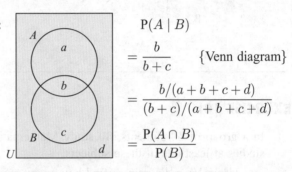

$P(A\,|\,B)$

$= \dfrac{b}{b+c}$ {Venn diagram}

$= \dfrac{b/(a+b+c+d)}{(b+c)/(a+b+c+d)}$

$= \dfrac{P(A \cap B)}{P(B)}$

It follows that $P(A \cap B) = P(A\,|\,B)\,P(B)$ or $P(A \cap B) = P(B\,|\,A)\,P(A)$

Example 24

In a class of 40 students, 34 like bananas, 22 like pineapples, and 2 dislike both fruits. If a student is randomly selected, find the probability that the student:

a likes both fruits   b likes at least one fruit
c likes bananas given that he or she likes pineapples
d dislikes pineapples given that he or she likes bananas.

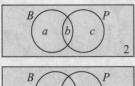

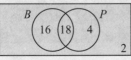

B represents students who like bananas.
P represents students who like pineapples.
We are given that $a + b = 34$
$b + c = 22$
$a + b + c = 38$

$\therefore\ c = 38 - 34$ and so $b = 18$
$= 4$ and $a = 16$

a P(likes both)   b P(likes at least one)   c $P(B\,|\,P)$ d $P(P'\,|\,B)$

$= \frac{18}{40}$ $= \frac{38}{40}$ $= \frac{18}{22}$ $= \frac{16}{34}$

$= \frac{9}{20}$ $= \frac{19}{20}$ $= \frac{9}{11}$ $= \frac{8}{17}$

Example 25

Bin A contains 3 red and 2 white tickets. Bin B contains 4 red and 1 white ticket. A die with 4 faces marked A and two faces marked B is rolled and used to select bin A or B. A ticket is then selected from this bin. Determine the probability that:

a   the ticket is red   **b**   the ticket was chosen from B given it is red.

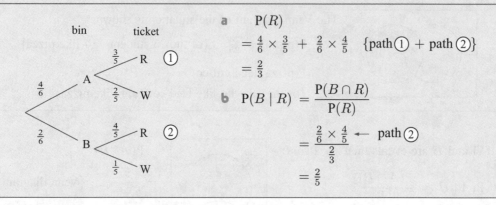

a $P(R)$

$= \frac{4}{6} \times \frac{3}{5} + \frac{2}{6} \times \frac{4}{5}$ {path① + path②}

$= \frac{2}{3}$

b $P(B \mid R) = \dfrac{P(B \cap R)}{P(R)}$

$= \dfrac{\frac{2}{6} \times \frac{4}{5}}{\frac{2}{3}}$ ← path②

$= \frac{2}{5}$

EXERCISE 18I

1   In a group of 50 students, 40 study Mathematics, 32 study Physics, and each student studies at least one of these subjects.

   a   Use a Venn diagram to find how many students study both subjects.

   b   If a student from this group is randomly selected, find the probability that he or she:

     i   studies Mathematics but not Physics

     ii   studies Physics given that he or she studies Mathematics.

2   In a group of 40 boys, 23 have dark hair, 18 have brown eyes, and 26 have dark hair, brown eyes or both. One of the boys is selected at random. Determine the probability that he has:

   a   dark hair and brown eyes   **b**   neither dark hair nor brown eyes

   c   dark hair but not brown eyes   **d**   brown eyes given that he has dark hair.

3   50 students go bushwalking. 23 get sunburnt, 22 get bitten by ants, and 5 are both sunburnt and bitten by ants. Determine the probability that a randomly selected student:

   a   escaped being bitten

   b   was either bitten or sunburnt

   c   was neither bitten nor sunburnt

   d   was bitten, given that he or she was sunburnt

   e   was sunburnt, given that he or she was not bitten.

4   400 families were surveyed. It was found that 90% had a TV set and 60% had a computer. Every family had at least one of these items. If one of these families is randomly selected, find the probability it has a TV set given that it has a computer.

5 In a certain town three newspapers are published. 20% of the population read A, 16% read B, 14% read C, 8% read A and B, 5% read A and C, 4% read B and C, and 2% read all 3 newspapers. A person is selected at random. Use a Venn diagram to help determine the probability that the person reads:

    a none of the papers   **b** at least one of the papers   **c** exactly one of the papers

    d either A or B **e** A, given that the person reads at least one paper

    f C, given that the person reads either A or B or both.

6 Urn A contains 2 red and 3 blue marbles, and urn B contains 4 red and 1 blue marble. Peter selects an urn by tossing a coin, and takes a marble from that urn.

    a Determine the probability that it is red.

    b Given that the marble is red, what is the probability that it came from B?

7 The probability that Greta's mother takes her shopping is $\frac{2}{5}$. When Greta goes shopping with her mother she gets an icecream 70% of the time. When Greta does not go shopping with her mother she gets an icecream 30% of the time.

Determine the probability that:

    a Greta's mother buys her an icecream when shopping.

    b Greta went shopping with her mother, given that her mother buys her an icecream.

8 On a given day, photocopier A has a 10% chance of malfunctioning and machine B has a 7% chance of the same. Given that at least one of the machines malfunctioned today, what is the chance that machine B malfunctioned?

9 On any day, the probability that a boy eats his prepared lunch is 0.5. The probability that his sister eats her lunch is 0.6. The probability that the girl eats her lunch given that the boy eats his is 0.9. Determine the probability that:

    a both eat their lunch   **b** the boy eats his lunch given that the girl eats hers

    c at least one of them eats lunch.

10 The probability that a randomly selected person has cancer is 0.02. The probability that he or she reacts positively to a test which detects cancer is 0.95 if he or she has cancer, and 0.03 if he or she does not. Determine the probability that a randomly tested person:

    a reacts positively   **b** has cancer given that he or she reacts positively.

11 A double-headed, a double-tailed, and an ordinary coin are placed in a tin can. One of the coins is randomly chosen without identifying it. The coin is tossed and falls "heads". Determine the probability that the coin is the "double-header".

12 The English Premier League consists of 20 teams. Tottenham is currently in 8th place on the table. It has 20% chance of winning and 60% chance of losing against any team placed above it. If a team is placed below it, Tottenham has a 50% chance of winning and a 30% chance of losing. Find the probability that Tottenham will draw its next game.

13 If events A and B are not mutually exclusive, $P(A \cup B) = P(A) + P(B) - P(A \cap B)$. Use a Venn diagram to find a corresponding rule for $P(A \cup B \cup C)$ where A, B and C are not mutually exclusive.

J   INDEPENDENT EVENTS

A and B are **independent events** if the occurrence of each one of them does not affect the probability that the other occurs,

i.e., $P(A \mid B) = P(A)$ and $P(B \mid A) = P(B)$.

So, as $P(A \cap B) = P(A \mid B) \, P(B)$,

A and B are **independent events** $\Leftrightarrow$ $P(A \cap B) = P(A) \, P(B)$.

Example 26

When two coins are tossed, A is the event of getting 2 heads. When a die is rolled, B is the event of getting a 5 or 6. Show that A and B are independent events.

$P(A) = \frac{1}{4}$ and $P(B) = \frac{2}{6}$.   Therefore, $P(A) \, P(B) = \frac{1}{4} \times \frac{2}{6} = \frac{1}{12}$

$P(A \cap B)$

$= P(2 \text{ heads } \textbf{and} \text{ a 5 or a 6})$

$= \frac{2}{24}$

$= \frac{1}{12}$

So, as $P(A \cap B) = P(A) \, P(B)$,   the events A and B are independent.

Example 27

$P(A) = \frac{1}{2}$, $P(B) = \frac{1}{3}$ and $P(A \cup B) = p$.   Find p if:

a A and B are mutually exclusive   **b** A and B are independent.

a   If A and B are mutually exclusive, $A \cap B = \varnothing$ and so $P(A \cap B) = 0$

But $P(A \cup B) = P(A) + P(B) - P(A \cap B)$

$\therefore \quad p = \frac{1}{2} + \frac{1}{3} - 0 = \frac{5}{6}$

b   If A and B are independent, $P(A \cap B) = P(A) \, P(B) = \frac{1}{2} \times \frac{1}{3} = \frac{1}{6}$

$\therefore \quad P(A \cup B) = \frac{1}{2} + \frac{1}{3} - \frac{1}{6}$ and hence $p = \frac{2}{3}$

Example 28

Given $P(A) = \frac{2}{5}$, $P(B \mid A) = \frac{1}{3}$ and $P(B \mid A') = \frac{1}{4}$ find:

a $P(B)$ **b** $P(A \cap B')$

$P(B \mid A) = \dfrac{P(B \cap A)}{P(A)}$ so $P(B \cap A) = P(B \mid A) \, P(A) = \frac{1}{3} \times \frac{2}{5} = \frac{2}{15}$

Similarly, $P(B \cap A') = P(B \mid A') \, P(A') = \frac{1}{4} \times \frac{3}{5} = \frac{3}{20}$

∴ the Venn diagram is:

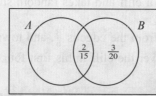

a $P(B) = \frac{2}{15} + \frac{3}{20} = \frac{17}{60}$

b $P(A \cap B') = P(A) - P(A \cap B)$
$$= \frac{2}{5} - \frac{2}{15}$$
$$= \frac{4}{15}$$

EXERCISE 18J

1 If $P(R) = 0.4$, $P(S) = 0.5$ and $P(R \cup S) = 0.7$, are R and S independent events?

2 If $P(A) = \frac{2}{5}$, $P(B) = \frac{1}{3}$ and $P(A \cup B) = \frac{1}{2}$, find:

   a $P(A \cap B)$ b $P(B \mid A)$ c $P(A \mid B)$

   Are A and B independent events?

3 If $P(X) = 0.5$, $P(Y) = 0.7$ and X and Y are independent events, determine the probability of the occurrence of:

   a both X and Y b X or Y c neither X nor Y
   d X but not Y e X given that Y occurs.

4 The probabilities that A, B and C can solve a particular problem are $\frac{3}{5}$, $\frac{2}{3}$ and $\frac{1}{2}$ respectively. If they all try, determine the probability that at least one of the group solves the problem.

5 a Find the probability of getting at least one six when a die is rolled 3 times.
   b If a die is rolled n times, find the smallest n such that
      P(at least one 6 in n throws) > 99%.

6 A and B are independent events. Prove that A' and B' are also independent events.

7 Two students, Karl and Hanna, play a game in which they take it in turns to select a card, with replacement, from a well-shuffled pack of 52 playing cards. The first person to select an ace wins the game. Karl has the first turn.

   a i   Find the probability that Karl wins on his third turn.
      ii Show that the probability that Karl wins prior to his $(n+1)$th turn is
          $\frac{13}{25}\left(1 - \left(\frac{12}{13}\right)^{2n}\right)$.
      iii Hence, find the probability that Karl wins the game.

   b If Karl and Hanna play this game seven times, find the probability that Karl will win more games than Hanna.

8 Given that $P(A \cap B) = 0.1$ and $P(A \cap B') = 0.4$, find $P(A \cup B')$ if A and B are independent.

9 Given $P(C) = \frac{9}{20}$, $P(C \mid D') = \frac{3}{7}$ and $P(C \mid D) = \frac{6}{13}$,

   a find i $P(D)$ ii $P(C' \cup D')$.
   b Are C and D independent events? Give a reason for your answer.

10 A delirious man stands on the edge of a cliff and takes random steps either towards or away from the cliff's edge.

The probability of him stepping away from the edge is $\frac{3}{5}$, and towards the edge is $\frac{2}{5}$.

Find the probability he does not step over the cliff in his first four steps.

 # PROBABILITIES USING PERMUTATIONS AND COMBINATIONS

Permutations and **combinations** can sometimes be used to find probabilities of various events. They are particularly useful if the sample size is large. It is useful to remember that:

$$P(\text{an event}) = \frac{\text{number of possibilities with the required properties of the event}}{\text{total number of unrestricted possibilities}}.$$

For example: Suppose we select at random a team of 7 players from a squad of 8 boys and 7 girls. The total number of unrestricted possibilities is $\binom{15}{7}$ since we are choosing 7 of the 15 available players.

The number of possibilities with the property of '4 boys **and** 3 girls' is $\binom{8}{4}\binom{7}{3}$ since we want any 4 of the 8 boys **and** any 3 of the 7 girls.

$$\therefore \quad P(\text{4 boys and 3 girls}) = \frac{\binom{8}{4}\binom{7}{3}}{\binom{15}{7}}.$$

The biggest difficulty in probability problems involving permutations or combinations seems to be in sorting out which to use.

Remember: • **permutations** involve the **ordering** of objects or things, whereas
          • **combinations** involve **selections** such as committees or teams.

Example 29

From a squad of 13 which includes 4 brothers, a team of 7 is randomly selected by drawing names from a hat. Determine the probability that the team contains:
a all the brothers   **b** at least 2 of the brothers.

There are $\binom{13}{7}$ different teams of 7 that can be chosen from 13 people.

a Of these teams, $\binom{4}{4}\binom{9}{3}$ contain all 4 brothers and any 3 others.

$$\therefore \quad P(\text{team contains all the brothers}) = \frac{\binom{4}{4}\binom{9}{3}}{\binom{13}{7}} \approx 0.0490$$

b P(at least 2 brothers) = P(2 brothers or 3 brothers or 4 brothers)

$$= \frac{\binom{4}{2}\binom{9}{5}}{\binom{13}{7}} + \frac{\binom{4}{3}\binom{9}{4}}{\binom{13}{7}} + \frac{\binom{4}{4}\binom{9}{3}}{\binom{13}{7}}$$

$$\approx 0.783$$

Example 30

5 letters U, S, T, I, N are placed at random in a row.
What is the probability that the word UNITS is spelled out?

There are 5! different permutations of the letters, one of which spells UNITS.

∴   P(UNITS is spelled) $= \frac{1}{5!} = \frac{1}{120}$

Notice that counting permutations is not essential here. We could have used:

P(UNITS) $= \frac{1}{5} \times \frac{1}{4} \times \frac{1}{3} \times \frac{1}{2} \times \frac{1}{1} = \frac{1}{120}$

5 to choose from   now 4 are left
and we want only U   and we want N

EXERCISE 18K

1   A committee of 4 is chosen from 11 people by random selection. What is the chance that sisters X and Y are on the committee?

2   4 alphabet blocks D, A, I and S are placed at random in a row. What is the likelihood that they spell out either AIDS or SAID?

3   A team of 7 is randomly chosen from a squad of 12. Determine the probability that both the captain and vice-captain are chosen.

4   Of the 22 people on board a plane, 3 are professional golfers. If the plane crashes and 4 people are killed, determine the chance that all three golfers survive.

5   5 boys sit at random on 5 seats in a row. Determine the probability that the two friends Keong and James sit: **a** at the ends of the row   **b** together.

6   A committee of 5 is randomly selected from 9 men and 7 women. Determine the likelihood that it consists of:

 a   all men   **b**   at least 3 men   **c**   at least one of each sex.

7   6 people including friends A, B and C are randomly seated on a row of 6 chairs. Determine the likelihood that A, B and C are seated together.

8   A school committee of 7 is to be chosen at random from 11 senior students and 3 junior students. Find the probability that:

 a   only senior students are chosen

 b   all three junior students are chosen.

BAYES' THEOREM

Suppose a sample space U is partitioned into two mutually exclusive regions by an event A and its complement A'.

We can show this on a Venn diagram as

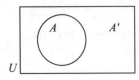   or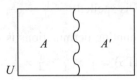

Now consider another event B in the sample space U. We can show this on a Venn diagram as

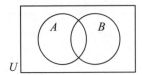   or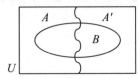

Bayes' theorem states that

$$P(A \mid B) = \frac{P(B \mid A)\, P(A)}{P(B)}$$

where $P(B) = P(B \mid A)\, P(A) + P(B \mid A')\, P(A')$.

Proof:
$$P(A \mid B) = \frac{P(A \cap B)}{P(B)} = \frac{P(B \mid A)\, P(A)}{P(B)}$$

where
$$P(B) = P(B \cap A) + P(B \cap A')$$
$$= P(B \mid A)\, P(A) + P(B \mid A')\, P(A')$$

Example 31

A can contains 4 blue and 2 green marbles. One marble is randomly drawn from the can without replacement and its colour is noted. A second marble is then drawn. What is the probability that:

a   the second marble is blue

b   the first was green given that the second is blue?

Let A be the event that the first marble is green.

Let B be the event that the second marble is blue.

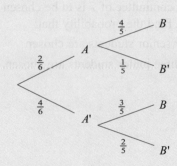

a   P(second marble is blue)

$= P(B)$

$= P(B \mid A)\,P(A) + P(B \mid A')\,P(A')$

$= \frac{2}{6} \times \frac{4}{5} + \frac{4}{6} \times \frac{3}{5}$

$= \frac{2}{3}$

b   P(first was green | second is blue)

$= P(A \mid B)$

$= \dfrac{P(B \mid A)\,P(A)}{P(B)}$ {Bayes' theorem}

$= \dfrac{\frac{2}{6} \times \frac{4}{5}}{\frac{2}{3}}$ {using **a**}

$= \frac{2}{5}$

EXERCISE 18L

1   Coffee making machines Alpha and Beta produce coffee in identically shaped plastic cups. Alpha produces 65% of the coffee sold each day, and Beta produces the remainder. Alpha underfills a cup 4% of the time while Beta underfills a cup 5% of the time.

a   If a cup of coffee is chosen at random, what is the probability it is underfilled?

b   A cup of coffee is randomly chosen and is found to be underfilled. What is the probability it came from Alpha?

2   54% of the students at a university are females. 8% of the male students are colour-blind and 2% of the female students are colour-blind. If a randomly chosen student:

a   is colour-blind, find the probability that the student is male

b   is not colour-blind, find the probability that the student is female.

3   A marble is randomly chosen from a can containing 3 red and 5 blue marbles. It is replaced by two marbles of the other colour. Another marble is then randomly chosen from the can. If the marbles chosen are the same colour, what is the probability that they are both blue?

4   35% of the animals in a deer herd carry the TPC gene. 58% of these deer also carry the SD gene, while 23% of the deer without the TPC gene carry the SD gene. If a deer is randomly chosen and is found to carry the SD gene, what is the probability it does not carry the TPC gene?

5   A new blood test has been shown to be effective in the early detection of a form of cancer. The probability that the test correctly identifies someone with the cancer is 0.97, and the probability that the test correctly identifies someone without the cancer is 0.93. Approximately 0.1% of the general population are known to contract this cancer.

A patient had a blood test and the test results were positive for the cancer. Find the probability that the patient actually had the cancer.

6   A man drives his car to work 80% of the time; otherwise he rides his bicycle. When he rides his bicycle to work he is late 25% of the time, whereas when he drives his car to work he is late 15% of the time. On a particular day, the man arrives on time. Find the probability that he rode his bicycle to work on that day.

7   The probabilities that Hiran's mother and father will be alive in one year's time are 0.99 and 0.98 respectively. What is the probability that if only one of them is alive in 12 months, it is his mother?

8 A manufacturer produces drink bottles. He uses 2 machines which produce 60% and 40% of the bottles respectively. 3% of the bottles made by the first machine are defective and 5% of the bottles made by the second machine are defective. What is the probability that a defective bottle came from:

    a   the first machine   **b**   the second machine?

9

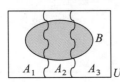

Suppose a sample space U is partitioned into three by the mutually exclusive events A_1, A_2 and A_3 as shown in the Venn diagram.

The sample space also contains another event B.

    a   Show that $P(B) = P(B \mid A_1)\, P(A_1) + P(B \mid A_2)\, P(A_2) + P(B \mid A_3)\, P(A_3)$.

    b   Hence show that Bayes' theorem for the case of three partitions is

$$P(A_i \mid B) = \frac{P(B \mid A_i)\, P(A_i)}{P(B)}, \ \ i \in \{1, 2, 3\} \ \ \text{where} \ \ P(B) = \sum_{j=1}^{3} P(B \mid A_j)\, P(A_j).$$

10 A printer has three presses A, B and C which print 30%, 40% and 30% of daily production respectively. Due to the age of the machines and other problems, the presses cannot be used 3%, 5% and 7% of the day, respectively. A printed page is randomly chosen.

    a   What is the probability that the press which printed the page is in use?

    b   If the press in **a** is in use, what is the probability it is press A?

    c   If the press in **a** is not in use, what is the probability it is either A or C?

11 12% of the over-60 population of Agento have lung cancer. Of those with lung cancer, 50% were heavy smokers, 40% were moderate smokers, and 10% were non-smokers. Of those without lung cancer, 5% were heavy smokers, 15% were moderate smokers, and 80% were non-smokers. If a member of the over-60 population of Agento is chosen at random, what is the probability that:

    a   the person was a heavy smoker

    b   the person has lung cancer given the person was a moderate smoker

    c   the person has lung cancer given the person was a non-smoker?

REVIEW SET 18A

1 List the different orders in which 4 people A, B, C and D could line up. If they line up at random, determine the probability that:

    a   A is next to C   **b**   there is exactly one person between A and C.

2 A coin is tossed and a square spinner labelled A, B, C, D, is twirled. Determine the probability of obtaining:

    a   a head and consonant   **b**   a tail and C   **c**   a tail or a vowel.

3 A class contains 25 students. 13 play tennis, 14 play volleyball, and 1 plays neither of these sports. If a student is randomly selected from the class, determine the probability that the student:

    a plays both tennis and volleyball   **b** plays at least one of these sports

    c plays volleyball given that he or she does not play tennis.

4 Niklas and Rolf play tennis with the winner being the first to win two sets. Niklas has a 40% chance of beating Rolf in any set. Draw a tree diagram showing the possible outcomes and hence determine the probability that Niklas will win the match.

5 The probability that a man will be alive in 25 years is $\frac{3}{5}$, and the probability that his wife will be alive is $\frac{2}{3}$. Determine the probability that in 25 years:

    a both will be alive   **b** at least one will be alive   **c** only the wife will be alive.

6 Each time Mae and Ravi play chess, Mae has probability $\frac{4}{5}$ of winning. If they play 5 games, determine the probability that:

    a Mae wins 3 of the games   **b** Mae wins either 4 or 5 of the games.

7 If I buy 4 tickets in a 500 ticket lottery, determine the probability that I win:

    a the first 3 prizes   **b** at least one of the first 3 prizes.

8 A school photocopier has a 95% chance of working on any particular day. Find the probability that it will be working on at least one of the next two days.

9 A team of five is randomly chosen from six doctors and four dentists. Determine the likelihood that it consists of: **a** all doctors   **b** at least two doctors.

10 3 girls and 3 boys sit at random on 6 seats in a row. Determine the probability that:

    a they alternate with girls sitting between boys   **b** the girls are seated together.

11 The students in a school are all vaccinated against measles. 48% of the students are males, of whom 16% have an allergic reaction to the vaccine. 35% of the girls also have an allergic reaction. If a student is randomly chosen from the school, what is the probability that the student:

    a has an allergic reaction

    b is female given that a reaction occurs?

REVIEW SET 18B

1 Systematically list the possible sexes of a 4-child family. Hence determine the probability that a randomly selected 4-child family consists of two children of each sex.

2 In a group of 40 students, 22 study Economics, 25 study Law, and 3 study neither of these subjects. Determine the probability that a randomly chosen student studies:

    a both Economics and Law   **b** at least one of these subjects

    c Economics given that he or she studies Law.

3   A bag contains 3 red, 4 yellow and 5 blue marbles. Two marbles are randomly selected from the bag without replacement. What is the probability that:

    a   both are blue   **b**   both are the same colour

    c   at least one is red   **d**   exactly one is yellow?

4   What is meant by: **a**   independent events   **b**   disjoint events?

5   On any one day it could rain with 25% chance and be windy with 36% chance. Draw a tree diagram showing the possibilities with regard to wind and rain on a particular day. Hence determine the probability that on a particular day there will be:

    a   rain and wind   **b**   rain or wind.

6   A, B and C have 10%, 20% and 30% chance of independently solving a certain maths problem. If they all try independently of one another, what is the probability that this group will solve the problem?

7   Jon goes cycling on three random mornings of each week. When he goes cycling he has eggs for breakfast 70% of the time. When he does not go cycling he has eggs for breakfast 25% of the time. Determine the probability that he:

    a   has eggs for breakfast   **b**   goes cycling given that he has eggs for breakfast.

8   **a**   Expand $\left(\frac{3}{5} + \frac{2}{5}\right)^4$.

    b   A tin contains 20 pens of which 12 have blue ink. Four pens are randomly selected (with replacement) from the tin. What is the probability that:

        i   two of them have blue ink   **ii**   at most two have blue ink?

9   X plays Y at table tennis and from past experience wins 3 sets in every 5 played. If they play 6 sets, write down the probability generator and hence determine the probability that   **a**   Y wins 3 of them   **b**   Y wins at least 5 of them.

10   With every attempt, Jack has an 80% chance of kicking a goal. In one quarter of a match he has 5 kicks for goal.

Determine the probability that he scores:

    a   3 goals then misses twice

    b   3 goals and misses twice.

REVIEW SET 18C

1   In a certain class, 91% of the students passed Mathematics and 88% of the students passed Chemistry. 85% of students passed both Mathematics and Chemistry.

    a   Show that the events of passing Mathematics and passing Chemistry are not independent.

    b   A randomly selected student passed Chemistry. Find the probability that this student did not pass Mathematics.

2 A group of ten students included three from year 12 and four from year 11. The principal called a meeting with five of the group, and randomly selected students to attend. Calculate the probability that exactly two year 12 and two year 11 students were called to the meeting.

3 Given $P(Y) = 0.35$ and $P(X \cup Y) = 0.8$, and that X and Y are independent events, find:

   a $P(X)$

   b the probability that X occurs or Y occurs, but not both X and Y.

4 A person with a university degree has a 0.33 chance of getting an executive position. A person without a university degree has a 0.17 chance of the same. If 78% of all applicants for an executive position have a university degree, find the probability that the successful applicant does not have one.

5 Given $P(X' \mid Y) = \frac{2}{3}$, $P(Y) = \frac{5}{6}$ and $X' \cap Y' = \varnothing$, find $P(X)$.

6 All of the 28 boys in an Australian school class play either Australian Rules football or soccer. 13 of the boys are migrants and 9 of these 13 play soccer. Of the remaining 15 boys, 4 play soccer. A boy is selected at random and plays Australian rules. Find the probability that he is a migrant.

7 The probability that a particular salesman will leave his sunglasses behind in any store is $\frac{1}{5}$. Suppose the salesman visits two stores in succession and leaves his sunglasses behind in one of them. What is the probability that the salesman left his sunglasses in the first store?

8 How many tosses of a fair coin are necessary to have a better than even chance of getting at least four heads?

9 An urn contains three red balls and six blue balls.

   a A ball is drawn at random and found to be blue. What is the probability that a second draw with no replacement will also produce a blue ball?

   b Two balls are drawn without replacement and the second is found to be red. What is the probability that the first ball was also red?

   c Based on the toss of a coin, either a red ball or a blue ball is added to the urn. Given that a random draw now produces a blue ball, what is the probability the added ball was   **i** red   **ii** blue?

10 Using a 52 card pack, a 'perfect' poker hand contains 10, J, Q, K, A of one suit. What is the probability of dealing:

   a a 'perfect' poker hand in any order

   b a 'perfect' poker hand in the order 10, J, Q, K, A?

11 With each pregnancy a particular woman will give birth to either a single baby or twins. There is a 15% chance of having twins during each pregnancy. If after 2 pregnancies she has given birth to 3 children, what is the probability she had twins first?

REVIEW SET 18D

1 **a** What is meant by saying that two events are independent?

   b If A and B are independent events, prove that A and B' are also independent.

2 Two coins A and B are tossed and the probability of a 'match' (either two heads or two tails) is $\frac{1}{2}$. Prove that at least one of the coins is unbiased.

3 **a** If $P(x) = \binom{n}{x} p^{n-x} q^x$ where $p + q = 1$ and $x = 0, 1, 2, 3, \ldots, n$

   prove that $P(x+1) = \left(\dfrac{n-x}{x+1}\right)\left(\dfrac{q}{p}\right) P(x)$ where $P(0) = p^n$.

   b If $n = 5$ and $p = \frac{1}{2}$, use **a** to find $P(0), P(1), P(2), \ldots, P(5)$.

4 A and B are independent events where $P(A) = 0.8$ and $P(B) = 0.65$.
   Determine: **a** $P(A \cup B)$ **b** $P(A \mid B)$ **c** $P(A' \mid B')$ **d** $P(B \mid A)$.

5 An unbiased coin is tossed n times. Find the smallest value of n for which the probability of getting at least two heads is greater than 99%.

6 The independent probabilities that 3 components of a TV set will need replacing within one year are $\frac{1}{20}$, $\frac{1}{50}$ and $\frac{1}{100}$ respectively. Calculate the probability that there will need to be a replacement of:

   a at least one component within a year   **b** exactly one component within a year.

7 When Peter plays John at tennis, the probability that Peter wins his service game is p and the probability that John wins his service game is q where $p > q$, $p + q > 1$.
   Which is more likely:
   A Peter will win at least two consecutive games out of 3 when he serves first
   B Peter will win at least two consecutive games out of 3 when John serves first?

8 Four different numbers are randomly chosen from $S = \{1, 2, 3, 4, 5, \ldots 10\}$.
   X is the second largest of the numbers selected.
   Determine the probability that X is: **a** 2   **b** 7   **c** 9.

9 Two different numbers were chosen at random from the digits 1 to 9 inclusive and it was observed that their sum was even. Determine the probability that both numbers were odd.

10 A dart thrower has a one in three chance of hitting the correct number with any throw. He throws 5 darts at the board and X is the number of successful hits. Find the probability generator for X, and hence calculate the probability of him scoring an odd number of successful hits given that he has at least two successful hits.

11 The diagram alongside shows an electrical circuit with switches. The probability that any switch is open is $\frac{1}{3}$. Determine the probability that the current flows from A to B.

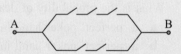

12 One letter is randomly selected from each of the names   JONES, PETERS and EVANS.

   a Determine the probability that the three letters are the same.

   b What is the likelihood that only two of the letters are the same?

Chapter 19

Introduction to calculus

Contents:

Calculus is a major branch of mathematics which builds on algebra, trigonometry, and analytic geometry. It has widespread applications in science, engineering, and financial mathematics.

The study of calculus is divided into two fields, **differential calculus** and **integral calculus**, both of which we will study in this course. These fields are linked by the **Fundamental theorem of calculus** which we will study in **Chapter 24**.

HISTORICAL NOTE

 Calculus is a Latin word meaning 'pebble'. Ancient Romans used stones for counting.

The history of calculus begins with the **Egyptian Moscow papyrus** from about 1850 BC. Its study continued in Egypt before being taken up by the Greek mathematician **Archimedes of Syracuse**.

It was further developed through the centuries by mathematicians of many nations.

Two of the most important contributors were **Gottfried Wilhelm Leibniz** and **Sir Isaac Newton** who independently developed the **fundamental theorem of calculus**.

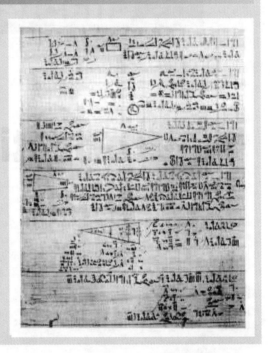

A   LIMITS

The idea of a **limit** is essential to differential calculus. We will see that it is necessary for finding the slope of a tangent to a curve at any point on the curve.

Consider the following table of values for $f(x) = x^2$ in the vicinity of $x = 2$.

x	1	1.9	1.99	1.999	1.9999	2.0001	2.001	2.01	2.1	3
$f(x)$	1	3.61	3.9601	3.996 00	3.999 60	4.000 40	4.004 00	4.0401	4.41	9

Notice that as x approaches 2 from the left, then $f(x)$ approaches 4 from below.

Likewise, as x approaches 2 from the right, then $f(x)$ approaches 4 from above.

We say that as x approaches 2 from either direction, $f(x)$ approaches a limit of 4, and write

$$\lim_{x \to 2} x^2 = 4.$$

INFORMAL DEFINITION OF A LIMIT

The following definition of a limit is informal but adequate for the purposes of this course:

> If $f(x)$ can be made as close as we like to some real number A by making x sufficiently close to a, we say that $f(x)$ approaches a **limit** of A as x approaches a, and we write
> $$\lim_{x \to a} f(x) = A.$$

We also say that as x approaches a, $f(x)$ **converges** to A.

Notice that we have not used the value of $f(x)$ when $x = a$, i.e., $f(a)$. This is very important to the concept of limits.

For example, if $f(x) = \dfrac{5x + x^2}{x}$ and we wish to find the limit as $x \to 0$, it is tempting for us to simply substitute $x = 0$ into $f(x)$.

Not only do we get the meaningless value of $\frac{0}{0}$, but also we destroy the basic limit method.

Observe that if $f(x) = \dfrac{5x + x^2}{x}$ then $f(x) \begin{cases} = 5 + x & \text{if } x \neq 0 \\ \text{is undefined if } x = 0. \end{cases}$

$f(x)$ has the graph shown.

It is the straight line $y = x + 5$ with the point $(0, 5)$ missing, called a **point of discontinuity** of the function.

However, even though this point is missing, the *limit* of $f(x)$ as x approaches 0 does exist. In particular, as $x \to 0$ from either direction, $f(x) \to 5$.

$\therefore \lim\limits_{x \to 0} \dfrac{5x + x^2}{x} = 5$

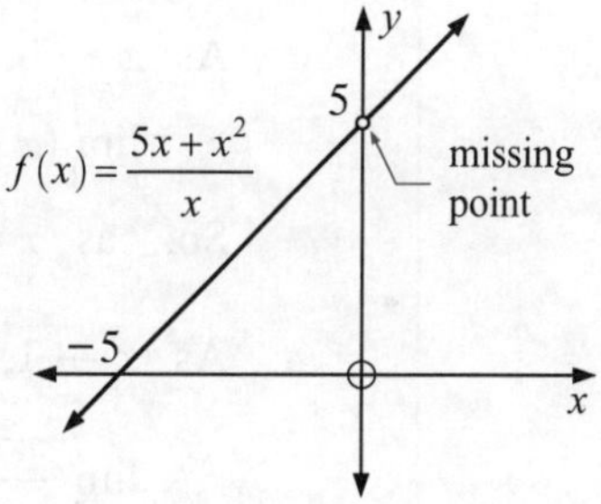

Rather than graph functions each time to determine limits, most can be found algebraically.

Example 1

Evaluate: **a** $\lim\limits_{x \to 2} x^2$ **b** $\lim\limits_{x \to 0} \dfrac{5x + x^2}{x}$

a x^2 can be made as close as we like to 4 by making x sufficiently close to 2.
$$\therefore \lim_{x \to 2} x^2 = 4$$

b $\dfrac{5x + x^2}{x} \begin{cases} = 5 + x & \text{if } x \neq 0 \\ \text{is undefined if } x = 0. \end{cases}$

$\therefore \lim\limits_{x \to 0} \dfrac{5x + x^2}{x}$

$= \lim\limits_{x \to 0} 5 + x, \quad x \neq 0$

$= 5$

RULES FOR LIMITS

If $f(x)$ and $g(x)$ are functions and c is a constant:

- $\displaystyle\lim_{x\to a} c = c$

- $\displaystyle\lim_{x\to a} c\,f(x) = c \lim_{x\to a} f(x)$

- $\displaystyle\lim_{x\to a} [f(x) \pm g(x)] = \lim_{x\to a} f(x) \pm \lim_{x\to a} g(x)$

- $\displaystyle\lim_{x\to a} [f(x)g(x)] = \lim_{x\to a} f(x) \times \lim_{x\to a} g(x)$

- $\displaystyle\lim_{x\to a} \frac{f(x)}{g(x)} = \lim_{x\to a} f(x) \div \lim_{x\to a} g(x)$ provided $\displaystyle\lim_{x\to a} g(x) \neq 0$

Example 2

Use these rules to evaluate:

a $\displaystyle\lim_{x\to 3} (x+2)(x-1)$

b $\displaystyle\lim_{x\to 1} \frac{x^2+2}{x-2}$

a As $x \to 3$, $x+2 \to 5$ and $x-1 \to 2$

$\therefore \displaystyle\lim_{x\to 3} (x+2)(x-1) = 5 \times 2 = 10$

So, as $x \to 3$, $(x+2)(x-1)$ *converges* to 10.

b As $x \to 1$, $x^2+2 \to 3$ and $x-2 \to -1$

$\therefore \displaystyle\lim_{x\to 1} \frac{x^2+2}{x-2} = \frac{3}{-1} = -3$

So, as $x \to 1$, $\dfrac{x^2+2}{x-2}$ *converges* to -3.

LIMITS AT INFINITY

We can use the idea of limits to discuss the behaviour of functions for extreme values of x.

We write $x \to \infty$ to mean when x gets as large as we like and positive,

and $x \to -\infty$ to mean when x gets as large as we like and negative.

We read $x \to \infty$ as "x tends to plus infinity" and $x \to -\infty$ as "x tends to minus infinity".

Notice that as $x \to \infty$, $1 < x < x^2 < x^3 < \ldots$

$\therefore \displaystyle\lim_{x\to\infty} \frac{1}{x} = 0$, $\displaystyle\lim_{x\to\infty} \frac{x}{x^2} = 0$, and so on.

Example 3

Evaluate the following limits:

a $\lim\limits_{x\to\infty} \dfrac{2x+3}{x-4}$

b $\lim\limits_{x\to\infty} \dfrac{x^2-3x+2}{1-x^2}$

a $\lim\limits_{x\to\infty} \dfrac{2x+3}{x-4}$

$= \lim\limits_{x\to\infty} \dfrac{2+\dfrac{3}{x}}{1-\dfrac{4}{x}}$ {dividing each term in both numerator and denominator by x}

$= \dfrac{2}{1}$ {as $x\to\infty$, $\dfrac{3}{x}\to 0$

$= 2$ and $\dfrac{4}{x}\to 0$}

or $\lim\limits_{x\to\infty} \dfrac{2x+3}{x-4}$

$= \lim\limits_{x\to\infty} \dfrac{2(x-4)+8+3}{x-4}$

$= \lim\limits_{x\to\infty} \left(2+\dfrac{11}{x-4}\right)$

$= 2$ {since $\lim\limits_{x\to\infty} \dfrac{11}{x-4}=0$}

b $\lim\limits_{x\to\infty} \dfrac{x^2-3x+2}{1-x^2}$

$= \lim\limits_{x\to\infty} \dfrac{1-\dfrac{3}{x}+\dfrac{2}{x^2}}{\dfrac{1}{x^2}-1}$ {dividing each term by x^2}

$= \dfrac{1}{-1}$ {as $x\to\infty$, $\dfrac{3}{x}\to 0$,

$= -1$ $\dfrac{2}{x^2}\to 0$, and $\dfrac{1}{x^2}\to 0$}

or $\lim\limits_{x\to\infty} \dfrac{x^2-3x+2}{1-x^2}$

$= \lim\limits_{x\to\infty} \dfrac{-x^2+3x-2}{x^2-1}$

$= \lim\limits_{x\to\infty} \dfrac{-(x^2-1)+3x-3}{x^2-1}$

$= \lim\limits_{x\to\infty} \left(-1+\dfrac{3x-3}{x^2-1}\right)$

$= -1$ {since $\lim\limits_{x\to\infty} \dfrac{3x-3}{x^2-1}=0$}

EXERCISE 19A

1 Evaluate the limits:

a $\lim\limits_{x\to 3} (x+4)$

b $\lim\limits_{x\to -1} (5-2x)$

c $\lim\limits_{x\to 4} (3x-1)$

d $\lim\limits_{x\to 2} 5x^2-3x+2$

e $\lim\limits_{h\to 0} h^2(1-h)$

f $\lim\limits_{x\to -1} \dfrac{1-2x}{x^2+1}$

g $\lim\limits_{x\to 0} (x^2+5)$

h $\lim\limits_{x\to -2} \dfrac{4}{x}$

i $\lim\limits_{x\to 0} \dfrac{x^2-3x}{x}$

j $\lim\limits_{h\to 0} \dfrac{2h^2+6h}{h}$

k $\lim\limits_{h\to 0} \dfrac{h^3-8h}{h}$

l $\lim\limits_{x\to 1} \dfrac{x^2-x}{x^2-1}$

m $\lim\limits_{x\to 2} \dfrac{x^2-2x}{x^2-4}$

n $\lim\limits_{x\to 3} \dfrac{x^2-x-6}{x^2-5x+6}$

o $\lim\limits_{x\to -5} \dfrac{2x^2-50}{3x^2+13x-10}$

p $\lim\limits_{x\to 1} \dfrac{x^3-1}{x^2-1}$

q $\lim\limits_{x\to 2} \dfrac{x^3-8}{2x-4}$

r $\lim\limits_{x\to -2} \dfrac{3x^2+5x-2}{x^2-2x-8}$

2 Examine $\displaystyle\lim_{x\to\infty} \frac{1}{x}$.

3 Evaluate:

a $\displaystyle\lim_{x\to\infty} \frac{3x-2}{x+1}$ **b** $\displaystyle\lim_{x\to\infty} \frac{1-2x}{3x+2}$ **c** $\displaystyle\lim_{x\to\infty} \frac{x}{1-x}$

d $\displaystyle\lim_{x\to\infty} \frac{x^2+3}{x^2-1}$ **e** $\displaystyle\lim_{x\to\infty} \frac{x^2-2x+4}{x^2+x-1}$ **f** $\displaystyle\lim_{x\to\infty} \frac{x^3-8}{3x^3+x^2-8x-4}$

B   FINDING ASYMPTOTES USING LIMITS

Rational functions are functions of the form $\dfrac{f(x)}{g(x)}$ where $f(x)$, $g(x)$ are polynomials.

Rational functions are characterised by the existence of **asymptotes** which may be vertical, horizontal, or oblique.

An **oblique asymptote** is neither horizontal nor vertical.

We can investigate the asymptotes of a function by using limits.

Consider the function $\ f:x\mapsto \dfrac{2x+3}{x-4}$.

Clearly the domain of f is: $\{x\in\mathbb{R},\ x\neq 4\}$ or $x\in\,]-\infty,4[\,\cup\,]4,\infty[$.

1 There is a vertical asymptote (VA) at $x=4$.

To discuss the behaviour near the VA, we find what happens to $f(x)$ as $x\to 4$ from the left and right.

- First we draw a sign diagram of $f(x)$.

- Hence as $x\to 4$ (left), $f(x)\to -\infty$

  $x\to 4$ (right), $f(x)\to +\infty$.

This describes the behaviour of the graph of $f(x)$ near the VA $x=4$.

2 Is there another type of asymptote?

Now $\ f(x)=\dfrac{2x+3}{x-4}=\dfrac{2(x-4)+11}{x-4}=2+\dfrac{11}{x-4}$.

- As $x\to +\infty$, $f(x)\to 2$ (above)   {as $\dfrac{11}{x-4}\to 0$ from above}

- As $x\to -\infty$, $f(x)\to 2$ (below)   {as $\dfrac{11}{x-4}\to 0$ from below}

Hence, there is a horizontal asymptote (HA) at $y=2$.

This horizontal asymptote corresponds to the answer in **Example 3** part **a**.

Example 4

Find any asymptotes of the function $f : x \to \dfrac{x^2 - 3x + 2}{1 - x^2}$ and discuss the behaviour of $f(x)$ near these asymptotes.

We notice that $f(x) = \dfrac{(x-2)(x-1)^{-1}}{(1-x)(1+x)} = \dfrac{-(x-2)}{1+x}$ provided $x \neq 1$.

So, there is a point discontinuity at $x = 1$.

Also, when $x = -1$, $f(x)$ is undefined.   {dividing by zero}

This indicates that $x = -1$ is a vertical asymptote.

The sign diagram for $f(x)$ is:

As $x \to -1$ (left), $f(x) \to -\infty$.

As $x \to -1$ (right), $f(x) \to +\infty$.

$\therefore$ $x = -1$ is a VA.

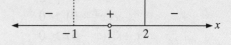

For $x \neq 1$, $f(x) = \dfrac{-(x-2)}{1+x} = \dfrac{-x+2}{x+1} = \dfrac{-(x+1)+3}{x+1} = -1 + \dfrac{3}{x+1}$

As $x \to \infty$, $f(x) \to -1$ (above) as $\dfrac{3}{x+1} \to 0$ and is > 0.

As $x \to -\infty$, $f(x) \to -1$ (below) as $\dfrac{3}{x+1} \to 0$ and is < 0.

$\therefore$ HA is $y = -1$ (see **Example 3** part **b**)

Example 5

Determine all asymptotes and discuss the behaviour of $f(x) = \dfrac{x^3 + x^2 + 4}{x^2 + x + 2}$ near its asymptotes.

First consider the quadratic denominator. Its discriminant is negative so it is positive for all x. $\therefore$ no VAs exist.

For other asymptotes we need to carry out the division.

$$
\begin{array}{r}
x \\
x^2 + x + 2 \overline{\smash{\big)}\, x^3 + x^2 + 4} \\
\underline{x^3 + x^2 + 2x } \\
-2x + 4
\end{array}
$$

Hence, $f(x) = x + \dfrac{4 - 2x}{x^2 + x + 2}$

As $x \to \infty$, $\dfrac{4 - 2x}{x^2 + x + 2} \to 0$ and is < 0, so $f(x) \to x$ from below.

As $x \to -\infty$, $\dfrac{4 - 2x}{x^2 + x + 2} \to 0$ and is > 0, so $f(x) \to x$ from above.

So, we have the oblique asymptote (OA) $y = x$.

Check this result by sketching the function on your GDC.

Example 6

For each of the following, determine all asymptotes and discuss the behaviour of the graph near these asymptotes:

a $y = 3 - 4e^{-x}$ **b** $y = \ln(x^3 - 9x)$

a The domain is $]-\infty, \infty[$ or $\mathbb{R}$, and so no VA exists.

As $x \to \infty$, $y \to 3$ (below).   {as $-4e^{-x} < 0$ and $\displaystyle\lim_{x \to \infty} 4e^{-x} = 0$}

As $x \to -\infty$, $y \to -\infty$.

So, we have a HA of $y = 3$.

b To find the domain we notice that $\ln(x^3 - 9x)$ is defined only when

$$x^3 - 9x > 0$$
$$\therefore \quad x(x^2 - 9) > 0$$
$$\therefore \quad x(x+3)(x-3) > 0$$

Now $x(x+3)(x-3)$ has sign diagram:

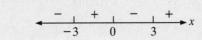

$\therefore$ the domain is: $]-3, 0[\,\cup\,]3, \infty[$

As $x \to -3$ (right), $y \to -\infty$.

As $x \to 0$ (left), $y \to -\infty$.

As $x \to 3$ (right), $y \to -\infty$.

As $x \to \infty$, $y \to +\infty$.

> Check the asymptotes by sketching the graph.

EXERCISE 19B

1 For each of the following, determine all asymptotes and discuss the behaviour of the graph near its asymptotes:

a $f(x) = \dfrac{3x - 2}{x + 3}$

b $y = \dfrac{2x^2 + 10}{x}$

c $W = 5000 - \dfrac{4900}{t^2 + 1}, \quad t \geqslant 0$

d $y = \dfrac{x^2 - 1}{x^2 + 1}$

e $f(x) = \dfrac{x}{x^2 + 1}$

f $f(x) = \dfrac{x - 2}{x^2 + x - 2}$

g $y = \dfrac{x^3 - 2}{x^2 + 1}$

h $f(x) = e^{x - \frac{1}{x}}$

i $y = x + \ln x$

j $f(x) = e^{2x} - 7e^x + 12$

k $y = e^x - x$

l $y = \dfrac{1000}{1 + 2e^{-0.16t}}$

C | TRIGONOMETRIC LIMITS

INVESTIGATION 1   EXAMINING $\frac{\sin\theta}{\theta}$ NEAR $\theta = 0$

This investigation examines $\frac{\sin\theta}{\theta}$ when θ is close to 0 and θ is in radians.

We consider this ratio graphically, numerically, and geometrically.

What to do:

1 Show that $f(\theta) = \frac{\sin\theta}{\theta}$ is an even function. What does this mean graphically?

2 Since $\frac{\sin\theta}{\theta}$ is even we need only examine $\frac{\sin\theta}{\theta}$ for positive θ.

   a What is the value of $\frac{\sin\theta}{\theta}$ when $\theta = 0$?

   b Graph $y = \frac{\sin\theta}{\theta}$ for $-\frac{\pi}{2} \leqslant \theta \leqslant \frac{\pi}{2}$ using a graphics   **GRAPHING PACKAGE**

     calculator or graphing package.

   c Explain why the graph indicates that $\lim\limits_{\theta \to 0} \frac{\sin\theta}{\theta} = 1$.

3 Copy and complete the given table, using your calculator:
Extend your table to include negative
values of θ which approach 0.

4 Explain why the area of the
shaded segment is $A = \frac{1}{2}r^2(\theta - \sin\theta)$.

θ	$\sin\theta$	$\frac{\sin\theta}{\theta}$
1		
0.5		
0.1		
0.01		
0.001		
⋮		

Indicate how to use the given figure and the shaded
area to show that, if θ is in radians and $\theta > 0$, then

$$\lim_{\theta \to 0} \frac{\sin\theta}{\theta} = 1.$$

5 Repeat the above investigation to find $\lim\limits_{\theta \to 0} \frac{\sin\theta}{\theta}$ using degrees rather than radians.

Theorem: If θ is in radians, then $\lim\limits_{\theta \to 0} \frac{\sin\theta}{\theta} = 1$, i.e., as $\theta \to 0$, $\frac{\sin\theta}{\theta}$ converges to 1.

Proof: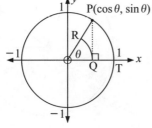

Suppose P($\cos\theta$, $\sin\theta$) lies on the unit circle in the
first quadrant.

PQ is drawn perpendicular to the x-axis, and arc QR
with centre O is drawn. Now,

area of sector OQR $\leqslant$ area $\triangle$OQP $\leqslant$ area sector OTP

$$\therefore \quad \tfrac{1}{2}(\text{OQ})^2 \times \theta \leqslant \tfrac{1}{2}(\text{OQ})(\text{PQ}) \leqslant \tfrac{1}{2}(\text{OT})^2 \times \theta$$

$$\therefore \quad \tfrac{1}{2}\theta\cos^2\theta \leqslant \tfrac{1}{2}\cos\theta\sin\theta \leqslant \tfrac{1}{2}\theta$$

$$\therefore \quad \cos\theta \leqslant \frac{\sin\theta}{\theta} \leqslant \frac{1}{\cos\theta} \quad \{\text{dividing throughout by } \tfrac{1}{2}\theta\cos\theta, \text{ which} > 0\}$$

Now as $\theta \to 0$, both $\cos\theta \to 1$ and $\dfrac{1}{\cos\theta} \to 1$

$$\therefore \quad \text{as } \theta \to 0 \text{ (right)}, \quad \frac{\sin\theta}{\theta} \to 1.$$

But $\dfrac{\sin\theta}{\theta}$ is an even function, so as $\theta \to 0$ (left), $\dfrac{\sin\theta}{\theta} \to 1$ also.

$$\text{Thus} \quad \lim_{\theta \to 0} \frac{\sin\theta}{\theta} = 1.$$

Note: We have established the behaviour of $\dfrac{\sin\theta}{\theta}$ as $\theta \to 0$ from both the right *and* the left before concluding the value of $\displaystyle\lim_{\theta \to 0} \frac{\sin\theta}{\theta}$.   This is very important when we deduce limits.

Example 7

Find $\displaystyle\lim_{\theta \to 0} \frac{\sin 3\theta}{\theta}$.

$$\lim_{\theta \to 0} \frac{\sin 3\theta}{\theta}$$

$$= \lim_{\theta \to 0} \frac{\sin 3\theta}{3\theta} \times 3$$

$$= 3 \times \lim_{3\theta \to 0} \frac{\sin 3\theta}{3\theta} \quad \{\text{as } \theta \to 0, \ 3\theta \to 0 \ \text{also}\}$$

$$= 3 \times 1$$

$$= 3$$

EXERCISE 19C

1   Find:

a $\displaystyle\lim_{\theta \to 0} \frac{\sin 2\theta}{\theta}$

b $\displaystyle\lim_{\theta \to 0} \frac{\theta}{\sin\theta}$

c $\displaystyle\lim_{\theta \to 0} \frac{\tan\theta}{\theta}$

d $\displaystyle\lim_{\theta \to 0} \frac{\sin\theta \sin 4\theta}{\theta^2}$

e $\displaystyle\lim_{h \to 0} \frac{\sin\left(\frac{h}{2}\right)\cos h}{h}$

f $\displaystyle\lim_{n \to \infty} n\sin\left(\frac{2\pi}{n}\right)$

2   A circle contains n congruent isosceles triangles, all with apex O and with base vertices on the circle as shown.

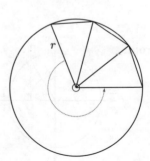

a   Explain why the sum of the areas of the triangles is $S_n = \tfrac{1}{2}nr^2\sin\left(\frac{2\pi}{n}\right)$.

b   Find $\displaystyle\lim_{n \to \infty} S_n$ **i**   geometrically

                                         ii   algebraically.

c   What can be deduced from **b**?

3 **a** Show that $\cos(A + B) - \cos(A - B) = -2\sin A \sin B$.

b If $A+B = S$ and $A-B = D$, show that $\cos S - \cos D = -2\sin\left(\frac{S+D}{2}\right)\sin\left(\frac{S-D}{2}\right)$.

c Hence find $\lim\limits_{h \to 0} \dfrac{\cos(x + h) - \cos x}{h}$.

D CALCULATION OF AREAS UNDER CURVES

Consider the function $f(x) = x^2 + 1$.

We wish to estimate the area A enclosed by $y = f(x)$, the x-axis, and the vertical lines $x = 1$ and $x = 4$.

Suppose we divide the x-interval into three strips of width 1 unit as shown.

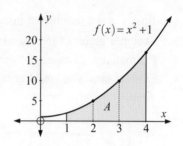

The diagram alongside shows **upper rectangles**, which are rectangles with top edges at the maximum value of the curve on that interval.

The area of the upper rectangles,

$$A_U = 1 \times f(2) + 1 \times f(3) + 1 \times f(4)$$
$$= 5 + 10 + 17$$
$$= 32 \text{ units}^2$$

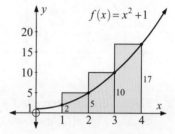

The next diagram shows **lower rectangles**, which are rectangles with top edges at the minimum value of the curve on that interval.

The area of the lower rectangles,

$$A_L = 1 \times f(1) + 1 \times f(2) + 1 \times f(3)$$
$$= 2 + 5 + 10$$
$$= 17 \text{ units}^2$$

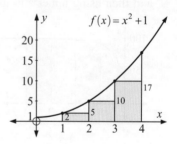

Now clearly $A_L < A < A_U$, so the required area lies between 17 units^2 and 32 units^2.

If the interval $1 \leqslant x \leqslant 4$ was divided into 6 equal intervals, each of length $\frac{1}{2}$, then

$$A_U = \tfrac{1}{2}f(1\tfrac{1}{2}) + \tfrac{1}{2}f(2) + \tfrac{1}{2}f(2\tfrac{1}{2}) + \tfrac{1}{2}f(3) + \tfrac{1}{2}f(3\tfrac{1}{2}) + \tfrac{1}{2}f(4)$$
$$= \tfrac{1}{2}\left(\tfrac{13}{4} + 5 + \tfrac{29}{4} + 10 + \tfrac{53}{4} + 17\right)$$
$$= 27.875 \text{ units}^2$$

and $A_L = \tfrac{1}{2}f(1) + \tfrac{1}{2}f(1\tfrac{1}{2}) + \tfrac{1}{2}f(2) + \tfrac{1}{2}f(2\tfrac{1}{2}) + \tfrac{1}{2}f(3) + \tfrac{1}{2}f(3\tfrac{1}{2})$

$$= \tfrac{1}{2}\left(2 + \tfrac{13}{4} + 5 + \tfrac{29}{4} + 10 + \tfrac{53}{4}\right)$$
$$= 20.375 \text{ units}^2$$

From this refinement we conclude that the required area lies between 20.375 and 27.875 units^2.

As we create more subdivisions, the estimates A_L and A_U will become more and more accurate. In fact, as the subdivision width is reduced further and further, both A_L and A_U will **converge** to A.

Example 8

A car travels at the speed of $v(t) = 100 - \dfrac{50}{5t^2 + 1}$ km h^{-1} away from a city.

The time t is the number of hours after the car leaves the city.

a Sketch a graph of the speed against time.
b Estimate the distance the car has travelled after 4 hours.
c Explain how you could obtain a better estimate for the distance in **b**.

a

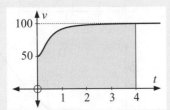

The graph shows that the function

$v(t) = 100 - \dfrac{50}{5t^2 + 1}$ is increasing.

As $t \to \infty$, $\dfrac{50}{5t^2 + 1} \to 0$

$\therefore$ a HA is $v = 100$.

b Since distance travelled = speed $\times$ time,   the distance travelled is the area enclosed by $v(t)$, the t-axis, and the vertical lines $t = 0$ and $t = 4$.

We estimate the distance travelled by dividing the interval into four subdivisions and then using upper and lower rectangles.

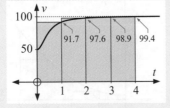

$A_U = 1 \times v(1) + 1 \times v(2) + 1 \times v(3) + 1 \times v(4)$
$= 1 \times 91.7 + 1 \times 97.6 + 1 \times 98.9 + 1 \times 99.4$
≈ 387.6

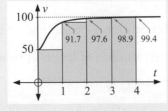

$A_L = 1 \times v(0) + 1 \times v(1) + 1 \times v(2) + 1 \times v(3)$
$= 1 \times 50 + 1 \times 91.7 + 1 \times 97.6 + 1 \times 98.9$
≈ 338.2

Now $A_L <$ distance travelled $< A_U$,   so the distance travelled is between 338.2 km and 387.6 km.

A good estimate might be the average of the distances,

$$A \approx \frac{338.2 + 387.6}{2} \approx 363 \text{ km}$$

c   We could obtain a better estimate by using more subdivisions.

For example, for the case of 8 subdivisions we have:

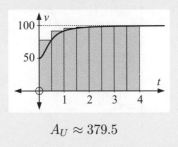   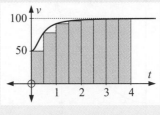

$$A_U \approx 379.5 \qquad\qquad A_L \approx 354.8$$

$\therefore$ a better estimate would be $A = \dfrac{354.8 + 379.5}{2} \approx 367$ km

EXERCISE 19D.1

1   At time $t = 0$ hours a car starts from Port Wakefield, a distance of 95 km from Adelaide, and travels with speed given by $v(t) = 50 + 50e^{-t}$ km h^{-1} towards Adelaide.

a   Sketch a graph of the speed of the car for $0 \leqslant t \leqslant 1$.

b   What are the maximum and minimum speeds of the car for $0 \leqslant t \leqslant 1$?

c   Show that the distance d of the car from Adelaide after one hour is less than 27 km.

d   By dividing the time of travel into 2 half hour intervals, estimate the distance of the car from Adelaide after 1 hour of travel.

e   Improve the estimate you made in d by considering 4 time intervals of a quarter of an hour each.

2   When items are sold, we say the *marginal profit* is the profit on the sale of each item. The marginal profit usually increases as the number of articles sold increases.
Suppose that the marginal profit of selling the nth house is $p(n) = 200n - n^2$ dollars.

a   Sketch a graph of the marginal profit for $0 \leqslant n \leqslant 100$.

b   Show that the total profit for selling 100 houses is less than \$1 000 000.

c   By considering the maximum and minimum marginal profit of the first 50 and the second 50 houses sold, estimate the profit made for selling 100 houses.

d   Improve the estimate you have made in c by considering four equal intervals.

e   Suggest a way of finding the exact profit made by selling 100 houses.

USING TECHNOLOGY

By subdividing the horizontal axis into small enough intervals, we can in theory find estimates for the area under a curve which are as close as we like to the actual value.

We illustrate this process by estimating the area A between the graph of $y = x^2$ and the x-axis for $0 \leqslant x \leqslant 1$.

This example is of historical interest. **Archimedes** (287 - 212 BC) found the exact area. In an article that contains 24 propositions he developed the essential theory of what is now known as integral calculus.

Consider $f(x) = x^2$ and divide the interval $0 \leqslant x \leqslant 1$ into 4 equal subdivisions.

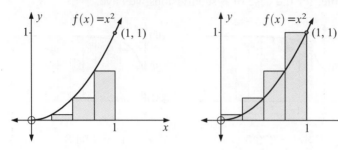

$A_L = \frac{1}{4}(0)^2 + \frac{1}{4}(\frac{1}{4})^2 + \frac{1}{4}(\frac{1}{2})^2 + \frac{1}{4}(\frac{3}{4})^2$ and $A_U = \frac{1}{4}(\frac{1}{4})^2 + \frac{1}{4}(\frac{1}{2})^2 + \frac{1}{4}(\frac{3}{4})^2 + \frac{1}{4}(1)^2$

≈ 0.219 ≈ 0.469

Now suppose there are n subdivisions, each of width $\dfrac{1}{n}$.

AREA FINDER

We can use technology to help calculate A_L and A_U for large values of n.

Click on the appropriate icon to access our **area finder** software or instructions for the procedure on a **graphics calculator**.

The following table summarises the results you should obtain for $n = 4$, 10, 25 and 50.

n	A_L	A_U	Average
4	0.218 75	0.468 75	0.343 75
10	0.285 00	0.385 00	0.335 00
25	0.313 60	0.353 60	0.333 60
50	0.323 40	0.343 40	0.333 40

The exact value of A is in fact $\frac{1}{3}$. Notice how both A_L and A_U are converging to this value as n increases.

EXERCISE 19D.2

1   Use rectangles to find lower and upper sums for the area between the graph of $y = x^2$ and the x-axis for $1 \leqslant x \leqslant 2$. Use $n = 10$, 25, 50, 100 and 500.
Give your answers to 4 decimal places.
As n gets larger, both A_L and A_U converge to the same number which is a simple fraction. What is it?

2   Use rectangles to find lower and upper sums for the areas between the graphs of each of the following functions and the x-axis for $0 \leqslant x \leqslant 1$.
Use values of $n = 5$, 10, 50, 100, 500, 1000 and 10 000.
Give your answer to 5 decimal places in each case.

     a   **i** $y = x^3$ **ii** $y = x$ **iii** $y = x^{\frac{1}{2}}$ **iv** $y = x^{\frac{1}{3}}$

     b   For each case in **a**, A_L and A_U converge to the same number which is a simple fraction. What fractions are they?

c On the basis of your answer to **b**, conjecture what the area between the graph of $y = x^a$ and the x-axis for $0 \leqslant x \leqslant 1$ might be for any number $a > 0$.

3 Consider the quarter circle of centre (0, 0) and radius 2 units illustrated.

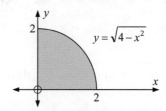

Its area is $\frac{1}{4}$ (full circle of radius 2)

$$= \tfrac{1}{4} \times \pi \times 2^2$$

$$= \pi$$

a By calculating the areas of lower and upper rectangles for $n = 10$, 50, 100, 200, 1000, $10\,000$, find rational bounds for π.

b Archimedes found the famous approximation $3\frac{10}{71} < \pi < 3\frac{1}{7}$.

For what value of n is your estimate for π better than that of Archimedes?

THE DEFINITE INTEGRAL

Consider the lower and upper rectangle sums for a function which is positive and increasing on the interval $[a, b]$.

We divide $[a, b]$ into n subdivisions of width $\delta x = \dfrac{b - a}{n}$.

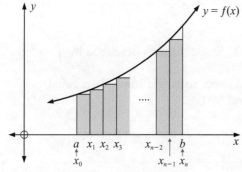
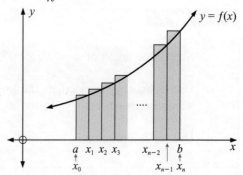

Since the function is increasing,

$$A_L = \delta x \, f(x_0) + \delta x \, f(x_1) + \delta x \, f(x_2) + \ldots\ldots + \delta x \, f(x_{n-2}) + \delta x \, f(x_{n-1})$$

$$= \sum_{i=0}^{n-1} f(x_i)\delta x$$

and $A_U = \delta x \, f(x_1) + \delta x \, f(x_2) + \delta x \, f(x_3) + \ldots\ldots + \delta x \, f(x_{n-1}) + \delta x \, f(x_n)$

$$= \sum_{i=1}^{n} f(x_i)\delta x$$

Notice that $A_U - A_L = \delta x \, (f(x_n) - f(x_0))$

$$= \frac{1}{n}(b - a)\,(f(b) - f(a))$$

$\therefore \displaystyle\lim_{n \to \infty} (A_U - A_L) = 0$

$\therefore \displaystyle\lim_{n \to \infty} A_L = \lim_{n \to \infty} A_U$

$\therefore$ since $A_L < A < A_U$, $\displaystyle\lim_{n \to \infty} A_L = A = \lim_{n \to \infty} A_U$

This fact is true for all positive continuous functions on the interval $[a, b]$.

The value A is known as the "**definite integral** of $f(x)$ from a to b", written

$$A = \int_a^b f(x)\, dx.$$

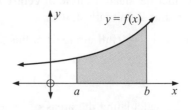

If $f(x) \geqslant 0$ for all $x \in [a, b]$,   then

$\int_a^b f(x)\, dx$ is the shaded area.

HISTORICAL NOTE

The word **integration** means "*to put together into a whole*". An **integral** is the "whole" produced from integration, since the areas $f(x_i) \times \delta x$ of the thin rectangular strips are put together into one whole area.

The symbol $\int$ is called an **integral sign**. In the time of **Newton** and **Leibniz** it was the stretched out letter s, but it is no longer part of the alphabet.

Example 9

a Sketch the graph of $y = x^4$ for $0 \leqslant x \leqslant 1$. Shade the area described by $\int_0^1 x^4\, dx$.

b Use technology to calculate the lower and upper rectangle sums for n equal subdivisions where $n = 5, 10, 50, 100$ and 500.

c Use the information in **b** to find $\int_0^1 x^4\, dx$ to 2 significant figures.

a

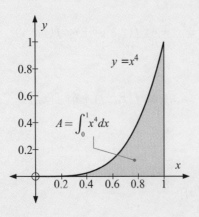

$$A = \int_0^1 x^4 dx$$

b

n	A_L	A_U
5	0.1133	0.3133
10	0.1533	0.2533
50	0.1901	0.2101
100	0.1950	0.2050
500	0.1990	0.2010

c When $n = 500$, $A_L \approx A_U \approx 0.20$,   to 2 significant figures.

$\therefore$ since $A_L < \int_0^1 x^4\, dx < A_U$, $\int_0^1 x^4\, dx \approx 0.20$ (2 s.f.)

Example 10

Use graphical evidence and known area facts to find:

a $\displaystyle\int_0^2 (2x+1)\, dx$ b $\displaystyle\int_0^1 \sqrt{1-x^2}\, dx$

a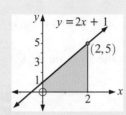

$\displaystyle\int_0^2 (2x+1)\, dx$

= shaded area

$= \left(\frac{1+5}{2}\right) \times 2$

$= 6$

b   If $y = \sqrt{1-x^2}$ then $y^2 = 1 - x^2$ and so $x^2 + y^2 = 1$ which is the equation of the unit circle. $y = \sqrt{1-x^2}$ is the upper half.

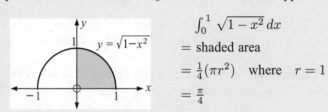

$\displaystyle\int_0^1 \sqrt{1-x^2}\, dx$

= shaded area

$= \frac{1}{4}(\pi r^2)$ where $r = 1$

$= \frac{\pi}{4}$

EXERCISE 19D.3

1   a   Sketch the graph of $y = \sqrt{x}$ for $0 \leqslant x \leqslant 1$.

Shade the area described by $\displaystyle\int_0^1 \sqrt{x}\, dx$.

   b   Find the lower and upper rectangle sums for $n = 5, 10, 50, 100$ and 500.

   c   Use the information in b to find $\displaystyle\int_0^1 \sqrt{x}\, dx$ to 2 significant figures.

2   a   Sketch the graph of $y = \sqrt{1 + x^3}$ and the x-axis for $0 \leqslant x \leqslant 2$.

   b   Find the lower and upper rectangle sums for $n = 50, 100, 500$.

   c   What is your best estimate for $\displaystyle\int_0^2 \sqrt{1 + x^3}\, dx$?

3   Use graphical evidence and known area facts to find:

   a $\displaystyle\int_1^3 (1 + 4x)\, dx$ b $\displaystyle\int_{-1}^2 (2 - x)\, dx$ c $\displaystyle\int_{-2}^2 \sqrt{4 - x^2}\, dx$

INVESTIGATION 2   ESTIMATING $\displaystyle\int_{-3}^{3} e^{-\frac{x^2}{2}}\, dx$

The integral $\displaystyle\int_{-3}^{3} e^{-\frac{x^2}{2}}\, dx$ is of considerable interest to statisticians.

In this investigation we shall estimate the value of this integral using upper and lower rectangular sums for $n = 4500$.

This value of n is too large for most calculators to handle in a single list, so we will perform it in sections.

What to do:

1 Sketch the graph of $y = e^{-\frac{x^2}{2}}$ for $-3 \leqslant x \leqslant 3$.

2 Calculate the upper and lower rectangular sums for the three intervals $0 \leqslant x \leqslant 1$, $1 \leqslant x \leqslant 2$ and $2 \leqslant x \leqslant 3$ using $n = 750$ for each.

3 Combine the upper rectangular sums and the lower rectangular sums you found in **2** to obtain an upper and lower rectangular sum for $0 \leqslant x \leqslant 3$ for $n = 2250$.

4 Use the fact that the function $y = e^{-\frac{x^2}{2}}$ is symmetric to find upper and lower rectangular sums for $-3 \leqslant x \leqslant 0$ for $n = 2250$.

5 Use your results of **3** and **4** to find an estimate for $\displaystyle\int_{-3}^{3} e^{-\frac{x^2}{2}}\, dx$.
How accurate is your estimate?

AREA FINDER

6 Compare your estimate in **5** with $\sqrt{2\pi}$.

REVIEW SET 19

1 Evaluate the limits:

a $\displaystyle\lim_{x \to 2} \frac{x^2 - 4}{2 - x}$

b $\displaystyle\lim_{x \to -2} \frac{3x^2 - 12}{5x^2 + 10x}$

c $\displaystyle\lim_{x \to 4} \frac{\sqrt{x} - 2}{x - 4}$

d $\displaystyle\lim_{x \to 4} \frac{x^2 - 16}{x - 4}$

e $\displaystyle\lim_{x \to -1} \frac{2x + 2}{x^2 - 1}$

f $\displaystyle\lim_{x \to \infty} \frac{1 - 2x - x^2}{2x^2 - 4}$

2 Find any asymptotes of the following functions and discuss the behaviour of the graph near them:

a $y = \dfrac{x^2 + x - 2}{x - 2}$

b $y = e^{x-2} - 3$

c $y = \ln(x^2 + 3)$

d $f(x) = e^{-x} \ln x$

e $y = x + \ln(2x - 3)$

f $x \mapsto \ln(-x) + 2$

3 Find:

a $\displaystyle\lim_{\theta \to 0} \frac{\sin 4\theta}{\theta}$

b $\displaystyle\lim_{\theta \to 0} \frac{2\theta}{\sin 3\theta}$

c $\displaystyle\lim_{n \to \infty} n \sin\left(\frac{\pi}{n}\right)$

4 **a** Sketch the region between the curve $y = \dfrac{4}{1 + x^2}$ and the x-axis for $0 \leqslant x \leqslant 1$.

Divide the interval into 5 equal parts and display the 5 upper and lower rectangles.

b Find the lower and upper rectangle sums for $n = 5, 50, 100$ and 500.

c Give your best estimate for $\displaystyle\int_0^1 \dfrac{4}{1 + x^2} \, dx$ and compare this answer with π.

5 The rate at which drugs are eliminated from the body is called the clearance rate. The clearance rate depends on the individual person as well as the amount of drugs present.

Suppose that in a healthy adult the clearance rate $r(t)$ of 110 mg of caffeine (about one cup of coffee) is given by $r(t) = 25e^{-0.22t}$ mg h^{-1}, where t is the number of hours after which the caffeine is taken.

a Sketch the graph of $r(t)$ for $0 \leqslant t \leqslant 4$.

b Show that 4 hours after the intake of 110 mg of caffeine, the amount of caffeine left in the body is between 10 and 70 mg.

c By considering the maximum and minimum clearance for each hour, estimate the amount of caffeine left in the body 4 hours after an intake of 110 mg.

d Suggest a way of improving the accuracy of your estimate in **c**.

6 Find $\displaystyle\lim_{h \to 0} \dfrac{2 \cos \left(x + \frac{h}{2} \right) \sin \left(\frac{h}{2} \right)}{h}$.

State any assumptions made in finding your answer.

7 **a** Show that $\sin(A + B) - \sin(A - B) = 2 \cos A \sin B$.

b If $A + B = S$ and $A - B = D$, show that
$$\sin S - \sin D = 2 \cos \left(\tfrac{S+D}{2} \right) \sin \left(\tfrac{S-D}{2} \right).$$

c Hence, find $\displaystyle\lim_{h \to 0} \dfrac{\sin(x + h) - \sin x}{h}$.

8 **a** Sketch the graph of the function $f(x) = \dfrac{1}{x}$ for $2 \leqslant x \leqslant 6$.

b Find the maximum and minimum value of $f(x) = \dfrac{1}{x}$ for $2 \leqslant x \leqslant 6$.

Use these values to show that the area between the graph of $f(x)$ and the x-axis for $2 \leqslant x \leqslant 6$ lies between $\frac{2}{3}$ and 2.

c Divide the interval $2 \leqslant x \leqslant 6$ into 4 smaller intervals of equal length. By considering the smallest and the largest values of f on each of these subdivisions, find an estimate for the area between the graph of f and the x-axis for $2 \leqslant x \leqslant 6$.

d Suggest a way of improving the accuracy of your estimate in **c**.

9 Consider the graph of $f(x) = e^{-x}$.

    a Sketch the graph of $y = f(x)$ for $0 \leqslant x \leqslant 2$.

    b Find upper and lower bounds for $\displaystyle\int_0^2 e^{-x}\,dx$ using upper and lower rectangles with 8 subdivisions.

    c Use technology to find, correct to 4 significant figures, upper and lower bounds for $\displaystyle\int_0^2 e^{-x}\,dx$ when $n = 100$.

10 The graph of $y = f(x)$ is illustrated:

    Evaluate the following using area interpretation:

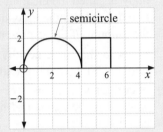

    a $\displaystyle\int_0^4 f(x)\,dx$ **b** $\displaystyle\int_4^6 f(x)\,dx$

11 Prove that for θ in radians:

    a $\theta > 0 \;\Rightarrow\; \displaystyle\lim_{\theta \to 0} \frac{\sin\theta}{\theta} = 1$

    b $\theta < 0 \;\Rightarrow\; \displaystyle\lim_{\theta \to 0} \frac{\sin\theta}{\theta} = 1$ also.

    c   the area of the shaded segment is given by $\frac{1}{2}r^2(\theta - \sin\theta)$.

    d Use **c** to give geometric evidence that **a** is true.

12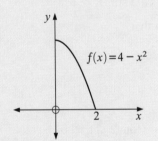

    a Use *four* upper and lower rectangles to find rationals A and B such that:
$$A < \int_0^2 (4 - x^2)\,dx < B.$$

    b Hence, find a good estimate of
$$\int_0^2 (4 - x^2)\,dx.$$

13 **a** Sketch the graph of $x \mapsto \sin^2 x$ for $x \in [0, \pi]$.

    b Hence, show that $\displaystyle\int_0^\pi \sin^2 x\,dx \approx \frac{\pi}{2}$ by considering triangle and trapezium approximations.

Chapter 20

Differential calculus

Contents:

In the previous chapter we discussed how the topic of calculus is divided into two fields: differential calculus and integral calculus. In this chapter we begin to examine **differential calculus** and how it relates to rate problems and the gradient of curves.

HISTORICAL NOTE

The topic of **differential calculus** originated in the 17th century with the work of **Sir Isaac Newton** and **Gottfried Wilhelm Leibniz**. These mathematicians developed the necessary theory while attempting to find algebraic methods for solving problems dealing with:

- the **gradients of tangents** to curves at any point on the curve, and

- finding the **rate of change** in one variable with respect to another.

Isaac Newton 1642 – 1727   Gottfried Leibniz 1646 – 1716

RATES OF CHANGE

A **rate** is a comparison between two quantities with different units.

We often judge performances by using rates. For example:

- Sir Donald Bradman's batting rate at Test cricket level was 99.94 *runs per innings*.
- Michael Jordan's basketball scoring rate was 20.0 *points per game*.
- Rangi's typing speed is 63 *words per minute* with an error rate of 2.3 *errors per page*.

Speed is a commonly used rate. It is the rate of change in distance per unit of time. We are familiar with the formula

$$\text{average speed} = \frac{\text{distance travelled}}{\text{time taken}}.$$

However, if a car has an average speed of 60 km h^{-1} for a journey, it does not mean that the car travels at exactly 60 km h^{-1} the whole time.

In fact, the speed will probably vary continuously throughout the journey. So, how can we calculate the car's speed at any particular time?

Suppose we are given a graph of the car's distance travelled against time taken. If this graph is a straight line then we know the speed is constant and is given by the gradient of the line.

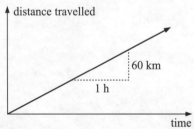

If the graph is a curve, then the car's instantaneous speed is given by the gradient of the tangent to the curve at that time.

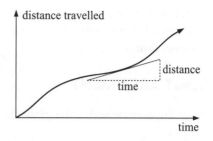

THE TANGENT TO A CURVE

A **chord** or **secant** of a curve is a straight line segment which joins any two points on the curve.

The gradient of the chord [AB] measures the average rate of change of the function for the given change in x-values.

A **tangent** is a straight line which touches a curve at a point.

The gradient of the tangent at point A measures the instantaneous rate of change of the function at point A.

In the limit as B approaches A, the gradient of the chord [AB] will be the gradient of the tangent at A.

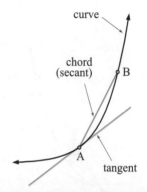

INVESTIGATION 1   THE GRADIENT OF A TANGENT

Given a curve $f(x)$, how can we find the gradient of the tangent at the point $(a, f(a))$?

For example, the point A(1, 1) lies on the curve $f(x) = x^2$. What is the gradient of the tangent at A?   **DEMO**

What to do:

1

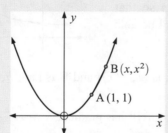

Suppose B lies on $f(x) = x^2$ and B has coordinates (x, x^2).

   a Show that the chord [AB] has gradient
$$\frac{f(x) - f(1)}{x - 1} \quad \text{or} \quad \frac{x^2 - 1}{x - 1}.$$

   b Copy and complete:

x	Point B	gradient of [AB]
5	(5, 25)	6
3		
2		
1.5		
1.1		
1.01		
1.001		

2 Comment on the gradient of [AB] as x gets closer to 1.

3 Repeat the process as x gets closer to 1, but from the left of A.

4 Click on the icon to view a demonstration of the process.

5 What do you suspect is the gradient of the tangent at A?

Fortunately we do not have to use a graph and table of values each time we wish to find the gradient of a tangent. Instead we can use an algebraic and geometric approach which involves **limits**.

LIMIT ARGUMENT

From the investigation, the gradient of $[AB] = \dfrac{x^2 - 1}{x - 1}$

$$\therefore \quad \text{gradient of } [AB] = \frac{(x+1)(x-1)}{x-1} = x + 1 \qquad \text{provided that } x \neq 1$$

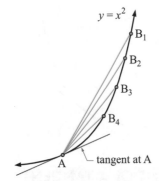

In the limit as B approaches A, $x \to 1$ and the gradient of $[AB] \to$ the gradient of the tangent at A.

So, the gradient of the tangent at the point A is

$$m_T = \lim_{x \to 1} \frac{x^2 - 1}{x - 1}$$
$$= \lim_{x \to 1} x + 1, \quad x \neq 1$$
$$= 2$$

As B approaches A, the gradient of [AB] approaches or **converges** to 2.

Limit arguments like that above form the foundation of differential calculus.

A   THE DERIVATIVE FUNCTION

For a non-linear function with equation $y = f(x)$, gradients of tangents at various points continually change.

Our task is to determine a **gradient function** so that when we replace x by some value a then we will be able to find the gradient of the tangent at $x = a$.

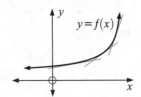

Consider a general function $y = f(x)$ where A is $(x, f(x))$ and B is $(x + h, f(x + h))$.

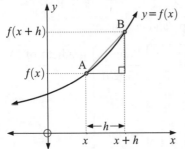

The chord [AB] has gradient $= \dfrac{f(x+h) - f(x)}{x + h - x}$

$$= \frac{f(x+h) - f(x)}{h}.$$

If we now let B approach A, then the gradient of [AB] approaches the gradient of the tangent at A.

So, the gradient of the tangent at the variable point $(x, f(x))$ is the limiting value of

$\dfrac{f(x+h) - f(x)}{h}$ as h approaches 0, or $\displaystyle\lim_{h \to 0} \dfrac{f(x+h) - f(x)}{h}$.

This formula gives the gradient for any value of the variable x. Since there is only one value of the gradient for each value of x, the formula is actually a function.

> The **gradient function**, also known as the **derived function** or **derivative function** or simply the **derivative** is defined as
>
> $$f'(x) = \lim_{h \to 0} \frac{f(x+h) - f(x)}{h}.$$
>
> We read the derivative function as 'eff dashed x'.

INVESTIGATION 2   FINDING GRADIENTS OF FUNCTIONS WITH TECHNOLOGY

This investigation can be done by **graphics calculator** or by clicking on the icon to open the **demonstration**. The idea is to find the gradients at various points on a simple curve and use these to predict the gradient function for the curve.

What to do:

1. Use a graphical argument to explain why:
   a if $f(x) = c$ where c is a constant, then $f'(x) = 0$
   b if $f(x) = mx + c$ where m and c are constants, then $f'(x) = m$.

2. Consider $f(x) = x^2$. Find $f'(x)$ for $x = 1, 2, 3, 4, 5, 6$ using technology. Predict $f'(x)$ from your results.

3. Use technology and modelling techniques to find $f'(x)$ for:

   CALCULUS DEMO

   a $f(x) = x^3$ b $f(x) = x^4$ c $f(x) = x^5$

   d $f(x) = \dfrac{1}{x}$ e $f(x) = \dfrac{1}{x^2}$ f $f(x) = \sqrt{x} = x^{\frac{1}{2}}$

4. Use the results of **3** to complete the following:
   "if $f(x) = x^n$, then $f'(x) = \ldots\ldots$"

For more complicated functions the method presented in the investigation cannot be used to find the gradient function.

To find the gradient function $f'(x)$ for a general function $f(x)$, we need to evaluate the limit $\lim_{h \to 0} \dfrac{f(x+h) - f(x)}{h}$. We call this the **method of first principles**.

Example 1

Use the definition of $f'(x)$ to find the gradient function of $f(x) = x^2$.

$$
\begin{aligned}
f'(x) &= \lim_{h \to 0} \frac{f(x+h) - f(x)}{h} \\
&= \lim_{h \to 0} \frac{(x+h)^2 - x^2}{h} \\
&= \lim_{h \to 0} \frac{x^2 + 2hx + h^2 - x^2}{h} \\
&= \lim_{h \to 0} \frac{h(2x + h)}{h} \quad \{\text{as } h \neq 0\} \\
&= 2x
\end{aligned}
$$

Example 2

Find, from first principles, $f'(x)$ if $f(x) = \dfrac{1}{x}$.

If $f(x) = \dfrac{1}{x}$, $f'(x) = \displaystyle\lim_{h \to 0} \frac{f(x+h) - f(x)}{h}$

$$= \lim_{h \to 0} \left[\frac{\dfrac{1}{x+h} - \dfrac{1}{x}}{h} \right] \times \frac{(x+h)x}{(x+h)x}$$

$$= \lim_{h \to 0} \frac{x - (x+h)}{hx(x+h)}$$

$$= \lim_{h \to 0} \frac{\cancel{-h}^{-1}}{\cancel{h}x(x+h)_1} \qquad \{\text{as } h \neq 0\}$$

$$= -\frac{1}{x^2} \qquad\qquad \{\text{as } h \to 0, \ x + h \to x\}$$

Example 3

Find, from first principles, the gradient function of $f(x) = \sqrt{x}$.

If $f(x) = \sqrt{x}$, $f'(x) = \displaystyle\lim_{h \to 0} \frac{f(x+h) - f(x)}{h}$

$$= \lim_{h \to 0} \frac{\sqrt{x+h} - \sqrt{x}}{h}$$

$$= \lim_{h \to 0} \left(\frac{\sqrt{x+h} - \sqrt{x}}{h} \right) \left(\frac{\sqrt{x+h} + \sqrt{x}}{\sqrt{x+h} + \sqrt{x}} \right)$$

$$= \lim_{h \to 0} \frac{x + h - x}{h(\sqrt{x+h} + \sqrt{x})}$$

$$= \lim_{h \to 0} \frac{\cancel{h}}{\cancel{h}(\sqrt{x+h} + \sqrt{x})} \qquad \{\text{as } h \neq 0\}$$

$$= \frac{1}{\sqrt{x} + \sqrt{x}}$$

$$= \frac{1}{2\sqrt{x}}$$

EXERCISE 20A

1 Find, from first principles, the gradient function of $f(x)$ where $f(x)$ is:

    a x **b** 5 **c** x^3 **d** x^4

Reminder: $(a + b)^3 = a^3 + 3a^2 b + 3ab^2 + b^3$

                  $(a + b)^4 = a^4 + 4a^3 b + 6a^2 b^2 + 4ab^3 + b^4$

2 Find, from first principles, $f'(x)$ given that $f(x)$ is:

   a $2x + 5$ **b** $x^2 - 3x$ **c** $x^3 - 2x^2 + 3$

3 Find, from first principles, the derivative of $f(x)$ where $f(x)$ is:

   a $\dfrac{1}{x + 2}$ **b** $\dfrac{1}{2x - 1}$ **c** $\dfrac{1}{x^2}$ **d** $\dfrac{1}{x^3}$

4 Find, from first principles, the derivative of $f(x)$ equal to:

   a $\sqrt{x + 2}$ **b** $\dfrac{1}{\sqrt{x}}$ **c** $\sqrt{2x + 1}$

5 Using the results from the questions above, copy and complete:

Function	Derivative (in form kx^n)
x	
x^2	$2x = 2x^1$
x^3	
x^4	
x^{-1}	
x^{-2}	
x^{-3}	
$x^{\frac{1}{2}}$	$\dfrac{1}{2\sqrt{x}} = \dfrac{1}{2}x^{-\frac{1}{2}}$
$x^{-\frac{1}{2}}$	

Use your table to predict a formula for $f'(x)$ where $f(x) = x^n$ and n is rational.

6 Using first principles, prove that: "if $f(x) = x^n$ then $f'(x) = nx^{n-1}$ for $n \in \mathbb{Z}^+$".

B   DERIVATIVES AT A GIVEN x-VALUE

Suppose we are given a function $f(x)$ and asked to find its derivative at the point where $x = a$. This is actually the gradient of the tangent to the curve at $x = a$, which we write as $f'(a)$.

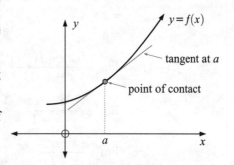

There are two methods for finding $f'(a)$ using first principles:

The first method is to start with the definition of the gradient function.

Since $f'(x) = \lim\limits_{h \to 0} \dfrac{f(x + h) - f(x)}{h}$,

we can simply substitute $x = a$ to give

$$f'(a) = \lim\limits_{h \to 0} \dfrac{f(a + h) - f(a)}{h}.$$

The second method is to consider two points on the graph of $y = f(x)$, a fixed point $A(a, f(a))$ and a variable point $B(x, f(x))$.

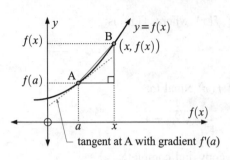

tangent at A with gradient $f'(a)$

The gradient of chord $[AB] = \dfrac{f(x) - f(a)}{x - a}$.

In the limit as B approaches A, $x \to a$ and the gradient of chord $[AB] \to$ gradient of the tangent at A.

$$\therefore \quad f'(a) = \lim_{x \to a} \dfrac{f(x) - f(a)}{x - a}.$$

Thus $\quad \boldsymbol{f'(a) = \lim\limits_{x \to a} \dfrac{f(x) - f(a)}{x - a}} \quad$ is an alternative definition for the gradient of the tangent at $x = a$.

Note: The gradient of the tangent at $x = a$ is defined as the **gradient of the curve** at the point where $x = a$, and is the instantaneous rate of change in y with respect to x at that point.

Example 4

Find, from first principles, the gradient of the tangent to:

a $\quad y = 2x^2 + 3 \quad$ at $\quad x = 2$
b $\quad y = 3 - x - x^2 \quad$ at $\quad x = -1$

a $\qquad f'(2) = \lim\limits_{x \to 2} \dfrac{f(x) - f(2)}{x - 2} \quad$ where $\quad f(2) = 2(2)^2 + 3 = 11$

$\therefore \quad f'(2) = \lim\limits_{x \to 2} \dfrac{2x^2 + 3 - 11}{x - 2}$

$\qquad\qquad = \lim\limits_{x \to 2} \dfrac{2x^2 - 8}{x - 2}$

$\qquad\qquad = \lim\limits_{x \to 2} \dfrac{2(x + 2)(x - 2)}{x - 2} \quad \{\text{as } x \neq 2\}$

$\qquad\qquad = 2 \times 4$

$\qquad\qquad = 8$

b $\quad f'(-1) = \lim\limits_{x \to -1} \dfrac{f(x) - f(-1)}{x - (-1)} \qquad$ where $\quad f(-1) = 3 - (-1) - (-1)^2$

$\qquad\qquad\qquad\qquad\qquad\qquad\qquad\qquad\qquad\qquad = 3 + 1 - 1$

$\qquad\qquad = \lim\limits_{x \to -1} \dfrac{3 - x - x^2 - 3}{x + 1} \qquad\qquad\qquad\quad = 3$

$\qquad\qquad = \lim\limits_{x \to -1} \dfrac{-x - x^2}{x + 1}$

$\qquad\qquad = \lim\limits_{x \to -1} \dfrac{-x(1 + x)}{x + 1} \quad \{\text{as } x \neq -1\}$

$\qquad\qquad = 1$

Example 5

Find, from first principles, the derivative of:

a $f(x) = \dfrac{9}{x}$ at $x = 2$ **b** $f(x) = \dfrac{2x - 1}{x + 3}$ at $x = -1$

a $f'(2) = \lim\limits_{x \to 2} \dfrac{f(x) - f(2)}{x - 2}$

$\qquad\quad = \lim\limits_{x \to 2} \left(\dfrac{\frac{9}{x} - \frac{9}{2}}{x - 2} \right)$

$\qquad\quad = \lim\limits_{x \to 2} \left(\dfrac{\frac{9}{x} - \frac{9}{2}}{x - 2} \right) \dfrac{2x}{2x}$ $\{2x$ is the LCD of $\frac{9}{x}$ and $\frac{9}{2}\}$

$\qquad\quad = \lim\limits_{x \to 2} \dfrac{18 - 9x}{2x(x - 2)}$ $\{$Do not 'multiply out' the denominator since we need to find and cancel the common factor.$\}$

$\qquad\quad = \lim\limits_{x \to 2} \dfrac{-9\overset{1}{\cancel{(x - 2)}}}{2x\underset{1}{\cancel{(x - 2)}}}$ $\{$as $x \neq 2\}$

$\qquad\quad = -\dfrac{9}{4}$

b $f'(-1) = \lim\limits_{x \to -1} \dfrac{f(x) - f(-1)}{x - (-1)}$ where $f(-1) = \dfrac{2(-1) - 1}{(-1) + 3} = -\dfrac{3}{2}$

$\qquad\quad = \lim\limits_{x \to -1} \left(\dfrac{\frac{2x - 1}{x + 3} + \frac{3}{2}}{x + 1} \right)$

$\qquad\quad = \lim\limits_{x \to -1} \left(\dfrac{\frac{2x - 1}{x + 3} + \frac{3}{2}}{x + 1} \right) \times \dfrac{2(x + 3)}{2(x + 3)}$

$\qquad\quad = \lim\limits_{x \to -1} \dfrac{2(2x - 1) + 3(x + 3)}{2(x + 1)(x + 3)}$

$\qquad\quad = \lim\limits_{x \to -1} \dfrac{4x - 2 + 3x + 9}{2(x + 1)(x + 3)}$

$\qquad\quad = \lim\limits_{x \to -1} \dfrac{7x + 7}{2(x + 1)(x + 3)}$

$\qquad\quad = \lim\limits_{x \to -1} \dfrac{7\overset{1}{\cancel{(x + 1)}}}{2\underset{1}{\cancel{(x + 1)}}(x + 3)}$

$\qquad\quad = \dfrac{7}{2(2)}$

$\qquad\quad = \dfrac{7}{4}$

Example 6

Find, using first principles, the instantaneous rate of change in $y = \sqrt{x}$ at $x = 9$.

$$f(x) = \sqrt{x} \quad \text{and} \quad f(9) = \sqrt{9} = 3$$

Now $\quad f'(9) = \lim\limits_{x \to 9} \dfrac{f(x) - f(9)}{x - 9}$

so $\quad f'(9) = \lim\limits_{x \to 9} \dfrac{\sqrt{x} - 3}{x - 9}$

$\qquad \qquad = \lim\limits_{x \to 9} \dfrac{\sqrt{x} - 3}{(\sqrt{x} + 3)(\sqrt{x} - 3)}$ $\qquad$ {treating $x - 9$ as the difference of two squares, $x \neq 9$}

$\qquad \qquad = \dfrac{1}{\sqrt{9} + 3}$

$\qquad \qquad = \tfrac{1}{6}$

$\therefore \quad$ the instantaneous rate of change in $y = \sqrt{x}$ at $x = 9$ is $\tfrac{1}{6}$.

Example 7

Use the first principles formula $\quad f'(a) = \lim\limits_{h \to 0} \dfrac{f(a + h) - f(a)}{h} \quad$ to find:

a the gradient of the tangent to $f(x) = x^2 + 2x$ at $x = 5$

b the instantaneous rate of change of $f(x) = \dfrac{4}{x}$ at $x = -3$

a $\quad f'(5) = \lim\limits_{h \to 0} \dfrac{f(5 + h) - f(5)}{h} \quad$ where $\quad f(5) = 5^2 + 2(5) = 35$

$\qquad \qquad = \lim\limits_{h \to 0} \dfrac{(5 + h)^2 + 2(5 + h) - 35}{h}$

$\qquad \qquad = \lim\limits_{h \to 0} \dfrac{25 + 10h + h^2 + 10 + 2h - 35}{h}$

$\qquad \qquad = \lim\limits_{h \to 0} \dfrac{h^2 + 12h}{h}$

$\qquad \qquad = \lim\limits_{h \to 0} \dfrac{h(h + 12)}{h} \qquad$ {as $h \neq 0$}

$\qquad \qquad = 12$

$\therefore \quad$ the gradient of the tangent at $x = 5$ is 12.

b $\quad f'(-3) = \lim\limits_{h \to 0} \dfrac{f(-3 + h) - f(-3)}{h} \quad$ where $\quad f(-3) = \tfrac{4}{-3} = -\tfrac{4}{3}$

$\qquad \qquad = \lim\limits_{h \to 0} \left(\dfrac{\frac{4}{-3+h} + \frac{4}{3}}{h} \right)$

$$= \lim_{h \to 0} \left(\frac{\frac{4}{h-3} + \frac{4}{3}}{h} \right) \times \frac{3(h-3)}{3(h-3)}$$

$$= \lim_{h \to 0} \frac{12 + 4(h-3)}{3h(h-3)}$$

$$= \lim_{h \to 0} \frac{4\cancel{h}^{\,1}}{3\cancel{h}(h-3)_{1}} \qquad \{\text{as } h \neq 0\}$$

$$= -\tfrac{4}{9}$$

$\therefore$ the instantaneous rate of change in $f(x)$ at $x = -3$ is $-\tfrac{4}{9}$.

EXERCISE 20B

Questions **1**, **2** and **3** may be done using either of the two methods given.

1 Find, from first principles, the gradient of the tangent to:

    a $f(x) = 1 - x^2$ at $x = 2$ **b** $f(x) = 2x^2 + 5x$ at $x = -1$

    c $f(x) = 5 - 2x^2$ at $x = 3$ **d** $f(x) = 3x + 5$ at $x = -2$

2 Find, from first principles, the derivative of:

    a $f(x) = \dfrac{4}{x}$ at $x = 2$ **b** $f(x) = -\dfrac{3}{x}$ at $x = -2$

    c $f(x) = \dfrac{1}{x^2}$ at $x = 4$ **d** $f(x) = \dfrac{4x}{x-3}$ at $x = 2$

    e $f(x) = \dfrac{4x+1}{x-2}$ at $x = 5$ **f** $f(x) = \dfrac{3x}{x^2+1}$ at $x = -4$

3 Find, from first principles, the instantaneous rate of change in:

    a $\sqrt{x}$ at $x = 4$ **b** $\sqrt{x}$ at $x = \tfrac{1}{4}$ **c** $\dfrac{2}{\sqrt{x}}$ at $x = 9$ **d** $\sqrt{x-6}$ at $x = 10$

4 Use the first principles formula $f'(a) = \lim\limits_{h \to 0} \dfrac{f(a+h) - f(a)}{h}$ to find:

    a the gradient of the tangent to $f(x) = x^2 + 3x - 4$ at $x = 3$

    b the gradient of the tangent to $f(x) = 5 - 2x - 3x^2$ at $x = -2$

    c the instantaneous rate of change in $f(x) = \dfrac{1}{2x - 1}$ at $x = -2$

    d the gradient of the tangent to $f(x) = \dfrac{1}{x^2}$ at $x = 3$

    e the instantaneous rate of change in $f(x) = \sqrt{x}$ at $x = 4$

    f the instantaneous rate of change in $f(x) = \dfrac{1}{\sqrt{x}}$ at $x = 1$

5 Using $f'(a) = \lim\limits_{h \to 0} \dfrac{f(a+h) - f(a)}{h}$ find: **a** $f'(2)$ for $f(x) = x^3$

                                                        b $f'(3)$ for $f(x) = x^4$

C | SIMPLE RULES OF DIFFERENTIATION

> **Differentiation** is the process of finding a derivative or gradient function.

From **questions 5** and **6** in **Exercise 20A** you should have discovered that if $f(x) = x^n$ then $f'(x) = nx^{n-1}$.

There are other rules which can be used to differentiate more complicated functions without having to resort to the tedious method of first principles. We will discover some of these rules in the following investigation.

INVESTIGATION 3   SIMPLE RULES OF DIFFERENTIATION

In this investigation we attempt to differentiate functions of the form cx^n where c is a constant, and functions which are a sum (or difference) of terms of the form cx^n.

What to do:

1 Find, from first principles, the derivatives of:

    a $4x^2$ **b** $2x^3$ **c** $5\sqrt{x}$

2 Compare your results with the derivatives of x^2, x^3 and $\sqrt{x}$ obtained earlier.

    Copy and complete: "If $f(x) = cx^n$,   then $f'(x) = \ldots\ldots$"

3 Use first principles to find $f'(x)$ for:

    a $f(x) = x^2 + 3x$ **b** $f(x) = x^3 - 2x^2$

4 Use 3 to copy and complete: "If $f(x) = u(x) + v(x)$ then $f'(x) = \ldots\ldots$"

You should have discovered the following rules for differentiating functions:

$f(x)$	$f'(x)$	Name of rule
c (a constant)	0	**differentiating a constant**
x^n	nx^{n-1}	**differentiating x^n**
$c\,u(x)$	$c\,u'(x)$	**constant times a function**
$u(x) + v(x)$	$u'(x) + v'(x)$	**addition rule**

Each of these rules can be proved using the first limit definition of $f'(x)$. For example:

- If $f(x) = cu(x)$ where c is a constant then $f'(x) = cu'(x)$.

    Proof: $f'(x) = \lim\limits_{h \to 0} \dfrac{f(x+h) - f(x)}{h}$

                     $= \lim\limits_{h \to 0} \dfrac{cu(x+h) - cu(x)}{h}$

                     $= \lim\limits_{h \to 0} c\left[\dfrac{u(x+h) - u(x)}{h}\right]$

$$= c \lim_{h \to 0} \frac{u(x+h) - u(x)}{h}$$

$$= c \, u'(x)$$

- If $f(x) = u(x) + v(x)$ then $f'(x) = u'(x) + v'(x)$

   Proof: $\quad f'(x) = \lim_{h \to 0} \dfrac{f(x+h) - f(x)}{h}$

   $$= \lim_{h \to 0} \left(\frac{u(x+h) + v(x+h) - [u(x) + v(x)]}{h} \right)$$

   $$= \lim_{h \to 0} \left(\frac{u(x+h) - u(x) + v(x+h) - v(x)}{h} \right)$$

   $$= \lim_{h \to 0} \frac{u(x+h) - u(x)}{h} + \lim_{h \to 0} \frac{v(x+h) - v(x)}{h}$$

   $$= u'(x) + v'(x)$$

Using the rules we have now developed we can differentiate sums of powers of x.

For example, if $f(x) = 3x^4 + 2x^3 - 5x^2 + 7x + 6$ then

$$f'(x) = 3(4x^3) + 2(3x^2) - 5(2x) + 7(1) + 0 = 12x^3 + 6x^2 - 10x + 7$$

Example 8

Find $f'(x)$ for $f(x)$ equal to: **a** $5x^3 + 6x^2 - 3x + 2$ **b** $7x - \dfrac{4}{x} + \dfrac{3}{x^3}$

a $f(x) = 5x^3 + 6x^2 - 3x + 2$

$\therefore \ f'(x) = 5(3x^2) + 6(2x) - 3(1)$

$\qquad\quad = 15x^2 + 12x - 3$

b $f(x) = 7x - \dfrac{4}{x} + \dfrac{3}{x^3}$

$\qquad\quad = 7x - 4x^{-1} + 3x^{-3}$

$\therefore \ f'(x) = 7(1) - 4(-1x^{-2}) + 3(-3x^{-4})$

$\qquad\quad = 7 + 4x^{-2} - 9x^{-4}$

$\qquad\quad = 7 + \dfrac{4}{x^2} - \dfrac{9}{x^4}$

Example 9

Find the gradient function of $f(x) = x^2 - \dfrac{4}{x}$ and hence find the gradient of the tangent to the function at the point where $x = 2$.

$f(x) = x^2 - \dfrac{4}{x}$

$\qquad = x^2 - 4x^{-1}$

$\therefore \ f'(x) = 2x - 4(-1x^{-2})$

$\qquad\quad = 2x + 4x^{-2}$

$\qquad\quad = 2x + \dfrac{4}{x^2}$

Now $f'(2) = 4 + 1 = 5$,

So, the tangent has gradient of 5.

Example 10

Find the gradient function of $f(x)$ where $f(x)$ is: **a** $3\sqrt{x} + \dfrac{2}{x}$ **b** $x^2 - \dfrac{4}{\sqrt{x}}$

a $f(x) = 3\sqrt{x} + \dfrac{2}{x} = 3x^{\frac{1}{2}} + 2x^{-1}$ $\therefore$ $f'(x) = 3(\frac{1}{2}x^{-\frac{1}{2}}) + 2(-1x^{-2})$

$$= \tfrac{3}{2}x^{-\frac{1}{2}} - 2x^{-2}$$

$$= \dfrac{3}{2\sqrt{x}} - \dfrac{2}{x^2}$$

b $f(x) = x^2 - \dfrac{4}{\sqrt{x}} = x^2 - 4x^{-\frac{1}{2}}$ $\therefore$ $f'(x) = 2x - 4(-\frac{1}{2}x^{-\frac{3}{2}})$

$$= 2x + 2x^{-\frac{3}{2}}$$

$$= 2x + \dfrac{2}{x\sqrt{x}}$$

ALTERNATIVE NOTATION

If we are given a function $f(x)$ then $f'(x)$ represents the derivative function.

If we are given y in terms of x then y' or $\dfrac{dy}{dx}$ are commonly used to represent the derivative.

Note:
- $\dfrac{dy}{dx}$ reads "dee y by dee x" or "the derivative of y with respect to x".

- $\dfrac{dy}{dx}$ is **not a fraction**.

- $\dfrac{d(.....)}{dx}$ reads "the derivative of (....) with respect to x".

The notation $\dfrac{dy}{dx}$ stems from the fact that the gradient function is found by considering

$\displaystyle\lim_{\delta x \to 0} \dfrac{\delta y}{\delta x}$ where δy and δx are small changes in y and x respectively.

Example 11

If $y = 3x^2 - 4x$, find $\dfrac{dy}{dx}$ and interpret its meaning.

As $y = 3x^2 - 4x$, $\dfrac{dy}{dx} = 6x - 4$.

$\dfrac{dy}{dx}$ is:
- the gradient function or derivative of $y = 3x^2 - 4x$ from which the gradient at any point can be found
- the instantaneous rate of change in y as x changes.

EXERCISE 20C

1 Find $f'(x)$ given that $f(x)$ is:

    a x^3 **b** $2x^3$ **c** $7x^2$

    d $x^2 + x$ **e** $4 - 2x^2$ **f** $x^2 + 3x - 5$

    g $x^3 + 3x^2 + 4x - 1$ **h** $5x^4 - 6x^2$ **i** $\dfrac{3x - 6}{x}$

    j $\dfrac{2x - 3}{x^2}$ **k** $\dfrac{x^3 + 5}{x}$ **l** $\dfrac{x^3 + x - 3}{x}$

    m $\dfrac{1}{\sqrt{x}}$ **n** $(2x - 1)^2$ **o** $(x + 2)^3$

2 Find $\dfrac{dy}{dx}$ for:

    a $y = 2x^3 - 7x^2 - 1$ **b** $y = \pi x^2$ **c** $y = \dfrac{1}{5x^2}$

    d $y = 100x$ **e** $y = 10(x + 1)$ **f** $y = 4\pi x^3$

3 Differentiate with respect to x :

    a $6x + 2$ **b** $x\sqrt{x}$ **c** $(5 - x)^2$

    d $\dfrac{6x^2 - 9x^4}{3x}$ **e** $4x - \dfrac{1}{4x}$ **f** $x(x + 1)(2x - 5)$

4 Find the gradient of the tangent to:

    a $y = x^2$ at $x = 2$ **b** $y = \dfrac{8}{x^2}$ at $x = 9$

    c $y = 2x^2 - 3x + 7$ at $x = -1$ **d** $y = \dfrac{2x^2 - 5}{x}$ at $x = 2$

    e $y = \dfrac{x^2 - 4}{x^2}$ at $x = 4$ **f** $y = \dfrac{x^3 - 4x - 8}{x^2}$ at $x = -1$

5 Find the gradient function of $f(x)$ where $f(x)$ is:

    a $4\sqrt{x} + x$ **b** $\sqrt[3]{x}$ **c** $-\dfrac{2}{\sqrt{x}}$ **d** $2x - \sqrt{x}$

    e $\dfrac{4}{\sqrt{x}} - 5$ **f** $3x^2 - x\sqrt{x}$ **g** $\dfrac{5}{x^2\sqrt{x}}$ **h** $2x - \dfrac{3}{x\sqrt{x}}$

6 **a** If $y = 4x - \dfrac{3}{x}$, find $\dfrac{dy}{dx}$ and interpret its meaning.

    b The position of a car moving along a straight road is given by $S = 2t^2 + 4t$ metres where t is the time in seconds. Find $\dfrac{dS}{dt}$ and interpret its meaning.

    c The cost of producing x toasters each week is given by

       $C = 1785 + 3x + 0.002x^2$ dollars. Find $\dfrac{dC}{dx}$ and interpret its meaning.

D   THE CHAIN RULE

In **Chapter 1** we defined the **composite** of two functions f and g as $f(g(x))$.

We can often write complicated functions as the composite of two or more simpler functions.

For example, consider $y = (x^2 + 3x)^4$.

This could be rewritten as $y = u^4$ where $u = x^2 + 3x$, or as $y = f(g(x))$ where $f(x) = x^4$ and $g(x) = x^2 + 3x$.

Example 12

Find: **a** $f(g(x))$ if $f(x) = \sqrt{x}$ and $g(x) = 2 - 3x$

b $f(x)$ and $g(x)$ such that $f(g(x)) = \dfrac{1}{x - x^2}$.

a $f(g(x))$

$= f(2 - 3x)$

$= \sqrt{2 - 3x}$

b $f(g(x)) = \dfrac{1}{x - x^2} = \dfrac{1}{g(x)}$

$\therefore f(x) = \dfrac{1}{x}$ and $g(x) = x - x^2$

EXERCISE 20D.1

1 Find $f(g(x))$ if:

a $f(x) = x^2$ and $g(x) = 2x + 7$ **b** $f(x) = 2x + 7$ and $g(x) = x^2$

c $f(x) = \sqrt{x}$ and $g(x) = 3 - 4x$ **d** $f(x) = 3 - 4x$ and $g(x) = \sqrt{x}$

e $f(x) = \dfrac{2}{x}$ and $g(x) = x^2 + 3$ **f** $f(x) = x^2 + 3$ and $g(x) = \dfrac{2}{x}$

2 Find $f(x)$ and $g(x)$ such that $f(g(x))$ is:

a $(3x + 10)^3$ **b** $\dfrac{1}{2x + 4}$ **c** $\sqrt{x^2 - 3x}$ **d** $\dfrac{10}{(3x - x^2)^3}$

DERIVATIVES OF COMPOSITE FUNCTIONS

The reason we are interested in writing complicated functions as composite functions is to make finding derivatives easier. In the following investigation we look for a rule that will help us to differentiate composite functions.

INVESTIGATION 4   DIFFERENTIATING COMPOSITES

The purpose of this investigation is to gain insight into how we can differentiate composite functions.

Based on our previous rule "if $y = x^n$ then $\dfrac{dy}{dx} = nx^{n-1}$", we might

suspect that if $y = (2x + 1)^2$ then $\dfrac{dy}{dx} = 2(2x + 1)^1 = 2(2x + 1)$.

But is this so?

What to do:

1 Consider $y = (2x+1)^2$. Expand the brackets and then find $\dfrac{dy}{dx}$. Is $\dfrac{dy}{dx} = 2(2x+1)$?

2 Consider $y = (3x+1)^2$. Expand the brackets and then find $\dfrac{dy}{dx}$. Is $\dfrac{dy}{dx} = 2(3x+1)^1$?

3 Consider $y = (ax+1)^2$. Expand the brackets and find $\dfrac{dy}{dx}$. Is $\dfrac{dy}{dx} = 2(ax+1)^1$?

4 If $y = u^2$ where u is a function of x, what do you suspect $\dfrac{dy}{dx}$ will be equal to?

5 Consider $y = (x^2 + 3x)^2$. Expand it and find $\dfrac{dy}{dx}$.

Does your answer agree with the rule you suggested in **4**?

In the previous investigation you probably found that if $y = u^2$ then

$$\frac{dy}{dx} = 2u \times \frac{du}{dx} = \frac{dy}{du}\frac{du}{dx}.$$

Now consider $y = (2x + 1)^3$ which has the form $y = u^3$ where $u = 2x + 1$.

Expanding we have
$$\begin{aligned} y &= (2x + 1)^3 \\ &= (2x)^3 + 3(2x)^2 1 + 3(2x)1^2 + 1^3 \quad \text{\{binomial expansion\}} \\ &= 8x^3 + 12x^2 + 6x + 1 \end{aligned}$$

$$\begin{aligned} \therefore \quad \frac{dy}{dx} &= 24x^2 + 24x + 6 \\ &= 6(4x^2 + 4x + 1) \\ &= 6(2x + 1)^2 \\ &= 3(2x + 1)^2 \times 2 \\ &= 3u^2 \times \frac{du}{dx} \quad \text{which is again} \quad \frac{dy}{du}\frac{du}{dx}. \end{aligned}$$

From the investigation and from the above example we formulate the **chain rule**:

> If $\boldsymbol{y = f(u)}$ where $\boldsymbol{u = u(x)}$ then $\dfrac{\boldsymbol{dy}}{\boldsymbol{dx}} = \dfrac{\boldsymbol{dy}}{\boldsymbol{du}}\dfrac{\boldsymbol{du}}{\boldsymbol{dx}}.$

This rule is extremely important and enables us to differentiate complicated functions much faster.

For example, we can readily see that for any function $f(x)$:

> If $\boldsymbol{y = [f(x)]^n}$ then $\dfrac{\boldsymbol{dy}}{\boldsymbol{dx}} = \boldsymbol{n[f(x)]^{n-1} \times f'(x)}.$

A non-examinable proof of this rule is included for completeness.

Proof: Consider $y = f(u)$ where $u = u(x)$.

For a small change of δx in x, there is a small change of $u(x + \delta x) - u(x) = \delta u$ in u and a small change of δy in y.

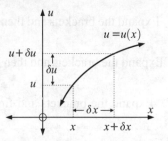
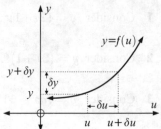

Now $\dfrac{\delta y}{\delta x} = \dfrac{\delta y}{\delta u} \times \dfrac{\delta u}{\delta x}$ {fraction multiplication}

As $\delta x \to 0$, $\delta u \to 0$ also. $\therefore \displaystyle\lim_{\delta x \to 0} \dfrac{\delta y}{\delta x} = \lim_{\delta u \to 0} \dfrac{\delta y}{\delta u} \times \lim_{\delta x \to 0} \dfrac{\delta u}{\delta x}$ {limit rule}

$$\therefore \quad \dfrac{dy}{dx} = \dfrac{dy}{du}\dfrac{du}{dx}$$

Note: If in $f'(x) = \displaystyle\lim_{h \to 0} \dfrac{f(x + h) - f(x)}{h}$,   we replace h by δx and $f(x + h) - f(x)$

by δy,   we have $f'(x) = \dfrac{dy}{dx} = \displaystyle\lim_{\delta x \to 0} \dfrac{\delta y}{\delta x}$.

Example 13

Find $\dfrac{dy}{dx}$ if: **a** $y = (x^2 - 2x)^4$ **b** $y = \dfrac{4}{\sqrt{1 - 2x}}$

a $\quad y = (x^2 - 2x)^4$

$\therefore \quad y = u^4$ where $u = x^2 - 2x$

Now $\dfrac{dy}{dx} = \dfrac{dy}{du}\dfrac{du}{dx}$ {chain rule}

$\qquad = 4u^3(2x - 2)$

$\qquad = 4(x^2 - 2x)^3(2x - 2)$ ←

> Notice that the brackets around $2x - 2$ are essential.

b $\quad y = \dfrac{4}{\sqrt{1 - 2x}}$

$\therefore \quad y = 4u^{-\frac{1}{2}}$ where $u = 1 - 2x$

Now $\dfrac{dy}{dx} = \dfrac{dy}{du}\dfrac{du}{dx}$ {chain rule}

$\qquad = 4 \times (-\tfrac{1}{2}u^{-\frac{3}{2}}) \times (-2)$

$\qquad = 4u^{-\frac{3}{2}}$

$\qquad = 4(1 - 2x)^{-\frac{3}{2}}$

EXERCISE 20D.2

1 Write in the form au^n, clearly stating what u is:

    a $\dfrac{1}{(2x-1)^2}$

    b $\sqrt{x^2-3x}$

    c $\dfrac{2}{\sqrt{2-x^2}}$

    d $\sqrt[3]{x^3-x^2}$

    e $\dfrac{4}{(3-x)^3}$

    f $\dfrac{10}{x^2-3}$

2 Find the gradient function $\dfrac{dy}{dx}$ for:

    a $y=(4x-5)^2$

    b $y=\dfrac{1}{5-2x}$

    c $y=\sqrt{3x-x^2}$

    d $y=(1-3x)^4$

    e $y=6(5-x)^3$

    f $y=\sqrt[3]{2x^3-x^2}$

    g $y=\dfrac{6}{(5x-4)^2}$

    h $y=\dfrac{4}{3x-x^2}$

    i $y=2\left(x^2-\dfrac{2}{x}\right)^3$

3 Find the gradient of the tangent to:

    a $y=\sqrt{1-x^2}$ at $x=\frac{1}{2}$

    b $y=(3x+2)^6$ at $x=-1$

    c $y=\dfrac{1}{(2x-1)^4}$ at $x=1$

    d $y=6\times\sqrt[3]{1-2x}$ at $x=0$

    e $y=\dfrac{4}{x+2\sqrt{x}}$ at $x=4$

    f $y=\left(x+\dfrac{1}{x}\right)^3$ at $x=1$

4 If $y=x^3$ then $x=y^{\frac{1}{3}}$.

    a   Find $\dfrac{dy}{dx}$ and $\dfrac{dx}{dy}$ and hence show that $\dfrac{dy}{dx}\times\dfrac{dx}{dy}=1$.

    b   Explain why $\dfrac{dy}{dx}\times\dfrac{dx}{dy}=1$ whenever these derivatives exist for any general function $y=f(x)$.

E   PRODUCT AND QUOTIENT RULES

If $f(x)=u(x)+v(x)$ then $f'(x)=u'(x)+v'(x)$.

So, the derivative of a sum of two functions is the sum of the derivatives.

But, what if $f(x)=u(x)v(x)$? Is $f'(x)=u'(x)v'(x)$?

In other words, is the derivative of a product of two functions equal to the product of the derivatives of the two functions?

The following example shows that this cannot be true:

If $f(x) = x\sqrt{x}$ we could say $f(x) = u(x)v(x)$ where $u(x) = x$ and $v(x) = \sqrt{x}$.

Now $f(x) = x^{\frac{3}{2}}$ so $f'(x) = \frac{3}{2}x^{\frac{1}{2}}$. But $u'(x)v'(x) = 1 \times \frac{1}{2}x^{-\frac{1}{2}} = \frac{1}{2}x^{-\frac{1}{2}} \neq f'(x)$.

THE PRODUCT RULE

If $u(x)$ and $v(x)$ are two functions of x and $y = uv$ then

$$\frac{dy}{dx} = \frac{du}{dx}v + u\frac{dv}{dx} \quad \text{or} \quad y' = u'(x)v(x) + u(x)v'(x).$$

Consider again the example $f(x) = x\sqrt{x}$.

This is a product $u(x)v(x)$ where $\quad u(x) = x$ and $\quad v(x) = x^{\frac{1}{2}}$

$$\therefore \quad u'(x) = 1 \quad \text{and} \quad v'(x) = \frac{1}{2}x^{-\frac{1}{2}}.$$

According to the product rule $\quad f'(x) = u'v + uv' = 1 \times x^{\frac{1}{2}} + x \times \frac{1}{2}x^{-\frac{1}{2}}$.

$$= x^{\frac{1}{2}} + \frac{1}{2}x^{\frac{1}{2}}$$

$$= \frac{3}{2}x^{\frac{1}{2}} \quad \text{which is correct} \quad \checkmark$$

Example 14

Find $\dfrac{dy}{dx}$ if: **a** $y = \sqrt{x}(2x+1)^3$ **b** $y = x^2(x^2 - 2x)^4$

a $y = \sqrt{x}(2x+1)^3$ is the product of $u = x^{\frac{1}{2}}$ and $v = (2x+1)^3$

$$\therefore \quad u' = \frac{1}{2}x^{-\frac{1}{2}} \quad \text{and} \quad v' = 3(2x+1)^2 \times 2$$
$$= 6(2x+1)^2$$

Now $\dfrac{dy}{dx} = u'v + uv' \quad$ {product rule}

$$= \frac{1}{2}x^{-\frac{1}{2}}(2x+1)^3 + x^{\frac{1}{2}} \times 6(2x+1)^2$$

$$= \frac{1}{2}x^{-\frac{1}{2}}(2x+1)^3 + 6x^{\frac{1}{2}}(2x+1)^2$$

b $y = x^2(x^2 - 2x)^4$ is the product of $u = x^2$ and $v = (x^2 - 2x)^4$

$$\therefore \quad u' = 2x \quad \text{and} \quad v' = 4(x^2 - 2x)^3(2x - 2)$$

Now $\dfrac{dy}{dx} = u'v + uv' \quad$ {product rule}

$$= 2x(x^2 - 2x)^4 + x^2 \times 4(x^2 - 2x)^3(2x - 2)$$

$$= 2x(x^2 - 2x)^4 + 4x^2(x^2 - 2x)^3(2x - 2)$$

For completeness we now prove the product rule.

Proof: Let $y = u(x)v(x)$. Suppose there is a small change of δx in x which causes corresponding changes of δu in u, δv in v, and δy in y.

As $y = uv$, $\quad y + \delta y = (u + \delta u)(v + \delta v)$

$$\therefore \quad y + \delta y = uv + (\delta u)v + u(\delta v) + \delta u \delta v$$

$$\therefore \quad \delta y = (\delta u)v + u(\delta v) + \delta u \delta v$$

$$\therefore \quad \frac{\delta y}{\delta x} = \left(\frac{\delta u}{\delta x}\right) v + u\left(\frac{\delta v}{\delta x}\right) + \left(\frac{\delta u}{\delta x}\right) \delta v \qquad \text{\{dividing each term by } \delta x\text{\}}$$

$$\therefore \quad \lim_{\delta x \to 0} \frac{\delta y}{\delta x} = \left(\lim_{\delta x \to 0} \frac{\delta u}{\delta x}\right) v + u\left(\lim_{\delta x \to 0} \frac{\delta v}{\delta x}\right) + 0 \qquad \text{\{as } \delta x \to 0, \, \delta v \to 0 \text{ also\}}$$

$$\therefore \quad \frac{dy}{dx} = \frac{du}{dx} v + u\frac{dv}{dx}$$

EXERCISE 20E.1

1 Find $\dfrac{dy}{dx}$ using the product rule:

    a $y = x^2(2x - 1)$ **b** $y = 4x(2x + 1)^3$ **c** $y = x^2\sqrt{3 - x}$

    d $y = \sqrt{x}(x - 3)^2$ **e** $y = 5x^2(3x^2 - 1)^2$ **f** $y = \sqrt{x}(x - x^2)^3$

2 Find the gradient of the tangent to:

    a $y = x^4(1 - 2x)^2$ at $x = -1$ **b** $y = \sqrt{x}(x^2 - x + 1)^2$ at $x = 4$

    c $y = x\sqrt{1 - 2x}$ at $x = -4$ **d** $y = x^3\sqrt{5 - x^2}$ at $x = 1$

3 If $y = \sqrt{x}(3 - x)^2$ show that $\dfrac{dy}{dx} = \dfrac{(3 - x)(3 - 5x)}{2\sqrt{x}}$.

Find the x-coordinates of all points on $y = \sqrt{x}(3 - x)^2$ where the tangent is horizontal.

THE QUOTIENT RULE

Expressions like $\dfrac{x^2 + 1}{2x - 5}$, $\dfrac{\sqrt{x}}{1 - 3x}$ and $\dfrac{x^3}{(x - x^2)^4}$ are called **quotients**.

Quotient functions have the form $Q(x) = \dfrac{u(x)}{v(x)}$.

Notice that $u(x) = Q(x)\,v(x)$

and by the product rule $u'(x) = Q'(x)\,v(x) + Q(x)\,v'(x)$

$$\therefore \quad u'(x) - Q(x)\,v'(x) = Q'(x)\,v(x)$$

$$\therefore \quad Q'(x)\,v(x) = u'(x) - \frac{u(x)}{v(x)}v'(x)$$

$$\therefore \quad Q'(x)\,v(x) = \frac{u'(x)\,v(x) - u(x)\,v'(x)}{v(x)}$$

$$\therefore \quad Q'(x) = \frac{u'(x)\,v(x) - u(x)\,v'(x)}{[v(x)]^2} \qquad \text{and this formula is called the \textbf{quotient rule}.}$$

So, if $Q(x) = \dfrac{u(x)}{v(x)}$ then $Q'(x) = \dfrac{u'(x)v(x) - u(x)v'(x)}{[v(x)]^2}$

or if $y = \dfrac{u}{v}$ where u and v are functions of x then $\dfrac{dy}{dx} = \dfrac{u'v - uv'}{v^2}$.

Example 15

Use the quotient rule to find $\dfrac{dy}{dx}$ if: **a** $y = \dfrac{1 + 3x}{x^2 + 1}$ **b** $y = \dfrac{\sqrt{x}}{(1 - 2x)^2}$

a $y = \dfrac{1 + 3x}{x^2 + 1}$ is a quotient with $u = 1 + 3x$ and $v = x^2 + 1$

$$\therefore \quad u' = 3 \qquad \text{and} \quad v' = 2x$$

Now $\dfrac{dy}{dx} = \dfrac{u'v - uv'}{v^2}$ {quotient rule}

$$= \frac{3(x^2 + 1) - (1 + 3x)2x}{(x^2 + 1)^2}$$

$$= \frac{3x^2 + 3 - 2x - 6x^2}{(x^2 + 1)^2}$$

$$= \frac{3 - 2x - 3x^2}{(x^2 + 1)^2}$$

b $y = \dfrac{\sqrt{x}}{(1 - 2x)^2}$ is a quotient where $u = x^{\frac{1}{2}}$ and $v = (1 - 2x)^2$

$$\therefore \quad u' = \tfrac{1}{2} x^{-\frac{1}{2}} \quad \text{and} \quad v' = 2(1 - 2x)^1 \times (-2)$$
$$= -4(1 - 2x)$$

Now $\dfrac{dy}{dx} = \dfrac{u'v - uv'}{v^2}$ {quotient rule}

$$= \frac{\tfrac{1}{2} x^{-\frac{1}{2}} (1 - 2x)^2 - x^{\frac{1}{2}} \times (-4(1 - 2x))}{(1 - 2x)^4}$$

$$= \frac{\tfrac{1}{2} x^{-\frac{1}{2}} (1 - 2x)^2 + 4x^{\frac{1}{2}} (1 - 2x)}{(1 - 2x)^4}$$

$$= \frac{(1 - 2x) \left[\dfrac{1 - 2x}{2\sqrt{x}} + 4\sqrt{x} \left(\dfrac{2\sqrt{x}}{2\sqrt{x}} \right) \right]}{(1 - 2x)^{4\,3}} \qquad \begin{array}{l} \text{\{look for common} \\ \text{factors\}} \end{array}$$

$$= \frac{1 - 2x + 8x}{2\sqrt{x}(1 - 2x)^3}$$

$$= \frac{6x + 1}{2\sqrt{x}(1 - 2x)^3}$$

Note: Simplification of $\dfrac{dy}{dx}$ as in the above example is often unnecessary, especially if you want to find the gradient of a tangent at a given point. In such cases you can substitute a value for x without simplifying.

EXERCISE 20E.2

1 Use the quotient rule to find $\dfrac{dy}{dx}$ if:

   a $y = \dfrac{1+3x}{2-x}$ **b** $y = \dfrac{x^2}{2x+1}$ **c** $y = \dfrac{x}{x^2-3}$

   d $y = \dfrac{\sqrt{x}}{1-2x}$ **e** $y = \dfrac{x^2-3}{3x-x^2}$ **f** $y = \dfrac{x}{\sqrt{1-3x}}$

2 Find the gradient of the tangent to:

   a $y = \dfrac{x}{1-2x}$ at $x = 1$ **b** $y = \dfrac{x^3}{x^2+1}$ at $x = -1$

   c $y = \dfrac{\sqrt{x}}{2x+1}$ at $x = 4$ **d** $y = \dfrac{x^2}{\sqrt{x^2+5}}$ at $x = -2$

3   **a**   If $y = \dfrac{2\sqrt{x}}{1-x}$,   show that $\dfrac{dy}{dx} = \dfrac{x+1}{\sqrt{x}(1-x)^2}$.

   b   For what values of x is $\dfrac{dy}{dx}$ **i**   zero   **ii**   undefined?

4   **a**   If $y = \dfrac{x^2-3x+1}{x+2}$,   show that $\dfrac{dy}{dx} = \dfrac{x^2+4x-7}{(x+2)^2}$.

   b   For what values of x is $\dfrac{dy}{dx}$ **i**   zero   **ii**   undefined?

   c   What is the graphical significance of your answers in **b**?

F   TANGENTS AND NORMALS

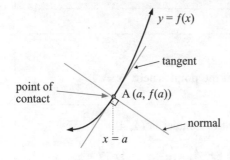

Consider a curve $y = f(x)$.

If A is the point with x-coordinate a, then the gradient of the tangent at this point is $f'(a) = m_T$.

The equation of the tangent is

$$\frac{y - f(a)}{x - a} = f'(a) \quad \{\text{equating gradients}\}$$

$$or \quad y - f(a) = f'(a)(x - a)$$

Alternatively, if the point A is at (a, b), then the equation of the tangent is

$$\frac{y - b}{x - a} = f'(a) \quad or \quad y - b = f'(a)(x - a).$$

A **normal** to a curve is a line which is perpendicular to the tangent at the point of contact.
The gradients of perpendicular lines are negative reciprocals of each other.

Thus,   the gradient of a **normal** at $x = a$ is $m_N = -\dfrac{1}{f'(a)}$.

For example, if $f(x) = x^2$ then $f'(x) = 2x$.

At $x = 2$, $f'(2) = 4$ and $-\dfrac{1}{f'(2)} = -\frac{1}{4}$.

So, at $x = 2$ the tangent has gradient 4 and the normal has gradient $-\frac{1}{4}$.

Since $f(2) = 4$, the tangent has equation $y - 4 = 4(x - 2)$ or $y = 4x - 4$ and the normal has equation $y - 4 = -\frac{1}{4}(x - 2)$ or $y = -\frac{1}{4}x + \frac{9}{2}$.

Note: If a line has gradient $\frac{4}{5}$ say, and passes through $(2, -3)$ say, another quick way to write down its equation is $4x - 5y = 4(2) - 5(-3)$, i.e., $4x - 5y = 23$.

If the gradient was $-\frac{4}{5}$, we would have:

$$4x + 5y = 4(2) + 5(-3), \quad \text{i.e.,} \quad 4x + 5y = -7.$$

Example 16

Find the equation of the tangent to $f(x) = x^2 + 1$ at the point where $x = 1$.

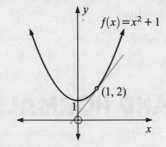

Since $f(1) = 1 + 1 = 2$, the point of contact is $(1, 2)$.

Now $f'(x) = 2x$ $\therefore$ $f'(1) = 2$

$\therefore$ the tangent has equation $\dfrac{y - 2}{x - 1} = 2$

which is $y - 2 = 2x - 2$ or $y = 2x$

Example 17

Find the equation of the normal to $y = \dfrac{8}{\sqrt{x}}$ at the point where $x = 4$.

When $x = 4$, $y = \frac{8}{\sqrt{4}} = \frac{8}{2} = 4$ so the point of contact is $(4, 4)$.

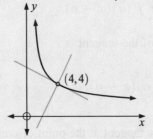

Now as $y = 8x^{-\frac{1}{2}}$, $\dfrac{dy}{dx} = -4x^{-\frac{3}{2}}$

and when $x = 4$, $\dfrac{dy}{dx} = -4 \times 4^{-\frac{3}{2}} = -\frac{1}{2}$

$\therefore$ the normal at $(4, 4)$ has gradient $\frac{2}{1}$.

$\therefore$ the equation of the normal is

$$2x - 1y = 2(4) - 1(4) \quad \text{or} \quad 2x - y = 4$$

Example 18

Find the equations of any horizontal tangents to $y = x^3 - 12x + 2$.

Since $y = x^3 - 12x + 2$, $\dfrac{dy}{dx} = 3x^2 - 12$

Horizontal tangents have gradient 0, so $3x^2 - 12 = 0$

$$\therefore \quad 3(x^2 - 4) = 0$$
$$\therefore \quad 3(x + 2)(x - 2) = 0$$
$$\therefore \quad x = -2 \text{ or } 2$$

When $x = 2$, $y = 8 - 24 + 2 = -14$
When $x = -2$, $y = -8 + 24 + 2 = 18$

$\therefore$ the points of contact are
$(2, -14)$ and $(-2, 18)$

$\therefore$ the tangents are $y = -14$ and $y = 18$.

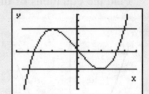

Example 19

Find the equation of the tangent to $y = \sqrt{10 - 3x}$ at the point where $x = 3$.

Let $f(x) = (10 - 3x)^{\frac{1}{2}}$

$\therefore \quad f'(x) = \frac{1}{2}(10 - 3x)^{-\frac{1}{2}} \times (-3)$

$\therefore \quad f'(3) = \frac{1}{2}(1)^{-\frac{1}{2}} \times (-3) = -\frac{3}{2}$

When $x = 3$, $y = \sqrt{10 - 9} = 1$

$\therefore$ the point of contact is $(3, 1)$.

So, the tangent has equation $\dfrac{y - 1}{x - 3} = -\dfrac{3}{2}$ i.e., $2y - 2 = -3x + 9$

or $3x + 2y = 11$

Example 20

Find the coordinates of the point(s) where the tangent to $y = x^3 + x + 2$ at $(1, 4)$ meets the curve again.

Let $f(x) = x^3 + x + 2$ $\therefore$ $f'(x) = 3x^2 + 1$

$\therefore \quad f'(1) = 3 + 1 = 4$

$\therefore$ the tangent at $(1, 4)$ has gradient 4

and its equation is $4x - y = 4(1) - 4$ or $y = 4x$

Now $y = 4x$ meets $y = x^3 + x + 2$ where $x^3 + x + 2 = 4x$

$$\therefore \quad x^3 - 3x + 2 = 0$$

This cubic must have a repeated zero of $x = 1$ because of the tangent which touches the curve at $x = 1$

$$\therefore \quad (x-1)^2(x+2) = 0$$

$$x^2 \times x = x^3 \qquad (-1)^2 \times 2 = 2$$

$\therefore \quad x = 1$ or -2

When $x = -2$, $y = (-2)^3 + (-2) + 2 = -8$

$\therefore$ the tangent meets the curve again at $(-2, -8)$.

Example 21

Find the equations of the tangents to $y = x^2$ from the external point $(2, 3)$.

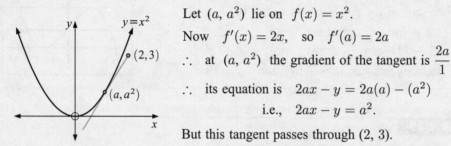

Let (a, a^2) lie on $f(x) = x^2$.

Now $f'(x) = 2x$, so $f'(a) = 2a$

$\therefore$ at (a, a^2) the gradient of the tangent is $\dfrac{2a}{1}$

$\therefore$ its equation is $2ax - y = 2a(a) - (a^2)$

i.e., $2ax - y = a^2$.

But this tangent passes through $(2, 3)$.

$$\therefore \quad 2a(2) - 3 = a^2$$

$$\therefore \quad a^2 - 4a + 3 = 0$$

$$\therefore \quad (a-1)(a-3) = 0$$

$$\therefore \quad a = 1 \text{ or } 3$$

If $a = 1$, the tangent has equation $2x - y = 1$ with point of contact $(1, 1)$.

If $a = 3$, the tangent has equation $6x - y = 9$ with point of contact $(3, 9)$.

EXERCISE 20F

1 Find the equation of the tangent to:

    a $y = x - 2x^2 + 3$ at $x = 2$

    b $y = \sqrt{x} + 1$ at $x = 4$

    c $y = x^3 - 5x$ at $x = 1$

    d $y = \dfrac{4}{\sqrt{x}}$ at $(1, 4)$

2 Find the equation of the normal to:

    a $y = x^2$ at the point $(3, 9)$

    b $y = x^3 - 5x + 2$ at $x = -2$

    c $y = \dfrac{5}{\sqrt{x}} - \sqrt{x}$ at the point $(1, 4)$

    d $y = 8\sqrt{x} - \dfrac{1}{x^2}$ at $x = 1$

3   **a** Find the equations of the horizontal tangents to $y = 2x^3 + 3x^2 - 12x + 1$.

    b Find all points of contact of horizontal tangents to the curve $y = 2\sqrt{x} + \dfrac{1}{\sqrt{x}}$.

    c Find k if the tangent to $y = 2x^3 + kx^2 - 3$ at the point where $x = 2$ has gradient 4.

    d Find the equation of the tangent to $y = 1 - 3x + 12x^2 - 8x^3$ which is parallel to the tangent at $(1, 2)$.

4 **a** The tangent to the curve $y = x^2 + ax + b$ where a and b are constants, is $2x + y = 6$ at the point where $x = 1$. Find the values of a and b.

   b The normal to the curve $y = a\sqrt{x} + \dfrac{b}{\sqrt{x}}$ where a and b are constants, has equation $4x + y = 22$ at the point where $x = 4$. Find the values of a and b.

5 Find the equation of the tangent to:

   a $y = \sqrt{2x + 1}$ at $x = 4$

   b $y = \dfrac{1}{2 - x}$ at $x = -1$

   c $f(x) = \dfrac{x}{1 - 3x}$ at $(-1, -\frac{1}{4})$

   d $f(x) = \dfrac{x^2}{1 - x}$ at $(2, -4)$

6 Find the equation of the normal to:

   a $y = \dfrac{1}{(x^2 + 1)^2}$ at $(1, \frac{1}{4})$

   b $y = \dfrac{1}{\sqrt{3 - 2x}}$ at $x = -3$

   c $f(x) = \sqrt{x}(1 - x)^2$ at $x = 4$

   d $f(x) = \dfrac{x^2 - 1}{2x + 3}$ at $x = -1$.

7 $y = a\sqrt{1 - bx}$ where a and b are constants, has a tangent with equation $3x + y = 5$ at the point where $x = -1$. Find a and b.

8 **a** Find where the tangent to the curve $y = x^3$ at the point where $x = 2$, meets the curve again.

   b Find where the tangent to the curve $y = -x^3 + 2x^2 + 1$ at the point where $x = -1$, meets the curve again.

   c Find where the tangent to the curve $y = x^3 + \dfrac{4}{x}$ at the point where $x = 1$, meets the curve again.

9 **a** Find the equation of the tangent to $y = x^2 - x + 9$ at the point where $x = a$. Hence, find the equations of the two tangents from $(0, 0)$ to the curve. State the coordinates of the points of contact.

   b Find the equations of the tangents to $y = x^3$ from the external point $(-2, 0)$.

   c Find the equation(s) of the normal(s) to $y = \sqrt{x}$ from the external point $(4, 0)$.

10 Consider $f(x) = \dfrac{8}{x^2}$.

   a Sketch the graph of the function.

   b Find the equation of the tangent at the point where $x = a$.

   c If the tangent in **b** cuts the x-axis at A and the y-axis at B, find the coordinates of A and B.

   d Find the area of triangle OAB and discuss the area of the triangle as $a \to \infty$.

11 Consider $f : x \mapsto \dfrac{x}{\sqrt{2 - x}}$.

   a State the domain of f.

   b Show that $f'(x) = \dfrac{4 - x}{2(2 - x)^{\frac{3}{2}}}$.

   c Find the equation of the normal to f at the point where $f(x) = -1$.

12 The graphs of $y = \sqrt{x+a}$ and $y = \sqrt{2x-x^2}$ have the same gradient at their point of intersection.

Find a and the point of intersection.

13 If P is at $(-2, 3)$ and Q is at $(6, -3)$, the line segment [PQ] is a tangent to $y = \dfrac{b}{(x+1)^2}$.
Find b.

G HIGHER DERIVATIVES

THE SECOND DERIVATIVE

> Given a function $f(x)$, the derivative $f'(x)$ is known as the **first derivative**.
>
> The **second derivative** of $f(x)$ is the derivative of $f'(x)$,
>
> i.e., **the derivative of the first derivative**.
>
> We use $f''(x)$ or y'' or $\dfrac{d^2y}{dx^2}$ to represent the second derivative.

Note that:
- $\dfrac{d^2y}{dx^2} = \dfrac{d}{dx}\left(\dfrac{dy}{dx}\right)$

- $\dfrac{d^2y}{dx^2}$ reads *"dee two y by dee x squared"*.

THE SECOND DERIVATIVE IN CONTEXT

Michael rides up a hill and down the other side to his friend's house. The dots on the graph show Michael's position at various times t.

$t=0$ $t=5$ $t=15$ $t=17$ $t=19$

$t=10$

Michael's place   friend's house

The distance Michael has travelled at various times is given in the following table:

Time (t min)	0	2.5	5	7.5	10	12.5	15	17	19
Distance travelled (s m)	0	498	782	908	989	1096	1350	1792	2500

The cubic model $s \approx 1.18t^3 - 30.47t^2 + 284.52t - 16.08$ metres   fits this data well.

However, notice that the model gives $s(0) \approx -16.08$ m   whereas the actual data gives $s(0) = 0$. This sort of problem often occurs when modelling from data.

A graph of the data points and the cubic curve follows:

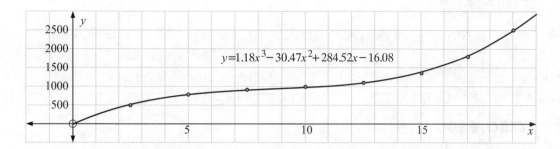

$$y = 1.18x^3 - 30.47x^2 + 284.52x - 16.08$$

Now $\dfrac{ds}{dt} \approx 3.54t^2 - 60.94t + 284.52$ metres per minute is the instantaneous rate of change in displacement per unit of time, or instantaneous velocity.

The instantaneous rate of change in velocity at any point in time is Michael's **acceleration**,

$$\text{so} \quad \frac{d}{dt}\left(\frac{ds}{dt}\right) = \frac{d^2 s}{dt^2} \quad \text{is the instantaneous acceleration,}$$

$$\text{i.e.,} \quad \frac{d^2 s}{dt^2} = 7.08t - 60.94 \quad \text{metres per minute per minute.}$$

Notice that when $t = 12$, $s \approx 1050$ m

$\dfrac{ds}{dt} \approx 63$ metres per minute and $\dfrac{d^2 s}{dt^2} \approx 24$ metres per minute per minute.

We will examine displacement, velocity and acceleration in greater detail in the next chapter.

Example 22	
Find $f''(x)$ given that $$f(x) = x^3 - \frac{3}{x}.$$	Now $f(x) = x^3 - 3x^{-1}$ $\therefore \quad f'(x) = 3x^2 + 3x^{-2}$ $\therefore \quad f''(x) = 6x - 6x^{-3}$ $\qquad\qquad = 6x - \dfrac{6}{x^3}$

HIGHER DERIVATIVES

Given $f''(x) = \dfrac{d^2 y}{dx^2}$ is obtained by differentiating $y = f(x)$ twice, it is clear that we can continue to differentiate to obtain the 3rd, 4th, 5th derivatives, and so on.

We call these: $\quad f^{(3)}(x) = \dfrac{d^3 y}{dx^3}, \quad f^{(4)}(x) = \dfrac{d^4 y}{dx^4}, \quad f^{(5)}(x) = \dfrac{d^5 y}{dx^5}, \quad$ respectively.

In general:

the **nth derivative of y with respect to x** is obtained by differentiating $y = f(x)$ n times.

We use the notation $\quad f^{(n)}(x) \quad$ or $\quad \dfrac{d^n y}{dx^n} \quad$ for the nth derivative.

Example 23

Find $f^{(3)}(x)$ given

$f(x) = x^7 + x^3 + x - \dfrac{2}{x^2}.$

$f(x) = x^7 + x^3 + x - 2x^{-2}$

$\therefore \quad f'(x) = 7x^6 + 3x^2 + 1 + 4x^{-3}$

$\therefore \quad f''(x) = 42x^5 + 6x - 12x^{-4}$

$\therefore \quad f^{(3)}(x) = 210x^4 + 6 + 48x^{-5}$

EXERCISE 20G

1 Find $f''(x)$ given that:

   a $f(x) = 3x^2 - 6x + 2$ **b** $f(x) = 2x^3 - 3x^2 - x + 5$

   c $f(x) = \dfrac{2}{\sqrt{x}} - 1$ **d** $f(x) = \dfrac{2 - 3x}{x^2}$

   e $f(x) = (1 - 2x)^3$ **f** $f(x) = \dfrac{x + 2}{2x - 1}$

2 Find $\dfrac{d^2y}{dx^2}$ and $\dfrac{d^3y}{dx^3}$ given that:

   a $y = x - x^3$ **b** $y = x^2 - \dfrac{5}{x^2}$ **c** $y = 2 - \dfrac{3}{\sqrt{x}}$

   d $y = \dfrac{4 - x}{x}$ **e** $y = (x^2 - 3x)^3$ **f** $y = x^2 - x + \dfrac{1}{1 - x}$

3 Find x when $f''(x) = 0$ for:

   a $f(x) = 2x^3 - 6x^2 + 5x + 1$ **b** $f(x) = \dfrac{x}{x^2 + 2}$

4 **a** If $y = \dfrac{1}{1 - x}$ find $\dfrac{dy}{dx}$.

   b Use the principle of mathematical induction to prove that if $y = \dfrac{1}{1 - x}$ then
$\dfrac{d^n y}{dx^n} = \dfrac{n!}{(1 - x)^{n+1}}$ for all $n \in \mathbb{Z}^+$.

REVIEW SET 20A

1 Find the equation of the tangent to $y = -2x^2$ at the point where $x = -1$.

2 Find $\dfrac{dy}{dx}$ for: **a** $y = 3x^2 - x^4$ **b** $y = \dfrac{x^3 - x}{x^2}$

3 Find, from first principles, the derivative of $f(x) = x^2 + 2x$.

4 Find the equation of the normal to $y = \dfrac{1 - 2x}{x^2}$ at the point where $x = 1$.

5 Find where the tangent to $y = 2x^3 + 4x - 1$ at $(1, 5)$ cuts the curve again.

6 The tangent to $y = \dfrac{ax + b}{\sqrt{x}}$ at $x = 1$ is $2x - y = 1$. Find a and b.

7 Find a given that the tangent to $y = \dfrac{4}{(ax+1)^2}$ at $x = 0$ passes through $(1,\,0)$.

8 Find the equation of the normal to $y = \dfrac{1}{\sqrt{x}}$ at the point where $x = 4$.

9 Determine the derivative with respect to t of:

    a $M = (t^2 + 3)^4$ **b** $A = \dfrac{\sqrt{t+5}}{t^2}$

10 Use the rules of differentiation to find $\dfrac{dy}{dx}$ for:

    a $y = \dfrac{4}{\sqrt{x}} - 3x$ **b** $y = (x - \dfrac{1}{x})^4$ **c** $y = \sqrt{x^2 - 3x}$

11 If $y = \sqrt{5 - 4x}$, find: **a** $\dfrac{dy}{dx}$ **b** $\dfrac{d^2y}{dx^2}$ **c** $\dfrac{d^3y}{dx^3}$

REVIEW SET 20B

1 Differentiate with respect to x:

    a $5x - 3x^{-1}$ **b** $(3x^2 + x)^4$ **c** $(x^2 + 1)(1 - x^2)^3$

2 Determine the equation of any horizontal tangents to the curve with equation $y = x^3 - 3x^2 - 9x + 2$.

3 Find the equation of the normal to $y = \dfrac{x+1}{x^2 - 2}$ at the point where $x = 1$.

4 Differentiate with respect to x: **a** $f(x) = \dfrac{(x+3)^3}{\sqrt{x}}$ **b** $f(x) = x^4\sqrt{x^2 + 3}$

5 Find $f''(x)$ for: **a** $f(x) = 3x^2 - \dfrac{1}{x}$ **b** $f(x) = \sqrt{x}$

6 The tangent to $y = x^2\sqrt{1-x}$ at $x = -3$ cuts the axes at A and B. Determine the area of triangle OAB.

7 $y = 2x$ is a tangent to the curve $y = x^3 + ax + b$ at $x = 1$. Find a and b.

8 The tangent to $y = x^3 + ax^2 - 4x + 3$ at $x = 1$ is parallel to the line $y = 3x$. Find the value of a and the equation of the tangent at $x = 1$. Where does the tangent cut the curve again?

9 The curve $f(x) = 2x^3 + Ax + B$ has a tangent with gradient 10 at the point $(-2, 33)$. Find the values of A and B.

10 Use the product rule for differentiation to prove that:

    a if $y = uv$ where u and v are functions of x, then

$$\frac{d^2y}{dx^2} = \left(\frac{d^2u}{dx^2}\right)v + 2\frac{du}{dx}\frac{dv}{dx} + u\left(\frac{d^2v}{dx^2}\right)$$

Chapter 21

Applications of differential calculus

Contents:

We saw in the previous chapter that one application of differential calculus is in finding the equations of tangents and normals to curves. There are many other uses, however, including the following which we will consider in this chapter:

- functions of time
- rates of change
- motion in a straight line
- curve properties
- optimisation
- applications in economics

TIME RATE OF CHANGE

There are countless quantities in the real world that vary with time.

For example:
- temperature varies continuously
- the height of a tree varies as it grows
- the prices of stocks and shares vary with each day's trading

Varying quantities can be modelled using functions of time.

For example, we could use:

- $s(t)$ to model the distance travelled by a runner
- $H(t)$ to model the height of a person riding in a Ferris wheel
- $C(t)$ to model the capacity of a person's lungs, which changes when the person breathes.

We saw in the previous chapter that if $y = f(x)$ then $f'(x)$ or $\dfrac{dy}{dx}$ is the gradient of the tangent at any value of x, and also the rate of change in y with respect to x.

We can likewise find the derivative of a function of time to tell us the **rate** at which something is happening.

For the examples above:

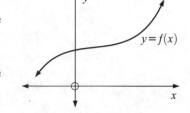

- $\dfrac{ds}{dt}$ or $s'(t)$ is the instantaneous *speed* of the runner. It might have units metres per second or $m\,s^{-1}$.

- $\dfrac{dH}{dt}$ or $H'(t)$ is the instantaneous rate of ascent of the person in the Ferris wheel. It might also have units metres per second or $m\,s^{-1}$.

- $\dfrac{dC}{dt}$ or $C'(t)$ is the person's instantaneous rate of change in lung capacity. It might have units litres per second or $L\,s^{-1}$.

EXERCISE 21A

1   The estimated future profits of a small business are given by $P(t) = 2t^2 - 12t + 118$ thousand dollars, where t is the time in years from now.

   a   What is the current annual profit?
   b   Find $\dfrac{dP}{dt}$ and state its units.

c What is the significance of $\dfrac{dP}{dt}$?

d When will the profit i decrease ii increase?

e What is the minimum profit and when does it occur?

f Find $\dfrac{dP}{dt}$ at $t = 4$, 10 and 25.   What do these figures represent?

2 Water is draining from a swimming pool such that the remaining volume of water after t minutes is $V = 200(50 - t)^2$ m^3.   Find:

a the average rate at which the water leaves the pool in the first 5 minutes

b the instantaneous rate at which the water is leaving at $t = 5$ minutes.

3 A ball is thrown vertically and its height above the ground is given by $s(t) = 1.2 + 28.1t - 4.9t^2$ metres where t is the time in seconds.

a From what distance above the ground was the ball released?

b Find $s'(t)$ and state what it represents.

c Find t when $s'(t) = 0$.   What is the significance of this result?

d What is the maximum height reached by the ball?

e Find the ball's speed: i when released ii at $t = 2$ s iii at $t = 5$ s
State the significance of the sign of the derivative.

f How long will it take for the ball to hit the ground?

g What is the significance of $\dfrac{d^2 s}{dt^2}$?

4 A shell is accidentally fired vertically from a mortar at ground level and reaches the ground again after 14.2 seconds.

a Given that its height above the ground at any time t seconds is given by $s(t) = bt - 4.9t^2$ metres, show that the initial velocity of the shell is b m s^{-1}.

b Find the initial velocity of the shell.

B   GENERAL RATES OF CHANGE

Earlier we discovered that: if $s(t)$ is a distance function then $s'(t)$ or $\dfrac{ds}{dt}$ is the instantaneous rate of change in distance with respect to time, which is speed.

In general, $\dfrac{dy}{dx}$ gives the **rate of change in y with respect to x.**

Note: If y increases as x increases, then $\dfrac{dy}{dx}$ will be positive.

If y decreases as x increases, then $\dfrac{dy}{dx}$ will be negative.

Example 1

According to a psychologist, the ability of a person to understand spatial concepts is given by $A = \frac{1}{3}\sqrt{t}$ where t is the age in years, $t \in [5, 18]$.

a Find the rate of improvement in ability to understand spatial concepts when a person is: **i** 9 years old   **ii** 16 years old.

b Explain why $\dfrac{dA}{dt} > 0$, $t \in [5, 18]$. Comment on the significance of this result.

c Explain why $\dfrac{d^2 A}{dt^2} < 0$, $t \in [5, 18]$. Comment on the significance of this result.

---

a $A = \frac{1}{3}\sqrt{t} = \frac{1}{3}t^{\frac{1}{2}}$ $\therefore$ $\dfrac{dA}{dt} = \frac{1}{6}t^{-\frac{1}{2}} = \dfrac{1}{6\sqrt{t}}$

    i When $t = 9$, $\dfrac{dA}{dt} = \frac{1}{18}$ $\therefore$ the rate of improvement is $\frac{1}{18}$ units per year for a 9 year old.

    ii When $t = 16$, $\dfrac{dA}{dt} = \frac{1}{24}$ $\therefore$ the rate of improvement is $\frac{1}{24}$ units per year for a 16 year old.

b As $\sqrt{t}$ is never negative, $\dfrac{1}{6\sqrt{t}}$ is never negative

$\therefore$ $\dfrac{dA}{dt} > 0$ for all $t \in [5, 18]$.

This means that the ability to understand spatial concepts increases with age.

c $\dfrac{dA}{dt} = \frac{1}{6}t^{-\frac{1}{2}}$ so $\dfrac{d^2 A}{dt^2} = -\frac{1}{12}t^{-\frac{3}{2}} = -\dfrac{1}{12t\sqrt{t}}$

$\therefore$ $\dfrac{d^2 A}{dt^2} < 0$ for all $t \in [5, 18]$.

This means that while the ability to understand spatial concepts increases with time, the rate of increase slows down with age.

Example 2

The cost of producing x items in a factory each day is given by

$$C(x) = \underbrace{0.000\,13x^3 + 0.002x^2}_{} + \underbrace{5x}_{} + \underbrace{2200}_{}$$

                        ↑   ↑   ↖

         cost of   raw material   fixed or overhead costs such as
        labour   costs   heating, cooling, maintenance, rent

a Find $C'(x)$, which is called the marginal cost function.
b Find the marginal cost when 150 items are produced. Interpret this result.
c Find $C(151) - C(150)$.   Compare this with the answer in **b**.

a   The marginal cost function is
$$C'(x) = 0.000\,39x^2 + 0.004x + 5$$

b $C'(150) = \$14.38$
This is the rate at which the costs are increasing with respect to the production level x when 150 items are made per day. It gives an estimate of the cost for making the 151st item.

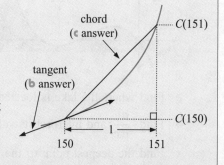

chord
(**c** answer)

$C(151)$

tangent
(**b** answer)

$C(150)$

150   151

c $C(151) - C(150) \approx \$3448.19 - \$3433.75$
$$\approx \$14.44$$

This is the actual cost of making the 151st item each week, so the answer in **b** gives a good estimate.

EXERCISE 21B

You are encouraged to use technology to graph the function for each question. This is often useful in interpreting results.

1   The quantity of a chemical in human skin which is responsible for its 'elasticity' is given by $Q = 100 - 10\sqrt{t}$ where t is the age of a person in years.

   a   Find Q at: **i** $t = 0$ **ii** $t = 25$ **iii** $t = 100$.

   b   At what rate is the quantity of the chemical changing at the ages of:
      i   25 years   **ii**   50 years?

   c   Show that the rate at which the skin loses the chemical is decreasing for all $t > 0$.

2   The height of *pinus radiata*, grown in ideal conditions, is given by $H = 20 - \dfrac{97.5}{t+5}$

metres, where t is the number of years after the tree was planted from an established seedling.

   a   How high is the tree at planting?

   b   Find the height of the tree at $t = 4$, $t = 8$ and $t = 12$ years.

   c   Find the rate at which the tree is growing at $t = 0$, 5 and 10 years.

   d   Show that $\dfrac{dH}{dt} > 0$ for all $t \geqslant 0$.   What is the significance of this result?

3   The total cost of running a train from Paris to Marseille is given by
$$C(v) = \tfrac{1}{5}v^2 + \frac{200\,000}{v} \text{ euros}$$
where v is the average speed of the train in $\text{km}\,\text{h}^{-1}$.

   a   Find the total cost of the journey if the average speed is:
      i $50 \text{ km}\,\text{h}^{-1}$ **ii** $100 \text{ km}\,\text{h}^{-1}$.

   b   Find the rate of change in the cost of running the train at speeds of:
      i $30 \text{ km}\,\text{h}^{-1}$ **ii** $90 \text{ km}\,\text{h}^{-1}$.

   c   At what speed will the cost be a minimum?

4

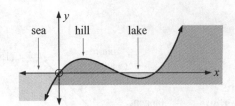

Alongside is a land and sea profile where the x-axis is sea level. The function $y = \frac{1}{10}x(x-2)(x-3)$ km   gives the height of the land or sea bed relative to sea level.

a Find where the lake is located relative to the shore line of the sea.

b Find $\dfrac{dy}{dx}$ and interpret its value when $x = \frac{1}{2}$ and when $x = 1\frac{1}{2}$ km.

c Find the deepest point of the lake and the depth at this point.

5 A tank contains 50 000 litres of water. The tap is left fully on and all the water drains from the tank in 80 minutes. The volume of water remaining in the tank after t minutes is given by $V = 50\,000 \left(1 - \dfrac{t}{80}\right)^2$ where $0 \leqslant t \leqslant 80$.

a Find $\dfrac{dV}{dt}$ and draw the graph of $\dfrac{dV}{dt}$ against t.

b At what time was the outflow fastest?

c Show that $\dfrac{d^2V}{dt^2}$ is always constant and positive. Interpret this result.

6 A fish farm grows and harvests barramundi in a large dam. The population of fish after t years is given by the function $P(t)$. The rate of change in the population $\dfrac{dP}{dt}$ is modelled by $\dfrac{dP}{dt} = aP\left(1 - \dfrac{P}{b}\right) - \left(\dfrac{c}{100}\right)P$

where a, b and c are known constants. a is the birth rate of the barramundi, b is the maximum carrying capacity of the dam and c is the percentage that is harvested each year.

a Explain why the fish population is stable when $\dfrac{dP}{dt} = 0$.

b If the birth rate is 6%, the maximum carrying capacity is 24 000, and 5% is harvested each year, find the stable population.

c If the harvest rate changes to 4%, what will the stable population increase to?

7 Seablue make denim jeans. The cost model for making x pairs per day is
$$C(x) = 0.0003x^3 + 0.02x^2 + 4x + 2250 \text{ dollars.}$$

a Find the marginal cost function $C'(x)$.

b Find $C'(220)$. What does it estimate?

c Find $C(221) - C(220)$. What does this represent?

d Find $C''(x)$ and the value of x when $C''(x) = 0$. What is the significance of this point?

C   MOTION IN A STRAIGHT LINE

DISPLACEMENT

Suppose an object P moves along a straight line so that its position s from an origin O is given as some function of time t,

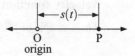

i.e., $s = s(t)$ where $t \geqslant 0$.

$s(t)$ is a **displacement function** and for any value of t it gives the displacement from O.

$s(t)$ is a vector quantity. Its magnitude is the distance from O, and its sign indicates the direction from O.

It is clear that   if $s(t) > 0$,   P is located to the **right of O**

                    if $s(t) = 0$,   P is located **at O**

                    if $s(t) < 0$,   P is located to the **left of O**.

MOTION GRAPHS

Consider $s(t) = t^2 + 2t - 3$ cm.

$s(0) = -3$ cm, $s(1) = 0$ cm, $s(2) = 5$ cm, $s(3) = 12$ cm, $s(4) = 21$ cm.

To appreciate the motion of P we draw a **motion graph**.

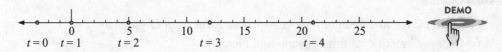

Click on the demo icon to get a better idea of the motion.

Fully animated, we not only get a good idea of the position of P, but also of what is happening to its velocity and acceleration.

VELOCITY AND ACCELERATION

AVERAGE VELOCITY

The **average velocity** of an object moving in a straight line in the time interval from $t = t_1$ to $t = t_2$ is the ratio of the change in displacement to the time taken.

average velocity $= \dfrac{s(t_2) - s(t_1)}{t_2 - t_1}$,   where $s(t)$ is the displacement function.

On a graph of $s(t)$, the average velocity is the gradient of a chord.

INSTANTANEOUS VELOCITY

In **Chapter 19** we established that $\dfrac{s(1 + h) - s(1)}{h}$ approached a fixed value as h approached 0 and this value must be the instantaneous velocity at $t = 1$.

If $s(t)$ is a displacement function of an object moving in a straight line, then

$$v(t) = s'(t) = \lim_{h \to 0} \frac{s(t+h) - s(t)}{h} \quad \text{is the } \textbf{instantaneous velocity or}$$

velocity function of the object at time t.

On a graph of $s(t)$, the instantaneous velocity is the gradient of a tangent.

AVERAGE ACCELERATION

If an object moves in a straight line with velocity function $v(t)$ then its **average acceleration** on the time interval from $t = t_1$ to $t = t_2$ is the ratio of the change in velocity to the time taken.

$$\textbf{average acceleration} = \frac{v(t_2) - v(t_1)}{t_2 - t_1}.$$

INSTANTANEOUS ACCELERATION

If a particle moves in a straight line with velocity function $v(t)$, then the

instantaneous acceleration at time t is $\quad a(t) = v'(t) = \lim_{h \to 0} \frac{v(t+h) - v(t)}{h}.$

Example 3

A particle moves in a straight line with displacement from O given by
$s(t) = 3t - t^2$ metres at time t seconds.   Find:
a the average velocity in the time interval from $t = 2$ to $t = 5$ seconds
b the average velocity in the time interval from $t = 2$ to $t = 2 + h$ seconds
c $\displaystyle \lim_{h \to 0} \frac{s(2+h) - s(2)}{h}$ and comment on its significance.

a   average velocity

$$= \frac{s(5) - s(2)}{5 - 2}$$

$$= \frac{(15 - 25) - (6 - 4)}{3}$$

$$= \frac{-10 - 2}{3}$$

$$= -4 \text{ m s}^{-1}$$

b   average velocity

$$= \frac{s(2+h) - s(2)}{2 + h - 2}$$

$$= \frac{3(2+h) - (2+h)^2 - 2}{h}$$

$$= \frac{6 + 3h - 4 - 4h - h^2 - 2}{h}$$

$$= \frac{-h - h^2}{h}$$

$$= -1 - h \text{ m s}^{-1} \quad \text{provided } h \neq 0$$

c $\displaystyle \lim_{h \to 0} \frac{s(2+h) - s(2)}{h} = \lim_{h \to 0} (-1 - h)$

$$= -1 \text{ m s}^{-1}$$

This is the instantaneous velocity of the particle at time $t = 2$ seconds.

EXERCISE 21C.1

1 A particle P moves in a straight line with a displacement function of
$s(t) = t^2 + 3t - 2$ metres, where $t \geqslant 0$, t in seconds.

   a Find the average velocity from $t = 1$ to $t = 3$ seconds.

   b Find the average velocity from $t = 1$ to $t = 1 + h$ seconds.

   c Find the value of $\displaystyle\lim_{h \to 0} \frac{s(1 + h) - s(1)}{h}$ and comment on its significance.

   d Find the average velocity from time t to time $t + h$ seconds and interpret

$$\lim_{h \to 0} \frac{s(t + h) - s(t)}{h}.$$

2 A particle P moves in a straight line with a displacement function of
$s(t) = 5 - 2t^2$ cm, where $t \geqslant 0$, t in seconds.

   a Find the average velocity from $t = 2$ to $t = 5$ seconds.

   b Find the average velocity from $t = 2$ to $t = 2 + h$ seconds.

   c Find the value of $\displaystyle\lim_{h \to 0} \frac{s(2 + h) - s(2)}{h}$ and state the meaning of this value.

   d Interpret $\displaystyle\lim_{h \to 0} \frac{s(t + h) - s(t)}{h}$.

3 A particle moves in a straight line with velocity function $v(t) = 2\sqrt{t} + 3$ cm s^{-1},
$t \geqslant 0$.

   a Find the average acceleration from $t = 1$ to $t = 4$ seconds.

   b Find the average acceleration from $t = 1$ to $t = 1 + h$ seconds.

   c Find the value of $\displaystyle\lim_{h \to 0} \frac{v(1 + h) - v(1)}{h}$. Interpret this value.

   d Interpret $\displaystyle\lim_{h \to 0} \frac{v(t + h) - v(t)}{h}$.

4 An object moves in a straight line with displacement function $s(t)$ and velocity
function $v(t)$, $t \geqslant 0$. State the meaning of:

   a $\displaystyle\lim_{h \to 0} \frac{s(4 + h) - s(4)}{h}$ **b** $\displaystyle\lim_{h \to 0} \frac{v(4 + h) - v(4)}{h}$

VELOCITY AND ACCELERATION FUNCTIONS

If a particle P moves in a straight line and its position is given by the displacement
function $s(t)$, $t \geqslant 0$, then:

- the **velocity** of P at time t is given by
  $$v(t) = s'(t) \qquad \text{\{the derivative of the displacement function\}}$$
- the **acceleration** of P at time t is given by
  $$a(t) = v'(t) = s''(t) \qquad \text{\{the derivative of the velocity function\}}$$

- $s(0)$, $v(0)$ and $a(0)$ give us the position, velocity and acceleration of the particle at time $t = 0$, and these are called the **initial conditions**.

SIGN INTERPRETATION

Suppose a particle P moves in a straight line with displacement function $s(t)$ relative to an origin O. Its velocity function is $v(t)$ and its acceleration function is $a(t)$.

We can use **sign diagrams** to interpret:

- where the particle is located relative to O
- the direction of motion and where a change of direction occurs
- when the particle's velocity is increasing or decreasing.

SIGNS OF $s(t)$:

$s(t)$	Interpretation
$= 0$	P is at O
> 0	P is located to the right of O
< 0	P is located to the left of O

$$v(t) = \lim_{h \to 0} \frac{s(t+h) - s(t)}{h}$$

If $v(t) > 0$ then $s(t+h) - s(t) > 0$

$$\therefore \quad s(t+h) > s(t)$$

For $h > 0$ the particle is moving from $s(t)$ to $s(t+h)$.

SIGNS OF $v(t)$:

$v(t)$	Interpretation
$= 0$	P is instantaneously at rest
> 0	P is moving to the right
< 0	P is moving to the left

$\therefore$ P is moving to the right.

SIGNS OF $a(t)$:

$a(t)$	Interpretation
> 0	velocity is increasing
< 0	velocity is decreasing
$= 0$	velocity may be a maximum or minimum

A useful table:

Phrase used in a question	t	s	v	a
initial conditions	0			
at the origin		0		
stationary			0	
reverses			0	
maximum height			0	
constant velocity				0
max. or min. velocity				0

When a particle reverses direction, its velocity must change sign.

We need a sign diagram of a to determine if the point is a maximum or minimum.

SPEED

As we have seen, velocities have size (magnitude) and sign (direction). The speed of an object is a measure of how fast it is travelling regardless of the direction of travel.

Thus   the **speed** at any instant is the modulus of the object's velocity,

i.e.,   if $S(t)$ represents speed then $S = |v|$.

To determine when the speed of an object is increasing or decreasing, we need to employ a **sign test**. This is:

- If the signs of $v(t)$ and $a(t)$ are the same (both positive or both negative), then the **speed** of P is **increasing**.
- If the signs of $v(t)$ and $a(t)$ are opposite, then the **speed** of P is **decreasing**.

We prove *the first* of these as follows:

Proof: Let $S = |v|$ be the speed of P at any instant $\therefore$ $S = \begin{cases} v & \text{if } v \geqslant 0 \\ -v & \text{if } v < 0 \end{cases}$

      Case 1:   If $v > 0$, $S = v$ and $\therefore$ $\dfrac{dS}{dt} = \dfrac{dv}{dt} = a(t)$

          If $a(t) > 0$ then $\dfrac{dS}{dt} > 0$ which implies that S is increasing.

      Case 2:   If $v < 0$, $S = -v$ and $\therefore$ $\dfrac{dS}{dt} = -\dfrac{dv}{dt} = -a(t)$

          If $a(t) < 0$ then $\dfrac{dS}{dt} > 0$ which also implies that S is increasing.

Thus if $v(t)$ and $a(t)$ have the same sign then the speed of P is increasing.

INVESTIGATION   **DISPLACEMENT, VELOCITY AND ACCELERATION GRAPHS**

   In this investigation we examine the motion of a projectile which is fired in a vertical direction. The projectile is affected by gravity, which is responsible for the projectile's constant acceleration.   **MOTION DEMO**

We then extend the investigation to consider other cases of motion in a straight line.

What to do:

1 Click on the icon to examine vertical projectile motion in a straight line. Observe first the displacement along the line, then look at the velocity or rate of change in displacement.

2 Examine the three graphs
- *displacement* v *time*
- *velocity* v *time*
- *acceleration* v *time*

Comment on the shape of these graphs.

3 Pick from the menu or construct functions of your own choosing to investigate the relationship between displacement, velocity and acceleration.

You are encouraged to use the motion demo above to answer questions in the following exercise.

Example 4

A particle moves in a straight line with position relative to some origin O given by
$s(t) = t^3 - 3t + 1$ cm, where t is the time in seconds ($t \geqslant 0$).

a Find expressions for the particle's velocity and acceleration, and draw sign diagrams for each of them.

b Find the initial conditions and hence describe the motion at this instant.

c Describe the motion of the particle at $t = 2$ seconds.

d Find the position of the particle when changes in direction occur.

e Draw a motion diagram for the particle.

f For what time interval(s) is the particle's speed increasing?

g What is the total distance travelled for $t \in [0, 2]$?

> **Note:** $t \geqslant 0$
> $\therefore$ critical value
> $t = -1$ is not required.

a $s(t) = t^3 - 3t + 1$ cm

$$\therefore \ v(t) = 3t^2 - 3 \qquad \{\text{as } v(t) = s'(t)\}$$
$$= 3(t^2 - 1)$$
$$= 3(t+1)(t-1) \text{ cm s}^{-1} \quad \text{which has sign diagram}$$

and $a(t) = 6t$ cm s^{-2} $\{\text{as } a(t) = v'(t)\}$

which has sign diagram

b When $t = 0$, $s(0) = 1$ cm
$$v(0) = -3 \text{ cm s}^{-1}$$
$$a(0) = 0 \text{ cm s}^{-2}$$

$\therefore$ the particle is 1 cm to the right of O, moving to the left at a speed of
3 cm s^{-1}.

c When $t = 2$, $s(2) = 8 - 6 + 1 = 3$ cm
$$v(2) = 12 - 3 = 9 \text{ cm s}^{-1}$$
$$a(2) = 12 \text{ cm s}^{-2}$$

$\therefore$ the particle is 3 cm to the right of O, moving to the right at a speed of
9 cm s^{-1}. Since a and v have the same sign, the speed is increasing.

d Since $v(t)$ changes sign when $t = 1$, a change of direction occurs at this instant.
$s(1) = 1 - 3 + 1 = -1$,   so the particle changes direction when it is 1 cm left
of O.

e

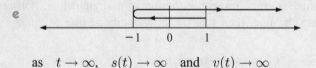

> **Note:** The motion is actually **on the line**, not above it as shown.

as $t \to \infty$, $s(t) \to \infty$ and $v(t) \to \infty$

f Speed is increasing when $v(t)$ and $a(t)$ have the same sign, i.e., $t \geqslant 1$.

g Total distance travelled $= 2 + 4 = 6$ cm.

Note: In later chapters on integral calculus another technique for finding the distances travelled and displacement over time will be explored.

EXERCISE 21C.2 (Use a graphics calculator to check sign diagrams.)

1   An object moves in a straight line with position given by $s(t) = t^2 - 4t + 3$ cm   from an origin O, where t is in seconds, $t \geqslant 0$.

   a   Find expressions for the object's velocity and acceleration at any instant and draw sign diagrams for each function.

   b   Find the initial conditions and explain what is happening to the object at that instant.

   c   Describe the motion of the object at time $t = 2$ seconds.

   d   At what time(s) does the object reverse direction? Find the position of the object at these instants.

   e   Draw a motion diagram for the object.

   f   For what time intervals is the speed of the object decreasing?

2   A stone is projected vertically so that its position above ground level after t seconds is given by $s(t) = 98t - 4.9t^2$ metres, $t \geqslant 0$.

   a   Find the velocity and acceleration functions for the stone and draw sign diagrams for each function.

   b   Find the initial position and velocity of the stone.

   c   Describe the stone's motion at times $t = 5$ and $t = 12$ seconds.

   d   Find the maximum height reached by the stone.

   e   Find the time taken for the stone to hit the ground.

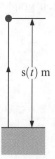

3   A particle moves in a straight line with displacement function
   $$s(t) = 12t - 2t^3 - 1 \text{ centimetres where } t \text{ is in seconds, } t \geqslant 0.$$

   a   Find velocity and acceleration functions for the particle's motion.

   b   Find the initial conditions and interpret their meaning.

   c   Find the times and positions when the particle reverses direction.

   d   At what times is the particle's: i speed increasing ii velocity increasing?

4   The position of a particle moving along the x-axis is given by $x(t) = t^3 - 9t^2 + 24t$ metres where t is in seconds, $t \geqslant 0$.

   a   Draw sign diagrams for the particle's velocity and acceleration functions.

   b   Find the position of the particle at the times when it reverses direction, and hence draw a motion diagram for the particle.

   c   At what times is the particle's: i speed decreasing ii velocity decreasing?

   d   Find the total distance travelled by the particle in the first 5 seconds of motion.

5   An experiment to determine the position of an object fired vertically from the earth's surface was performed. From the results, a two dimensional graph of the position above the earth's surface $s(t)$ metres was plotted, where t was the time in seconds.

   It was noted that the graph was *parabolic*.

   Assuming a constant gravitational acceleration g, show that if the initial velocity is $v(0)$ then:

   a $v(t) = v(0) + gt$ b $s(t) = v(0) \times t + \frac{1}{2}gt^2$.

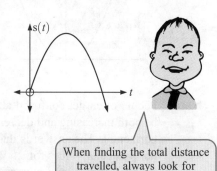

When finding the total distance travelled, always look for direction reversals first.

D SOME CURVE PROPERTIES

In this section we consider some properties of curves which can be established using derivatives. These include intervals in which curves are increasing and decreasing, and the stationary points of functions.

INCREASING AND DECREASING INTERVALS

The concepts of increasing and decreasing are closely linked to **intervals** of a function's domain.

Some examples of intervals and their graphical representations are:

Algebraic form	Means	Alternative notation
$x \geqslant 4$	●——→ at 4	$x \in [\,4, \infty\,[$
$x > 4$	○——→ at 4	$x \in\,]\,4, \infty\,[$
$x \leqslant 2$	←——● at 2	$x \in\,]-\infty, 2\,]$
$x < 2$	←——○ at 2	$x \in\,]-\infty, 2\,[$
$2 \leqslant x \leqslant 4$	●——● at 2 and 4	$x \in [\,2, 4\,]$
$2 \leqslant x < 4$	●——○ at 2 and 4	$x \in [\,2, 4\,[$

Suppose S is an interval in the domain of $f(x)$, so $f(x)$ is defined for all x in S.

- $f(x)$ is **increasing** on S $\Leftrightarrow$ $f(a) < f(b)$ for all $a, b \in S$ such that $a < b$.
- $f(x)$ is **decreasing** on S $\Leftrightarrow$ $f(a) > f(b)$ for all $a, b \in S$ such that $a < b$.

Reminder: $\Leftrightarrow$ is read "if and only if".

For example:

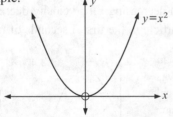

$y = x^2$ is decreasing for $x \leqslant 0$ and increasing for $x \geqslant 0$.

Note: People often get confused about the point $x = 0$. They wonder how the curve can be both increasing and decreasing at the same point when it is clear that the tangent is horizontal. The answer is that increasing and decreasing are associated with *intervals*, not particular values for x. We must clearly state that $y = x^2$ is decreasing *on the interval* $x \leqslant 0$ and increasing *on the interval* $x \geqslant 0$.

We can deduce when a curve is increasing or decreasing by considering $f'(x)$ on the interval in question. For most functions that we deal with in this course:

- $f(x)$ is **increasing** on S $\Leftrightarrow$ $f'(x) \geqslant 0$ for all x in S
- $f(x)$ is **decreasing** on S $\Leftrightarrow$ $f'(x) \leqslant 0$ for all x in S.

MONOTONICITY

Many functions are either increasing or decreasing for all $x \in \mathbb{R}$. We say these functions are **monotone increasing** or **monotone decreasing**.

For example:

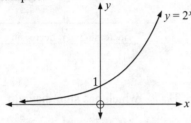

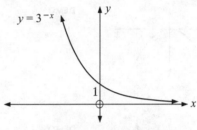

$y = 2^x$ is increasing for all x. $y = 3^{-x}$ is decreasing for all x.

Notice that:

- for an **increasing** function, an increase in x produces an increase in y
- for a **decreasing** function, an increase in x produces a decrease in y.

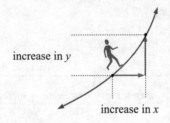

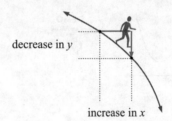

Example 5

Find intervals where $f(x)$ is:
a   increasing
b   decreasing.

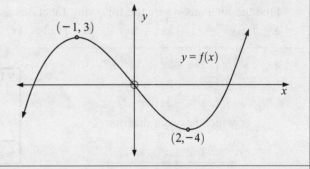

a $f(x)$ is increasing for $x \leqslant -1$ and for $x \geqslant 2$
   since all tangents have gradients $\geqslant 0$ on these intervals.

b $f(x)$ is decreasing for $-1 \leqslant x \leqslant 2$.

Sign diagrams for the derivative are extremely useful for determining intervals where a function is increasing or decreasing. Consider the following examples:

- $f(x) = x^2$

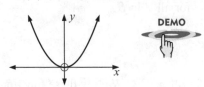

$f'(x) = 2x$ which has sign diagram

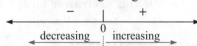

So $f(x) = x^2$ is   decreasing for $x \leqslant 0$
and   increasing for $x \geqslant 0$.

- $f(x) = -x^2$

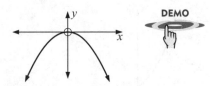

$f'(x) = -2x$ which has sign diagram

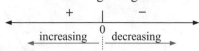

- $f(x) = x^3$

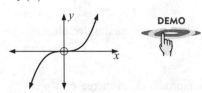

$f'(x) = 3x^2$ which has sign diagram

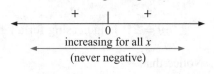

- $f(x) = x^3 - 3x + 4$

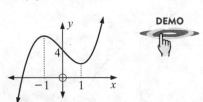

$f'(x) = 3x^2 - 3$
$= 3(x^2 - 1)$
$= 3(x + 1)(x - 1)$

which has sign diagram

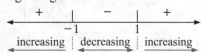

Example 6

Find the intervals where the following functions are increasing or decreasing:

a $f(x) = -x^3 + 3x^2 + 5$ b $f(x) = 3x^4 - 8x^3 + 2$

a $f(x) = -x^3 + 3x^2 + 5$
∴ $f'(x) = -3x^2 + 6x$
∴ $f'(x) = -3x(x - 2)$

which has sign diagram

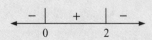

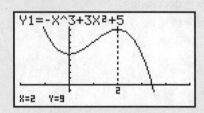

So, $f(x)$ is decreasing for
$x \leqslant 0$ and for $x \geqslant 2$ and
is increasing for $0 \leqslant x \leqslant 2$.

b
$$f(x) = 3x^4 - 8x^3 + 2$$
$$\therefore \quad f'(x) = 12x^3 - 24x^2$$
$$= 12x^2(x - 2)$$

which has sign diagram

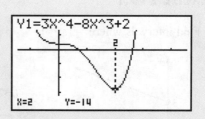

$$\begin{array}{c} - \quad | \quad - \quad | \quad + \\ \hline \quad 0 \qquad 2 \end{array}$$

So, $f(x)$ is decreasing for $x \leqslant 2$ and is increasing for $x \geqslant 2$.

Remember that $f(x)$ must be defined for all x on an interval before we can classify the interval as increasing or decreasing. We must exclude points where a function is undefined, and need to take care with vertical asymptotes.

Example 7

Consider $f(x) = \dfrac{3x - 9}{x^2 - x - 2}$.

a Show that $f'(x) = \dfrac{-3(x - 5)(x - 1)}{(x - 2)^2(x + 1)^2}$ and draw its sign diagram.

b Hence, find intervals where $y = f(x)$ is increasing or decreasing.

a $f(x) = \dfrac{3x - 9}{x^2 - x - 2}$

$$f'(x) = \frac{3(x^2 - x - 2) - (3x - 9)(2x - 1)}{(x - 2)^2(x + 1)^2} \qquad \text{\{quotient rule\}}$$

$$= \frac{3x^2 - 3x - 6 - [6x^2 - 21x + 9]}{(x - 2)^2(x + 1)^2}$$

$$= \frac{-3x^2 + 18x - 15}{(x - 2)^2(x + 1)^2}$$

$$= \frac{-3(x^2 - 6x + 5)}{(x - 2)^2(x + 1)^2}$$

$$= \frac{-3(x - 5)(x - 1)}{(x - 2)^2(x + 1)^2} \quad \text{which has sign diagram}$$

b $f(x)$ is increasing for $1 \leqslant x < 2$ and for $2 < x \leqslant 5$.

$f(x)$ is decreasing for $x < -1$ and for $-1 < x \leqslant 1$ and for $x \geqslant 5$.

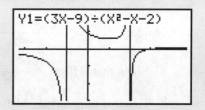

EXERCISE 21D.1

1 Find intervals where $f(x)$ is   **i** increasing   **ii** decreasing:

a
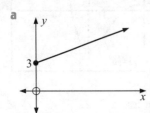

b
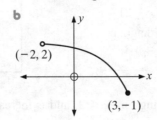

c
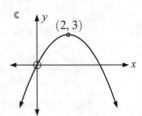

d
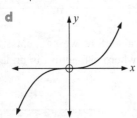

e
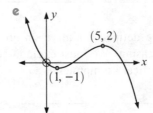

f
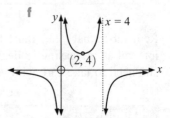

2 Find intervals where $f(x)$ is increasing or decreasing:

a $f(x) = x^2$
b $f(x) = -x^3$

c $f(x) = 2x^2 + 3x - 4$
d $f(x) = \sqrt{x}$

e $f(x) = \dfrac{2}{\sqrt{x}}$
f $f(x) = x^3 - 6x^2$

g $f(x) = -2x^3 + 4x$
h $f(x) = -4x^3 + 15x^2 + 18x + 3$

i $f(x) = 3x^4 - 16x^3 + 24x^2 - 2$
j $f(x) = 2x^3 + 9x^2 + 6x - 7$

k $f(x) = x^3 - 6x^2 + 3x - 1$
l $f(x) = x - 2\sqrt{x}$

m $f(x) = 3x^4 - 8x^3 - 6x^2 + 24x + 11$
n $f(x) = x^4 - 4x^3 + 2x^2 + 4x + 1$

3 **a** Consider $f(x) = \dfrac{4x}{x^2 + 1}$.

   i Show that $f'(x) = \dfrac{-4(x+1)(x-1)}{(x^2 + 1)^2}$ and draw its sign diagram.

   ii Hence, find intervals where $y = f(x)$ is increasing or decreasing.

b Consider $f(x) = \dfrac{4x}{(x-1)^2}$.

   i Show that $f'(x) = \dfrac{-4(x+1)}{(x-1)^3}$ and draw its sign diagram.

   ii Hence, find intervals where $y = f(x)$ is increasing or decreasing.

c Consider $f(x) = \dfrac{-x^2 + 4x - 7}{x - 1}$.

   i Show that $f'(x) = \dfrac{-(x+1)(x-3)}{(x-1)^2}$ and draw its sign diagram.

   ii Hence, find intervals where $y = f(x)$ is increasing or decreasing.

4 Find intervals where $f(x)$ is increasing or decreasing if:

a $f(x) = \dfrac{x^3}{x^2 - 1}$

b $f(x) = x^2 + \dfrac{4}{x-1}$

STATIONARY POINTS

A **stationary point** of a function is a point such that $f'(x) = 0$.

MAXIMA AND MINIMA

Consider the following graph which has a restricted domain of $-5 \leqslant x \leqslant 6$.

B$(-2, 4)$ D$(6, 18)$ C$(2, -4)$ A$(-5, -16\frac{1}{2})$ $y = f(x)$

A is a **global minimum** as it is the minimum value of y on the entire domain.

B is a **local maximum** as it is a turning point where the curve has shape ⌢ and $f'(x) = 0$ at that point.

C is a **local minimum** as it is a turning point where the curve has shape ⌣ and $f'(x) = 0$ at that point.

D is a **global maximum** as it is the maximum value of y on the entire domain.

Note:
- Local maxima and minima are stationary points where $f'(x) = 0$. The tangents at these points are **horizontal**.
- It is possible for a local maximum or minimum to also be the global maximum or minimum of a function.
  For example, for $y = x^2$ the point $(0, 0)$ is a local minimum and is also the global minimum.

HORIZONTAL INFLECTIONS OR STATIONARY POINTS OF INFLECTION (SPI)

It is not always true that whenever we find a value of x where $f'(x) = 0$ we have a local maximum or minimum.

For example, $f(x) = x^3$ has $f'(x) = 3x^2$
and $f'(x) = 0$ when $x = 0$.

Notice that the x-axis is a tangent to the curve which actually crosses over the curve at O(0, 0). This tangent is horizontal but O(0, 0) is neither a local maximum nor a local minimum.

It is called a **horizontal inflection** (or **inflexion**) as the curve changes its curvature or shape.

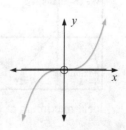

SUMMARY

A **stationary point** is a point where $f'(x) = 0$. It could be a local maximum, local minimum, or a horizontal inflection (SPI).

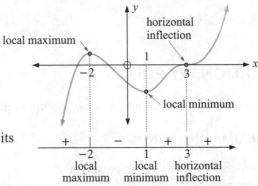

Consider the following graph:

The sign diagram of its gradient function is:

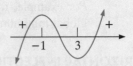

Stationary point	Sign diagram of $f'(x)$ near $x = a$	Shape of curve near $x = a$
local maximum	$\xrightarrow{\quad + \;\big|\; - \quad}$ a	$x = a$
local minimum	$\xrightarrow{\quad - \;\big|\; + \quad}$ a	$x = a$
horizontal inflection or stationary inflection	$\xrightarrow{+\,\big|\,+}$ a or $\xrightarrow{-\,\big|\,-}$ a	$x = a$ or $x = a$

Example 8

Find and classify all stationary points of $f(x) = x^3 - 3x^2 - 9x + 5$.

$$f(x) = x^3 - 3x^2 - 9x + 5$$
$$\therefore \quad f'(x) = 3x^2 - 6x - 9$$
$$= 3(x^2 - 2x - 3)$$
$$= 3(x - 3)(x + 1) \quad \text{which has sign diagram:}$$

So, we have a local maximum at $x = -1$ and a local minimum at $x = 3$.

$$f(-1) = (-1)^3 - 3(-1)^2 - 9(-1) + 5 \qquad\qquad f(3) = 3^3 - 3 \times 3^2 - 9 \times 3 + 5$$
$$= 10 \qquad\qquad\qquad\qquad\qquad = -22$$

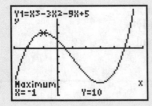

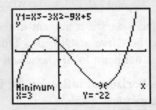

$\therefore$ local maximum at $(-1, 10)$ $\qquad\qquad$ $\therefore$ local minimum at $(3, -22)$

If we are asked to find the greatest or least value on an interval, then we should always check the endpoints. We seek the *global* maximum or minimum on the given domain.

Example 9

Find the greatest and least value of $x^3 - 6x^2 + 5$ on the interval $-2 \leqslant x \leqslant 5$.

First we graph $y = x^3 - 6x^2 + 5$ on $[-2, 5]$.
In this case the greatest value is clearly at the local maximum when $\dfrac{dy}{dx} = 0$.

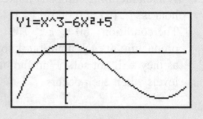

Now $\dfrac{dy}{dx} = 3x^2 - 12x$
$= 3x(x - 4)$
$= 0$ when $x = 0$ or 4.

So, the greatest value is $f(0) = 5$ when $x = 0$.
The least value is either $f(-2)$ or $f(4)$, whichever is smaller.
Now $f(-2) = -27$ and $f(4) = -27$
$\therefore$ least value is -27 when $x = -2$ and $x = 4$.

EXERCISE 21D.2

1 The tangents at points A, B and C are horizontal.
  a Classify points A, B and C.
  b Draw a sign diagram for the gradient function $f'(x)$ for all x.
  c State intervals where $y = f(x)$ is:
    i increasing   ii decreasing.
  d Draw a sign diagram for $f(x)$ for all x.
  e Comment on the differences between the sign diagrams found above.

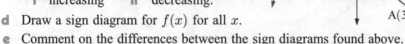

2 For each of the following functions, find and classify the stationary points, and hence sketch the function showing all important features.
  a $f(x) = x^2 - 2$
  b $f(x) = x^3 + 1$
  c $f(x) = x^3 - 3x + 2$
  d $f(x) = x^4 - 2x^2$
  e $f(x) = x^3 - 6x^2 + 12x + 1$
  f $f(x) = \sqrt{x} + 2$
  g $f(x) = x - \sqrt{x}$
  h $f(x) = x^4 - 6x^2 + 8x - 3$
  i $f(x) = 1 - x\sqrt{x}$
  j $f(x) = x^4 - 2x^2 - 8$

3 At what value of x does the quadratic function $f(x) = ax^2 + bx + c$, $a \neq 0$, have a stationary point? Under what conditions is the stationary point a local maximum or a local minimum?

4 $f(x) = 2x^3 + ax^2 - 24x + 1$ has a local maximum at $x = -4$. Find a.

5 $f(x) = x^3 + ax + b$ has a stationary point at $(-2, 3)$.
  a Find the values of a and b.
  b Find the position and nature of all stationary points.

6 A cubic polynomial $P(x)$ touches the line with equation $y = 9x + 2$ at the point $(0, 2)$, and has a stationary point at $(-1, -7)$. Find $P(x)$.

7 Find the greatest and least value of:

a $x^3 - 12x - 2$ for $-3 \leqslant x \leqslant 5$ **b** $4 - 3x^2 + x^3$ for $-2 \leqslant x \leqslant 3$

8 A manufacturing company makes door hinges. The cost function for making x hinges per hour is $C(x) = 0.0007x^3 - 0.1796x^2 + 14.663x + 160$ dollars where $50 \leqslant x \leqslant 150$. The condition $50 \leqslant x \leqslant 150$ applies as the company has a standing order filled by producing 50 each hour, but knows that production of more than 150 per hour is useless as they will not sell. Find the minimum and maximum hourly costs and the production levels when each occurs.

E   RATIONAL FUNCTIONS

Rational functions have the form $f(x) = \dfrac{g(x)}{h(x)}$ where $g(x)$ and $h(x)$ are polynomials.

For example, $f(x) = \dfrac{2x - 1}{x^2 + 2}$ and $f(x) = \dfrac{x^2 - 4}{x^2 - 3x + 2}$ are rational functions.

We have seen that one feature of a rational function is the presence of **asymptotes**.

These are lines (or curves) that the graph of the function approaches when x or y takes large values.

> **Vertical asymptotes** can be found by solving $h(x) = 0$.
>
> **Horizontal asymptotes** can be found by finding what value $f(x)$ approaches as $|x| \to \infty$.
>
> **Oblique asymptotes** are neither horizontal nor vertical. They can be found using the division process and then finding what function $f(x)$ approaches as $|x| \to \infty$.

When finding the position and nature of stationary points for rational functions, we usually begin by using the quotient rule to find the derivative.

Rational functions of the form $y = \dfrac{\text{linear}}{\text{linear}}$ were covered earlier in this text.

FUNCTIONS OF THE FORM $y = \dfrac{\text{linear}}{\text{quadratic}}$

For these functions the order of the polynomial in the denominator is higher than that in the numerator.

As $|x| \to \infty$, $f(x) \to 0$, and so they all have the horizontal asymptote $y = 0$.

Example 10

Consider $f(x) = \dfrac{3x - 9}{x^2 - x - 2}$.

a Determine the equations of any asymptotes.

b Find $f'(x)$ and determine the position and nature of any stationary points.

c Find the axes intercepts.   **d** Sketch the graph of the function.

a $f(x) = \dfrac{3x - 9}{x^2 - x - 2} = \dfrac{3x - 9}{(x - 2)(x + 1)}$

Vertical asymptotes are $x = 2$ and $x = -1$ {when the denominator is 0}

Horizontal asymptote is $y = 0$ {as $|x| \to \infty$, $f(x) \to 0$}

b $f'(x) = \dfrac{3(x^2 - x - 2) - (3x - 9)(2x - 1)}{(x - 2)^2(x + 1)^2}$ {Quotient rule}

$= \dfrac{3x^2 - 3x - 6 - [6x^2 - 21x + 9]}{(x - 2)^2(x + 1)^2}$ So, $f'(x)$ has sign diagram:

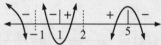

$= \dfrac{-3x^2 + 18x - 15}{(x - 2)^2(x + 1)^2}$

$= \dfrac{-3(x^2 - 6x + 5)}{(x - 2)^2(x + 1)^2}$ $\therefore$ a local maximum when $x = 5$ and a local minimum when $x = 1$

$= \dfrac{-3(x - 5)(x - 1)}{(x - 2)^2(x + 1)^2}$ The local max. is $(5, \frac{1}{3})$.

The local min. is $(1, 3)$.

c Cuts the x-axis when $y = 0$

$\therefore$ $3x - 9 = 0$ or $x = 3$

So, the x-intercept is 3.

Cuts the y-axis when $x = 0$

$\therefore$ $y = \dfrac{-9}{-2} = 4\frac{1}{2}$

So, the y-intercept is $4\frac{1}{2}$.

d

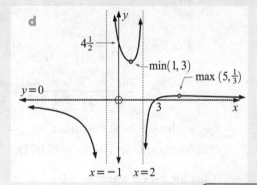

FUNCTIONS OF THE FORM $y = \dfrac{\text{quadratic}}{\text{quadratic}}$

Functions such as $y = \dfrac{2x^2 - x + 3}{x^2 + x - 2}$ have a **horizontal asymptote**

which can be found by dividing every term by x^2.

Notice that $y = \dfrac{2 - \dfrac{1}{x} + \dfrac{3}{x^2}}{1 + \dfrac{1}{x} - \dfrac{2}{x^2}}$ so as $|x| \to \infty$, $y \to \dfrac{2}{1} = 2$

> Sign diagrams must show vertical asymptotes.

Alternatively, by the division process

$$y = 2 + \frac{7 - 3x}{x^2 + x - 2} \to 2 \quad \text{as} \quad |x| \to \infty$$

$$
\begin{array}{r}
2 \\
x^2 + x - 2 \overline{\smash{\big)}\ 2x^2 - x + 3} \\
2x^2 + 2x - 4 \\
\hline
-3x + 7
\end{array}
$$

Example 11

For $f(x) = \dfrac{x^2 - 3x + 2}{x^2 + 3x + 2}$.

a   Determine the equations of its asymptotes.

b   Find $f'(x)$ and determine the position and nature of any turning points.

c   Find the axes intercepts.

d   Sketch the graph of the function.

---

a $f(x) = \dfrac{x^2 - 3x + 2}{x^2 + 3x + 2} = \dfrac{1 - \dfrac{3}{x} + \dfrac{2}{x^2}}{1 + \dfrac{3}{x} + \dfrac{2}{x^2}}$ so as $|x| \to \infty$, $y \to 1$

        $\therefore$ HA is $y = 1$

   $f(x) = \dfrac{x^2 - 3x + 2}{(x+1)(x+2)}$ $\therefore$ vertical asymptotes are $x = -1$ and $x = -2$

b $f'(x) = \dfrac{(2x - 3)(x^2 + 3x + 2) - (x^2 - 3x + 2)(2x + 3)}{(x+1)^2 (x+2)^2}$

   $\therefore$ $f'(x) = \dfrac{6x^2 - 12}{(x+1)^2 (x+2)^2}$ {on simplifying}

        $= \dfrac{6(x + \sqrt{2})(x - \sqrt{2})}{(x+1)^2 (x+2)^2}$ and has sign diagram

So, we have a local maximum at $x = -\sqrt{2}$ and a local minimum at $x = \sqrt{2}$.
The local max. is $(-\sqrt{2}, -33.971)$.   The local min. is $(\sqrt{2}, -0.029)$.

c   Cuts the x-axis when $y = 0$

     $\therefore$ $x^2 - 3x + 2 = 0$

     $\therefore$ $(x - 1)(x - 2) = 0$

         $\therefore$ $x = 1$ or 2

So, the x-intercepts are 1 and 2.

Cuts the y-axis when $x = 0$

       $\therefore$ $y = \frac{2}{2} = 1$

So, the y-intercept is 1.

d

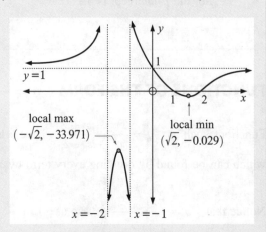

local max $(-\sqrt{2}, -33.971)$

local min $(\sqrt{2}, -0.029)$

FUNCTIONS OF THE FORM $\quad y = \dfrac{\text{quadratic}}{\text{linear}}$

For these functions the order of the polynomial in the numerator is higher than that in the denominator. This results in an oblique asymptote which is found by the division process.

For example, $\quad y = \dfrac{x^2 + 2x - 1}{x + 3} = x - 1 + \dfrac{2}{x + 3}\quad$ on division.

As $|x| \to \infty$, $\dfrac{2}{x+3} \to 0$ and so $y \to x - 1$. Thus $y = x - 1$ is an oblique asymptote.

Example 12

For $f(x) = \dfrac{-x^2 + 4x - 7}{x - 1}$:

a Determine the equation of its asymptotes.

b Find $f'(x)$ and determine the position and nature of any turning points.

c Find the axes intercepts.   **d** Sketch the graph of the function.

---

a $\quad f(x) = \dfrac{-x^2 + 4x - 7}{x - 1} = -x + 3 - \dfrac{4}{x - 1}$

$$\begin{array}{r|rrr} 1 & -1 & 4 & -7 \\ & 0 & -1 & 3 \\ \hline & -1 & 3 & -4 \end{array}$$

$\therefore$ a vertical asymptote is $\ x = 1 \qquad$ {as $x \to 1$, $|f(x)| \to \infty$}

and an oblique asymptote is $\ y = -x + 3 \quad$ {as $|x| \to \infty$, $y \to -x + 3$}

b $\quad f'(x) = \dfrac{(-2x + 4)(x - 1) - (-x^2 + 4x - 7) \times 1}{(x - 1)^2}$

$\qquad\quad = \dfrac{-2x^2 + 6x - 4 + x^2 - 4x + 7}{(x - 1)^2}$

$\qquad\quad = \dfrac{-x^2 + 2x + 3}{(x - 1)^2}$

$\qquad\quad = \dfrac{-(x^2 - 2x - 3)}{(x - 1)^2}$

$\qquad\quad = -\dfrac{(x + 1)(x - 3)}{(x - 1)^2}$

which has sign diagram:

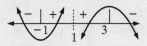

$\therefore$ a local maximum at $(3, -2)$
and a local minimum at $(-1, 6)$

c Cuts the x-axis when $y = 0$,

$\qquad \therefore\ -x^2 + 4x - 7 = 0$

$\qquad \therefore\ x^2 - 4x + 7 = 0$

$\therefore\ \Delta = 16 - 4 \times 1 \times 7 < 0$

so there are no real roots

$\therefore$ does not cut the x-axis

Cuts the y-axis when $x = 0$.

$\therefore\ y = \dfrac{-7}{-1} = 7\ \therefore\ y$-intercept is 7.

d

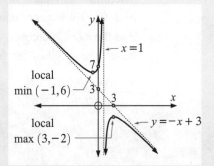

EXERCISE 21E

1 Determine the equations of the asymptotes of:

a $y = \dfrac{2x}{x^2 - 4}$

b $y = \dfrac{1 - x}{(x + 2)^2}$

c $y = \dfrac{3x + 2}{x^2 + 1}$

d $y = \dfrac{2x^2 - x + 2}{x^2 - 1}$

e $y = \dfrac{-x^2 + 2x - 1}{x^2 + x + 1}$

f $y = \dfrac{3x^2 - x + 2}{(x + 2)^2}$

g $y = \dfrac{3x^3 + x^2 - 1}{x - 2}$

h $y = \dfrac{2x^2 - 5x - 1}{x + 1}$

i $y = \dfrac{3x^2 + x}{2x - 1}$

2 For each of the following functions:

    i   determine the equation(s) of the asymptotes .

    ii   find $\dfrac{dy}{dx}$ and hence determine the position and nature of any stationary points

    iii   find the axes intercepts

    iv   sketch the function, showing all information obtained in **i**, **ii** and **iii**.

a $y = \dfrac{x^2 - x}{x^2 - x - 6}$

b $y = \dfrac{x^2 - 1}{x^2 + 1}$

c $y = \dfrac{x^2 - 5x + 4}{x^2 + 5x + 4}$

d $y = \dfrac{x^2 - 6x + 5}{(x + 1)^2}$

3 For each of the following functions:

    i   determine the equation(s) of the asymptotes

    ii   find $f'(x)$ and hence determine the position and nature of any stationary points

    iii   find the axes intercepts

    iv   sketch the graph of the function, showing all information in **i**, **ii**, and **iii**.

a $f(x) = \dfrac{4x}{x^2 + 1}$

b $f(x) = \dfrac{4x}{x^2 - 4x - 5}$

c $f(x) = \dfrac{4x}{(x - 1)^2}$

d $f(x) = \dfrac{3x - 3}{(x + 2)^2}$

4 For each of the following functions:

    i   determine the equation(s) of the asymptotes

    ii   find $f'(x)$ and hence determine the position and nature of any stationary points

    iii   find the axes intercepts

    iv   sketch the graph of the function

a $y = \dfrac{x^2 + 4x + 5}{x + 2}$

b $y = \dfrac{x^2 + 3x}{x + 1}$

c $y = -2x + 1 - \dfrac{2}{x - 2}$

d $f(x) = \dfrac{x^3}{x^2 - 1}$

e $f(x) = \dfrac{x^3}{x^2 + 1}$

F   INFLECTIONS AND SHAPE

When a curve, or part of a curve, has shape:

   we say that the shape is **concave downwards**

   we say that the shape is **concave upwards**.

TEST FOR SHAPE

Consider the **concave downwards** curve:

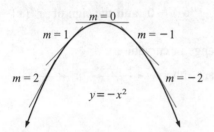

Wherever we are on the curve, as x is increased, the gradient of the tangent decreases.

∴ $f'(x)$ is decreasing,

∴   its derivative is negative,

so $f''(x) < 0$.

Likewise, if the curve is **concave upwards**:

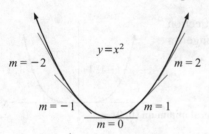

Wherever we are on the curve, as x is increased, the gradient of the tangent increases.

∴ $f'(x)$ is increasing,

∴   its derivative is positive,

so $f''(x) > 0$.

POINTS OF INFLECTION (INFLEXION)

A **point of inflection** is a point on a curve at which a change of curvature (shape) occurs,

i.e.,

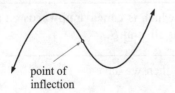   or

point of inflection   point of inflection

DEMO

Notes: • If the tangent at a point of inflection is horizontal then this point is also a stationary point. We say that we have a **horizontal** or **stationary inflection** **(SPI)**.

For example,

stationary inflection

tangent ←   → gradient = 0

a

$y = f(x)$

SD $f'(x)$ ← $\dfrac{-\;|\;-}{a}$ → x SD $f''(x)$ ← $\dfrac{+\;|\;-}{a}$ → x

- If the tangent at a point of inflection is not horizontal we say that we have a **non-horizontal** or **non-stationary inflection (NSPI)**.

  For example,

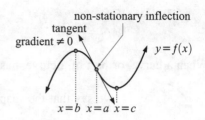

non-stationary inflection

tangent gradient $\neq 0$

$y = f(x)$

$x = b \quad x = a \quad x = c$

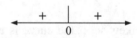

SD $f'(x)$ $\xleftarrow{\quad + \mid - \mid + \quad}_{\;b\quad c} x$ SD $f''(x)$ $\xleftarrow{\quad - \mid + \quad}_{\;\;a} x$

- The tangent at the point of inflection, also called the **inflecting tangent**, crosses the curve at that point.

There is a **point of inflection** at $x = a$ if $f''(a) = 0$ **and** the sign of $f''(x)$ changes on either side of $x = a$.

The point of inflection corresponds to a change in curvature.

In the vicinity of a, $f''(x)$ has sign diagram either $\xleftarrow{\; + \mid - \;}_{\;a}$ or $\xleftarrow{\; - \mid + \;}_{\;a}$

Observe that if $f(x) = x^4$ then

$f'(x) = 4x^3$ and $f''(x) = 12x^2$ and $f''(x)$ has sign diagram

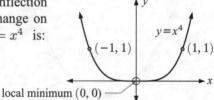

Although $f''(0) = 0$ we do not have a point of inflection at $(0, 0)$ because the sign of $f''(x)$ does not change on either side of $x = 0$. In fact the graph of $f(x) = x^4$ is:

y

$y = x^4$

$(-1, 1)$ $(1, 1)$

local minimum $(0, 0)$

x

SUMMARY

For a curve (or part curve) which is **concave downwards** on an interval S, $f''(x) \leqslant 0$ for all x in S.

For a curve (or part curve) which is **concave upwards** on an interval S, $f''(x) \geqslant 0$ for all x in S.

If $f''(x)$ changes sign at $x = a$, and $f''(a) = 0$, then we have a
- **horizontal inflection** if $f'(a) = 0$
- **non-horizontal inflection** if $f'(a) \neq 0$.

Click on the demo icon to examine some standard functions for turning points, points of inflection, and intervals where the function is increasing, decreasing, and concave up or down.

DEMO

Example 13

Find and classify all points of inflection of $f(x) = x^4 - 4x^3 + 5$.

$f(x) = x^4 - 4x^3 + 5$

$\therefore \quad f'(x) = 4x^3 - 12x^2$

$\therefore \quad f''(x) = 12x^2 - 24x$

$\qquad = 12x(x - 2)$

$\therefore \quad f''(x) = 0$ when $x = 0$ or 2

Since the signs of $f''(x)$ change about $x = 0$ and $x = 2$, these two points are points of inflection.

$\qquad$ Also $\quad f'(0) = 0, \quad f'(2) = 32 - 48 \neq 0$

$\qquad$ and $\quad f(0) = 5, \quad f(2) = 16 - 32 + 5 = -11$

Thus $(0, 5)$ is a horizontal inflection, and $(2, -11)$ is a non-horizontal inflection.

Example 14

For $f(x) = 3x^4 - 16x^3 + 24x^2 - 9$:

a find and classify all points where $f'(x) = 0$

b find and classify all points of inflection

c find intervals where the function is increasing or decreasing

d find intervals where the function is concave up or down.

e Hence, sketch the graph showing *all* important features.

a $\qquad f(x) = 3x^4 - 16x^3 + 24x^2 - 9$

$\therefore \quad f'(x) = 12x^3 - 48x^2 + 48x$

$\qquad = 12x(x^2 - 4x + 4)$

$\qquad = 12x(x - 2)^2$

Now $f(0) = -9$ and $f(2) = 7$

$\therefore$ $(0, -9)$ is a local minimum and

$(2, 7)$ is a horizontal inflection.

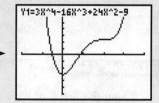

b $f''(x) = 36x^2 - 96x + 48$

$\qquad = 12(3x^2 - 8x + 4)$

$\qquad = 12(x - 2)(3x - 2)$

$\therefore$ $(2, 7)$ is a horizontal inflection

and $\left(\frac{2}{3}, f\left(\frac{2}{3}\right)\right)$ or $\left(\frac{2}{3}, -2.48\right)$ is a

non-horizontal inflection.

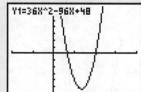

c $f(x)$ is decreasing for $x \leqslant 0$

$f(x)$ is increasing for $x \geqslant 0$.

d $f(x)$ is concave up for $x \leqslant \frac{2}{3}$ and $x \geqslant 2$

$f(x)$ is concave down for $\frac{2}{3} \leqslant x \leqslant 2$.

e

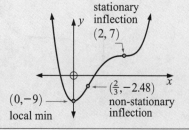

stationary inflection $(2, 7)$

$\left(\frac{2}{3}, -2.48\right)$

non-stationary inflection

$(0, -9)$ local min

$f''(x) = 0$ corresponds to the stationary points of $y = f'(x)$, so $f''(x)$ will change sign at a local maximum or minimum of $y = f'(x)$. Such points correspond to the points of inflection of $y = f(x)$.

If a local maximum or minimum of $y = f'(x)$ *touches* the x-axis, then it corresponds to a stationary point of inflection of $y = f(x)$. Otherwise it corresponds to a non-stationary point of inflection.

Example 15

The graph below shows a gradient function $y = f'(x)$. Sketch a graph which could be $y = f(x)$, showing clearly the x-values corresponding to all stationary points and points of inflection.

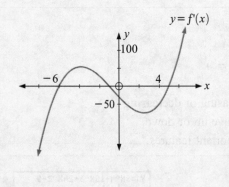

Sign diagram of $f'(x)$ is:

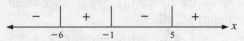

$f'(x)$ is a maximum when $x = -4$ and a minimum when $x \approx 2\frac{1}{2}$.

At these points $f''(x) = 0$ but $f'(x) \neq 0$, so they correspond to non-stationary points of inflection.

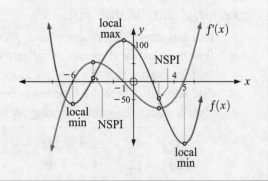

Example 16

Using the graph of $y = f(x)$ below, sketch the graphs of $y = f'(x)$ and $y = f''(x)$.

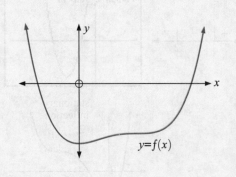

The local minimum corresponds to $f'(x) = 0$ and $f''(x) \neq 0$.

The NSPI corresponds to $f'(x) \neq 0$ and $f''(x) = 0$.

The SPI corresponds to $f'(x) = 0$ and $f''(x) = 0$.

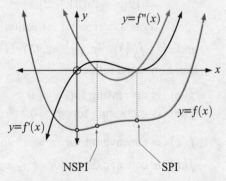

EXERCISE 21F

1 Find and classify all points of inflection of:

    a $f(x) = x^2 + 3$ **b** $f(x) = 2 - x^3$

    c $f(x) = x^3 - 6x^2 + 9x + 1$ **d** $f(x) = x^3 + 6x^2 + 12x + 5$

    e $f(x) = -3x^4 - 8x^3 + 2$ **f** $f(x) = 3 - \dfrac{1}{\sqrt{x}}$

2 For each of the following functions:

    i find and classify all points where $f'(x) = 0$
    ii find and classify all points of inflection
    iii find intervals where the function is increasing or decreasing
    iv find intervals where the function is concave up or down.
    v Sketch the graph showing *all* important features.

    a $f(x) = x^2$ **b** $f(x) = x^3$ **c** $f(x) = \sqrt{x}$

    d $f(x) = x^3 - 3x^2 - 24x + 1$ **e** $f(x) = 3x^4 + 4x^3 - 2$ **f** $f(x) = (x - 1)^4$

    g $f(x) = x^4 - 4x^2 + 3$ **h** $f(x) = 3 - \dfrac{4}{\sqrt{x}}$

3 For the graphs of $y = f'(x)$ below, sketch a graph which could be $y = f(x)$. Show clearly the location of any stationary points and points of inflection.

    a   **b**

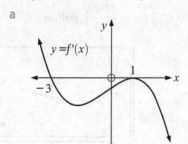 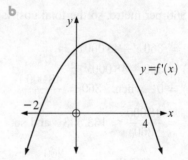

4 Using the graphs of $y = f(x)$ below, sketch the graphs of $y = f'(x)$ and $y = f''(x)$. Show clearly any axes intercepts and turning points.

    a   **b**   **c**

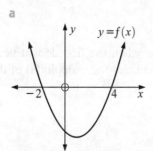 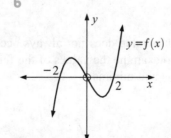 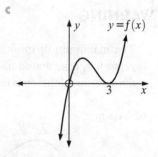

G | OPTIMISATION

There are many problems for which we need to find the **maximum** or **minimum** value of a function. We can solve such problems using differential calculus techniques. The solution is often referred to as the **optimum** solution and the process is called **optimisation**.

Consider the following problem:

An industrial shed is to have a total floor space of 600 m² and is to be divided into 3 rectangular rooms of equal size. The walls, internal and external, will cost $60 per metre to build. What dimensions should the shed have to minimise the cost of the walls?

We let each room be x m by y m as shown.

Clearly $x > 0$ and $y > 0$.

The total length of wall material is $L = 6x + 4y$ m.

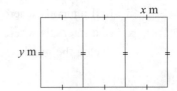

We know that the total area is 600 m²,

so $3x \times y = 600$ and hence $y = \dfrac{200}{x}$.

Knowing this relationship enables us to write L in terms of one variable, in this case x.

$$L = 6x + 4\left(\frac{200}{x}\right) = \left(6x + \frac{800}{x}\right) \text{ m}$$

The cost is $60 per metre, so the total cost is $C(x) = 60\left(6x + \dfrac{800}{x}\right)$ dollars.

Now $C(x) = 360x + 48\,000x^{-1}$

$\therefore\ C'(x) = 360 - 48\,000x^{-2}$

$\therefore\ C'(x) = 0$ when $360 = \dfrac{48\,000}{x^2}$

i.e., $x^2 = \dfrac{48\,000}{360} \approx 133.333$ and so $x \approx 11.547$

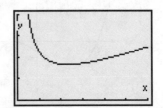

Now when $x \approx 11.547$, $y \approx \dfrac{200}{11.547} \approx 17.321$ and $C(11.547) \approx 8313.84$ dollars.

So, the minimum cost is about $8310 when the shed is 34.6 m by 17.3 m.

WARNING

The maximum or minimum value does not always occur when the first derivative is zero. It is essential to also examine the values of the function at the endpoint(s) of the domain for global maxima and minima.

For example:

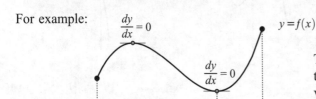

The maximum value of y occurs at the endpoint $x = b$. The minimum value of y occurs at the local minimum $x = p$.

TESTING OPTIMAL SOLUTIONS

If one is trying to optimise a function $f(x)$ and we find values of x such that $f'(x) = 0$, how do we know whether we have a maximum or a minimum solution? The following are acceptable tests:

SIGN DIAGRAM TEST

If near to $x = a$ where $f'(a) = 0$ the sign diagram is:

- $\overset{+\quad-}{\underset{a}{\diagup\frown\diagdown}}$ we have a **local maximum**
- $\overset{-\quad+}{\underset{a}{\diagdown\smile\diagup}}$ we have a **local minimum**.

SECOND DERIVATIVE TEST

If near $x = a$ where $f'(a) = 0$ and:

- $\dfrac{d^2y}{dx^2} < 0$ we have $\frown$ shape,

  which is a **local maximum**
- $\dfrac{d^2y}{dx^2} > 0$ we have $\smile$ shape,

  which is a **local minimum**.

GRAPHICAL TEST

If the graph of $y = f(x)$ shows:

- $\frown$ we have a **local maximum**
- $\smile$ we have a **local minimum**.

OPTIMISATION PROBLEM SOLVING METHOD

The following steps should be followed:

Step 1: Draw a large, clear diagram(s) of the situation.

Step 2: Construct a formula with the variable to be **optimised** (maximised or minimised) as the subject. It should be written in terms of **one** convenient **variable**, x say. You should write down what restrictions there are on x.

Step 3: Find the **first derivative** and find the value(s) of x when it is **zero**.

Step 4: If there is a restricted domain such as $a \leqslant x \leqslant b$, the maximum or minimum may occur either when the derivative is zero or else at an endpoint.
Show by the **sign diagram test**, the **second derivative test** or the **graphical test**, that you have a maximum or a minimum situation.

Example 17

A rectangular cake dish is made by cutting out squares from the corners of a 25 cm by 40 cm rectangle of tin-plate, and then folding the metal to form the container.

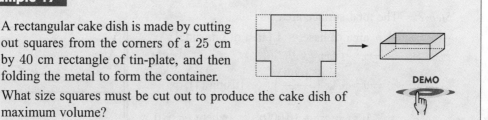

What size squares must be cut out to produce the cake dish of maximum volume?

Step 1:   Let x cm be the side lengths of the squares that are cut out.

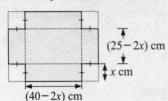

Step 2:

Volume = length × width × depth

$= (40 - 2x)(25 - 2x)x$ cm^3

$\therefore \ V = (40 - 2x)(25x - 2x^2)$ cm^3

Notice that $x > 0$ and $25 - 2x > 0$

$\therefore \ 0 < x < 12.5$

Step 3:   Now $\dfrac{dV}{dx} = -2(25x - 2x^2) + (40 - 2x)(25 - 4x)$ {product rule}

$= -50x + 4x^2 + 1000 - 50x - 160x + 8x^2$

$= 12x^2 - 260x + 1000$

$= 4(3x^2 - 65x + 250)$

$= 4(3x - 50)(x - 5)$ which is 0 when $x = \frac{50}{3} = 16\frac{2}{3}$ or $x = 5$

Step 4:   **Sign diagram test**

$\dfrac{dV}{dx}$ has sign diagram:

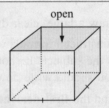

or   **Second derivative test**

$\dfrac{d^2V}{dx^2} = 24x - 260$ and at $x = 5$, $\dfrac{d^2V}{dx^2} = -140$ which is < 0

$\therefore$ the shape is ⌢ and we have a local maximum.

So, the maximum volume is obtained when $x = 5$,

i.e.,   when 5 cm squares are cut from the corners.

Example 18

Find the most economical shape (minimum surface area) for a box with a square base, vertical sides and an open top, given that it must contain 4 litres.

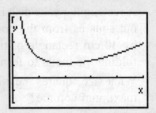

Step 1:

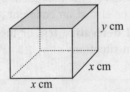

Let the base lengths be x cm and the depth be y cm. The volume

$V = $ length × width × depth

$\therefore \ V = x^2 y$

$\therefore \ 4000 = x^2 y$ .... (1) {as 1 litre $\equiv$ 1000 cm^3}

Step 2:   The total surface area

$A = $ area of base $+$ 4 (area of one side)

$= x^2 + 4xy$

$= x^2 + 4x\left(\dfrac{4000}{x^2}\right)$ {using (1)}

$\therefore \ A(x) = x^2 + 16\,000x^{-1}$ where $x > 0$

Step 3: $A'(x) = 2x - 16\,000x^{-2}$

$$\therefore \; A'(x) = 0 \quad \text{when} \quad 2x = \frac{16\,000}{x^2}$$

$$\therefore \; 2x^3 = 16\,000$$

$$\therefore \; x = \sqrt[3]{8000} = 20$$

Step 4:   **Sign diagram test**   *or*   **Second derivative test**

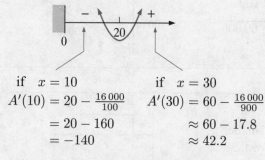

$$A''(x) = 2 + 32\,000x^{-3}$$

$$= 2 + \frac{32\,000}{x^3}$$

which is always positive as $x^3 > 0$ for all $x > 0$.

if $x = 10$	if $x = 30$
$A'(10) = 20 - \frac{16\,000}{100}$	$A'(30) = 60 - \frac{16\,000}{900}$
$= 20 - 160$	$\approx 60 - 17.8$
$= -140$	≈ 42.2

Both tests establish that the minimum material is used to make the container

when $x = 20$ and $y = \dfrac{4000}{20^2} = 10$.   So,

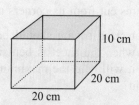

is the most economical shape.

Sometimes the variable to be optimised is in the form of a single square root function. In these situations it is convenient to square the function and use the fact that if $A > 0$, the optimum value of $A(x)$ occurs at the same value of x as the optimum value of $[A(x)]^2$.

Example 19

An animal enclosure is a right angled triangle with one leg being a drain. The farmer has 300 m of fencing available for the other two sides, AB and BC.

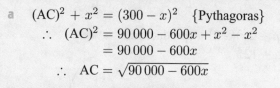

a   Show that $AC = \sqrt{90\,000 - 600x}$ if $AB = x$ m.

b   Find the maximum area of the triangular enclosure.
   Hint: If the area is A m^2, find A^2 in terms of x.
          A is a maximum when A^2 takes its maximum value.

---

a $(AC)^2 + x^2 = (300 - x)^2$ {Pythagoras}

$\therefore \; (AC)^2 = 90\,000 - 600x + x^2 - x^2$

$= 90\,000 - 600x$

$\therefore \; AC = \sqrt{90\,000 - 600x}$

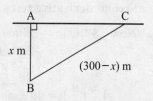

$0 < x < 300$

b   The area of triangle ABC is

$$A(x) = \tfrac{1}{2}(\text{base} \times \text{altitude})$$

$$= \tfrac{1}{2}(AC \times x)$$

$$= \tfrac{1}{2}x\sqrt{90\,000 - 600x}$$

$$\therefore \quad [A(x)]^2 = \frac{x^2}{4}(90\,000 - 600x) = 22\,500x^2 - 150x^3$$

$$\therefore \quad \frac{d}{dx}[A(x)]^2 = 45\,000x - 450x^2$$

$$= 450x(100 - x) \qquad \text{with sign}$$
diagram:

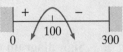

$A(x)$ is maximised when $x = 100$

so $A_{\max} = \frac{1}{2}(100)\sqrt{90\,000 - 60\,000}$

$\approx 8660 \text{ m}^2$

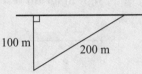

Example 20

A square sheet of metal has smaller squares cut from its corners as shown.

What sized square should be cut out so that when the sheet is bent into an open box it will hold the maximum amount of liquid?

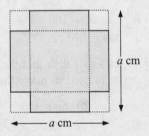

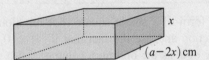

Let x cm by x cm squares be cut out.

Volume = length × width × depth

$$= (a - 2x) \times (a - 2x) \times x$$

$$\therefore \quad V(x) = x(a - 2x)^2$$

Now $V'(x) = 1(a - 2x)^2 + x \times 2(a - 2x)^1 \times (-2)$ {product rule}

$$= (a - 2x)[a - 2x - 4x]$$

$$= (a - 2x)(a - 6x)$$

$\therefore \quad V'(x) = 0$ when $x = \dfrac{a}{2}$ or $\dfrac{a}{6}$

However, $a - 2x$ must be > 0 and so $x < \dfrac{a}{2}$

Thus $x = \dfrac{a}{6}$ is the only value in $0 < x < \dfrac{a}{2}$ with $V'(x) = 0$.

Second derivative test:

Now $V''(x) = -2(a - 6x) + (a - 2x)(-6)$ {product rule}

$$= -2a + 12x - 6a + 12x$$

$$= 24x - 8a$$

$\therefore \quad V''\left(\dfrac{a}{6}\right) = 4a - 8a = -4a$ which is < 0

$\therefore$ the volume is maximised when $x = \dfrac{a}{6}$.

convex
downwards

Conclusion: When $x = \dfrac{a}{6}$, the resulting container has maximum capacity.

EXERCISE 21G

Use **calculus techniques** in the following problems.

1 A manufacturer can produce x fittings per day where $0 \leqslant x \leqslant 10\,000$. The costs are:
- €1000 per day for the workers   • €2 per day per fitting
- €$\dfrac{5000}{x}$ per day for running costs and maintenance.

How many fittings should be produced daily to minimise costs?

2 For the cost function $C(x) = 720 + 4x + 0.02x^2$ dollars and price function $p(x) = 15 - 0.002x$ dollars, find the production level that will maximise profits.

3 The total cost of producing x blankets per day is $\frac{1}{4}x^2 + 8x + 20$ dollars, and for this production level each blanket may be sold for $(23 - \frac{1}{2}x)$ dollars.

How many blankets should be produced per day to maximise the total profit?

4 The cost of running a boat is $£\dfrac{v^2}{10}$ per hour where v is the speed of the boat.

All other costs amount to £62.50 per hour. Find the speed which will minimise the total cost per kilometre.

5 A duck farmer wishes to build a rectangular enclosure of area 100 m². The farmer must purchase wire netting for three of the sides as the fourth side is an existing fence. Naturally, the farmer wishes to minimise the length (and therefore cost) of fencing required to complete the job.

   a If the shorter sides have length x m, show that the required length of wire netting to be purchased is $L = 2x + \dfrac{100}{x}$.

   b Use *technology* to help you sketch the graph of $y = 2x + \dfrac{100}{x}$.

   c Find the minimum value of L and the corresponding value of x when this occurs.

   d Sketch the optimum situation showing all dimensions.

6 Radioactive waste is to be disposed of in fully enclosed lead boxes of inner volume 200 cm³. The base of the box has dimensions in the ratio 2 : 1.

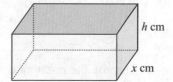

   a What is the inner length of the box?

   b Explain why $x^2 h = 100$.

   c Explain why the inner surface area of the box is given by $A(x) = 4x^2 + \dfrac{600}{x}$ cm².

   d Use *technology* to help sketch the graph of $y = 4x^2 + \dfrac{600}{x}$.

   e Find the minimum inner surface area of the box and the corresponding value of x.

   f Sketch the optimum box shape showing all dimensions.

7 Consider the manufacture of cylindrical tin cans of 1 L capacity where the cost of the metal used is to be minimised. This means that the surface area must be as small as possible.

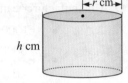

  a Explain why the height h is given by $h = \dfrac{1000}{\pi r^2}$ cm.

  b Show that the total surface area A is given by
  $$A = 2\pi r^2 + \dfrac{2000}{r} \text{ cm}^2.$$

  c Use *technology* to help you sketch the graph of A against r.

  d Find the value of r which makes A as small as possible.

  e Sketch the can of smallest surface area.

8 Sam has sheets of metal which are 36 cm by 36 cm square. He wants to cut out identical squares which are x cm by x cm from the corners of each sheet. He will then bend the sheets along the dashed lines to form an open container.

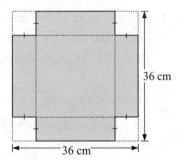

  a Show that the capacity of the container is given by $V(x) = x(36 - 2x)^2$ cm^3.

  b What sized squares should be cut out to produce the container of greatest capacity?

9 An athletics track has two 'straights' of length l m and two semicircular ends of radius x m. The perimeter of the track is 400 m.

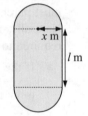

  a Show that $l = 200 - \pi x$ and hence write down the possible values that x may have.

  b Show that the area inside the track is $A = 400x - \pi x^2$.

  c What values of l and x produce the largest area inside the track?

10 A sector of radius 10 cm is bent to form a conical cup as shown.

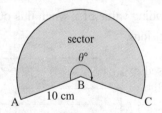
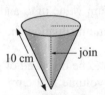

becomes   10 cm   — join   when edges AB and CB are joined with tape

Suppose the resulting cone has base radius r cm and height h cm.

  a Show that in the sector, $\text{arc AC} = \dfrac{\theta\pi}{18}$.

  b If r is the radius of the cone, explain why $r = \dfrac{\theta}{36}$.

  c If h is the height of the cone show that $h = \sqrt{100 - \left(\dfrac{\theta}{36}\right)^2}$.

  d Find the cone's capacity V in terms of θ only.

  e Use technology to sketch the graph of $V(\theta)$.

  f Find θ when $V(\theta)$ is a maximum.

11 B is a row boat 5 km out at sea from A. AC is a straight sandy beach, 6 km long. Peter can row the boat at 8 km h^{-1} and run along the beach at 17 km h^{-1}. Suppose Peter rows directly from B to point X on [AC] such that AX $= x$ km.

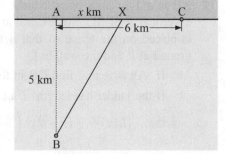

  a Explain why $0 \leqslant x \leqslant 6$.

  b If $T(x)$ is the *total time* Peter takes to row to X and then run along the beach to C, show that $T(x) = \dfrac{\sqrt{x^2 + 25}}{8} + \dfrac{6 - x}{17}$ hrs.

  c Find x such that $\dfrac{dT}{dx} = 0$. What is the significance of this value of x? Prove your statement.

12 A pumphouse is to be placed at some point X along a river.

Two pipelines will then connect the pumphouse to homesteads A and B.

How far from M should point X be so that the total length of pipeline is minimised?

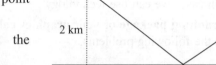

13 Open cylindrical bins are to contain 100 litres. Find the radius and height of the bin shape which requires the least amount of material (minimises the surface area).

14 Two lamps have intensities 40 and 5 candle-power and are 6 m apart. If the intensity of illumination I at any point is directly proportional to the power of the source, and inversely proportional to the square of the distance from the source, find the darkest point on the line joining the two lamps.

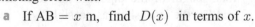

15 A right angled triangular pen is made from 24 m of fencing, all used for sides AB and BC. Side AC is an existing brick wall.

  a If AB $= x$ m, find $D(x)$ in terms of x.

  b Find $\dfrac{d[D(x)]^2}{dx}$ and hence draw a sign diagram for it.

  c Find the smallest and the greatest possible value of $D(x)$ and the design of the pen in each case.

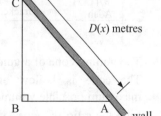

16 At 1.00 pm a ship A leaves port P, and sails in the direction 30°T at 12 km h^{-1}. At the same time, ship B is 100 km due east of P and is sailing at 8 km h^{-1} towards P.

  a Show that the distance $D(t)$ between the two ships is given by
  $D(t) = \sqrt{304t^2 - 2800t + 10\,000}$ km, where t is the number of hours after 1.00 pm.

  b Find the minimum value of $[D(t)]^2$ for all $t \geqslant 0$.

  c At what time, to the nearest minute, are the ships closest?

17 AB is a 1 m high fence which is 2 m from a vertical wall RQ. An extension ladder PQ is placed on the fence so that it touches the ground at P and the wall at Q.

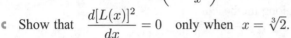

   a If $AP = x$ m, find QR in terms of x.

   b If the ladder has length L m, show that $[L(x)]^2 = (x+2)^2 \left(1 + \dfrac{1}{x^2}\right)$.

   c Show that $\dfrac{d[L(x)]^2}{dx} = 0$ only when $x = \sqrt[3]{2}$.

   d Find, correct to the nearest centimetre, the shortest length of the extension ladder. You must prove that this length is the shortest.

Sometimes finding the zeros of the derivative is difficult, and in such cases we can use technology.

Use the **graphing package** or your **graphics calculator** to help solve the following problems.

18 A, B and C are computers. A printer P is networked to each computer. Where should P be located so that the total cable length AP + BP + CP is a minimum?

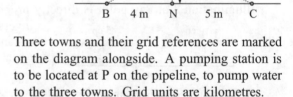

19

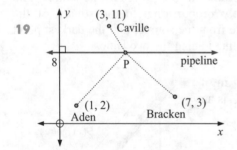

Three towns and their grid references are marked on the diagram alongside. A pumping station is to be located at P on the pipeline, to pump water to the three towns. Grid units are kilometres.

Exactly where should P be located so that the total length of the pipelines to Aden, Bracken and Caville is as short as possible?

20 The trailing cone of a guided long range torpedo is to be conical with slant edge s cm. The cone is hollow and must contain the maximum possible volume of fuel.

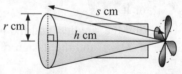

Find the ratio of $s : r$ such that the maximum fuel carrying capacity occurs.

21

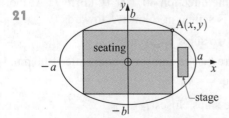

A company constructs rectangular seating arrangements for pop concerts on sports grounds. The oval shown has equation $\dfrac{x^2}{a^2} + \dfrac{y^2}{b^2} = 1$ where a and b are the lengths of the semi-major and semi-minor axes.

a Show that $y = \dfrac{b}{a}\sqrt{a^2 - x^2}$ for A as shown.

b Show that the seating area is given by $A(x) = \dfrac{4bx}{a}\sqrt{a^2 - x^2}$.

c Show that $A'(x) = 0$ when $x = \dfrac{a}{\sqrt{2}}$.

d Prove that the seating area is a maximum when $x = \dfrac{a}{\sqrt{2}}$.

e Given that the area of the ellipse is πab, what percentage of the ground is occupied by the seats in the optimum case?

H   IMPLICIT DIFFERENTIATION

For relations such as $y^3 + 3xy^2 - xy + 11 = 0$ it is often difficult or impossible to make y the subject of the formula. Such relationships between x and y are called **implicit relations**.

To gain insight into how such relations can be differentiated we will examine a familiar case.

Consider the circle with centre (0, 0) and radius 2.

The equation of the circle is $x^2 + y^2 = 4$.

Suppose A(x, y) lies on the circle.

The radius OA has gradient $= \dfrac{y\text{-step}}{x\text{-step}} = \dfrac{y - 0}{x - 0} = \dfrac{y}{x}$

$\therefore$ the tangent at A has gradient $= -\dfrac{x}{y}$ {the negative reciprocal}

Thus $\dfrac{dy}{dx} = -\dfrac{x}{y}$ for all points (x, y) on the circle.

So, in this case we have found $\dfrac{dy}{dx}$ by using a circle property.

Another way of finding $\dfrac{dy}{dx}$ for a circle is to split the relation into two parts.

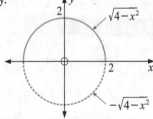

If $x^2 + y^2 = 4$ then $y^2 = 4 - x^2$

and so $y = \pm\sqrt{4 - x^2}$.

Case 1:

$y = \sqrt{4 - x^2} = (4 - x^2)^{\frac{1}{2}}$

$\therefore \quad \dfrac{dy}{dx} = \tfrac{1}{2}(4 - x^2)^{-\frac{1}{2}} \times (-2x)$

$= \dfrac{-x}{\sqrt{4 - x^2}}$

$= -\dfrac{x}{y}$

Case 2:

$y = -\sqrt{4 - x^2} = -(4 - x^2)^{\frac{1}{2}}$

$\therefore \quad \dfrac{dy}{dx} = -\tfrac{1}{2}(4 - x^2)^{-\frac{1}{2}} \times (-2x)$

$= \dfrac{x}{\sqrt{4 - x^2}}$

$= \dfrac{x}{-y}$

So, in both cases $\dfrac{dy}{dx} = -\dfrac{x}{y}$.   The question is: *"Is there a better way of finding $\dfrac{dy}{dx}$?"*

IMPLICIT DIFFERENTIATION

The process by which we differentiate implicit relations is called **implicit differentiation**.

If we are given an implicit relation between y and x and we want $\dfrac{dy}{dx}$, we differentiate both sides of the equation with respect to x, applying the chain, product, quotient and any other rules as appropriate. This will generate terms containing $\dfrac{dy}{dx}$, which we then proceed to make the subject of the equation.

For example, if $x^2 + y^2 = 4$,   then $\dfrac{d}{dx}(x^2 + y^2) = \dfrac{d}{dx}(4)$

$$\therefore \quad 2x + 2y\frac{dy}{dx} = 0$$

$$\therefore \quad \frac{dy}{dx} = -\frac{x}{y} \quad \text{as required.}$$

A useful property is that $\qquad \dfrac{d}{dx}(y^n) = ny^{n-1}\dfrac{dy}{dx} \qquad$ using the *chain rule*.

Example 21

If y is a function of x find: **a** $\dfrac{d}{dx}(y^3)$ **b** $\dfrac{d}{dx}\left(\dfrac{1}{y}\right)$ **c** $\dfrac{d}{dx}(xy^2)$

a $\quad \dfrac{d}{dx}(y^3)$

$\quad = 3y^2\dfrac{dy}{dx}$

b $\quad \dfrac{d}{dx}\left(\dfrac{1}{y}\right)$

$\quad = \dfrac{d}{dx}(y^{-1})$

$\quad = -y^{-2}\dfrac{dy}{dx}$

c $\quad \dfrac{d}{dx}(xy^2)$

$\quad = 1 \times y^2 + x \times 2y\dfrac{dy}{dx}$ {product rule}

$\quad = y^2 + 2xy\dfrac{dy}{dx}$

Example 22

a Find $\dfrac{dy}{dx}$ if: **i** $x^2 + y^3 = 8$ **ii** $x + x^2y + y^3 = 100$

b For part **a i** only, find $\dfrac{d^2y}{dx^2}$.

a **i** $\qquad x^2 + y^3 = 8$

$\therefore \quad \dfrac{d}{dx}(x^2) + \dfrac{d}{dx}(y^3) = \dfrac{d}{dx}(8)$

$\therefore \quad 2x + 3y^2\dfrac{dy}{dx} = 0$

$\therefore \quad \dfrac{dy}{dx} = \dfrac{-2x}{3y^2}$

ii $\qquad x + x^2y + y^3 = 100$

$\therefore \quad \dfrac{d(x)}{dx} + \dfrac{d}{dx}(x^2y) + \dfrac{d}{dx}(y^3) = \dfrac{d}{dx}(100)$

$\therefore \quad 1 + \underbrace{\left[2xy + x^2\dfrac{dy}{dx}\right]}_{\text{\{product rule\}}} + 3y^2\dfrac{dy}{dx} = 0$

$\therefore \quad (x^2 + 3y^2)\dfrac{dy}{dx} = -1 - 2xy$

$\therefore \quad \dfrac{dy}{dx} = \dfrac{-1 - 2xy}{x^2 + 3y^2}$

b $\dfrac{d^2y}{dx^2} = \dfrac{d}{dx}\left(\dfrac{dy}{dx}\right) = \dfrac{d}{dx}\left(\dfrac{-2x}{3y^2}\right)$

$\qquad\qquad = \dfrac{-2(3y^2) - (-2x)6y\dfrac{dy}{dx}}{9y^4}$ {quotient rule}

$\qquad\qquad = \dfrac{-6y^2 + 12xy\left(\dfrac{-2x}{3y^2}\right)}{9y^4}$

$\qquad\qquad = \dfrac{-6y^2 - \dfrac{8x^2}{y}}{9y^4} \times \left(\dfrac{y}{y}\right)$

$\qquad\qquad = \dfrac{-6y^3 - 8x^2}{9y^5}$

Example 23

Find the gradient of the tangent to $x^2 + y^3 = 5$ at the point where $x = 2$.

First we find $\dfrac{dy}{dx}$: $\qquad 2x + 3y^2\dfrac{dy}{dx} = 0$ {implicit differentiation}

$\qquad\qquad \therefore \ 3y^2\dfrac{dy}{dx} = -2x \ $ and so $\ \dfrac{dy}{dx} = \dfrac{-2x}{3y^2}$

$\qquad$ When $\ x = 2, \ \ 4 + y^3 = 5 \ $ and $\ \therefore \ y = 1$

$\qquad$ Consequently $\ \dfrac{dy}{dx} = \dfrac{-2(2)}{3(1)^2} = -\tfrac{4}{3}$

So, the gradient of the tangent at $x = 2$ is $-\tfrac{4}{3}$.

EXERCISE 21H

1 If y is a function of x, find:

   a $\dfrac{d}{dx}(2y)$ **b** $\dfrac{d}{dx}(-3y)$ **c** $\dfrac{d}{dx}(y^3)$ **d** $\dfrac{d}{dx}(\dfrac{1}{y})$ **e** $\dfrac{d}{dx}(y^4)$

   f $\dfrac{d}{dx}(\sqrt{y})$ **g** $\dfrac{d}{dx}\left(\dfrac{1}{y^2}\right)$ **h** $\dfrac{d}{dx}(xy)$ **i** $\dfrac{d}{dx}(x^2y)$ **j** $\dfrac{d}{dx}(xy^2)$

2 Find $\dfrac{dy}{dx}$ if: **a** $x^2 + y^2 = 25$ **b** $x^2 + 3y^2 = 9$ **c** $y^2 - x^2 = 8$

                     d $x^2 - y^3 = 10$ **e** $x^2 + xy = 4$ **f** $x^3 - 2xy = 5$

3 Find the gradient of the tangent to:

   a $x + y^3 = 4y$ at $y = 1$ **b** $x + y = 8xy$ at $x = \tfrac{1}{2}$

4 Find $\dfrac{d^2y}{dx^2}$ for each implicit relation in question **2**.

5 Given that $3V^2 + 2q = 2Vq$, find   **a** $\dfrac{dV}{dq}$ **b** $\dfrac{d^2q}{dV^2}$.

REVIEW SET 21A

1 A particle P moves in a straight line with position relative to the origin O given by $s(t) = 2t^3 - 9t^2 + 12t - 5$ cm, where t is the time in seconds, $t \geqslant 0$.

  a Find expressions for the particle's velocity and acceleration and draw sign diagrams for each of them.

  b Find the initial conditions.

  c Describe the motion of the particle at time $t = 2$ seconds.

  d Find the times and positions where the particle changes direction.

  e Draw a diagram to illustrate the motion of P.

  f Determine the time intervals when the particle's speed is increasing.

2 The cost per hour of running a freight train is given by $C(v) = \dfrac{v^2}{30} + \dfrac{9000}{v}$ dollars where v is the average speed of the train in km h^{-1}.

  a Find the cost of running the train for:

   i two hours at 45 km h^{-1} **ii** 5 hours at 64 km h^{-1}.

  b Find the rate of change in the hourly cost of running the train at speeds of:

   i 50 km h^{-1} **ii** 66 km h^{-1}.

  c At what speed will the cost be a minimum?

3 For the function $f(x) = 2x^3 - 3x^2 - 36x + 7$:

  a find and classify all stationary points and points of inflection

  b find intervals where the function is increasing and decreasing

  c find intervals where the function is concave up or down

  d sketch the graph of $y = f(x)$ showing all important features.

4 Rectangle ABCD is inscribed within the parabola $y = k - x^2$ and the x-axis, as shown.

  a If $OD = x$, show that the rectangle ABCD has area function $A(x) = 2kx - 2x^3$.

  b If the area of ABCD is a maximum when $AD = 2\sqrt{3}$, find k.

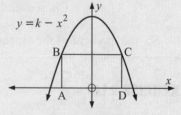

5 A manufacturer of open steel boxes has to make one with a square base and a capacity of 1 m^3. The steel costs \$2 per square metre.

  a If the base measures x m by x m and the height is y m, find y in terms of x.

  b Hence, show that the total cost of the steel is $C(x) = 2x^2 + \dfrac{8}{x}$ dollars.

  c Find the dimensions of the box which would cost the least in steel to make.

6 **a** Find $\dfrac{dy}{dx}$ given that $x^2 y + 2xy^3 = -18$.

  b Find the equation of the tangent to $x^2 y + 2xy^3 = -18$ at the point $(1, -2)$.

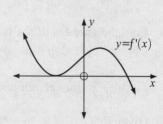

7 Given the graph of $y = f'(x)$ drawn alongside, sketch a possible curve for $y = f(x)$. Show clearly any turning points and points of inflection.

REVIEW SET 21B

1 A triangular pen is enclosed by two fences AB and BC each of length 50 m, with the river being the third side.

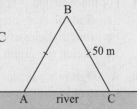

  a If $AC = 2x$ m, show that the area of triangle ABC is $A(x) = x\sqrt{2500 - x^2}$ m^2.

  b Find $\dfrac{d[A(x)]^2}{dx}$ and hence find x such that the area is a maximum.

2 A particle P moves in a straight line with position from O given by

$$s(t) = 15t - \frac{60}{(t-1)^2} \text{ cm}, \quad \text{where } t \text{ is the time in seconds, } t \geqslant 0.$$

  a Find velocity and acceleration functions for P's motion.

  b Describe the motion of P at $t = 3$ seconds.

  c For what values of t is the particle's speed increasing?

3 A rectangular gutter is formed by bending a 24 cm wide sheet of metal as shown in the illustration.

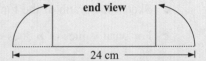

Where must the bends be made in order to maximise the capacity of the gutter?

4 Consider the curve with equation $x^2 - 2xy^2 + y^3 = k$ where k is a constant.

  a If $(2, -1)$ lies on the curve, find k.

  b Find $\dfrac{dy}{dx}$.   **c** Find the equation of the normal to $x^2 - 2xy^2 + y^3 = k$ at $(2, -1)$.

5 A particle moves along the x-axis with position relative to origin O given by $x(t) = 3t - \sqrt{t}$ cm, where t is the time in seconds, $t \geqslant 0$.

  a Find expressions for the particle's velocity and acceleration at any time t, and draw sign diagrams for each function.

  b Find the initial conditions and hence describe the motion at that instant.

  c Describe the motion of the particle at $t = 9$ seconds.

  d Find the time and position when the particle reverses direction.

  e Determine the time interval when the particle's speed is decreasing.

6 For the function $f(x) = \dfrac{x^2 - 1}{x^2 + 1}$:

  a find the axes intercepts   **b** explain why $f(x)$ has no vertical asymptotes

  c find the position and nature of any stationary points

  d show that $y = f(x)$ has non-stationary inflections at $x = \pm\sqrt{\frac{1}{3}}$

  e sketch the graph of $y = f(x)$ showing all features found in **a**, **b**, **c** and **d** above.

7 The graph of $y = f(x)$ is given.

On the same axes sketch the graph of $y = |f'(x)|$.

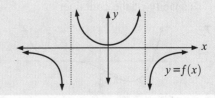

REVIEW SET 21C

1 For the function $f(x) = x^3 - 4x^2 + 4x$:
  a find all axes intercepts
  b find and classify all stationary points and points of inflection
  c sketch the graph of $y = f(x)$ showing features from **a** and **b**.

2 A 200 m fence is placed around a lawn which has the shape of
a rectangle with a semi-circle on one of its sides.

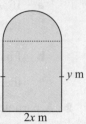

  a Using the dimensions shown on the figure,
     show that $y = 100 - x - \frac{\pi}{2}x$.
  b Hence, find the area of the lawn A in terms of x only.
  c Find the dimensions of the lawn if it has the maximum possible area.

y m

$2x$ m

3 Consider $f(x) = \dfrac{x^2 + 2x}{x - 2}$.

  a Determine the equations of any asymptotes.
  b Find the position and nature of its turning points.   **c** Find its axes intercepts.
  d Sketch the graph of the function showing the important features of **a**, **b** and **c**.

  e For what values of p does $\dfrac{x^2 + 2x}{x - 2} = p$ have two real distinct roots?

4 A machinist has a spherical ball of brass with
diameter 10 cm. The ball is placed in a lathe and
machined into a cylinder.

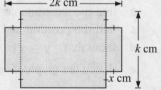

h cm

x cm

  a If the cylinder has radius x cm, show that
     the cylinder's volume is given by
     $$V(x) = \pi x^2 \sqrt{100 - 4x^2} \text{ cm}^3.$$
  b Hence, find the dimensions of the cylinder of largest volume which can be made.

5 Two roads AB and BC meet at right angles. A straight
pipeline LM is to be laid between the two roads with
the requirement that it must pass through point X.

  a If PM $= x$ km, find LQ in terms of x.
  b Hence show that the length of the pipeline is
     given by $L(x) = \sqrt{x^2 + 1}\left(1 + \dfrac{8}{x}\right)$ km.

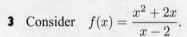

  c Find $\dfrac{d[L(x)]^2}{dx}$ and hence find the shortest possible length for the pipeline.

6 A rectangular sheet of tin-plate is $2k$ cm by
k cm and four squares each with sides x cm
are cut from its corners. The remainder is bent
into the shape of an open rectangular container.
Find the value of x which will maximise the
capacity of the container.

$2k$ cm

k cm

x cm

7

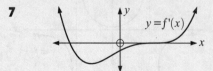

$y = f'(x)$

The graph of $y = f'(x)$ is drawn.

On the same axes clearly draw a possible
graph of $y = f(x)$. Show all turning points
and points of inflection.

Chapter 22

Derivatives of exponential and logarithmic functions

Contents:

The simplest **exponential functions** are of the form $f(x) = a^x$ where a is any positive constant, $a \neq 1$.

The graphs of all members of the exponential family $f(x) = a^x$ have the following properties:

- pass through the point $(0, 1)$
- asymptotic to the x-axis at one end
- lie above the x-axis for all x
- concave up for all x
- monotone increasing for $a > 1$
- monotone decreasing for $0 < a < 1$.

For example,

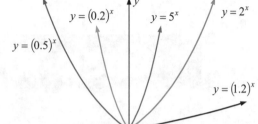

EXPONENTIAL e

A

INVESTIGATION 1   **THE DERIVATIVE OF** $y = a^x$

This investigation could be done by using a **graphics calculator** or by clicking on the icon.

The purpose of this investigation is to observe the nature of the derivative of $f(x) = a^x$ for $a = 2, 3, 4, 5, \frac{1}{2}$ and $\frac{1}{4}$.

What to do:

1 For $y = 2^x$ find the gradient of the tangent at $x = 0, 0.5, 1,$ 1.5, 2 and 2.5.   Use modelling techniques from your graphics calculator or the software provided to show that $\dfrac{dy}{dx} \approx 0.693 \times 2^x$.

CALCULUS DEMO

2 Repeat **1** for $y = 3^x$.

3 Repeat **1** for $y = 5^x$.

4 Repeat **1** for $y = (0.5)^x$.

5 Use **1**, **2**, **3** and **4** to help write a statement about the derivative of the general exponential $y = a^x$ for $a > 0$, $a \neq 1$.

From the previous investigation you should have discovered that:

- if $f(x) = a^x$ then $f'(x) = ka^x$ where k is a constant
- k is the derivative of $y = a^x$ at $x = 0$,   i.e., $k = f'(0)$.

This result is easily proved algebraically.

If $f(x) = a^x$, then $f'(x) = \lim\limits_{h \to 0} \dfrac{f(x+h) - f(x)}{h}$ {first principles definition of derivative}

$$= \lim_{h \to 0} \frac{a^{x+h} - a^x}{h}$$

$$= \lim_{h \to 0} \frac{a^x(a^h - 1)}{h}$$

$$= a^x \times \left(\lim_{h \to 0} \frac{a^h - 1}{h} \right) \quad \text{\{as } a^x \text{ is independent of } h\text{\}}$$

But $f'(0) = \lim\limits_{h \to 0} \dfrac{f(0+h) - f(0)}{h}$

$$= \lim_{h \to 0} \frac{a^h - 1}{h}$$

$\therefore \quad f'(x) = a^x f'(0)$

$y = a^x$

gradient is $f'(0)$

So, if we can find a value of a such that $f'(0) = 1$, then we have found *a function which is its own derivative.*

INVESTIGATION 2   **FINDING a WHEN $y = a^x$ AND $\dfrac{dy}{dx} = a^x$**

Click on the icon to graph $f(x) = a^x$ and its derivative function $y = f'(x)$.   **DEMO**

Experiment with different values of a until the graphs of $f(x) = a^x$ and $y = f'(x)$ appear the same.

Estimate the corresponding value of a to 2 decimal places.

From **Investigation 2** you should have discovered that if $a \approx 2.72$ and $f(x) = a^x$ then $f'(x) = a^x$ also.

To find this value of a more accurately we return to the algebraic approach:

We showed that if $f(x) = a^x$ then $f'(x) = a^x \left(\lim\limits_{h \to 0} \dfrac{a^h - 1}{h} \right)$.

So if $f'(x) = a^x$ we require $\lim\limits_{h \to 0} \dfrac{a^h - 1}{h} = 1$.

$\therefore \quad \dfrac{a^h - 1}{h} \approx 1$ for values of h which are close to 0

$\therefore \quad a^h \approx 1 + h$ for h close to 0.

Letting $h = \dfrac{1}{n}$, $a^{\frac{1}{n}} \approx 1 + \dfrac{1}{n}$ for large values of n $\{h = \dfrac{1}{n} \to 0 \text{ as } n \to \infty\}$

$$\therefore \quad a \approx \left(1 + \frac{1}{n}\right)^n \quad \text{for large values of } n.$$

We now examine $\left(1 + \dfrac{1}{n}\right)^n$ as $n \to \infty$.

n	$\left(1 + \dfrac{1}{n}\right)^n$	n	$\left(1 + \dfrac{1}{n}\right)^n$
10	$2.593\,742\,460$	10^7	$2.718\,281\,693$
10^2	$2.704\,813\,829$	10^8	$2.718\,281\,815$
10^3	$2.716\,923\,932$	10^9	$2.718\,281\,827$
10^4	$2.718\,145\,927$	10^{10}	$2.718\,281\,828$
10^5	$2.718\,268\,237$	10^{11}	$2.718\,281\,828$
10^6	$2.718\,280\,469$	10^{12}	$2.718\,281\,828$

In fact as $n \to \infty$, $\left(1 + \dfrac{1}{n}\right)^n \to 2.718\,281\,828\,459\,045\,235\,....$

and this irrational number is denoted by the symbol e.

$$e = 2.718\,281\,828\,459\,045\,235\,.... \quad \text{and is called } \textbf{exponential } e.$$

$$\text{If} \quad f(x) = e^x \quad \text{then} \quad f'(x) = e^x.$$

Alternative notation: e^x is sometimes written as $\exp(x)$.

For example, $\exp(1 - x) = e^{1-x}$.

e is an important number with similarities to the number π. Both numbers are irrational (not surds) with non-recurring, non-terminating decimal expansions, and both are discovered naturally.

We also saw e in an earlier chapter when looking at continuous compound interest.

PROPERTIES OF $y = e^x$

Notice that $\dfrac{dy}{dx} = e^x = y.$

As $x \to \infty$, $y \to \infty$ very rapidly,

and so $\dfrac{dy}{dx} \to \infty.$

This means that the gradient of the curve is very large for large values of x. The curve increases in steepness as x gets larger.

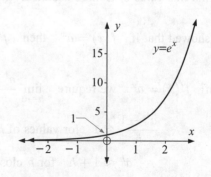

As $x \to -\infty$, $y \to 0$ and so $\dfrac{dy}{dx} \to 0$.

This means for large negative x, the graph becomes flatter and approaches the asymptote $y = 0$.

$e^x > 0$ for all x, so the range of $f : x \mapsto e^x$ is $\mathbb{R}^+$ or $]0, \infty[$.

THE DERIVATIVE OF $e^{f(x)}$

The functions e^{-x}, e^{2x+3} and e^{-x^2} are all of the form $e^{f(x)}$. Such functions are often used in problem solving.

In general, $e^{f(x)} > 0$ for all x, no matter what the function $f(x)$.

Consider $y = e^{f(x)}$.

Now $y = e^u$ where $u = f(x)$.

But $\dfrac{dy}{dx} = \dfrac{dy}{du}\dfrac{du}{dx}$ {chain rule}

$\therefore \dfrac{dy}{dx} = e^u \dfrac{du}{dx} = e^{f(x)} \times f'(x)$

Summary:

Function	Derivative
e^x	e^x
$e^{f(x)}$	$e^{f(x)} \times f'(x)$

Example 1

Find the gradient function for y equal to:

a $\quad 2e^x + e^{-3x}$ b $\quad x^2 e^{-x}$ c $\quad \dfrac{e^{2x}}{x}$

a If $y = 2e^x + e^{-3x}$ then $\dfrac{dy}{dx} = 2e^x + e^{-3x}(-3)$

$= 2e^x - 3e^{-3x}$

b If $y = x^2 e^{-x}$ then $\dfrac{dy}{dx} = 2xe^{-x} + x^2 e^{-x}(-1)$ {product rule}

$= 2xe^{-x} - x^2 e^{-x}$

c If $y = \dfrac{e^{2x}}{x}$ then $\dfrac{dy}{dx} = \dfrac{e^{2x}(2)x - e^{2x}(1)}{x^2}$ {quotient rule}

$= \dfrac{e^{2x}(2x - 1)}{x^2}$

Example 2

Find the gradient function for y equal to: **a** $(e^x - 1)^3$ **b** $\dfrac{1}{\sqrt{2e^{-x} + 1}}$

a $y = (e^x - 1)^3$

$\quad = u^3$ where $u = e^x - 1$

$\dfrac{dy}{dx} = \dfrac{dy}{du}\dfrac{du}{dx}$

$\quad = 3u^2 \dfrac{du}{dx}$

$\quad = 3(e^x - 1)^2 \times e^x$

$\quad = 3e^x(e^x - 1)^2$

b $y = (2e^{-x} + 1)^{-\frac{1}{2}}$

$\quad = u^{-\frac{1}{2}}$ where $u = 2e^{-x} + 1$

$\dfrac{dy}{dx} = \dfrac{dy}{du}\dfrac{du}{dx}$

$\quad = -\tfrac{1}{2}u^{-\frac{3}{2}}\dfrac{du}{dx}$

$\quad = -\tfrac{1}{2}(2e^{-x} + 1)^{-\frac{3}{2}} \times 2e^{-x}(-1)$

$\quad = e^{-x}(2e^{-x} + 1)^{-\frac{3}{2}}$

Example 3

Find the position and nature of any turning points of $y = (x - 2)e^{-x}$.

$\dfrac{dy}{dx} = (1)e^{-x} + (x - 2)e^{-x}(-1)$ {product rule}

$\quad = e^{-x}(1 - (x - 2))$

$\quad = \dfrac{3 - x}{e^x}$ where e^x is positive for all x.

So, $\dfrac{dy}{dx} = 0$ when $x = 3$.

The sign diagram of $\dfrac{dy}{dx}$ is:

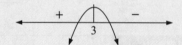

$\therefore$ at $x = 3$ we have a maximum turning point.

But when $x = 3$, $y = (1)e^{-3} = \dfrac{1}{e^3}$

$\therefore$ the maximum turning point is $(3, \dfrac{1}{e^3})$.

EXERCISE 22A

1 Find the gradient function for $f(x)$ equal to:

a	e^{4x}	**b**	$e^x + 3$	**c**	$\exp(-2x)$	**d**	$e^{\frac{x}{2}}$
e	$2e^{-\frac{x}{2}}$	**f**	$1 - 2e^{-x}$	**g**	$4e^{\frac{x}{2}} - 3e^{-x}$	**h**	$\dfrac{e^x + e^{-x}}{2}$
i	e^{-x^2}	**j**	$e^{\frac{1}{x}}$	**k**	$10(1 + e^{2x})$	**l**	$20(1 - e^{-2x})$
m	e^{2x+1}	**n**	$e^{\frac{x}{4}}$	**o**	$e^{1 - 2x^2}$	**p**	$e^{-0.02x}$

2 Find the derivative of:

     a xe^x **b** $x^3 e^{-x}$ **c** $\dfrac{e^x}{x}$ **d** $\dfrac{x}{e^x}$

     e $x^2 e^{3x}$ **f** $\dfrac{e^x}{\sqrt{x}}$ **g** $\sqrt{x}\,e^{-x}$ **h** $\dfrac{e^x + 2}{e^{-x} + 1}$

3 Find the gradient function for $f(x)$ equal to:

     a $(e^x + 2)^4$ **b** $\dfrac{1}{1 - e^{-x}}$ **c** $\sqrt{e^{2x} + 10}$

     d $\dfrac{1}{(1 - e^{3x})^2}$ **e** $\dfrac{1}{\sqrt{1 - e^{-x}}}$ **f** $x\sqrt{1 - 2e^{-x}}$

4 If $y = Ae^{kx}$, where A and k are constants:

     a show that   **i** $\dfrac{dy}{dx} = ky$ **ii** $\dfrac{d^2 y}{dx^2} = k^2 y$

     b predict the connection between $\dfrac{d^n y}{dx^n}$ and y and prove your conjecture using the principle of mathematical induction.

5 If $y = 2e^{3x} + 5e^{4x}$, show that $\dfrac{d^2 y}{dx^2} - 7\dfrac{dy}{dx} + 12y = 0$.

6 Find $\dfrac{dy}{dx}$ if $x^3 e^{3y} + 4x^2 y^3 = 27e^{-2x}$.

7 Find the position and nature of the turning point(s) of:

     a $y = xe^{-x}$ **b** $y = x^2 e^x$ **c** $y = \dfrac{e^x}{x}$ **d** $y = e^{-x}(x + 2)$

B   NATURAL LOGARITHMS

In **Chapter 4** we found that:

- if $e^x = a$ then $x = \ln a$ and vice versa i.e., $e^x = a \Leftrightarrow x = \ln a$.

- The graph of $y = \ln x$ is the reflection of the graph of $y = e^x$ in the mirror line $y = x$.

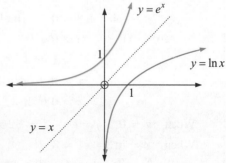

- $y = e^x$ and $y = \ln x$ are inverse functions.

- From the definition $e^x = a \iff x = \ln a$ we observe that $e^{\ln a} = a$.

  This means that any positive real number a can be written as a power of e, or alternatively,

  the **natural logarithm** of any positive number is its power of e, i.e., $\ln e^n = n$.

Recall that the **laws of logarithms** in base e are identical to those for base 10 and indeed for any base.

These are: For $a > 0$, $b > 0$ • $\ln(ab) = \ln a + \ln b$

                                      • $\ln\left(\dfrac{a}{b}\right) = \ln a - \ln b$

                                      • $\ln(a^n) = n \ln a$ **Note:** $\ln e^n = n$

           Notice also that: • $\ln 1 = 0$ and $\ln e = 1$

                                      • $\ln\left(\dfrac{1}{a}\right) = -\ln a$

                                      • $\log_b a = \dfrac{\ln a}{\ln b}$, $b \neq 1$

Notice that: $a^x = (e^{\ln a})^x = e^{(\ln a)x}$

$$\therefore \quad \frac{d(a^x)}{dx} = e^{(\ln a)x} \times \ln a = a^x \ln a$$

So,   if $y = a^x$ then $\dfrac{dy}{dx} = a^x \ln a$.

Example 4

Find algebraically, the exact points of intersection of $y = e^x - 3$ and $y = 1 - 3e^{-x}$. Check your solution using technology.

The functions meet where

$$e^x - 3 = 1 - 3e^{-x}$$
$$\therefore \quad e^x - 4 + 3e^{-x} = 0$$
$$\therefore \quad e^{2x} - 4e^x + 3 = 0 \quad \text{\{multiplying each term by } e^x\text{\}}$$
$$\therefore \quad (e^x - 1)(e^x - 3) = 0$$
$$\therefore \quad e^x = 1 \text{ or } 3$$
$$\therefore \quad x = \ln 1 \text{ or } \ln 3$$
$$\therefore \quad x = 0 \text{ or } \ln 3$$

When $x = 0$, $y = e^0 - 3 = -2$

When $x = \ln 3$, $e^x = 3$ $\therefore$ $y = 3 - 3 = 0$

$\therefore$ the functions meet at $(0, -2)$ and at $(\ln 3, 0)$.

GRAPHING PACKAGE

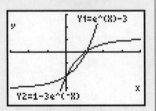

Example 5

Consider the function $y = 2 - e^{-x}$.

a Find the x-intercept.   **b** Find the y-intercept.

c Show algebraically that the function is increasing for all x.

d Show algebraically that the function is concave down for all x.

e Use technology to help graph $y = 2 - e^{-x}$.

f Explain why $y = 2$ is a horizontal asymptote.

---

a The x-intercept occurs when $y = 0$, $\therefore$ $e^{-x} = 2$

$$\therefore \quad -x = \ln 2$$
$$\therefore \quad x = -\ln 2$$

$\therefore$ the x-intercept is $-\ln 2 \approx -0.69$

b The y-intercept occurs when $x = 0$

$\therefore$ $y = 2 - e^0 = 2 - 1 = 1$

c $\dfrac{dy}{dx} = 0 - e^{-x}(-1) = e^{-x} = \dfrac{1}{e^x}$

Now $e^x > 0$ for all x, so $\dfrac{dy}{dx} > 0$ for all x

$\therefore$ the function is increasing for all x.

d $\dfrac{d^2y}{dx^2} = e^{-x}(-1) = \dfrac{-1}{e^x}$ which is < 0 for all x

$\therefore$ the function is concave down for all x.

e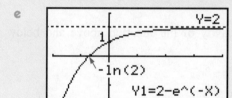

f As $x \to \infty$, $e^x \to \infty$
and $e^{-x} \to 0$
$\therefore$ $y \to 2$ (below)
Hence, HA is $y = 2$.

EXERCISE 22B

1 Write as a natural logarithmic equation:

a $N = 50e^{2t}$ **b** $P = 8.69e^{-0.0541t}$ **c** $S = a^2 e^{-kt}$

2 Without using a calculator, evaluate:

a $\ln e^2$ **b** $\ln \sqrt{e}$ **c** $\ln\left(\dfrac{1}{e}\right)$ **d** $\ln\left(\dfrac{1}{\sqrt{e}}\right)$

e $e^{\ln 3}$ **f** $e^{2\ln 3}$ **g** $e^{-\ln 5}$ **h** $e^{-2\ln 2}$

3 Write as a power of e: **a** 2 **b** 10 **c** a **d** a^x

4 Solve for x:

   a $e^x = 2$

   d $e^{2x} = 2e^x$

   g $e^x + 2 = 3e^{-x}$

   b $e^x = -2$

   e $e^x = e^{-x}$

   h $1 + 12e^{-x} = e^x$

   c $e^x = 0$

   f $e^{2x} - 5e^x + 6 = 0$

   i $e^x + e^{-x} = 3$

5 Find $\dfrac{dy}{dx}$ for

   a $y = 2^x$

   d $y = x^3 6^{-x}$

   b $y = 5^x$

   e $y = \dfrac{2^x}{x}$

   c $y = x2^x$

   f $y = \dfrac{x}{3^x}$

6 Find algebraically, the point(s) of intersection of:

   a $y = e^x$ and $y = e^{2x} - 6$

   c $y = 3 - e^x$ and $y = 5e^{-x} - 3$

   b $y = 2e^x + 1$ and $y = 7 - e^x$

   Check your answers using technology.

7 $f(x) = e^x - 3$ and $g(x) = 3 - 5e^{-x}$.

   a Find the x and y-intercepts of both functions.

   b Discuss $f(x)$ and $g(x)$ as $x \to \infty$ and as $x \to -\infty$.

   c Find algebraically the point(s) of intersection of the functions.

   d Sketch the graph of both functions on the same set of axes. Show all important features on your graph.

8 The function $y = e^x - 3e^{-x}$ cuts the x-axis at P and the y-axis at Q.

   a Determine the coordinates of P and Q.

   b Prove that the function is increasing for all x.

   c Show that $\dfrac{d^2y}{dx^2} = y$.

   What can be deduced about the concavity of the function above and below the x-axis?

   d Use technology to help graph $y = e^x - 3e^{-x}$.

   Show the features of **a**, **b** and **c** on the graph.

9 For the function $y = 4^x - 2^x$:

   a find the axes intercepts

   b discuss the graph as $x \to \infty$ and as $x \to -\infty$

   c find the position and nature of any turning points

   d discuss the concavity of the function

   e draw a graph showing the features found above.

C | DERIVATIVES OF LOGARITHMIC FUNCTIONS

INVESTIGATION 3 — THE DERIVATIVE OF $\ln x$

If $y = \ln x$, what is the gradient function?

CALCULUS DEMO

What to do:

1 Click on the icon to see the graph of $y = \ln x$.

A tangent is drawn to a point on the graph and the gradient of this tangent is given.

As the point moves from left to right, a graph of the gradient of the tangent is displayed.

2 What do you conjecture that the equation of the gradient is?

3 Find the gradient at $x = 0.25$, $x = 0.5$, $x = 1$, $x = 2$, $x = 3$, $x = 4$, $x = 5$.

Do your results confirm your conjecture from **2**?

From the investigation you should have observed that   if $y = \ln x$ then $\dfrac{dy}{dx} = \dfrac{1}{x}$.

Proof: If $y = \ln x$ then $x = e^y$

Using implicit differentiation with respect to x,

$$1 = e^y \frac{dy}{dx} \qquad \{\text{chain rule}\}$$

$$\therefore \quad 1 = x \frac{dy}{dx} \qquad \{\text{as} \quad e^y = x\}$$

$$\therefore \quad \frac{1}{x} = \frac{dy}{dx}$$

By use of the chain rule, we can also show that   if $y = \ln f(x)$ then $\dfrac{dy}{dx} = \dfrac{f'(x)}{f(x)}$.

Proof: If $y = \ln f(x)$ then $y = \ln u$ where $u = f(x)$.

Now $\dfrac{dy}{dx} = \dfrac{dy}{du}\dfrac{du}{dx}$

$= \dfrac{1}{u} f'(x)$

$= \dfrac{f'(x)}{f(x)}$

Summary:

Function	Derivative
$\ln x$	$\dfrac{1}{x}$
$\ln f(x)$	$\dfrac{f'(x)}{f(x)}$

Example 6

Find the gradient function of: **a** $y = \ln(kx)$ where k is a constant
                                    b $y = \ln(1 - 3x)$ **c** $y = x^3 \ln x$

a If $y = \ln(kx)$ then $\dfrac{dy}{dx} = \dfrac{k}{kx} = \dfrac{1}{x}$

Note: $\ln(kx) = \ln k + \ln x = \ln x + \text{constant}$

b If $y = \ln(1 - 3x)$ then $\dfrac{dy}{dx} = \dfrac{-3}{1 - 3x} = \dfrac{3}{3x - 1}$

c If $y = x^3 \ln x$ then $\dfrac{dy}{dx} = 3x^2 \ln x + x^3 \left(\dfrac{1}{x}\right)$ {product rule}

$$= 3x^2 \ln x + x^2$$

$$= x^2(3 \ln x + 1)$$

The laws of logarithms can help us to differentiate some logarithmic functions more easily.

Example 7

Differentiate with respect to x:
a $y = \ln(xe^{-x})$ **b** $y = \ln\left[\dfrac{x^2}{(x + 2)(x - 3)}\right]$

a If $y = \ln(xe^{-x})$ then $y = \ln x + \ln e^{-x}$ {log of a product law}
                                    $\therefore\ \ y = \ln x - x$ {$\ln e^a = a$}

Differentiating with respect to x, we get $\dfrac{dy}{dx} = \dfrac{1}{x} - 1$

b If $y = \ln\left[\dfrac{x^2}{(x + 2)(x - 3)}\right]$ then $y = \ln x^2 - \ln[(x + 2)(x - 3)]$

$$= 2 \ln x - [\ln(x + 2) + \ln(x - 3)]$$

$$= 2 \ln x - \ln(x + 2) - \ln(x - 3)$$

$$\therefore\ \ \dfrac{dy}{dx} = \dfrac{2}{x} - \dfrac{1}{x + 2} - \dfrac{1}{x - 3}$$

EXERCISE 22C

1 Find the gradient function of:

   a $y = \ln(7x)$ **b** $y = \ln(2x + 1)$ **c** $y = \ln(x - x^2)$

   d $y = 3 - 2 \ln x$ **e** $y = x^2 \ln x$ **f** $y = \dfrac{\ln x}{2x}$

   g $y = e^x \ln x$ **h** $y = (\ln x)^2$ **i** $y = \sqrt{\ln x}$

   j $y = e^{-x} \ln x$ **k** $y = \sqrt{x} \ln(2x)$ **l** $y = \dfrac{2\sqrt{x}}{\ln x}$

2 Find $\dfrac{dy}{dx}$ for:

    a $y = x \ln 5$
    b $y = \ln(x^3)$
    c $y = \ln(x^4 + x)$

    d $y = \ln(10 - 5x)$
    e $y = [\ln(2x + 1)]^3$
    f $y = \dfrac{\ln(4x)}{x}$

    g $y = \ln\left(\dfrac{1}{x}\right)$
    h $y = \ln(\ln x)$
    i $y = \dfrac{1}{\ln x}$

3 Differentiate with respect to x:

    a $y = \ln\sqrt{1 - 2x}$
    b $y = \ln\left(\dfrac{1}{2x + 3}\right)$
    c $y = \ln\left(e^x \sqrt{x}\right)$

    d $y = \ln\left(x\sqrt{2 - x}\right)$
    e $y = \ln\left(\dfrac{x + 3}{x - 1}\right)$
    f $y = \ln\left(\dfrac{x^2}{3 - x}\right)$

    g $f(x) = \ln\left((3x - 4)^3\right)$
    h $f(x) = \ln\left(x(x^2 + 1)\right)$
    i $f(x) = \ln\left(\dfrac{x^2 + 2x}{x - 5}\right)$

4   **a**   Find $\dfrac{dy}{dx}$ for: **i** $y = \log_2 x$ **ii** $y = \log_{10} x$ **iii** $y = x\log_3 x$

    b   By substituting $e^{\ln 2}$ for 2 in $y = 2^x$ find $\dfrac{dy}{dx}$.

    c   Show that if $y = a^x$, then $\dfrac{dy}{dx} = a^x \times \ln a$.

5 Consider $f(x) = \ln(2x - 1) - 3$.

    a   Find the x-intercept.

    b   Can $f(0)$ be found? What is the significance of this result?

    c   Find the gradient of the tangent to the curve at $x = 1$.

    d   For what values of x does $f(x)$ have meaning?

    e   Find $f''(x)$ and hence explain why $f(x)$ is concave down whenever $f(x)$ has meaning.

    f   Graph the function.

6 Prove that $\dfrac{\ln x}{x} \leqslant \dfrac{1}{e}$ for all $x > 0$. **Hint:** Let $f(x) = \dfrac{\ln x}{x}$ and find its greatest value.

7 Consider the function $f(x) = x - \ln x$.

Show that the graph of $y = f(x)$ has a local minimum and that this is the only turning point. Hence prove that $\ln x \leqslant x - 1$ for all $x > 0$.

8 Find $\dfrac{da}{db}$ if $e^{2a}\ln b^2 - a^3b + \ln(ab) = 21$.

D   APPLICATIONS

The applications we consider here are:

- tangents and normals
- rates of change
- curve properties
- displacement, velocity and acceleration
- optimisation (maxima and minima)

EXERCISE 22D

1 Find the equation of the tangent to $y = e^{-x}$ at the point where $x = 1$.

2 Find the equation of the tangent to $y = \ln(2 - x)$ at the point where $x = -1$.

3 The tangent to $y = x^2 e^x$ at $x = 1$ cuts the x and y-axes at A and B respectively. Find the coordinates of A and B.

4 Find the equation of the normal to $y = \ln \sqrt{x}$ at the point where $y = -1$.

5 Find the equation of the tangent to $y = e^x$ at the point where $x = a$.
   Hence, find the equation of the tangent to $y = e^x$ which passes through the origin.

6 Consider $f(x) = \ln x$.
   a For what values of x is $f(x)$ defined?
   b Find the signs of $f'(x)$ and $f''(x)$ and comment on the geometrical significance of each.
   c Sketch the graph of $f(x) = \ln x$ and find the equation of the normal at the point where $y = 1$.

7 Find, correct to 2 decimal places, the angle between the tangents to $y = 3e^{-x}$ and $y = 2 + e^x$ at their point of intersection.

8 A radioactive substance decays according to the formula $W = 20e^{-kt}$ grams where t is the time in hours.
   a Find k given that the weight is 10 grams after 50 hours.
   b Find the weight of radioactive substance present at:
      i $t = 0$ hours   ii $t = 24$ hours   iii $t = 1$ week.
   c How long will it take for the weight to reach 1 gram?
   d Find the rate of radioactive decay at: i $t = 100$ hours   ii $t = 1000$ hours.
   e Show that $\dfrac{dW}{dt}$ is proportional to the weight of substance remaining.

9 The temperature of a liquid after being placed in a refrigerator is given by $T = 5 + 95e^{-kt}$ °C   where k is a positive constant and t is the time in minutes.
   a Find k if the temperature of the liquid is 20°C after 15 minutes.
   b What was the temperature of the liquid when it was first placed in the refrigerator?
   c Show that $\dfrac{dT}{dt} = c(T - 5)$ for some constant c.
   d At what rate is the temperature changing at:
      i $t = 0$ mins   ii $t = 10$ mins   iii $t = 20$ mins?

10 The height of a certain species of shrub t years after it is planted is given by $H(t) = 20 \ln(3t + 2) + 30$ cm, $t \geqslant 0$.
    a How high was the shrub when it was planted?
    b How long will it take for the shrub to reach a height of 1 m?
    c At what rate is the shrub's height changing:
       i   3 years after being planted   ii   10 years after being planted?

11 In the conversion of sugar solution to alcohol, the chemical reaction obeys the law $A = s(1 - e^{-kt})$, $t \geqslant 0$ where t is the number of hours after the reaction commenced, s is the original sugar concentration (%), and A is the alcohol produced, in litres.

    a Find A when $t = 0$.

    b If $s = 10$ and $A = 5$ after 3 hours, find k.

    c If $s = 10$, find the speed of the reaction at time 5 hours.

    d Show that the speed of the reaction is proportional to $A - s$.

12 Consider the function $f(x) = \dfrac{e^x}{x}$.

    a Does the graph of $y = f(x)$ have any x or y-intercepts?

    b Discuss $f(x)$ as $x \to \infty$ and as $x \to -\infty$.

    c Find and classify any stationary points of $y = f(x)$.

    d Sketch the graph of $y = f(x)$ showing all important features.

    e Find the equation of the tangent to $f(x) = \dfrac{e^x}{x}$ at the point where $x = -1$.

13 A particle P moves in a straight line. Its displacement from the origin O is given by $s(t) = 100t + 200e^{-\frac{t}{5}}$ cm where t is the time in seconds, $t \geqslant 0$.

    a Find the velocity and acceleration functions.

    b Find the initial position, velocity and acceleration of P.

    c Discuss the velocity of P as $t \to \infty$.

    d Sketch the graph of the velocity function.

    e Find when the velocity of P is 80 cm per second.

14 A psychologist claims that the ability A to memorise simple facts during infancy years can be calculated using the formula $A(t) = t \ln t + 1$ where $0 < t \leqslant 5$, t being the age of the child in years.

    a At what age is the child's memorising ability a minimum?

    b Sketch the graph of $A(t)$.

15 One of the most common functions used in statistics is the *normal distribution function* $f(x) = \dfrac{1}{\sqrt{2\pi}} e^{-\frac{1}{2}x^2}$.

    a Find the stationary points of the function and find intervals where the function is increasing and decreasing.

    b Find all points of inflection.

    c Discuss $f(x)$ as $x \to \infty$ and as $x \to -\infty$.

    d Sketch the graph of $y = f(x)$ showing all important features.

16 A manufacturer of electric kettles performs a cost control study and discovers that to produce x kettles per day, the cost per kettle $C(x)$ is given by

$$C(x) = 4 \ln x + \left(\frac{30 - x}{10} \right)^2 \text{ hundred dollars}$$

with a minimum production capacity of 10 kettles per day.

How many kettles should be manufactured to keep the cost per kettle a minimum?

17 Infinitely many rectangles which sit on the x-axis can be inscribed under the curve $y = e^{-x^2}$.

Determine the coordinates of C such that rectangle ABCD has maximum area.

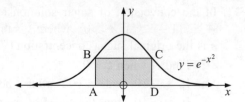

18 The revenue generated when a manufacturer sells x torches per day is given by

$$R(x) \approx 1000 \ln \left(1 + \frac{x}{400}\right) + 600 \text{ dollars.}$$

Each torch costs the manufacturer \$1.50 to produce plus fixed costs of \$300 per day. How many torches should be produced daily to maximise the profits made?

19 A quadratic of the form $y = ax^2$, $a > 0$, touches the logarithmic function $y = \ln x$.

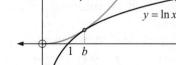

a If the x-coordinate of the point of contact is b, explain why $ab^2 = \ln b$ and $2ab = \dfrac{1}{b}$.

b Deduce that the point of contact is $(\sqrt{e}, \frac{1}{2})$.

c What is the value of a?

d What is the equation of the common tangent?

20 A small population of wasps is observed. After t weeks the population is modelled by

$$P(t) = \frac{50\,000}{1 + 1000e^{-0.5t}} \quad \text{wasps,} \quad \text{where} \quad 0 \leqslant t \leqslant 25.$$

Find when the wasp population is growing fastest.

21 $f(t) = ate^{bt^2}$ has a maximum value of 1 when $t = 2$. Find constants a and b.

22 For the function $f(x) = e^{ax}(x+1)$, $a \in \mathbb{R}$, show that:

a $f'(x) = e^{ax}(a[x+1]+1)$

b $f''(x) = ae^{ax}(a[x+1]+2)$

c if $f^{(k)}(x) = a^{k-1}e^{ax}(a[x+1]+k)$, $k \in \mathbb{Z}$, then
$f^{(k+1)}(x) = a^k e^{ax}(a[x+1]+[k+1])$.

23 Consider the function $f(x) = e^{-x}(x+2)$.

a Find **i** $f'(x)$ **ii** $f''(x)$ **iii** $f'''(x)$ **iv**

b Conjecture a formula for finding $f^{(n)}(x)$, $n \in \mathbb{Z}^+$.

c Use the principle of mathematical induction to prove your conjecture in **b**.

24 Consider the function $f(x) = xe^{ax}$.

a Find $f^{(n)}(x)$ for $n = 1, 2, 3$ and 4.

b Conjecture a formula for $f^{(n)}(x)$, $n \in \mathbb{Z}^+$.

c Use the principle of mathematical induction to prove your conjecture in **b**.

E ┃ SOME SPECIAL EXPONENTIAL FUNCTIONS

▶ **surge functions:** $y = Ate^{-bt}$, $t \geqslant 0$ where A and b are positive constants.

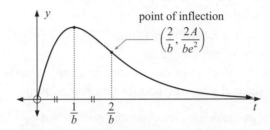

This model is used extensively when studying medicinal doses.
There is an initial rapid increase to a maximum and then a slower decay to zero.
The independent variable t is usually time, $t \geqslant 0$.

▶ **logistic functions:** $y = \dfrac{C}{1 + Ae^{-bt}}$, $t \geqslant 0$ where A, b and C are positive constants.

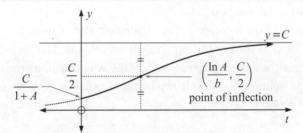

The logistical model is useful for studying the growth of populations that are limited by resources or predators.
The independent variable t is usually time, $t \geqslant 0$.

EXERCISE 22E

1   When a new pain killing injection is administered the effect is modelled by $E = 750te^{-1.5t}$ units, where $t \geqslant 0$ is the time in hours after the injection of the drug.

   a   Sketch the graph of E against t.
   b   What is the effect of the drug after
      i   30 minutes ii   2 hours?
   c   When is the drug most effective?
   d   During the operating period, the level of the drug must be at least 100 units.
      i   When can the operation commence?
      ii   How long has the surgeon to complete the operation if no further injection is possible?
   e   Find t at the point of inflection of the graph. What is the significance of this point?

2 **a** Prove that $f(t) = Ate^{-bt}$ has

     i a local maximum at $t = \dfrac{1}{b}$ **ii** a point of inflection at $t = \dfrac{2}{b}$.

  b Use question **1** to check the facts obtained in **a**.

3 The velocity of a body after t seconds, $t \geqslant 0$, is given by $v = 25te^{-2t}$ cm s^{-1}.

  a Sketch the velocity function.

  b Show that the body's acceleration at time t is $25(1 - 2t)e^{-2t}$ cm s^{-2}.

  c When is the velocity increasing?

  d Find the point of inflection of the velocity function. What is its significance?

  e Find the time interval when the acceleration is increasing.

4 The number of ants in a colony after t months is modelled by $A(t) = \dfrac{25\,000}{1 + 0.8e^{-t}}$.

  a Sketch the graph of $A(t)$.

  b What is the inital ant population?

  c What is the ant population after 3 months?

  d Is there a limit to the population size? If so, what is it?

  e At what time does the population reach 24 500?

5 The number of bees in a hive after t months is modelled by $B(t) = \dfrac{C}{1 + 0.5e^{-1.73t}}$.

  a What is the inital bee population?

  b Find the percentage increase in the population after 1 month.

  c Is there a limit to the population size? If so, what is it?

  d If after 2 months the bee population is 4500, what was the original population size?

  e Find $B'(t)$ and use it to explain why the population is increasing over time.

  f Sketch the graph of $B(t)$.

6 For the logistic function $f(t) = \dfrac{C}{1 + Ae^{-bt}}$, show that:

  a $f(t) = C$ is its horizontal asymptote

  b it has a point of inflection with y-coordinate $\dfrac{C}{2}$.

REVIEW SET 22A

1 Find $\dfrac{dy}{dx}$ if:

  a $y = e^{x^3 + 2}$ **b** $y = \dfrac{e^x}{x^2}$ **c** $\ln(2y + 1) = xe^y$

2 Find the equation of the normal to $y = e^{-x^2}$ at the point where $x = 1$.

3 Sketch the graphs of $y = e^x + 3$ and $y = 9 - 5e^{-x}$ on the same set of axes. Determine the exact coordinates of the points of intersection.

4 Consider the function $f(x) = \dfrac{e^x}{x - 1}$.

  a Find the x and y-intercepts.

  b For what values of x is $f(x)$ defined?

    c Find the signs of $f'(x)$ and $f''(x)$ and comment on the geometrical significance of each.

    d Sketch the graph of $y = f(x)$ and find the equation of the tangent at the point where $x = 2$.

5 The height of a tree t years after it was planted is given by

    $H(t) = 60 + 40 \ln(2t + 1)$ cm, $t \geqslant 0$.

    a How high was the tree when it was planted?

    b How long does it take for the tree to reach: **i** 150 cm   **ii** 300 cm?

    c At what rate is the tree's height increasing after: **i** 2 years   **ii** 20 years?

6 A particle P moves in a straight line with position given by $\;s(t) = 80e^{-\frac{t}{10}} - 40t$ m where t is the time in seconds, $t \geqslant 0$.

    a Find the velocity and acceleration functions.

    b Find the initial position, velocity, and acceleration of P.

    c Discuss the velocity of P as $t \to \infty$.

    d Sketch the graph of the velocity function.

    e Find when the velocity is -44 metres per second.

7 Infinitely many rectangles can be inscribed under the curve $y = e^{-2x}$ as shown. Determine the coordinates of A such that the rectangle OBAC has maximum area.

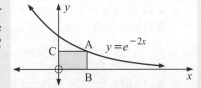

8 A shirt maker sells x shirts per day with revenue function

$$R(x) = 200 \ln \left(1 + \frac{x}{100}\right) + 1000 \text{ dollars.}$$

The manufacturing costs are determined by the cost function

$$C(x) = (x - 100)^2 + 200 \text{ dollars.}$$

How many shirts should be sold daily to maximise profits? What is the maximum daily profit?

9 Find where the tangent to $\;y = \ln(x^2 + 3)\;$ at $x = 0$ cuts the x-axis.

10 Find $\dfrac{dy}{dx}$ by first taking natural logarithms of both sides:

    a $y = x2^x$
        b $y = \dfrac{(x^2 + 2)(x - 3)}{1 - x^3}$

REVIEW SET 22B

1 Find $\dfrac{dy}{dx}$ if:

    a $y = \ln(x^3 - 3x)$ **b** $y = \ln\left(\dfrac{x + 3}{x^2}\right)$ **c** $e^{x+y} = \ln(y^2 + 1)$ **d** $y = x^{x^2}$

2 Find where the tangent to $\;y = \ln(x^4 + 3)\;$ at $x = 1$ cuts the y-axis.

3 Solve exactly for x: **a** $e^{2x} = 3e^x$ **b** $e^{2x} - 7e^x + 12 = 0$

4 Consider the function $f(x) = e^x - x$.

    a Find and classify any stationary points of $y = f(x)$.

    b Discuss $f(x)$ as $x \to -\infty$ and as $x \to \infty$.

    c Find $f''(x)$ and draw its sign diagram. Give geometrical interpretations for the signs of $f''(x)$.

    d Sketch the graph of $y = f(x)$.

    e Deduce that $e^x \geqslant x + 1$ for all x.

5 Differentiate with respect to x: **a** $f(x) = \ln(e^x + 3)$ **b** $f(x) = \ln\left[\dfrac{(x+2)^3}{x}\right]$

6 Find the exact roots of the following equations:

    a $3e^x - 5 = -2e^{-x}$ **b** $2\ln x - 3\ln\left(\dfrac{1}{x}\right) = 10$

7 A particle P moves in a straight line with position given by $s(t) = 25t - 10\ln t$ cm, $t \geqslant 1$, where t is the time in minutes.

    a Find the velocity and acceleration functions.

    b Find the position, velocity, and acceleration when $t = e$ minutes.

    c Discuss the velocity as $t \to \infty$.

    d Sketch the graph of the velocity function.

    e Find when the velocity of P is 12 cm per minute.

8 A manufacturer determines that the total weekly cost C of producing x clocks per day is given by $C(x) = 10\ln x + \left(20 - \dfrac{x}{10}\right)^2$ dollars.

    How many clocks per day should be produced to minimise the costs given that at least 50 clocks per day must be made to fill fixed daily orders?

9 The graph of $y = ae^{-x}$ for $a > 0$ is shown.

    P lies on the graph and the rectangle OAPB is drawn.

    As P moves along the curve, the rectangle constantly changes shape.

    Find the x-coordinate of P such that the rectangle OAPB has minimum perimeter.

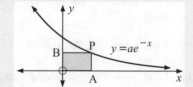

10 For the function $f(x) = x + \ln x$:

    a find the values of x for which $f(x)$ is defined

    b find the signs of $f'(x)$ and $f''(x)$ and comment on the geometrical significance of each

    c sketch the graph of $y = f(x)$ and find the equation of the normal at the point where $x = 1$.

Chapter 23

Derivatives of circular functions and related rates

Contents:

INTRODUCTION

In **Chapter 12** we saw that sine and cosine curves arise naturally from motion in a circle.

Click on the icon to observe the motion of point P around the unit circle. Observe the graphs of P's height relative to the x-axis, and then P's displacement from the y-axis. The resulting graphs are those of $y = \cos t$ and $y = \sin t$.

DEMO

Suppose P moves anticlockwise around the unit circle with constant linear speed of 1 unit per second.

After 2π seconds, P will travel 2π units which is one full revolution.

So, after t seconds P will travel through t radians, and at time t, P is at $(\cos t, \sin t)$.

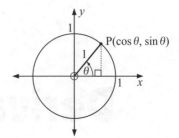

Note:
- The **angular velocity** of P is the time rate of change in $\angle AOP$.

  Angular velocity is only meaningful in motion along a circular or elliptical arc.

  For the example above, the angular velocity of P is $\dfrac{d\theta}{dt}$ and $\dfrac{d\theta}{dt} = 1$ radian per sec.

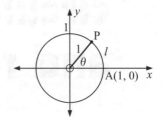

- If l is arc length AP, the **linear speed** of P is the time rate of change in l, which is $\dfrac{dl}{dt}$.

  For the example above, $l = \theta r = \theta \times 1 = \theta$

  and $\dfrac{dl}{dt} = \dfrac{d\theta}{dt} = 1$ radian per sec.

A | DERIVATIVES OF CIRCULAR FUNCTIONS

INVESTIGATION   DERIVATIVES OF $\sin t$ AND $\cos t$

Our aim is to use a computer demonstration to investigate the derivatives of $\sin t$ and $\cos t$.

What to do:

1 Click on the icon to observe the graph of $y = \sin t$. A tangent with t-step of length 1 unit moves across the curve, and its y-step is translated onto the slope graph. Suggest the derivative of the function $y = \sin t$.

DERIVATIVES DEMO

2 Repeat the process in **1** for the graph of $y = \cos t$. Hence suggest the derivative of the function $y = \sin t$.

From the investigation you may have deduced that

$$\frac{d}{dt}(\sin t) = \cos t \quad \text{and} \quad \frac{d}{dt}(\cos t) = -\sin t.$$

We will now show these derivatives using first principles. To do this we make use of the two results:

- If θ is in radians, then $\displaystyle\lim_{\theta \to 0} \frac{\sin \theta}{\theta} = 1$ {established in **Chapter 19**}

- $\sin S - \sin D = 2\cos\left(\frac{S+D}{2}\right)\sin\left(\frac{S-D}{2}\right)$ {established on page **314**}

THE DERIVATIVE OF $\sin x$

Consider $f(x) = \sin x$.

Now $\displaystyle f'(x) = \lim_{h \to 0} \frac{f(x+h) - f(x)}{h}$

$$= \lim_{h \to 0} \frac{\sin(x+h) - \sin x}{h}$$

$$= \lim_{h \to 0} \frac{2\cos\left(\frac{x+h+x}{2}\right)\sin\left(\frac{x+h-x}{2}\right)}{h} \qquad \text{\{identity above\}}$$

$$= \lim_{h \to 0} \frac{2\cos\left(x+\frac{h}{2}\right)\sin\left(\frac{h}{2}\right)}{h}$$

$$= \lim_{h \to 0} \frac{2\cos\left(x+\frac{h}{2}\right)}{2} \times \frac{\sin\left(\frac{h}{2}\right)}{\frac{h}{2}}$$

$$= \cos x \times 1 \qquad \text{\{as } h \to 0, \ \frac{h}{2} \to 0, \ \frac{\sin\left(\frac{h}{2}\right)}{\frac{h}{2}} \to 1\}$$

$$= \cos x$$

So, if $f(x) = \sin x$ then $f'(x) = \cos x$, provided that x is in radians.

Alternatively, $\displaystyle f'(x) = \lim_{h \to 0} \frac{\sin(x+h) - \sin x}{h}$

$$= \lim_{h \to 0} \frac{\sin x \cos h + \cos x \sin h - \sin x}{h}$$

$$= \lim_{h \to 0} \frac{\sin x(\cos h - 1) + \cos x \sin h}{h}$$

$$= \lim_{h \to 0} \frac{\sin x\left(-2\sin^2\left(\frac{h}{2}\right)\right)}{h} + \lim_{h \to 0} \cos x \left(\frac{\sin h}{h}\right)$$

$$= \lim_{h \to 0} -2\sin x \, \frac{\sin\left(\frac{h}{2}\right)}{\frac{h}{2}} \, \frac{\sin\left(\frac{h}{2}\right)}{2} + \cos x \times \lim_{h \to 0} \frac{\sin h}{h}$$

$$= -2\sin x \times 1 \times 0 + \cos x \times 1$$

$$= \cos x$$

THE DERIVATIVE OF $\cos x$

Consider $y = \cos x = \sin\left(\frac{\pi}{2} - x\right)$

$\therefore \quad y = \sin u \quad$ where $\quad u = \frac{\pi}{2} - x$

Now $\quad \dfrac{dy}{dx} = \dfrac{dy}{du}\dfrac{du}{dx} \qquad$ {chain rule}

$\qquad\qquad = \cos u \times (-1)$

$\qquad\qquad = -\cos(\frac{\pi}{2} - x)$

$\qquad\qquad = -\sin x$

So, if $f(x) = \cos x$ then $f'(x) = -\sin x$, provided that x is in radians.

THE DERIVATIVE OF $\tan x$

Consider $\quad y = \tan x = \dfrac{\sin x}{\cos x}$

$\therefore \quad \dfrac{dy}{dx} = \dfrac{\cos x \cos x - \sin x(-\sin x)}{[\cos x]^2} \qquad$ {quotient rule}

$\qquad\quad = \dfrac{\cos^2 x + \sin^2 x}{\cos^2 x}$

$\qquad\quad = \dfrac{1}{\cos^2 x} \quad$ which is $\quad \sec^2 x$

Summary:

For x in radians

Function	Derivative
$\sin x$	$\cos x$
$\cos x$	$-\sin x$
$\tan x$	$\sec^2 x$

THE DERIVATIVES OF $\sin[f(x)]$, $\cos[f(x)]$ AND $\tan[f(x)]$

Consider $y = \sin[f(x)]$

$\therefore \quad y = \sin u \quad$ where $\quad u = f(x)$

Now $\quad \dfrac{dy}{dx} = \dfrac{dy}{du}\dfrac{du}{dx} \qquad$ {chain rule}

$\qquad\qquad = \cos u \times f'(x)$

$\qquad\qquad = \cos[f(x)] \times f'(x)$

Summary:

For x in radians

Function	Derivative
$\sin[f(x)]$	$\cos[f(x)]\,f'(x)$
$\cos[f(x)]$	$-\sin[f(x)]\,f'(x)$
$\tan[f(x)]$	$\sec^2[f(x)]\,f'(x)$

Example 1

Differentiate with respect to x: **a** $x\sin x$ **b** $4\tan^2(3x)$

a If $y = x\sin x$

then by the product rule

$\dfrac{dy}{dx} = (1)\sin x + (x)\cos x$

$\qquad = \sin x + x\cos x$

b If $y = 4\tan^2(3x) = 4[\tan(3x)]^2$

then by the chain rule

$\dfrac{dy}{dx} = 8[\tan(3x)]^1 \times \dfrac{d}{dx}[\tan(3x)]$

$\qquad = 8\tan(3x)\,3\sec^2(3x)$

$\qquad = 24\tan(3x)\sec^2(3x)$

Example 2

Find the equation of the tangent to $y = \tan x$ at the point where $x = \frac{\pi}{4}$.

Let $f(x) = \tan x$ so $f(\frac{\pi}{4}) = \tan \frac{\pi}{4} = 1$

$f'(x) = \sec^2 x$ so $f'(\frac{\pi}{4}) = [\sec (\frac{\pi}{4})]^2 = (\sqrt{2})^2 = 2$

At $(\frac{\pi}{4}, 1)$, the tangent has slope 2

$\therefore$ the equation is $\dfrac{y-1}{x-\frac{\pi}{4}} = 2$ which is $y - 1 = 2x - \frac{\pi}{2}$

or $y = 2x + \left(1 - \frac{\pi}{2}\right)$

Example 3

Find the rate of change in the area of triangle ABC as θ changes, at the time when $\theta = 60^o$.

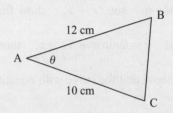

Area $A = \frac{1}{2} \times 10 \times 12 \times \sin \theta$ $\{$Area $= \frac{1}{2}ab\sin C\}$

$\therefore$ $A = 60 \sin \theta$

$\therefore$ $\dfrac{dA}{d\theta} = 60 \cos \theta$

When $\theta = \frac{\pi}{3}$, $\cos \theta = \frac{1}{2}$ **Note:** θ must be in radians.

$\therefore$ $\dfrac{dA}{d\theta} = 30$ cm^2 / radian

EXERCISE 23A

1 Find $\dfrac{dy}{dx}$ for:

   a $y = \sin(2x)$ **b** $y = \sin x + \cos x$ **c** $y = \cos(3x) - \sin x$

   d $y = \sin(x+1)$ **e** $y = \cos(3 - 2x)$ **f** $y = \tan(5x)$

   g $y = \sin\left(\frac{x}{2}\right) - 3 \cos x$ **h** $y = 3 \tan(\pi x)$ **i** $y = 4 \sin x - \cos(2x)$

2 Differentiate with respect to x:

   a $x^2 + \cos x$ **b** $\tan x - 3 \sin x$ **c** $e^x \cos x$ **d** $e^{-x} \sin x$

   e $\ln(\sin x)$ **f** $e^{2x} \tan x$ **g** $\sin(3x)$ **h** $\cos\left(\frac{x}{2}\right)$

   i $3 \tan(2x)$ **j** $x \cos x$ **k** $\dfrac{\sin x}{x}$ **l** $x \tan x$

3 Differentiate with respect to x:

    a $\sin(x^2)$ **b** $\cos(\sqrt{x})$ **c** $\sqrt{\cos x}$ **d** $\sin^2 x$

    e $\cos^3 x$ **f** $\cos x \sin(2x)$ **g** $\cos(\cos x)$ **h** $\cos^3(4x)$

    i $\csc x$ **j** $\sec(2x)$ **k** $\dfrac{2}{\sin^2(2x)}$ **l** $8\cot^3\left(\frac{x}{2}\right)$

4 If $y = x^4$ then $\dfrac{dy}{dx} = 4x^3$, $\dfrac{d^2y}{dx^2} = 12x^2$, $\dfrac{d^3y}{dx^3} = 24x$, $\dfrac{d^4y}{dx^4} = 24$ and higher derivatives are all zero. Now consider $y = \sin x$.

    a Find $\dfrac{dy}{dx}, \dfrac{d^2y}{dx^2}, \dfrac{d^3y}{dx^3}, \dfrac{d^4y}{dx^4}.$ **b** Explain why $\dfrac{d^ny}{dx^n}$ can have four different values.

5 **a** If $y = \sin(2x + 3)$, show that $\dfrac{d^2y}{dx^2} + 4y = 0$.

    b If $y = 2\sin x + 3\cos x$, show that $y'' + y = 0$ where y'' represents $\dfrac{d^2y}{dx^2}$.

    c Show that the curve with equation $y = \dfrac{\cos x}{1 + \sin x}$ cannot have horizontal tangents.

6 Find the equation of:

    a the tangent to $y = \sin x$ at the origin

    b the tangent to $y = \tan x$ at the origin

    c the normal to $y = \cos x$ at the point where $x = \frac{\pi}{6}$

    d the normal to $y = \csc(2x)$ at the point where $x = \frac{\pi}{4}$.

7 On the Indonesian coast, the depth of water at time t hours after midnight is given by $d = 9.3 + 6.8\cos(0.507t)$ metres.

    a Is the tide rising or falling at 8.00 am?

    b What is the rate of change in the depth of water at 8.00 am?

8 The voltage in a circuit is given by $V(t) = 340\sin(100\pi t)$ where t is the time in seconds. At what rate is the voltage changing:

    a when $t = 0.01$ **b** when $V(t)$ is a maximum?

9 A piston is operated by rod AP attached to a flywheel of radius 1 m. AP = 2 m. P has coordinates $(\cos t, \sin t)$ and point A is $(-x, 0)$.

    a Show that $x = \sqrt{4 - \sin^2 t} - \cos t$.

    b Find the rate at which x is changing at the instant when:

        i $t = 0$ s   **ii** $t = \frac{\pi}{2}$ s   **iii** $t = \frac{2\pi}{3}$ s

10 For each of the following functions, determine the position and nature of the stationary points on the interval $0 \leqslant x \leqslant 2\pi$, then show them on a graph of the function.

    a $f(x) = \sin x$ **b** $f(x) = \cos(2x)$ **c** $f(x) = \sin^2 x$

11 Consider the function $f(x) = \sec x$ for $0 \leqslant x \leqslant 2\pi$.

    a For what values of x is $f(x)$ undefined on this interval?

    b Find the position and nature of any stationary points on this interval.

    c Prove that $f(x+2\pi) = f(x)$, $x \in \mathbb{R}$. What is the geometrical significance of this?

    d Sketch the graph of $y = \sec x$, $x \in [-\frac{\pi}{2}, \frac{5\pi}{2}]$ and show its stationary points.

12 Determine the position and nature of the stationary points of $y = \sin(2x) + 2\cos x$ on $0 \leqslant x \leqslant 2\pi$. Sketch the graph of the function on this interval, and show the positions of the stationary points you found.

13 A particle P moves along the x-axis with position given by $x(t) = 1 - 2\cos t$ cm where t is the time in seconds.

    a State the initial position, velocity and acceleration of P.

    b Describe the motion when $t = \frac{\pi}{4}$ seconds.

    c Find the times when the particle reverses direction on $0 \leqslant t \leqslant 2\pi$ and find the position of the particle at these instants.

    d When is the particle's speed increasing on $0 \leqslant t \leqslant 2\pi$?

B THE DERIVATIVES OF RECIPROCAL CIRCULAR FUNCTIONS

If $y = \csc x$, then $y = \dfrac{1}{\sin x} = u^{-1}$ where $u = \sin x$

$$\therefore \quad \frac{dy}{dx} = -1u^{-2}\frac{du}{dx} = \frac{-1}{(\sin x)^2}\cos x$$

$$= -\frac{1}{\sin x}\frac{\cos x}{\sin x}$$

$$= -\csc x \cot x$$

Likewise: • if $y = \sec x$, then $\dfrac{dy}{dx} = \sec x \tan x$

         • if $y = \cot x$, then $\dfrac{dy}{dx} = -\csc^2 x$

Summary:

Function	Derivative
$\csc x$	$-\csc x \cot x$
$\sec x$	$\sec x \tan x$
$\cot x$	$-\csc^2 x$

Example 4

Find $\dfrac{dy}{dx}$ for: **a** $y = \csc(3x)$ **b** $y = \sqrt{\cot(\frac{x}{2})}$

a $y = \csc(3x)$

$$\therefore \quad \frac{dy}{dx} = -\csc(3x)\cot(3x)\frac{d}{dx}(3x)$$

$$= -3\csc(3x)\cot(3x)$$

b $y = \left(\cot(\tfrac{x}{2})\right)^{\frac{1}{2}}$

$$\therefore \quad \frac{dy}{dx} = \tfrac{1}{2}\left(\cot(\tfrac{x}{2})\right)^{-\frac{1}{2}} \times -\csc^2(\tfrac{x}{2}) \times \tfrac{1}{2}$$

$$= \frac{-\csc^2(\tfrac{x}{2})}{4\sqrt{\cot(\tfrac{x}{2})}}$$

EXERCISE 23B

1 **a** Use $y = (\cos x)^{-1}$ to prove that $\dfrac{d}{dx}(\sec x) = \sec x \tan x$.

 b If $y = \cot x$, prove that $\dfrac{dy}{dx} = -\csc^2 x$ using the quotient rule.

2 Find $\dfrac{dy}{dx}$ for:
 a $y = x \sec x$ **b** $y = e^x \cot x$ **c** $y = 4\sec(2x)$

  d $y = e^{-x} \cot(\frac{x}{2})$ **e** $y = x^2 \csc x$ **f** $y = x\sqrt{\csc x}$

  g $y = \ln(\sec x)$ **h** $y = x\csc(x^2)$ **i** $y = \dfrac{\cot x}{\sqrt{x}}$

3 Find the equation of the tangent to:
 a $y = \sec x$ at $x = \frac{\pi}{4}$ **b** $y = \cot(\frac{x}{2})$ at $x = \frac{\pi}{3}$

4 Find the equation of the normal to:
 a $y = \csc x$ at $x = \frac{\pi}{6}$ **b** $y = \sqrt{\sec(\frac{x}{3})}$ at $x = \pi$

C | THE DERIVATIVES OF INVERSE CIRCULAR FUNCTIONS

$y = \sin x$, $x \in [-\frac{\pi}{2}, \frac{\pi}{2}]$ is a 1-1 function and so has an inverse function f^{-1}.

This function is called

$$f^{-1}(x) = \arcsin x \quad \text{or} \quad \sin^{-1} x.$$

Note: $\sin^{-1} x$ **is not** $\dfrac{1}{\sin x}$ or $\csc x$

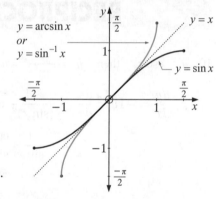

 $\sin^{-1} x$ is the **inverse** function of $y = \sin x$.

 $\csc x$ is the **reciprocal** function of $y = \sin x$.

Likewise, $y = \cos x$, $x \in [0, \pi]$ has inverse function

$$f^{-1}(x) = \arccos x \quad \text{or} \quad \cos^{-1} x.$$

and $y = \tan x$, $x \in]-\frac{\pi}{2}, \frac{\pi}{2}[$ has inverse function

$$f^{-1}(x) = \arctan x \quad \text{or} \quad \tan^{-1} x.$$

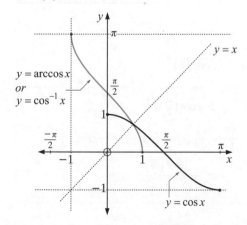

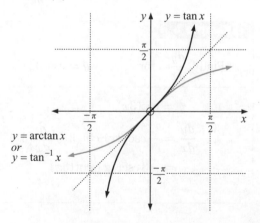

Example 5

Show that: $\arctan(\frac{1}{2}) + \arctan(\frac{1}{3}) = \frac{\pi}{4}$

Let $\arctan(\frac{1}{2}) = \theta$ and $\arctan(\frac{1}{3}) = \phi$,   so $\tan\theta = \frac{1}{2}$ and $\tan\phi = \frac{1}{3}$

Now $\tan(\theta + \phi) = \dfrac{\tan\theta + \tan\phi}{1 - \tan\theta\tan\phi} = \dfrac{\frac{1}{2} + \frac{1}{3}}{1 - (\frac{1}{2})(\frac{1}{3})} = 1$

$\therefore \quad \theta + \phi = \frac{\pi}{4} + k\pi, \quad k \in \mathbb{Z}$

But $0 < \arctan(\frac{1}{2}) < \frac{\pi}{2}$ and $0 < \arctan(\frac{1}{3}) < \frac{\pi}{2}$

$\therefore \quad 0 < \arctan(\frac{1}{2}) + \arctan(\frac{1}{3}) < \pi$

$\therefore \quad \arctan(\frac{1}{2}) + \arctan(\frac{1}{3}) = \theta + \phi = \frac{\pi}{4}$

EXERCISE 23C.1

1 Use a calculator to check the graphs of $y = \arcsin x$, $y = \arccos x$ and $y = \arctan x$.

2 Find, giving your answer in radians:

    a $\arccos(1)$ **b** $\arcsin(-1)$ **c** $\arctan(1)$ **d** $\arctan(-1)$

    e $\arcsin(\frac{1}{2})$ **f** $\arccos(\frac{-\sqrt{3}}{2})$ **g** $\arctan(\sqrt{3})$ **h** $\arccos(-\frac{1}{\sqrt{2}})$

    i $\arctan(-\frac{1}{\sqrt{3}})$ **j** $\sin^{-1}(-0.767)$ **k** $\cos^{-1}(0.327)$ **l** $\tan^{-1}(-50)$

3 Find the exact solution of: **a** $\arcsin x = \frac{\pi}{3}$ **b** $\arctan(3x) = -\frac{\pi}{4}$

4 Use $\tan(\theta - \phi) = \dfrac{\tan\theta - \tan\phi}{1 + \tan\theta\tan\phi}$ to show that $\arctan(5) - \arctan(\frac{2}{3}) = \frac{\pi}{4}$.

5 Without using technology, show that:

    a $\arctan(\frac{1}{5}) + \arctan(\frac{2}{3}) = \frac{\pi}{4}$ **b** $\arctan(\frac{4}{3}) = 2\arctan(\frac{1}{2})$

6 Find the exact value of $4\arctan(\frac{1}{5}) - \arctan(\frac{1}{239})$.

DERIVATIVES OF INVERSE CIRCULAR FUNCTIONS

Consider the differentiation of $y = \arcsin x$ by these methods:

Method 1:

    If $y = \arcsin x$ then $x = \sin y$

    $\therefore \quad \dfrac{dx}{dy} = \cos y = \sqrt{1 - \sin^2 y}$

    $\therefore \quad \dfrac{dx}{dy} = \sqrt{1 - x^2}$

    $\therefore \quad \dfrac{dy}{dx} = \dfrac{1}{\sqrt{1 - x^2}}, \quad x \in\,]-1, 1[$

    {From the chain rule, $\dfrac{dy}{dx}\dfrac{dx}{dy} = \dfrac{dy}{dy} = 1$,   so $\dfrac{dy}{dx}$ and $\dfrac{dx}{dy}$ are reciprocals.}

Method 2:   If $y = \arcsin x$ then $x = \sin y$

Using implicit differentiation, $1 = \cos y \dfrac{dy}{dx}$

$$\therefore \quad \frac{dy}{dx} = \frac{1}{\cos y}$$

$$\therefore \quad \frac{dy}{dx} = \frac{1}{\sqrt{1 - \sin^2 y}} \quad \{y \in [-\tfrac{\pi}{2}, \tfrac{\pi}{2}] \ \Rightarrow \ \cos y \geqslant 0\}$$

$$\therefore \quad \frac{dy}{dx} = \frac{1}{\sqrt{1 - x^2}}, \quad x \in \,]-1, 1[$$

If $y = \arcsin x$,	If $y = \arccos x$,	If $y = \arctan x$,
$\dfrac{dy}{dx} = \dfrac{1}{\sqrt{1 - x^2}}, \ x \in \,]-1, 1[$	$\dfrac{dy}{dx} = \dfrac{-1}{\sqrt{1 - x^2}}, \ x \in \,]-1, 1[$	$\dfrac{dy}{dx} = \dfrac{1}{1 + x^2}, \ x \in \mathbb{R}$

EXERCISE 23C.2

1 If $y = \arccos x$,   show that $\dfrac{dy}{dx} = \dfrac{-1}{\sqrt{1 - x^2}}, \quad x \in \,]-1, 1[$.

2 If $y = \arctan x$,   show that $\dfrac{dy}{dx} = \dfrac{1}{1 + x^2}, \quad x \in \mathbb{R}$.

3 Find $\dfrac{dy}{dx}$ for:

    a $y = \arctan(2x)$ **b** $y = \arccos(3x)$ **c** $y = \arcsin(\tfrac{x}{4})$

    d $y = \arccos(\tfrac{x}{5})$ **e** $y = \arctan(x^2)$ **f** $y = \arccos(\sin x)$

4 Find $\dfrac{dy}{dx}$ for: **a** $y = x \arcsin x$ **b** $y = e^x \arccos x$ **c** $y = e^{-x} \arctan x$

5 **a** Prove that if $y = \arcsin(\tfrac{x}{a})$,   then $\dfrac{dy}{dx} = \dfrac{1}{\sqrt{a^2 - x^2}}$ for $x \in \,]-a, a[$.

    b Prove that if $y = \arctan(\tfrac{x}{a})$,   then $\dfrac{dy}{dx} = \dfrac{a}{a^2 + x^2}$ for $x \in \mathbb{R}$.

    c If $y = \arccos(\tfrac{x}{a})$,   find $\dfrac{dy}{dx}$.

6 Sonia approaches a painting which has its bottom edge 2 m above
    eye level and its top edge 3 m above eye level.

    a Given α and θ as shown in the diagram, find
        $\tan \alpha$ and $\tan(\alpha + \theta)$.

    b Find θ in terms of x only.
        Hint: $\theta = (\alpha + \theta) - \alpha$.

    c Show that $\dfrac{d\theta}{dx} = \dfrac{2}{x^2 + 4} - \dfrac{3}{x^2 + 9}$ and

        hence find x when $\dfrac{d\theta}{dx} = 0$.

    d Interpret the result you have found in **c**.

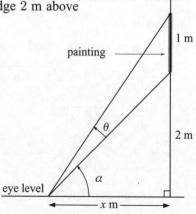

D   MAXIMA AND MINIMA WITH TRIGONOMETRY

Example 6

Two corridors meet at right angles and are 2 m and 3 m wide respectively. θ is the angle marked on the given figure and AB is a thin metal tube which must be kept horizontal and cannot be bent as it moves around the corner from one corridor to the other.

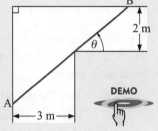

a   Show that the length AB is given by

$$L = 3\sec\theta + 2\csc\theta$$

b   Show that $\dfrac{dL}{d\theta} = 0$ when $\theta = \arctan\left(\sqrt[3]{\frac{2}{3}}\right) \approx 41.14^{\circ}$.

c   Find L when $\theta = \arctan\left(\sqrt[3]{\frac{2}{3}}\right)$ and comment on the significance of this value.

---

a $\cos\theta = \dfrac{3}{a}$ and $\sin\theta = \dfrac{2}{b}$ so $\sec\theta = \dfrac{a}{3}$ and $\csc\theta = \dfrac{b}{2}$

$\therefore\ \ L = a + b = 3\sec\theta + 2\csc\theta$

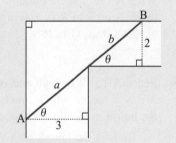

b $\dfrac{dL}{d\theta} = 3\sec\theta\tan\theta + 2(-\csc\theta\cot\theta)$

$= \dfrac{3\sin\theta}{\cos^2\theta} - \dfrac{2\cos\theta}{\sin^2\theta}$

$= \dfrac{3\sin^3\theta - 2\cos^3\theta}{\cos^2\theta\sin^2\theta}$

Thus $\dfrac{dL}{d\theta} = 0 \ \Leftrightarrow\ 3\sin^3\theta = 2\cos^3\theta$

$\therefore\ \tan^3\theta = \frac{2}{3}$

$\therefore\ \tan\theta = \sqrt[3]{\frac{2}{3}}$ and so $\theta = \arctan\left(\sqrt[3]{\frac{2}{3}}\right) \approx 41.14^{\circ}$

c   *Sign diagram of* $\dfrac{dL}{d\theta}$:

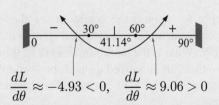

$$\dfrac{dL}{d\theta} \approx -4.93 < 0, \quad \dfrac{dL}{d\theta} \approx 9.06 > 0$$

Thus, AB is minimised when $\theta \approx 41.14^{\circ}$. At this time $L \approx 7.023$ metres, so if we ignore the width of the rod then the greatest length of rod able to be horizontally carried around the corner is 7.023 m.

EXERCISE 23D

1 A circular piece of tinplate of radius 10 cm has 3 segments removed as illustrated.

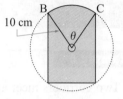

If θ is the measure of angle COB, show that the remaining area is given by $A = 50(\theta + 3\sin\theta)$.

Hence, find θ to the nearest $\frac{1}{10}$ of a degree when the area A is a maximum.

2 A symmetrical gutter is made from a sheet of metal 30 cm wide by bending it twice as shown.

For θ as indicated:

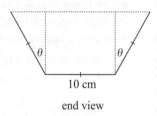

end view

a deduce that the cross-sectional area is given by
$$A = 100\cos\theta(1 + \sin\theta)$$

b show that $\dfrac{dA}{d\theta} = 0$ when $\sin\theta = \frac{1}{2}$ or -1

c for what value of θ does the gutter have maximum carrying capacity?

3 Hieu can row a boat across a circular lake of radius 2 km at 3 km h^{-1}. He can walk around the edge of the lake at 5 km h^{-1}.

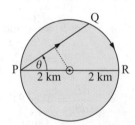

What is the longest possible time Hieu could take to get from P to R by rowing from P to Q and then walking from Q to R?

4 Fence AB is 2 m high and is 2 m from a house. XY is a ladder which touches the ground at X, the house at Y, and the fence at B.

a If L is the length of XY, show that
$$L = 2\sec\theta + 2\csc\theta$$

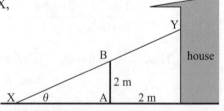

b Show that $\dfrac{dL}{d\theta} = \dfrac{2\sin^3\theta - 2\cos^3\theta}{\sin^2\theta\cos^2\theta}$

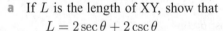

c What is the length of the shortest ladder XY which touches at X, B and Y?

5 In **Example 6**, suppose the corridors are those in a hospital and are 4 m wide and 3 m wide respectively. What is the maximum length of thin metal tube that can be moved around the corner? Remember it must be kept horizontal and must not be bent.

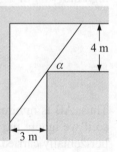

6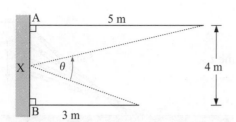

How far should X be from A if angle θ is to be a maximum?

7   A and B are two homesteads. A pump house is to be located at P on the canal to pump water to both A and B.

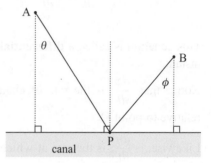

a   If A and B are a km and b km from the canal respectively, show that:

$$AP + PB = a\sec\theta + b\sec\phi = L, \quad \text{say.}$$

b   Show that $\dfrac{dL}{d\theta} = \dfrac{a\sin\theta}{\cos^2\theta} + \dfrac{b\sin\phi}{\cos^2\phi}\dfrac{d\phi}{d\theta}$.

c   Explain why $a\tan\theta + b\tan\phi$ is a constant and hence show that $\dfrac{d\phi}{d\theta} = \dfrac{-a\cos^2\phi}{b\cos^2\theta}$.

d   Hence, show that $\dfrac{dL}{d\theta} = 0 \iff \sin\theta = \sin\phi$.

e   What can be deduced from **d**? Include all reasoning and an appropriate test.

Note: Question **7** is solvable using geometry only. The solution is to reflect point B in the line representing the canal. We call the image B' and join this point to A. The location of point P which minimises AP + PB is the intersection of $[AB']$ and the edge of the canal.

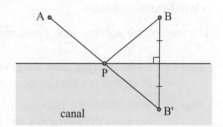

E   **RELATED RATES**

A 5 m ladder rests against a vertical wall at point B, with its feet at point A on horizontal ground.

The ladder slips and slides down the wall. The following diagram shows the positions of the ladder at certain instances.

Click on the icon to view the motion of the sliding ladder.

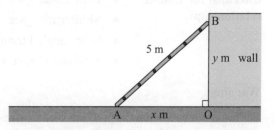

DEMO

If $AO = x$ m and $OB = y$ m,

then $x^2 + y^2 = 5^2$. {Pythagoras}

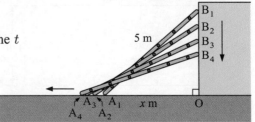

Differentiating this equation with respect to time t

gives $\qquad 2x\dfrac{dx}{dt} + 2y\dfrac{dy}{dt} = 0$

$\qquad$ or $\quad x\dfrac{dx}{dt} + y\dfrac{dy}{dt} = 0.$

This equation is called a **differential equation** and describes the motion of the ladder at any instant.

Notice that $\dfrac{dx}{dt}$ is the rate of change in x with respect to time t, and is the speed of A relative to point O.

Likewise, $\dfrac{dy}{dt}$ is the rate at which B moves downwards.

Observe that:
- $\dfrac{dx}{dt}$ is *positive* as x is increasing

- $\dfrac{dy}{dt}$ is *negative* as y is decreasing.

Problems involving differential equations where one of the variables is t (time) are called **related rates** problems.

The method for solving such problems is:

Step 1:	Draw a large, clear **diagram** of the general situation. Sometimes two or more diagrams are necessary.
Step 2:	Write down the information, label the diagram(s), and make sure you distinguish between the **variables** and the **constants**.
Step 3:	Write down an **equation** connecting the variables.
Step 4:	**Differentiate** the equation with respect to t to obtain a **differential equation**.
Step 5:	Finally, solve for the **particular case** which is some instant in time.

Checklist for finding relationships:
- Pythagoras' theorem.
- Similar triangles where corresponding sides are in proportion.
- Right angled triangle trigonometry.
- Sine and Cosine Rules.

Warning:

We **must not** substitute the particular case values too early. Otherwise we will incorrectly treat variables as constants. The differential equation in fully generalised form must be established first.

Example 7

A 5 m long ladder rests against a vertical wall with its feet on horizontal ground. The feet on the ground slip, and at the instant when they are 3 m from the wall, they are moving at 10 m s^{-1}.

At what speed is the other end of the ladder moving at this instant?

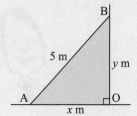

Let $OA = x$ m and $OB = y$ m

$\therefore \ x^2 + y^2 = 5^2$ {Pythagoras}

Differentiating with respect to t gives

$$2x\frac{dx}{dt} + 2y\frac{dy}{dt} = 0 \quad \text{or} \quad x\frac{dx}{dt} + y\frac{dy}{dt} = 0$$

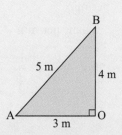

Particular case:

At the instant $\quad \dfrac{dx}{dt} = 10 \text{ m s}^{-1}$,

$$\therefore \ 3(10) + 4\frac{dy}{dt} = 0$$

$$\therefore \ \frac{dy}{dt} = -\frac{15}{2} = -7.5 \text{ m s}^{-1}$$

Thus OB is decreasing at 7.5 m s^{-1}.

$\therefore$ B is moving down the wall at 7.5 m s^{-1} at that instant.

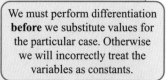

We must perform differentiation **before** we substitute values for the particular case. Otherwise we will incorrectly treat the variables as constants.

Example 8

The volume of a cube increases at a constant rate of 10 cm^3 per second. Find the rate of change in its total surface area at the instant when its sides are 20 cm long.

Let x cm be the lengths of the sides of the cube, so $\ A = 6x^2 \ $ and $\ V = x^3$.

$$\therefore \ \frac{dA}{dt} = 12x\frac{dx}{dt} \quad \text{and} \quad \frac{dV}{dt} = 3x^2\frac{dx}{dt}$$

Particular case:

At the instant when $\ x = 20, \ \dfrac{dV}{dt} = 10$

$$\therefore \ 10 = 3 \times 20^2 \times \frac{dx}{dt}$$

$$\therefore \ \frac{dx}{dt} = \frac{10}{1200} = \frac{1}{120} \text{ cm s}^{-1}$$

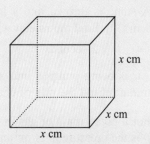

Thus $\ \dfrac{dA}{dt} = 12 \times 20 \times \frac{1}{120} \text{ cm}^2 \text{ s}^{-1} = 2 \text{ cm}^2 \text{ s}^{-1}$

$\therefore$ the surface area is increasing at 2 cm^2 per second.

Example 9

Triangle ABC is right angled at A, and AB = 20 cm. The angle ABC increases at a constant rate of $1°$ per minute. At what rate is BC changing at the instant when angle ABC measures $30°$?

> Remember that $\frac{d\theta}{dt}$ must be measured as radians/time unit.

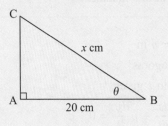

Let $\widehat{ABC} = \theta$ and $BC = x$ cm

Now $\cos\theta = \dfrac{20}{x} = 20x^{-1}$

$\therefore \; -\sin\theta \dfrac{d\theta}{dt} = -20x^{-2}\dfrac{dx}{dt}$

Particular case: $\cos 30° = \dfrac{20}{x}$

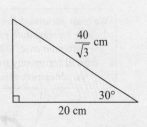

$\therefore \; \dfrac{\sqrt{3}}{2} = \dfrac{20}{x}$ and $\dfrac{d\theta}{dt} = 1°$ per min

$\therefore \; x = \dfrac{40}{\sqrt{3}}$ $\qquad\qquad\quad = \dfrac{\pi}{180}$ radians per min

Thus $-\sin 30° \times \frac{\pi}{180} = -20 \times \dfrac{3}{1600} \times \dfrac{dx}{dt}$

$\therefore \; -\frac{1}{2} \times \frac{\pi}{180} = -\frac{3}{80}\dfrac{dx}{dt}$

$\therefore \; \dfrac{dx}{dt} = \frac{\pi}{360} \times \frac{80}{3}$ cm per min

≈ 0.2327 cm per min

$\therefore$ BC is increasing at approximately 0.233 cm per min.

EXERCISE 23E

1 a and b are variables related by the equation $ab^3 = 40$. At the instant when $a = 5$, b is increasing at 1 unit per second. What is happening to a at this instant?

2 The area of a variable rectangle remains constant at 100 cm^2. The length of the rectangle is decreasing at 1 cm per minute. At what rate is the breadth increasing at the instant when the rectangle is a square?

3 A stone is thrown into a lake and a circular ripple moves out at a constant speed of 1 m s^{-1}. Find the rate at which the circle's area is increasing at the instant when:

    a $t = 2$ seconds   **b** $t = 4$ seconds.

4 Air is being pumped into a spherical weather balloon at a constant rate of 6π m^3 per minute. Find the rate of change in its surface area at the instant when its radius is 2 m.

5 For a given mass of gas in a piston, $pV^{1.5} = 400$ where p is the pressure in N/m^2 and V is the volume in m^3.

If the pressure increases at 3 N/m^2 per minute, find the rate at which the volume is changing at the instant when the pressure is 50 N/m^2.

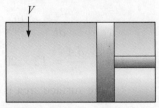

6 Wheat runs from a hole in a silo at a constant rate and forms a conical heap whose base radius is treble its height. If after 1 minute, the height of the heap is 20 cm, find the rate at which the height is rising at this instant.

7 A trough of length 6 m has a uniform cross-section which is an equilateral triangle with sides 1 m. Water leaks from the bottom of the trough at a constant rate of 0.1 m³/min.

Find the rate at which the water level is falling at the instant when it is 20 cm deep.

1 m

end view

8 Two jet aeroplanes fly on parallel courses which are 12 km apart. Their air speeds are 200 m s⁻¹ and 250 m s⁻¹ respectively. How fast is the distance between them changing at the instant when the slower jet is 5 km ahead of the faster one?

9 A ground-level floodlight located 40 m from the foot of a building shines in the direction of the building. A 2 m tall person walks directly towards the building at 1 m s⁻¹. How fast is the person's shadow on the building shortening at the instant when the person is:

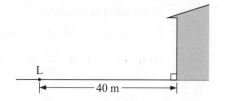

L

40 m

    a 20 m from the building **b** 10 m from the building?

10 A right angled triangle ABC has a fixed hypotenuse AC of length 10 cm, and side AB increases at 0.1 cm per second. At what rate is angle CAB increasing at the instant when the triangle is isosceles?

11 An aeroplane passes directly overhead then flies horizontally away from an observer at an altitude of 5000 m with an air speed of 200 m s⁻¹. At what rate is its angle of elevation to the observer changing at the instant when the angle of elevation is:

    a 60°   **b** 30° ?

12 A rectangle PQRS has PQ of length 20 cm and QR increases at a constant rate of 2 cm s⁻¹. At what rate is the acute angle between the diagonals of the rectangle changing at the instant when QR is 15 cm long?

13 Triangle PQR is right angled at Q and PQ is 6 cm long. If QR increases at 2 cm per minute, find the rate of change in angle P at the instant when QR is 8 cm.

14 Two cyclists A and B leave X simultaneously at 120° to one another with constant speeds of 12 m s⁻¹ and 16 m s⁻¹ respectively. Find the rate at which the distance between them is changing after 2 minutes.

15 AOB is a fixed diameter of a circle of radius 5 cm. A point P moves around the circle at a constant rate of 1 revolution in 10 seconds. Find the rate at which AP is changing at the instant when:

    a AP is 5 cm and increasing

    b P is at B.

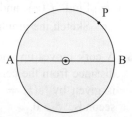

P

A   B

16 Shaft AB is 30 cm long and is attached to a flywheel at A. B is confined to motion along OX. The radius of the wheel is 15 cm, and the wheel rotates clockwise at 100 revolutions per second. Find the rate of change in angle ABO when angle AOX is:

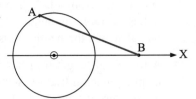

  a $120°$ **b** $180°$.

17 A farmer has a water trough of length 8 m which has a semi-circular cross-section of diameter 1 m. Water is pumped into the trough at a constant rate of 0.1 m^3 per minute.

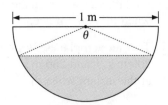

  a Show that the volume of water in the trough is given by $V = \theta - \sin\theta$ where θ is the angle as illustrated (in radians).

  b Find the rate at which the water level is rising at the instant when it is 25 cm deep.

  Hint: First find $\dfrac{d\theta}{dt}$ and then find $\dfrac{dh}{dt}$ at the given instant.

REVIEW SET 23A

1 Differentiate with respect to x:

  a $\sin(5x)\ln(x)$ **b** $\sin(x)\cos(2x)$ **c** $e^{-2x}\tan x$

2 Show that the equation of the tangent to $y = x\tan x$ at $x = \frac{\pi}{4}$ is

$$(2+\pi)x - 2y = \frac{\pi^2}{4}.$$

3 Find $f'(x)$ and $f''(x)$ for:

  a $f(x) = 3\sin x - 4\cos(2x)$ **b** $f(x) = \sqrt{x}\cos(4x)$

4 A particle moves in a straight line along the x-axis with position given by $x(t) = 3 + \sin(2t)$ cm   after t seconds.

  a Find the initial position, velocity and acceleration of the particle.

  b Find the times when the particle changes direction during $0 \leqslant t \leqslant \pi$ secs.

  c Find the total distance travelled by the particle in the first π seconds.

5 Consider $f(x) = \sqrt{\cos x}$ for $0 \leqslant x \leqslant 2\pi$.

  a For what values of x is $f(x)$ meaningful?

  b Find $f'(x)$ and hence find intervals where $f(x)$ is increasing and decreasing.

  c Sketch the graph of $y = f(x)$ on $0 \leqslant x \leqslant 2\pi$.

6 A cork moves up and down in a bucket of water such that the distance from the centre of the cork to the bottom of the bucket is given by $s(t) = 30 + \cos(\pi t)$ cm   where t is the time in seconds, $t \geqslant 0$.

  a Find the cork's velocity at times $t = 0, \frac{1}{2}, 1, 1\frac{1}{2}, 2$ sec.

  b Find the time intervals when the cork is falling.

7 The point $(3\cos\theta, \, 2\sin\theta)$ lies on a curve, $\theta \in [0, \, 2\pi]$.

    a Find the equation of the curve in Cartesian form.

    b Find $\dfrac{dy}{dx}$ in terms of θ.

    c Suppose a tangent to the curve meets the x-axis at A and the y-axis at B. Find the smallest area of triangle OAB and the values of θ when it occurs.

8 Four straight sticks of fixed length a, b, c and d are hinged together at P, Q, R and S.

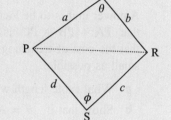

    a Use the cosine rule to find an equation which connects a, b, c, d, $\cos\theta$ and $\cos\phi$ and hence show that $\dfrac{d\theta}{d\phi} = \dfrac{cd\sin\phi}{ab\sin\theta}$.

    b Hence, show that the area of quadrilateral PQRS is a maximum when it is a cyclic quadrilateral.

9 A light bulb hangs from the ceiling at height h metres above the floor, directly above point N. At any point A on the floor which is x metres from the light bulb, the illumination I is given by
$$I = \frac{\sqrt{8}\cos\theta}{x^2} \text{ units.}$$

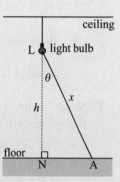

    a If NA $= 1$ metre, show that at A, $I = \sqrt{8}\cos\theta\sin^2\theta$.

    b The light bulb may be lifted or lowered to change the intensity at A. Assuming NA $= 1$ metre, find the height the bulb should be above the floor for greatest illumination at A.

REVIEW SET 23B

1 Find $\dfrac{dy}{dx}$ for: **a** $y = \dfrac{x}{\sqrt{\sec x}}$ **b** $y = e^x \cot(2x)$ **c** $y = \arccos(\tfrac{x}{2})$

2 Find the equation of:

    a the tangent to $y = \sec x$ at the point where $x = \tfrac{\pi}{3}$

    b the normal to $y = \arctan x$ at the point where $x = \sqrt{3}$.

3 A man on a jetty pulls a boat directly towards him so the rope is coming in at a rate of 20 metres per minute. The rope is attached to the boat 1 m above water level and his hands are 6 m above water level. How fast is the boat approaching the jetty at the instant when it is 15 m from the jetty?

4 Two runners run in different directions, $60°$ apart. A runs at 5 m s^{-1} and B runs at 4 m s^{-1}. B passes through X 3 seconds after A passes through X.

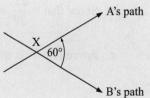

At what rate is the distance between them increasing at the time when A is 20 metres past X?

5 **a** If $f(x) = \arcsin x + \arccos x$, find $f'(x)$. What can we conclude about $f(x)$?

  b Simplify $\arctan\left(\dfrac{1-a}{1+a}\right) + \arctan a$

  c Find the value of $\arctan(\frac{1}{2}) + \arctan(\frac{1}{5}) + \arctan(\frac{1}{8})$

6 A and B are two houses directly opposite one another and 1 km from a straight road CD. MC is 3 km and C is a house at the roadside.

A power unit is to be located on DC at P such that PA + PB + PC is to be a minimum so that the cost of trenching and cable will be as small as possible.

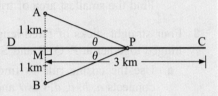

  a What cable length would be required if P is at **i** M   **ii** C?

  b Show that if $\theta = A\widehat{P}M = B\widehat{P}M$, then the length of cable will be
$$L = 2\csc\theta + 3 - \cot\theta \text{ metres.}$$

  c Show that $\dfrac{dL}{d\theta} = \dfrac{1 - 2\cos\theta}{\sin^2\theta}$ and hence show that the minimum length of cable required is $(3 + \sqrt{3})$ km.

7 Water exits a conical tank at a constant rate of 0.2 m³/minute. If the surface of the water has radius r:

  a find $V(r)$, the volume of the water remaining

  b find the rate at which the surface radius is changing at the instant when the height of water is 5 m.

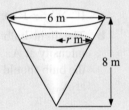

8 Consider a circle with centre O and radius r. A, B and C are fixed points.

An ant starts at B and moves at constant speed v in a straight line to point P.

The ant then moves along the arc from P to C via D at constant speed w where $w > v$.

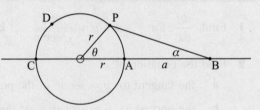

  a Show that the total time for the journey is
$$T = \frac{\sqrt{r^2 + (a+r)^2 - 2r(a+r)\cos\theta}}{v} + \frac{r(\pi - \theta)}{w}.$$

  b Show that $\dfrac{dT}{d\theta} = \dfrac{a+r}{v}\left(\sin\alpha - \dfrac{rv}{(a+r)w}\right)$.

  c Prove that T is minimised when $\sin\alpha = \dfrac{rv}{(a+r)w}$.

Chapter 24

Integration

Contents:

In the previous chapters we used differential calculus to find the derivatives of many types of functions. We also used it in problem solving, in particular to find the slopes of graphs and rates of changes, and to solve optimisation problems.

In this chapter we consider **integral calculus**. This involves **antidifferentiation** which is the reverse process of differentiation. We will see that integral calculus also has many useful applications, including:

- finding areas where curved boundaries are involved
- finding volumes of revolution
- finding distances travelled from velocity functions
- finding hydrostatic pressure
- finding work done by a force
- finding centres of mass and moments of inertia
- solving problems in economics and biology
- solving problems in statistics
- solving differential equations.

A   ANTIDIFFERENTIATION

In many problems in calculus we know the rate of change of one variable with respect to another, but we do not have a formula which relates the variables. In other words, we know $\dfrac{dy}{dx}$, but we need to know y in terms of x.

Examples of problems we need to solve include:

- The slope function $f'(x)$ of a curve is $2x + 3$ and the curve passes through the origin. What is the function $y = f(x)$?

- The rate of change in temperature is $\dfrac{dT}{dt} = 10e^{-t}$ °C per minute where $t \geqslant 0$. What is the temperature function given that initially the temperature was 11°C?

The process of finding y from $\dfrac{dy}{dx}$ or $f(x)$ from $f'(x)$ is the reverse process of differentiation. We call it **antidifferentiation**.

Consider the following problem: If $\dfrac{dy}{dx} = x^2$, what is y in terms of x?

From our work on differentiation we know that when we differentiate power functions the index reduces by 1. We hence know that y must involve x^3.

Now if $y = x^3$ then $\dfrac{dy}{dx} = 3x^2$, so if we start with $y = \frac{1}{3}x^3$ then $\dfrac{dy}{dx} = x^2$.

However, if $y = \frac{1}{3}x^3 + 2$, $y = \frac{1}{3}x^3 + 100$ or $y = \frac{1}{3}x^3 - 7$ then $\dfrac{dy}{dx} = x^2$.

In fact, there are infinitely many such functions of the form $y = \frac{1}{3}x^3 + c$ where c is an arbitrary constant which will give $\dfrac{dy}{dx} = x^2$. Ignoring the arbitrary constant, we say that $\frac{1}{3}x^3$ is the **antiderivative** of x^2. It is the simplest function which when differentiated gives x^2.

> If $F(x)$ is a function where $F'(x) = f(x)$ we say that:
> - the **derivative** of $F(x)$ is $f(x)$ and
> - the **antiderivative** of $f(x)$ is $F(x)$.

Example 1

Find the antiderivative of: a x^3 b e^{2x} c $\dfrac{1}{\sqrt{x}}$

a   We know that the derivative of x^4 involves x^3.

Since $\dfrac{d}{dx}(x^4) = 4x^3$, $\dfrac{d}{dx}\left(\frac{1}{4}x^4\right) = x^3$

∴   the antiderivative of x^3 is $\frac{1}{4}x^4$.

b   Since $\dfrac{d}{dx}(e^{2x}) = e^{2x} \times 2$, $\dfrac{d}{dx}\left(\frac{1}{2}e^{2x}\right) = \frac{1}{2} \times e^{2x} \times 2 = e^{2x}$

∴   the antiderivative of e^{2x} is $\frac{1}{2}e^{2x}$.

c $\dfrac{1}{\sqrt{x}} = x^{-\frac{1}{2}}$ Now $\dfrac{d}{dx}(x^{\frac{1}{2}}) = \frac{1}{2}x^{-\frac{1}{2}}$ ∴ $\dfrac{d}{dx}(2x^{\frac{1}{2}}) = 2(\frac{1}{2})x^{-\frac{1}{2}} = x^{-\frac{1}{2}}$

∴   the antiderivative of $\dfrac{1}{\sqrt{x}}$ is $2\sqrt{x}$.

EXERCISE 24A

1   a   Find the antiderivative of:
   i x ii x^2 iii x^5 iv x^{-2} v x^{-4} vi $x^{\frac{1}{3}}$ vii $x^{-\frac{1}{2}}$
   b   From your answers in a, predict a general rule for the antiderivative of x^n.

2   a   Find the antiderivative of:
   i e^{2x} ii e^{5x} iii $e^{\frac{1}{2}x}$ iv $e^{0.01x}$ v $e^{\pi x}$ vi $e^{\frac{x}{3}}$
   b   From your answers in a, predict a general rule for the antiderivative of e^{kx} where k is a constant.

3   Find the antiderivative of:
   a $6x^2+4x$ by differentiating x^3+x^2 b e^{3x+1} by differentiating e^{3x+1}
   c $\sqrt{x}$ by differentiating $x\sqrt{x}$ d $(2x+1)^3$ by differentiating $(2x+1)^4$

B   THE FUNDAMENTAL THEOREM OF CALCULUS

Sir Isaac Newton and **Gottfried Wilhelm Leibniz** showed the link between differential calculus and the definite integral or limit of an area sum. This link is called the **fundamental theorem of calculus**. The beauty of this theorem is that it enables us to evaluate complicated summations.

We have already observed in **Chapter 19** that:

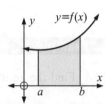

If $f(x)$ is a continuous positive function on an interval $[a, b]$ then the

area under the curve between $x = a$ and $x = b$ is $\displaystyle\int_a^b f(x)\,dx$.

INVESTIGATION   THE AREA FUNCTION

Consider the constant function $f(x) = 5$.

The corresponding area function is

$$A(t) = \int_a^t 5\,dx$$

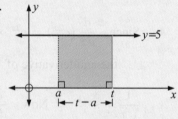

$$= \text{shaded area in graph}$$
$$= (t - a)5$$
$$= 5t - 5a$$

$\therefore$ we can write $A(t)$ in the form $F(t) - F(a)$ where $F(t) = 5t$ or equivalently, $F(x) = 5x$.

What to do:

1 What is the derivative $F'(x)$ of the function $F(x) = 5x$? How does this relate to the function $f(x)$?

2 Consider the simplest linear function $f(x) = x$.
   The corresponding area function is

$$A(t) = \int_a^t x\,dx$$

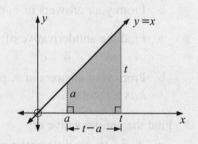

$$= \text{shaded area in graph}$$
$$= \left(\frac{t + a}{2}\right)(t - a)$$

   a Can you write $A(t)$ in the form $F(t) - F(a)$?
   b If so, what is the derivative $F'(x)$? How does it relate to the function $f(x)$?

3 Consider $f(x) = 2x + 3$.   The corresponding area function is

$$A(t) = \int_a^t (2x + 3)\, dx$$

$\qquad$ = shaded area in graph

$$= \left(\frac{2t + 3 + 2a + 3}{2} \right)(t - a)$$

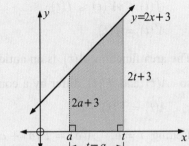

a Can you write $A(t)$ in the form $F(t) - F(a)$?

b If so, what is the derivative $F'(x)$?
How does it relate to the function $f(x)$?

4 Repeat the procedure in **2** and **3** for finding the area functions of
$\quad$ **a** $f(x) = \frac{1}{2}x + 3$ $\qquad$ **b** $f(x) = 5 - 2x$

Do your results fit with your earlier observations?

5 If $f(x) = 3x^2 + 4x + 5$, predict what $F(x)$ would be without performing the algebraic procedure.

From the investigation you should have discovered that, for $f(x) \geqslant 0$,

$$\int_a^t f(x)\, dx = F(t) - F(a) \text{ where } F'(x) = f(x). \quad F(x) \text{ is the } \textbf{antiderivative} \text{ of } f(x).$$

The following argument shows why this is true for all functions $f(x) \geqslant 0$.

Consider a function $y = f(x)$ which has antiderivative $F(x)$ and an area function $A(t)$
which is the area from $x = a$ to $x = t$,

$\qquad$ i.e., $A(t) = \displaystyle\int_a^t f(x)\, dx.$

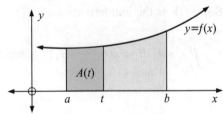

$A(t)$ is clearly an increasing function and

$A(a) = 0$ ..... (1)

Now consider a narrow strip of the region between
$x = t$ and $x = t + h$.

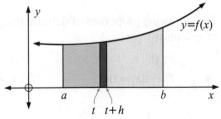

The area of this strip is $A(t + h) - A(t)$.

Since the narrow strip is contained within two
rectangles then

$\quad$ area of smaller $\leqslant A(t + h) - A(t) \leqslant$ area of larger
$\qquad$ rectangle $\qquad\qquad\qquad\qquad\qquad$ rectangle

$\qquad \therefore \quad hf(t) \leqslant A(t + h) - A(t) \leqslant hf(t + h)$

$\qquad \therefore \quad f(t) \leqslant \dfrac{A(t + h) - A(t)}{h} \leqslant f(t + h)$

Taking the limit as $h \to 0$ gives

$\qquad f(t) \leqslant A'(t) \leqslant f(t)$

$\therefore \quad A'(t) = f(t)$

The area function $A(t)$ is an antiderivative of $f(t)$,

so $A(t)$ and $F(t)$ differ by a constant.

$\therefore \quad A(t) = F(t) + c$

Letting $t = a, \quad A(a) = F(a) + c$

$\qquad$ But $\quad A(a) = 0 \quad$ {from (1)}

$\qquad\qquad$ so $\quad c = -F(a)$

$\qquad\qquad \therefore \quad A(t) = F(t) - F(a)$

$f(t)$ $\qquad$ $f(t+h)$

$t \quad t+h$

enlarged strip

$\therefore \quad$ letting $t = b, \qquad \displaystyle\int_a^b f(x)\,dx = F(b) - F(a)$

This result is in fact true for all continuous functions $f(x)$, and can be stated as the **fundamental theorem of calculus**:

For a continuous function $f(x)$ with antiderivative $F(x)$, $\displaystyle\int_a^b \boldsymbol{f(x)\,dx = F(b) - F(a)}$.

The fundamental theorem of calculus has many applications beyond the calculation of areas.

For example, given a velocity function $v(t)$ we know that $\dfrac{ds}{dt} = v$.

So, $s(t)$ is the antiderivative of $v(t)$ and by the fundamental theorem of calculus,

$\displaystyle\int_{t_1}^{t_2} v(t)\,dt = s(t_2) - s(t_1)$ $\quad$ gives the **displacement** over the time interval $[t_1, t_2]$.

PROPERTIES OF DEFINITE INTEGRALS

The following properties of definite integrals can all be deduced from the fundamental theorem of calculus:

- $\displaystyle\int_a^a f(x)\,dx = 0$

- $\displaystyle\int_a^b c\,dx = c(b - a) \qquad$ {c is a constant}

- $\displaystyle\int_b^a f(x)\,dx = -\int_a^b f(x)\,dx$

- $\displaystyle\int_a^b f(x)\,dx + \int_b^c f(x)\,dx = \int_a^c f(x)\,dx$

- $\displaystyle\int_a^b c\,f(x)\,dx = c\int_a^b f(x)\,dx$

- $\displaystyle\int_a^b [f(x) \pm g(x)]\,dx = \int_a^b f(x)\,dx \pm \int_a^b g(x)\,dx$

Example proof:

$$\int_a^b f(x)\,dx + \int_b^c f(x)\,dx$$

$$= F(b) - F(a) + F(c) - F(b)$$

$$= F(c) - F(a)$$

$$= \int_a^c f(x)\,dx$$

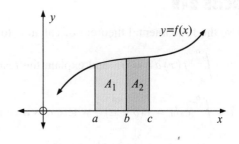

$$\int_a^b f(x)\,dx + \int_b^c f(x)\,dx = A_1 + A_2 = \int_a^c f(x)\,dx$$

Example 2

Use the fundamental theorem of calculus to find the area:

a between the x-axis and $y = x^2$ from $x = 0$ to $x = 1$

b between the x-axis and $y = \sqrt{x}$ from $x = 1$ to $x = 9$

a

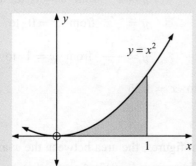

$f(x) = x^2$ has antiderivative $F(x) = \dfrac{x^3}{3}$

$\therefore$ the area $= \int_0^1 x^2\,dx$

$\qquad\qquad = F(1) - F(0)$

$\qquad\qquad = \frac{1}{3} - 0$

$\qquad\qquad = \frac{1}{3}$ units^2

b

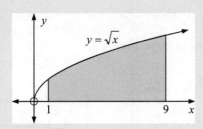

$f(x) = \sqrt{x} = x^{\frac{1}{2}}$ has antiderivative

$F(x) = \dfrac{x^{\frac{3}{2}}}{\frac{3}{2}} = \frac{2}{3}x\sqrt{x}$

$\therefore$ the area $= \int_1^9 x^{\frac{1}{2}}\,dx$

$\qquad\qquad = F(9) - F(1)$

$\qquad\qquad = \frac{2}{3} \times 27 - \frac{2}{3} \times 1$

$\qquad\qquad = 17\frac{1}{3}$ units^2

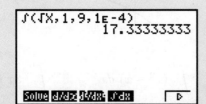

EXERCISE 24B

1   Use the fundamental theorem of calculus to show that:

a $\displaystyle\int_a^a f(x)\,dx = 0$ and explain the result graphically

b $\displaystyle\int_a^b c\,dx = c(b-a)$ where c is a constant

c $\displaystyle\int_b^a f(x)\,dx = -\int_a^b f(x)\,dx$

d $\displaystyle\int_a^b c\,f(x)\,dx = c\int_a^b f(x)\,dx$ where c is a constant

e $\displaystyle\int_a^b [f(x) + g(x)]\,dx = \int_a^b f(x)\,dx + \int_a^b g(x)\,dx$

2   Use the fundamental theorem of calculus to find the area between the x-axis and:

a $y = x^3$ from $x = 0$ to $x = 1$ b $y = x^3$ from $x = 1$ to $x = 2$

c $y = x^2 + 3x + 2$ from $x = 1$ to $x = 3$ d $y = \sqrt{x}$ from $x = 0$ to $x = 2$

e $y = e^x$ from $x = 0$ to $x = 1.5$ f $y = \dfrac{1}{\sqrt{x}}$ from $x = 1$ to $x = 4$

g $y = x^3 + 2x^2 + 7x + 4$ from $x = 1$ to $x = 1.25$

Check each answer using technology.

3   Using technology, find correct to 3 significant figures, the area between the x-axis and:

a $y = e^{x^2}$ from $x = 0$ to $x = 1.5$ b $y = (\ln x)^2$ from $x = 2$ to $x = 4$

c $y = \sqrt{9 - x^2}$ from $x = 1$ to $x = 2$

4   a   Use the fundamental theorem of calculus to show that

$$\int_a^b (-f(x))\,dx = -\int_a^b f(x)\,dx$$

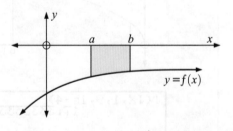

b   Use the result in **a** to show that if
$f(x) \leqslant 0$ for all x on $[a, b]$ then

the shaded area $= -\displaystyle\int_a^b f(x)\,dx$.

c   Calculate: i $\displaystyle\int_0^1 (-x^2)\,dx$ ii $\displaystyle\int_0^1 (x^2 - x)\,dx$ iii $\displaystyle\int_{-2}^0 3x\,dx$

d   Use graphical evidence and known area facts to find $\displaystyle\int_0^2 (-\sqrt{4 - x^2})\,dx$

C | **INTEGRATION**

Earlier we showed that the **antiderivative** of x^2 was $\frac{1}{3}x^3$.

We also showed that any function of the form $\frac{1}{3}x^3 + c$ where c is any constant, has derivative x^2.

We say that the **integral** of x^2 is $\frac{1}{3}x^3 + c$ and write $\int x^2\,dx = \frac{1}{3}x^3 + c$

We read this as "the integral of x^2 with respect to x".

In general,   if $F'(x) = f(x)$ then $\int f(x)\,dx = F(x) + c.$

DISCOVERING INTEGRALS

Since integration is the reverse process of differentiation we can sometimes discover integrals by differentiation. For example:

- if $F(x) = x^4$, then $F'(x) = 4x^3$ $\therefore$ $\int 4x^3\,dx = x^4 + c$

- if $F(x) = \sqrt{x} = x^{\frac{1}{2}}$, then $F'(x) = \frac{1}{2}x^{-\frac{1}{2}} = \dfrac{1}{2\sqrt{x}}$

$$\therefore \int \frac{1}{2\sqrt{x}}\,dx = \sqrt{x} + c$$

The following rules may prove useful:

- Any constant may be written in front of the integral sign.

$$\int k\,f(x)\,dx = k\int f(x)\,dx, \quad k \text{ is a constant}$$

Proof:

Consider differentiating $kF(x)$ where $F'(x) = f(x)$.

$$\frac{d}{dx}\left(k\,F(x)\right) = k\,F'(x) = k\,f(x)$$
$$\therefore \int k\,f(x)\,dx = k\,F(x)$$
$$= k\int f(x)\,dx$$

- The integral of a sum is the sum of the separate integrals. This rule enables us to integrate term by term.

$$\int [f(x) + g(x)]\,dx = \int f(x)\,dx + \int g(x)\,dx$$

Example 3	
If $y = x^4 + 2x^3$, find $\dfrac{dy}{dx}$ and hence find $\displaystyle\int (2x^3 + 3x^2)\,dx.$	If $y = x^4 + 2x^3$, then $\dfrac{dy}{dx} = 4x^3 + 6x^2$ $\therefore \int 4x^3 + 6x^2\,dx = x^4 + 2x^3 + c_1$ $\therefore \int 2(2x^3 + 3x^2)\,dx = x^4 + 2x^3 + c_1$ $\therefore 2\int (2x^3 + 3x^2)\,dx = x^4 + 2x^3 + c_1$ $\therefore \int (2x^3 + 3x^2)\,dx = \frac{1}{2}x^4 + x^3 + c$

EXERCISE 24C.1

1 If $y = x^7$, find $\dfrac{dy}{dx}$ and hence find $\int x^6 \, dx$.

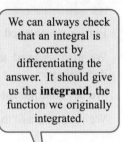

We can always check that an integral is correct by differentiating the answer. It should give us the **integrand**, the function we originally integrated.

2 If $y = x^3 + x^2$, find $\dfrac{dy}{dx}$ and hence find $\int (3x^2 + 2x) \, dx$.

3 If $y = e^{2x+1}$, find $\dfrac{dy}{dx}$ and hence find $\int e^{2x+1} \, dx$.

4 If $y = (2x + 1)^4$, find $\dfrac{dy}{dx}$ and hence find $\int (2x + 1)^3 \, dx$.

5 If $y = x\sqrt{x}$, find $\dfrac{dy}{dx}$ and hence find $\int \sqrt{x} \, dx$.

6 If $y = \dfrac{1}{\sqrt{x}}$, find $\dfrac{dy}{dx}$ and hence find $\displaystyle\int \dfrac{1}{x\sqrt{x}} \, dx$.

7 Prove the rule $\int [f(x) + g(x)] \, dx = \int f(x) \, dx + \int g(x) \, dx$.

8 Find $\dfrac{dy}{dx}$ if $y = \sqrt{1 - 4x}$ and hence find $\displaystyle\int \dfrac{1}{\sqrt{1 - 4x}} \, dx$.

9 By considering $\dfrac{d}{dx} \ln(5 - 3x + x^2)$, find $\displaystyle\int \dfrac{4x - 6}{5 - 3x + x^2} \, dx$.

10 By considering $\dfrac{d}{dx} (2^x)$, find $\int 2^x \, dx$.   **Hint:** $2^x = (e^{\ln 2})^x$.

11 By considering $\dfrac{d}{dx} (x \ln x)$, find $\int \ln x \, dx$.

RULES FOR INTEGRATION

In earlier chapters we developed rules to help us differentiate functions more efficiently. Following is a summary of these rules:

Function	Derivative	Name
c, a constant	0	
$mx + c$, m and c are constants	m	
x^n	nx^{n-1}	**power rule**
$cu(x)$	$cu'(x)$	
$u(x) + v(x)$	$u'(x) + v'(x)$	**addition rule**
$u(x)v(x)$	$u'(x)v(x) + u(x)v'(x)$	**product rule**
$\dfrac{u(x)}{v(x)}$	$\dfrac{u'(x)v(x) - u(x)v'(x)}{[v(x)]^2}$	**quotient rule**
$y = f(u)$ where $u = u(x)$	$\dfrac{dy}{dx} = \dfrac{dy}{du}\dfrac{du}{dx}$	**chain rule**
e^x	e^x	
$e^{f(x)}$	$e^{f(x)} f'(x)$	

Function	Derivative
$\ln x$	$\dfrac{1}{x}$
$\ln f(x)$	$\dfrac{f'(x)}{f(x)}$
$[f(x)]^n$	$n[f(x)]^{n-1}\,f'(x)$

These rules or combinations of them can be used to differentiate almost all functions.

However, the task of finding **antiderivatives** is not so easy and cannot be written as a simple list of rules as we did above. In fact huge books of different types of functions and their integrals have been written. Fortunately our course is restricted to a few special cases.

SIMPLE INTEGRALS

Notice that:

For k a constant, $\dfrac{d}{dx}(kx+c)=k$ $\therefore \int k\,dx = kx + c$

If $n \neq -1$, $\dfrac{d}{dx}\left(\dfrac{x^{n+1}}{n+1}+c\right)=\dfrac{(n+1)x^n}{n+1}=x^n$ $\therefore \int x^n\,dx = \dfrac{x^{n+1}}{n+1}+c,\ n \neq -1$

$\dfrac{d}{dx}(e^x+c)=e^x$ $\therefore \int e^x\,dx = e^x + c$

If $x > 0$, $\dfrac{d}{dx}(\ln x + c) = \dfrac{1}{x}$

If $x < 0$, $\dfrac{d}{dx}(\ln(-x)+c)=\dfrac{-1}{-x}=\dfrac{1}{x}$ $\Bigg\} \quad \therefore \int \dfrac{1}{x}\,dx = \ln|x| + c$

Note:
- c is always an arbitrary constant called the **integrating constant** or **constant of integration**.

- Remember that we can check our integration by differentiating the resulting function.

Example 4

Find:

a $\int (x^3 - 2x^2 + 5)\,dx$

b $\int \left(\dfrac{1}{x^3} - \sqrt{x}\right)dx$

a $\int (x^3 - 2x^2 + 5)\,dx$

$= \dfrac{x^4}{4} - \dfrac{2x^3}{3} + 5x + c$

b $\int \left(\dfrac{1}{x^3} - \sqrt{x}\right)dx$

$= \int (x^{-3} - x^{\frac{1}{2}})\,dx$

$= \dfrac{x^{-2}}{-2} - \dfrac{x^{\frac{3}{2}}}{\frac{3}{2}} + c$

$= -\dfrac{1}{2x^2} - \dfrac{2}{3}x^{\frac{3}{2}} + c$

There is no product or quotient rule for integration. Consequently we often have to carry out multiplication or division before we integrate.

Example 5

Find: **a** $\int \left(3x + \dfrac{2}{x}\right)^2 dx$ **b** $\int \left(\dfrac{x^2 - 2}{\sqrt{x}}\right) dx$

a $\int \left(3x + \dfrac{2}{x}\right)^2 dx$

$= \int \left(9x^2 + 12 + \dfrac{4}{x^2}\right) dx$

$= \int (9x^2 + 12 + 4x^{-2}) dx$

$= \dfrac{9x^3}{3} + 12x + \dfrac{4x^{-1}}{-1} + c$

$= 3x^3 + 12x - \dfrac{4}{x} + c$

b $\int \left(\dfrac{x^2 - 2}{\sqrt{x}}\right) dx$

$= \int \left(\dfrac{x^2}{\sqrt{x}} - \dfrac{2}{\sqrt{x}}\right) dx$

$= \int (x^{\frac{3}{2}} - 2x^{-\frac{1}{2}}) dx$

$= \dfrac{x^{\frac{5}{2}}}{\frac{5}{2}} - \dfrac{2x^{\frac{1}{2}}}{\frac{1}{2}} + c$

$= \dfrac{2}{5}x^2\sqrt{x} - 4\sqrt{x} + c$

Notice that we expanded the brackets and simplified to a form that can be integrated.

We can find c if we are given a point on the curve.

Example 6

Find $f(x)$ given that $f'(x) = x^3 - 2x^2 + 3$ and $f(0) = 2$.

Since $f'(x) = x^3 - 2x^2 + 3$,

$f(x) = \int (x^3 - 2x^2 + 3) dx$

$\therefore f(x) = \dfrac{x^4}{4} - \dfrac{2x^3}{3} + 3x + c$

But $f(0) = 2$, so $0 - 0 + 0 + c = 2$ and so $c = 2$.

Thus $f(x) = \dfrac{x^4}{4} - \dfrac{2x^3}{3} + 3x + 2$

If we are given the second derivative we need to integrate twice to find the function. This creates two integrating constants and so we need two other facts about the curve in order to find them.

Example 7

Find $f(x)$ given that $f''(x) = 12x^2 - 4$, $f'(0) = -1$ and $f(1) = 4$.

If $f''(x) = 12x^2 - 4$

then $f'(x) = \dfrac{12x^3}{3} - 4x + c$ \qquad {integrating with respect to x}

$\therefore$ $f'(x) = 4x^3 - 4x + c$

But $f'(0) = -1$ so $0 - 0 + c = -1$ and so $c = -1$

Thus $f'(x) = 4x^3 - 4x - 1$

$\therefore$ $f(x) = \dfrac{4x^4}{4} - \dfrac{4x^2}{2} - x + d$ \qquad {integrating again}

$\therefore$ $f(x) = x^4 - 2x^2 - x + d$

But $f(1) = 4$ so $1 - 2 - 1 + d = 4$ and so $d = 6$

Thus $f(x) = x^4 - 2x^2 - x + 6$

EXERCISE 24C.2

1 Find:

a $\int (x^4 - x^2 - x + 2)\, dx$ \quad **b** $\int (\sqrt{x} + e^x)\, dx$ \quad **c** $\int \left(3e^x - \dfrac{1}{x}\right) dx$

d $\int \left(x\sqrt{x} - \dfrac{2}{x}\right) dx$ \quad **e** $\int \left(\dfrac{1}{x\sqrt{x}} + \dfrac{4}{x}\right) dx$ \quad **f** $\int \left(\tfrac{1}{2}x^3 - x^4 + x^{\frac{1}{3}}\right) dx$

g $\int \left(x^2 + \dfrac{3}{x}\right) dx$ \quad **h** $\int \left(\dfrac{1}{2x} + x^2 - e^x\right) dx$ \quad **i** $\int \left(5e^x + \tfrac{1}{3}x^3 - \dfrac{4}{x}\right) dx$

2 Find:

a $\int (x^2 + 3x - 2)\, dx$ \quad **b** $\int \left(\sqrt{x} - \dfrac{1}{\sqrt{x}}\right) dx$ \quad **c** $\int \left(2e^x - \dfrac{1}{x^2}\right) dx$

d $\int \dfrac{1 - 4x}{x\sqrt{x}}\, dx$ \quad **e** $\int (2x + 1)^2\, dx$ \quad **f** $\int \dfrac{x^2 + x - 3}{x}\, dx$

g $\int \dfrac{2x - 1}{\sqrt{x}}\, dx$ \quad **h** $\int \dfrac{x^2 - 4x + 10}{x^2\sqrt{x}}\, dx$ \quad **i** $\int (x + 1)^3\, dx$

3 Find y if:

a $\dfrac{dy}{dx} = 6$ \qquad **b** $\dfrac{dy}{dx} = 4x^2$ \qquad **c** $\dfrac{dy}{dx} = 5x - x^2$

d $\dfrac{dy}{dx} = \dfrac{1}{x^2}$ \qquad **e** $\dfrac{dy}{dx} = 2e^x - 5$ \qquad **f** $\dfrac{dy}{dx} = 4x^3 + 3x^2$

4 Find y if:

    a $\dfrac{dy}{dx} = (1 - 2x)^2$ **b** $\dfrac{dy}{dx} = \sqrt{x} - \dfrac{2}{\sqrt{x}}$ **c** $\dfrac{dy}{dx} = \dfrac{x^2 + 2x - 5}{x^2}$

5 Find $f(x)$ if:

    a $f'(x) = x^3 - 5x + 3$ **b** $f'(x) = 2\sqrt{x}(1 - 3x)$ **c** $f'(x) = 3e^x - \dfrac{4}{x}$

6 Find $f(x)$ given that:

    a $f'(x) = 2x - 1$ and $f(0) = 3$ **b** $f'(x) = 3x^2 + 2x$ and $f(2) = 5$

    c $f'(x) = e^x + \dfrac{1}{\sqrt{x}}$ and $f(1) = 1$ **d** $f'(x) = x - \dfrac{2}{\sqrt{x}}$ and $f(1) = 2.$

7 Find $f(x)$ given that:

    a $f''(x) = 2x + 1, \quad f'(1) = 3$ and $f(2) = 7$

    b $f''(x) = 15\sqrt{x} + \dfrac{3}{\sqrt{x}}, \quad f'(1) = 12$ and $f(0) = 5$

    c $f''(x) = 2x$ and the points (1, 0) and (0, 5) lie on the curve.

D   INTEGRATING e^{ax+b} AND $(ax + b)^n$

Notice that $\dfrac{d}{dx}\left(\dfrac{1}{a}e^{ax+b}\right) = \dfrac{1}{a}e^{ax+b} \times a = e^{ax+b}$

$$\therefore \quad \int e^{ax+b}\, dx = \dfrac{1}{a}e^{ax+b} + c$$

Likewise if $n \neq -1$,

$$\dfrac{d}{dx}\left(\dfrac{1}{a(n+1)}(ax+b)^{n+1}\right) = \dfrac{1}{a(n+1)}(n+1)(ax+b)^n \times a,$$

$$= (ax+b)^n$$

$$\therefore \quad \int (ax+b)^n\, dx = \dfrac{1}{a}\dfrac{(ax+b)^{n+1}}{n+1} + c, \quad n \neq -1$$

Also, $\dfrac{d}{dx}\left(\dfrac{1}{a}\ln(ax+b)\right) = \dfrac{1}{a}\left(\dfrac{a}{ax+b}\right) = \dfrac{1}{ax+b}$ for $ax + b > 0$

$$\therefore \quad \int \dfrac{1}{ax+b}\, dx = \dfrac{1}{a}\ln(ax+b) + c$$

In fact, $\displaystyle\int \dfrac{1}{ax+b}\, dx = \dfrac{1}{a}\ln|ax+b| + c$

Example 8

Find:

a $\int (2x+3)^4 \, dx$

b $\int \dfrac{1}{\sqrt{1-2x}} \, dx$

a $\int (2x+3)^4 \, dx$

$= \tfrac{1}{2} \times \dfrac{(2x+3)^5}{5} + c$

$= \tfrac{1}{10}(2x+3)^5 + c$

b $\int \dfrac{1}{\sqrt{1-2x}} \, dx$

$= \int (1-2x)^{-\frac{1}{2}} \, dx$

$= \dfrac{1}{-2} \times \dfrac{(1-2x)^{\frac{1}{2}}}{\frac{1}{2}} + c$

$= -\sqrt{1-2x} + c$

Example 9

Find: a $\int (2e^{2x} - e^{-3x}) \, dx$

b $\int \dfrac{4}{1-2x} \, dx$

a $\int (2e^{2x} - e^{-3x}) \, dx$

$= 2(\tfrac{1}{2})e^{2x} - (\tfrac{1}{-3})e^{-3x} + c$

$= e^{2x} + \tfrac{1}{3}e^{-3x} + c$

b $\int \dfrac{4}{1-2x} \, dx = 4 \int \dfrac{1}{1-2x} \, dx$

$= 4 \left(\dfrac{1}{-2} \right) \ln|1-2x| + c$

$= -2 \ln|1-2x| + c$

EXERCISE 24D

1 Find:

a $\int (2x+5)^3 \, dx$ b $\int \dfrac{1}{(3-2x)^2} \, dx$ c $\int \dfrac{4}{(2x-1)^4} \, dx$ d $\int (4x-3)^7 \, dx$

e $\int \sqrt{3x-4} \, dx$ f $\int \dfrac{10}{\sqrt{1-5x}} \, dx$ g $\int 3(1-x)^4 \, dx$ h $\int \dfrac{4}{\sqrt{3-4x}} \, dx$

2 a Find $y = f(x)$ given $\dfrac{dy}{dx} = \sqrt{2x-7}$ and that $y = 11$ when $x = 8$.

b Function $f(x)$ has slope function $\dfrac{4}{\sqrt{1-x}}$ and passes through the point $(-3, -11)$.

Find the point on the graph of $y = f(x)$ with x-coordinate -8.

3 Find:

a $\int 3(2x-1)^2 \, dx$ b $\int (x^2 - x)^2 \, dx$ c $\int (1-3x)^3 \, dx$

d $\int (1-x^2)^2 \, dx$ e $\int 4\sqrt{5-x} \, dx$ f $\int (x^2+1)^3 \, dx$

4 Find:

a $\int \left(2e^x + 5e^{2x} \right) \, dx$ b $\int \left(3e^{5x-2} \right) \, dx$ c $\int \left(e^{7-3x} \right) \, dx$

d $\int \dfrac{1}{2x-1} \, dx$ e $\int \dfrac{5}{1-3x} \, dx$ f $\int \left(e^{-x} - \dfrac{4}{2x+1} \right) \, dx$

g $\int (e^x + e^{-x})^2 \, dx$ h $\int (e^{-x} + 2)^2 \, dx$ i $\int \left(x - \dfrac{5}{1-x} \right) \, dx$

5 Find y given that:

    a $\dfrac{dy}{dx} = (1 - e^x)^2$ **b** $\dfrac{dy}{dx} = 1 - 2x + \dfrac{3}{x+2}$ **c** $\dfrac{dy}{dx} = e^{-2x} + \dfrac{4}{2x-1}$

6 To find $\displaystyle\int \dfrac{1}{4x}\,dx,$ Tracy's answer was $\displaystyle\int \dfrac{1}{4x}\,dx = \tfrac{1}{4}\ln|4x| + c$

and Nadine's answer was $\displaystyle\int \dfrac{1}{4x}\,dx = \tfrac{1}{4}\int \dfrac{1}{x}\,dx = \tfrac{1}{4}\ln|x| + c$

Which of them has found the correct answer?   Prove your statement.

7   **a** If $f'(x) = 2e^{-2x}$ and $f(0) = 3,$ find $f(x)$.

    b If $f'(x) = 2x - \dfrac{2}{1-x}$ and $f(-1) = 3,$ find $f(x)$.

    c If a curve has slope function $\sqrt{x} + \tfrac{1}{2}e^{-4x}$ and passes through $(1,\ 0)$, find the equation of the function.

8 Show that $\dfrac{3}{x+2} - \dfrac{1}{x-2} = \dfrac{2x-8}{x^2-4},$ and hence find $\displaystyle\int \dfrac{2x-8}{x^2-4}\,dx.$

9 Show that $\dfrac{1}{2x-1} - \dfrac{1}{2x+1} = \dfrac{2}{4x^2-1},$ and hence find $\displaystyle\int \dfrac{2}{4x^2-1}\,dx.$

E   INTEGRATING $f(u)u'(x)$ BY SUBSTITUTION

$\displaystyle\int (x^2+3x)^4(2x+3)\,dx$ is of the form $\displaystyle\int f(u)\,u'(x)\,dx$

where $f(u) = u^4,$ $u = x^2 + 3x$ and $u'(x) = 2x + 3$.

Likewise, $\displaystyle\int e^{x^2-x}(2x-1)\,dx$ is of the form $\displaystyle\int f(u)\,u'(x)\,dx$

where $f(u) = e^u,$ $u = x^2 - x$ and $u'(x) = 2x - 1,$

and $\displaystyle\int \dfrac{3x^2+2}{x^3+2x}\,dx$ is of the form $\displaystyle\int f(u)\,u'(x)\,dx$

where $f(u) = \dfrac{1}{u},$ $u = x^3 + 2x$ and $u'(x) = 3x^2 + 2$.

We can integrate funtions of this form using the theorem

$$\int f(u)\,\frac{du}{dx}\,dx = \int f(u)\,du$$

Proof: Suppose $F(u)$ is the antiderivative of $f(u)$, so $F'(u) = f(u)$

$$\therefore \int f(u)\,du = F(u) + c \ \text{......} \ (1)$$

$$\text{But} \quad \frac{d}{dx}F(u) = \frac{d}{du}F(u)\frac{du}{dx} \quad \{\text{chain rule}\}$$

$$= F'(u)\frac{du}{dx}$$

$$= f(u)\frac{du}{dx}$$

$$\therefore \int f(u)\frac{du}{dx}\,dx = F(u) + c$$

$$= \int f(u)\,du \quad \{\text{from (1)}\}$$

So, for the first example:

$$\int (x^2 + 3x)^4(2x + 3)\,dx = \int u^4\frac{du}{dx}\,dx \quad \{u = x^2 + 3x, \quad \frac{du}{dx} = 2x + 3\}$$

$$= \int u^4\,du \quad \{\text{replacing } \frac{du}{dx}\,dx \text{ by } du\}$$

$$= \frac{u^5}{5} + c \quad \text{which is} \quad \tfrac{1}{5}(x^2 + 3x)^5 + c$$

Example 10

Use substitution to find:

$\int \sqrt{x^3 + 2x}\,(3x^2 + 2)\,dx$

$$\int \sqrt{x^3 + 2x}\,(3x^2 + 2)\,dx$$

$$= \int \sqrt{u}\frac{du}{dx}\,dx \quad \text{where} \quad u = x^3 + 2x$$

$$= \int u^{\frac{1}{2}}\,du$$

$$= \frac{u^{\frac{3}{2}}}{\frac{3}{2}} + c$$

$$= \tfrac{2}{3}(x^3 + 2x)^{\frac{3}{2}} + c$$

Example 11

Use substitution to find: **a** $\displaystyle\int \frac{3x^2 + 2}{x^3 + 2x}\,dx$ **b** $\displaystyle\int xe^{1-x^2}\,dx$

a
$$\int \frac{3x^2 + 2}{x^3 + 2x}\,dx$$

$$= \int \frac{1}{x^3 + 2x}(3x^2 + 2)\,dx$$

$$= \int \frac{1}{u}\frac{du}{dx}\,dx \quad \{u = x^3 + 2x\}$$

$$= \int \frac{1}{u}\,du$$

$$= \ln|u| + c$$

$$= \ln|x^3 + 2x| + c$$

b
$$\int xe^{1-x^2}\,dx$$

$$= -\tfrac{1}{2}\int (-2x)\,e^{1-x^2}\,dx$$

$$= -\tfrac{1}{2}\int e^u\frac{du}{dx}\,dx \quad \{u = 1 - x^2,$$

$$\qquad\qquad\qquad\qquad \frac{du}{dx} = -2x\}$$

$$= -\tfrac{1}{2}\int e^u\,du$$

$$= -\tfrac{1}{2}e^u + c$$

$$= -\tfrac{1}{2}e^{1-x^2} + c$$

EXERCISE 24E

1 Integrate with respect to x:

   a $3x^2(x^3+1)^4$
   b $\dfrac{2x}{\sqrt{x^2+3}}$
   c $\sqrt{x^3+x}\,(3x^2+1)$

   d $4x^3(2+x^4)^3$
   e $(x^3+2x+1)^4(3x^2+2)$
   f $\dfrac{x^2}{(3x^3-1)^4}$

   g $\dfrac{x}{(1-x^2)^5}$
   h $\dfrac{x+2}{(x^2+4x-3)^2}$
   i $x^4(x+1)^4(2x+1)$

2 Find:

   a $\displaystyle \int -2e^{1-2x}\,dx$
   b $\displaystyle \int 2xe^{x^2}\,dx$
   c $\displaystyle \int x^2 e^{x^3+1}\,dx$

   d $\displaystyle \int \dfrac{e^{\sqrt{x}}}{\sqrt{x}}\,dx$
   e $\displaystyle \int (2x-1)e^{x-x^2}\,dx$
   f $\displaystyle \int \dfrac{e^{\frac{x-1}{x}}}{x^2}\,dx$

3 Find:

   a $\displaystyle \int \dfrac{2x}{x^2+1}\,dx$
   b $\displaystyle \int \dfrac{x}{2-x^2}\,dx$
   c $\displaystyle \int \dfrac{2x-3}{x^2-3x}\,dx$

   d $\displaystyle \int \dfrac{6x^2-2}{x^3-x}\,dx$
   e $\displaystyle \int \dfrac{4x-10}{5x-x^2}\,dx$
   f $\displaystyle \int \dfrac{1-x^2}{x^3-3x}\,dx$

4 Find $f(x)$ if $f'(x)$ is:

   a $x^2(3-x^3)^2$
   b $\dfrac{4}{x\ln x}$
   c $x\sqrt{1-x^2}$

   d xe^{1-x^2}
   e $\dfrac{1-3x^2}{x^3-x}$
   f $\dfrac{(\ln x)^3}{x}$

F   INTEGRATING CIRCULAR FUNCTIONS

Observe the following:

$$\frac{d}{dx}(\sin x + c) = \cos x + 0 = \cos x \qquad \therefore \ \int \cos x \, dx = \sin x + c$$

$$\frac{d}{dx}(-\cos x + c) = -(-\sin x) + 0 = \sin x \qquad \therefore \ \int \sin x \, dx = -\cos x + c$$

$$\frac{d}{dx}(\tan x + c) = \sec^2 x \qquad \therefore \ \int \sec^2 x \, dx = \tan x + c$$

We can now complete our list of basic integrals:

Function	Integral	Function	Integral
k (a constant)	$kx + c$	e^x	$e^x + c$
x^n ($n \neq -1$)	$\dfrac{x^{n+1}}{n+1} + c$	$\cos x$	$\sin x + c$
		$\sin x$	$-\cos x + c$
$\dfrac{1}{x}$	$\ln|x| + c$	$\sec^2 x$	$\tan x + c$

Example 12

Integrate with respect to x:

a $2\sin x - \cos x$

b $3\sec^2 x - \dfrac{2}{x} + \sqrt{x}$

a $\int [2\sin x - \cos x]dx$

$= 2(-\cos x) - \sin x + c$

$= -2\cos x - \sin x + c$

b $\displaystyle\int \left[3\sec^2 x - \frac{2}{x} + x^{\frac{1}{2}}\right] dx$

$= 3\tan x - 2\ln|x| + \dfrac{x^{\frac{3}{2}}}{\frac{3}{2}} + c$

$= 3\tan x - 2\ln|x| + \frac{2}{3}x^{\frac{3}{2}} + c$

Example 13

Find $\dfrac{d}{dx}(x\sin x)$ and hence deduce $\int x\cos x\, dx$.

$\dfrac{d}{dx}(x\sin x) = (1)\sin x + (x)\cos x$ {product rule of differentiation}

$= \sin x + x\cos x$

Thus $\int(\sin x + x\cos x)dx = x\sin x + c_1$ {antidifferentiation}

$\therefore \int \sin x\, dx + \int x\cos x\, dx = x\sin x + c_1$

$\therefore -\cos x + c_2 + \int x\cos x\, dx = x\sin x + c_1$

$\therefore \int x\cos x\, dx = x\sin x + \cos x + c$

Example 14

By considering $\dfrac{d}{dx}(\csc x)$, determine $\displaystyle\int \frac{\cos x}{\sin^2 x}\, dx$.

$\dfrac{d}{dx}(\csc x) = \dfrac{d}{dx}[\sin x]^{-1}$

$= -[\sin x]^{-2} \times \dfrac{d}{dx}(\sin x)$

$= -\dfrac{1}{\sin^2 x} \times \cos x$

$= -\dfrac{\cos x}{\sin^2 x}$

Hence $\displaystyle\int -\frac{\cos x}{\sin^2 x}\, dx = \csc x + c_1$

$\therefore \displaystyle\int \frac{\cos x}{\sin^2 x}\, dx = -\csc x + c$

Example 15

Find $f(x)$ given that
$f'(x) = 2\sin x - \sqrt{x}$
and $f(0) = 4$.

$$f(x) = \int \left[2\sin x - x^{\frac{1}{2}} \right] dx$$

$$\therefore \quad f(x) = 2 \times (-\cos x) - \frac{x^{\frac{3}{2}}}{\frac{3}{2}} + c$$

$$\therefore \quad f(x) = -2\cos x - \tfrac{2}{3}x^{\frac{3}{2}} + c$$

$$\text{But} \quad f(0) = -2\cos 0 - 0 + c$$

$$\therefore \quad 4 = -2 + c \quad \text{and so} \quad c = 6$$

$$\text{Thus} \quad f(x) = -2\cos x - \tfrac{2}{3}x^{\frac{3}{2}} + 6.$$

EXERCISE 24F.1

1 Integrate with respect to x:

    a $3\sin x - 2$ **b** $4x - 2\cos x$ **c** $2\sqrt{x} + 4\sec^2 x$

    d $\sec^2 x + 2\sin x$ **e** $\dfrac{x}{2} - \sec^2 x$ **f** $\sin x - 2\cos x + e^x$

    g $x^2\sqrt{x} - 10\sin x$ **h** $\dfrac{x(x-1)}{3} + \cos x$ **i** $5\sec^2 x - \sin x + 2\sqrt{x}$

2 Find:

    a $\int \left(\sqrt{x} + \tfrac{1}{2}\cos x \right) dx$ **b** $\int (\theta - \sin \theta)\, d\theta$ **c** $\int \left(t\sqrt{t} + 2\sec^2 t \right) dt$

    d $\int (2e^t - 4\sin t)\, dt$ **e** $\int \left(3\cos t - \dfrac{1}{t} \right) dt$ **f** $\int \left(3 - \dfrac{2}{\theta} + \sec^2 \theta \right) d\theta$

3   **a**   Find $\dfrac{d}{dx}(e^x \sin x)$ and hence find $\int e^x(\sin x + \cos x)\, dx$.

    b   By considering $\dfrac{d}{dx}(e^{-x} \sin x)$,   determine $\displaystyle\int \dfrac{\cos x - \sin x}{e^x}\, dx$.

    c   Find $\dfrac{d}{dx}(x \cos x)$ and hence find $\int x \sin x\, dx$.

    d   By considering $\dfrac{d}{dx}(\sec x)$,   determine $\displaystyle\int \tan x \sec x\, dx$.

4 Find $f(x)$ given that:

    a $f'(x) = x^2 - 4\cos x$ and $f(0) = 3$

    b $f'(x) = 2\cos x - 3\sin x$ and $f\left(\tfrac{\pi}{4}\right) = \tfrac{1}{\sqrt{2}}$

    c $f'(x) = \sqrt{x} - 2\sec^2 x$ and $f(\pi) = 0$.

INTEGRALS OF CIRCULAR FUNCTIONS OF THE FORM $f(ax+b)$

Observe the following: As $\dfrac{d}{dx}(\sin(ax+b)) = \cos(ax+b) \times a$,

$$\therefore \quad \int a\cos(ax+b)\,dx = \sin(ax+b) + c_1$$

$$\therefore \quad a\int \cos(ax+b)\,dx = \sin(ax+b) + c_1$$

$$\therefore \quad \int \cos(ax+b)\,dx = \frac{1}{a}\sin(ax+b) + c$$

Likewise we can show $\displaystyle\int \sin(ax+b)\,dx = -\frac{1}{a}\cos(ax+b) + c$

and $\displaystyle\int \sec^2(ax+b)\,dx = \frac{1}{a}\tan(ax+b) + c$

SUMMARY OF INTEGRALS FOR FUNCTIONS OF THE FORM $f(ax+b)$

Function	Integral	Function	Integral
$\cos(ax+b)$	$\dfrac{1}{a}\sin(ax+b) + c$	e^{ax+b}	$\dfrac{1}{a}e^{ax+b} + c$
$\sin(ax+b)$	$-\dfrac{1}{a}\cos(ax+b) + c$	$(ax+b)^n$	$\dfrac{1}{a}\dfrac{(ax+b)^{n+1}}{n+1} + c, \quad n \neq -1$
$\sec^2(ax+b)$	$\dfrac{1}{a}\tan(ax+b) + c$	$\dfrac{1}{ax+b}$	$\dfrac{1}{a}\ln|ax+b| + c$

Example 16

Integrate with respect to x: **a** $e^{-2x} - 4\sec^2(2x)$ **b** $2\sin(3x) + \cos(4x+\pi)$

a
$$\int (e^{-2x} - 4\sec^2(2x))\,dx$$
$$= \tfrac{1}{-2}e^{-2x} - 4 \times \tfrac{1}{2}\tan(2x) + c$$
$$-\tfrac{1}{2}e^{-2x} - 2\tan(2x) + c$$

b
$$\int (2\sin(3x) + \cos(4x+\pi))\,dx$$
$$= 2 \times \tfrac{1}{3}(-\cos(3x)) + \tfrac{1}{4}\sin(4x+\pi) + c$$
$$= -\tfrac{2}{3}\cos(3x) + \tfrac{1}{4}\sin(4x+\pi) + c$$

INTEGRALS OF POWERS OF CIRCULAR FUNCTIONS

Integrals involving $\sin^2(ax+b)$ and $\cos^2(ax+b)$ can be found by first using

$$\sin^2\theta = \tfrac{1}{2} - \tfrac{1}{2}\cos(2\theta) \quad \text{or} \quad \cos^2\theta = \tfrac{1}{2} + \tfrac{1}{2}\cos(2\theta).$$

These formulae are simply rearrangements of $\cos(2\theta)$ formulae.

For example,
- $\sin^2(3x - \frac{\pi}{2})$ becomes $\frac{1}{2} - \frac{1}{2}\cos(6x - \pi)$
- $\cos^2\left(\frac{x}{2}\right)$ becomes $\frac{1}{2} + \frac{1}{2}\cos 2\left(\frac{x}{2}\right) = \frac{1}{2} + \frac{1}{2}\cos x$

Example 17

Integrate $(2 - \sin x)^2$.

$$\int (2 - \sin x)^2 dx$$
$$= \int (4 - 4\sin x + \sin^2 x) dx$$
$$= \int \left(4 - 4\sin x + \frac{1}{2} - \frac{1}{2}\cos(2x)\right) dx$$
$$= \int \left(\frac{9}{2} - 4\sin x - \frac{1}{2}\cos(2x)\right) dx$$
$$= \frac{9}{2}x + 4\cos x - \frac{1}{2} \times \frac{1}{2}\sin(2x) + c$$
$$= \frac{9}{2}x + 4\cos x - \frac{1}{4}\sin(2x) + c$$

INTEGRATION BY SUBSTITUTION

Example 18

Integrate with respect to x: **a** $\cos^3 x \sin x$ **b** $\cot x$

a
$$\int \cos^3 x \sin x \, dx$$
$$= \int [\cos x]^3 \sin x \, dx$$
We let $u = \cos x$, $\dfrac{du}{dx} = -\sin x$
$$\therefore \int \cos^3 x \sin x \, dx$$
$$= \int u^3 \left(-\frac{du}{dx}\right) dx$$
$$= -\int u^3 \, du$$
$$= -\frac{u^4}{4} + c$$
$$= -\frac{1}{4}\cos^4 x + c$$

b
$$\int \cot x \, dx = \int \frac{\cos x}{\sin x} \, dx$$
We let $u = \sin x$, $\dfrac{du}{dx} = \cos x$
$$\therefore \int \cot x \, dx = \int \frac{1}{u}\frac{du}{dx} \, dx$$
$$= \int \frac{1}{u} \, du$$
$$= \ln|u| + c$$
$$= \ln|\sin x| + c$$

Note: The substitutions we make need to be chosen with care.

For example, in **Example 18** part **b**, if we let $u = \cos x$, $\dfrac{du}{dx} = -\sin x$ then
$$\int \frac{\cos x}{\sin x} dx = \int \frac{u}{-\dfrac{du}{dx}} \, dx.$$

This substitution leads nowhere as we cannot perform this integration.

Example 19

Find $\int \sin^3 x \, dx$.

$\int \sin^3 x \, dx$

$= \int \sin^2 x \sin x \, dx$

$= \int (1 - \cos^2 x) \sin x \, dx$

$= \int (1 - u^2) \left(-\dfrac{du}{dx} \right) dx \quad \{u = \cos x, \ \dfrac{du}{dx} = -\sin x\}$

$= \int (u^2 - 1) \, du$

$= \dfrac{u^3}{3} - u + c$

$= \frac{1}{3} \cos^3 x - \cos x + c$

EXERCISE 24F.2

1 Integrate with respect to x:

   a $\sin(3x)$

   b $2\cos(4x)$

   c $\sec^2(2x)$

   d $3\cos\left(\frac{x}{2}\right)$

   e $3\sin(2x) - e^{-x}$

   f $e^{2x} - 2\sec^2\left(\frac{x}{2}\right)$

   g $2\sin\left(2x + \frac{\pi}{6}\right)$

   h $-3\cos\left(\frac{\pi}{4} - x\right)$

   i $4\sec^2\left(\frac{\pi}{3} - 2x\right)$

   j $\cos(2x) + \sin(2x)$

   k $2\sin(3x) + 5\cos(4x)$

   l $\frac{1}{2}\cos(8x) - 3\sin x$

2 Integrate with respect to x:

   a $\cos^2 x$

   b $\sin^2 x$

   c $1 + \cos^2(2x)$

   d $3 - \sin^2(3x)$

   e $\frac{1}{2}\cos^2(4x)$

   f $(1 + \cos x)^2$

3 Use the identity $\cos^2 \theta = \frac{1}{2} + \frac{1}{2}\cos(2\theta)$ to show that

$$\cos^4 x = \frac{1}{8}\cos(4x) + \frac{1}{2}\cos(2x) + \frac{3}{8} \quad \text{and hence find} \quad \int \cos^4 x \, dx.$$

4 Integrate by substitution:

   a $\sin^4 x \cos x$

   b $\dfrac{\sin x}{\sqrt{\cos x}}$

   c $\tan x$

   d $\sqrt{\sin x} \cos x$

   e $\dfrac{\cos x}{(2 + \sin x)^2}$

   f $\dfrac{\sin x}{\cos^3 x}$

   g $\dfrac{\sin x}{1 - \cos x}$

   h $\dfrac{\cos(2x)}{\sin(2x) - 3}$

   i $x\sin(x^2)$

   j $\dfrac{\sin^3 x}{\cos^5 x}$

   k $\csc^3(2x)\cot(2x)$

   l $\cos^3 x$

5 Find:

   a $\int \sin^5 x \, dx$

   b $\int \sin^4 x \cos^3 x \, dx$

6 Find $f(x)$ if $f'(x)$ is:

    a $\sin x\, e^{\cos x}$ **b** $\sin^3(2x)\cos(2x)$ **c** $\dfrac{\sin x + \cos x}{\sin x - \cos x}$ **d** $\dfrac{e^{\tan x}}{\cos^2 x}$

7 Find:

    a $\int \cot x\, dx$ **b** $\int \cot(3x)\, dx$ **c** $\int \csc^2 x\, dx$

    d $\int \sec x \tan x\, dx$ **e** $\int \csc x \cot x\, dx$ **f** $\int \tan(3x)\sec(3x)\, dx$

    g $\int \csc\left(\tfrac{x}{2}\right)\cot\left(\tfrac{x}{2}\right) dx$ **h** $\int \sec^3 x \sin x\, dx$ **i** $\displaystyle\int \frac{\csc^2 x}{\sqrt{\cot x}}\, dx$

G   DEFINITE INTEGRALS

If $F(x)$ is the antiderivative of $f(x)$ where $f(x)$ is continuous on the interval $a \leqslant x \leqslant b$ then the **definite integral** of $f(x)$ on this interval is $\displaystyle\int_a^b f(x)\, dx = F(b) - F(a)$.

$\displaystyle\int_a^b f(x)\, dx$ reads "the integral from $x = a$ to $x = b$ of $f(x)$ with respect to x".

Notation: We write $F(b) - F(a) = [F(x)]_a^b$.

Example 20

Find $\displaystyle\int_1^3 (x^2 + 2)\, dx$

$\displaystyle\int_1^3 (x^2 + 2)\, dx$

$= \left[\dfrac{x^3}{3} + 2x\right]_1^3$

$= \left(\dfrac{3^3}{3} + 2(3)\right) - \left(\dfrac{1^3}{3} + 2(1)\right)$

$= (9 + 6) - (\tfrac{1}{3} + 2)$

$= 12\tfrac{2}{3}$

```
fnInt(X²+2,X,1,3
)
        12.66666667
```

Example 21

Evaluate: **a** $\displaystyle\int_0^{\frac{\pi}{3}} \sin x\, dx$ **b** $\displaystyle\int_0^{\frac{\pi}{8}} \sec^2(2x)\, dx$

a $\displaystyle\int_0^{\frac{\pi}{3}} \sin x\, dx$

$= \left[-\cos x\right]_0^{\frac{\pi}{3}}$

$= \left(-\cos \tfrac{\pi}{3}\right) - \left(-\cos 0\right)$

$= -\tfrac{1}{2} + 1$

$= \tfrac{1}{2}$

```
fnInt(sin(X),X,0
,π/3)
          .50000
```

b $\displaystyle\int_0^{\frac{\pi}{8}} \sec^2(2x)\, dx$

$= \left[\tfrac{1}{2}\tan(2x)\right]_0^{\frac{\pi}{8}}$

$= \left(\tfrac{1}{2}\tan\tfrac{\pi}{4}\right) - \left(\tfrac{1}{2}\tan 0\right)$

$= \tfrac{1}{2} \times 1 - \tfrac{1}{2} \times 0$

$= \tfrac{1}{2}$

When we solve a definite integral by substitution, we need to make sure the endpoints are converted to the new variable.

Example 22

Evaluate: **a** $\displaystyle\int_2^3 \frac{x}{x^2-1}\,dx$ **b** $\displaystyle\int_0^1 \frac{6x}{(x^2+1)^3}\,dx$

a

$$\int_2^3 \frac{x}{x^2-1}\,dx$$

$$= \int_2^3 \frac{1}{u}\left(\frac{1}{2}\frac{du}{dx}\right)dx$$

$$= \frac{1}{2}\int_3^8 \frac{1}{u}\,du$$

$$= \frac{1}{2}[\ln|u|]_3^8$$

$$= \frac{1}{2}(\ln 8 - \ln 3)$$

$$= \frac{1}{2}\ln\left(\frac{8}{3}\right)$$

Let $u = x^2 - 1$ $\therefore$ $\dfrac{du}{dx} = 2x$

When $x = 2$, $u = 2^2 - 1 = 3$
When $x = 3$, $u = 3^2 - 1 = 8$

```
.5ln (8÷3)
            0.4904146265
∫(X÷(X²-1),2,3,1E-4)
            0.4904146265



Solve d/dx ∫dx∫ ∫'dx      ▷
```

b

$$\int_0^1 \frac{6x}{(x^2+1)^3}\,dx$$

$$= \int_0^1 \frac{1}{u^3}\left(3\frac{du}{dx}\right)dx$$

$$= 3\int_1^2 u^{-3}\,du$$

$$= 3\left[\frac{u^{-2}}{-2}\right]_1^2$$

$$= 3\left(\frac{2^{-2}}{-2} - \frac{1^{-2}}{-2}\right)$$

$$= \frac{9}{8}$$

Let $u = x^2 + 1$ $\therefore$ $\dfrac{du}{dx} = 2x$

When $x = 0$, $u = 1$
When $x = 1$, $u = 2$

```
∫(6×X÷(X²+1)^3,0,1,1E
-4)
            1.125



Solve d/dx ∫dx∫ ∫'dx      ▷
```

Example 23

Evaluate: $\displaystyle\int_{\frac{\pi}{6}}^{\frac{\pi}{2}} \sqrt{\sin x}\,\cos x\,dx$

$$\int_{\frac{\pi}{6}}^{\frac{\pi}{2}} \sqrt{\sin x}\,\cos x\,dx$$

$$= \int_{\frac{\pi}{6}}^{\frac{\pi}{2}} \sqrt{u}\,\frac{du}{dx}\,dx$$

Let $u = \sin x$ $\therefore$ $\dfrac{du}{dx} = \cos x$

When $x = \frac{\pi}{2}$, $u = \sin\frac{\pi}{2} = 1$

When $x = \frac{\pi}{6}$, $u = \sin\frac{\pi}{6} = \frac{1}{2}$

$$= \int_{\frac{1}{2}}^{1} u^{\frac{1}{2}} \, du$$

$$= \left[\frac{u^{\frac{3}{2}}}{\frac{3}{2}} \right]_{\frac{1}{2}}^{1}$$

$$= \tfrac{2}{3}(1)^{\frac{3}{2}} - \tfrac{2}{3}\left(\tfrac{1}{2}\right)^{\frac{3}{2}}$$

$$= \tfrac{2}{3} - \tfrac{1}{3\sqrt{2}}$$

```
∫(∫(sin X)×cos X,π÷6,
π÷2,1ε-6)
              0.43096
```

EXERCISE 24G.1

1 Evaluate the following and check with your graphics calculator:

  a $\displaystyle\int_{0}^{1} x^3 \, dx$
  b $\displaystyle\int_{0}^{2} (x^2 - x) \, dx$
  c $\displaystyle\int_{0}^{1} e^x \, dx$

  d $\displaystyle\int_{1}^{4} \left(x - \frac{3}{\sqrt{x}} \right) dx$
  e $\displaystyle\int_{4}^{9} \frac{x-3}{\sqrt{x}} \, dx$
  f $\displaystyle\int_{1}^{3} \frac{1}{x} \, dx$

  g $\displaystyle\int_{1}^{2} (e^{-x} + 1)^2 \, dx$
  h $\displaystyle\int_{2}^{6} \frac{1}{\sqrt{2x-3}} \, dx$
  i $\displaystyle\int_{0}^{1} e^{1-x} \, dx$

2 Evaluate:

  a $\displaystyle\int_{0}^{\frac{\pi}{6}} \cos x \, dx$
  b $\displaystyle\int_{\frac{\pi}{3}}^{\frac{\pi}{2}} \sin x \, dx$
  c $\displaystyle\int_{\frac{\pi}{4}}^{\frac{\pi}{3}} \sec^2 x \, dx$

  d $\displaystyle\int_{0}^{\frac{\pi}{6}} \sin(3x) \, dx$
  e $\displaystyle\int_{0}^{\frac{\pi}{4}} \cos^2 x \, dx$
  f $\displaystyle\int_{0}^{\frac{\pi}{2}} \sin^2 x \, dx$

3 Evaluate the following and check with your graphics calculator:

  a $\displaystyle\int_{1}^{2} \frac{x}{(x^2+2)^2} \, dx$
  b $\displaystyle\int_{0}^{1} x^2 e^{x^3+1} \, dx$
  c $\displaystyle\int_{0}^{3} x\sqrt{x^2+16} \, dx$

  d $\displaystyle\int_{1}^{2} xe^{-2x^2} \, dx$
  e $\displaystyle\int_{2}^{3} \frac{x}{2-x^2} \, dx$
  f $\displaystyle\int_{1}^{2} \frac{\ln x}{x} \, dx$

  g $\displaystyle\int_{0}^{1} \frac{1-3x^2}{1-x^3+x} \, dx$
  h $\displaystyle\int_{2}^{4} \frac{6x^2-4x+4}{x^3-x^2+2x} \, dx$
  i $\displaystyle\int_{0}^{1} (x^2+2x)^n (x+1) \, dx$

                                                                          (Careful!)

4 Evaluate:

  a $\displaystyle\int_{0}^{\frac{\pi}{3}} \frac{\sin x}{\sqrt{\cos x}} \, dx$
  b $\displaystyle\int_{0}^{\frac{\pi}{6}} \sin^2 x \cos x \, dx$
  c $\displaystyle\int_{0}^{\frac{\pi}{4}} \tan x \, dx$

  d $\displaystyle\int_{\frac{\pi}{6}}^{\frac{\pi}{2}} \cot x \, dx$
  e $\displaystyle\int_{0}^{\frac{\pi}{6}} \frac{\cos x}{1-\sin x} \, dx$
  f $\displaystyle\int_{0}^{\frac{\pi}{4}} \sec^2 x \tan^3 x \, dx$

PROPERTIES OF DEFINITE INTEGRALS

Earlier in the chapter we proved the following properties of definite integrals using the fundamental theorem of calculus:

- $$\int_a^b [-f(x)]\, dx = -\int_a^b f(x)\, dx$$

- $$\int_a^b cf(x)\, dx = c\int_a^b f(x)\, dx, \quad c \text{ is any constant}$$

- $$\int_a^b f(x)\, dx + \int_b^c f(x)\, dx = \int_a^c f(x)\, dx$$

- $$\int_a^b [f(x) + g(x)]\, dx = \int_a^b f(x)\, dx + \int_a^b g(x)\, dx$$

EXERCISE 24G.2

Use questions **1** to **4** to check the properties of definite integrals.

1 Find: **a** $\displaystyle\int_1^4 \sqrt{x}\, dx$ and $\displaystyle\int_1^4 (-\sqrt{x})\, dx$ **b** $\displaystyle\int_0^1 x^7\, dx$ and $\displaystyle\int_0^1 (-x^7)\, dx$

2 Find: **a** $\displaystyle\int_0^1 x^2\, dx$ **b** $\displaystyle\int_1^2 x^2\, dx$ **c** $\displaystyle\int_0^2 x^2\, dx$ **d** $\displaystyle\int_0^1 3x^2\, dx$

3 Find: **a** $\displaystyle\int_0^2 (x^3 - 4x)\, dx$ **b** $\displaystyle\int_2^3 (x^3 - 4x)\, dx$ **c** $\displaystyle\int_0^3 (x^3 - 4x)\, dx$

4 Find: **a** $\displaystyle\int_0^1 x^2\, dx$ **b** $\displaystyle\int_0^1 \sqrt{x}\, dx$ **c** $\displaystyle\int_0^1 (x^2 + \sqrt{x})\, dx$

5 Evaluate the following integrals using area interpretation:

a $\displaystyle\int_0^3 f(x)\, dx$ **b** $\displaystyle\int_3^7 f(x)\, dx$

c $\displaystyle\int_2^4 f(x)\, dx$ **d** $\displaystyle\int_0^7 f(x)\, dx$

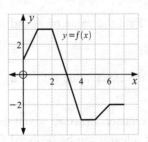

6 Evaluate the following integrals using area interpretation:

a $\displaystyle\int_0^4 f(x)\, dx$ **b** $\displaystyle\int_4^6 f(x)\, dx$

c $\displaystyle\int_6^8 f(x)\, dx$ **d** $\displaystyle\int_0^8 f(x)\, dx$

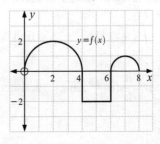

7 Write as a single integral:

   a $\displaystyle\int_2^4 f(x)\,dx + \int_4^7 f(x)\,dx$ **b** $\displaystyle\int_1^3 g(x)\,dx + \int_3^8 g(x)\,dx + \int_8^9 g(x)\,dx$

8   **a** If $\displaystyle\int_1^3 f(x)\,dx = 2$ and $\displaystyle\int_1^6 f(x)\,dx = -3$, find $\displaystyle\int_3^6 f(x)\,dx$.

   b If $\displaystyle\int_0^2 f(x)\,dx = 5$, $\displaystyle\int_4^6 f(x)\,dx = -2$ and $\displaystyle\int_0^6 f(x)\,dx = 7$, find $\displaystyle\int_2^4 f(x)\,dx$.

REVIEW SET 24A

1 Integrate with respect to x:

   a $\dfrac{4}{\sqrt{x}}$ **b** $\dfrac{3}{1-2x}$ **c** xe^{1-x^2} **d** e^{4-3x}

2 Integrate with respect to x: **a** $\sin^7 x \cos x$ **b** $\tan(2x)$ **c** $e^{\sin x}\cos x$

3 Find the exact value of: **a** $\displaystyle\int_{-5}^{-1} \sqrt{1-3x}\,dx$ **b** $\displaystyle\int_0^1 \dfrac{4x^2}{(x^3+2)^3}\,dx$

4 By differentiating $y = \sqrt{x^2 - 4}$, find $\displaystyle\int \dfrac{x}{\sqrt{x^2-4}}\,dx$.

5 A curve $y = f(x)$ has $f''(x) = 18x+10$. Find $f(x)$ if $f(0) = -1$ and $f(1) = 13$.

6 Evaluate: **a** $\displaystyle\int_0^{\frac{\pi}{3}} \cos^2\left(\tfrac{x}{2}\right)\,dx$ **b** $\displaystyle\int_0^{\frac{\pi}{3}} \tan x\,dx$

7 $\dfrac{4x-3}{2x+1}$ can be written in the form $A + \dfrac{B}{2x+1}$.

   a Find the value of A and B.   **b** Hence find $\displaystyle\int_0^2 \dfrac{4x-3}{2x+1}\,dx$.

8 Find the exact value of: **a** $\displaystyle\int_3^4 \dfrac{1}{\sqrt{2x+1}}\,dx$ **b** $\displaystyle\int_0^2 x^2 e^{x^3+1}\,dx$

9 Differentiate $\ln \sec x$, given that $\sec x > 0$.
   What integral can be deduced from this derivative?

10 If $\displaystyle\int_0^a e^{1-2x}\,dx = \tfrac{e}{4}$, find a in the form $\ln k$.

11 Find $\dfrac{d}{dx}(e^{-2x}\sin x)$ and hence find $\displaystyle\int_0^{\frac{\pi}{2}} \left[e^{-2x}(\cos x - 2\sin x)\right]\,dx$

REVIEW SET 24B

1 Find:

    a $\displaystyle\int \left(2e^{-x} - \frac{1}{x} + 3\right) dx$ **b** $\displaystyle\int \left(\sqrt{x} - \frac{1}{\sqrt{x}}\right)^2 dx$ **c** $\displaystyle\int (3 + e^{2x-1})^2 \, dx$

2 Evaluate: **a** $\displaystyle\int_1^2 (x^2 - 1)^2 \, dx$ **b** $\displaystyle\int_1^2 x(x^2 - 1)^2 \, dx$

3 Integrate: **a** $4\sin^2\left(\frac{x}{2}\right)$ **b** $(2 - \cos x)^2$

4 By differentiating $(3x^2 + x)^3$, find $\int (3x^2 + x)^2 (6x + 1)\, dx$.

5 Given that $f'(x) = x^2 - 3x + 2$ and $f(1) = 3$, find $f(x)$.

6 Differentiate $\sin(x^2)$ and hence find $\int x\cos(x^2)dx$.

7 Find the exact value of $\displaystyle\int_2^3 \frac{1}{\sqrt{3x-4}}\, dx$.

8 $f''(x) = 3x^2 + 2x$ and $f(0) = f(2) = 3$.

    Find: **a** $f(x)$ **b** the equation of the normal to $y = f(x)$ at $x = 2$.

9 Evaluate $\displaystyle\int_{\frac{\pi}{6}}^{\frac{\pi}{2}} \cot\theta\, d\theta$

10 Find A, B, C and D using the division algorithms, if:

    $\dfrac{x^3 - 3x + 2}{x - 2} = Ax^2 + Bx + C + \dfrac{D}{x - 2}$. Hence find $\displaystyle\int \frac{x^3 - 3x + 2}{x - 2}\, dx$.

11 **a** Find $\displaystyle\int \frac{1}{x+2}\, dx - \int \frac{2}{x-1}\, dx$.   **b** Hence find $\displaystyle\int \frac{x+5}{(x+2)(x-1)}\, dx$.

12 **a** Find constants A, B and C given that $\dfrac{4}{x(1-x^2)} = \dfrac{A}{x} + \dfrac{B}{x+1} + \dfrac{C}{x-1}$.

    b Hence find $\displaystyle\int \frac{4}{x(1-x^2)}\, dx$.

    c Find in simplest form, the exact value of $\displaystyle\int_2^4 \frac{4}{x(1-x^2)}\, dx$.

REVIEW SET 24C

1 Find y if: **a** $\dfrac{dy}{dx} = (x^2 - 1)^2$ **b** $\dfrac{dy}{dx} = 400 - 20e^{-\frac{x}{2}}$

2 Evaluate: **a** $\displaystyle\int_{-2}^{0} \dfrac{4}{2x-1}\, dx$ **b** $\displaystyle\int_{0}^{1} \dfrac{10x}{\sqrt{3x^2+1}}\, dx$

3 Find $\displaystyle\int \dfrac{\sin x}{\cos^4 x}\, dx$.

4 Find $\dfrac{d}{dx}(\ln x)^2$ and hence find $\displaystyle\int \dfrac{\ln x}{x}\, dx$.

5 Given that $f''(x) = 4x^2 - 3$, $f'(0) = 6$ and $f(2) = 3$, find $f(3)$.

6 Find the derivative of $x \tan x$ and hence determine $\int x \sec^2 x\, dx$.

7 Find $\int (2x+3)^n\, dx$ for all integers n.

8 **a** Find $(e^x + 2)^3$ using the binomial expansion.

   b Hence find the exact value of $\displaystyle\int_{0}^{1} (e^x + 2)^3\, dx$.

   c Check **b** using technology.

9 Evaluate: **a** $\displaystyle\int_{0}^{\frac{\pi}{6}} \sin^2\left(\tfrac{x}{2}\right) dx$ **b** $\displaystyle\int_{\frac{\pi}{4}}^{\frac{\pi}{3}} \dfrac{\sec^2 x}{\tan x}\, dx$

10 A function has slope function $2\sqrt{x} + \dfrac{a}{\sqrt{x}}$ and passes through the points $(0, 2)$ and $(1, 4)$. Find a and hence explain why the function $y = f(x)$ has no stationary points.

11 $\displaystyle\int_{a}^{2a} (x^2 + ax + 2)\, dx = \dfrac{73a}{2}$.   Find a.

12 Find $\dfrac{d}{dx}\left(\dfrac{e^{1-x}}{x^2}\right)$ and hence find the exact value of $\displaystyle\int_{1}^{2} \dfrac{e^{1-x}(x+2)}{x^3}\, dx$.

13 Find $\displaystyle\int \dfrac{\sin x}{\sqrt{\cos^n x}}\, dx$.   Comment on the existence of this integral.

Chapter **25**

Applications of integration

Contents: A   Finding areas between curves
B   Motion problems
C   Problem solving by integration

We have already seen how definite integrals can be related to the areas between functions and the x-axis. In this chapter we explore this relationship further, and consider other applications of integral calculus such as motion problems.

INVESTIGATION $\int_a^b f(x)\,dx$ AND AREAS

Does $\displaystyle\int_a^b f(x)\,dx$ always give us an area?

What to do:

1 Find $\displaystyle\int_0^1 x^3\,dx$ and $\displaystyle\int_{-1}^1 x^3\,dx$.

2 Explain why the first integral in **1** gives an area whereas the second integral does not. Graphical evidence is essential.

3 Find $\displaystyle\int_{-1}^0 x^3\,dx$ and explain why the answer is negative.

4 Check that $\displaystyle\int_{-1}^0 x^3\,dx + \int_0^1 x^3\,dx = \int_{-1}^1 x^3\,dx$.

A   FINDING AREAS BETWEEN CURVES

We have already established in **Chapter 24** that:

If $f(x)$ is positive and continuous on the interval $a \leqslant x \leqslant b$, then the area bounded by $y = f(x)$, the x-axis, and the vertical lines $x = a$ and $x = b$

is given by $\displaystyle\int_a^b f(x)\,dx$.

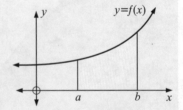

Notice also that the area bounded by $x = f(y)$, the y-axis, and the horizontal lines $y = a$ and $y = b$

is given by $\displaystyle\int_a^b f(y)\,dy$.

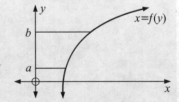

Example 1

Find the area of the region enclosed by $y = x^2 + 1$, the x-axis, $x = 1$ and $x = 2$.

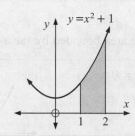

$$\text{Area} = \int_1^2 (x^2 + 1)\,dx$$

$$= \left[\frac{x^3}{3} + x\right]_1^2$$

$$= \left(\tfrac{8}{3} + 2\right) - \left(\tfrac{1}{3} + 1\right)$$

$$= 3\tfrac{1}{3} \text{ units}^2$$

We can check this result using a graphics calculator or graphing package.

GRAPHING
PACKAGE

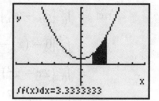

AREA BETWEEN TWO FUNCTIONS

If two functions $f(x)$ and $g(x)$ intersect at $x = a$ and $x = b$ and $f(x) \geqslant g(x)$ for all $x \in [a, b]$, then the area of the shaded region between their points of intersection is given by

$$\int_a^b [f(x) - g(x)]\,dx.$$

Alternatively, if we describe the upper and lower functions as $y = y_U$ and $y = y_L$ respectively, then the area is

$$\int_a^b [y_U - y_L]\,dx.$$

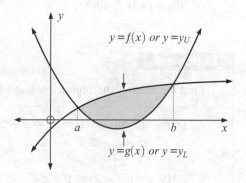

Proof: If we translate each curve vertically through $[0, k]$ until it is completely above the x-axis, the area does not change.

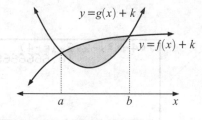

Area of shaded region

$$= \int_a^b [f(x) + k]\,dx - \int_a^b [g(x) + k]\,dx$$

$$= \int_a^b [f(x) - g(x)]\,dx$$

We can see immediately that if $y = f(x) = 0$ then the enclosed area is $\int_a^b [-g(x)]\,dx$.

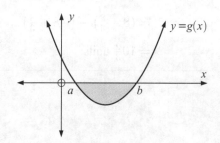

Example 2

Use $\int_a^b [y_U - y_L]\,dx$ to find the area bounded by the x-axis and $y = x^2 - 2x$.

The curve cuts the x-axis when $y = 0$

$\therefore \quad x^2 - 2x = 0$

$\therefore \quad x(x - 2) = 0$

$\therefore \quad x = 0 \text{ or } 2$

$\therefore$ the x-intercepts are 0 and 2.

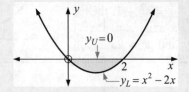

$$\text{Area} = \int_0^2 [y_U - y_L]\,dx$$

$$= \int_0^2 [0 - (x^2 - 2x)]\,dx$$

$$= \int_0^2 (2x - x^2)\,dx$$

$$= \left[x^2 - \frac{x^3}{3} \right]_0^2$$

$$= \left(4 - \tfrac{8}{3} \right) - (0)$$

$\therefore$ the area is $\frac{4}{3}$ units^2.

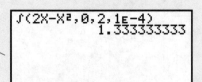

$\int (2X - X^2, 0, 2, 1_E - 4)$
$\qquad\qquad 1.333333333$

Solve d/dx ∫dx ∫dx   ▷

Example 3

Find the area of the region enclosed by $y = x + 2$ and $y = x^2 + x - 2$.

$y = x + 2$ meets $y = x^2 + x - 2$ where

$\qquad x^2 + x - 2 = x + 2$

$\therefore \quad x^2 - 4 = 0$

$\therefore \quad (x + 2)(x - 2) = 0$

$\therefore \quad x = \pm 2$

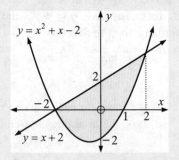

$$\text{Area} = \int_{-2}^2 [y_U - y_L]\,dx$$

$$= \int_{-2}^2 [(x + 2) - (x^2 + x - 2)]\,dx$$

$$= \int_{-2}^2 (4 - x^2)\,dx$$

$$= \left[4x - \frac{x^3}{3} \right]_{-2}^2$$

$$= \left(8 - \tfrac{8}{3} \right) - \left(-8 + \tfrac{8}{3} \right)$$

$$= 10\tfrac{2}{3} \text{ units}^2$$

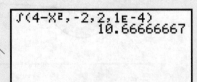

$\int (4 - X^2, -2, 2, 1_E - 4)$
$\qquad\qquad 10.66666667$

Solve d/dx ∫dx ∫dx   ▷

Example 4

Find the total area of the regions contained by $y = f(x)$ and the x-axis for $f(x) = x^3 + 2x^2 - 3x$.

$f(x) = x^3 + 2x^2 - 3x$
$\quad = x(x^2 + 2x - 3)$
$\quad = x(x - 1)(x + 3)$

$\therefore \quad y = f(x)$ cuts the x-axis at 0, 1, -3.

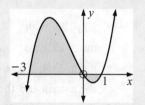

Total area

$= \int_{-3}^{0} (x^3 + 2x^2 - 3x)\,dx - \int_{0}^{1} (x^3 + 2x^2 - 3x)\,dx \quad \longleftarrow$

$= \left[\dfrac{x^4}{4} + \dfrac{2x^3}{3} - \dfrac{3x^2}{2} \right]_{-3}^{0} - \left[\dfrac{x^4}{4} + \dfrac{2x^3}{3} - \dfrac{3x^2}{2} \right]_{0}^{1}$

$= (0 - -11\tfrac{1}{4}) - (-\tfrac{7}{12} - 0) = 11\tfrac{5}{6}$ units^2

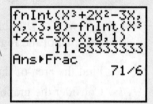

The area in **Example 4** may also be found using technology

as   total area $= \int_{-3}^{1} \left| x^3 + 2x^2 - 3x \right| \, dx$.

In general,   the area between the functions $f(x)$
and $g(x)$ on the interval $[a, b]$ is

$$\int_{a}^{b} |f(x) - g(x)| \, dx.$$

EXERCISE 25A

1 Find the exact value of the area of the region bounded by:

    a $y = x^2$, the x-axis and $x = 1$

    b $y = x^3$, the x-axis, $x = 1$ and $x = 4$

    c $y = e^x$, the x-axis, the y-axis and $x = 1$

    d the x-axis and the part of $y = 6 + x - x^2$ above the x-axis

    e $x = y^2 + 1$, the y-axis, and the lines $y = 1$ and $y = 2$

    f $x = \sqrt{y + 5}$, the y-axis, and the lines $y = -1$ and $y = 4$

2 Use $\int_{a}^{b} [f(x) - g(x)]\,dx$ or $\int_{a}^{b} [y_U - y_L]\,dx$ to find the exact value of the area between:

    a the axes and $y = \sqrt{9 - x}$ **b** $y = \dfrac{1}{x}$, the x-axis, $x = 1$ and $x = 4$

    c $y = \dfrac{1}{x}$, the x-axis, $x = -1$ and $x = -3$

    d $y = 2 - \dfrac{1}{\sqrt{x}}$, the x-axis and $x = 4$

    e $y = e^x + e^{-x}$, the x-axis, $x = -1$ and $x = 1$

    f $y = e^x$, the y-axis, the lines $y = 2$ and $y = 3$ using $\int \ln y \, dy = y \ln y - y + c$

3 **a** Find the area enclosed by one arch of $y = \sin(2x)$.

  b Show that the area enclosed by $y = \sin x$ and the x-axis from $x = 0$ to $x = \pi$ is 2 units^2.

  c Find the area enclosed by $y = \sin^2 x$ and the x-axis from $x = 0$ to $x = \pi$.

4 Use $\int_a^b [y_U - y_L]\, dx$ to find the exact value of the area bounded by:

  a the x-axis and $y = x^2 + x - 2$

  b the x-axis, $y = e^{-x} - 1$ and $x = 2$

  c the x-axis and the part of $y = 3x^2 - 8x + 4$ below the x-axis

  d $y = x^3 - 4x$, the x-axis, $x = 1$, and $x = 2$.

5 A region with $x \geqslant 0$ has boundaries defined by $y = \sin x$, $y = \cos x$ and the y-axis. Find the area of the region.

6 **a** Find the area of the region enclosed by $y = x^2 - 2x$ and $y = 3$.

  b Consider the graphs of $y = x - 3$ and $y = x^2 - 3x$.

   i Sketch the graphs on the same set of axes.

   ii Find the coordinates of the points where the graphs meet.

   iii Find the area of the region enclosed by the two graphs.

  c Determine the area of the region enclosed by $y = \sqrt{x}$ and $y = x^2$.

  d On the same set of axes, graph $y = e^x - 1$ and $y = 2 - 2e^{-x}$, showing axes intercepts and asymptotes.

   Find algebraically, the points of intersection of $y = e^x - 1$ and $y = 2 - 2e^{-x}$.

   Find the area of the region enclosed by the two curves.

  e Determine the exact value of the area of the region bounded by $y = 2e^x$, $y = e^{2x}$ and $x = 0$.

7 On the same set of axes, draw the graphs of the relations $y = 2x$ and $y^2 = 4x$. Determine the area of the region enclosed by these relations.

8 The graph alongside shows a small portion of the graph of $y = \tan x$.

A is a point on the graph with a y-coordinate of 1.

  a Find the coordinates of A.

  b Find the shaded area.

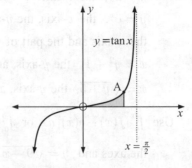

9 Sketch the circle with equation $x^2 + y^2 = 9$.

  a Explain why the upper half of the circle has equation $y = \sqrt{9 - x^2}$.

  b Hence, determine $\int_0^3 \sqrt{9 - x^2}\, dx$ without actually integrating the function.

  c Check your answer using technology.

10 Find the area enclosed by the function $y = f(x)$ and the x-axis for:

  a $f(x) = x^3 - 9x$ **b** $f(x) = -x(x-2)(x-4)$ **c** $f(x) = x^4 - 5x^2 + 4$.

11 The illustrated curves are those of $y = \sin x$ and $y = \sin(2x)$.

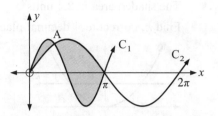

  a Identify each curve.

  b Find algebraically the coordinates of A.

  c Find the total area enclosed by C_1 and C_2 for $0 \leqslant x \leqslant \pi$.

12

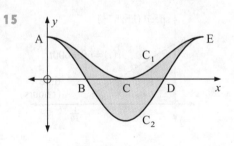

For the given graphs of $y = x^3 - 4x$ and $y = 3x + 6$:

  a write the shaded area as

   i the sum of two definite integrals

   ii a single definite integral involving modulus.

  b Find the total shaded area.

13 Find the areas enclosed by:

  a $y = x^3 - 5x$ and $y = 2x^2 - 6$

  b $y = -x^3 + 3x^2 + 6x - 8$ and $y = 5x - 5$

  c $y = 2x^3 - 3x^2 + 18$ and $y = x^3 + 10x - 6$

14 a Explain why the total area shaded is *not* equal to $\int_1^7 f(x)\,dx$.

  b What is the total shaded area equal to in terms of integrals?

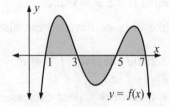

15

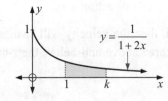

The illustrated curves are those of $y = \cos(2x)$ and $y = \cos^2 x$.

  a Identify each curve.

  b Determine the coordinates of A, B, C, D and E.

  c Show that the area of the shaded region is $\frac{\pi}{2}$ units^2.

16 Find, correct to 3 significant figures, the areas of the regions enclosed by the curves:

  a $y = e^{-x^2}$ and $y = x^2 - 1$ **b** $y = x^x$ and $y = 4x - \frac{1}{10}x^4$

17 The shaded area is 0.2 units^2.

Find k, correct to 4 decimal places.

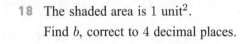

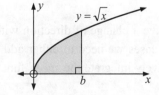

18 The shaded area is 1 unit^2.

Find b, correct to 4 decimal places.

19   The shaded area is 2.4 units^2.

Find k, correct to 4 decimal places.

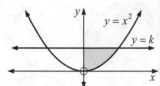

20   The shaded area is $6a$ units^2.

Find the exact value of a.

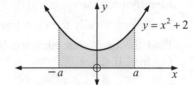

B   MOTION PROBLEMS

DISTANCES FROM VELOCITY GRAPHS

Suppose a car travels at a constant positive velocity of 60 km h^{-1} for 15 minutes. We know
the distance travelled = speed × time

$$= 60 \text{ km h}^{-1} \times \tfrac{1}{4} \text{ h}$$
$$= 15 \text{ km}.$$

When we graph *speed* against *time*, the graph is
a horizontal line and it is clear that the distance
travelled is the area shaded.

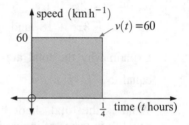

So, the distance travelled can also be found by

the definite integral $\displaystyle\int_0^{\frac{1}{4}} 60\,dt = 15$.

Now suppose the speed decreases at a constant
rate so that the car, initially travelling at
60 km h^{-1}, stops in 6 minutes.

In this case the average speed must be 30 km h^{-1},
so the distance travelled = 30 km h$^{-1} \times \tfrac{1}{10}$ h
$$= 3 \text{ km}$$

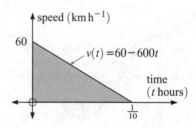

But the triangle has area $= \tfrac{1}{2} \times$ base × altitude

$$= \tfrac{1}{2} \times \tfrac{1}{10} \times 60 = 3$$

So, once again the shaded area gives us the distance travelled, and we can find it using the

definite integral $\displaystyle\int_0^{\frac{1}{10}} (60 - 600t)\,dt = 3$.

These results suggest that: distance travelled $= \displaystyle\int_{t_1}^{t_2} v(t)\,dt$ provided we do not change
direction.

If we have a change of direction within the time interval then the velocity will change sign. In
such cases we need to either add the components of area above and below the t-axis, or
alternatively integrate the *speed* function $|v(t)|$.

In general, distance travelled $= \displaystyle\int_{t_1}^{t_2} |v(t)| \, dt$

Example 5

The velocity-time graph for a train journey is illustrated in the graph alongside. Find the total distance travelled by the train.

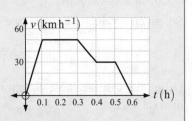

Total distance travelled
= total area under the graph
= area A + area B + area C + area D + area E
$= \frac{1}{2}(0.1)50 + (0.2)50 + \left(\frac{50+30}{2}\right)(0.1) + (0.1)30$
$\quad + \frac{1}{2}(0.1)30$
$= 2.5 + 10 + 4 + 3 + 1.5$
$= 21$ km

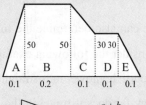

$\text{area} = \dfrac{a+b}{2} \times c$

EXERCISE 25B.1

1 A runner has the velocity-time graph shown. Find the total distance travelled by the runner.

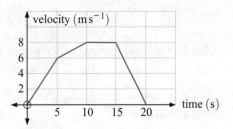

2

A car travels along a straight road with the velocity-time function illustrated.

a What is the significance of the graph:
  i above the t-axis
  ii below the t-axis?

b Find the total distance travelled by the car.

c Find the final displacement of the car.

3 A cyclist rides off from rest, accelerating at a constant rate for 3 minutes until she reaches 40 km h^{-1}. She then maintains a constant speed for 4 minutes until reaching a hill. She slows down at a constant rate to 30 km h^{-1} in one minute, then continues at this rate for 10 minutes. At the top of the hill she reduces her speed uniformly and is stationary 2 minutes later. After drawing a graph, find how far she has travelled.

DISPLACEMENT AND VELOCITY FUNCTIONS

In this section we are concerned with **motion in a straight line**, or **linear motion**.

Recall that for some displacement function $s(t)$ the velocity function is $s'(t)$ and that $t \geqslant 0$ in all situations.

So, given a velocity function we can determine the displacement function by the integral

$$s(t) = \int v(t) \, dt$$

Using the displacement function we can quickly determine the displacement in a time interval $[a, b]$.

$$\textbf{Displacement} = s(b) - s(a) = \int_a^b v(t) \, dt$$

We can also determine the **total distance travelled** in some time interval $a \leqslant t \leqslant b$.

Consider the following example:

A particle moves in a straight line with velocity function $v(t) = t - 3 \text{ cm s}^{-1}$.

How far does it travel in the first 4 seconds of motion?

We notice that $v(t)$ has sign diagram:

Since the velocity function changes sign at $t = 3$ seconds, the particle **reverses direction** at this time.

Now $s(t) = \int (t - 3) \, dt = \dfrac{t^2}{2} - 3t + c$ but we have no information to find c.

Clearly, the *displacement* of the particle in the first 4 seconds is
$$s(4) - s(0) = c - 4 - c = -4 \text{ cm}.$$

However, when calculating the distance travelled we need to remember the reversal of direction at $t = 3$.

We find the positions of the particle at $t = 0$, $t = 3$ and $t = 4$:
$$s(0) = c, \qquad s(3) = c - 4\tfrac{1}{2}, \qquad s(4) = c - 4.$$

Hence, we can draw a diagram of the motion:

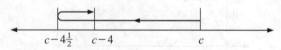

Thus the total distance travelled is $(4\tfrac{1}{2} + \tfrac{1}{2}) \text{ cm} = 5 \text{ cm}.$

Summary:

To find the total distance travelled given a velocity function $v(t) = s'(t)$ on $a \leqslant t \leqslant b$:

- Draw a sign diagram for $v(t)$ so that we can determine any directional changes.
- Determine $s(t)$ by integration, with integrating constant c, say.
- Find $s(a)$ and $s(b)$. Also find $s(t)$ at every point where there is a direction reversal.
- Draw a motion diagram.
- Determine the total distance travelled from the motion diagram.

$$\text{total distance travelled} = \int_a^b |v(t)|\, dt \qquad \text{displacement} = \int_a^b v(t)\, dt$$

Example 6

A particle P moves in a straight line with velocity function $v(t) = t^2 - 3t + 2 \text{ m s}^{-1}$.

a How far does P travel in the first 4 seconds of motion?

b Find the displacement of P after 4 seconds.

a $v(t) = s'(t) = t^2 - 3t + 2 \qquad \therefore$ sign diagram of v is:

$= (t-1)(t-2)$

Since the signs change, P reverses direction at $t = 1$ and $t = 2$ secs.

Now $s(t) = \int (t^2 - 3t + 2)\, dt = \dfrac{t^3}{3} - \dfrac{3t^2}{2} + 2t + c$

Now $s(0) = c$ $\qquad\qquad\qquad\qquad s(1) = \frac{1}{3} - \frac{3}{2} + 2 + c = c + \frac{5}{6}$

$s(2) = \frac{8}{3} - 6 + 4 + c = c + \frac{2}{3}$ $\qquad s(4) = \frac{64}{3} - 24 + 8 + c = c + 5\frac{1}{3}$

Motion diagram:

$\therefore$ total distance $= \left(c + \frac{5}{6} - c\right) + \left(c + \frac{5}{6} - [c + \frac{2}{3}]\right) + \left(c + 5\frac{1}{3} - [c + \frac{2}{3}]\right)$

$= \frac{5}{6} + \frac{5}{6} - \frac{2}{3} + 5\frac{1}{3} - \frac{2}{3}$

$= 5\frac{2}{3}$ m

```
fnInt(abs(X²-3X+
2),X,0,4)
          5.666666667
```

b Displacement $=$ final position $-$ original position

$= s(4) - s(0)$

$= c + 5\frac{1}{3} - c$

$= 5\frac{1}{3}$ m   i.e., $5\frac{1}{3}$ m to the right.

```
fnInt(X²-3X+2,X,
0,4)
          5.333333333
```

EXERCISE 25B.2

1 A particle has velocity function $v(t) = 1 - 2t \text{ cm s}^{-1}$ as it moves in a straight line.

a Find the total distance travelled in the first second of motion.

b Find the displacement of the particle at the end of one second.

2 Particle P has velocity $v(t) = t^2 - t - 2 \text{ cm s}^{-1}$.

a Find the total distance travelled in the first 3 seconds of motion.

b Find the displacement of the particle at the end of three seconds.

3 A particle moves along the x-axis with velocity function $x'(t) = 16t - 4t^3$ units/s. Find the total distance travelled in the time interval:

   a $0 \leqslant t \leqslant 3$ seconds   **b** $1 \leqslant t \leqslant 3$ seconds.

4 A particle moves in a straight line with velocity function $v(t) = \cos t$ $\mathrm{m\,s^{-1}}$.

   a Show that the particle oscillates between two points.

   b Find the distance between the two points in **a**.

VELOCITY AND ACCELERATION FUNCTIONS

We know that the acceleration function is the derivative of velocity, so $a(t) = v'(t)$.

So, given an acceleration function, we can determine the velocity function by the integral

$$v(t) = \int a(t)\ dt$$

EXERCISE 25B.3

1 The velocity of a particle travelling in a straight line is given by $v(t) = 50 - 10e^{-0.5t}$ $\mathrm{m\,s^{-1}}$, where $t \geqslant 0$, t in seconds.

   a State the initial velocity of the particle.

   b Find the velocity of the particle after 3 seconds.

   c How long will it take for the particle's velocity to increase to 45 $\mathrm{m\,s^{-1}}$?

   d Discuss $v(t)$ as $t \to \infty$.

   e Show that the particle's acceleration is always positive.

   f Draw the graph of $v(t)$ against t.

   g Find the total distance travelled by the particle in the first 3 seconds of motion.

2 A train moves along a straight track with acceleration $\frac{t}{10} - 3$ $\mathrm{m\,s^{-2}}$. If the initial velocity of the train is 45 $\mathrm{m\,s^{-1}}$, determine the total distance travelled in the first minute.

3 An object has initial velocity 20 $\mathrm{m\,s^{-1}}$ as it moves in a straight line with acceleration function $4e^{-\frac{t}{20}}$ $\mathrm{m\,s^{-2}}$.

   a Show that as t increases the object approaches a limiting velocity.

   b Find the total distance travelled in the first 10 seconds of motion.

C   PROBLEM SOLVING BY INTEGRATION

When we studied differential calculus, we saw how to find the rate of change of a function by differentiation.

In practical situations it is sometimes easier to measure the rate of change of a variable, for example, the rate of water flow through a pipe. In such situations we can use integration to find a function for the quantity concerned.

Example 7

The marginal cost of producing x urns per week is given by
$2.15 - 0.02x + 0.00036x^2$ dollars per urn provided $0 \leqslant x \leqslant 120$.
The initial costs before production starts are \$185. Find the total cost of producing 100 urns per day.

The marginal cost is $\quad \dfrac{dC}{dx} = 2.15 - 0.02x + 0.00036x^2$ \$/urn

$$\therefore \quad C(x) = \int (2.15 - 0.02x + 0.00036x^2)\, dx$$

$$= 2.15x - 0.02\frac{x^2}{2} + 0.00036\frac{x^3}{3} + c$$

$$= 2.15x - 0.01x^2 + 0.00012x^3 + c$$

But $\quad C(0) = 185 \qquad \therefore \quad c = 185$

$$\therefore \quad C(x) = 2.15x - 0.01x^2 + 0.00012x^3 + 185$$

$$\therefore \quad C(100) = 2.15(100) - 0.01(100)^2 + 0.00012(100)^3 + 185$$

$$= 420$$

$\therefore$ the total cost is \$420.

Example 8

A metal tube has an annulus cross-section as shown. The outer radius is 4 cm and the inner radius is 2 cm. Within the tube, water is maintained at a temperature of $100°C$. Within the metal the temperature drops off from inside to outside according to $\quad \dfrac{dT}{dx} = -\dfrac{10}{x} \quad$ where x is the distance from the central axis and $2 \leqslant x \leqslant 4$.

Find the temperature of the outer surface of the tube.

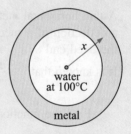
tube cross-section

$$\frac{dT}{dx} = \frac{-10}{x}, \quad \text{so} \quad T = \int \frac{-10}{x}\, dx$$

$$\therefore \quad T = -10\ln|x| + c$$

But when $x = 2$, $T = 100$

$$\therefore \quad 100 = -10\ln 2 + c$$

$$\therefore \quad c = 100 + 10\ln 2$$

Thus $\quad T = -10\ln x + 100 + 10\ln 2$

$$T = 100 + 10\ln\left(\tfrac{2}{x}\right)$$

When $\quad x = 4, \quad T = 100 + 10\ln\left(\tfrac{1}{2}\right) \approx 93.1$

$\therefore$ the outer surface temperature is $93.1°C$.

EXERCISE 25C

1   The marginal cost per day of producing x gadgets is $C'(x) = 3.15 + 0.004x$ euros per gadget.   What is the total cost of daily production of 800 gadgets given that the fixed costs before production commences are €450 per day?

2   The marginal profit for producing x dinner plates per week is given by $P'(x) = 15 - 0.03x$ dollars per plate.   If no plates are made a loss of $650 each week occurs.

   a   Find the profit function.

   b   What is the maximum profit and when does it occur?

   c   What production levels enable a profit to be made?

3   Jon needs to bulk-up for the football season. His energy needs t days after starting his weight gain program are given by $E'(t) = 350(80 + 0.15t)^{0.8} - 120(80 + 0.15t)$ calories per day. Find Jon's total energy needs over the first week of the program.

4   The tube cross-section shown has inner radius of 3 cm and outer radius 6 cm.   Within the tube, water is maintained at a temperature of $100°C$. Within the metal the temperature falls off at the rate

   $\dfrac{dT}{dx} = \dfrac{-20}{x^{0.63}}$ where x is the distance from the central

   axis and $3 \leqslant x \leqslant 6$.

   Find the temperature of the outer surface of the tube.

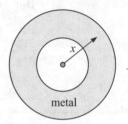

metal

5   A thin horizontal metal strip of length 1 metre has a deflection of y metres at a distance of x m from the fixed end.

   It is known that $\dfrac{d^2y}{dx^2} = -\frac{1}{10}(1 - x)^2$.

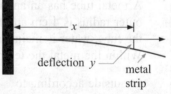

deflection y — metal strip

   a   Find the function $y(x)$ which measures the deflection from the horizontal at any

   point on the metal strip.   **Hint:**   When $x = 0$, what are y and $\dfrac{dy}{dx}$?

   b   Determine the greatest deflection of the metal strip.

6   A 4 m plank of wood is supported only at its ends, O and P. The plank sags under its own weight by y metres at a distance x metres from end O.

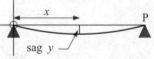

sag y —

   The differential equation $\dfrac{d^2y}{dx^2} = 0.01\left(2x - \dfrac{x^2}{2}\right)$ relates the variables x and y.

   a   Find the function $y(x)$ which measures the sag from the horizontal at any point along the plank.

   b   Find the maximum sag from the horizontal.

   c   Find the sag at a distance 1 m from P.

   d   Find the angle the plank makes with the horizontal at the point 1 m from P.

7 A contractor digs roughly cylindrical wells to a depth of h metres. He estimates that the cost of digging at the depth x metres is $\frac{1}{2}x^2+4$ dollars per m^3 of earth and rock extracted.

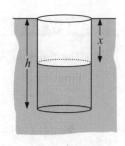

If a well is to have a radius r m, show that the total cost of digging a well is given by

$$C(h) = \pi r^2 \left(\frac{h^3 + 24h}{6} \right) + C_0 \text{ dollars.} \quad \textbf{Hint: } \frac{dC}{dx} = \frac{dC}{dV}\frac{dV}{dx}$$

8 The length of a continuous function $y = f(x)$ on $a \leqslant x \leqslant b$ is found using

$$L = \int_a^b \sqrt{1 + \left(\frac{dy}{dx} \right)^2} \, dx.$$

Find, correct to 5 decimal places, the length of $y = \sin x$ on $0 \leqslant x \leqslant \pi$.

9 A farmer with a large property plans a rectangular fruit orchard with one boundary being an irrigation canal. He has 4 km of fencing to fence the orchard.

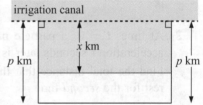

The farmer knows that the yield per unit of area changes the further you are away from the canal in proportion to

$\dfrac{1}{\sqrt{x+4}}$ where x is as shown in the figure.

If the yield from the field is denoted Y, and the area of the orchard is denoted A:

a explain why $\dfrac{dY}{dA} = \dfrac{k}{\sqrt{x+4}}$ where k is a constant

b show that $\dfrac{dY}{dx} = \dfrac{k(4-2p)}{\sqrt{x+4}}$ by using the chain rule

c explain why $Y = \displaystyle\int_0^p \dfrac{k(4-2p)}{\sqrt{x+4}} \, dx$

d show that $Y = 4k(2-p)[\sqrt{p+4} - 2]$.

e What dimensions should the orchard be to maximise the yield?

REVIEW SET 25A

1 The function $y = f(x)$ is graphed.

Find:

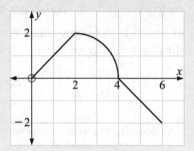

   a $\int_0^4 f(x)\,dx$

   b $\int_4^6 f(x)\,dx$

   c $\int_0^6 f(x)\,dx$

2 Write the total shaded area:

   a as the sum of three definite integrals

   b as one definite integral involving a modulus.

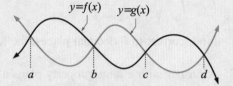

3 At time $t = 0$ a particle passes through the origin with velocity 27 cm s^{-1}. Its acceleration t seconds later is $6t - 30$ cm s^{-2}.

Find the total distance that the particle has travelled when it momentarily comes to rest for the *second* time.

4 Draw the graphs of $y^2 = x - 1$ and $y = x - 3$.

   a Find the coordinates where the graphs meet.   **b** Find the enclosed area.

5 Determine k if the enclosed region has area $5\frac{1}{3}$ units^2.

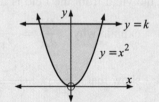

6 By appealing only to geometrical evidence, explain why: $\displaystyle\int_0^1 e^x\,dx + \int_1^e \ln x\,dx = e$.

7 A boat travelling in a straight line has its engine turned off at time $t = 0$. Its velocity at time t seconds thereafter is given by $v(t) = \dfrac{100}{(t+2)^2}$ m s^{-1}.

   a Find the initial velocity of the boat, and its velocity after 3 seconds.

   b Discuss $v(t)$ as $t \to \infty$.

   c Sketch the graph of $v(t)$ against t.

   d Find how long it takes for the boat to travel 30 metres.

   e Find the acceleration of the boat at any time t.

   f Show that $\dfrac{dv}{dt} = -kv^{\frac{3}{2}}$, and find the value of the constant k.

8 Find the total finite area enclosed by $y = x^3$ and $y = 7x^2 - 10x$.

9 Find a given that the area of the region between $y = e^x$ and the x-axis from $x = 0$ to $x = a$ is 2 units^2.

Hence determine b, given that the area of the region between $x = a$ and $x = b$ is also 2 units^2.

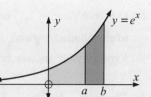

10 A cantilever of length L m has a deflection of y m at a distance x m from the fixed end. The variables are connected by $\dfrac{d^2y}{dx^2} = k(L - x)^2$ where k is the proportionality constant.

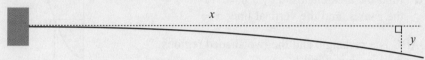

Find the greatest deflection of the cantilever in terms of k and L.

11 Determine the area enclosed by $y = \frac{2}{\pi}x$ and $y = \sin x$.

12 The figure shows the graphs of $y = \cos(2x)$ and $y = e^{3x}$ for $x \in [-\pi, \frac{\pi}{2}]$.

Find correct to 4 decimal places:

a the value of b

b the area of the shaded region.

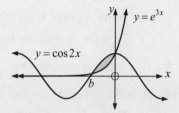

13 a Find $\dfrac{d}{dx}[\ln(\tan x + \sec x)]$ and hence find $\int \sec x\, dx$.

b Consider $x \mapsto \sec(2x)$ for $x \in [0, \pi]$.

    i Sketch the graph of the function on the given domain.

    ii Find the area of the region bounded by $y = \sec(2x)$, the y-axis, and the line $y = 3$.

REVIEW SET 25B

1 A particle moves in a straight line with velocity $v(t) = 2t - 3t^2$ m s^{-1}.
Find the distance travelled in the first second of motion.

2 Find the area of the region enclosed by $y = x^2 + 4x + 1$ and $y = 3x + 3$.

3 Determine $\int_0^2 \sqrt{4 - x^2}\, dx$ using graphical evidence only.

4 The current $I(t)$ milliamps in a circuit falls off in accordance with $\dfrac{dI}{dt} = \dfrac{-100}{t^2}$ where t is the time in seconds, $t \geqslant 0.2$.

It is known that when $t = 2$, the current is 150 milliamps. Find a formula for the current at any time $t \geqslant 0.2$, and hence find:

    a the current after 20 seconds   **b** what happens to the current as $t \to \infty$.

5 Is it true that $\int_{-1}^{3} f(x)\,dx$ represents the area of the shaded region?

Explain your answer briefly.

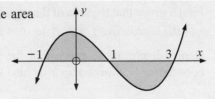

6 Consider $f(x) = \dfrac{x}{1+x^2}$.

  a Find the position and nature of all turning points of $y = f(x)$.

  b Discuss $f(x)$ as $x \to \infty$ and as $x \to -\infty$.

  c Sketch the graph of $y = f(x)$.

  d Find the area enclosed by $y = f(x)$, the x-axis, and the vertical line $x = -2$.

7 OABC is a rectangle and the two shaded regions are equal in area. Find k.

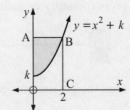

8   **a** Sketch the region bounded by $y = x^3 + 2$, the y-axis, and the horizontal lines $y = 3$ and $y = 6$.

  b Write x in the form $f(y)$.

  c Find the area of the region graphed in **a**.

9 Find the area enclosed by $y = 2x^3 - 9x$ and $y = 3x^2 - 10$.

10 Consider $f(x) = 2 - \sec^2 x$ on $[-4,\,4]$.

  a Use technology to help sketch the graph of the function.

  b Find the equations of the function's vertical asymptotes.

  c Find the axes intercepts.

  d Find the area of the region bounded by one arch of the function and the x-axis.

11

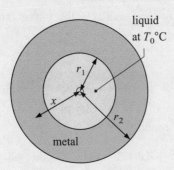

A metal tube has an annulus cross-section with radii r_1 and r_2 as shown.

Within the tube a liquid is maintained at temperature $T_0 \,^\circ$C.

Within the metal, the temperature drops from inside to outside according to $\dfrac{dT}{dx} = \dfrac{k}{x}$ where k is a negative constant and x is the distance from the central axis.

Show that the outer surface has temperature $T_0 + k \ln \left(\dfrac{r_2}{r_1} \right)$.

12 Find the area of the region enclosed by $y = \tan x$, the x-axis, and the vertical line $x = \frac{\pi}{3}$.

13 A particle moves in a straight line with velocity given by $v(t) = \sin t$ metres per second. Find the total distance travelled by the particle in the first 4 seconds of motion.

REVIEW SET 25C

1 A particle moves in a straight line with velocity $v(t) = t^2 - 6t + 8 \text{ m s}^{-1}$, $t \geqslant 0$.
  a Draw a sign diagram for $v(t)$.
  b Explain exactly what happens to the particle in the first 5 seconds of motion.
  c After 5 seconds, how far is the particle from its original position?
  d Find the total distance travelled in the first 5 seconds of motion.

2 Determine the area enclosed by the y-axis, the line $y = 3$ and the curve
$$x = \ln\left(\frac{y+3}{2}\right).$$

3 **a** Find a given that the shaded area is 4 units^2.
  b Find the x-coordinate of A if OA divides the shaded region into equal areas.

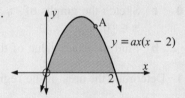

4 **a** The graph of $y = \sin x$ is drawn alongside. Use the graph to explain why
$$\tfrac{\pi}{2} < \int_0^\pi \sin x \, dx < \pi.$$

  b A is $\left(\frac{\pi}{4}, \frac{1}{\sqrt{2}}\right)$ and C is $\left(\frac{3\pi}{4}, \frac{1}{\sqrt{2}}\right)$.

  Use the diagram to show that the area under one arch of $y = \sin x$ (as illustrated) is close to $\frac{\pi}{4}(1 + \sqrt{2})$ units^2, but more than it.

  c Find exactly the area under one arch of $y = \sin x$.

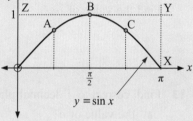

5 For the given function $y = f(x)$, $0 \leqslant x \leqslant 6$:
  a Show that A has equation $y_A = \sqrt{4x - x^2}$.
  b Show that B has equation
$$y_B = -\sqrt{10x - x^2 - 24}.$$
  c Find $\int_0^4 y_A \, dx$ and $\int_4^6 y_B \, dx$.
  d Hence, find $\int_0^6 f(x) \, dx$.

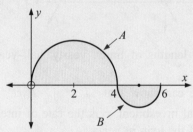

6 Determine m and c if the enclosed region has area $4\frac{1}{2}$ units^2.

Hint: You may need your graphics calculator to do the algebra.

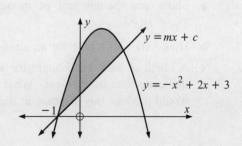

7 The ellipse shown has equation $\dfrac{x^2}{16} + \dfrac{y^2}{4} = 1$.

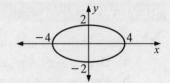

  a Sketch the graph again and mark on it the area represented by $\int_0^4 \frac{1}{2}\sqrt{16 - x^2}\, dx$.

  b Explain from the graph why we can say $8 < \int_0^4 \sqrt{16 - x^2}\, dx < 16$.

8 Find the area of the region enclosed by $y = x^3 + x^2 + 2x + 6$ and $y = 7x^2 - x - 4$.

9 Without actually integrating $\sin^3 x$, prove that $\int_0^\pi \sin^3 x\, dx < 4$.

  Hint: Graph $y = \sin^3 x$ for $0 \leqslant x \leqslant \pi$.

10 **a** Sketch the graphs of $y = \sin^2 x$ and $y = \sin x$ on the same set of axes for $x \in [0, \pi]$.

  b Find the exact value of the area enclosed by these curves for $x \in [0, \frac{\pi}{2}]$.

11 Determine the area of the region enclosed by $y = x$, $y = \sin x$ and $x = \pi$.

12 The shaded region has area $\frac{1}{2}$ unit^2.

Find the value of m.

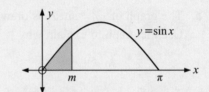

13 Find, correct to 4 decimal places:

  a the value of a

  b the area of the shaded region.

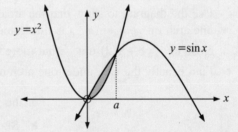

14 A bank may compound interest over various lengths of time: yearly, half-yearly, quarterly, monthly, daily, and so on.

If interest is compounded instantaneously, we can show that $I = \int_0^T P_0 r e^{rt}\, dt$ where I is the interest accrued, P_0 is the initial investment, r is the rate of interest per annum as a decimal, and T is the period of the loan in years.

  a Show that the amount of money in an account at time T is given by $P_T = P_0 e^{rT}$.

  b How long will it take for an amount to double at a rate of 8% p.a.?

  c A block of land was bought for \$55 in 1940 and sold for \$196 000 in 2007 at the same time of the year. What rate of interest, compounded instantaneously, would produce this increase in the same time?

Chapter 26

Volumes of revolution

Contents:

A   SOLIDS OF REVOLUTION

Consider the curve $y = f(x)$ for $a \leqslant x \leqslant b$.

If the shaded part is **rotated about the x-axis** through $360°$, a 3-dimensional solid will be formed. This solid is called a **solid of revolution**.

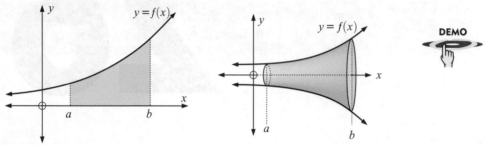

A solid of revolution will also be formed if the part of the curve is **rotated about the y-axis** through $360°$.

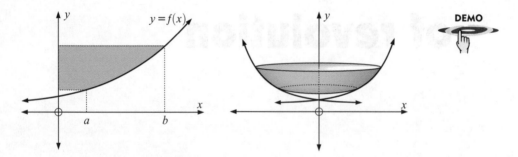

VOLUME OF REVOLUTION

We can use integration to find volumes of revolution between $x = a$ and $x = b$.

The solid can be thought to be made up of an infinite number of thin cylindrical discs.

Since the volume of a cylinder $= \pi r^2 h$, the left-most disc has approximate volume $\pi[f(a)]^2 \delta x$, and

the right-most disc has approximate volume $\pi[f(b)]^2 \delta x$.

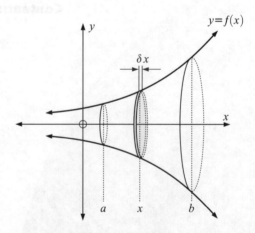

In general, $\pi[f(x)]^2 \delta x$ is the approximate volume for the illustrated disc.

As there are infinitely many discs, we let $\delta x \to 0$.

$$\therefore \quad V = \lim_{\delta x \to 0} \sum_{x=a}^{x=b} \pi[f(x)]^2 \, \delta x \ = \int_a^b \pi[f(x)]^2 \, dx = \pi \int_a^b y^2 \, dx$$

When the region enclosed by $y = f(x)$, the x-axis, and the vertical lines $x = a$, $x = b$ is rotated about the x-axis to generate a solid, the volume of the solid is given by

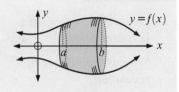

$$\text{Volume of revolution} = \pi \int_a^b y^2 \, dx.$$

Example 1

Use integration to find the volume of the solid generated when the line $y = x$ for $1 \leqslant x \leqslant 4$ is revolved around the x-axis.

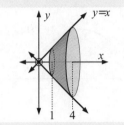

$$\begin{aligned}
\text{Volume of revolution} &= \pi \int_a^b y^2 \, dx \\
&= \pi \int_1^4 x^2 \, dx \\
&= \pi \left[\frac{x^3}{3} \right]_1^4 \\
&= \pi \left(\frac{64}{3} - \frac{1}{3} \right) \\
&= 21\pi \quad \text{cubic units}
\end{aligned}$$

Note: The volume of a cone can be calculated using
$$V_{\text{cone}} = \tfrac{1}{3}\pi r^2 h$$
So, in this example
$$\begin{aligned}
V &= \tfrac{1}{3}\pi 4^2(4) - \tfrac{1}{3}\pi 1^2(1) \\
&= \frac{64\pi}{3} - \frac{\pi}{3} \\
&= 21\pi \quad \text{which checks} \quad \checkmark
\end{aligned}$$

Example 2

Find the volume of the solid formed when the graph of the function $y = x^2$ for $0 \leqslant x \leqslant 5$ is revolved about the x-axis.

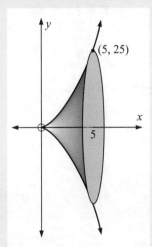

Volume of revolution
$$\begin{aligned}
&= \pi \int_a^b y^2 \, dx \\
&= \pi \int_0^5 (x^2)^2 \, dx \\
&= \pi \int_0^5 x^4 \, dx \\
&= \pi \left[\frac{x^5}{5} \right]_0^5 \\
&= \pi(625 - 0) \\
&= 625\pi \quad \text{cubic units}
\end{aligned}$$

Note:
Entering $Y_1 = X^2$ then $fnInt(\pi * Y_1^2, X, 0, 5)$ gives this volume.

Example 3

One arch of $y = \sin x$ is rotated about the x-axis.

What is the volume of revolution?

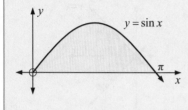

$y = \sin x$

$$\text{Volume} = \pi \int_a^b [f(x)]^2\, dx$$

$$= \pi \int_0^\pi \sin^2 x\, dx$$

$$= \pi \int_0^\pi \left[\tfrac{1}{2} - \tfrac{1}{2}\cos(2x)\right] dx$$

$$= \pi \left[\tfrac{x}{2} - \tfrac{1}{2}\left(\tfrac{1}{2}\right)\sin(2x)\right]_0^\pi$$

$$= \pi \left[\left(\tfrac{\pi}{2} - \tfrac{1}{4}\sin(2\pi)\right) - \left(0 - \tfrac{1}{4}\sin 0\right)\right]$$

$$= \pi \times \tfrac{\pi}{2}$$

$$= \tfrac{\pi^2}{2} \quad \text{units}^3$$

Using the same limit method we can derive a similar formula for a solid of revolution which has been rotated about the y-axis.

When the region enclosed by $x = f(y)$, the x-axis, and the horizontal lines $y = a$, $y = b$ is rotated about the y-axis to generate a solid, the volume of the solid is given by

$$\text{Volume of revolution} = \pi \int_a^b x^2\, dy$$

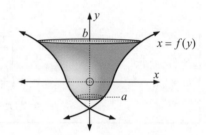

$x = f(y)$

Example 4

The graph of $y = \ln x$, $x \in [1, e]$ is rotated about the y-axis.

What is the volume of revolution?

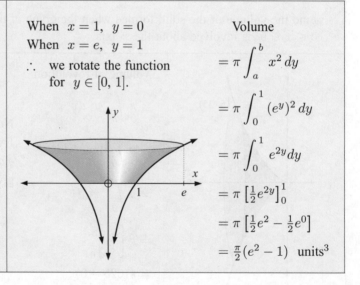

When $x = 1$, $y = 0$
When $x = e$, $y = 1$

$\therefore$ we rotate the function for $y \in [0, 1]$.

Volume

$$= \pi \int_a^b x^2\, dy$$

$$= \pi \int_0^1 (e^y)^2\, dy$$

$$= \pi \int_0^1 e^{2y}\, dy$$

$$= \pi \left[\tfrac{1}{2}e^{2y}\right]_0^1$$

$$= \pi \left[\tfrac{1}{2}e^2 - \tfrac{1}{2}e^0\right]$$

$$= \tfrac{\pi}{2}(e^2 - 1) \quad \text{units}^3$$

EXERCISE 26A

1 Find the volume of the solid formed when the following are revolved about the x-axis:

    a $y = 2x$ for $0 \leqslant x \leqslant 3$ **b** $y = \sqrt{x}$ for $0 \leqslant x \leqslant 4$

    c $y = x^3$ for $1 \leqslant x \leqslant 2$ **d** $y = x^{\frac{3}{2}}$ for $1 \leqslant x \leqslant 4$

    e $y = x^2$ for $2 \leqslant x \leqslant 4$ **f** $y = \sqrt{25 - x^2}$ for $0 \leqslant x \leqslant 5$

    g $y = \dfrac{1}{x - 1}$ for $2 \leqslant x \leqslant 3$ **h** $y = x + \dfrac{1}{x}$ for $1 \leqslant x \leqslant 3$

2 Use technology to find, correct to 3 significant figures, the volume of the solid of revolution formed when these functions are rotated through $360°$ about the x-axis:

    a $y = \dfrac{x^3}{x^2 + 1}$ for $x \in [1, 3]$ **b** $y = e^{\sin x}$ for $x \in [0, 2]$

3 Find the volume of revolution when the shaded region is revolved about the x-axis.

    a   **b**   **c**

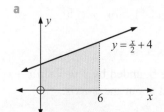 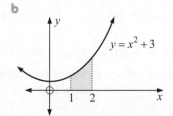 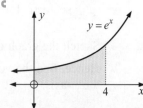

4

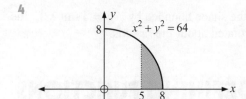

The shaded region is rotated about the x-axis.

    a   Find the volume of revolution.

    b   A hemispherical bowl of radius 8 cm contains water to a depth of 3 cm. What is the volume of water?

5   **a**   What is the name of the solid of revolution when the shaded region is revolved about the x-axis?

    b   Find the equation of the line segment AB in the form $y = ax + b$.

    c   Find a formula for the volume of the solid using

$$\pi \int_a^b y^2 \, dx.$$

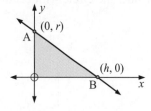

6

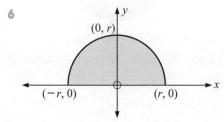

A circle with centre $(0, 0)$ and radius r units has equation $x^2 + y^2 = r^2$.

    a   If the shaded region is revolved about the x-axis, what solid is formed?

    b   Use integration to show that the volume of revolution is $\frac{4}{3}\pi r^3$.

7 Find the volumes of the solids formed when the following are revolved about the y-axis:

   a $y = x^2$ between $y = 0$ and $y = 4$

   b $y = \sqrt{x}$ between $y = 1$ and $y = 4$

   c $y = \ln x$ between $y = 0$ and $y = 2$

   d $y = \sqrt{x - 2}$ between $x = 2$ and $x = 11$

   e $y = (x - 1)^3$ between $x = 1$ and $x = 3$.

8 Find the exact value of the volume of the solid of revolution formed by rotating the relation $\dfrac{x^2}{9} + \dfrac{y^2}{16} = 1$, $x \geqslant 0$ through $360°$ about the y-axis.

9 Find the volume of revolution when these regions are rotated about the x-axis:

   a $y = \cos x$ for $0 \leqslant x \leqslant \frac{\pi}{2}$ **b** $y = \cos(2x)$ for $0 \leqslant x \leqslant \frac{\pi}{4}$

   c $y = \sqrt{\sin x}$ for $0 \leqslant x \leqslant \pi$ **d** $y = \dfrac{1}{\cos x}$ for $0 \leqslant x \leqslant \frac{\pi}{3}$

   e $y = \sec(3x)$ for $x \in [0, \frac{\pi}{12}]$ **f** $y = \tan\left(\frac{x}{2}\right)$ for $x \in [0, \frac{\pi}{2}]$

10 **a** Sketch the graph of $y = \sin x + \cos x$ for $0 \leqslant x \leqslant \frac{\pi}{2}$.

     b Hence, find the volume of revolution of the shape bounded by $y = \sin x + \cos x$, the x-axis, $x = 0$ and $x = \frac{\pi}{4}$ when it is rotated about the x-axis.

11 **a** Sketch the graph of $y = 4\sin(2x)$ from $x = 0$ to $x = \frac{\pi}{4}$.

     b Hence, find the volume of revolution of the shape bounded by $y = 4\sin(2x)$, the x-axis, $x = 0$ and $x = \frac{\pi}{4}$ when it is rotated about the x-axis.

B   VOLUMES FOR TWO DEFINING FUNCTIONS

Consider the circle with centre $(0, 3)$ and radius 1 unit.

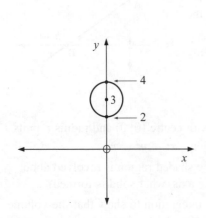

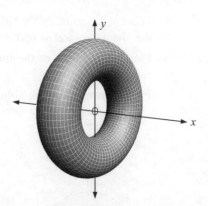

When this circle is revolved about the x-axis, we obtain a doughnut or *torus*.

In general, if the region bounded by $y = f(x)$ (on top) and $y = g(x)$ and the lines $x = a$, $x = b$ is revolved about the x-axis, then its volume of revolution is given by:

$$V = \pi \int_a^b [f(x)]^2 \, dx - \pi \int_a^b [g(x)]^2 \, dx$$

So, $\quad V = \pi \int_a^b \left([f(x)]^2 - [g(x)]^2 \right) dx \quad$ or $\quad V = \pi \int_a^b \left(y_U{}^2 - y_L{}^2 \right) dx$

Rotating

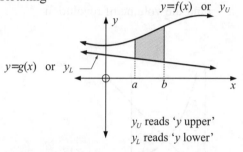

about the x-axis gives

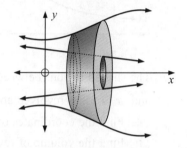

y_U reads 'y upper'
y_L reads 'y lower'

Example 5

Find the volume of revolution generated by revolving the region between $y = x^2$ and $y = \sqrt{x}$ about the x-axis.

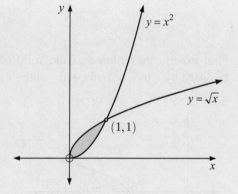

Volume $= \pi \int_0^1 \left(y_U{}^2 - y_L{}^2 \right) dx$

$= \pi \int_0^1 \left((\sqrt{x})^2 - (x^2)^2 \right) dx$

$= \pi \int_0^1 (x - x^4) \, dx$

$= \pi \left[\dfrac{x^2}{2} - \dfrac{x^5}{5} \right]_0^1$

$= \pi \left((\tfrac{1}{2} - \tfrac{1}{5}) - (0) \right)$

$= \tfrac{3\pi}{10}$ units^3

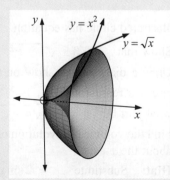

EXERCISE 26B

1 The shaded region between $y = 4 - x^2$ and
$y = 3$ is revolved about the x-axis.

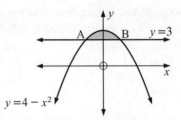

  a What are the coordinates of A and B?
  b Find the volume of revolution.

2

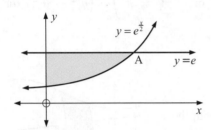

The shaded region is revolved about
the x-axis.

  a   Find the coordinates of A.
  b   Find the volume of revolution.

3 The shaded region (between $y = x$, $y = \dfrac{1}{x}$
and $x = 2$) is revolved about the x-axis.

  a Find the coordinates of A.
  b Find the volume of revolution.

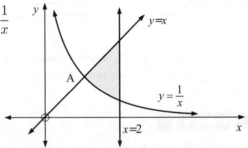

4 Find exactly the volume of the solid of revolution generated by rotating the region
enclosed by $y = x^2 - 4x + 6$ and $x + y = 6$ through $360°$ about the x-axis.

5

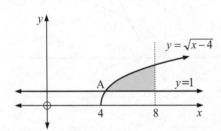

The shaded region (between $y = \sqrt{x-4}$,
$y = 1$ and $x = 8$) is revolved about the
x-axis.

  a   What are the coordinates of A?
  b   Find the volume of revolution.

6 The illustrated circle has equation $x^2 + (y - 3)^2 = 4$.

  a Show that $y = 3 \pm \sqrt{4 - x^2}$.

  b Draw a diagram and show on it what part of the
circle is represented by $y = 3 + \sqrt{4 - x^2}$ and
what part by $y = 3 - \sqrt{4 - x^2}$.

  c Find the volume of revolution of the shaded region
about the x-axis.

  Hint: Substitute $x = 2 \sin u$ to evaluate the
integral. Use your calculator to check
your answer.

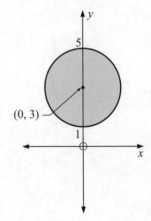

7 The length of a chord of the circle with equation $x^2 + y^2 = r^2$ is equal to the radius of the circle. The chord is parallel to the y-axis and a solid of revolution is generated by rotating the minor segment cut off by the chord through $360°$ about the y-axis.

Prove that the volume of the solid formed is given by $V = \dfrac{\pi r^3}{6}$.

8 A circle has equation $x^2 + y^2 = r^2$ where $r > 3$. A minor segment is cut off by a chord of length 6 units drawn parallel to the y-axis.

Show that the volume of the solid of revolution formed by rotating the segment through $360°$ about the y-axis is independent of the value of r.

9

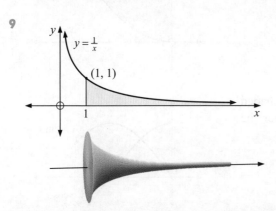

Prove that the shaded area from $x = 1$ to infinity is infinite whereas its volume of revolution is finite.

REVIEW SET 26

1 Find the volume of the solid of revolution formed when the following are rotated about the x-axis:

   a $y = x$ between $x = 4$ and $x = 10$

   b $y = x + 1$ between $x = 4$ and $x = 10$

   c $y = \sin x$ between $x = 0$ and $x = \pi$

   d $y = \sqrt{9 - x^2}$ between $x = 0$ and $x = 3$.

2 Find the volume of the solid of revolution formed when the shaded region is rotated through $360°$ about the x-axis:

   a

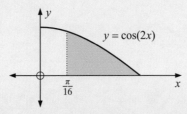

   b

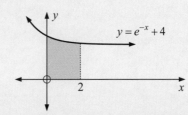

3 Find the volume of revolution when $y = \csc x$ is rotated through $360°$ about the x-axis for $\frac{\pi}{4} \leqslant x \leqslant \frac{3\pi}{4}$.

4 Find the volume of the solid of revolution formed when the following are rotated about the y-axis:

   a $x = y^2$ between $y = 1$ and $y = 2$

   b $y = \sqrt[3]{x^2}$ between $y = 2$ and $y = 3$

   c $y = x^3$ between $x = 1$ and $x = 2$

5 Find the volume of revolution generated by rotating the shaded region through $360°$ about the x-axis:

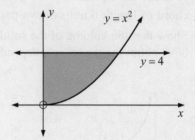

6 Find the volume of revolution if the shaded region is rotated through $360°$ about the x-axis:

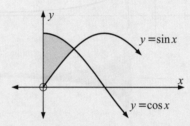

7

   a Use $V = \frac{1}{3}\pi r^2 h$ to find the volume of this cone.

   b Check your answer to **a** by integration.

8 Find the volume enclosed when $y = x^3$, from the x-axis to $y = 8$, is revolved about the y-axis.

Chapter 27

Further integration and differential equations

Contents:

In the previous chapters we have seen several techniques for finding integrals, including:

- integrating **term by term**
- integrating by using the **reverse process of differentiation**
- integration by **substitution**

In this chapter we consider some more special integrals and techniques for integration, including **integration by parts**.

We conclude the chapter with a study of **separable differential equations** which can be solved by integration.

A | THE INTEGRALS OF $\dfrac{1}{\sqrt{a^2 - x^2}}$ AND $\dfrac{1}{x^2 + a^2}$

The integrals of $\dfrac{1}{\sqrt{a^2 - x^2}}$ and $\dfrac{1}{x^2 + a^2}$ can be obtained by considering the derivatives

of $y = \arcsin\left(\frac{x}{a}\right)$ and $y = \arctan\left(\frac{x}{a}\right)$.

Consider $y = \arcsin\left(\frac{x}{a}\right)$

$$\therefore \quad x = a\sin y$$

$$\therefore \quad \frac{dx}{dy} = a\cos y$$

$$= a\sqrt{1 - \sin^2 y}$$

$$= a\sqrt{1 - \frac{x^2}{a^2}}$$

$$= \sqrt{a^2 - x^2}$$

$$\therefore \quad \frac{dy}{dx} = \frac{1}{\sqrt{a^2 - x^2}}$$

$$\therefore \quad \int \frac{1}{\sqrt{a^2 - x^2}}\, dx = \arcsin\left(\frac{x}{a}\right) + c$$

Consider $y = \arctan\left(\frac{x}{a}\right)$

$$\therefore \quad x = a\tan y$$

$$\therefore \quad \frac{dx}{dy} = a\sec^2 y$$

$$= a(1 + \tan^2 y)$$

$$= a\left(1 + \frac{x^2}{a^2}\right)$$

$$= \frac{a^2 + x^2}{a}$$

$$\therefore \quad \frac{dy}{dx} = \frac{a}{x^2 + a^2}$$

$$\therefore \quad \int \frac{1}{x^2 + a^2}\, dx = \frac{1}{a}\arctan\left(\frac{x}{a}\right) + c$$

Example 1

Find: **a** $\displaystyle\int \frac{1}{\sqrt{9 - x^2}}\, dx$ **b** $\displaystyle\int \frac{5}{4x^2 + 8}\, dx$

a $\displaystyle\int \frac{1}{\sqrt{9 - x^2}}\, dx$

$$= \arcsin\left(\frac{x}{3}\right) + c$$

b $\displaystyle\int \frac{5}{4x^2 + 8}\, dx$

$$= \frac{5}{4}\int \frac{1}{x^2 + (\sqrt{2})^2}\, dx$$

$$= \frac{5}{4} \times \frac{1}{\sqrt{2}}\arctan\left(\frac{x}{\sqrt{2}}\right) + c$$

$$= \frac{5}{4\sqrt{2}}\arctan\left(\frac{x}{\sqrt{2}}\right) + c$$

EXERCISE 27A

1 Find:

a $\int \dfrac{4}{\sqrt{1-x^2}}\,dx$ **b** $\int \dfrac{3}{\sqrt{4-x^2}}\,dx$ **c** $\int \dfrac{1}{x^2+16}\,dx$ **d** $\int \dfrac{1}{4x^2+1}\,dx$

e $\int \dfrac{1}{\sqrt{1-4x^2}}\,dx$ **f** $\int \dfrac{2}{\sqrt{4-9x^2}}\,dx$ **g** $\int \dfrac{1}{4+2x^2}\,dx$ **h** $\int \dfrac{5}{9+4x^2}\,dx$

2 **a** Sketch the graph of $y = \dfrac{1}{\sqrt{1-x^2}}$.

   b Explain algebraically why the function
     i is symmetrical about the y-axis   **ii** has domain $x \in \,]-1,1\,[$.

   c Find the exact area enclosed by the function and the x-axis, the y-axis, and the line $x = \frac{1}{2}$.

B   FURTHER INTEGRATION BY SUBSTITUTION

Here are some suggestions of possible substitutions to help integrate more difficult functions.

Note that these substitutions may not always lead to success, so sometimes other substitutions will be needed.

With practice you will develop a feeling for which substitution is best in a given situation.

When a function contains	Try substituting
$\sqrt{f(x)}$	$u = f(x)$
$\ln x$	$u = \ln x$
$\sqrt{a^2 - x^2}$	$x = a\sin\theta$
$x^2 + a^2$ or $\sqrt{x^2 + a^2}$	$x = a\tan\theta$
$\sqrt{x^2 - a^2}$	$x = a\sec\theta$

Example 2

Find $\int x\sqrt{x+2}\,dx$.

Let $u = x + 2$

$\therefore \dfrac{du}{dx} = 1$

$\therefore \displaystyle\int x\sqrt{x+2}\,dx$

$= \displaystyle\int (u-2)\sqrt{u}\,\dfrac{du}{dx}\,dx$

$= \displaystyle\int (u^{\frac{3}{2}} - 2u^{\frac{1}{2}})\,du$

$= \dfrac{u^{\frac{5}{2}}}{\frac{5}{2}} - \dfrac{2u^{\frac{3}{2}}}{\frac{3}{2}} + c$

$= \tfrac{2}{5}(x+2)^{\frac{5}{2}} - \tfrac{4}{3}(x+2)^{\frac{3}{2}} + c$

EXERCISE 27B

1 Find using a suitable substitution:

   a $\int x\sqrt{x-3}\,dx$ **b** $\int x^2\sqrt{x+1}\,dx$ **c** $\int x^3\sqrt{3-x^2}\,dx$

   d $\int t^3\sqrt{t^2+2}\,dt$ **e** $\int \dfrac{\sqrt{x-1}}{x}\,dx$ **Hint:** in **e** let $u = \sqrt{x-1}$.

Example 3

Find the exact value of $\displaystyle\int_{-4}^{6} x\sqrt{x+4}\,dx$.

Let $u = x + 4$ $\therefore$ $\dfrac{du}{dx} = 1$ $\therefore$ $\displaystyle\int_{-4}^{6} x\sqrt{x+4}\,dx = \int_{0}^{10} (u-4)\sqrt{u}\,du$

When $x = -4$, $u = 0$.
When $x = 6$, $u = 10$.

$$= \int_{0}^{10} (u^{\frac{3}{2}} - 4u^{\frac{1}{2}})\,du$$

```
Plot1  Plot2  Plot3
\Y1▤X√(X+4)
-----
fnInt(Y1,X,-4,6)
      42.16370172
-----
(40/3)√(10
      42.16370214
```

$$= \left[\tfrac{2}{5}u^{\frac{5}{2}} - \tfrac{8}{3}u^{\frac{3}{2}}\right]_{0}^{10}$$

$$= \tfrac{2}{5} \times 10^{\frac{5}{2}} - \tfrac{8}{3} \times 10^{\frac{3}{2}}$$

$$= 40\sqrt{10} - \tfrac{80}{3}\sqrt{10}$$

$$= \tfrac{40}{3}\sqrt{10}$$

Example 4

Find $\displaystyle\int \dfrac{\sqrt{x^2-9}}{x}\,dx$.

Let $x = 3\sec\theta$ $\therefore$ $\dfrac{dx}{d\theta} = 3\sec\theta\tan\theta$

So, $\displaystyle\int \dfrac{\sqrt{x^2-9}}{x}\,dx = \int \dfrac{\sqrt{9\sec^2\theta - 9}}{3\sec\theta}\,3\sec\theta\tan\theta\,d\theta$

$\sec\theta = \dfrac{x}{3}$

$$= \int 3\sqrt{\sec^2\theta - 1}\,\tan\theta\,d\theta$$

$\therefore$ $\cos\theta = \dfrac{3}{x}$

$$= \int 3\tan^2\theta\,d\theta$$

$$= \int (3\sec^2\theta - 3)\,d\theta$$

$$= 3\tan\theta - 3\theta + c$$

$$= \sqrt{x^2-9} - 3\arccos\left(\tfrac{3}{x}\right) + c$$

$\therefore$ $\tan\theta = \dfrac{\sqrt{x^2-9}}{3}$

2 Find the exact value of:

a $\displaystyle\int_{3}^{4} x\sqrt{x-1}\,dx$ b $\displaystyle\int_{0}^{3} x\sqrt{x+6}\,dx$ c $\displaystyle\int_{2}^{5} x^2\sqrt{x-2}\,dx$

Check each answer using technology.

3 Integrate with respect to x:

a $\dfrac{x^2}{9+x^2}$ b $\dfrac{x^2}{\sqrt{1-x^2}}$ c $\dfrac{2x}{x^2+9}$ d $\dfrac{4\ln x}{x\left(1 + [\ln x]^2\right)}$

e $\dfrac{\sqrt{x^2-4}}{x}$ f $\sin x \cos 2x$ g $\dfrac{1}{\sqrt{9-4x^2}}$ h $\dfrac{x^3}{1+x^2}$

i $\dfrac{1}{x\left(9+4\left[\ln x\right]^2\right)}$ **j** $\dfrac{1}{x(x^2+16)}$ **k** $\dfrac{1}{x^2\sqrt{16-x^2}}$ **l** $x^2\sqrt{4-x^2}$

C   INTEGRATION BY PARTS

Some functions can only be integrated using **integration by parts**, which is a method we derive from the product rule of differentiation.

Since $\dfrac{d}{dx}(uv) = u'v + uv'$ then $\int (u'v + uv')\,dx = uv$

$\therefore \quad \int u'v\,dx + \int uv'dx = uv$

$\therefore \quad \int uv'\,dx = uv - \int u'v\,dx$

So, providing $\int u'v\,dx$ can be easily found, we can find $\int uv'\,dx$ using

$$\int uv'\,dx = uv - \int u'v\,dx \quad \textbf{or} \quad \int u\,\dfrac{dv}{dx}\,dx = uv - \int v\,\dfrac{du}{dx}\,dx$$

Example 5

Find: **a** $\int xe^{-x}\,dx$ **b** $\int x\cos x\,dx$

a $u = x \qquad v' = e^{-x}$
$ \ u' = 1 \qquad v = -e^{-x}$

$\therefore \ \int xe^{-x}\,dx = -xe^{-x} - \int(-e^{-x})\,dx$
$\phantom{\therefore \ \int xe^{-x}\,dx} = -xe^{-x} + (-e^{-x}) + c$
$\phantom{\therefore \ \int xe^{-x}\,dx} = -e^{-x}(x+1) + c$

Check:

$\dfrac{d}{dx}(-e^{-x}(x+1) + c)$
$= e^{-x}(x+1) + -e^{-x}(1) + 0$
$= xe^{-x} + e^{-x} - e^{-x}$
$= xe^{-x} \ \checkmark$

b $u = x \qquad v' = \cos x$
$ \ u' = 1 \qquad v = \sin x$

$\therefore \ \int x\cos x\,dx = x\sin x - \int \sin x\,dx$
$ = x\sin x - (-\cos x) + c$
$ = x\sin x + \cos x + c$

Check:

$\dfrac{d}{dx}(x\sin x + \cos x + c)$
$= 1 \times \sin x + x\cos x - \sin x$
$= \sin x + x\cos x - \sin x$
$= x\cos x \ \checkmark$

EXERCISE 27C

1 Use integration by parts to find the integral of the following functions with respect to x:

a xe^x	**b** $x\sin x$	**c** $x^2\ln x$
d $x\sin 3x$	**e** $x\cos 2x$	**f** $x\sec^2 x$
g $\ln x$	**h** $(\ln x)^2$	**i** $\arctan x$

> When using 'integration by parts' the function u should be easy to differentiate and v should be easy to integrate.

Hint: In **g** write $\ln x$ as $1\ln x$.
$\phantom{\textbf{Hint:}\ }$ In **i** write $\arctan x$ as $1\arctan x$.

Sometimes it is necessary to use integration by parts *twice* in order to find an integral.

Example 6

Find $\int e^x \sin x \, dx$.

$\int e^x \sin x \, dx$

$= e^x(-\cos x) - \int e^x(-\cos x)\, dx$ ⟵ $\begin{cases} u = e^x & v' = \sin x \\ u' = e^x & v = -\cos x \end{cases}$

$= -e^x \cos x + \int e^x \cos x \, dx$

$= -e^x \cos x + e^x \sin x - \int e^x \sin x \, dx$ ⟵ $\begin{cases} u = e^x & v' = \cos x \\ u' = e^x & v = \sin x \end{cases}$

$\therefore \quad 2\int e^x \sin x \, dx = -e^x \cos x + e^x \sin x$

$\therefore \quad \int e^x \sin x \, dx = \frac{1}{2}e^x(\sin x - \cos x) + c$

---

2 Find these integrals:

   a $x^2 e^{-x}$ **b** $e^x \cos x$ **c** $e^{-x} \sin x$ **d** $x^2 \sin x$

3 **a** Use integration by parts to find $\int u^2 e^u \, du$.

   b Hence find $\int (\ln x)^2 \, dx$ using the substitution $u = \ln x$.

4 **a** Use integration by parts to find $\int u \sin u \, du$.

   b Hence find $\int \sin \sqrt{2x} \, dx$ using the substitution $u^2 = 2x$.

5 Find $\int \cos \sqrt{3x} \, dx$ using the substitution $u^2 = 3x$.

INVESTIGATION 1   **NUMERICAL INTEGRATION**

There are many functions that do not have indefinite integrals. In other words, we cannot write the indefinite integral as a function. However, definite integrals can still be determined by **numerical methods**. An example of such a method is the upper and lower rectangles we used in **Chapter 19**.

A slightly more accurate method is the **midpoint rule** in which we take the height of each rectangle to be the value of the function at the midpoint of the subinterval.

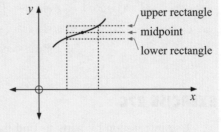

For example, consider finding the area between $f(x) = \sin(x^2)$ and the x-axis from $x = 0$ to $x = 1$.

The graph of $f(x) = \sin(x^2)$ is:

$f(x)$ is an even function and does not have an indefinite integral, so a numerical method is essential for

$\int_0^1 \sin(x^2) \, dx$ to be evaluated.

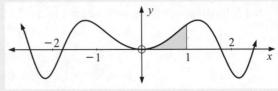

What to do:

1   Suppose the interval from 0 to 1 is divided into 10 equal subintervals of width 0.1.
    Using the midpoint rule, the shaded area is

$$\int_0^1 \sin(x^2)dx \approx [f(0.05) + f(0.15) + f(0.25) + \ldots\ldots + f(0.95)]\, \delta x$$

where $\delta x = 0.1$ is the subinterval width.

Use this formula to estimate the integral to 3 decimal places.

AREA FINDER

2   Click on the area finder icon and find the area estimate for
    $n = 10,\ 100,\ 1000,\ 10\,000$.

3   Use your graphics calculator's definite integral function to find the area.

4   Now find $\int_0^2 \sin(x^2)\, dx$.

5   What is the area enclosed between $y = \sin(x^2)$, the x-axis, and the vertical line
    $x = 2$?

D   MISCELLANEOUS INTEGRATION

We have now practised several integration techniques with clues given as to what method to
use. In this section we attempt to find integrals without clues.

EXERCISE 27D

1   Integrate with respect to x:

    a $\dfrac{e^x + e^{-x}}{e^x - e^{-x}}$ **b** 7^x **c** $(3x + 5)^5$ **d** $\dfrac{\sin x}{2 - \cos x}$

    e $x \sec^2 x$ **f** $\cot 2x$ **g** $x(x + 3)^3$ **h** $\dfrac{(x + 1)^3}{x}$

    i $x^2 e^{-x}$ **j** $x\sqrt{1 - x}$ **k** $x^2\sqrt{1 - x^2}$ **l** $\dfrac{3}{x\sqrt{x^2 - 4}}$

    m $x^2\sqrt{x - 3}$ **n** $\tan^3 x$ **o** $\dfrac{\ln(x + 2)}{(x + 2)^2}$ **p** $\dfrac{1}{x^2 + 2x + 3}$

2   Integrate with respect to x:

    a $\dfrac{1}{x^2 + 9}$ **b** $\dfrac{4}{\sqrt{x}\,\sqrt{1 - x}}$ **c** $\ln(2x)$ **d** $e^{-x}\cos x$

    e $\dfrac{1}{x(1 + x^2)}$ **f** $\dfrac{\arctan x}{1 + x^2}$ **g** $\sqrt{9 - x^2}$ **h** $\dfrac{(\ln x)^2}{x^2}$

    i $\dfrac{x}{\sqrt{x - 3}}$ **j** $\sin 4x \cos x$ **k** $\dfrac{2x + 3}{x^2 - 2x + 5}$ **l** $\cos^3 x$

    m $\dfrac{x + 4}{x^2 + 4}$ **n** $\dfrac{1 - 2x}{\sqrt{4 - x^2}}$ **o** $\dfrac{x^3}{(2 - x)^3}$ **p** $\sin^5 x \cos^5 x$

E | SEPARABLE DIFFERENTIAL EQUATIONS

Consider a function $y = f(x)$. We know the derivative $\dfrac{dy}{dx}$ is the rate at which the function changes with respect to its independent variable x.

> A **differential equation** is an equation which connects the derivative(s) of a function to the function itself and variables in which the function is defined.

Examples of differential equations are: $\dfrac{dy}{dx} = \dfrac{x^2}{y}$ and $\dfrac{d^2y}{dx^2} - 3\dfrac{dy}{dx} + 4y = 0$

These are some examples of situations where differential equations are observed:

A falling object

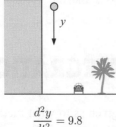

$$\dfrac{d^2y}{dt^2} = 9.8$$

A parachutist

$$m\dfrac{dv}{dt} = mg - av^2$$

Object on a spring

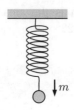

$$m\dfrac{d^2y}{dt^2} = -ky$$

SEPARABLE DIFFERENTIAL EQUATIONS

> Differential equations which can be written in the form $\dfrac{dy}{dx} = \dfrac{f(x)}{g(y)}$ are known as **separable differential equations**.

Notice that $g(y)\dfrac{dy}{dx} = f(x)$ and so $\displaystyle\int g(y)\dfrac{dy}{dx}\,dx = \int f(x)\,dx$ when we integrate both sides with respect to x.

Consequently, $\int g(y)\,dy = \int f(x)\,dx$ which enables us to solve the original differential equation.

When we integrate, the solution involves unknown constants, and this is called a **general solution** of the differential equation.

The constants are evaluated using **initial conditions** to give a **particular solution**.

Example 7

Find the general solutions to the following separable differential equations:

   a $\dfrac{dy}{dx} = ky$ **b** $\dfrac{dy}{dx} = k(A - y)$

---

   a $\dfrac{dy}{dx} = ky$ **b** $\dfrac{dy}{dx} = k(A - y) = -k(y - A)$

$$\therefore \quad \frac{1}{y}\frac{dy}{dx} = k \qquad\qquad \therefore \quad \frac{1}{y-A}\frac{dy}{dx} = -k$$

$$\therefore \quad \int \frac{1}{y}\frac{dy}{dx}\,dx = \int k\,dx \qquad \therefore \quad \int \frac{1}{y-A}\frac{dy}{dx}\,dx = \int -k\,dx$$

$$\therefore \quad \int \frac{1}{y}\,dy = \int k\,dx \qquad\qquad \therefore \quad \int \frac{1}{y-A}\,dy = \int -k\,dx$$

$$\therefore \quad \ln|y| = kx + c \qquad\qquad \therefore \quad \ln|y-A| = -kx + c$$

$$\therefore \quad y = \pm e^{kx+c} \qquad\qquad\qquad \therefore \quad |y-A| = e^{-kx+c}$$

$$\therefore \quad y = \pm e^{c}e^{kx} \qquad\qquad\qquad \therefore \quad y - A = \pm e^{c}e^{-kx}$$

$$\therefore \quad y = Ae^{kx} \quad \text{for some} \qquad \therefore \quad y - A = Be^{-kx} \quad \{B \text{ a constant}\}$$

$$\text{constant } A. \qquad\qquad\qquad\qquad \therefore \quad y = A + Be^{-kx}$$

Example 8

Solve $\dfrac{dV}{dh} = k\sqrt{V}$ given that $V(9) = 1$, $V(13) = 4$, and k is a constant.

> Don't forget to check your solution by differentiation.

$$\frac{dV}{dh} = k\sqrt{V}$$

$$\therefore \quad \frac{1}{\sqrt{V}}\frac{dV}{dh} = k$$

$$\therefore \quad \int V^{-\frac{1}{2}}\frac{dV}{dh}\,dh = \int k\,dh$$

$$\therefore \quad \int V^{-\frac{1}{2}}\,dV = \int k\,dh$$

$$\therefore \quad \frac{V^{\frac{1}{2}}}{\frac{1}{2}} = kh + c$$

> This is the general solution

$$\therefore \quad 2\sqrt{V} = kh + c$$

But $V(9) = 1$ and $V(13) = 4$

> These are the initial conditions

$$\therefore \quad 2\sqrt{1} = k(9) + c \quad \text{and} \qquad 2\sqrt{4} = k(13) + c$$

$$\therefore \quad 9k + c = 2 \qquad\qquad \text{and} \quad 13k + c = 4$$

Solving these equations simultaneously gives $k = \frac{1}{2}$ and $c = -\frac{5}{2}$

$$\therefore \quad 2\sqrt{V} = \tfrac{1}{2}h - \tfrac{5}{2} = \frac{h-5}{2}$$

$$\therefore \quad \sqrt{V} = \frac{h-5}{4}$$

$$\therefore \quad V = \left(\frac{h-5}{4}\right)^{2}$$

> This is the particular solution

Example 9

The curve $y = f(x)$ has a y-intercept of 3. The tangent to this curve at the point (x, y) has an x-intercept of $x + 2$.

Find the equation of this curve in the form $y = f(x)$.

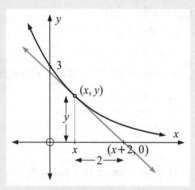

Gradient of tangent at (x, y) is $\dfrac{dy}{dx} = \dfrac{y - 0}{x - (x + 2)} = -\dfrac{y}{2}$

$\therefore \quad \dfrac{1}{y} \dfrac{dy}{dx} = -\dfrac{1}{2}$

$\therefore \quad \displaystyle\int \dfrac{1}{y} \dfrac{dy}{dx} \, dx = \int -\tfrac{1}{2} \, dx$

$\therefore \quad \displaystyle\int \dfrac{1}{y} \, dy = -\tfrac{1}{2}x + c$

$\therefore \quad \ln|y| = -\tfrac{1}{2}x + c$

$\therefore \quad y = Ae^{-\frac{1}{2}x}$

When $x = 0$, $y = 3$

$\therefore \quad 3 = A$

$\therefore \quad y = 3e^{-\frac{1}{2}x}$

Example 10

The number of bacteria present in a culture increases at a rate proportional to the number present. If the number increases by 10% in one hour, what percentage increase occurs after a further 5 hours?

If N is the number of bacteria present at time t hours, then $\dfrac{dN}{dt} \propto N$

$\therefore \quad \dfrac{dN}{dt} = kN$ where k is a constant

$\therefore \quad \dfrac{1}{N} \dfrac{dN}{dt} = k$

and $\displaystyle\int \dfrac{1}{N} \dfrac{dN}{dt} \, dt = \int k \, dt$

$\therefore \quad \displaystyle\int \dfrac{1}{N} \, dN = \int k \, dt$

$\therefore \quad \ln N = kt + c$ {$|N|$ is not necessary as $N > 0$}

Suppose the number of bacteria when $t = 0$ was $N = N_0$.

$\therefore \quad \ln N_0 = c$ and so $\ln N = kt + \ln N_0$ ...... (1)

When $t = 1$, $N = 1.1N_0$ {since 110% of N_0 is $1.1N_0$}

$\therefore$ in (1), $\ln(1.1N_0) = k + \ln N_0$

$\therefore$ $\ln(1.1) + \ln N_0 = k + \ln N_0$

$\therefore$ $k = \ln(1.1)$

So, (1) becomes $\ln N = t\ln(1.1) + \ln N_0$

$\therefore$ $N = N_0 \times (1.1)^t$

After a further 5 hours, $t = 6$

$\therefore$ $N = N_0(1.1)^6 \approx 1.7716N_0 \approx 177.16\%$ of N_0

$\therefore$ N has increased by 77.16%.

Example 11

A raindrop falls with acceleration $9.8 - \dfrac{v}{3}$ $\mathrm{m\,s^{-2}}$, where v is its velocity. Show

that the raindrop's velocity is $v = 29.4(1 - e^{-\frac{t}{3}})$ $\mathrm{m\,s^{-1}}$ and it approaches a limiting value of 29.4 $\mathrm{m\,s^{-1}}$.

Acceleration is $\dfrac{dv}{dt}$,   so $\dfrac{dv}{dt} = 9.8 - \dfrac{v}{3} = \dfrac{29.4 - v}{3}$ $\mathrm{m\,s^{-2}}$

$\therefore$ $\left(\dfrac{1}{v - 29.4}\right)\dfrac{dv}{dt} = -\frac{1}{3}$

$\therefore$ $\displaystyle\int \left(\dfrac{1}{v - 29.4}\right)\dfrac{dv}{dt}\,dt = \int -\frac{1}{3}\,dt$

$\therefore$ $\displaystyle\int \left(\dfrac{1}{v - 29.4}\right)dv = \int -\frac{1}{3}\,dt$

$\therefore$ $\ln|v - 29.4| = -\frac{1}{3}t + c$

$\therefore$ $v - 29.4 = Ae^{-\frac{t}{3}}$

$\therefore$ $v = 29.4 + Ae^{-\frac{t}{3}}$

Now when $t = 0$, $v = 0$ and so $A = -29.4$

$\therefore$ $v = 29.4 - 29.4e^{-\frac{t}{3}}$

$\therefore$ $v = 29.4(1 - e^{-\frac{t}{3}})$

Now as $t \to \infty$, $e^{-\frac{t}{3}} \to 0$

$\therefore$ $v - 29.4 \to 0$ and so $v \to 29.4$ $\mathrm{m\,s^{-1}}$

Example 12

A large cylindrical tank has radius 2 m. Water flows out of a tap at the bottom of the tank at a rate proportional to the square root of the depth of the water within it. Initially the tank is full to a depth of 9 m. After 15 minutes the depth of water is 4 m. How long will it take for the tank to empty?

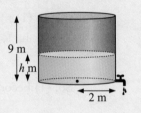

We are given that $\dfrac{dV}{dt} \propto \sqrt{h}$ where h is the depth of water

$\therefore \quad \dfrac{dV}{dt} = k\sqrt{h}$ where k is a constant.

Now $\dfrac{dV}{dt} = \dfrac{dV}{dh}\dfrac{dh}{dt}$ {chain rule}

The volume of water in the tank is $V = \pi r^2 h = 4\pi h$ $\therefore \quad \dfrac{dV}{dh} = 4\pi.$

$\therefore \quad k\sqrt{h} = 4\pi \dfrac{dh}{dt}$

$\therefore \quad \dfrac{4\pi}{\sqrt{h}}\dfrac{dh}{dt} = k$

$\therefore \quad \int 4\pi h^{-\frac{1}{2}} \dfrac{dh}{dt}\, dt = \int k\, dt$

$\therefore \quad 4\pi \int h^{-\frac{1}{2}}\, dh = \int k\, dt$

$\therefore \quad 4\pi \dfrac{h^{\frac{1}{2}}}{\frac{1}{2}} = kt + c$

$\therefore \quad 8\pi\sqrt{h} = kt + c$ ...... (1)

Now when $t = 0, \quad h = 9$

$\therefore$ in (1), $8\pi\sqrt{9} = c$ and so $c = 24\pi$

So, $8\pi\sqrt{h} = kt + 24\pi$ ...... (2)

And when $t = 15, \quad h = 4$

$\therefore$ in (2), $16\pi = 15k + 24\pi$ and so $k = -\frac{8\pi}{15}$

$\therefore \quad 8\pi\sqrt{h} = -\frac{8\pi}{15}t + 24\pi$

$\therefore \quad \sqrt{h} = -\frac{t}{15} + 3$

Now when it is empty $h = 0$

$\therefore \quad 0 = -\frac{t}{15} + 3$

$\therefore \quad t = 45$

So, the tank empties in 45 minutes.

EXERCISE 27E.1

1 Find the general solution of the following differential equations:

  a $\dfrac{dy}{dx} = 5y$

  b $\dfrac{dM}{dt} = -2M$

  c $\dfrac{dy}{dx} = \dfrac{2}{y}$

  d $\dfrac{dP}{dt} = 3\sqrt{P}$

  e $\dfrac{dQ}{dt} = 2Q + 3$

  f $\dfrac{dQ}{dt} = \dfrac{1}{2Q + 3}$

2 Find the particular solution of the following differential equations:

  a $\dfrac{dy}{dx} = 4y$ and when $x = 0$, $y = 10$

  b $\dfrac{dM}{dt} = -3M$ and $M(0) = 20$

  c $\dfrac{dy}{dt} = \dfrac{\sqrt{y}}{3}$ and when $t = 24$, $y = 9$

  d $\dfrac{dP}{dn} = 2P + 3$ and $P(0) = 2$

  e $\dfrac{dy}{dx} = k\sqrt{y}$ where k is a constant, $y(4) = 1$ and $y(5) = 4$

3 If the gradient of a curve at any point is equal to twice the y-coordinate at that point, show that the curve is an exponential function.

4 **a** If $\dfrac{dp}{dt} = -\frac{1}{2}p$, and $p = 10$ when $t = 0$, find p when $t = 2$.

  b If $\dfrac{dM}{dr} = 8 - 2M$, and $M = 2$ when $r = 0$, find r when $M = 3.5$.

5 $\dfrac{ds}{dt} + ks = 0$ where k is a constant, and $s = 50$ when $t = 0$.

  If it is also known that $s = 20$ when $t = 3$, show that $s = 50(0.4)^{\frac{t}{3}}$.

6 Find the general solution of:

  a $xy' = 3y$

  b $xy = 4y'$

  c $y' = ye^x$

  d $y' = xe^y$

7 Solve $\dfrac{dz}{dr} = z + zr^2$, $z(0) = 1$.

8 Solve $\dfrac{dy}{dx} = -2xy$ if $y = 1$ when $x = 0$.

9 Solve $ye^x \dfrac{dy}{dx} = x$ if $y = 2$ when $x = 0$.

10 Solve $(1 + x)\dfrac{dy}{dx} = 2xy$ if $y = e^2$ when $x = 0$.

11 Solve $(1 + x^2)\dfrac{dy}{dx} = 2xy$ if $y = 10$ when $x = 2$.

12 Solve $\dfrac{dy}{dx} = 4x + xy^2$ if $y = 2$ when $x = 0$.

13 The tangent to the curve $y = f(x)$ at the point (x, y) has an x-intercept of $x + 3$. If the curve has an y-intercept of 2, find $f(x)$.

14 A curve is known to have $\dfrac{dy}{dx} = \dfrac{x}{y}$. Find the general solution to this differential equation and hence find the curve that passes through the point $(5, -4)$.

Find a if $(a, 3)$ also lies on this curve.

15 A curve has $\dfrac{dy}{dx} = y^2(1 + x)$ and passes through the point $(1, 2)$.

    a Find the equation of this curve.

    b Find the equations for the curve's asymptotes.

16 Compare the differential equations: $\dfrac{dy}{dx} = -\dfrac{x}{y}$ with $\dfrac{dy}{dx} = \dfrac{y}{x}$.

    a Prove that the solution curves for these differential equations intersect at right angles.

    b Solve the differential equations analytically and give a geometrical interpretation of the situation.

17 A body moves with velocity v metres per second, and its acceleration is proportional to v. If $v = 4$ when $t = 0$ and $v = 6$ when $t = 4$, find the formula for v in terms of t. Hence, find v when $t = 5$ seconds.

18 In the 'inversion' of raw sugar, the rate of change in the weight w kg of raw sugar is directly proportional to w. If, after 10 hours, 80% reduction has occurred, how much raw sugar remains after 30 hours?

19 When a transistor ratio is switched off, the current falls away according to the differential equation $\dfrac{dI}{dt} = -kI$ where k is a constant. If the current drops to 10% in the first second, how long will it take to drop to 0.1% of its original value?

20 A lump of metal of mass 1 kg is released from rest in water. After t seconds its velocity is v m s^{-1} and the resistance due to the water is $4v$ Newtons.

The equation for the motion is $\dfrac{dv}{dt} = g - 4v$ where g is the gravitational constant.

    a Prove that $v = \dfrac{g}{4}(1 - e^{-4t})$ and hence show that there is a limiting velocity.

    b When is the metal falling at $\dfrac{g}{10}$ m s^{-1}?

21 Water evaporates from a lake at a rate proportional to the volume of water remaining.

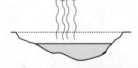

    a Explaining the symbols used, why does $\dfrac{dV}{dt} = k(V_0 - V)$ represent this situation?

    b If 50% of the water evaporates in 20 days, find the percentage of water remaining after 50 days without rain.

22 Water flows out of a tap at the bottom of a cylindrical tank of height 4 m and radius 2 m. The tank is initially full and the water escapes at a rate proportional to the square root of the depth of the water remaining. After 2 hours the depth of water is 1 m. How long will it take for the tank to empty?

23 Water evaporates from a hemispherical bowl of radius r cm such that $\dfrac{dV}{dt} = -r^2$, where t is the time in hours.

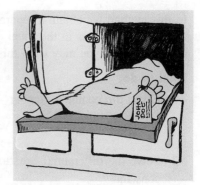

If the water has depth h cm then its volume is given by $V = \frac{1}{3}\pi h^2(3r - h)$.

a Assuming r is a constant, use $\dfrac{dV}{dt} = \dfrac{dV}{dh}\dfrac{dh}{dt}$ to set up a differential equation between h and t.

b Suppose the bowl's radius is 10 cm and that initially it is full of water.

Show that $t = \frac{\pi}{300}(h^3 - 30h^2 + 2000)$ and hence find the time taken for the depth of water to reach the 5 cm mark.

Newton's law of cooling is:

"The rate at which an object changes temperature is proportional to the difference between its temperature and that of the surrounding medium,

i.e., $\dfrac{dT}{dt} \propto (T - T_m)$".

Use Newton's law of cooling to solve questions **24** and **25**.

24 The temperature inside a refrigerator is maintained at 5°C. An object at 100°C is placed in the refrigerator to cool. After 1 minute its temperature drops to 80°C. How long will it take for the temperature to drop to 10°C?

25 At 6 am the temperature of a corpse is 13°C and 3 hours later it falls to 9°C. Given that living body temperature is 37°C and the temperature of the corpse's surroundings is constant at 5°C, estimate the time of death.

INVESTIGATION 2 $\qquad e^{i\theta} = \cos\theta + i\sin\theta$

In the 18th century **Leonhard Euler** made enormous contributions to mathematics and physics. Euler was responsible for introducing the symbols e and i, and for the famous identity $e^{i\theta} = \cos\theta + i\sin\theta$.

In this investigation we explore two methods which show this result.

METHOD 1: POWER SERIES EXPANSION

$$1 + x + x^2 + x^3 + \ldots = \frac{1}{1-x} \quad \text{for} \quad |x| < 1 \quad \{\text{sum of an infinite geometric series}\}$$

$$\therefore \ \frac{1}{1-x} = 1 + x + x^2 + x^3 + \ldots \quad \text{where the RHS is called the \textbf{power series expansion}}$$

$$\text{of} \ \frac{1}{1-x}.$$

Other functions also have power series expansions of the form $\displaystyle\sum_{j=0}^{\infty} a_j\, x^j$ where $\{a_j\}$ is a set of constant coefficients.

What to do:

1 Suppose e^x has a power series expansion, so
$$e^x = a_0 + a_1 x + a_2 x^2 + a_3 x^3 + a_4 x^4 + a_5 x^5 + \ldots\ldots \quad (1)$$

   a By letting $x = 0$, find a_0.

   b Differentiate both sides of (1) and by letting $x = 0$, find a_1.

   c Repeat the above process to find a_2, a_3, a_4 and a_5.

   d Conjecture the power series expansion of e^x by writing an expression for the general term a_n.

2 Repeat the procedure of **1** to obtain power series expansions for $\sin x$ and $\cos x$.

3 In your power series for e^x, replace x by $i\theta$.
   Hence, find $e^{i\theta}$ in the form $A + iB$.

4 Compare the results of **2** and **3** to find A and B.

METHOD 2:   DIFFERENTIAL EQUATION

In this method we obtain a separable differential equation involving the complex number i. We can solve this in the usual method by treating i as a constant, though in later years of mathematics you may learn this is not always such a wise tactic!

What to do:

1 Given the complex number $z = r \operatorname{cis} \theta = r\cos\theta + ir\sin\theta$ where $r = |z|$ is a constant and $\theta = \arg z$ is variable, show that $\dfrac{dz}{d\theta} = iz$.

2 Solve the differential equation $\dfrac{dz}{d\theta} = iz$, showing that $z = re^{i\theta}$ where r is a constant.

3 Compare your results in **1** and **2** to obtain the identity $e^{i\theta} = \cos\theta + i\sin\theta$.

RESULTS USING THE IDENTITY

Use the identity $e^{i\theta} = \cos\theta + i\sin\theta$ to show that:

   i $|zw| = |z|\,|w|$ and $\arg(zw) = \arg(z) + \arg(w)$ for complex numbers $z,\ w$.

   ii $\dfrac{\operatorname{cis}\theta}{\operatorname{cis}\phi} = \operatorname{cis}(\theta - \phi)$

   iii $e^{i\pi} + 1 = 0$ {called **Euler's identity**}

DIFFERENTIAL EQUATIONS WITH UNUSUAL SUBSTITUTIONS

In this final section we consider some interesting inseparable differential equations which can be converted to separable form using clever substitutions.

Example 13

Solve $x\dfrac{dy}{dx} = x + y$ by letting $y = ux$.

Let $y = ux$ $\therefore$ $\dfrac{dy}{dx} = \dfrac{du}{dx}x + u$ {product rule}

Substituting into the original DE,

$$x\left(\dfrac{du}{dx}x + u\right) = x + ux$$

$$\therefore \quad x^2\dfrac{du}{dx} + ux = x + ux$$

$$\therefore \quad x^2\dfrac{du}{dx} = x$$

$$\therefore \quad \dfrac{du}{dx} = \dfrac{1}{x}$$

$$\therefore \quad \int \dfrac{du}{dx}\,dx = \int \dfrac{1}{x}\,dx$$

$$\therefore \quad u = \ln|x| + c$$

But $y = ux$, so $y = x\ln|x| + cx$ is the general solution.

EXERCISE 27E.2

1 Solve $\dfrac{dy}{dx} - 2xe^x = y$ by letting $y = ue^x$.

2 Solve $\left(\dfrac{dy}{dx}\right)^2 = y^2 + 2e^x y + e^{2x}$ by letting $y = ue^x$.

3 Solve $4xy\dfrac{dy}{dx} = -x^2 - y^2$ for $x > 0$ by letting $y = ux$.

4 Solve $x\dfrac{dy}{dx} - y = 4x^2 y$ by letting $y = ux$ or otherwise.

REVIEW SET 27A

1 Find $\int x^2\sqrt{4 - x}\,dx$.

2 Use integration by parts to find $\int \arctan x\,dx$. Check your answer using differentiation.

3 Find integrals of: **a** $e^{-x}\cos x$ **b** $x^2 e^x$ **c** $\dfrac{x^3}{\sqrt{9 - x^2}}$

4 Find the solution to $y' = -\dfrac{2e^x}{y}$ given that $y(0) = 4$.

5 The current I which flows through an electrical circuit with resistance R and inductance L can be determined from the differential equation $L\dfrac{dI}{dt} = E - RI$. Both R and L are constants, and so is the electromotive force E.

Given that $R = 4$, $L = 0.2$ and $E = 20$, find how long it will take for the current, initially 0 amps, to reach 0.5 amps.

6 The graph of $y = f(x)$ has a y-intercept of 3 and the tangent at the point (x, y) has an x-intercept of $x - 3$. Find the function $f(x)$.

7 Solve the differential equation $2xy\dfrac{dy}{dx} = x^2 + y^2$ by letting $y = ux$.

Hence show that if $y = 2$ when $x = 1$, a particular solution is $y^2 = x^2 + 3x$.

REVIEW SET 27B

1 Find: **a** $\displaystyle\int \frac{5}{\sqrt{9 - x^2}}\, dx$ **b** $\displaystyle\int \frac{1}{9 + 4x^2}\, dx$ **c** $\displaystyle\int_{7}^{10} x\sqrt{x - 5}\, dx$

2 Find: **a** $\displaystyle\int x \cos x\, dx$ **b** $\displaystyle\int \frac{\sqrt{x^2 - 4}}{x}\, dx$

3 Given $\dfrac{dy}{dx} = \dfrac{1}{y + 2}$ and $y(0) = 0$, deduce that $y = \sqrt{2x + 4} - 2$.

4 Given $\dfrac{dy}{dx} = \dfrac{2x}{\cos y}$ with initial condition $y(1) = \frac{\pi}{2}$, show that $y = \arcsin(x^2)$.

5 OBLH is a seal slide at the zoo. At *any* point P, the gradient of the slide is equal to the gradient of a uniformly inclined plane with highest point P and with a 5 m long horizontal base along OB.

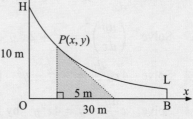

   a Show that $P(x, y)$ satisfies the equation $y = 10e^{-\frac{x}{5}}$.

   b Find the height of L above OB.

   c Find the gradient of the slide at H and at L.

6 Bacteria grow in culture at a rate proportional to the number of bacteria present.

   a Write down a differential equation connecting the number of bacteria $N(t)$ at time t, to its growth rate.

   b If the population of bacteria doubles every 37 minutes and there are 10^5 bacteria initially, how many bacteria are present in the culture after 4 hours?

7 If a curve has $\dfrac{dy}{dx} = (y - 1)^2(2 + x)$ and passes through the point $(-1, 2)$:

   a find the equation of the curve

   b find the equations of the asymptotes to the curve.

8 A cylindrical rainwater tank is initially full, and the water runs out of it at a rate proportional to the volume of water left in it. If the tank is half full after 20 minutes, find the fraction of water remaining in the tank after one hour.

Chapter 28

Statistical distributions of discrete random variables

Contents:

DISCRETE RANDOM VARIABLES

RANDOM VARIABLES

In previous work we have described events mainly by using words. Where possible, it is far more convenient to use numbers.

A **random variable** represents in number form the possible outcomes which could occur for some random experiment.

A **discrete random variable** X has possible values $x_1, x_2, x_3, \ldots$

For example:
- the number of houses in your suburb which have a 'power safety switch'
- the number of new bicycles sold each year by a bicycle store
- the number of defective light bulbs in the purchase order of a city store.

A **continuous random variable** X has all possible values in some interval on the number line.

For example:
- the heights of men could all lie in the interval $50 < x < 250$ cm
- the volume of water in a rainwater tank during a given month could lie in the interval $0 < x < 100$ m^3.

To determine the value of a discrete random variable we need to **count**.

To determine the value of a continuous random variable we need to **measure**.

For any random variable there is a corresponding **probability distribution**.

The probability that the variable X takes value x is written as $P(X = x)$ or p_x. We can also sometimes write a probability distribution as a function $P(x)$.

For example, when tossing two coins, the random variable X could be 0 heads, 1 head, or 2 heads, i.e., $X = 0, 1$ or 2. The associated probability distribution is $p_0 = \frac{1}{4}$, $p_1 = \frac{1}{2}$, and $p_2 = \frac{1}{4}$ with graph:

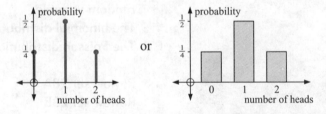

Example 1

A supermarket has three checkout points A, B and C. A government inspector checks for accuracy of the weighing scales at each checkout. If a weighing scale is accurate then yes (Y) is recorded, and if not, no (N). Suppose the random variable X is the number of accurate weighing scales at the supermarket.

a   List the possible outcomes.

b Describe using x the events of there being:

    i one accurate scale   **ii** at least one accurate scale.

a Possible outcomes:	A	B	C	x
	N	N	N	0
	Y	N	N	1
	N	Y	N	1
	N	N	Y	1
	N	Y	Y	2
	Y	N	Y	2
	Y	Y	N	2
	Y	Y	Y	3

b **i** $x = 1$

    ii $x = 1, 2$ or 3

EXERCISE 28A

1 Classify the following random variables as continuous or discrete.

  a The quantity of fat in a lamb chop.

  b The mark out of 50 for a Geography test.

  c The weight of a seventeen year old student.

  d The volume of water in a cup of coffee.

  e The number of trout in a lake.

  f The number of hairs on a cat.

  g The length of hairs on a horse.

  h The height of a sky-scraper.

2 For each of the following:

    i identify the random variable being considered

    ii give possible values for the random variable

    iii indicate whether the variable is continuous or discrete.

  a To measure the rainfall over a 24-hour period in Singapore, the height of water collected in a rain gauge (up to 200 mm) is used.

  b To investigate the stopping distance for a tyre with a new tread pattern, a braking experiment is carried out.

  c To check the reliability of a new type of light switch, switches are repeatedly turned off and on until they fail.

3 A supermarket has four checkouts A, B, C and D. Management checks the weighing devices at each checkout. If a weighing device is accurate a yes (Y) is recorded; otherwise, no (N) is recorded. The random variable being considered is the number of weighing devices which are accurate.

  a Suppose X is the random variable. What values can x have?

  b Tabulate the possible outcomes and the corresponding values for x.

  c Describe, using x, the events of:

    i 2 devices being accurate   **ii** at least two devices being accurate.

4   Consider tossing three coins simultaneously. The random variable under consideration
    is the number of heads that could result.

    a   List the possible values of x.

    b   Tabulate the possible outcomes and the corresponding values of x.

    c   Find the values of $P(X = x)$, the probability of each x value occurring.

    d   Graph the probability distribution $P(X = x)$ against x as a probability histogram.

B   DISCRETE PROBABILITY DISTRIBUTIONS

For each random variable there is a **probability distribution**.

> The probability p_i of any given outcome lies between 0 and 1 (inclusive),
> i.e., $0 \leqslant p_i \leqslant 1$.
>
> If there are n possible outcomes then
>
> $$\sum_{i=1}^{n} p_i = 1 \quad \text{or} \quad p_1 + p_2 + p_3 + \ldots + p_n = 1.$$

The **probability distribution** of a **discrete random variable** can be given

  • in table form

  • in graphical form

  • in functional form as a **probability mass function**.

It provides us with all possible values of the variable and the probability of the occurrence of
each value.

Example 2

A magazine store recorded the number of magazines purchased by its customers in
one week. 23% purchased one magazine, 38% purchased two, 21% purchased three,
13% purchased four, and 5% purchased five.

  a   What is the random variable?

  b   Make a probability table for the random variable.

  c   Graph the probability distribution using a spike graph.

---

a   The random variable X is the number of
    magazines sold.

    So, $x = 0, 1, 2, 3, 4$ or 5.

c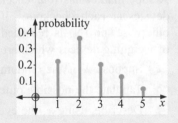

b

x_i	0	1	2	3	4	5
p_i	0.00	0.23	0.38	0.21	0.13	0.05

Example 3

Show that the following are probability distribution functions:

a $P(x) = \dfrac{x^2+1}{34}$, $x = 1, 2, 3, 4$

b $P(x) = C_x^3 (0.6)^x (0.4)^{3-x}$, $x = 0, 1, 2, 3$

---

a $P(1) = \frac{2}{34}$ $P(2) = \frac{5}{34}$ $P(3) = \frac{10}{34}$ $P(4) = \frac{17}{34}$

all of which obey $0 \leqslant P(x_i) \leqslant 1$, and $\sum P(x_i) = \frac{2}{34} + \frac{5}{34} + \frac{10}{34} + \frac{17}{34} = 1$

$\therefore$ $P(x)$ is a probability distribution function.

b For $P(x) = C_x^3 (0.6)^x (0.4)^{3-x}$

$P(0) = C_0^3 (0.6)^0 (0.4)^3 \quad = 1 \times 1 \times (0.4)^3 \quad = 0.064$

$P(1) = C_1^3 (0.6)^1 (0.4)^2 \quad = 3 \times (0.6) \times (0.4)^2 = 0.288$

$P(2) = C_2^3 (0.6)^2 (0.4)^1 \quad = 3 \times (0.6)^2 \times (0.4) = 0.432$

$P(3) = C_3^3 (0.6)^3 (0.4)^0 \quad = 1 \times (0.6)^3 \times 1 \quad = 0.216$

 Total $\underline{1.000}$

All probabilities lie between 0 and 1 and $\sum P(x_i) = 1$.

So, $P(x)$ is a probability distribution function.

Example 4

A bag contains 4 red and 2 blue marbles. Two marbles are randomly selected without replacement. If X denotes the number of reds selected, find the probability distribution of X.

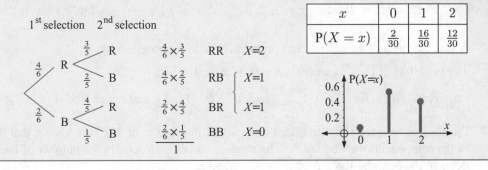

x	0	1	2
$P(X = x)$	$\frac{2}{30}$	$\frac{16}{30}$	$\frac{12}{30}$

EXERCISE 28B

1 Find k in these probability distributions:

a

x	0	1	2
$P(x)$	0.3	k	0.5

b

x	0	1	2	3
$P(x)$	k	$2k$	$3k$	k

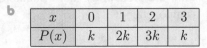

2 The probabilities of Jason scoring home runs in each game during his baseball career are given in the following table. X is the number of home runs per game.

x	0	1	2	3	4	5
$P(x)$	a	0.3333	0.1088	0.0084	0.0007	0.0000

   a What is the value of $P(2)$?

   b What is the value of a? Explain what this number means.

   c What is the value of $P(1) + P(2) + P(3) + P(4) + P(5)$? Explain what this represents.

   d Draw a probability distribution spike graph of $P(x)$ against x.

3 Explain why the following are not valid probability distributions:

   a

x	0	1	2	3
$P(x)$	0.2	0.3	0.4	0.2

   b

x	2	3	4	5
$P(x)$	0.3	0.4	0.5	-0.2

4 Sally's number of hits each softball match has the following probability distribution:

x	0	1	2	3	4	5
$P(x)$	0.07	0.14	k	0.46	0.08	0.02

   a State clearly what the random variable represents.

   b Find k.   **c** Find: **i** $P(x \geqslant 2)$ **ii** $P(1 \leqslant x \leqslant 3)$

5 A die is rolled twice.

   a Draw a grid which shows the sample space.

   b Suppose X denotes the sum of the results for the two rolls. Find the probability distribution of X.

   c Draw a probability distribution histogram for this situation.

6 Find k for the following probability distributions:

   a $P(x) = k(x + 2)$ for $x = 1, 2, 3$ **b** $P(x) = \dfrac{k}{x + 1}$ for $x = 0, 1, 2, 3$

7 A discrete random variable X has probability distribution given by:

$P(x) = k \left(\frac{1}{3}\right)^x \left(\frac{2}{3}\right)^{4-x}$ where $x = 0, 1, 2, 3, 4$.

   a Find $P(x)$ for $x = 0, 1, 2, 3$ and 4.   **b** Find k and hence find $P(x \geqslant 2)$.

8 Electrical components are produced and packed into boxes of 10. It is known that 4% of the components may be faulty. The random variable X denotes the number of faulty items in the box and has a probability distribution

$P(x) = C_x^{10} \, (0.04)^x \, (0.96)^{10-x}, \; x = 0, 1, 2, ..., 10.$

   a Find the probability that a randomly selected box will contain no faulty component.

   b Find the probability that a randomly selected box will contain at least one faulty component.

9 A bag contains 5 blue and 3 green tickets. Two tickets are randomly selected without replacement. X denotes the number of blue tickets selected.

    a Find the probability distribution of X.

    b Suppose instead that three tickets are randomly selected without replacement. Find the probability distribution of X for $X = 0, 1, 2, 3$.

10 When a pair of dice is rolled, D denotes the sum of the top faces.

    a Display the possible results in a table.

    b Find $P(D = 7)$.

    c Find the probability distribution of D.

    d Find $P(D \geqslant 8 \mid D \geqslant 6)$.

11 The number of cars X that pass a shop during the period from 3.00 pm to 3.03 pm is given by $P(X = x) = \dfrac{(0.2)^x e^{-0.2}}{x!}$ where $x = 0, 1, 2, 3, \ldots\ldots$

    a Find **i** $P(X = 0)$ **ii** $P(X = 1)$ **iii** $P(X = 2)$.

    b Find the probability that at least three cars will pass the shop in the given period.

12 When a pair of dice is rolled, N denotes the difference between the numbers on the top faces.

    a Display the possible results in a table.

    b Construct a probability distribution table for the possible values of N.

    c Find $P(N = 3)$.

    d Find $P(N \geqslant 3 \mid N \geqslant 1)$.

C   EXPECTATION

Consider the following problem:

> A die is to be rolled 120 times. On how many occasions would you *expect* the result to be a "six"?

In order to answer this question we must first consider all possible outcomes of rolling the die. The possibilities are 1, 2, 3, 4, 5 and 6, and each of these is equally likely to occur.

Therefore, we would expect $\frac{1}{6}$ of them to be a "six".

$\frac{1}{6}$ of 120 is 20, so we expect 20 of the 120 rolls of the die to yield a "six".

However, this does not mean that you *will* get 20 sixes if you roll a die 120 times.

> In general: If there are n outcomes in an event and the probability of each outcome in the event occurring is p, then the **expectation** that the event will occur is np.

Example 5

Each time a footballer kicks for goal he has a $\frac{3}{4}$ chance of being successful.

In a particular game he has 12 kicks for goal. How many goals would you expect him to kick?

$p = \text{P(goal)} = \frac{3}{4}$ $\therefore$ the expected number of goals is $np = 12 \times \frac{3}{4} = 9$

Example 6

In a game of chance, a player spins a square spinner labelled 1, 2, 3, 4. The player wins the amount of money shown in the table alongside, depending on which number comes up.

Number	1	2	3	4
Winnings	$1	$2	$5	$8

Determine:

a   the expected return for one spin of the spinner

b   whether you would recommend playing this game if it costs $5 for one game.

a   As each number is equally likely, the probability for each number is $\frac{1}{4}$
   $\therefore$ expected return $= \frac{1}{4} \times 1 \ + \ \frac{1}{4} \times 2 \ + \ \frac{1}{4} \times 5 \ + \ \frac{1}{4} \times 8 = \$4$.

b   As the expected return of $4 is less than the cost of $5 to play the game, you would not recommend that a person play the game.

EXPECTATION BY FORMULAE

For examples like **Example 6** part a we can define the expectation $\text{E}(X)$ of a random variable

to be $$\text{E}(X) = \sum_{i=1}^{n} p_i x_i \,.$$

EXERCISE 28C

1   In a particular region, the probability that it will rain on any one day is 0.28. On how many days of the year would you expect it to rain?

2   a   If 3 coins are tossed what is the chance that they all fall heads?

   b   If the 3 coins are tossed 200 times, on how many occasions would you expect them all to fall heads?

3   If two dice are rolled simultaneously 180 times, on how many occasions would you expect to get a double?

4   A single coin is tossed once. If a head appears you win $2 and if a tail appears you lose $1. How much would you expect to win when playing this game three times?

5 During the snow season there is a $\frac{3}{7}$ probability of snow falling on any particular day. If Udo skis for five weeks, on how many days could he expect to see snow falling?

6 In a random survey of her electorate, politician A discovered the residents' voting intentions in relation to herself and her two opponents B and C. The results are indicated alongside:

A	B	C
165	87	48

  a Estimate the probability that a randomly chosen voter in the electorate will vote for:

  i A   ii B   iii C.

  b If there are 7500 people in the electorate, how many of these would you expect to vote for:

  i A   ii B   iii C?

7 A person rolls a normal six-sided die and wins the number of dollars shown on the face.

  a How much does the person expect to win for one roll of the die?

  b If it costs $4 to play the game, would you advise the person to play several games?

8 A charity fundraiser gets a licence to run the following gambling game: A die is rolled and the returns to the player are given in the 'pay table' alongside. To play the game $4 is needed. A result of getting a 6 wins $10, so in fact you are ahead by $6 if you get a 6 on the first roll.

Result	Wins
6	$10
4, 5	$4
1, 2, 3	$1

  a What are your chances of playing one game and winning:

  i $10   ii $4   iii $1?

  b Your expected return from throwing a 6 is $\frac{1}{6} \times \$10$. What is your expected return from throwing:

  i a 4 or 5   ii a 1, 2 or 3   iii a 1, 2, 3, 4, 5 or 6?

  c What is your overall expected result at the end of one game?

  d What is your overall expected result at the end of 100 games?

9 A person plays a game with a pair of coins. If two heads appear then $10 is won. If a head and a tail appear then $3 is won. If two tails appear then $5 is lost.

  a How much would a person expect to win playing this game once?

  b If the organiser of the game is allowed to make an average of $1 per game, how much should be charged to play the game once?

THE MEASURES OF A DISCRETE RANDOM VARIABLE

Suppose x_i are the possible values of the random variable X, and f_i are the frequencies with which these values occur.

We calculate the **population mean** as $\mu = \dfrac{\sum f_i x_i}{\sum f_i}$,

the **population standard deviation** as $\sigma = \sqrt{\dfrac{\sum f_i (x_i - \mu)^2}{\sum f_i}}$,

and the **population variance** is σ^2.

Suppose we have 10 counters, one with a 1 written on it, four with a 2 written on them, three with a 3, and two with a 4. One counter is to be randomly selected from a hat.

We can summarise the possible results in a table:

outcome x_i	1	2	3	4
frequency f_i	1	4	3	2
probability p_i	$\frac{1}{10}$	$\frac{4}{10}$	$\frac{3}{10}$	$\frac{2}{10}$

Now $\mu = \dfrac{\sum f_i x_i}{\sum f_i}$

$= \dfrac{1 \times 1 + 2 \times 4 + 3 \times 3 + 4 \times 2}{1 + 4 + 3 + 2}$

$= 1 \times \frac{1}{10} + 2 \times \frac{4}{10} + 3 \times \frac{3}{10} + 4 \times \frac{2}{10}$

so $\mu = \sum x_i p_i$

Also, $\sigma^2 = \dfrac{\sum f_i (x_i - \mu)^2}{\sum f_i}$

$= \dfrac{1(x_1 - \mu)^2}{10} + \dfrac{4(x_2 - \mu)^2}{10} + \dfrac{3(x_3 - \mu)^2}{10} + \dfrac{2(x_4 - \mu)^2}{10}$

$= \frac{1}{10}(x_1 - \mu)^2 + \frac{4}{10}(x_2 - \mu)^2 + \frac{3}{10}(x_3 - \mu)^2 + \frac{2}{10}(x_4 - \mu)^2$

so $\sigma^2 = \sum (x_i - \mu)^2 p_i$

We can show that these formulae are also true in the **general case**.

Suppose a random variable has n possible values $x_1, x_2, x_3, ..., x_n$
with frequencies $f_1, f_2, f_3, ..., f_n$
and probabilities $p_1, p_2, p_3, ..., p_n$.

The population mean $\mu = \dfrac{\sum f_i x_i}{\sum f_i}$ {mean for tabled values}

$= \dfrac{f_1 x_1 + f_2 x_2 + f_3 x_3 + ... + f_n x_n}{N}$ {letting $\sum f_i = N$}

$$= x_1 \left(\frac{f_1}{N}\right) + x_2 \left(\frac{f_2}{N}\right) + x_3 \left(\frac{f_3}{N}\right) + ... + x_n \left(\frac{f_n}{N}\right)$$

$$= x_1 p_1 + x_2 p_2 + x_3 p_3 + ... + x_n p_n$$

$$= \sum x_i p_i$$

The variance $\sigma^2 = \dfrac{\sum f_i (x_i - \mu)^2}{\sum f_i}$

$$= \frac{f_1(x_1 - \mu)^2}{N} + \frac{f_2(x_2 - \mu)^2}{N} + \frac{f_3(x_3 - \mu)^2}{N} + ... + \frac{f_n(x_n - \mu)^2}{N}$$

$$= p_1(x_1 - \mu)^2 + p_2(x_2 - \mu)^2 + p_3(x_3 - \mu)^2 + ... + p_n(x_n - \mu)^2$$

$$= \sum (x_i - \mu)^2 p_i$$

If a discrete random variable has n possible values $x_1, x_2, x_3, ..., x_n$

with probabilities $p_1, p_2, p_3, ..., p_n$ of occurring,

then
- the population **mean** is $\mu = \sum x_i p_i$
- the population **variance** is $\sigma^2 = \sum (x_i - \mu)^2 p_i$
- the population **standard deviation** is $\sigma = \sqrt{\sum (x_i - \mu)^2 p_i}$.

The population mean of a discrete random variable is often referred to as the '*expected value of x*' or sometimes as the '*average value of x in the long run*'.

In practice, we can define:

- the **mean** as $E(X) = \mu = \sum x_i p_i$ and
- the **variance** as $\text{Var}(X) = \sigma^2 = \sum (x_i - \mu)^2 p_i = E(X - \mu)^2$.

Example 7

Find the mean and standard deviation of the data of **Example 2**.

The probability table is:

x_i	0	1	2	3	4	5
p_i	0.00	0.23	0.38	0.21	0.13	0.05

Now $\mu = \sum x_i p_i$

$$= 0(0.00) + (0.23) + 2(0.38) + 3(0.21) + 4(0.13) + 5(0.05)$$

$$= 2.39$$

so in the long run, the average number of magazines purchased per customer is 2.39 .

The standard deviation

$$\sigma = \sqrt{(x_i - \mu)^2 p_i}$$

$$= \sqrt{(1 - 2.39)^2 \times 0.23 + (2 - 2.39)^2 \times 0.38 + ... + (5 - 2.39)^2 \times 0.05}$$

$$\approx 1.122$$

An alternative formula for the population standard deviation is

$$\sigma = \sqrt{\sum x_i^2 p_i - \mu^2}\,.$$

This formula is often easier to use than the first one. For example, for a die:

$$\mu = \sum x_i p_i = 1(\tfrac{1}{6}) + 2(\tfrac{1}{6}) + 3(\tfrac{1}{6}) + 4(\tfrac{1}{6}) + 5(\tfrac{1}{6}) + 6(\tfrac{1}{6}) = 3.5$$

$$\text{and} \quad \sigma^2 = \sum x_i^2 p_i - \mu^2 = 1^2(\tfrac{1}{6}) + 2^2(\tfrac{1}{6}) + 3^2(\tfrac{1}{6}) + 4^2(\tfrac{1}{6}) + 5^2(\tfrac{1}{6}) + 6^2(\tfrac{1}{6}) - (3.5)^2$$

$$\approx 2.92$$

Consequently, $\sigma \approx 1.71$.

These results can be checked using your calculator by generating 800 random digits from 1 to 6. Then find the mean and standard deviation. You should get a good approximation to the theoretical values obtained above.

THE MEDIAN AND MODE

In **Chapter 17** we also found two other measures for the centre of a distribution or data set:

- the **median** of a data set is the middle score
- the **mode** is the most frequently occurring score.

Example 8

Find the median and mode of the data from **Example 2**.

The probability table is:

x_i	0	1	2	3	4	5
p_i	0.00	0.23	0.38	0.21	0.13	0.05

So, in 100 trials the *expected* frequencies f_i are:

x_i	0	1	2	3	4	5
f_i	0	23	38	21	13	5

$$\therefore \quad \text{middle score} = \frac{x_{50} + x_{51}}{2} = \frac{2 + 2}{2} = 2$$

$$\therefore \quad \text{median} = 2$$

The mode is the most frequently occurring score, which should be the score with highest probability.

$$\therefore \quad \text{mode} = 2$$

EXERCISE 28D.1

1 A country exports crayfish to overseas markets. The buyers are prepared to pay high prices when the crayfish arrive still alive.

If X is the number of deaths per dozen crayfish, the probability distribution for X is given by:

x_i	0	1	2	3	4	5	> 5
$P(x_i)$	0.54	0.26	0.15	k	0.01	0.01	0.00

   a Find k.

   b Over a long period, what is the mean number of deaths per dozen crayfish?

   c Find σ, the standard deviation for the probability distribution.

2 A random variable X has probability distribution given by

$$P(x) = \frac{x^2 + x}{20} \quad \text{for} \quad x = 1, 2, 3. \quad \text{Calculate } \mu \text{ and } \sigma \text{ for this distribution.}$$

3 A random variable X has probability distribution given by

$$P(x) = C_x^3 (0.4)^x (0.6)^{3-x} \quad \text{for} \quad x = 0, 1, 2, 3.$$

   a Find $P(x)$ for $x = 0, 1, 2$ and 3 and display the results in table form.

   b Find the mean and standard deviation for the distribution.

4 Using $\sigma^2 = \sum (x_i - \mu)^2 p_i$ show that $\sigma^2 = \sum x_i^2 p_i - \mu^2$.

5 A random variable X has the probability distribution shown.

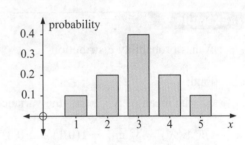

   a Copy and complete:

x_i	1	2	3	4	5
$P(x_i)$					

   b Find the mean μ and standard deviation σ for the distribution.

   c Determine   **i** $P(\mu - \sigma < x < \mu + \sigma)$ **ii** $P(\mu - 2\sigma < x < \mu + 2\sigma)$.

6 An insurance policy covers a $20\,000$ sapphire ring against theft and loss. If it is stolen then the insurance company will pay the policy owner in full. If it is lost then they will pay the owner 8000. From past experience, the insurance company knows that the probability of theft is 0.0025 and of being lost is 0.03. How much should the company charge to cover the ring if they want a $100 expected return?

7 A pair of dice is rolled and the random variable M is the larger of the two numbers that are shown uppermost.

   a In table form, obtain the probability distribution of M.

   b Find the mean and standard deviation of the M-distribution.

8 A uniform distribution has $P(x_1) = P(x_2) = P(x_3) = \ldots$ Give *two* examples of a uniform distribution.

9 Find the **median** and **mode** of the discrete random variables given in questions **1, 2, 3, 5, 7** above.

PROPERTIES OF $E(X)$

If $E(X)$ is the expected value of random variable X then:
- $E(k) = k$ for any constant k
- $E(kX) = kE(X)$ for any constant k
- $E(A(X) + B(X)) = E(A(X)) + E(B(X))$ for functions A and B
  i.e., the expectation of a sum is the sum of the individual expectations.

These properties enable us to deduce that:

$$E(5) = 5, \qquad E(3X) = 3E(X) \qquad \text{and} \qquad E(X^2 + 2X + 3) = E(X^2) + 2E(X) + 3$$

PROPERTY OF $Var(X)$

$$\mathbf{Var(X) = E(X^2) - \{E(X)\}^2} \qquad \text{or} \qquad \mathbf{Var(X) = E(X^2) - \mu^2}$$

Proof: $\begin{aligned} Var(X) &= E(X - \mu)^2 \\ &= E(X^2 - 2\mu X + \mu^2) \\ &= E(X^2) - 2\mu E(X) + \mu^2 \qquad \{\text{properties of } E(X)\} \\ &= E(X^2) - 2\mu^2 + \mu^2 \\ &= E(X^2) - \mu^2 \end{aligned}$

Example 9

X has probability distribution

x	1	2	3	4
p_x	0.1	0.3	0.4	0.2

Find:

a   the mean of X b   the variance of X c   the standard deviation of X.

a $E(X) = \sum x p_x = 1(0.1) + 2(0.3) + 3(0.4) + 4(0.2)$
$\therefore$ $E(X) = 2.7$ so $\mu = 2.7$

b $E(X^2) = \sum x^2 p_x = 1^2(0.1) + 2^2(0.3) + 3^2(0.4) + 4^2(0.2) = 8.1$
$\therefore$ $\begin{aligned} Var(X) &= E(X^2) - \{E(X)\}^2 \\ &= 8.1 - 2.7^2 \\ &= 0.81 \end{aligned}$

c $\sigma = \sqrt{Var(X)} = 0.9$

EXERCISE 28D.2

1   X has probability distribution:

x	2	3	4	5	6
p_x	0.3	0.3	0.2	0.1	0.1

Find:

a   the mean of X b   the variance of X c   the standard deviation of X.

2 X has probability distribution:

x	5	6	7	8
p_x	0.2	k	0.4	0.1

Find:

a the value of k **b** the mean of X **c** the variance of X.

3 X has probability distribution:

x	1	2	3	4
p_x	0.4	0.3	0.2	0.1

Find:

a $E(X)$ **b** $E(X^2)$ **c** $Var(X)$ **d** σ

e $E(X+1)$ **f** $Var(X+1)$ **g** $E(2X^2 + 3X - 7)$

4 X has probability distribution:

x	1	2	3	4
p_x	0.2	a	0.3	b

a Find a and b given that $E(X) = 2.8$.

b Hence show that $Var(X) = 1.26$.

5 Suppose X is the number of marsupials entering a park at night. It is suspected that X has a probability distribution of the form

$P(X = x) = a(x^2 - 8x)$ where $X = 0, 1, 2, 3, ... 8$.

a Find the constant a.

b Find the expected number of marsupials entering the park on a given night.

c Find the standard deviation of X.

6 An unbiased coin is tossed four times. X is the number of heads which could appear.

a Find the probability distribution of X.

b Find: **i** the mean of X **ii** the standard deviation of X.

7 A box contains 10 almonds, two of which are bitter and the remainder are normal. Brit randomly selects three almonds without replacement. Let X be the random variable for the number of bitter almonds Brit selects.

a Find the probability distribution of X.

b Find: **i** the mean of X **ii** the standard deviation of X.

8 The probability distribution of a discrete random variable Y is illustrated in the table below.

Y	-1	0	1	2
$P(Y = y)$	0.1	a	0.3	b

a Given $E(Y) = 0.9$, find the values of a and b.

b Calculate $Var(Y)$.

9 The score X obtained by rolling a biased pentagonal die has the following probability distribution:

X	1	2	3	4	5
$P(X = x)$	$\frac{1}{6}$	$\frac{1}{3}$	$\frac{1}{12}$	a	$\frac{1}{6}$

Find a and hence find $E(X)$ and $Var(X)$.

INVESTIGATION 1 $E(aX + b)$ AND $Var(aX + b)$

The purpose of this investigation is to discover a relationship between $E(aX + b)$ and $E(X)$ and also $Var(aX + b)$ and $Var(X)$.

What to do:

1 Consider the X-distribution: 1, 2, 3, 4, 5, each occurring with equal probability.
   a Find $E(X)$ and $Var(X)$.
   b If $Y = 2X+3$, find the Y-distribution.
      Hence find $E(2X+3)$ and $Var(2X+3)$.
   c Repeat **b** for $Y = 3X - 2$.   **d** Repeat **b** for $Y = -2X + 5$.
   e Repeat **b** for $Y = \dfrac{X+1}{2}$.

2 Make up your own sample distribution for a random variable X and repeat **1**.
3 Record all your results in table form for both distributions.
4 From **3**, what is the relationship between: • $E(X)$ and $E(aX + b)$
                                                 • $Var(X)$ and $Var(aX + b)$?

From the investigation you should have discovered that

$$E(aX + b) = aE(X) + b \quad \text{and} \quad Var(aX + b) = a^2 Var(X).$$

These results will be formally proved in the exercise which follows.

Example 10

X is distributed with mean 8.1 and standard deviation 2.37. If $Y = 4X - 7$, find the mean and standard deviation of the Y-distribution.

$E(X) = 8.1$ and $Var(X) = 2.37^2$ $E(4X - 7)$ $Var(4X - 7)$
                                        $= 4E(X) - 7$ $= 4^2 Var(X)$
                                        $= 4(8.1) - 7$ $= 4^2 \times 2.37^2$
                                        $= 25.4$

For the Y-distribution,
the mean is 25.4 and the standard deviation is $4 \times 2.37 = 9.48$.

EXERCISE 28D.3

1 X is distributed with mean 6 and standard deviation 2. If $Y = 2X + 5$, find the mean and standard deviation of the Y-distribution.

2 **a** Use the properties of $E(X)$ to prove that $E(aX + b) = aE(X) + b$.
   b The mean of an X-distribution is 3. Find the mean of the Y-distribution where:

   i $Y = 3X + 4$ **ii** $Y = -2X + 1$ **iii** $Y = \dfrac{4X - 2}{3}$

3 X is a random variable with mean 5 and standard deviation 2.

Find   **i** $E(Y)$ **ii** $Var(Y)$ for:

   a $Y = 2X + 3$ **b** $Y = -2X + 3$ **c** $Y = \dfrac{X - 5}{2}$

4 Suppose $Y = 2X + 3$ where X is a random variable.

Find in terms of $E(X)$ and $E(X^2)$:

   a $E(Y)$ **b** $E(Y^2)$ **c** $Var(Y)$

5 Using $Var(X) = E(X^2) - \{E(X)\}^2$,   prove that $Var(aX + b) = a^2 Var(X)$.

E   THE BINOMIAL DISTRIBUTION

Thus far in the chapter we have considered the general properties of discrete random variables.

We now examine a special discrete random variable which is applied to **sampling with replacement**. The probability distribution associated with this variable is the **binomial probability distribution**.

Note that for **sampling without replacement** the **hypergeometric probability distribution** is the model used. It is not part of this core course, but questions involving sampling of this type can be tackled using **combinations**.

BINOMIAL EXPERIMENTS

Consider an experiment for which there are two possible results: **success** if some event occurs, or **failure** if the event does not occur.

If we repeat this experiment in a number of **independent trials**, we call it a **binomial experiment**.

The probability of a success p must be constant for all trials.

If q is the probability of a failure, then $q = 1 - p$ (since $p + q = 1$).

The random variable X is the total number of successes in n trials.

THE BINOMIAL PROBABILITY DISTRIBUTION

Suppose a spinner has three blue edges and one white edge.
Clearly, for each spin we will get either a blue or a white.

The chance of finishing on blue is $\frac{3}{4}$ and on white is $\frac{1}{4}$.

If we call a blue result a 'success' and a white result a 'failure', then we have a binomial experiment.

We let p be the probability of getting a blue and q be the probability of getting a white

$\therefore$ $p = \frac{3}{4}$ and $q = \frac{1}{4}$.

Consider twirling the spinner $n = 3$ times.

Let the random variable X be the number of 'successes' or blue results, so $x = 0, 1, 2$ or 3.

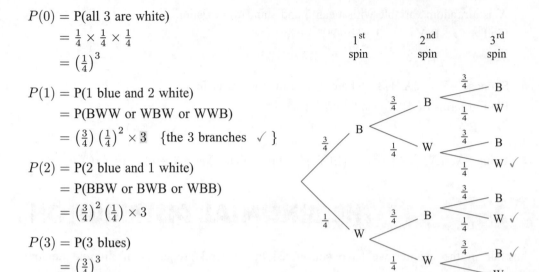

$P(0) = $ P(all 3 are white)

$\quad = \frac{1}{4} \times \frac{1}{4} \times \frac{1}{4}$

$\quad = \left(\frac{1}{4}\right)^3$

$P(1) = $ P(1 blue and 2 white)

$\quad = $ P(BWW or WBW or WWB)

$\quad = \left(\frac{3}{4}\right)\left(\frac{1}{4}\right)^2 \times \mathbf{3}$ {the 3 branches ✓ }

$P(2) = $ P(2 blue and 1 white)

$\quad = $ P(BBW or BWB or WBB)

$\quad = \left(\frac{3}{4}\right)^2 \left(\frac{1}{4}\right) \times 3$

$P(3) = $ P(3 blues)

$\quad = \left(\frac{3}{4}\right)^3$

The coloured factor $\mathbf{3}$ is the number of ways of getting one success in three trials, which is combination C_1^3 or $\binom{3}{1}$.

We note that

$$P(0) = \left(\frac{1}{4}\right)^3 \qquad = C_0^3 \left(\frac{3}{4}\right)^0 \left(\frac{1}{4}\right)^3 \approx 0.0156$$

$$P(1) = 3\left(\frac{1}{4}\right)^2 \left(\frac{3}{4}\right)^1 = C_1^3 \left(\frac{3}{4}\right)^1 \left(\frac{1}{4}\right)^2 \approx 0.1406$$

$$P(2) = 3\left(\frac{1}{4}\right)^1 \left(\frac{3}{4}\right)^2 = C_2^3 \left(\frac{3}{4}\right)^2 \left(\frac{1}{4}\right)^1 \approx 0.4219$$

$$P(3) = \left(\frac{3}{4}\right)^3 \qquad = C_3^3 \left(\frac{3}{4}\right)^3 \left(\frac{1}{4}\right)^0 \approx 0.4219$$

This suggests that: $P(x) = C_x^3 \left(\frac{3}{4}\right)^x \left(\frac{1}{4}\right)^{3-x}$ where $x = 0, 1, 2, 3$.

In general:

> Consider a binomial experiment for which p is the probability of a *success* and q is the probability of a *failure*.
>
> If there are n trials then the probability that there are r *successes* and $n - r$ *failures* is given by
>
> $P(X = r) = C_r^n \, p^r q^{n-r}$ where $q = 1 - p$ and $r = 0, 1, 2, 3, 4, \ldots, n$.
>
> $P(X = r)$ is the **binomial probability distribution function**.

Note:
- If X is the random variable of a binomial experiment with parameters n and p, then we write $X \sim \mathrm{B}(n, p)$.

  $\sim$ reads '*is distributed as*'

- $C_x^n = \binom{n}{x}$

$\mathrm{B}(n, p)$ is a useful notation. It indicates that the distribution is binomial and gives the values of n, the number of independent trials, and p, the probability of success in each trial.

- We can quickly calculate binomial probabilities using a graphics calculator.

  ▶ To find the probability $P(X = r)$ that the variable takes the value r, we use the function binompdf(n, p, r).
  binompdf stands for 'binomial probability distribution function'.

  ▶ To find the probability $P(X \leqslant r)$ that the variable takes a value which is *at most* r, we use the function binomcdf(n, p, r).
  binomcdf stands for 'binomial cumulative distribution function'.

Example 11

72% of union members are in favour of a certain change to their conditions of employment. A random sample of five members is taken. Find the probability that:

a three members are in favour of the change in conditions

b at least three members are in favour of the changed conditions.

Let X denote the number of members in favour of the changes.

$n = 5$, so $X = 0, 1, 2, 3, 4$ or 5, and $p = 72\% = 0.72$

$\therefore \quad X \sim B(5, 0.72)$.

a $\quad P(x = 3)$

$= C_3^5 (0.72)^3 (0.28)^2$

or binompdf(5, 0.72, 3)

≈ 0.293

b $\quad P(x \geqslant 3)$

$= 1 - P(x \leqslant 2)$

$= 1 - \text{binomcdf}(5, 0.72, 2)$

≈ 0.862

SUMMARY OF BINOMIAL DISTRIBUTIONS:

- The probability distribution is discrete.

- There are two outcomes which we usually call *success* and *failure*.

- The trials are **independent**, so the probability of success in a particular trial is not affected by the success or failure of previous trials. In other words, the probability of success is a constant for each trial of the experiment.

EXERCISE 28E.1

1 For which of these probability experiments does the binomial distribution apply? Justify your answers, using a full sentence.

  a A coin is thrown 100 times. The variable is the number of heads.

  b One hundred coins are each thrown once. The variable is the number of heads.

  c A box contains 5 blue and 3 red marbles. I draw out 5 marbles, replacing the marble each time. The variable is the number of red marbles drawn.

  d A box contains 5 blue and 3 red marbles. I draw 5 marbles without replacement. The variable is the number of red marbles drawn.

  e A large bin contains ten thousand bolts, 1% of which are faulty. I draw a sample of 10 bolts from the bin. The variable is the number of faulty bolts.

2 At a manufacturing plant, 35% of the employees work night-shift. If 7 employees were selected at random, find the probability that:

    a exactly 3 of them work night-shift

    b less than 4 of them work night-shift

    c at least 4 of them work night-shift.

3 Records show that 6% of the items assembled on a production line are faulty.
A random sample of 12 items is selected at random (with replacement).
Find the probability that:

    a none will be faulty   **b** at most one will be faulty

    c at least two will be faulty   **d** less than 4 will be faulty.

4 The local bus service does not have a good reputation. It is known that the 8 am bus will run late on average two days out of every five. For any week of the year taken at random, find the probability of the 8 am bus being on time:

    a all 7 days   **b** only on Monday

    c on any 6 days   **d** on at least 4 days.

5 An infectious flu virus is spreading through a school. The probability of a randomly selected student having the flu next week is 0.3.

    a Calculate the probability that out of a class of 25 students, 2 or more will have the flu next week.

    b If more than 20% of the students are away with the flu next week, a class test will have to be cancelled. What is the probability that the test will be cancelled?

MEAN AND STANDARD DEVIATION OF A BINOMIAL RANDOM VARIABLE

Suppose we toss a coin $n = 20$ times. For each toss, the probability of it falling 'heads' is $p = \frac{1}{2}$, so for the 20 trials we expect it to fall 'heads' $np = 10$ times.

Now suppose we roll a die $n = 30$ times. For each roll, the probability of it finishing as a 4 is $p = \frac{1}{6}$, so for the 30 trials we expect to obtain a 4 on $np = 5$ occasions.

So, in the general case:

> If a binomial experiment is repeated n times and a particular variable has probability p of occurring each time, then our expectation is that the mean μ will be $\mu = np$.

Finding the standard deviation is not so simple. We will start with a theoretical approach, after which we verify the generalised result by simulation.

ONE TRIAL ($n = 1$)

In the case of $n = 1$ where p is the probability of success and q is the probability of failure, the number of successes x could be 0 or 1.

x_i	0	1
p_i	q	p

Now $\mu = \sum p_i x_i$
$= q(0) + p(1)$
$= p$

and $\sigma^2 = \sum x_i^2 p_i - \mu^2$
$= [(0)^2 q + (1)^2 p] - p^2$
$= p - p^2$
$= p(1-p)$
$= pq \quad \{\text{as} \quad q = 1 - p\}$
$\therefore \quad \sigma = \sqrt{pq}$

TWO TRIALS $(n = 2)$

In the case where $n = 2$,
$$\left. \begin{array}{l} P(0) = C_0^2\, p^0 q^2 = q^2 \\ P(1) = C_1^2\, p^1 q^1 = 2pq \\ P(2) = C_2^2\, p^2 q^0 = p^2 \end{array} \right\} \quad \text{as} \quad x = 0,\, 1 \text{ or } 2$$

So, the table of probabilities is

x_i	0	1	2
p_i	q^2	$2pq$	p^2

$\mu = \sum p_i x_i$
$= q^2(0) + 2pq(1) + p^2(2)$
$= 2pq + 2p^2$
$= 2p(q + p)$
$= 2p \quad \{\text{as} \quad p + q = 1\}$

and $\sigma^2 = \sum x_i^2 p_i - \mu^2$
$= [0^2 \times q^2 + 1^2 \times 2pq + 2^2 \times p^2] - (2p)^2$
$= 2pq + 4p^2 - 4p^2$
$= 2pq$
$\therefore \quad \sigma = \sqrt{2pq}$

The case $n = 3$ produces $\mu = 3p$ and $\sigma = \sqrt{3pq}$ {see the following exercise}.

The case $n = 4$ produces $\mu = 4p$ and $\sigma = \sqrt{4pq}$.

These results suggest that in general:

> If X is a binomial random variable with parameters n and p i.e., $X \sim B(n, p)$
> then the mean of X is $\mu = np$ and the standard deviation of x is $\sigma = \sqrt{npq}$.

A general proof of this statement is beyond the scope of this course. However, the following investigation should help you appreciate the truth of the statement.

INVESTIGATION 2 THE MEAN AND STANDARD DEVIATION OF A BINOMIAL RANDOM VARIABLE

In this investigation we will examine binomial distributions randomly generated by a *sorting simulation*.

STATISTICS PACKAGE   SIMULATION

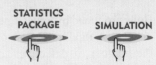

What to do:

1   Obtain experimental binomial distribution results for 1000 repetitions with

    a $n = 4, \ p = 0.5$ **b** $n = 5, \ p = 0.6$ **c** $n = 6, \ p = 0.75$

2   For each of the distributions obtained in **1**, find the mean μ and standard deviation σ from the statistics package.

3 Use $\mu = np$ and $\sigma = \sqrt{npq}$ to see how your experimental values for μ and σ in **2** agree with the theoretical expectation.

4 Finally, comment on the shape of a distribution for different values of p. For the fixed value of $n = 50$, consider the distribution with $p = 0.2,\ 0.35,\ 0.5,\ 0.68,\ 0.85$.

Example 12

5% of a batch of batteries are defective. A random sample of 80 is taken with replacement. Find the mean and standard deviation of the number of defectives in the sample.

This is a binomial sampling situation with $n = 80$, $p = 5\% = \frac{1}{20}$.

If X is the random variable for the number of defectives then X is $B(80, \frac{1}{20})$.

So, $\mu = np = 80 \times \frac{1}{20} = 4$ and $\sigma = \sqrt{npq} = \sqrt{80 \times \frac{1}{20} \times \frac{19}{20}} \approx 1.95$

We expect to find 4 defective batteries with standard deviation 1.95.

EXERCISE 28E.2

1 Suppose X is B(6, p). For each of the following cases:

    i find the mean and standard deviation of the X-distribution

    ii graph the distribution using a histogram

    iii comment on the shape of the distribution

  a when $p = 0.5$ **b** when $p = 0.2$ **c** when $p = 0.8$

2 A coin is tossed 10 times and X is the number of heads which occur. Find the mean and standard deviation of the X-distribution.

3 Suppose X is B(3, p).

  a Find $P(0)$, $P(1)$, $P(2)$ and $P(3)$ using

$$P(x) = C^3_x\, p^x\, q^{3-x}$$

and display your results in a table:

x_i	0	1	2	3
p_i				

  b Use $\mu = \sum p_i x_i$ to show that $\mu = 3p$.

  c Use $\sigma^2 = \sum x_i^2\, p_i - \mu^2$ to show that $\sigma = \sqrt{3pq}$.

4 Bolts produced by a machine vary in quality. The probability that a given bolt is defective is 0.04. A random sample of 30 bolts is taken from the week's production. If X denotes the number of defectives in the sample, find the mean and standard deviation of the X-distribution.

5 A city restaurant knows that 13% of reservations are not honoured, which means the group does not come. Suppose the restaurant receives five reservations and X is the random variable on the number of groups that do not come. Find the mean and standard deviation of the X-distribution.

F   THE POISSON DISTRIBUTION

PROOF

The **Poisson random variable** was first introduced by the French mathematician Siméon-Denis Poisson (1781 - 1840). He discovered it as a limit of the binomial distribution as the number of trials $n \to \infty$.

Whereas the binomial distribution $B(n,\, p)$ is used to determine the probability of obtaining a certain number of successes in a given number of independent trials, the **Poisson distribution** is used to determine the probability of obtaining a certain number of successes that can take place in a certain interval (of time or space).

Examples are:
- the number of incoming telephone calls to a given phone per hour
- the number of misprints on a typical page of a book
- the number of fish caught in a large lake per day
- the number of car accidents on a given road per month.

The probability distribution function for the discrete Poisson random variable is:

$$p_x = P(X = x) = \frac{m^x e^{-m}}{x!} \quad \text{for} \quad x = 0,\, 1,\, 2,\, 3,\, 4,\, 5,\, ...$$

where m is called the **parameter** of the distribution.

INVESTIGATION 3   POISSON MEAN AND VARIANCE

In this investigation you should discover the mean and variance of the Poisson distribution.

What to do:

1 Prove by solving the differential equation that there is only one solution of the differential equation $f'(x) = f(x)$ where $f(0) = 1$, and that this solution is $f(x) = e^x$.

2 Consider $f(x) = 1 + \dfrac{x}{1!} + \dfrac{x^2}{2!} + \dfrac{x^3}{3!} + ... + \dfrac{x^n}{n!} + ...$ which is an infinite power series.

   a Check that $f(0) = 1$ and find $f'(x)$. What do you notice?
   b From the result of question **1**, what can be deduced about $f(x)$?
   c Let $x = 1$ in your discovered result in **b**, and calculate the sum of the first 12 terms of the power series.

3 By observing that $\dfrac{2x}{1!} = \dfrac{x}{1!} + \dfrac{x}{1!}$, $\dfrac{3x^2}{2!} = \dfrac{x^2}{2!} + \dfrac{x^2}{1!}$, etc.,

   show that $1 + \dfrac{2x}{1!} + \dfrac{3x^2}{2!} + \dfrac{4x^3}{3!} + ... = e^x(1 + x)$.

4 If $p_x = P(X = x) = \dfrac{m^x e^{-m}}{x!}$ for $x = 0,\, 1,\, 2,\, 3,\, ...,$ show that:

   a $\displaystyle\sum_{x=0}^{\infty} p_x = 1$ **b** $E(X) = m$ **c** $Var(X) = m$

From the investigation, you should have discovered that the Poisson distribution has mean m and variance m.

$$\text{Thus} \quad \mu = m \quad \text{and} \quad \sigma^2 = m.$$

Since $\mu = \sigma^2 = m$, we can describe a Poisson distribution using the single parameter m. We can therefore denote the distribution simply by $\text{Po}(m)$.

If X is a Poisson random variable then we write $X \sim \text{Po}(m)$ where $m = \mu = \sigma^2$.

Conditions for a distribution to be Poisson:

1 The average number of occurrences μ is constant for each interval. This means it should be equally likely that the event occurs in one specific interval as in any other.

2 The probability of more than one occurrence in a given interval is very small. The typical number of occurrences in a given interval should be much less than is theoretically possible, say about 10% or less.

3 The number of occurrences in disjoint intervals are independent of each other.

Consider the following example:

When Sandra proof read 80 pages of a text book she observed the following distribution for X, the number of errors per page:

X	0	1	2	3	4	5	6	7	8	9	10
frequency	3	11	16	18	15	9	5	1	1	0	1

The mean for this data is $\mu = \dfrac{\sum f_i x_i}{\sum f_i} = \dfrac{257}{80} = 3.2125$.

Using the Poisson model with $m = 3.2125$ the expected frequencies are:

x_i	0	1	2	3	4	5	6	7	8	9	10
f_i	3.22	10.3	16.6	17.8	14.3	9.18	4.92	2.26	0.906	0.323	0.104

The expected frequencies are close to the observed frequencies, which suggests the Poisson model is a good model for representing this distribution.

Further evidence is that

$$\sigma^2 = \sum x_i {p_i}^2 - \mu^2$$

$$= 0^2(\tfrac{3}{80}) + 1^2(\tfrac{11}{80}) + 2^2(\tfrac{16}{80}) + \text{......} + 10^2(\tfrac{1}{80}) - 3.2125^2$$

$$\approx 3.367$$

which is fairly close to $m = 3.2125$.

Note that there is a formal statistic test for establishing whether a Poisson distribution is appropriate. This test is covered in the **Statistics Option Topic**.

EXERCISE 28F

1 Sven's Florist Shop receives the X distribution of phone calls shown between 9.00 am and 9.15 am on Fridays.

X	0	1	2	3	4	5	6
frequency	12	18	12	6	3	0	1

   a Find the mean of the X-distribution.

   b Compare the actual data with that generated by a Poisson model.

2   **a** A Poisson distribution has a standard deviation of 2.67.

      i What is its mean?   **ii** What is its probability generating function?

  b For the distribution in **a**, find:

     i $P(X = 2)$ **ii** $P(X \leqslant 3)$ **iii** $P(X \geqslant 5)$ **iv** $P(X \geqslant 3) \mid X \geqslant 1)$

3 One gram of radioactive substance is positioned so that each emission of an alpha-particle will flash on a screen. The emissions over 500 periods of 10 second duration are given in the following table:

number per period	0	1	2	3	4	5	6	7
frequency	91	156	132	75	33	9	3	1

  a Find the mean of the distribution.

  b Fit a Poisson model to the data and compare the actual data to that from the model.

  c Find the standard deviation of the distribution. How close is it to $\sqrt{m}$ found in **a**?

4 Top Cars rent cars to tourists. They have four cars which are hired out on a daily basis. The number of requests each day is distributed according to the Poisson model with a mean of 3. Determine the probability that:

  a none of its cars are rented   **b** at least 3 of its cars are rented

  c some requests will have to be refused

  d all are hired out given that at least two are.

5 Consider a random variable $X \sim Po(m)$.

  a Find m given that $P(X = 1) + P(X = 2) = P(X = 3)$.

  b If $m = 2.7$, find **i** $P(X \geqslant 3)$ **ii** $P(X \leqslant 4 \mid X \geqslant 2)$

6 Wind tunnel experiments on a new aerofoil produced data showing there was a 98% chance of the aerofoil not disintegrating at maximum airspeed. In a sample of 100 aerofoils, use the Poisson distribution to determine the probability that:

  a only one   **b** only two   **c** at most 2 aerofoils will disintegrate.

7 Road safety figures for a large city show that any driver has a 0.02% chance of being killed each time he or she drives a car.

  a Use the Poisson approximation to the binomial distribution to find the probability that a driver can use a car 10 times a week for a year and survive.

  b If this data does not change, how many years can you drive in Los Angeles and still have a better than even chance of surviving?

8 A supplier of clothing materials looks for flaws before selling it to customers. The number of flaws follows a Poisson distribution with a mean of 1.7 flaws per metre.

    a Find the probability that there are exactly 3 flaws in 1 metre of material.

    b Determine the probability that there is at least one flaw in 2 metres of material.

    c Find the modal value of this Poisson distribution.

9 The random variable Y is Poisson with mean m and satisfies

$$P(Y = 3) = P(Y = 1) + 2P(Y = 2)$$

    a Find the value of m correct to 4 decimal places.

    b Using the value of m found in **a** above, find $P(1 < Y < 5)$.

    c Calculate $P(2 \leqslant Y \leqslant 6 \mid Y \geqslant 4)$.

10 The random variable U has a Poisson distribution with mean x. Let y be the probability that U takes one of the values 0, 1 or 2.

    a Write down an expression for y as a function of x.

    b Sketch the graph of y for $0 \leqslant x \leqslant 3$.

    c Use calculus to show that as the mean increases, $P(U \leqslant 2)$ decreases.

REVIEW SET 28A

1 $f(x) = \dfrac{a}{x^2 + 1}$, $x = 0, 1, 2, 3$ is a probability distribution function.

    a Find a.   **b** Hence, find $P(x \geqslant 1)$.

2 A random variable X has probability distribution function $P(x) = C_x^4 \left(\frac{1}{2}\right)^x \left(\frac{1}{2}\right)^{4-x}$ for $x = 0, 1, 2, 3, 4$.

    a Find $P(x)$ for $x = 0, 1, 2, 3, 4$.   **b** Find μ and σ for this distribution.

3 A manufacturer finds that 18% of the items produced from its assembly lines are defective. During a floor inspection, the manufacturer randomly selects ten items. Find the probability that the manufacturer finds:

    a one defective   **b** two defective   **c** at least two defective items.

4 A random sample of 120 toothbrushes is made with replacement from a very large batch where 4% are known to be defective. Find:

    a the mean **b** the standard deviation of the number of defectives in the sample.

5 At a social club function, a dice game is played where on a single roll of a six-sided die the following payouts are made:

    $2 for an odd number, $3 for a 2, $6 for a 4, and $9 for a 6.

    a What is the expected return for a single roll of the die?

    b If the club charges $5 for each roll, how much money would the club expect to make if 75 people played the game once each?

6 A biased tetrahedral die has the numbers 6, 12 and 24 clearly indicated on 3 of its faces. The fourth number is unknown. The table below indicates the probability of each of these numbers occurring if the die is rolled once.

If the die is rolled once:

Number	6	12	x	24
Probability	$\frac{1}{3}$	$\frac{1}{6}$	$\frac{1}{4}$	y

  a Find the probability of obtaining the number 24.

  b Find the fourth number if the average result when rolling the die once is 14.

  c Find the median and modal score for this die.

7 The probability distribution for the discrete random variable X is given by the probability distribution function: $P(X = x) = a \left(\frac{5}{6}\right)^x$ for $x = 0, 1, 2, 3, \ldots$
Find the value of a.

8 A hot water unit relies on 20 solar components for its power and will operate provided at least one of its 20 components is working. The probability that an individual solar component will fail in a year is 0.85, and the components' failure or otherwise are independent of each other.

  a Find the probability that this hot water unit will fail within one year.

  b Find the smallest number of solar components required to ensure that the hot water service is operating at the end of one year with a probability of at least 0.98.

9 For a given binomial random variable X with 7 independent trials, we know that
$$P(X = 3) = 0.226\,89.$$

  a Find the smallest possible value of p, the probability of obtaining a success in one trial.

  b Hence calculate the probability of getting at most 4 successes in 10 trials.

10 During peak period, customers arrive at random at a fish and chip shop at the rate of 20 customers every 15 minutes.

  a Find the probability that during peak period, 15 customers will arrive in the next quarter of an hour.

  b If the probability that more than 10 customers will arrive at the fish and chip shop in a 10 minute period during peak period is greater than 80%, the manager will employ an extra shop assistant. Will the manager hire an extra shop assistant?

11 A Poisson random variable X is such that $P(X = 1) = P(2 \leqslant X \leqslant 4)$.

  a Find the mean and standard deviation of: **i** X **ii** $Y = \dfrac{X+1}{2}$.

  b Find $P(X \geqslant 2)$.

REVIEW SET 28B

1 A discrete random variable X has probability distribution function

   $P(x) = k \left(\frac{3}{4}\right)^x \left(\frac{1}{4}\right)^{3-x}$ where $x = 0, 1, 2, 3$ and k is a constant.

   a Find k.   **b** Find $P(x \geqslant 1)$.

2 An X-ray has probability of 0.96 of showing a fracture in the arm. If four different X-rays are taken of a particular fracture, find the probability that:

   a all four show the fracture   **b** the fracture does not show up

   c at least three X-rays show the fracture   **d** only one X-ray shows the fracture.

3 A random variable X has probability distribution function given by:

x	0	1	2	3	4
$P(x)$	0.10	0.30	0.45	0.10	k

   a Find k.

   b Find the mean μ and standard deviation σ for the distribution of X.

4 From data over the last fifteen years it is known that the chance of a netballer with a knee injury needing major knee surgery in any one season is 0.0132. In 2007 there were 487 cases of knee injuries. Find the mean and standard deviation of the number of major knee surgeries.

5 An author was known to make one mistake in 200 pages of her work. A second author was known to make 3 mistakes in 200 pages of her work. During one writing period, the first author produced 20 pages and the second author produced 40 pages. Assuming independent work of the authors, use the Poisson distribution to find the probability that the authors made 2 or more mistakes between them.

6 A die is biased such that the probability of obtaining a 6 is $\frac{2}{5}$. The die is rolled 1200 times. Let X be the number of sixes obtained. Find:

   a the mean of X **b** the standard deviation of X.

7 A discrete random variable has its probability distribution given by

   $P(X = x) = k \left(x + x^{-1}\right)$ where $x = 1, 2, 3, 4$.   Find:

   a the exact value of k **b** $E(X)$ and $Var(X)$ **c** the median and mode of X.

8 A Poisson random variable X satisfies the rule $5Var(X) = 2 \left[E(X)\right]^2 - 12$.

   a Find the mean of X.   **b** Find $P(X < 3)$

9 The random variable X has a binomial distribution for which $P(X > 2) \approx 0.070\,198$ for 10 independent trials. Find $P(X < 2)$.

10 The random variable Y has a Poisson distribution with $P(Y > 3) \approx 0.033\,768\,97$. Find $P(Y < 3)$.

11 The random variable X has mean μ and standard deviation σ.

   Prove that the random variable $Y = aX + b$ has mean $a\mu + b$ and standard deviation $|a|\,\sigma$.

Chapter 29

Statistical distributions of continuous random variables

Contents:

CONTINUOUS PROBABILITY DENSITY FUNCTIONS

In the previous chapter we looked at discrete random variables and examined some probability distributions where the random variable X could take the non-negative integer values $x = 0, 1, 2, 3, 4, ...$

For a **continuous random variable** X, x can take any real value.

Consequently, a function is used to specify the probability distribution, and that function is called the **probability density function**.

Probabilities are found by finding areas under the probability density function.

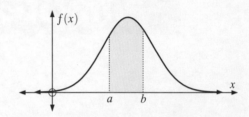

A **continuous probability density function (pdf)** is a function $f(x)$ such that

$f(x) \geqslant 0$ on a given interval $[a, b]$ and $\displaystyle\int_a^b f(x)\,dx = 1$.

For a continuous probability density function:

- The **mode** is the value of x at the maximum value of $f(x)$ on $[a, b]$.

- The **median** m is the solution for m of the equation $\displaystyle\int_a^m f(x)\,dx = \tfrac{1}{2}$.

- The **mean** μ or $\mathrm{E}(X)$ is defined as $\mu = \displaystyle\int_a^b x\,f(x)\,dx$.

- The **variance** $\mathrm{Var}(X) = \mathrm{E}(X^2) - \{\mathrm{E}(X)\}^2 = \displaystyle\int_a^b x^2 f(x)\,dx - \mu^2$

Example 1

$$f(x) = \begin{cases} \tfrac{1}{2}x & \text{on } [0, 2] \\ 0 & \text{elsewhere} \end{cases} \qquad \text{is a probability density function.}$$

a Check that the above statement is true.

b Find **i** the mode **ii** the median **iii** the mean of the distribution.

c Find $\mathrm{Var}(X)$ and σ.

---

a

Area $= \tfrac{1}{2} \times 2 \times 1 = 1$ ✓

or $\displaystyle\int_0^2 \tfrac{1}{2}x\,dx = \left[\tfrac{1}{4}x^2\right]_0^2 = 1$ ✓

b **i** $f(x)$ is a maximum when $x = 2$

$\therefore$ the mode $= 2$.

ii The median is the solution of

$$\int_0^m \tfrac{1}{2} x \, dx = \tfrac{1}{2}$$

$\therefore$ $\left[\tfrac{1}{4} x^2\right]_0^m = \tfrac{1}{2}$

$\therefore$ $\dfrac{m^2}{4} = \tfrac{1}{2}$

$\therefore$ $m^2 = 2$

$\therefore$ $m = \sqrt{2}$ {as $m \in [0, 2]$}

iii $\mu = \displaystyle\int_0^2 x \, f(x) \, dx$

$= \displaystyle\int_0^2 \tfrac{1}{2} x^2 \, dx$

$= \left[\tfrac{1}{6} x^3\right]_0^2$

$= 1\tfrac{1}{3}$

c $\mathrm{E}(X^2) = \displaystyle\int_0^2 x^2 \, f(x) \, dx$

$= \displaystyle\int_0^2 \tfrac{1}{2} x^3 \, dx$

$= \left[\tfrac{1}{8} x^4\right]_0^2$

$= 2$

$\therefore$ $\mathrm{Var}(X) = 2 - (1\tfrac{1}{3})^2$

$= \tfrac{2}{9}$

and $\sigma = \sqrt{\mathrm{Var}(X)}$

$= \dfrac{\sqrt{2}}{3}$

EXERCISE 29A

1 $f(x) = \begin{cases} ax(x-4), & 0 \leqslant x \leqslant 4 \\ 0 & \text{elsewhere} \end{cases}$ is a continuous probability density function.

   a Find a.   **b** Sketch the graph of $y = f(x)$.

   c Find: **i** the mean   **ii** the mode   **iii** the median   **iv** the variance.

2 $f(x) = \begin{cases} -0.2x(x-b), & 0 \leqslant x \leqslant b \\ 0 & \text{elsewhere} \end{cases}$ is a probability density function.

   a Find b.   **b** Find: **i** the mean   **ii** the variance.

3 $f(x) = \begin{cases} ke^{-x}, & 0 \leqslant x \leqslant 3 \\ 0 & \text{elsewhere} \end{cases}$ is a probability density function.

   a Find k to 4 decimal places.   **b** Find the median.

4 $f(x) = \begin{cases} kx^2(x-6), & 0 \leqslant x \leqslant 5 \\ 0 & \text{elsewhere} \end{cases}$ is a probability density function. Find:

   a k **b** the mode   **c** the median   **d** the mean   **e** the variance.

5 The probability density function of the random variable Y is given by

$$f(y) = \begin{cases} 5 - 12y, & 0 \leqslant y \leqslant k \\ 0 & \text{elsewhere.} \end{cases}$$

   a   Under what conditions can Y be a continuous random variable?

   b   Without using calculus, find k.

   c   Notice that $\displaystyle\int_0^{\frac{1}{2}} (5 - 12y)\, dy = 1$.   Explain why $k \neq \frac{1}{2}$ despite this result.

   d   Find the mean and median value of Y.

6   The probability density function for the random variable X is $f(x) = k$, $a \leqslant x \leqslant b$.

   a   Find k in terms of a and b.

   b   Calculate the mean, median and mode of X.

   c   Calculate $\text{Var}(X)$ and the standard deviation of X.

7   The continuous random variable X has the probability density function $f(x) = 2e^{-2x}$, $x \geqslant 0$.

   a   Calculate the median of X.   **b**   Calculate the mode of X.

8   A continuous random variable X has probability density function $f(x) = 6\cos 3x$ for $0 \leqslant x \leqslant a$.

   a   Find a.   **b**   Find the mean of X.   **c**   Find the 20th percentile of X.

   d   Find the standard deviation of X.

9   The continuous random variable X has the probability density function $f(x) = ax^4$, $0 \leqslant x \leqslant k$.

   Given that $P\left(X \leqslant \frac{2}{3}\right) = \frac{1}{243}$,   find a and k.

10   The time taken in hours to perform a particular task has the probability density function:

$$f(x) = \begin{cases} \dfrac{125}{18}x^2 & 0 \leqslant x < 0.6 \\[2mm] \dfrac{9}{10x^2} & 0.6 \leqslant x \leqslant 0.9 \\[2mm] 0 & \text{otherwise.} \end{cases}$$

   a   Sketch the graph of this function.

   b   Show that $f(x)$ is a well defined probability density function for the random variable X, the time taken to perform the task.

   c   Find the mean, median and mode of X.

   d   Find the variance and standard deviation of X.

   e   Find $P(0.3 < X < 0.7)$ and interpret your answer.

SUMMARY

Discrete random variable	Continuous random variable
• $\mu = E(X) = \sum x p_x$	• $\mu = E(X) = \int x f(x)\, dx$
• $\sigma^2 = \text{Var}(X) = E(X - \mu)^2$	• $\sigma^2 = \text{Var}(X) = E(X - \mu)^2$
$\quad = \sum (x - \mu)^2 p_x$	$\quad = \int (x - \mu)^2 f(x)\, dx$
$\quad = \sum x^2 p_x - \mu^2$	$\quad = \int x^2 f(x)\, dx - \mu^2$
$\quad = E(X^2) - \{E(X)\}^2$	$\quad = E(X^2) - \{E(X)\}^2$

B   NORMAL DISTRIBUTIONS

The normal distribution is the most important distribution for a continuous random variable. Many naturally occurring phenomena have a distribution that is normal, or approximately normal. Some examples are:

- physical attributes of a population such as height, weight, and arm length
- crop yields
- scores for tests taken by a large population

> If X is **normally distributed** then its **probability density function** is given by
>
> $$f(x) = \frac{1}{\sigma\sqrt{2\pi}}\, e^{-\frac{1}{2}\left(\frac{x-\mu}{\sigma}\right)^2} \quad \text{for} \quad -\infty < x < \infty$$
>
> where μ is the mean and σ^2 is the variance of the distribution.
>
> Each member of the family is specified by the **parameters** μ and σ^2, and we can write $X \sim N(\mu, \sigma^2)$.

This probability density function for the normal distribution represents a family of **bell-shaped normal curves**.

These curves are all symmetrical about the vertical line $x = \mu$.

A typical normal curve is illustrated alongside.

Notice that $f(\mu) = \dfrac{1}{\sigma\sqrt{2\pi}}$.

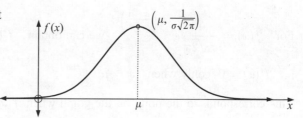

HOW THE NORMAL DISTRIBUTION ARISES

Consider the oranges picked from an orange tree. They do not all have the same weight. The variation may be due to several factors, including:

- genetics
- different times when the flowers were fertilised
- different amounts of sunlight reaching the leaves and fruit
- different weather conditions such as the prevailing winds.

The result is that most of the fruit will have weights close to the mean, while there are far fewer oranges that are *much* heavier or *much* lighter. This results in the bell-shaped distribution.

Once a normal model has been established, we can use it to make predictions about a distribution and to answer other relevant questions.

CHARACTERISTICS OF THE NORMAL PROBABILITY DENSITY FUNCTION

- The curve is symmetrical about the vertical line $x = \mu$.
- As $|x| \to \infty$ the normal curve approaches its asymptote, the x-axis.
- $f(x) > 0$ for all x.
- The area under the curve is one unit^2, and so $\displaystyle\int_{-\infty}^{\infty} f(x)\,dx = 1$.

- More scores are distributed closer to the mean than further away. This results in the typical **bell shape**.

A TYPICAL NORMAL DISTRIBUTION

A large sample of cockle shells was collected and the maximum distance across each shell was measured. Click on the video clip icon to see how a histogram of the data is built up. Now click on the demo icon to observe the effect of changing the class interval lengths for normally distributed data.

VIDEO CLIP

DEMO

THE GEOMETRICAL SIGNIFICANCE OF μ AND σ

For $\quad f(x) = \dfrac{1}{\sigma\sqrt{2\pi}}\, e^{-\frac{1}{2}\left(\frac{x-\mu}{\sigma}\right)^2} \quad$ we can obtain $\quad f'(x) = \dfrac{-1}{\sigma^2\sqrt{2\pi}}\left(\dfrac{x-\mu}{\sigma}\right) e^{-\frac{1}{2}\left(\frac{x-\mu}{\sigma}\right)^2}$

$\therefore \quad f'(x) = 0 \quad$ only when $\quad x = \mu$.

This corresponds to the point on the graph when $f(x)$ is a maximum.

Differentiating again, we can obtain $\quad f''(x) = \dfrac{-1}{\sigma^2\sqrt{2\pi}} e^{-\frac{1}{2}\left(\frac{x-\mu}{\sigma}\right)^2} \left[\dfrac{1}{\sigma} - \dfrac{(x-\mu)^2}{\sigma^3}\right]$

$\therefore \quad f''(x) = 0 \quad$ when $\quad \dfrac{(x-\mu)^2}{\sigma^3} = \dfrac{1}{\sigma}$

$\therefore \quad (x-\mu)^2 = \sigma^2$

$\therefore \quad x - \mu = \pm\sigma$

$\therefore \quad x = \mu \pm \sigma$

So, the points of inflection are at $x = \mu + \sigma$ and $x = \mu - \sigma$.

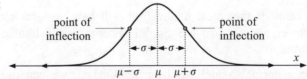

For a given normal curve, the standard deviation is uniquely determined as the horizontal distance from the vertical line $x = \mu$ to a point of inflection.

For a normal distribution with mean μ and standard deviation σ, the proportional breakdown of where the random variable could lie is given below.

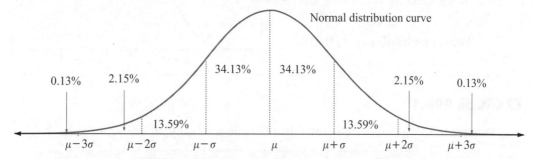

Notice that:
- $\approx 68.26\%$ of values lie between $\mu - \sigma$ and $\mu + \sigma$
- $\approx 95.44\%$ of values lie between $\mu - 2\sigma$ and $\mu + 2\sigma$
- $\approx 99.74\%$ of values lie between $\mu - 3\sigma$ and $\mu + 3\sigma$.

INVESTIGATION 1   STANDARD DEVIATION SIGNIFICANCE

The purpose of this investigation is to check the proportions of normal distribution data which lie within σ, 2σ and 3σ of the mean.

What to do:

DEMO

1 Click on the icon to start the demonstration in Microsoft® Excel.
2 Take a random sample of size $n = 1000$ from a normal distribution.
3 Find: **a** $\overline{x}$ and s **b** $\overline{x} - s$, $\overline{x} + s$ **c** $\overline{x} - 2s$, $\overline{x} + 2s$ **d** $\overline{x} - 3s$, $\overline{x} + 3s$
4 Count all values between:
   a $\overline{x} - s$ and $\overline{x} + s$ **b** $\overline{x} - 2s$ and $\overline{x} + 2s$ **c** $\overline{x} - 3s$ and $\overline{x} + 3s$
5 Determine the percentage of data values in these intervals. Do these confirm the theoretical percentages given above?
6 Repeat the procedure several times.

Example 2

The chest measurements of 18 year old male footballers is normally distributed with a mean of 95 cm and a standard deviation of 8 cm.

a Find the percentage of footballers with chest measurements between:
   i 87 cm and 103 cm   **ii** 103 cm and 111 cm

b Find the probability that the chest measurement of a randomly chosen footballer is between 87 cm and 111 cm.

a   **i** We need the percentage between $\mu - \sigma$ and $\mu + \sigma$. This is $\approx 68.3\%$.

   ii We need the percentage between $\mu + \sigma$ and $\mu + 2\sigma$.

    This is $\approx 13.6\%$.

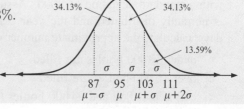

b This is between $\mu - \sigma$ and $\mu + 2\sigma$.

The percentage is $68.26\% + 13.59\%$
$\approx 81.9\%$.

So, the probability is ≈ 0.819.

EXERCISE 29B.1

1 Draw each of the following normal distributions accurately on one set of axes.

Distribution	mean (mL)	standard deviation (mL)
A	25	5
B	30	2
C	21	10

2 Explain why it is likely that the distributions of the following variables will be normal:

  a   the volume of soft drink in cans

  b   the diameter of bolts immediately after manufacture.

3 It is known that when a specific type of radish is grown without fertiliser, the weights of the radishes produced are normally distributed with a mean of 40 g and a standard deviation of 10 g. When the same type of radish is grown in the same way except for the inclusion of fertiliser, the weights of the radishes produced are also normally distributed, but with a mean of 140 g and a standard deviation of 40 g. Determine the proportion of radishes grown:

  a   without fertiliser with weights less than 50 grams

  b   with fertiliser with weights less than 60 grams

  c **i**   with and   **ii**   without fertiliser with weights between 20 and 60 g inclusive

  d **i**   with and   **ii**   without fertiliser with weights greater than or equal to 60 g.

4 The height of male students is normally distributed with a mean of 170 cm and a standard deviation of 8 cm.

  a   Find the percentage of male students whose height is:

    i   between 162 cm and 170 cm   **ii**   between 170 cm and 186 cm.

  b   Find the probability that a randomly chosen student from this group has a height:

    i   between 178 cm and 186 cm   **ii**   less than 162 cm

    iii   less than 154 cm   **iv**   greater than 162 cm.

5 A bottle filling machine fills an average of 20 000 bottles a day with a standard deviation of 2000. Assuming that production is normally distributed and the year comprises 260 working days, calculate the approximate number of working days that:

  a   under 18 000 bottles are filled

  b   over 16 000 bottles are filled

  c   between 18 000 and 24 000 bottles (inclusive) are filled.

PROBABILITIES BY GRAPHICS CALCULATOR

We can use a graphics calculator to quickly
find probabilities for a normal distribution.

Suppose $X \sim N(10, 2^2)$, so X is normally
distributed with mean 10 and standard
deviation 2.

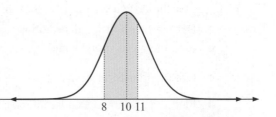

How do we find $P(8 \leqslant X \leqslant 11)$?

How do we find a if $P(X \geqslant a) = 0.479$?

Click on the icon for your graphics calculator to obtain instructions
for answering these questions.

EXERCISE 29B.2

Use a calculator to find these probabilities:

1 X is a random variable that is distributed normally with mean 70 and standard
deviation 4.   Find:

    a $P(70 \leqslant X \leqslant 74)$ **b** $P(68 \leqslant X \leqslant 72)$ **c** $P(X \leqslant 65)$

2 X is a random variable that is distributed normally with mean 60 and standard
deviation 5.   Find:

    a $P(60 \leqslant X \leqslant 65)$ **b** $P(62 \leqslant X \leqslant 67)$ **c** $P(X \geqslant 64)$

    d $P(X \leqslant 68)$ **e** $P(X \leqslant 61)$ **f** $P(57.5 \leqslant X \leqslant 62.5)$

3 Given that $X \sim N(23, 5^2)$,   find a if:

    a $P(X < a) = 0.378$ **b** $P(X \geqslant a) = 0.592$

    c $P(23 - a < X < 23 + a) = 0.427$

C   THE STANDARD NORMAL DISTRIBUTION (Z-DISTRIBUTION)

Every normal X-distribution can be **transformed** into the **standard normal distribution** or

Z-distribution using the transformation $Z = \dfrac{X - \mu}{\sigma}$.

In the following investigation we determine the mean and standard deviation of this
Z-distribution.

INVESTIGATION 2 MEAN AND STANDARD DEVIATION OF $Z = \dfrac{x - \mu}{\sigma}$

Suppose a random variable X is **normally distributed** with mean μ and
standard deviation σ.

For each value of X we can calculate a **Z-value** using the algebraic

transformation $Z = \dfrac{X - \mu}{\sigma}$.

What to do:

1 Consider the X-values: 1, 2, 2, 3, 3, 3, 3, 4, 4, 4, 4, 4, 5, 5, 5, 5, 6, 6, 7.

   a Draw a graph of the distribution to check that it is approximately normal.

   b Find the mean μ and standard deviation σ for the distribution of X-values.

   c Use the transformation $Z = \dfrac{X - \mu}{\sigma}$ to convert each X-value into a Z-value.

   d Find the mean and standard deviation for the distribution of Z-values.

2 Click on the icon to load a large sample drawn from a normal population. By clicking appropriately we can repeat the four steps of question **1**.

DEMO

3 Write a brief report of your findings.

You should have discovered that for a Z-distribution the mean is 0 and the standard deviation is 1. This is true for *all* Z-distributions generated by transformation of a normal distribution, and this is why we call it the *standard* normal distribution.

For a normal X-distribution we know the probability density function is:
$$f(x) = \frac{1}{\sigma\sqrt{2\pi}}\, e^{-\frac{1}{2}\left(\frac{x-\mu}{\sigma}\right)^2}.$$

Substituting $x = z$, $\mu = 0$ and $\sigma = 1$, we find

the **probability density function** for the Z-distribution is $f(z) = \frac{1}{\sqrt{2\pi}}\, e^{-\frac{1}{2}z^2}$, $-\infty < z < \infty$.

Notice that the normal distribution function $f(x)$ has two parameters μ and σ, whereas the standard normal distribution function $f(z)$ has no parameters.

This means that a unique table of values can be constructed for $f(z)$, and we can use this table to compare normal distributions.

Before graphics calculators and computer packages the standard normal distribution was used exclusively for normal probability calculations such as those which follow.

CALCULATING PROBABILITIES USING THE Z-DISTRIBUTION

Since z is continuous,

$$P(Z \leqslant a) = P(Z < a)$$

and $P(Z \leqslant a) = \displaystyle\int_{-\infty}^{a} \frac{1}{\sqrt{2\pi}}\, e^{-\frac{1}{2}z^2}\, dz.$

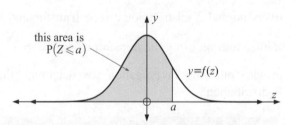

this area is
P($Z \leqslant a$)

$y = f(z)$

The table of curve areas on **page 824** enables us to find $P(Z \leqslant a)$.

USING A GRAPHICS CALCULATOR TO FIND PROBABILITIES

For a **TI-83**:   To find $P(Z \leqslant a)$ or $P(Z < a)$ use   normalcdf($-$E99, a).

              To find $P(Z \geqslant a)$ or $P(Z > a)$ use   normalcdf(a, E99).

              To find $P(a \leqslant Z \leqslant b)$ or $P(a < Z < b)$ use   normalcdf(a, b).

Example 3

If Z is a standard normal variable, find:

a $\quad P(Z \leqslant 1.5)$ b $\quad P(Z > 0.84)$ c $\quad P(-0.41 \leqslant Z \leqslant 0.67)$

a $\quad P(Z \leqslant 1.5)$
≈ 0.933

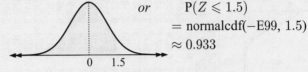

$or \quad P(Z \leqslant 1.5)$
$= \text{normalcdf}(-E99, 1.5)$
≈ 0.933

b $\quad P(Z > 0.84)$
$= 1 - P(Z \leqslant 0.84)$
$\approx 1 - 0.79954$
≈ 0.200

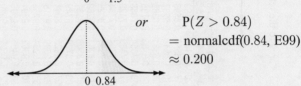

$or \quad P(Z > 0.84)$
$= \text{normalcdf}(0.84, E99)$
≈ 0.200

c $\quad P(-0.41 \leqslant Z \leqslant 0.67)$
$= P(Z \leqslant 0.67) - P(Z \leqslant -0.41)$
$\approx 0.7486 - 0.3409$
≈ 0.408

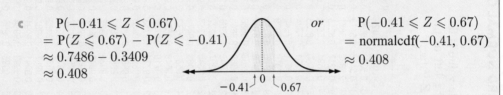

$or \quad P(-0.41 \leqslant Z \leqslant 0.67)$
$= \text{normalcdf}(-0.41, 0.67)$
≈ 0.408

WHAT DO Z-VALUES TELL US?

- If $z_1 = 1.84$ then z_1 is 1.84 standard deviations to the right of the mean.
- If $z_2 = -0.273$ then z_2 is 0.273 standard deviations to the left of the mean.

So, Z-values are useful when comparing results from two or more different distributions.

Example 4

Kelly scored 73% in History where the class mean was 68% and the standard deviation was 10.2%. In Mathematics she scored 66%, the class mean was 62%, and the standard deviation was 6.8%.

In which subject did Kelly perform better compared with the rest of her class? Assume the scores for both subjects were normally distributed.

Kelly's Z-score for History $= \dfrac{73 - 68}{10.2} \approx 0.490$

Kelly's Z-score for Maths $= \dfrac{66 - 62}{6.8} \approx 0.588$

So, Kelly's result in Maths was 0.588 standard deviations above the mean, whereas her result in History was 0.490 standard deviations above the mean.

$\therefore$ Kelly's result in Maths was better, even though it was a lower score.

STANDARD NORMAL CURVE AREAS ($Z \leqslant 0$)

Each table value is the area to the left of the specified Z-value.

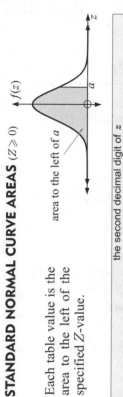

area to the left of a

z	.00	.01	.02	.03	.04	.05	.06	.07	.08	.09
					the second decimal digit of z					
-3.4	0.0003	0.0003	0.0003	0.0003	0.0003	0.0003	0.0003	0.0003	0.0003	0.0002
-3.3	0.0005	0.0005	0.0005	0.0004	0.0004	0.0004	0.0004	0.0004	0.0004	0.0003
-3.2	0.0007	0.0007	0.0006	0.0006	0.0006	0.0006	0.0006	0.0005	0.0005	0.0005
-3.1	0.0010	0.0009	0.0013	0.0012	0.0012	0.0011	0.0011	0.0011	0.0010	0.0010
-3.0	0.0013	0.0013	0.0013	0.0012	0.0012	0.0011	0.0011	0.0011	0.0010	0.0010
-2.9	0.0019	0.0018	0.0018	0.0017	0.0016	0.0016	0.0015	0.0015	0.0014	0.0014
-2.8	0.0026	0.0025	0.0024	0.0023	0.0023	0.0022	0.0021	0.0021	0.0020	0.0019
-2.7	0.0035	0.0034	0.0033	0.0032	0.0031	0.0030	0.0029	0.0028	0.0027	0.0026
-2.6	0.0047	0.0045	0.0044	0.0043	0.0041	0.0040	0.0039	0.0038	0.0037	0.0036
-2.5	0.0062	0.0060	0.0059	0.0057	0.0055	0.0054	0.0052	0.0051	0.0049	0.0048
-2.4	0.0082	0.0080	0.0078	0.0075	0.0073	0.0071	0.0069	0.0068	0.0066	0.0064
-2.3	0.0107	0.0104	0.0102	0.0099	0.0096	0.0094	0.0091	0.0089	0.0087	0.0084
-2.2	0.0139	0.0136	0.0132	0.0129	0.0125	0.0122	0.0119	0.0116	0.0113	0.0110
-2.1	0.0179	0.0174	0.0170	0.0166	0.0162	0.0158	0.0154	0.0150	0.0146	0.0143
-2.0	0.0228	0.0222	0.0217	0.0212	0.0207	0.0202	0.0197	0.0192	0.0188	0.0183
-1.9	0.0287	0.0281	0.0274	0.0268	0.0262	0.0256	0.0250	0.0244	0.0239	0.0233
-1.8	0.0359	0.0351	0.0344	0.0336	0.0329	0.0322	0.0314	0.0307	0.0301	0.0294
-1.7	0.0446	0.0436	0.0427	0.0418	0.0409	0.0401	0.0392	0.0384	0.0375	0.0367
-1.6	0.0548	0.0537	0.0526	0.0516	0.0505	0.0495	0.0485	0.0475	0.0465	0.0455
-1.5	0.0668	0.0655	0.0643	0.0630	0.0618	0.0606	0.0594	0.0582	0.0571	0.0559
-1.4	0.0808	0.0793	0.0778	0.0764	0.0749	0.0735	0.0721	0.0708	0.0694	0.0681
-1.3	0.0968	0.0951	0.0934	0.0918	0.0901	0.0885	0.0869	0.0853	0.0838	0.0823
-1.2	0.1151	0.1131	0.1112	0.1093	0.1075	0.1056	0.1038	0.1020	0.1003	0.0985
-1.1	0.1357	0.1335	0.1314	0.1292	0.1271	0.1251	0.1230	0.1210	0.1190	0.1170
-1.0	0.1587	0.1562	0.1539	0.1515	0.1492	0.1469	0.1446	0.1423	0.1401	0.1379
-0.9	0.1841	0.1814	0.1788	0.1762	0.1736	0.1711	0.1685	0.1660	0.1635	0.1611
-0.8	0.2119	0.2090	0.2061	0.2033	0.2005	0.1977	0.1949	0.1922	0.1894	0.1867
-0.7	0.2420	0.2389	0.2358	0.2327	0.2296	0.2266	0.2236	0.2206	0.2177	0.2148
-0.6	0.2743	0.2709	0.2676	0.2643	0.2611	0.2578	0.2546	0.2514	0.2483	0.2451
-0.5	0.3085	0.3050	0.3015	0.2981	0.2946	0.2912	0.2877	0.2843	0.2810	0.2776
-0.4	0.3446	0.3409	0.3372	0.3336	0.3300	0.3264	0.3228	0.3192	0.3156	0.3121
-0.3	0.3821	0.3783	0.3745	0.3707	0.3669	0.3632	0.3594	0.3557	0.3520	0.3483
-0.2	0.4207	0.4168	0.4129	0.4090	0.4052	0.4013	0.3974	0.3936	0.3897	0.3859
-0.1	0.4602	0.4562	0.4522	0.4483	0.4443	0.4404	0.4364	0.4325	0.4286	0.4247
0.0	0.5000	0.4960	0.4920	0.4880	0.4840	0.4801	0.4761	0.4721	0.4681	0.4641

STANDARD NORMAL CURVE AREAS ($Z \geqslant 0$)

Each table value is the area to the left of the specified Z-value.

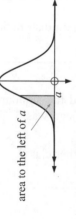

area to the left of a

z	.00	.01	.02	.03	.04	.05	.06	.07	.08	.09
					the second decimal digit of z					
0.0	0.5000	0.5040	0.5080	0.5120	0.5160	0.5199	0.5239	0.5279	0.5319	0.5359
0.1	0.5398	0.5438	0.5478	0.5517	0.5557	0.5596	0.5636	0.5675	0.5714	0.5753
0.2	0.5793	0.5832	0.5871	0.5910	0.5948	0.5987	0.6026	0.6064	0.6103	0.6141
0.3	0.6179	0.6217	0.6255	0.6293	0.6331	0.6368	0.6406	0.6443	0.6480	0.6517
0.4	0.6554	0.6591	0.6628	0.6664	0.6700	0.6736	0.6772	0.6808	0.6844	0.6879
0.5	0.6915	0.6950	0.6985	0.7019	0.7054	0.7088	0.7123	0.7157	0.7190	0.7224
0.6	0.7257	0.7291	0.7324	0.7357	0.7389	0.7422	0.7454	0.7486	0.7517	0.7549
0.7	0.7580	0.7611	0.7642	0.7673	0.7704	0.7734	0.7764	0.7794	0.7823	0.7852
0.8	0.7881	0.7910	0.7939	0.7967	0.7995	0.8023	0.8051	0.8078	0.8106	0.8133
0.9	0.8159	0.8186	0.8212	0.8238	0.8264	0.8289	0.8315	0.8340	0.8365	0.8389
1.0	0.8413	0.8438	0.8461	0.8485	0.8508	0.8531	0.8554	0.8577	0.8599	0.8621
1.1	0.8643	0.8665	0.8686	0.8708	0.8729	0.8749	0.8770	0.8790	0.8810	0.8830
1.2	0.8849	0.8869	0.8888	0.8907	0.8925	0.8944	0.8962	0.8980	0.8997	0.9015
1.3	0.9032	0.9049	0.9066	0.9082	0.9099	0.9115	0.9131	0.9147	0.9162	0.9177
1.4	0.9192	0.9207	0.9222	0.9236	0.9251	0.9265	0.9279	0.9292	0.9306	0.9319
1.5	0.9332	0.9345	0.9357	0.9370	0.9382	0.9394	0.9406	0.9418	0.9429	0.9441
1.6	0.9452	0.9463	0.9474	0.9484	0.9495	0.9505	0.9515	0.9525	0.9535	0.9545
1.7	0.9554	0.9564	0.9573	0.9582	0.9591	0.9599	0.9608	0.9616	0.9625	0.9633
1.8	0.9641	0.9649	0.9656	0.9664	0.9671	0.9678	0.9686	0.9693	0.9699	0.9706
1.9	0.9713	0.9719	0.9726	0.9732	0.9738	0.9744	0.9750	0.9756	0.9761	0.9767
2.0	0.9772	0.9778	0.9783	0.9788	0.9793	0.9798	0.9803	0.9808	0.9812	0.9817
2.1	0.9821	0.9826	0.9830	0.9834	0.9838	0.9842	0.9846	0.9850	0.9854	0.9857
2.2	0.9861	0.9864	0.9868	0.9871	0.9875	0.9878	0.9881	0.9884	0.9887	0.9890
2.3	0.9893	0.9896	0.9898	0.9901	0.9904	0.9906	0.9909	0.9911	0.9913	0.9916
2.4	0.9918	0.9920	0.9922	0.9925	0.9927	0.9929	0.9931	0.9932	0.9934	0.9936
2.5	0.9938	0.9940	0.9941	0.9943	0.9945	0.9946	0.9948	0.9949	0.9951	0.9952
2.6	0.9953	0.9955	0.9956	0.9957	0.9959	0.9960	0.9961	0.9962	0.9963	0.9964
2.7	0.9965	0.9966	0.9967	0.9968	0.9969	0.9970	0.9971	0.9972	0.9973	0.9974
2.8	0.9974	0.9975	0.9976	0.9977	0.9977	0.9978	0.9979	0.9979	0.9980	0.9981
2.9	0.9981	0.9982	0.9982	0.9983	0.9984	0.9984	0.9985	0.9985	0.9986	0.9986
3.0	0.9987	0.9987	0.9987	0.9988	0.9988	0.9989	0.9989	0.9989	0.9990	0.9990
3.1	0.9990	0.9991	0.9991	0.9991	0.9992	0.9992	0.9992	0.9992	0.9993	0.9993
3.2	0.9993	0.9993	0.9994	0.9994	0.9994	0.9994	0.9994	0.9995	0.9995	0.9995
3.3	0.9995	0.9995	0.9995	0.9996	0.9996	0.9996	0.9996	0.9996	0.9996	0.9997
3.4	0.9997	0.9997	0.9997	0.9997	0.9997	0.9997	0.9997	0.9997	0.9997	0.9998

EXERCISE 29C.1

1 For a random variable X the mean is μ and standard deviation is σ.

Using properties of E(X) and Var(X) find: **a** $\text{E}\left(\dfrac{X - \mu}{\sigma}\right)$ **b** $\text{Var}\left(\dfrac{X - \mu}{\sigma}\right)$.

2 If Z has standard normal distribution, find *using tables* and a sketch:

    a $\text{P}(Z \leqslant 1.2)$ **b** $\text{P}(Z \geqslant 0.86)$ **c** $\text{P}(Z \leqslant -0.52)$

    d $\text{P}(Z \geqslant -1.62)$ **e** $\text{P}(-0.86 \leqslant Z \leqslant 0.32)$

3 If Z has standard normal distribution, find *using technology*:

    a $\text{P}(Z \geqslant 0.837)$ **b** $\text{P}(Z \leqslant 0.0614)$ **c** $\text{P}(Z \geqslant -0.876)$

    d $\text{P}(-0.3862 \leqslant Z \leqslant 0.2506)$ **e** $\text{P}(-2.367 \leqslant Z \leqslant -0.6503)$

4 If Z has standard normal distribution, find:

    a $\text{P}(-0.5 < Z < 0.5)$ **b** $\text{P}(-1.960 < Z < 1.960)$

5 Find a if Z has standard normal distribution and:

    a $\text{P}(Z \leqslant a) = 0.95$ **b** $\text{P}(Z \geqslant a) = 0.90$

6 The table alongside shows Sergio's results in his mid-year examinations, along with the class means and standard deviations.

    a Find Sergio's Z-value for each subject.

    b Arrange Sergios performances in each subject in order from 'best' to 'worst'.

Sergio	μ	σ
Physics	83%	78%	10.8%
Chemistry	77%	72%	11.6%
Mathematics	84%	74%	10.1%
German	91%	86%	9.6%
Biology	72%	62%	12.2%

7 Pedro is studying Algebra and Geometry. He sits for the mid-year exams in each subject.

He is told that his Algebra mark is 56%, whereas the class mean and standard deviation are 50.2% and 15.8% respectively.

In Geometry he is told that the class mean and standard deviation are 58.7% and 18.7% respectively.

What percentage does Pedro need to have scored in Geometry to have an equivalent result to his Algebra mark?

STANDARDISING ANY NORMAL DISTRIBUTION

To find probabilities for a normally distributed random variable X:

Step 1:	Convert X-values to Z using $Z = \dfrac{X - \mu}{\sigma}$.
Step 2:	Sketch a standard normal curve and shade the required region.
Step 3:	Use the standard normal tables or a graphics calculator to find the probability.

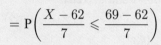

Example 5

Given that X is a normal variable with mean 62 and standard deviation 7, find:

a $P(X \leqslant 69)$ **b** $P(58.5 \leqslant X \leqslant 71.8)$

a $P(X \leqslant 69)$

$$= P\left(\frac{X - 62}{7} \leqslant \frac{69 - 62}{7}\right)$$

$$= P(Z \leqslant 1)$$

$$\approx 0.841$$

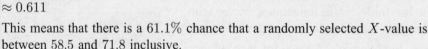

This means that there is an 84.1% chance that a randomly selected X-value is 69 or less.

b $P(58.5 \leqslant X \leqslant 71.8)$

$$= P\left(\frac{58.5 - 62}{7} \leqslant \frac{X - 62}{7} \leqslant \frac{71.8 - 62}{7}\right)$$

$$= P(-0.5 \leqslant Z \leqslant 1.4)$$

$$\approx 0.9192 - 0.3085$$

$$\approx 0.611$$

This means that there is a 61.1% chance that a randomly selected X-value is between 58.5 and 71.8 inclusive.

These probabilities can also be found using a graphics calculator without actually converting to standard normal Z-scores. Click on the icon for your calculator for instructions, and hence check the answers above.

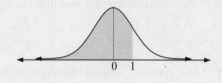

EXERCISE 29C.2

1 A random variable X is normally distributed with mean 70 and standard deviation 4. By converting to the standard variable Z and then using the tabled probability values for Z, find:

   a $P(X \geqslant 74)$ **b** $P(X \leqslant 68)$ **c** $P(60.6 \leqslant X \leqslant 68.4)$

2 A random variable X is normally distributed with mean 58.3 and standard deviation 8.96. By converting to the standard variable Z and then using your graphics calculator, find:

   a $P(X \geqslant 61.8)$ **b** $P(X \leqslant 54.2)$ **c** $P(50.67 \leqslant X \leqslant 68.92)$

3 The length L of a nail is normally distributed with mean 50.2 mm and standard deviation 0.93 mm. Find, by first converting to Z-values:

   a $P(L \geqslant 50)$ **b** $P(L \leqslant 51)$ **c** $P(49 \leqslant L \leqslant 50.5)$

FINDING QUANTILES OR k VALUES

Consider a population of crabs where the length of a shell, X mm, is normally distributed with mean 70 mm and standard deviation 10 mm.

A biologist wants to protect the population by allowing only the largest 5% of crabs to be harvested. He therefore asks the question: "95% of the crabs have lengths less than what?".

To answer this question we need to find the value of k such that $P(X \leqslant k) = 0.95$.

Example 6

Find k for which $P(X \leqslant k) = 0.95$ given that $X \sim N(70, 10^2)$ and X is measured in mm.

$$P(X \leqslant k) = 0.95$$

$$\therefore \; P\left(\frac{X - 70}{10} \leqslant \frac{k - 70}{10}\right) = 0.95$$

$$\therefore \; P\left(Z \leqslant \frac{k - 70}{10}\right) = 0.95$$

Searching amongst the standard normal tables or using your graphics calculator:

$$\frac{k - 70}{10} \approx 1.645$$

$$\therefore \; k \approx 86.5$$

So, approximately 95% of the values are expected to be 86.5 mm or less.

or Using technology:

If $P(X \leqslant k) = 0.95$

then $k = \text{invNorm}(0.95, 70, 10)$

$$\therefore \; k \approx 86.5$$

```
invNorm(0.95,70,
10)
          86.44853626
```

EXERCISE 29C.3

1 Z has a standard normal distribution. Find k using tabled values if:

   a $P(Z \leqslant k) = 0.81$ **b** $P(Z \leqslant k) = 0.58$ **c** $P(Z \leqslant k) = 0.17$

2 Z has a standard normal distribution. Find k using technology if:

   a $P(Z \leqslant k) = 0.384$ **b** $P(Z \leqslant k) = 0.878$ **c** $P(Z \leqslant k) = 0.1384$

3 **a** Show that $P(-k \leqslant Z \leqslant k) = 2\,P(Z \leqslant k) - 1$.

   b Suppose Z has a standard normal distribution. Find k if:

      i $P(-k \leqslant Z \leqslant k) = 0.238$ **ii** $P(-k \leqslant Z \leqslant k) = 0.7004$

4 **a** Find k if $P(X \leqslant k) = 0.9$ and $X \sim N(56, 18^2)$.

   b Find k if $P(X \geqslant k) = 0.8$ and $X \sim N(38.7, 8.8^2)$.

D

APPLICATIONS OF
THE NORMAL DISTRIBUTION

Example 7

In 1972 the heights of rugby players were found to be normally distributed with mean 179 cm and standard deviation 7 cm. Find the probability that a randomly selected player in 1972 was:

a   at least 175 cm tall   b   between 170 cm and 190 cm.

If X is the height of a player then X is normally distributed with $\mu = 179$, $\sigma = 7$.

a $P(X \geqslant 175)$ b $P(170 < X < 190)$
= normalcdf (175, E99, 179, 7)   = normalcdf (170, 190, 179, 7)
≈ 0.716 {graphics calculator} ≈ 0.843 {graphics calculator}

Example 8

A university professor determines that 80% of this year's History candidates should pass the final examination. The examination results are expected to be normally distributed with mean 62 and standard deviation 13. Find the expected lowest score necessary to pass the examination.

Let the random variable X denote the final examination result, so $X \sim N(62, 13^2)$.
We need to find k such that $P(X \geqslant k) = 0.8$
$\therefore$ $P(X \leqslant k) = 0.2$
$\therefore$ $k = \text{invNorm}(0.2, 62, 13)$
$\therefore$ $k \approx 51.1$

So, the minimum pass mark is more than 51%. If the final marks are given as integer percentages then the pass mark will be 52%.

Example 9

Find the mean and standard deviation of a normally distributed random variable X if $P(X \geqslant 50) = 0.2$ and $P(X \leqslant 20) = 0.3$.

$P(X \leqslant 20) = 0.3$ $P(X \geqslant 50) = 0.2$
$\therefore$ $P(Z \leqslant \dfrac{20 - \mu}{\sigma}) = 0.3$ $\therefore$ $P(X \leqslant 50) = 0.8$

$\therefore$ $\dfrac{20 - \mu}{\sigma} = \text{invNorm}(0.3)$ $\therefore$ $P(Z \leqslant \dfrac{50 - \mu}{\sigma}) = 0.8$

≈ -0.5244 $\therefore$ $\dfrac{50 - \mu}{\sigma} = 0.8416$

$\therefore$ $20 - \mu \approx -0.5244\sigma$ ..... (1) $\therefore$ $50 - \mu \approx 0.8416\sigma$ ..... (2)

Solving (1) and (2) simultaneously we get $\mu \approx 31.5$, $\sigma \approx 22.0$.

Note:
- In **Example 9** we **must** convert to Z-scores to answer the question. We always need to convert to Z-scores if we are trying to find an unknown mean μ or standard deviation σ.

- Z-scores are also useful when trying to compare two scores from different normal distributions.

- If possible, it is good practice to verify your results using an alternative method.

EXERCISE 29D

1 A machine produces metal bolts. The lengths of these bolts have a normal distribution with mean 19.8 cm and standard deviation 0.3 cm.

If a bolt is selected at random from the machine, find the probability that it will have a length between 19.7 cm and 20 cm.

2 Max's customers put money for charity in a collection box on the front counter of his shop. Assume that the average weekly collection is approximately normally distributed with a mean of \$40 and a standard deviation of \$6. What proportion of weeks would he expect to collect: **a**   between \$30.00 and \$50.00   **b**   at least \$50.00?

3 The students of Class X sat a Physics test. The average score was 46 with a standard deviation of 25. The teacher decided to award an A to the top 7% of the students in the class. Assuming that the scores were normally distributed, find the lowest score that a student needed to obtain in order to achieve an A.

4 Eels are washed onto a beach after a storm. Their lengths have a normal distribution with a mean of 41 cm and a variance of 11 cm^2.

- **a** If an eel is randomly selected, find the probability that it is at least 50 cm long.

- **b** Find the proportion of eels measuring between 40 cm and 50 cm long.

- **c** How many eels from a sample of 200 would you expect to measure at least 45 cm in length?

5 Find the mean and standard deviation of a normally distributed random variable X if $P(X \geqslant 35) = 0.32$ and $P(X \leqslant 8) = 0.26$.

6
- **a** A random variable X is normally distributed. Find the mean and the standard deviation of X, given that $P(X \geqslant 80) = 0.1$ and $P(X \leqslant 30) = 0.15$.

- **b** In the Mathematics examination at the end of the year, it was found that 10% of the students scored at least 80 marks, and no more than 15% scored less than 30 marks. Assuming the marks are normally distributed, what proportion of students scored more than 50 marks?

7 Circular metal tokens are used to operate a washing machine in a laundromat. The diameters of the tokens are normally distributed, and only tokens with diameters between 1.94 and 2.06 cm will operate the machine.

a   Find the mean and standard deviation of the distribution given that 2% of the tokens are too small, and 3% are too large.

b   Find the probability that at most one token out of a randomly selected sample of 20 will not operate the machine.

REVIEW SET 29A

1 The arm lengths of 18 year old females are normally distributed with mean 64 cm and standard deviation 4 cm.

a   Find the percentage of 18 year old females whose arm lengths are:

   i   between 60 cm and 72 cm   ii   greater than 60 cm.

b   Find the probability that a randomly chosen 18 year old female has an arm length in the range 56 cm to 68 cm.

2 The length of steel rods produced by a machine is normally distributed with a standard deviation of 3 mm. It is found that 2% of all rods are less than 25 mm long. Find the mean length of rods produced by the machine.

3 $f(x) = \begin{cases} ax(x-3), & 0 \leqslant x \leqslant 2 \\ 0 & \text{elsewhere} \end{cases}$ is a continuous probability distribution function.

a   Find a.   b   Sketch the graph of $y = f(x)$.

c   Find: i   the mean   ii   the mode   iii   the median   iv   the variance.

d   Find $P(1 \leqslant x \leqslant 2)$.

4 A factory has a machine designed to fill bottles of drink with a volume of 375 mL. It is found that the average amount of drink in each bottle is 376 mL, and that 2.3% of the drink bottles have a volume smaller than 375 mL. Assuming that the amount of drink in each bottle is distributed normally, find the standard deviation.

5 The continuous random variable Z is distributed such that $Z \sim N(0, 1)$.

Find the value of k if $P(|Z| > k) = 0.376$.

6 X is a continuous random variable where $X \sim N(\mu, 2^2)$. Find $P(|X - \mu| < 0.524)$.

7 The marks of 2376 candidates in an IB examination are normally distributed with a mean of 49 marks and variance 225.

a   If the pass mark is 45, estimate the number of candidates who passed the examination.

b   If 7% of the candidates scored scored a '7', find the minimum mark required to obtained a '7'.

c   Find the interquartile range of the distribution of marks obtained.

8 The lengths of metal rods produced in a manufacturing process are distributed normally with mean μ cm and standard deviation 6 cm. It is known that 5.63% of the rods have length greater than 89.52 cm. Find the mean, median, and modal length of these metal rods.

9 The continuous random variable X has probability density function

$$f(x) = \begin{cases} e^{-\frac{1}{2}x} & \text{for } 0 \leqslant x \leqslant k. \\ 0 & \text{otherwise.} \end{cases}$$

  a Find the exact value of k, writing your answer in the form $\ln a$ where $a \in \mathbb{Z}$.

  b What is the probability that X lies between $\frac{1}{4}$ and $\frac{7}{8}$?

  c Find the exact values of the mean and variance of X.

10 The random variable X is distributed normally with mean 50 and $P(X < 90) \approx 0.975$.

Find the shaded area in the given diagram which illustrates the probability density function for the random variable X.

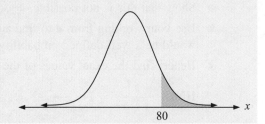

80

x

REVIEW SET 29B

1 The contents of a certain brand of soft drink can is normally distributed with mean 377 mL and standard deviation 4.2 mL.

  a Find the percentage of cans with contents:

   i less than 368.6 mL   **ii** between 372.8 mL and 389.6 mL

  b Find the probability that a randomly selected can has contents between 364.4 mL and 381.2 mL.

2 The life of a Xenon battery is known to be normally distributed with a mean of 33.2 weeks and a standard deviation of 2.8 weeks.

  a Find the probability that a randomly selected battery will last at least 35 weeks.

  b Find the maximum number of weeks for which the manufacturer can expect that not more than 8% of batteries will fail.

3 The edible part of a batch of Coffin Bay oysters is normally distributed with mean 38.6 grams and standard deviation 6.3 grams. If the random variable X is the mass of a Coffin Bay oyster:

  a find a if $P(38.6 - a \leqslant X \leqslant 38.6 + a) = 0.6826$

  b find b if $P(X \geqslant b) = 0.8413$.

4 A random variable X has probability density function $f(x) = ax^2(2 - x)$ for $0 < x < 2$.

  a Show that $a = \frac{3}{4}$.   **b** Find the mode of X.

  c Find the median of X.   **d** Find $P(0.6 < X < 1.2)$.

5 The random variable T represents the lifetime in years of a component of a solar cell. Its probability density function is $F(t) = 0.4e^{-0.4t}, \ t \geqslant 0$.

    a Find the probability that this component of the solar cell fails within 1 year. Give your answer correct to 5 decimal places.

    b Each solar cell has 5 of these components which operate independently of each other. The cell will work provided at least 3 of the components continue to work. Find the probability that a solar cell will still operate after 1 year.

6 It is claimed that the continuous random variable X has probability density function

$$f(x) = \begin{cases} \dfrac{4}{1+x^2} & \text{for } 0 \leqslant x \leqslant 1 \\ 0 & \text{otherwise.} \end{cases}$$

    a Show that this is not possible.

    b Use your working from **a** to find an exact value of k for which $F(x) = kf(x)$ would be a well-defined probability density function.

    c Hence, find the exact values of the mean and variance of X.

    Hint: $\dfrac{x^2}{1+x^2} = 1 - \dfrac{1}{1+x^2}$.

7 A continuous random variable X has probability density function

$$f(x) = \begin{cases} ax(4 - x^2), & 0 \leqslant x \leqslant 2 \\ 0 & \text{elsewhere.} \end{cases}$$

    a Find the exact value of a.

    b Find the exact value of the mode of X.

    c Calculate the median value of X.

    d Find the exact value of the mean of X.

8 The heights of 18 year old boys are normally distributed with a mean of 187 cm. Fifteen percent of all these boys have heights greater than 193 cm. Find the probability that two 18 year old boys chosen at random will have heights greater than 185 cm.

9 The random variable X is normally distributed with $P(X \leqslant 30) = 0.0832$ and $P(X \geqslant 90) = 0.101$.

    a Find the mean μ and standard deviation σ for X, correct to 3 decimal places.

    b Hence find $P(|X - \mu| > 7)$.

10 The continuous random variable X has a probability density function defined on the interval $[0, k]$ by

$$f(x) = \begin{cases} \dfrac{x}{5} & \text{for } 0 \leqslant x \leqslant 2 \\ \dfrac{8}{5x^2} & 2 \leqslant x \leqslant k. \end{cases}$$

    a Find the value of k.

    b Find the exact value of the median of X.

    c Find the mean and variance of X.

Chapter 30

Miscellaneous questions

EXERCISE 30

1   a   Simplify $(-1+i\sqrt{2})^3$.

    b   Write $5+i\sqrt{2}$ in the form $a^3\text{cis}\,\theta$ stating the exact values of a and θ.

    c   Find the exact solutions of $z^3 = 5+i\sqrt{2}$.

    d   Hence, show that $\arctan\left(\frac{\sqrt{2}}{5}\right) + 2\pi = 3\arccos\left(\frac{-1}{\sqrt{3}}\right)$.

2   a   Find the cube roots of $-2-2i$.

    b   Display the cube roots of $-2-2i$ on an Argand diagram.

    c   If the cube roots are α_1, α_2 and α_3, show that $\alpha_1 + \alpha_2 + \alpha_3 = 0$.

    d   Using an algebraic argument, prove that if β is any complex number then the sum of the zeros of $z^n = \beta$ is 0.

3   a   Evaluate $(1-i)^2$ and simplify $(1-i)^{4n}$.

    b   Hence, evaluate $(1-i)^{16}$.

    c   Use your answers above to find two solutions of $z^{16} = 256$.   Give clear reasons for your answers.

4   Let $z = \dfrac{-1+i\sqrt{3}}{4}$ and $w = \dfrac{\sqrt{2}+i\sqrt{2}}{4}$.

    a   Write z and w in the form $r(\cos\theta + i\sin\theta)$ where $0 \leqslant \theta \leqslant \pi$.

    b   Show that $zw = \frac{1}{4}\left(\cos\frac{11\pi}{12} + i\sin\frac{11\pi}{12}\right)$.

    c   Evaluate zw in the form $a+ib$ and hence find the exact values of $\cos\frac{11\pi}{12}$ and $\sin\frac{11\pi}{12}$.

5   The sum of the first n terms of a series is given by $S_n = n^3 + 2n - 1$. Find u_n, the nth term of the series.

6   The tangent to the curve $y = f(x)$ at the point A$(x,\,y)$ meets the x-axis at the point B$(x-\frac{1}{2},\,0)$. The curve meets the y-axis at the point C$(0,\,\frac{1}{e})$. Find the equation of the curve.

7   The diagram shows a sector POR of a circle of radius 1 unit and centre O. The angle $\widehat{POR} = \theta$, and the line segments [PQ], [P$_1$Q$_1$], [P$_2$Q$_2$], [P$_3$Q$_3$], ... are all perpendicular to [OR].

Calculate, in terms of θ, the sum to infinity of the lengths
PQ + P$_1$Q$_1$ + P$_2$Q$_2$ + P$_3$Q$_3$ + ...

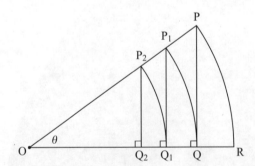

8   Use the method of integration by parts to find $\int x\arctan x\, dx$.
Check that your answer is correct using differentiation.

9   Solve the following equations:

    a $\log_2\left(x^2 - 2x + 1\right) = 1 + \log_2(x-1)$ b $3^{2x+1} = 5(3^x) + 2$

10 Solve *exactly* for x: $\dfrac{3x-1}{|x+1|} > 2$.

11 Find the *exact* values of x for which $\sin^2 x + \sin x - 2 = 0$ and $-2\pi \leqslant x \leqslant 2\pi$.

12 If $f : x \mapsto \ln x$ and $g : x \mapsto 3 + x$ find: **a** $f^{-1}(2) \times g^{-1}(2)$ **b** $(f \circ g)^{-1}(2)$.

13 Given an angle θ where $\sin\theta = -\frac{7}{25}$ and $-\frac{\pi}{2} < \theta < 0$,   find the exact values of:
    a $\cos\theta$ **b** $\tan\theta$ **c** $\sin 2\theta$ **d** $\sec 2\theta$.

14 Solve $\sqrt{3}\cos x \csc x + 1 = 0$ for $0 \leqslant x \leqslant 2\pi$.

15 The number of snails in a garden plot follows a Poisson distribution with standard deviation d. Find d if the chance of finding exactly 8 snails is half that of finding exactly 7 snails in this plot.

16 Find the coordinates of the point on the line L that is nearest to the origin if the equation of L is $r = 2\mathbf{i} - 3\mathbf{j} + \mathbf{k} + \lambda(-\mathbf{i} + \mathbf{j} - \mathbf{k})$, $\lambda \in \mathbb{R}$.

17 The function $f(x)$ satisfies the following criteria: $f'(x) > 0$ and $f''(x) < 0$ for all x, $f(2) = 1$, and $f'(2) = 2$.
    a Find the equation of the tangent to $f(x)$ at $x = 2$ and sketch it on a graph.
    b Hence, sketch a graph of $f(x)$ on the same axes.
    c Explain why $f(x)$ has exactly one zero.
    d Estimate an interval in which the zero of $f(x)$ lies.

18 If $n \in \mathbb{Z}$, $n \geqslant -2$, prove by induction that $2n^3 - 3n^2 + n + 31 \geqslant 0$.

19 Prove by induction that $\displaystyle\sum_{r=1}^{n} r3^r = \frac{3}{4}\left[(2n-1)3^n + 1\right]$ for all $n \in \mathbb{Z}^+$.

20 Prove by induction that for all $n \in \mathbb{Z}^+$,
$$\frac{1}{a(a+1)} + \frac{1}{(a+1)(a+2)} + \frac{1}{(a+2)(a+3)} + \dotsb + \frac{1}{(a+n-1)(a+n)} = \frac{n}{a(a+n)}.$$

21 Prove by induction that $x^n - y^n$ has a factor of $x - y$ for all $n \in \mathbb{Z}^+$.

22 Prove that $3\left(5^{2n+1}\right) + 2^{3n+1}$ is divisible by 17 for all $n \in \mathbb{Z}^+$.

23 Assuming Pascal's rule $\binom{n}{r} + \binom{n}{r+1} = \binom{n+1}{r+1}$,
    a prove that $(1+x)^n = 1 + \binom{n}{1}x + \binom{n}{2}x^2 + \dotsb + \binom{n}{n}x^n$ for all $n \in \mathbb{Z}^+$.
    b Establish the binomial expansion for $(a+b)^n$ by letting $x = \dfrac{b}{a}$ in **a**.

24 Prove that $\dfrac{1}{\sin 2x} + \dfrac{1}{\sin 4x} + \dotsb + \dfrac{1}{\sin(2^n x)} = \cot x - \cot(2^n x)$ for all $n \in \mathbb{Z}^+$.

25 Show that if $y = mx + c$ is a tangent to $y^2 = 4x$ then $c = \dfrac{1}{m}$ and the coordinates of the point of contact are $\left(\dfrac{1}{m^2}, \dfrac{2}{m}\right)$.

26 The illustrated ellipse has equation $\dfrac{x^2}{a^2} + \dfrac{y^2}{b^2} = 1.$

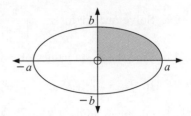

 a Show that the shaded region has area given by

$$\frac{b}{a} \int_0^a \sqrt{a^2 - x^2}\, dx\,.$$

 b Find the area of the ellipse in terms of a and b.

 c An ellipsoid is obtained by rotating the ellipse about the x-axis through $360°$.

  Prove that the volume of the ellipsoid is given by $V = \tfrac{4}{3}\pi ab^2.$

27 Consider the following quadratic function where $a_i,\, b_i \in \mathbb{R}$:

$$f(x) = (a_1 x - b_1)^2 + (a_2 x - b_2)^2 + (a_3 x - b_3)^2 + \ldots\ldots + (a_n x - b_n)^2.$$

Use quadratic theory to prove the 'Cauchy-Schwartz inequality':

$$\left(\sum_{i=1}^n a_i^2 \right) \left(\sum_{i=1}^n b_i^2 \right) \geqslant \left(\sum_{i=1}^n a_i b_i \right)^2.$$

28 Show that the equation of the tangent to the ellipse with equation

$$\frac{x^2}{a^2} + \frac{y^2}{b^2} = 1 \quad \text{at the point P}(x_1,\, y_1) \ \text{ is } \ \left(\frac{x_1}{a^2} \right) x + \left(\frac{y_1}{b^2} \right) y = 1.$$

29 Prove that in any triangle with angles A, B and C:

 a $\sin 2A + \sin 2B + \sin 2C = 4 \sin A \sin B \sin C$

 b $\tan A + \tan B + \tan C = \tan A \tan B \tan C.$

30 **a** A circle has radius r and the acute angled triangle ABC has vertices on the circle.

  Show that the area of the triangle is given by $\dfrac{abc}{4r}.$

 b In triangle ABC it is known that $\sin A = \cos B + \cos C.$
  Show that the triangle is right angled.

31

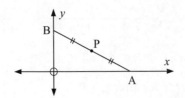

[AB] is a thin metal rod of fixed length and P is its centre. A is free to move on the x-axis and B is free to move on the y-axis.

What path or *locus* is traced out by point P as the rod moves to all possible places?

32 **a** Show that $\sqrt{14 - 4\sqrt{6}}$ cannot be written in the form $a + b\sqrt{6}$ where $a,\, b \in \mathbb{Z}$.

 b Can $\sqrt{14 - 4\sqrt{6}}$ be written in the form $a\sqrt{m} + b\sqrt{n}$ where $a,\, b,\, m,\, n \in \mathbb{Z}$?

33 $(1 + x)^n = \binom{n}{0} + \binom{n}{1} x + \binom{n}{2} x^2 + \binom{n}{3} x^3 + \ldots\ldots + \binom{n}{n} x^n$ for all $n \in \mathbb{Z}^+.$
Prove that:

 a $\binom{n}{1} + 2\binom{n}{2} + 3\binom{n}{3} + \ldots\ldots + n\binom{n}{n} = n 2^{n-1}$

 b $\binom{n}{0} + 2\binom{n}{1} + 3\binom{n}{2} + \ldots\ldots + (n+1)\binom{n}{n} = (n+2)2^{n-1}$

 c $\binom{n}{0} + \tfrac{1}{2}\binom{n}{1} + \tfrac{1}{3}\binom{n}{2} + \ldots\ldots + \dfrac{1}{n+1}\binom{n}{n} = \dfrac{2^{n+1} - 1}{n+1}.$

34   **a**   If $\dfrac{x+5}{(x^2+5)(1-x)} = \dfrac{Ax+B}{x^2+5} + \dfrac{C}{x-1}$,   find A, B and C.

    b   Hence, find the exact value of $\displaystyle\int_2^4 \dfrac{x+5}{(x^2+5)(1-x)}\,dx$.

35   Consider the series $\dfrac{1}{1\times 3} + \dfrac{1}{2\times 4} + \dfrac{1}{3\times 5} + \ldots\ldots + \dfrac{1}{n(n+2)}$.

    a   By writing $\dfrac{1}{n(n+2)}$ in the form $\dfrac{A}{n} + \dfrac{B}{n+2}$,   find the values of A and B.

    b   Use **a** to show that the sum of the series is $\dfrac{3}{4} - \dfrac{1}{2n+2} - \dfrac{1}{2n+4}$.

    c   Find $\displaystyle\sum_{r=1}^{\infty} \dfrac{1}{r(r+2)}$.   **d**   Check **b** using mathematical induction.

36   Find: **a** $\displaystyle\int \dfrac{x}{\sqrt{1-x^2}}\,dx$ **b** $\displaystyle\int \dfrac{1+x}{1+x^2}\,dx$ **c** $\displaystyle\int \dfrac{1}{\sqrt{1-x^2}}\,dx$

37   A flagpole is erected at A and its top is B. At C, due west of A, the angle of elevation to B is α. At D, due south of A, the angle of elevation to B is β.

    Point E is due south of C and due west of D. Show that at E, the angle of elevation to B is $\operatorname{arccot}\left(\sqrt{\cot^2\alpha + \cot^2\beta}\right)$.

38   **a**   Use complex number methods to show that $\tan 4\theta = \dfrac{4\tan\theta - 4\tan^3\theta}{1 - 6\tan^2\theta + \tan^4\theta}$.

    b   Hence, find the roots of the equation $x^4 + 4x^3 - 6x^2 - 4x + 1 = 0$.

39   Find the sum of the series:

    a $1 + a\cos\theta + a^2\cos 2\theta + a^3\cos 3\theta + \ldots\ldots + a^n\cos n\theta$

    b $a\sin\theta + a^2\sin 2\theta + a^3\sin 3\theta + \ldots\ldots + a^n\sin n\theta$ for $n \in \mathbb{Z}^+$.

40   Suppose e^x can be written as the infinite series $e^x = a_0 + a_1 x + a_2 x^2 + \ldots\ldots + a_n x^n + \ldots\ldots$

    a   Show that $a_0 = 1$, $a_1 = 1$, $a_2 = \frac{1}{2!}$, $a_3 = \frac{1}{3!}$, $\ldots\ldots$

    b   Hence conjecture an infinite geometric series representation for e^x.

    c   Check your answer to **b** using the substitution $x = 1$.

41   **a**   By considering $\dfrac{1}{a^2 - x^2} = \dfrac{P}{a-x} + \dfrac{Q}{a+x}$,   find P and Q.

    b   Use **a** to show that $\displaystyle\int \dfrac{1}{a^2 - x^2}\,dx = \dfrac{1}{2a}\ln\left|\dfrac{a+x}{a-x}\right| + c$.

    c   Check **b** using differentiation.

42   **a**   Assuming that

    $\cos S + \cos D = 2\cos\left(\frac{S+D}{2}\right)\cos\left(\frac{S-D}{2}\right)$ and $\sin S + \sin D = 2\sin\left(\frac{S+D}{2}\right)\cos\left(\frac{S-D}{2}\right)$,

    prove that $\operatorname{cis}\theta + \operatorname{cis}\phi = 2\cos\left(\frac{\theta-\phi}{2}\right)\operatorname{cis}\left(\frac{\theta+\phi}{2}\right)$.

    b From **a**, what is the modulus and argument of $\text{cis}\,\theta + \text{cis}\,\phi$?

    c Show that your answers in **b** are correct using a geometrical argument.

    d Prove that the solutions of $\left(\dfrac{z+1}{z-1}\right)^5 = 1$ are $z = -i\cot\left(\dfrac{k\pi}{5}\right)$, $k = 1, 2, 3, 4$.

43   **a** If $z + \dfrac{1}{z}$ is real, prove that either $|z| = 1$ or z is real.

    b If $|z+w| = |z-w|$ prove that $\arg z$ and $\arg w$ differ by $\frac{\pi}{2}$.

    c If $z = r\,\text{cis}\,\theta$,   write z^4, $\dfrac{1}{z}$ and iz^* in a similar form.

44 $x^2 + ax + bc = 0$ and $x^2 + bx + ca = 0$ where $a \neq 0$, $b \neq 0$, $c \neq 0$, have a single common root. Prove that the other roots satisfy $x^2 + cx + ab = 0$.

45 If $x = a^{\frac{1}{3}} + b^{\frac{1}{3}}$,   show that $x^3 = 3(ab)^{\frac{1}{3}} x + (a+b)$.

    Hence, find all real solutions of the equation $x^3 = 6x + 6$.

46 Solve simultaneously: $x = 16y$ and $\log_y x - \log_x y = \frac{8}{3}$.

47 Find all values of m for which the quartic equation $x^4 - (3m+2)x^2 + m^2 = 0$ has 4 real roots in arithmetic progression.

48 α and β are two of the roots of $x^3 + ax^2 + bx + c = 0$.

    Prove that $\alpha\beta$ is a root of $x^3 - bx^2 + acx - c^2 = 0$.

49 x and y satisfy the equations $x^2 + 3xy + 9 = 0$ and $y^2 + x - 1 = 0$.

    Solve these equations simultaneously for x given that x is real.

50   **a** Find the value of the sum: $\dfrac{1}{1+\sqrt{2}} + \dfrac{1}{\sqrt{2}+\sqrt{3}} + \dfrac{1}{\sqrt{3}+\sqrt{4}} + \dots + \dfrac{1}{\sqrt{99}+\sqrt{100}}$.

    b Can you make any generalizations from **a**?

51 The three numbers x, y and z are such that $x > y > z > 0$.

    Show that if $\frac{1}{x}$, $\frac{1}{y}$ and $\frac{1}{z}$ are in arithmetic progression, then $x - z$, y and $x - y + z$ are the lengths of the sides of a right angled triangle.

52 Each summer, 10% of the trees on a certain plantation die out, and each winter, workmen plant 100 new trees. At the end of the winter in 1980 there were 1200 trees in the plantation.

    a How many living trees were there at the end of winter in 1970?

    b What will happen to the number of trees in the plantation during the 21st century providing the conditions remain unchanged?

53   **a** I wish to borrow $20000 for 10 years at 12% p.a. where the interest is compounded quarterly. I intend to pay off the loan in quarterly instalments. How much do I need to pay back each quarter?

    b Find a formula for calculating the repayments R if the total amount borrowed is P, for n years, at r% p.a., and there are to be m equal payments at equal intervals each year.

54 A rectangle is divided by m lines parallel to one pair of opposite sides and n lines parallel to the other pair. How many rectangles are there in the figure obtained?

55 **a** Schools A and B each preselect 11 members for a team to be sent interstate. However, circumstances allow only a combined team of 11 to be sent away. In how many ways can a team of 11 be selected and a captain be chosen if the captain must come from A?

   b Use **a** to show that: $1 \binom{n}{1}^2 + 2 \binom{n}{2}^2 + 3 \binom{n}{3}^2 + \ \ldots\ldots\ + n \binom{n}{n}^2 = n \binom{2n-1}{n-1}$.

56 Two different numbers are randomly chosen out of the set $\{1, 2, 3, 4, 5, \ldots\ldots\ , n\}$, where n is a multiple of four. Determine the probability that one of the numbers is four times larger than the other.

57 A hundred seeds are planted in ten rows of ten seeds per row. Assuming that each seed independently germinates with probability $\frac{1}{2}$, find the probability that the row with the maximum number of germinations contains at least 8 seedlings.

58 Consider a randomly chosen n child family, where $n > 1$. Let A be the event that the family has at most one boy, and B be the event that every child in the family is of the same sex. For what values of n are the events A and B independent?

59 Two marksmen, A and B, fire simultaneously at a target. If A is twice as likely to hit the target as B, and if the probability that the target does get hit is $\frac{1}{2}$, find the probability of A hitting the target.

60 A quadratic equation $ax^2 + bx + c = 0$ is copied by a typist. However, the numbers standing for a, b and c are blurred and she can only see that they are integers of one digit. What is the probability that the equation she types has real roots?

61 Two people agree to meet each other at the corner of two city streets between 1 pm and 2 pm, but neither will wait for the other for more than 30 minutes. If each person is equally likely to arrive at any time during the one hour period, determine the probability that they will in fact meet.

62 Use the figure alongside to show that $\cos 36° = \dfrac{1 + \sqrt{5}}{4}$.

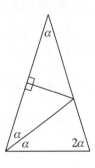

63 Find α:

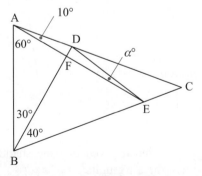

64 For A, B, C not necessarily the angles of a triangle, what can be deduced about $A + B + C$ if $\tan A + \tan B + \tan C = \tan A \tan B \tan C$?

65 Without using a calculator, show how to find $\arctan(\frac{1}{7}) + 2\arctan(\frac{1}{3})$.

66 A mountain is perfectly conical in shape. The base is a circle of radius 2 km, and the steepest slopes leading up to the top are 3 km long.

From the southernmost point A on the base, a path leads up on the side of the mountain to B, a point on the northern slope which is 1.5 km up the slope from C. A and C are diametrically opposite.

If the path leading from A to B is the shortest possible distance from A to B along the mountainside, find the length of this path.

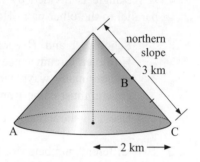

67

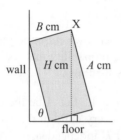

An A cm by B cm rectangular refrigerator leans at an angle of θ to the floor against a wall.

a Find H in terms of A, B and θ.

b Explain how the figure can be used to prove that $A\sin\theta + B\cos\theta \leqslant \sqrt{A^2 + B^2}$, with equality when $\tan\theta = \dfrac{A}{B}$.

68 Over 2000 years ago, **Heron** or **Hero** discovered a formula for finding the area of a triangle with sides a, b and c. It is $A = \sqrt{s(s-a)(s-b)(s-c)}$ where $2s = a+b+c$. Prove that this formula is correct.

69 **a** Given that $y = \ln(\tan x)$, $x \in \left]0, \frac{\pi}{2}\right[$, show that $\dfrac{dy}{dx} = k\csc(2x)$ for some constant k.

b The graph of $y = \csc(2x)$ is illustrated on the interval $\left]0, \frac{\pi}{2}\right[$.

Find the area of the shaded region.

Give your answer in the form $a\ln b$ where $a \in \mathbb{Q}$ and $b \in \mathbb{Z}^+$.

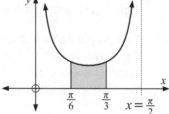

70 P is a point and line l, with direction vector $\mathbf{v}$, passes through points A and Q.

a Prove that $PQ = \dfrac{\left| \overrightarrow{AP} \times \mathbf{v} \right|}{|\mathbf{v}|}$.

b Hence, find the shortest distance from $(2, -1, 3)$ to the line $\begin{pmatrix} x \\ y \\ z \end{pmatrix} = \begin{pmatrix} -1 \\ 1 \\ 2 \end{pmatrix} + \lambda \begin{pmatrix} 3 \\ -1 \\ 1 \end{pmatrix}$.

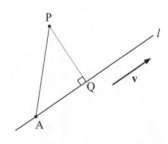

71

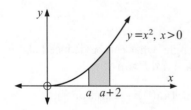

Find a given that the shaded region has area $5\frac{1}{6}$ units^2.

72 If $\dfrac{dy}{dx} = x \csc y$ and $y(2) = 0$,   find y as a function of x.

73 By considering $\dfrac{d}{dx}(\tan^3 x)$,   find $\int \sec^4 x \, dx$.

74 What can be deduced if $A \cap B$ and $A \cup B$ are independent events?

75 For a continuous function defined on the interval $[a, b]$, the length of the curve can be
found using $L = \displaystyle\int_a^b \sqrt{1 + [f'(x)]^2} \, dx$.   Find the length of:

    a $y = x^2$ on the interval $[0, 1]$ **b** $y = \sin x$ on the interval $[0, \pi]$.

76   **a** Simplify: **i** $(A \cup B) \cap A'$ **ii** $(A \cap B) \cup (A' \cap B)$.
    b Verify that $(A \cap B) \cup C = (A \cup C) \cap (B \cup C)$.
    c Prove that if A and B are independent events then so are:
        i A' and B' **ii** A and B'.

77 Write $(3 - i\sqrt{2})^4$ in the form $x + y\sqrt{2}i$ where $x,\ y \in \mathbb{Z}$.

78 Solve the equation $\sin \theta \cos \theta = \frac{1}{4}$ for the interval $\theta \in [-\pi, \pi]$.

79 z and w are two complex numbers such that $2z + w = i$ and $z - 3w = 7 - 10i$.
Find $z + w$ in the form $a + bi$, where a and $b \in \mathbb{Z}$.

80 Solve the differential equation $(x + 1)^2 \dfrac{dy}{dx} = 2xy$, $x > -1$ given that $y(1) = 4$.

81 f is defined by $x \mapsto \ln(x(x - 2))$.
    a State the domain of f.   **b** Find $f'(x)$.
    c Find the equation of the tangent to f at the point where $x = 3$.

82 Hat 1 contains three green and four blue tickets. Hat 2 contains four green and three
blue tickets. One ticket is randomly selected from each hat.
    a What is the probability that the tickets are the same colour?
    b Given that the tickets are different colours, what is the probability that the green
ticket came from Hat 2?

83 If $\mathbf{A}^3 = \mathbf{A}$, what can be said about: **a** $|\mathbf{A}|$ **b** $\mathbf{A}^{-1}$?

84 If $P(x)$ is divided by $(x - a)^2$, prove that the remainder is $P'(a)(x - a) + P(a)$ where
$P'(x)$ is the derivative of $P(x)$.

85 A lampshade is a truncated cone open
at the bottom.

Find the pattern needed to make this
lampshade from a flat sheet of material.

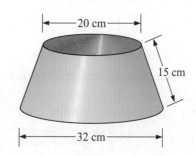

86 [AB] represents a painting on a wall. AB = 2 m and BC = 1 m.

The angle of view observed by a girl between the top and bottom of the painting is $30°$.

How far is the girl from the wall?

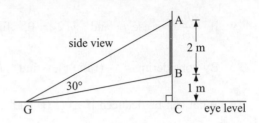

87

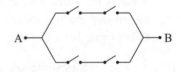

A circle is centred at the origin O. A second circle has half the diameter of the original circle and touches it internally. P is a fixed point on the smaller circle as shown, and lies on the x-axis.

The smaller circle now rolls around the inside of the larger one without slipping.

Show that for all positions of the smaller circle, P remains on the x-axis.

88 **a** Write $-8i$ in polar form.

    b Hence find the three cube roots of $-8i$, calling them z_1, z_2 and z_3.

    c Illustrate the roots from **b** on an Argand diagram.

    d Show that $z_1{}^2 = z_2 z_3$ where z_1 is any one of the three cube roots.

    e Find the product of the three cube roots.

89 **a** Complex number z has an argument of θ. Show that iz has an argument of $\theta + \frac{\pi}{2}$.

    b In an Argand plane, points P, Q and R represent the complex numbers z_1, z_2 and z_3 respectively. If $i(z_3 - z_2) = z_1 - z_2$, what can be deduced about triangle PQR?

90 $z = re^{i\theta}$, $r > 0$, is a non-zero complex number such that $z + \dfrac{1}{z} = a + bi$, $a, b \in \mathbb{R}$.

    a Find expressions for a and b in terms of r and θ.

    b Hence, find all complex numbers z such that $z + \dfrac{1}{z}$ is real.

91 The diagram shows a simple electrical network.

Each symbol —✓•— represents a switch.

All four switches operate independently, and the probability of each one of them being closed is p.

    a In terms of p, find the probability that the current flows from A to B.

    b Find the least value of p for which the probability of current flow is more than 0.5.

92 If $\mathbf{A} = \begin{pmatrix} 2 & 1 \\ 0 & 2 \end{pmatrix}$:

    a find $\mathbf{A}^2$ and $\mathbf{A}^3$.

    b prove using mathematical induction that $\mathbf{A}^n = \begin{pmatrix} 2^n & n2^{n-1} \\ 0 & 2^n \end{pmatrix}$ for all $n \in \mathbb{Z}^+$.

93 By considering the identity $(1+x)^n = (1+x)^2 (1+x)^{n-2}$, deduce that

$\binom{n}{r} = \binom{n-2}{r} + 2\binom{n-2}{r-1} + \binom{n-2}{r-2}$.

94 While driving, Bernard passes through n intersections which are independently controlled by traffic lights. Each set of lights has probability p of stopping him.

   a What is the probability that Bernard will be stopped *at least once*.

   b Suppose A_k is the event that Bernard is stopped at *exactly* k intersections and B_k is the event that Bernard is stopped at *at least* k intersections.

     Write down the conditional probability $P(A_k \mid B_k)$.

   c If A_1 and B_1 are independent, find p.

   d Find p if $P(A_2 \mid B_2) = P(A_1)$ and $n = 2$.

95 A club has n female members and n male members. A committee of *three* members is to be randomly chosen, and must contain more females than males.

   a How many committees consist of 2 females and 1 male?

   b How many committees consist of 3 females?

   c Use **a** and **b** to deduce that $n\binom{n}{2} + \binom{n}{3} = \frac{1}{2}\binom{2n}{3}$.

   d Suppose the club consists of 12 people, and that Mr and Mrs Jones are both members. Find the probability that a randomly selected committee contains:

     i Mrs Jones   **ii** Mr Jones given that it contains Mrs Jones.

96 In triangle ABC, the angle at A is double the angle at B.
If AC = 5 cm and BC = 6 cm, find:

   a the cosine of the angle at B   **b** the length of [AB] using the cosine rule.

   c Are both solutions in **b** valid?

97 $x^2 + b_1 x + c_1 = 0$ and $x^2 + b_2 x + c_2 = 0$ are two quadratic equations where $b_1 b_2 = 2(c_1 + c_2)$.

Prove that at least one of the equations has real roots.

98 Suppose that for all $n \in \mathbb{Z}^+$, $(2 - \sqrt{3})^n = a_n - b_n\sqrt{3}$ where a_n and b_n are integers.

   a Show that $a_{n+1} = 2a_n + 3b_n$ and $b_{n+1} = a_n + 2b_n$.

   b Calculate $a_n^2 - 3b_n^2$ for $n = 1, 2$ and 3.

   c What do you propose from **b**?

   d Prove your proposition from **c**.

99 A sequence u_n is defined by $u_1 = u_2 = 1$ and $u_{n+2} = u_{n+1} + u_n$ for all $n \in \mathbb{Z}^+$.
Prove by induction that $u_n \leqslant 2^n$ for all $n \in \mathbb{Z}^+$.

100 Use the Principle of mathematical induction to prove that, if $n \geqslant 2, n \in \mathbb{Z}^+$,

   then $(1 - \frac{1}{2^2})(1 - \frac{1}{3^2})(1 - \frac{1}{4^2}) \ldots (1 - \frac{1}{n^2}) = \frac{n+1}{2n}$.

101   **a** Graph $y = x^3 - 12x^2 + 45x$ and on the graph mark the coordinates of its turning points.

   b If $x^3 - 12x^2 + 45x = k$ has three real roots, what values can k have?

102   **a** Use complex number methods to prove that $\cos^3 \theta = \frac{3}{4}\cos\theta + \frac{1}{4}\cos 3\theta$.

   b Solve the equation $x^3 - 3x + 1 = 0$ by letting $y = mx$.

103 Triangle ABC has perimeter 20 cm.

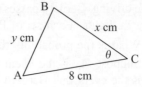

- **a** Find y^2 in terms of x and θ and hence find $\cos\theta$ in terms of x only.
- **b** If the triangle has area A, show that $A^2 = -20(x^2 - 12x + 20)$.
- **c** Hence, without calculus, find the maximum area of the triangle and comment on the triangle's shape when its area is a maximum.

104
- **a** If $\mathbf{A} = \begin{pmatrix} 2 & 1 \\ 0 & 1 \end{pmatrix}$, predict the form of $\mathbf{A}^n$.
- **b** Use mathematical induction to prove your conjecture in **a** correct.
- **c** If $\mathbf{S}_n = \mathbf{A} + \mathbf{A}^2 + \mathbf{A}^3 + ... + \mathbf{A}^n$, find $\mathbf{S}_n$ in simplest form and hence find $\mathbf{S}_{20}$.

105 If $\displaystyle\sum_{n=1}^{m} f(n) = m^3 + 3m$, find $f(n)$.

106 ABC is an equilateral triangle with sides 10 cm long. P is a point within the triangle which is 5 cm from A and 6 cm from B. How far is it from C?

107 A normally distributed random variable X has a mean of 90. Given that the probability $P(X < 85) \approx 0.16$:
- **a** find the proportion of scores between 90 and 95, i.e., find $P(90 < X < 95)$
- **b** find an *estimate* of the standard deviation for the random variable X.

108 A normally distributed random variable X has a mean of 90. Given that the probability $P(X < 88) \approx 0.28925$, find the:
- **a** standard deviation of X to 5 decimal places
- **b** probability that a randomly chosen score is *either* greater than 91 or less than 89.

109 In an International school there are 78 students preparing for the IB Diploma. Of these students, 38 are male and 17 of these males are studying Mathematics at the higher level. Of the female students, 25 are not studying Mathematics at the higher level.
A student is selected at random and found to be studying Mathematics at the higher level. Find the probability that this student is male.

110 A company manufactures computer chips, and it is known that 3% of them are faulty. In a batch of 500 such chips, find the probability that between 1 and 2 percent (inclusive) of the chips are faulty.

111 A factory manufactures rope, and the rope has an average of 0.7 flaws per metre. It is known that the number of flaws produced in the rope follows a Poisson distribution.
- **a** Determine the probability that there will be exactly 2 flaws in 2 metres of rope.
- **b** Find the probability that there will be at least 2 flaws in 4 metres of rope.

112 A random variable X is known to be distributed normally with standard deviation 2.83. Find the probability that a randomly selected score from X will differ from the mean by less than 4.

113 A discrete random variable X has a probability function given by the rule
$P(X = x) = a\left(\frac{2}{5}\right)^x$, $x = 0, 1, 2, 3, ...$ Find the value of a.

114 Given that events A and B are independent with $P(A \mid B) = \frac{1}{4}$ and $P(B \mid A) = \frac{2}{5}$, find $P(A \cup B')$.

115 In a game, a player rolls a biased tetrahedral (four-faced) die. The probability of each possible score is shown alongside in the table.

Score	1	2	3	4
Probability	$\frac{1}{12}$	k	$\frac{1}{4}$	$\frac{1}{3}$

  a Find the value of k.

  b Let the random variable X denote the number of 2s that occur when the die is rolled 2400 times. Calculate the exact mean and standard deviation of X.

116 The lifetime n (in years) of a particular component of a solar cell is given by the

probability density function $f(n) = \begin{cases} 0.6e^{-0.6n}, & n \geqslant 0 \\ 0, & \text{otherwise.} \end{cases}$

  a What is the chance that a randomly chosen component will last for at least one year?

  b A solar cell has 8 components, each of which operates independently of each other. The solar cell will continue to operate provided at least one of the components are operating. Find the probability that a randomly chosen solar cell fails within one year.

117 The random variable X has a Poisson distribution with standard deviation σ such that $P(X = 2) - P(X = 1) = 3P(X = 0)$.   Find the *exact* value of σ in surd form.

118 A machine produces soft drink in bottles. The volumes in millilitres (mL) of a sample of drinks chosen at random are shown below.

Volume (mL)	374.7	374.8	374.9	375.0	375.1	375.2	375.3	375.4
Frequency	6	12	15	16	9	11	8	3

Find unbiased estimates of:
  a the mean of the population from which this sample is taken
  b the variance of the population from which this sample is taken.

119 In a particular year, a randomly chosen Year 12 group completed a calculus test with the following results:

$$\sum_{i=1}^{25} x_i = 1650 \quad \text{and} \quad \sum_{i=1}^{25} x_i^2 = 115\,492,$$ where x_i denotes the percentage result of the

i th student in the class. Calculate an unbiased estimate of:
  a the mean percentage result of all Year 12 students in the calculus test
  b the variance of the percentage result of all Year 12 students in the calculus test.

120 **a** Using integration by parts, find $\int \ln x \, dx$.   Show how to check that your answer is correct.

  b The continuous random variable X has probability density function defined by

$f(x) = \begin{cases} \ln x, & 1 \leqslant x \leqslant k \\ 0, & \text{otherwise.} \end{cases}$ Find the *exact* value of k.

  c Write down an equation that you would need to solve to find the *median* value of the random variable X. Do not attempt to solve this equation.

121 Use the cosine rule and the given kite to show that $\sin^2\theta = \frac{1}{2} - \frac{1}{2}\cos 2\theta$ and $\cos^2\theta = \frac{1}{2} + \frac{1}{2}\cos 2\theta$.

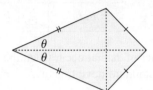

122 Show that $\tan\theta = 3\tan\alpha$.

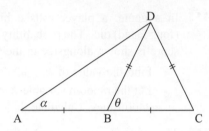

123 Points P and Q are free to move on the coordinate axes. N is the foot of the perpendicular from the origin to the line segment [PQ]. [PQ] makes an angle of θ with the y-axis.

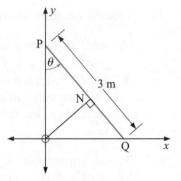

  a Show that N is at $(3\sin\theta\cos^2\theta,\ 3\sin^2\theta\cos\theta)$.

  b Use technology to sketch the graph of the curve defined by: $x = 3\sin\theta\cos^2\theta$, $y = 3\sin^2\theta\cos\theta$.

124 **a** Find the general term u_n of the sequence:
$$\frac{1}{\sin\theta} - \sin\theta,\ \cos\theta,\ \sin\theta,\ \frac{1}{\cos\theta} - \cos\theta, ...$$

  b Find an equation connecting consecutive terms of the sequence:
$1, \cos\theta, \cos^3\theta, \cos^7\theta, \cos^{15}\theta, ...$

125 $\frac{1}{k}$, k, $k^2 + 1$ where $k \in \mathbb{Q}$ are the 3rd, 4th and 6th terms of an arithmetic sequence respectively.

  a Find k.   **b** Find the general term u_n.

126 ABC is an equilateral triangle with sides of length $2k$. P is any point within the triangle. [PX], [PY] and [PZ] are altitudes from P to the sides [AB], [BC] and [CA] respectively.

  a By letting $P\hat{C}Z$ be θ, find $PX + PY + PZ$ in terms of θ, and hence show that $PX + PY + PZ$ is constant for all positions of P.

  b Check that your solution to **a** is correct when P is at A.

  c Prove that the result in **a** is true using areas of triangles only.

127 R and Q are two fixed points on either side of line segment [AB]. P is free to move on the line segment so that the angles θ and ϕ vary. a and b are the distances of Q and R respectively from [AB].

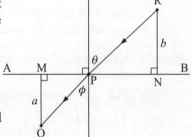

  a Show that for all positions of P,
$$\frac{d\phi}{d\theta} = \frac{-b\cos^2\phi}{a\cos^2\theta}.$$

  b A particle moves from R to P with constant speed v_1 and from P to Q with constant speed v_2.

Deduce that the time taken to go from R to P to Q is a minimum when $\dfrac{\sin\theta}{\sin\phi} = \dfrac{v_1}{v_2}$.

128 At A on the surface of the Earth, a rocket is launched vertically upwards. After t hours it is at R, h km above the surface. B is the horizon seen from R.

Suppose $\widehat{BOR}$ is θ and arc AB is y km long.

  a If the Earth's radius is r km, show that
$$\frac{dy}{dt} = \frac{\cos^2 \theta}{\sin \theta}\frac{dh}{dt}.$$

  b If the velocity of the rocket after t hours is given by $r \sin t$ for any $t \in [0, \pi]$, find the height of the rocket at $t = \frac{\pi}{2}$ hours.

  c If $r \approx 6000$, find the rate at which arc AB is changing at the instant when $t = \frac{\pi}{2}$.

129 Prove that the roots of $(m-1)x^2 + x - m = 0$ are always real and positive for $0 < m < 1$.

130 **a** Show that $\sin 15^\circ = \frac{\sqrt{6}-\sqrt{2}}{4}$ using $\sin 45^\circ = \frac{1}{\sqrt{2}}$ and $\sin 30^\circ = \frac{1}{2}$, together with a suitable trigonometric formula.

  b Find the exact value of $\cos^2 165^\circ + \cos^2 285^\circ$.

131 For $-\pi \leqslant x \leqslant \pi$, find the exact solutions to $3 \sec 2x = \cot 2x + 3 \tan 2x$.

132 Solve exactly for x if $4 \sin x = \sqrt{3} \csc x + 2 - 2\sqrt{3}$ where $0 \leqslant x \leqslant 2\pi$.

133 The first 3 terms of a geometric sequence have a sum of 39. If the middle term is increased by $66\frac{2}{3}\%$, the first three terms now form an arithmetic sequence. Find the smallest possible value of the first term.

134 Show algebraically that the equation $\log_3(x-k) + \log_3(x+2) = 1$ has a real solution for every real value of k.

135 Solve the following equations, giving exact answers:

  a $8^{2x+3} = 4\sqrt[3]{2}$ **b** $3^{2x+1} + 8(3^x) = 3$

  c $\ln(\ln x) = 1$ **d** $\log_{\frac{1}{9}} x = \log_9 5$

136 Solve the following inequalities, giving exact answers:

  a $(0.5)^{x+1} > 0.125$ **b** $\left(\frac{2}{3}\right)^x > \left(\frac{3}{2}\right)^{x-1}$ **c** $4^x + 2^{x+3} < 48$

137 If $x^2 + y^2 = 52xy$, show that $\log\left(\frac{x-y}{5}\right) = \frac{1}{2}(\log x + \log 2y)$.

138 If $z = \cos \theta + i \sin \theta$ where $0 < \theta < \frac{\pi}{4}$, find the modulus and argument of $1 - z^2$.

139 Find z in the form $a + bi$ if $z^2 = 1 + i + \dfrac{58}{9(3-7i)}$.

140 Solve the following equations simultaneously: $4^x = 8^y$ and $9^y = \dfrac{243}{3^x}$.

141 Given $w = \dfrac{z-1}{z^*+1}$ where $z = a + bi$ and z^* is the complex conjugate of z, write w in the form $x + yi$. Hence determine the conditions under which w is purely imaginary.

142 Given that $x = \log_3 y^2$, express $\log_y 81$ in terms of x.

143 An infinite number of circles are drawn in a sector of a circle of radius 10 cm and angle $\alpha = \frac{\pi}{3}$ as shown.

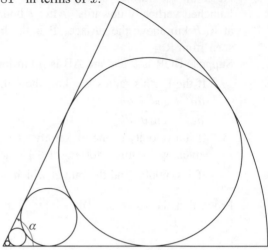

    a What is the total area of this infinite series of circles?

    b Find an expression for the total area of all circles for a general angle α such that $0 \leqslant \alpha \leqslant \frac{\pi}{2}$.

144 The ratio of the zeros of $x^2 + ax + b$ is $2 : 1$. Find a relationship between a and b.

145 Find real numbers a and b if the polynomial $z^3 + az^2 + bz + 15 = 0$ has a root $2 + i$.

146 If $x^n + ax^2 - 6$ leaves a remainder of -3 when divided by $(x - 1)$ and a remainder of -15 when divided by $(x + 3)$, find the values of a and n.

147 When a cubic polynomial $P(x)$ is divided by $x(2x - 3)$, the remainder is $ax + b$ where a and b are real.

    a If the quotient is the same as the remainder, write down an expression for $P(x)$.

    b Prove that $(2x - 1)$ and $(x - 1)$ are both factors of $P(x)$.

    c Find the equation of $P(x)$ given that it has a y-intercept $(0, 7)$ and passes through the point $(2, 39)$.

148 Factorise $f(x) = 2x^3 - x^2 - 8x - 5$, and hence find the values of x for which $f(x) \geqslant 0$.

149 The graph of a quartic polynomial $y = f(x)$ cuts the x-axis at $x = -3$ and at $x = -\frac{1}{4}$, and touches it at $x = \frac{3}{2}$. The y-intercept is 9. Find $f(x)$.

150 The polynomial $p(x) = x^3 + (5 + 4a)x + 5a$ where a is real, has a zero $-2 + i$.

    a Find a real quadratic factor of $p(x)$.

    b Hence, find the value of a and the real zero of $p(x)$.

151 Let $h(x) = x^3 - 6tx^2 + 11t^2 x - 6t^3$ where t is real.

    a Show that t is a zero of $h(x)$.

    b Factorise $h(x)$ as a product of linear factors.

    c Hence or otherwise, find the coordinates of the points where the graphs of $y = x^3 + 6x^2$ and $y = -6 - 11x$ meet.

152 A real polynomial $P(x) = x^4 + ax^3 + bx^2 + cx - 10$ has two integer zeros p and q.

    a If $P(x)$ also has a complex zero $1 + ki$, where k is an integer:

        i use this zero to write an expression for a real quadratic factor of $P(x)$

        ii state all possible values of k.

    b Using p and q, write another expression for a real quadratic factor of $P(x)$. Hence list all possible values of pq.

    c Given that $p + q = -1$, show that there is only one possible value for pq. Hence find all zeros of $P(x)$.

153 The real polynomial $P(z)$ of degree 4 has one complex zero of the form $1 - 2i$, and another of the form ai, where $a \neq 0$ and a is real.

    Find $P(z)$ if $P(0) = 10$ and the coefficient of z^4 is 1. Leave the answer in factorised form.

154 The point A$(-2, 3)$ lies on the graph of $y = f(x)$. Give the coordinates of the point that A moves to under the following transformations:

    a $y = f(x - 2) + 1$ **b** $y = 2f(x - 2)$ **c** $y = -\,|\,f(x)\,|\,-2$

    d $y = f(2x - 3)$ **e** $y = \dfrac{1}{f(x)}$ **f** $y = f^{-1}(x)$

155 The points A$(-1, 0)$, B$(1, 0)$ and C$(0, -0.5)$ are the x- and y-intercepts of $y = f(x)$.

On the same set of axes, sketch the following graphs. For each case, explain what happens to the points A, B and C.

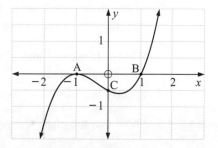

    a $y = f(x + 1) - 1$ **b** $y = -2f(x - 1)$

    c $y = |f(x)|$ **d** $y = \dfrac{1}{f(x)}$

156 The real quadratic function $f(x)$ has a zero of $3 + 2i$, and a y-intercept of -13. Write the function in the form:

    a $f(x) = ax^2 + bx + c$ **b** $f(x) = a(x - h)^2 + k$.

157 Find a trigonometric equation of the form $y = a\sin(b(x + c)) + d$ that represents the following graph with the information given below.

You may assume that $(3, -5)$ is a minimum point and $(6, -1)$ lies on the principal axis.

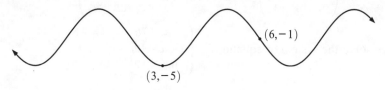

(6,−1)

(3,−5)

158 Solve the system using an inverse matrix:
$$\begin{cases} x + 3y - z = 15 \\ 2x + y + z = 7 \\ x - y - 2z = 0 \end{cases}.$$

159 The Ferris wheel at the Royal Show turns one full circle every minute. The lowest point is 1 metre from the ground, whilst the highest point is 25 metres above the ground.

    a The height of the Ferris wheel above ground level after t seconds is given by the model $h(t) = a + b\sin(c(t - d))$. Find the values of a, b, c and d given that you start your ride after entering your seat at the lowest point.

    b If the motor driving the Ferris wheel breaks down after 91 seconds, how high up would you be while waiting to be rescued?

160 The equations of two lines are:

l_1: $\mathbf{r} = \begin{pmatrix} -4 \\ 2 \\ -1 \end{pmatrix} + \lambda \begin{pmatrix} 3 \\ 1 \\ 2 \end{pmatrix}$, $\lambda \in \mathbb{R}$,   and l_2: $x = \dfrac{y-5}{2} = \dfrac{-z-1}{2}$.

- **a** Determine the point of intersection of l_1 and the plane $2x + y - z = 2$.
- **b** Clearly explain why l_1 and l_2 are not parallel.
- **c** Find the point of intersection of l_1 and l_2.
- **d** Find the equation of the plane that contains l_1 and l_2.

161 Find the acute angle between the plane $2x + 2y - z = 3$ and the line
$x = \lambda - 1$, $y = -2\lambda + 4$, $z = -\lambda + 3$.

162 Consider the following system of
linear equations in which p and q
are constants:
$$\begin{cases} x - 2y + 3z = 1 \\ x + py + 2z = 0 \\ -2x + p^2 y - 4z = q. \end{cases}$$

- **a** Write this system of equations in augmented matrix form.
- **b** Show, using clearly defined row operations, that this augmented matrix can be reduced to: $\begin{pmatrix} 1 & -2 & 3 & | & 1 \\ 0 & p+2 & -1 & | & -1 \\ 0 & 0 & p & | & p+q \end{pmatrix}$.
- **c** What values can p and q take when the system has
  - **i** a unique solution   **ii** no solutions   **iii** infinite solutions?
- **d** Specify the infinite solutions in parametric form.

163
- **a** Show that the plane $2x + y + z = 5$ contains the line l_1: $x = -2t + 2$, $y = t$, $z = 3t + 1$, $t \in \mathbb{R}$.
- **b** For what values of k does the plane $x + ky + z = 3$ contain l_1?
- **c** Without using row operations, find the values of p and q for which the following system of equations has an infinite number of solutions. Clearly explain your reasoning. $\begin{cases} 2x + y + z = 5 \\ x - y + z = 3 \\ 2x + py + 2z = q \end{cases}$
- **d** Check your result using row operations.

164 For $\mathbf{A} = \begin{pmatrix} 2 & 1 & -1 \\ -1 & 2 & 1 \\ 0 & 6 & 1 \end{pmatrix}$ and $\mathbf{B} = \begin{pmatrix} 4 & 7 & -3 \\ -1 & -2 & 1 \\ 6 & 12 & -5 \end{pmatrix}$,   calculate $\mathbf{AB}$ and

hence solve the system of equations $\begin{cases} 4a + 7b - 3c = -8 \\ -a - 2b + c = 3 \\ 6a + 12b - 5c = -15. \end{cases}$

165 Use vector methods to prove that joining the midpoints of the sides of a rhombus gives a rectangle.

166
- **a** Given $\mathbf{a} = \mathbf{i} + \mathbf{j} - 3\mathbf{k}$ and $\mathbf{b} = \mathbf{j} + 2\mathbf{k}$,   find $\mathbf{a} \times \mathbf{b}$.
- **b** Find a vector of length 5 units which is perpendicular to both $\mathbf{a}$ and $\mathbf{b}$.

167 Let $\mathbf{r} = 2\mathbf{i} - 2\mathbf{j} + \mathbf{k}$, $\mathbf{s} = 3\mathbf{i} + \mathbf{j} + 2\mathbf{k}$ and $\mathbf{t} = \mathbf{i} + 2\mathbf{j} - \mathbf{k}$ be the position vectors of the points R, S, and T respectively. Find the area of the triangle RST.

168 In the given figure, ABCD is a parallelogram. X is the midpoint of [BC], and Y is on [AX] such that $AY : YX = 2 : 1$. The coordinates of A, B and C are $(1, 3, -4)$, $(4, 4, -2)$ and $(10, 2, 0)$ respectively.

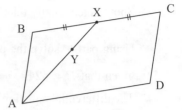

   a Find the coordinates of D, X and Y.
   b Prove that B, D and Y are collinear.

169 Let $\mathbf{a} = 3\mathbf{i} + 2\mathbf{j} - \mathbf{k}$, $\mathbf{b} = \mathbf{i} + \mathbf{j} - \mathbf{k}$ and $\mathbf{c} = 2\mathbf{i} - \mathbf{j} + \mathbf{k}$.
   a Show that $\mathbf{b} \times \mathbf{c} = -3\mathbf{j} - 3\mathbf{k}$.
   b Verify for the given vectors that $\mathbf{a} \times (\mathbf{b} \times \mathbf{c}) = \mathbf{b}\,(\mathbf{a} \bullet \mathbf{c}) - \mathbf{c}\,(\mathbf{a} \bullet \mathbf{b})$.

170 Given the vectors $\mathbf{p} = \begin{pmatrix} 1 \\ 2 \\ -2 \end{pmatrix}$ and $\mathbf{q} = \begin{pmatrix} -t \\ 1+t \\ 2t \end{pmatrix}$, find t such that:

   a $\mathbf{p}$ and $\mathbf{q}$ are perpendicular   **b** $\mathbf{p}$ and $\mathbf{q}$ are parallel.

171 Suppose A and B are events such $P(A) = 0.3 + x$, $P(B) = 0.2 + x$ and $P(A \cap B) = x$.
   a Find x if A and B are mutually exclusive events.
   b Calculate the possible values of x if A and B are independent events.

172 Find exact solutions for the following:

   a $|\, 1 - 4x \,| > \frac{1}{3} \,|\, 2x - 1 \,|$ **b** $\dfrac{x - 2}{6 - 5x - x^2} \leqslant 0$

173 The average number of amoebas in 50 mL of pond water is 20.

   a Assuming that the number of amoebas in pond water follows a Poisson distribution, find the probability that no more than 5 amoebas are present in 10 mL of randomly sampled pond water.
   b If a researcher collected 10 mL of pond water each weekday over 4 weeks (20 days in all), find the probability that the researcher collected no more than 5 amoebas on more than 10 occasions in that 4 week period.

174 Solve $\dfrac{dy}{dx} = \cos^2 x$ given that $y(0) = 4$.

175 Solve the differential equation $xy\dfrac{dy}{dx} = 1 + y^2$ given that $y = 0$ when $x = 2$.

176 A current of I amperes flows through a coil of inductance L henrys and resistance R ohms with electromotive force $E = L\dfrac{dI}{dt} + RI$ volts.

Assuming that E, L and R are constants, show by separating the variables that

$I = \dfrac{E}{R}\left(1 - e^{-\frac{R}{L}t}\right)$, given that $I = 0$ when $t = 0$.

177 A pair of guinea pigs was released onto an island in early January. Infrared scans of the island in early May showed the guinea pig population to be 180. Given that the rate of increase in such a population is proportional to the population at that time, estimate the island's guinea pig population in early October.

178   **a**   Show algebraically that $\dfrac{1}{y} + \dfrac{1}{P-y} = \dfrac{P}{y(P-y)}$.

   b   Using part **a**, solve the differential equation $y' = k\,y\left(1 - \dfrac{y}{P}\right)$

   given that $P = 624$, $y = 2$ when $t = 0$,   and that $y = 12$ when $t = 1$.

   c   The differential equation above describes how a rumour is spread at Beijing College by 2 people starting at 12 noon. 12 people have heard the rumour by 1 pm.

   i   Find the number of people at Beijing College, giving a reason for your answer.

   ii   How many people have heard the rumour by 2 pm?

   iii   At what time have 90% of the people heard the rumour?

179   **a**   Express $1 + i$ and $\sqrt{3} - i$ in the form $re^{i\theta}$.

   Hence write $z = \dfrac{-1-i}{\sqrt{3}-i}$ in the form $re^{i\theta}$.

   b   What is the smallest positive integer n such that z^n is a real number?

180   There are 12 students in a school's Hungarian class. Being well-mannered, they line up in a single file to enter the class.

   a   How many orders are possible?

   b   How many orders are there if:

   i   Irena and Eva are among the last four in the line

   ii   Istvan is between Paul and Laszlo and they are all together

   iii   Istvan is between Paul and Laszlo but they are not necessarily together

   iv   there are exactly three students between Annabelle and Holly?

   c   Once inside, the class is split into 3 groups of four students each for a vocabulary quiz. How many ways can this be done:

   i   if there are no restrictions

   ii   if Ben and Marton must be in the same group?

181   The velocity of a particle travelling in a straight line is given by $v = \cos(\tfrac{1}{3}t)$ cm s^{-1}.

   Find the distance travelled by this particle in the first 10π seconds of motion.

182   Year 12 students at a government school can choose from 16 subjects for their Certificate. Seven of these subjects are in group I, six are in group II, and the other three are in group III. Students must study six subjects to qualify for the Certificate. How many combinations of subjects are possible if:

   a   there are no restrictions

   b   students must choose 2 subjects from groups I and II and the remaining subjects could be from any group

   c   French (a group I subject) is compulsory, and they must choose at least one subject from group III?

183   Solve the equation: $\binom{n}{3} = 3\binom{n-1}{2} - \binom{n-1}{1}$.

184   Find the coefficient of:

   a x^{12} in the expansion of $\left(2x^3 - \dfrac{1}{2x}\right)^8$ **b** x^2 in the expansion of $(1+2x)^5(2-x)^6$

   c x^3 in the expansion of $(1 + 2x - 3x^2)^4$.

185 The function f is defined by $f : x \mapsto e^{\sin^2 x}, \quad x \in [0, \pi]$.

    a Use calculus to find the exact value(s) of x for which $f(x)$ has a maximum value.

    b Find $f''(x)$ and write down an equation that will enable you to find any points of inflection in the given domain.

    c Find the point(s) of inflection in the given domain.

186 Solve for x: $\quad \log_x 4 + \log_2 x = 3$

187 Find the exact value of a if $a > 0$ and $\quad \displaystyle\int_0^a \frac{x}{x^2 + 1}\, dx = 3$.

188 Given that A is an acute angle and $\tan 2A = \frac{3}{2}$, find the exact value of $\tan A$.

189 The scores a, b, 6, 13 and 7 where $b > a$ have a mean and variance of 8. Find the values of a and b.

190 The graph of $y = f(x)$ for $-9 \leqslant x \leqslant 9$ is shown alongside.

The function has vertical asymptotes at $x = 2$ and $x = -3$ and a horizontal asymptote at $y = 2$.

Copy and sketch the graph of

$y = \dfrac{1}{f(x)}$, indicating clearly the axes

intercepts and all asymptotes.

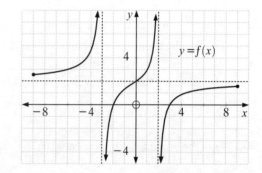

191 For what values of x is the matrix $\quad \mathbf{A} = \begin{pmatrix} x - 1 & -2 & 5 \\ -4 & 3 - x & -2 \\ -2 & 5 & -8 \end{pmatrix}$ singular?

192 Find a and b if the matrix $\quad \mathbf{A} = \begin{pmatrix} a & -1 \\ b & 2 \end{pmatrix}$ is its own inverse. Hence find $\mathbf{A}^{11}$.

193 If $z = x + 2i$ and $u = 3 + iy$ where $x, y \in \mathbb{R}$, find the smallest positive value of x for which $\dfrac{z + u}{z - u}$ is purely imaginary.

194 If $1 - 2i$ is a zero of $P(x) = x^4 + 11x^2 - 10x + 50$, find all the other zeros.

195 Find the exact value of the volume of the solid formed when the region enclosed by $y = xe^{x^3}$, the x-axis, and the line $x = 1$, is rotated through $360°$ about the x-axis.

196 Determine the sequence of transformations which transform the function $f(x) = 3x^2 - 12x + 5$ to $g(x) = -3x^2 + 18x - 10$.

197 Find the area of the region bounded by the curve $y = \tan^2 x + 2\sin^2 x$, the x-axis, and the line $x = \frac{\pi}{4}$.

198 Simplify $\sin(2 \arcsin x)$ and hence find $\displaystyle\int_0^1 \sin(2 \arcsin x)\, dx$.

199 For the system of linear equations:
$$\begin{cases} 2x - y + 3z = 4 \\ 2x + y + (a+3)z = 10 - a \\ 4x + 6y + (a^2 + 6)z = a^2, \end{cases}$$

find the value(s) of a for which the system has:
- **a** no solutions
- **b** infinitely many solutions, and find the form of these solutions
- **c** a unique solution, and find the solution in the case where $a = 2$.

200 A function f is defined by $f(x) = \dfrac{x^2 + 1}{(x+1)^2}$.

- **a** Write down the equations of the asymptotes of the graph of $y = f(x)$.
- **b** Find $f'(x)$ and hence find the position and nature of any stationary points.
- **c** Find $f''(x)$ and hence find the coordinates of all points of inflection.
- **d** Sketch the graph of $y = f(x)$ showing all the above features.

201 A particle moves in a straight line such that its displacement from point O is s.
The acceleration of the particle is a and its velocity is v where $a = \frac{1}{2}v^2$.
- **a** Find $v(t)$ given that $v(0) = -1$.
- **b** Find the distance travelled in the first 2 seconds of motion.

202 Determine the domain of $f(x) = \arccos(1 + x - x^2)$, and find $f'(x)$.

203 Find the area of the region enclosed by the graph of $y = \dfrac{\tan x}{\cos(2x) + 1}$, the x-axis, and the line $x = \frac{\pi}{3}$.

204 Find the equations of all asymptotes of the graph of the function $y = \dfrac{\tan x}{\sin(2x) + 1}$ where $-\pi \leqslant x \leqslant \pi$.

205 Find the exact coordinates of the stationary points on the curve $y = \dfrac{\sin x}{\tan x + 1}$ where $-\pi \leqslant x \leqslant \frac{\pi}{2}$.

206 The sum of an infinite geometric series is 49 and the second term of the series is 10. Find the possible values for the sum of the first three terms of the series.

207 If $f : x \mapsto 2x + 1$ and $g : x \mapsto \dfrac{x+1}{x-2}$, find: **a** $(f \circ g)(x)$ **b** $g^{-1}(x)$.

208
- **a** Find $\dfrac{dy}{dx}$ if $x^2 - 3xy + y^2 = 7$.
- **b** Hence find the coordinates of all points on the curve for which the gradient is $\frac{2}{3}$.

209 A and B are two events such that $P(A) = \frac{1}{3}$ and $P(B) = \frac{2}{7}$.
- **a** Find $P(A \cup B)$ if A and B are: **i** mutually exclusive **ii** independent.
- **b** Find $P(A \mid B)$ if $P(A \cup B) = \frac{3}{7}$.

210   **a**   Find the coordinates of A, the point of intersection of l_1 and l_2, where l_1 is given

by $\mathbf{r} = \begin{pmatrix} 8 \\ -13 \\ -3 \end{pmatrix} + \lambda \begin{pmatrix} 3 \\ -5 \\ -2 \end{pmatrix}$ and l_2 is given by $\dfrac{x+10}{6} = \dfrac{y-7}{-5} = \dfrac{z-11}{-5}$.

   b   Find the coordinates of B, where l_1 meets the plane $3x + 2y - z = -2$.
   c   The point $C(p,\, 0,\, q)$ lies on the plane in **b**.

   Find the possible values of p if the area of triangle ABC is $\frac{\sqrt{3}}{2}$ units^2.

211   Find x in terms of a if $a > 1$ and $\log_a(x+2) = \log_a x + 2$.

212   Solve for y: $(x^2 + 1)\dfrac{dy}{dx} = y + 1$ given that $y = 2$ when $x = 0$.

213   Find $\int x^2 \sin x \, dx$.

214   If $f(2x + 3) = 5x - 7$, find $f^{-1}(x)$.

215   Find, to 3 significant figures, the area of the region enclosed by the graphs of
$y = xe^{\sin x}$ and $y = x^2 - 4x + 6$.

216   Find $\dfrac{dy}{dx}$ if $e^{xy} + xy^2 - \sin y = 2$.

217   Solve for x: $\dfrac{|\,2x - 1\,| + 3}{|\,x + 3\,| - 2} < -x$

218   Find $\displaystyle\int \dfrac{x}{1 + \sqrt{x + 2}}\, dx$.

219   Find $\dfrac{dy}{dx}$ if $\sin(xy) + y^2 = x$.

220   The lines $\mathbf{r} = \begin{pmatrix} 3 \\ -2 \\ 2 \end{pmatrix} + \lambda \begin{pmatrix} a \\ -1 \\ 2 \end{pmatrix}$ and $\dfrac{x-4}{2} = 1 - y = \dfrac{z+2}{3}$ intersect at point P.

   a   Find the value of a and hence find the coordinates of P.
   b   Find the acute angle between the two lines.
   c   Find the equation of the plane which contains the two lines.

221   For what values of a does the graph of $y = ax + 2$ cut the graph of $y = 3x^2 - 2x + 5$ in two distinct points?

222   The height of a cone is always twice the radius of its base. The volume of the cone is increasing at a constant rate of 5 cm^3 s^{-1}. Find the rate of change in the radius when the height is 20 cm.

223   Find the value of a if the line passing through the points A$(0,\, 5,\, 6)$ and B$(4,\, 1,\, -2)$

and the line $\mathbf{r} = \begin{pmatrix} a \\ 3 \\ 2 \end{pmatrix} + s \begin{pmatrix} 2 \\ -1 \\ 1 \end{pmatrix}$ are coplanar.

224 Let $f(x) = x \tan \sqrt{1 - x^2}$, $-1 \leqslant x \leqslant 1$.

   a Sketch the graph of $y = f(x)$.

   b Write down an expression for V, the volume of the solid formed by rotating the region bounded by $y = f(x)$, $x = 0$ and $x = 1$ through $360°$ about the x-axis.

225 Let $f(x) = xe^{1-2x^2}$.

   a Find $f'(x)$ and $f''(x)$.

   b Find the exact coordinates of the stationary points of the function and determine their nature.

   c Find the exact values of the x-coordinates of the points of inflexion of the function.

   d Discuss the behaviour of the function as $x \to \pm\infty$.

   e Sketch the graph of the function.

   f Find the exact value of k if $k > 0$ and the region bounded by $y = f(x)$, the x-axis, and the line $x = k$ has area equal to $\frac{1}{4}(e - 1)$ units^2.

226 **a** Find a and k if the line l_1 given by $\mathbf{r} = \begin{pmatrix} 1 \\ -1 \\ 2 \end{pmatrix} + \lambda \begin{pmatrix} 1 \\ a \\ -1 \end{pmatrix}$ lies on the plane P_1 with equation $3x - ky + z = 3$.

   b Show that the plane P_2 with equation $2x - y - 4z = 9$ is perpendicular to P_1.

   c Find the equation of l_2, the line of intersection of P_1 and P_2.

   d Find the point of intersection of l_1 and l_2.

   e Find the angle between the lines l_1 and l_2.

227 Construct a quartic polynomial $f(x)$ with integer coefficients such that $f(x) < 0$ for all $x \in \mathbb{R}$. Write your polynomial in expanded form.

228 $P(z) = z^3 + az^2 + bz + c$ where a, b and $c \in \mathbb{R}$.

Two of the roots of $P(z)$ are -2 and $-3 + 2i$.

Find a, b and c and also find possible values of z when $P(z) \geqslant 0$.

229 $f(x) = 2\tan(3(x - 1)) + 4$ for $x \in [-1, 1]$. Find:

   a the period of $y = f(x)$

   b the equations of any asymptotes

   c the transformations that transform $y = \tan x$ into $y = f(x)$.

   d the domain and range of $y = f(x)$.

ANSWERS

EXERCISE 1A

1 a, d, e **2** a, b, c, e, g **3** No, e.g., $x = 1$ **4** $y = \pm\sqrt{9 - x^2}$

EXERCISE 1B.1

1 **a** 2 **b** 8 **c** -1 **d** -13 **e** 1

2 **a** 2 **b** 2 **c** -16 **d** -68 **e** $\frac{17}{4}$

3 **a** $7 - 3a$ **b** $7 + 3a$ **c** $-3a - 2$ **d** $10 - 3b$ **e** $1 - 3x$
   f $7 - 3x - 3h$

4 **a** $2x^2 + 19x + 43$ **b** $2x^2 - 11x + 13$ **c** $2x^2 - 3x - 1$
   d $2x^4 + 3x^2 - 1$ **e** $2x^4 - x^2 - 2$
   f $2x^2 + 4xh + 2h^2 + 3x + 3h - 1$

5 **a** **i** $-\frac{7}{2}$ **ii** $-\frac{3}{4}$ **iii** $-\frac{4}{9}$ **b** $x = 4$ **c** $\frac{2x + 7}{x - 2}$ **d** $x = \frac{9}{5}$

6 f is the function which converts x into $f(x)$ whereas $f(x)$ is the value of the function at any value of x.

7 **a** 6210 Euros value after 4 years **b** $t = 4.5$, the time for the photocopier to reach a value of 5780 Euros. **c** 9650 Euros

8
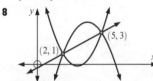
Points labelled: $(5, 3)$, $(2, 1)$

9 $f(x) = -2x + 5$

10 $a = 3$, $b = -1$,
   $c = -4$,
   $T(x) = 3x^2 - x - 4$

EXERCISE 1B.2

1 **a** Domain $\{1, 2, 3\}$, Range $\{3, 5, 7\}$
   b Domain $\{-1, 0, 2\}$, Range $\{3, 5\}$
   c Domain $\{-3, -2, -1, 3\}$, Range $\{1\}$
   d Domain $\{-2, -1, 0, 1, 2\}$, Range $\{0, \sqrt{3}, 2\}$

2 **a** Domain $\{x|\ -1 < x \leqslant 5\}$, Range $\{y|\ 1 < y \leqslant 3\}$
   b Domain $\{x\ |\ x \neq 2\}$, Range $\{y\ |\ y \neq -1\}$
   c Domain $\{x\ |\ x \in \mathbb{R}\}$, Range $\{y\ |\ 0 < y \leqslant 2\}$
   d Domain $\{x\ |\ x \in \mathbb{R}\}$, Range $\{y\ |\ y \geqslant -1\}$
   e Domain $\{x\ |\ x \geqslant -4\}$, Range $\{y:\ y \geqslant -3\}$
   f Domain $\{x\ |\ x \neq \pm 2\}$, Range $\{y:\ y \leqslant -1 \text{ or } y > 0\}$

3 **a** Domain $\{x\ |\ x \text{ is in } \mathbb{R}\}$, Range $\{y\ |\ y \text{ is in } \mathbb{R}\}$
   b Domain $\{x\ |\ x \text{ is in } \mathbb{R}\}$, Range $\{3\}$
   c Domain $\{x\ |\ x \text{ is in } \mathbb{R}\}$, Range $\{y\ |\ y \geqslant 2\}$
   d Domain $\{x\ |\ x \text{ is in } \mathbb{R}\}$, Range $\{y\ |\ y \geqslant 2\}$
   e Domain $\{x\ |\ x \leqslant -2,\ x \geqslant 2\}$, Range $\{y\ |\ y \geqslant 0\}$
   f Domain $\{x\ |\ x \neq 2\}$, Range $\{y\ |\ y \neq 0\}$
   g Domain $\{x\ |\ x \leqslant 2\}$, Range $\{y\ |\ y \geqslant 0\}$
   h Domain $\{x\ |\ x > \frac{5}{2}\}$, Range $\{y\ |\ y > 0\}$
   i Domain $\{x\ |\ x \neq 5\}$, Range $\{y\ |\ y \neq 2\}$

4 **a** Domain $\{x\ |\ x \geqslant 0\}$, Range $\{y\ |\ y \geqslant 0\}$
   b Domain $\{x\ |\ x \neq 0\}$, Range $\{y\ |\ y > 0\}$
   c Domain $\{x\ |\ x \leqslant 4\}$, Range $\{y\ |\ y \geqslant 0\}$
   d Domain $\{x\ |\ x \in \mathbb{R}\}$, Range $\{y\ |\ y \geqslant -2\frac{1}{4}\}$
   e Domain $\{x\ |\ x \in \mathbb{R}\}$, Range $\{y\ |\ y \leqslant 2\frac{1}{12}\}$
   f Domain $\{x\ |\ x \neq 0\}$, Range $\{y\ |\ y \leqslant -2 \text{ or } y \geqslant 2\}$
   g Domain $\{x\ |\ x \neq 2\}$, Range $\{y\ |\ y \neq 1\}$
   h Domain $\{x\ |\ x \in \mathbb{R}\}$, Range $\{y\ |\ y \in \mathbb{R}\}$
   i Domain $\{x\ |\ x \neq -1 \text{ or } 2\}$, Range $\{y\ |\ y \leqslant \frac{1}{3} \text{ or } y \geqslant 3\}$
   j Domain $\{x\ |\ x \neq 0\}$, Range $\{y\ |y \geqslant 2\}$
   k Domain $\{x\ |\ x \neq 0\}$, Range $\{y\ |\ y \leqslant -2 \text{ or } y \geqslant 2\}$
   l Domain $\{x\ |\ x \in \mathbb{R}\}$, Range $\{y\ |\ y \geqslant -8\}$

EXERCISE 1C

1 **a** $5 - 2x$ **b** $-2x - 2$ **c** 11

2 $f(g(x)) = (2 - x)^2$, Domain $\{x\ |\ x \text{ is in } \mathbb{R}\}$, Range $\{y\ |\ y \geqslant 0\}$
   $g(f(x)) = 2 - x^2$, Domain $\{x\ |\ x \text{ is in } \mathbb{R}\}$, Range $\{y\ |\ y \leqslant 2\}$

3 **a** $x^2 - 6x + 10$ **b** $2 - x^2$ **c** $x = \pm\frac{1}{\sqrt{2}}$

4 **a** $f \circ g = \{(0, 1), (1, 0), (2, 3), (3, 2)\}$
   b $g \circ f = \{(0, 1), (1, 0), (2, 3), (3, 2)\}$
   c $f \circ f = \{(0, 0), (1, 1), (2, 2), (3, 3)\}$

5 $f \circ g = \{(0, 0), (1, 1), (2, 2), (3, 3)\}$

6 **a** $f \circ g = \{(2, 7), (5, 2), (7, 5), (9, 9)\}$
   b $g \circ f = \{(0, 2), (1, 0), (2, 1), (3, 3)\}$

7 **a** $(f \circ g)(x) = \dfrac{4x - 2}{3x - 1}$, $x \neq 1$, Domain $\{x\ |\ x \neq \frac{1}{3} \text{ or } 1\}$
   b $(f \circ g)(x) = 2x + 5$, $x \neq -2$, Domain $\{x\ |\ x \neq -2\}$
   c $(g \circ g)(x) = x$, $x \neq 1$, Domain $\{x\ |\ x \neq 1\}$

8 **a** Let $x = 0$, $\therefore$ $b = d$ and so
   $$ax + b = cx + b$$
   $$\therefore \quad ax = cx \quad \text{for all } x$$
   Let $x = 1$, $\therefore$ $a = c$
   b $(f \circ g)(x) = [2a]x + [2b + 3] = 1x + 0$ for all x
   $$\therefore \quad 2a = 1 \quad \text{and} \quad 2b + 3 = 0$$
   $$\therefore \quad a = \tfrac{1}{2} \quad \text{and} \quad b = -\tfrac{3}{2}$$
   c Yes, $\{(g \circ f)(x) = [2a]x + [3a + b]\}$

EXERCISE 1D

1 **a**
```
  −     +
─────┼─────
     2
```
b
```
  −     +     −
──┼───────────┼──
 −1           3
```
c
```
  +     −     +
──┼───────────┼──
  0           2
```
d
```
  +           +
──────────┼──────
          1
```
e
```
  −           −
─────────┼───────
        −2
```
f
```
  +     −     +     −
──┼───────────┼────┼──
 −2           0    2
```
g
```
  −     ┊     +
────────┼────────
        0
```
h
```
  +     +           −
──┼───────────┼──────
 −1           2
```
i
```
  −  +     +     −
──┼──┼───────────┼──
 −3  0           4
```
j
```
  +┊     −           +
───┼───────────┼───────
   1           2
```
k
```
  −┊  +     −  ┊+
───┼──────────┼──
  −1  0       3
```
l
```
  −┊     +     −     +┊  −
───┼───────────────┼──┼───
  −2 −1           1    2
```

2 **a**
```
  +     −           +
──┼───────────┼──────
 −4           2
```
b
```
  +     −     +
──┼───────────┼──
  0           3
```
c
```
  +     −     +
──┼───────────┼──
 −2           0
```
d
```
  −     +     −
──┼───────────┼──
 −1           3
```
e
```
  −     +     −
──┼───────────┼──
 ½           3
```
f
```
  +     −     +
──┼───────────┼──
 ½           5
```
g
```
  +     −     +
──┼───────────┼──
 −3           3
```
h
```
  −     +     −
──┼───────────┼──
 −2           2
```
i
```
  −     +     −
──┼───────────┼──
  0           5
```
j
```
  +     −     +
──┼───────────┼──
  1           2
```
k
```
  −     +     −
──┼───────────┼──
 −½          ½
```
l
```
  +     −     +
──┼───────────┼──
 −⅔          ½
```
m
```
  −     +     −
──┼───────────┼──
 −3           ⅓
```
n
```
  −     +     −
──┼───────────┼──
 −½           5
```
o
```
  −     +     −
──┼───────────┼──
 −⅖          ⅓
```

3 a
+   +
———————
−2

b
+   +
———————
3

c
−   −
———————
−2

d
−   −
———————
4

e
+   +
———————
1

f
−   −
———————
2

g
+   +
———————
$\frac{1}{2}$

h
−   −
———————
−3

i
−   −
———————
$\frac{3}{2}$

4 a
+   −   +
———————
−2   1

b
+   −   +
———————
−3   0

c
−   +   −
———————
$-\frac{3}{2}$ 4

d
−   +   −
———————
$\frac{1}{4}$ 2

e
+   −   +
———————
0   2

f
+   −   +
———————
0   3

g
−   +   +
———————
0   1

h
−   −   +
———————
−1   0

i
+   −   +   −
———————
−2   1   3

j
+   −   +   −
———————
0   1   2

k
+   −   +   −
———————
−2   0   2

l
+   −   +   −
———————
$-\frac{3}{2}$ 2   3

m
−   +   −   +
———————
$-\sqrt{3}$ −1 $\sqrt{3}$

n
−   +
———————
0

o
−   +
———————
−1

p
+   −   −
———————
−3   3

q
+   −   −   +
———————
−2   0   5

r
−   +   +
———————
1   3

s
+   −   +
———————
−1 $\frac{1}{2}$

t
−   +   −
———————
$-\frac{14}{3}$ −3

u
+   −   +   −   +
———————
−8 −3 0 2

EXERCISE 1E

1 a $x \in [-3, 2]$ **b** no solutions **c** $x \in]-\frac{1}{2}, 3[$

d $x \in]-\infty, 0]$ or $[1, \infty[$ **e** $x \in]-\infty, 0]$ or $[3, \infty[$

f $x \in]-\frac{2}{3}, 0[$ **g** $x \in]-2, 2[$

h $x \in]-\infty, -\sqrt{2}]$ or $[\sqrt{2}, \infty[$ **i** $x \neq -2$

j $x \in]-\infty, -1]$ or $[\frac{3}{2}, \infty[$ **k** no solutions

l $x \in]-\frac{3}{2}, \frac{1}{3}[$ **m** $x \in]-\infty, -\frac{4}{3}[$ or $]4, \infty[$ **n** $x \neq 1$

o $x \in [\frac{1}{3}, \frac{1}{2}]$ **p** $x \in]-\infty, -\frac{1}{6}[$ or $]1, \infty[$

q $x \in]-\infty, -\frac{1}{4}]$ or $[\frac{2}{3}, \infty[$ **r** $x \in]-\infty, \frac{3}{2}[$ or $]3, \infty[$

2 a $x \in]-\infty, -4[$ or $]\frac{1}{2}, \infty[$ **b** $x \in]-\infty, -1[$ or $]4, \infty[$

c $x \in]-\infty, -3]$ or $]-\frac{3}{2}, \infty[$ **d** $x \in]-\infty, -3]$ or $]3, \infty[$

e $x \in]-\infty, \frac{1}{4}]$ or $]1, \infty[$ **f** $x \in]-\infty, \frac{1}{2}[$ **g** $x \in]0, \frac{1}{100}[$

h $x \in]\frac{1}{2}, \frac{5}{9}]$ **i** $x \in]-\infty, -1[$ or $]-\frac{3}{5}, \infty[$ **j** $x \in]-7, \frac{5}{2}[$

k $x \in]-3, 0[$ or $]2, \infty[$ **l** $x \in [-5, -2[$ or $[0, 2[$

m $x \in]-\infty, -2[$ or $]-1, 0[$ or $]2, \infty[$

n $x \in]-2, 0[$ or $]2, \infty[$ **o** $x \in [-1, 0[$ or $[1, \infty[$

p $x \in [-1, 0]$ or $[1, \infty[$ **q** $x \in]-2, \frac{6}{11}[$ or $]2, \infty[$

r $x \in]-\infty, \frac{2}{3}[$ or $[1, 2]$

EXERCISE 1F.1

1 a 2 **b** 3 **c** 6 **d** 6 **e** 5 **f** −1 **g** 1 **h** 5 **i** 4
j 4 **k** 2 **l** 2

2 a 8 **b** 2 **c** $\frac{5}{4}$ **d** 0 **3 a** No **b** No

4

a	b	$\lvert ab \rvert$	$\lvert a \rvert\lvert b \rvert$	$\left\lvert \frac{a}{b} \right\rvert$	$\frac{\lvert a \rvert}{\lvert b \rvert}$
6	2	12	12	3	3
6	−2	12	12	3	3
−6	2	12	12	3	3
−6	−2	12	12	3	3

$$\lvert ab \rvert = \lvert a \rvert\lvert b \rvert, \quad \left\lvert \frac{a}{b} \right\rvert = \frac{\lvert a \rvert}{\lvert b \rvert} \quad (b \neq 0)$$

6 a $y = \lvert x - 2 \rvert$

$$y = \begin{cases} x - 2, & x \geqslant 2 \\ 2 - x, & x < 2 \end{cases}$$

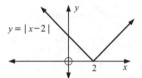

b $y = \lvert x + 1 \rvert$

$$y = \begin{cases} x + 1, & x \geqslant -1 \\ -x - 1, & x < -1 \end{cases}$$

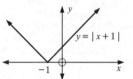

c $y = \begin{cases} -x, & x \geqslant 0 \\ x, & x < 0 \end{cases}$

d $y = \begin{cases} 2x, & x \geqslant 0 \\ 0, & x < 0 \end{cases}$

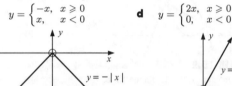

e $y = \begin{cases} 1, & x > 0 \\ \text{undefined}, & x = 0 \\ -1, & x < 0 \end{cases}$

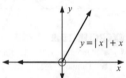

f $y = \begin{cases} -x, & x \geqslant 0 \\ 3x, & x < 0 \end{cases}$

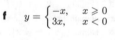

g $y = \lvert x \rvert + \lvert x - 2 \rvert$

$$y = \begin{cases} 2x - 2, & x \geqslant 2 \\ 2, & 0 \leqslant x < 2 \\ 2 - 2x, & x < 0 \end{cases}$$

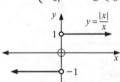

h $y = \lvert x \rvert - \lvert x - 1 \rvert$

$$y = \begin{cases} 1, & x \geqslant 1 \\ 2x - 1, & 0 \leqslant x < 1 \\ -1, & x < 0 \end{cases}$$

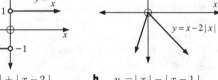

i $y = \lvert x^2 + 1 \rvert$
$y = x^2 + 1$ for all x

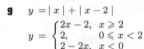

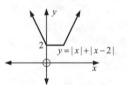

j $y = \lvert x^2 - 1 \rvert$

$$y = \begin{cases} x^2 - 1, & x \geqslant 1, \ x \leqslant -1 \\ 1 - x^2, & -1 < x < 1 \end{cases}$$

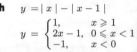

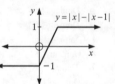

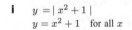

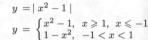

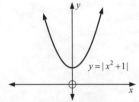

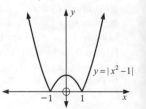

k $y = |x^2 - 2x|$

$y = \begin{cases} x^2 - 2x, & x \geqslant 2, \ x \leqslant 0 \\ 2x - x^2, & 0 < x < 2 \end{cases}$

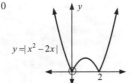

$y = |x^2 - 2x|$

l $y = |x^2 + 3x + 2|$

$y = \begin{cases} x^2 + 3x + 2, & x \geqslant -1, \ x \leqslant -2 \\ -x^2 - 3x - 2, & -2 < x < -1 \end{cases}$

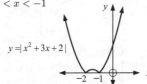

$y = |x^2 + 3x + 2|$

EXERCISE 1F.2

1 a $x = \pm 3$ **b** no solution **c** $x = 0$ **d** $x = 4$ or -2
  e $x = -1$ or 7 **f** no solution **g** $x = 1$ or $\frac{1}{3}$
  h $x = 0$ or 3 **i** $x = -2$ or $\frac{14}{5}$

2 a $x = \frac{3}{2}$ or $\frac{3}{2}$ **b** $x = -2$ or $-\frac{4}{7}$ **c** $x = -1$ or 7

3 a $x = \frac{1}{2}$ **b** $x = \frac{5}{2}$ **c** $x = -\frac{1}{4}$ or $\frac{3}{2}$ **d** $x = -6$ or $-\frac{4}{3}$
  e $x = \pm\frac{1}{2}$ **f** $x = -6$ or $\frac{2}{5}$

4 a $x = 1$ **b** $x = -\frac{4}{5}$ or 4 **c** $x = \frac{5}{7}$ or 5

EXERCISE 1F.3

1 a $x \in \,]-4, 4[$ **b** $x \in \,]-\infty, -3]$ or $[3, \infty[$
  c $x \in [-4, -2]$ **d** $x \in \,]-\infty, -6]$ or $[-2, \infty[$
  e $x \in \,]-1, 2[$ **f** $x \in \,]-\infty, \frac{1}{4}[$ or $]\frac{5}{4}, \infty[$
  g $x \in \,]-\frac{5}{2}, \frac{3}{2}[$ **h** $x \in [-1, 3]$ **i** $x \in \,]-\frac{1}{7}, 1[$
  j $x \in \,]-\infty, -\frac{3}{7}]$ or $[1, \infty[$ **k** $x \in [\frac{4}{3}, 2]$ **l** $x \in [-2, 8]$

2 a $x \in [-1, 7]$ **b** $x \in [-1, 2]$
  c $x \in \,]-\infty, -1[$ or $x \in \,]\frac{1}{3}, \infty[$
  d $x \in \,]-\infty, -1]$ or $x \in [6, \infty[$ **e** $x \in [1, \infty[$
  f $x \in [-1, \frac{1}{5}]$ **g** $x \in [\frac{3}{2}, 2[$ or $x \in \,]2, 3]$
  h $x \in [-\frac{1}{4}, 1[$ or $x \in \,]1, \infty[$

3 a $x \in \,]1, 3[$ **b** $x \in \,]-\infty, 3[$
  c $x \in \,]-\infty, -1[$ or $x \in \,]2, \infty[$ **d** $x \in [3, \infty[$

4

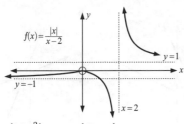

$f(x) = \frac{|x|}{x-2}$

$x \in [-2, \frac{2}{3}]$ or $x \in \,]2, \infty[$

5 a

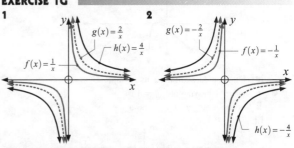

$y = -4x - 4$ $y = 4x + 4$

$y = -2x + 6$ $y = 2x + 10$

$y = 10$

b ii Anywhere between O and Q, min. length of cable is 10 km.
  iii At O, minimum length of cable is 17 km.

6 a True **b** True

EXERCISE 1G

1

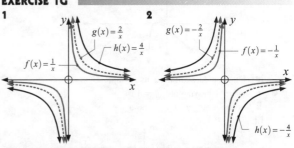

$g(x) = \frac{2}{x}$
$h(x) = \frac{4}{x}$
$f(x) = \frac{1}{x}$

2

$g(x) = -\frac{2}{x}$
$f(x) = -\frac{1}{x}$
$h(x) = -\frac{4}{x}$

EXERCISE 1H

1 a i vertical asymptote $x = 2$, horizontal asymptote $y = 0$
  ii as $x \to 2^-$, $y \to -\infty$ as $x \to \infty$, $y \to 0^+$
    as $x \to 2^+$, $y \to \infty$ as $x \to -\infty$, $y \to 0^-$
  iii

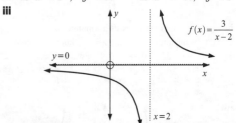

$f(x) = \frac{3}{x-2}$

$y = 0$

$x = 2$

  iv Function does not cross its asymptotes.

b i vertical asymptote $x = -1$, horizontal asymptote $y = 2$
  ii as $x \to -1^-$, $y \to \infty$ as $x \to \infty$, $y \to 2^-$
    as $x \to -1^+$, $y \to -\infty$ as $x \to -\infty$, $y \to 2^+$
  iii

$f(x) = 2 - \frac{3}{x+1}$

$y = 2$

$x = -1$

  iv Function does not cross its asymptotes.

c i vertical asymptotes $x = -1$, $x = 2$,
    horizontal asymptote $y = 0$
  ii as $x \to -1^-$, $y \to \infty$ as $x \to \infty$, $y \to 0^+$
    as $x \to -1^+$, $y \to -\infty$ as $x \to -\infty$, $y \to 0^-$
    as $x \to 2^-$, $y \to -\infty$
    as $x \to 2^+$, $y \to \infty$
  iii

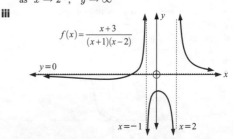

$f(x) = \frac{x+3}{(x+1)(x-2)}$

$y = 0$

$x = -1$ $x = 2$

  iv Function crosses the horizontal asymptote at $(-3, 0)$.

d i vertical asymptote $x = 3$, oblique asymptote $y = x$
  ii as $x \to 3^-$, $y \to -\infty$ as $x \to \infty$, $y \to x^+$
    as $x \to 3^+$, $y \to \infty$ as $x \to -\infty$, $y \to x^-$

iii

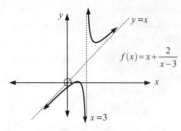

$$f(x)=x+\frac{2}{x-3}$$

iv Function does not cross its asymptotes.

e i horizontal asymptote $y=1$

ii as $x\to\infty$, $y\to1^-$ as $x\to-\infty$, $y\to1^-$

iii

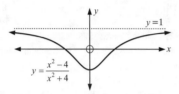

$$y=\frac{x^2-4}{x^2+4}$$

iv Function does not cross its asymptote.

f i vert. asymptotes $x=-2$, $x=2$, horiz. asymptote $y=2$

ii as $x\to-2^-$, $y\to\infty$ as $x\to\infty$, $y\to2^+$

as $x\to-2^+$, $y\to-\infty$ as $x\to-\infty$, $y\to2^+$

as $x\to2^-$, $y\to-\infty$

as $x\to2^+$, $y\to\infty$

iii

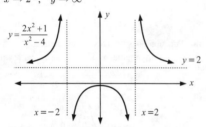

$$y=\frac{2x^2+1}{x^2-4}$$

iv Function does not cross its asymptotes.

g i vertical asymptote $x=-1$, oblique asymptote $y=x+3$

ii as $x\to-1^-$, $y\to\infty$ as $x\to\infty$, $y\to(x+3)^-$

as $x\to-1^+$, $y\to-\infty$ as $x\to-\infty$, $y\to(x+3)^+$

iii

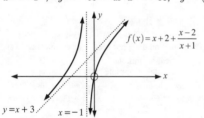

$$f(x)=x+2+\frac{x-2}{x+1}$$

iv Function does not cross its asymptotes.

h i oblique asymptote $y=2x$

ii as $x\to\infty$, $y\to(2x)^-$

as $x\to-\infty$, $y\to(2x)^+$

iii

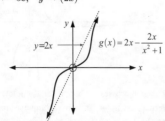

$$g(x)=2x-\frac{2x}{x^2+1}$$

iv Function crosses the oblique asymptote at $(0, 0)$.

i i vert. asymptotes $x=-1$, $x=5$, horiz. asymptote $y=0$

ii as $x\to-1^-$, $y\to-\infty$ as $x\to\infty$, $y\to0^+$

as $x\to-1^+$, $y\to\infty$ as $x\to-\infty$, $y\to0^-$

as $x\to5^-$, $y\to-\infty$

as $x\to5^+$, $y\to\infty$

iii

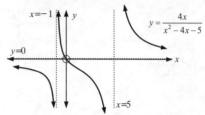

$$y=\frac{4x}{x^2-4x-5}$$

iv Function crosses the horizontal asymptote at $(0, 0)$.

j i vertical asymptote $x=0$, parabolic asymptote $y=x^2$

ii as $x\to0^-$, $y\to\infty$ as $x\to\infty$, $y\to(x^2)^-$

as $x\to0^+$, $y\to-\infty$ as $x\to-\infty$, $y\to(x^2)^+$

iii

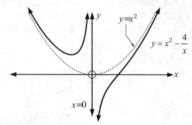

$$y=x^2-\frac{4}{x}$$

iv Function does not cross its asymptotes.

EXERCISE 1I

1 a i

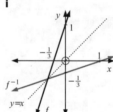

b i

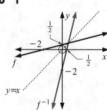

ii, iii

$$f^{-1}(x)=\frac{x-1}{3}$$

ii, iii

$$f^{-1}(x)=4x-2$$

2 a i $f^{-1}(x)=\dfrac{x-5}{2}$ **b i** $f^{-1}(x)=-2x+\dfrac{3}{2}$

ii

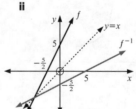

ii

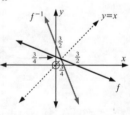

c i $f^{-1}(x)$ **ii**

$=x-3$

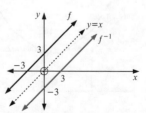

3 a
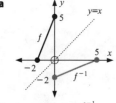
b
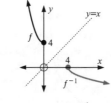

c
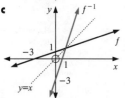
d
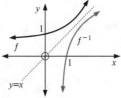

e
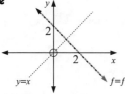
f
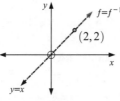

4 a
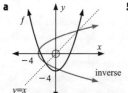
5

b No **c** Yes, it is $y = \sqrt{x + 4}$

EXERCISE 1J

1 a $\{(2, 1), (4, 2), (5, 3)\}$ **b** not invertible
  c $\{(0, -1), (1, 2), (2, 0), (3, 1)\}$ **d** $\{(-1, -1), (0, 0), (1, 1)\}$

2 a $f : x \mapsto \dfrac{1}{x}$, $x \neq 0$ satisfies both the vertical and
   horizontal line tests and $\therefore$ has an inverse function.
  b $f^{-1}(x) = \dfrac{1}{x}$ and $f(x) = \dfrac{1}{x}$ i.e., $f = f^{-1}$
   $\therefore$ f is a self-inverse function

3 a $y = \dfrac{3x - 8}{x - 3}$ is symmetrical about $y = x$,
   $\therefore$ f is a self-inverse function.
  b $f^{-1}(x) = \dfrac{3x - 8}{x - 3}$ and $f(x) = \dfrac{3x - 8}{x - 3}$
   i.e., $f = f^{-1}$ $\therefore$ f is a self-inverse function

4 b i is the only one
  c ii Domain $\{x \mid x \leqslant 1\}$ **iii** Domain $\{x \mid x \geqslant 1\}$

5 a $f^{-1}(x) = -\sqrt{x}$ **b**
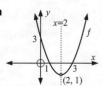

6 a

A horizontal line above the vertex cuts the graph **twice**. So, it does not have an inverse.

b For $x \geqslant 2$, all horizontal lines cut 0 or once only, $\therefore$ has an inverse.

---

c Hint: Inverse is $x = y^2 - 4y + 3$ for $y \geqslant 2$
d i Domain is $\{x \mid x \geqslant 2\}$, Range is $\{y \mid y \geqslant -1\}$
  ii Domain is $\{x \mid x \geqslant -1\}$, Range is $\{y \mid y \geqslant 2\}$
e Hint: Find $(f \circ f^{-1})(x)$ and $(f^{-1} \circ f)(x)$ and show that they both equal x.

7 a $f^{-1}(x) = \sqrt{x - 3} - 1$, $x \geqslant 3$
b
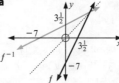
c i Domain $\{x \mid x \geqslant -1\}$
   Range $\{y \mid y \geqslant 3\}$
  ii Domain $\{x \mid x \geqslant 3\}$
   Range $\{y \mid y \geqslant -1\}$

8 a 10 **b** $x = 3$ **9 a i** 25 **ii** 16 **b** $x = 1$

10 $(f^{-1} \circ g^{-1})(x) = \dfrac{x + 3}{8}$ and $(g \circ f)^{-1}(x) = \dfrac{x + 3}{8}$

11 a Is not **b** Is **c** Is **d** Is **e** Is
13 a B is $(f(x), x)$ **b** $x = f^{-1}(f(x)) = (f^{-1} \circ f)(x)$
  c Start with B first and repeat the process used in **a** and **b**.

REVIEW SET 1A

1 a 0 **b** -15 **c** $-\frac{5}{4}$

2 a i Range $= \{y \mid y \geqslant -5\}$, Domain $= \{x \mid x \text{ is in } \mathbb{R}\}$
  ii x-int. -1, 5; y-int. $-\frac{25}{9}$ **iii** is a function **iv** no
  b i Range $= \{y \mid y = 1 \text{ or } -3\}$ Domain $= \{x \mid x \text{ is in } \mathbb{R}\}$
  ii no x-intercepts; y-intercept 1 **iii** is a function **iv** no

3 $a = 1$, $b = -6$, $c = 5$
4 a
$$\begin{array}{ccc} - & + & - \\ \hline & -\frac{2}{3} \quad 4 & \end{array}$$
b
$$\begin{array}{ccc} - & - & + \\ \hline & -2 \quad 3 & \end{array}$$

5 a $2x^2 + 1$ **b** $4x^2 - 12x + 11$
6 a $x \in \,]-\infty, -5]$ or $]-2, 2]$ **b** $x \in \,]-8, -\frac{1}{2}[\,$ or $]1, \infty[$
7 a
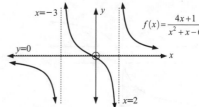
b $f^{-1}(x) = \dfrac{x + 7}{2}$

8 a $x = 1$ or 7 **b** $x \in \,]-\infty, -\frac{1}{5}]$ or $[5, \infty[$
9 a vertical asymptotes $x = -3$, $x = 2$
   horizontal asymptote $y = 0$
  b as $x \to -3^-$, $y \to -\infty$ as $x \to \infty$, $y \to 0^+$
   as $x \to -3^+$, $y \to \infty$ as $x \to -\infty$, $y \to 0^-$
   as $x \to 2^-$, $y \to -\infty$
   as $x \to 2^+$, $y \to \infty$
  c

$f(x) = \dfrac{4x + 1}{x^2 + x - 6}$

10 $(f^{-1} \circ h^{-1})(x) = x - 2$ and $(h \circ f)^{-1}(x) = x - 2$

REVIEW SET 1B

1 a $x^2 - x - 2$ **b** $x^4 - 7x^2 + 10$
2 a $f^{-1}(x) = \dfrac{7 - x}{4}$ **b** $f^{-1}(x) = \dfrac{5x - 3}{2}$
3 a Domain $\{x \mid x \in \mathbb{R}\}$, Range $\{y \mid y \geqslant -4\}$
  b Domain $\{x \mid x \neq 0, 2\}$, Range $\{y \mid y \leqslant -1 \text{ or } y > 0\}$

4 a

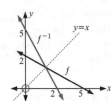

b

5 a

$$\begin{array}{c} - \quad + \quad - \quad + \\ \hline \quad -2 \quad 3 \quad 8 \end{array}$$

b

$$\begin{array}{c} - \quad | \quad + \quad + \\ \hline \quad -5 \quad -3 \end{array}$$

6 a $x \in [-\frac{5}{2}, 2]$ **b** $x \in \,]-2, -1[\;$ or $\;]4, \infty[$

7 a $f(x) = \sqrt{x}$, $g(x) = 1 - x^2$ **b** $g(x) = x^2$, $f(x) = \dfrac{x-2}{x+1}$

8 a $x = -1$ or 3 **b** $x \in \,]-\infty, -\frac{1}{3}]\;$ or $\;[5, \infty[$

9 a vertical asymptotes $x = \pm 2$, horizontal asymptote $y = 3$

b as $x \to -2^-$, $y \to -\infty$ as $x \to \infty$, $y \to 3^+$
as $x \to -2^+$, $y \to \infty$ as $x \to -\infty$, $y \to 3^-$
as $x \to 2^-$, $y \to -\infty$
as $x \to 2^+$, $y \to \infty$

c

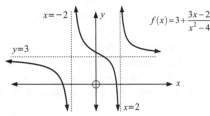

d Function crosses horizontal asymptote at $(\frac{2}{3}, 3)$.

10 a $h^{-1}(x) = 4 + \sqrt{x - 3}$

REVIEW SET 1C

1 a $10 - 6x$ **b** $x = 2$

2 a Domain $\{x \mid x > -3\}$,   Range $\{y \mid -3 < y < 5\}$
b Domain $\{x \mid x \neq 1\}$,   Range $\{y \mid y \leqslant -3, \; y \geqslant 5\}$

3 a i $1 - 2\sqrt{x}$ **ii** $\sqrt{1 - 2x}$
b For $f \circ g$, Domain $\{x \mid x \geqslant 0\}$, Range $\{y \mid y \leqslant 1\}$
For $g \circ f$, Domain $\{x \mid x \leqslant \frac{1}{2}\}$, Range $\{y \mid y \geqslant 0\}$

4 a $x \in \,]-\infty, 2[$ **b** $x \in \,]-2, -\frac{5}{4}]\;$ or $\;]1, \infty[$

5 a $x = 0$ **b**

c Domain $= \{x \mid x \neq 0\}$,
Range $= \{y \mid y > 0\}$

$y = \dfrac{1}{x^2}$

6 a $x \in \,]-\infty, 1[\;$ or $\;]9, \infty[$

b

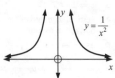

$y = \dfrac{x}{|x|+1}$

$y = \frac{1}{3}$

$(\frac{1}{2}, \frac{1}{3})$

$\therefore \dfrac{x}{|x|+1} \geqslant \dfrac{1}{3}$ for $x \in [\frac{1}{2}, \infty[$

7 a

$$\begin{array}{c} - \quad + \quad | \quad - \quad + \\ \hline \quad -2 \quad 1 \quad 3 \end{array}$$

b $x \in \,]-\infty, -2[\;$ or $\;]1, 3[$

8 a vertical asymptote $x = 1$, oblique asymptote $y = x - 2$
b as $x \to 1^-$, $y \to \infty$ as $x \to \infty$, $y \to (x-2)^+$
as $x \to 1^+$, $y \to \infty$ as $x \to -\infty$, $y \to (x-2)^+$

c

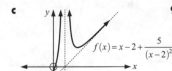

$f(x) = x - 2 + \dfrac{5}{(x-2)^2}$

$y = x - 2$

$x = 1$

9 a $f^{-1}(x) = \dfrac{x-2}{4}$

b $f^{-1}(x) = \dfrac{3 - 4x}{5}$

10 a, d

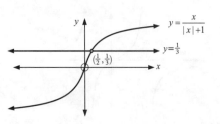

b If $x \leqslant -3$, we have the graph to the left of $x = -3$ and any horizontal line cuts it at most once.

c $y = -3 - \sqrt{x + 2}$

e Range of g $\{y \mid y \geqslant -2\}$, Domain of g^{-1} $\{x \mid x \geqslant -2\}$
Range of g^{-1} $\{y \mid y \leqslant -3\}$

EXERCISE 2A

1 a 4, 13, 22, 31, ... **b** 45, 39, 33, 27, ...
c 2, 6, 18, 54, ... **d** 96, 48, 24, 12, ...

2 a Starts at 8 and each term is 8 more than the previous term.
Next two terms 40, 48.
b Starts at 2, each term is 3 more than the previous term; 14, 17.
c Starts at 36, each term is 5 less than the previous term; 16, 11.
d Starts at 96, each term is 7 less than the previous term; 68, 61.
e Starts at 1, each term is 4 times the previous term; 256, 1024.
f Starts at 2, each term is 3 times the previous term; 162, 486.
g Starts at 480, each term is half the previous term; 30, 15.
h Starts at 243, each term is $\frac{1}{3}$ of the previous term; 3, 1.
i Starts at 50 000, each term is $\frac{1}{5}$ of the previous term; 80, 16.

3 a Each term is the square of the term number; 25, 36, 49.
b Each term is the cube of the term number; 125, 216, 343.
c Each term is $n(n + 1)$ where n is the term number; 30, 42, 56.

EXERCISE 2B

1 a 2, 4, 6, 8, 10 **b** 4, 6, 8, 10, 12 **c** 1, 3, 5, 7, 9
d −1, 1, 3, 5, 7 **e** 5, 7, 9, 11, 13 **f** 13, 15, 17, 19, 21
g 4, 7, 10, 13, 16 **h** 1, 5, 9, 13, 17
2 a 2, 4, 8, 16, 32 **b** 6, 12, 24, 48, 96
c 3, $1\frac{1}{2}$, $\frac{3}{4}$, $\frac{3}{8}$, $\frac{3}{16}$ **d** −2, 4, −8, 16, −32

3 17, 11, 23, −1, 47

EXERCISE 2C

1 a $u_1 = 6$, $d = 11$ **b** $u_n = 11n - 5$ **c** 545
d yes, u_{30} **e** no
2 a $u_1 = 87$, $d = -4$, **b** $u_n = 91 - 4n$ **c** −69 **d** no
3 b $u_1 = 1$, $d = 3$ **c** 169 **d** $u_{151} = 451$
4 b $u_1 = 32$, $d = -\frac{7}{2}$ **c** −227 **d** $n \geqslant 68$
5 a $k = 17\frac{1}{2}$ **b** $k = 4$ **c** $k = 3$, $k = -1$
6 a $u_n = 6n - 1$ **b** $u_n = -\frac{3}{2}n + \frac{11}{2}$ **c** $u_n = -5n + 36$
d $u_n = -\frac{3}{2}n + \frac{1}{2}$
7 a $6\frac{1}{4}$, $7\frac{1}{2}$, $8\frac{3}{4}$ **b** $3\frac{5}{7}$, $8\frac{3}{7}$, $13\frac{1}{7}$, $17\frac{6}{7}$, $22\frac{4}{7}$, $27\frac{2}{7}$
8 a $u_1 = 36$, $d = -\frac{2}{3}$ **b** 100 **9** 100 006

EXERCISE 2D.1

1 a $b = 18$, $c = 54$ **b** $b = 2\frac{1}{2}$, $c = 1\frac{1}{4}$ **c** $b = 3$, $c = -1\frac{1}{2}$
2 a $u_1 = 5$, $r = 2$ **b** $u_n = 5 \times 2^{n-1}$, $u_{15} = 81\,920$
3 a $u_1 = 12$, $r = -\frac{1}{2}$ **b** $u_n = 12 \times (-\frac{1}{2})^{n-1}$, $u_{13} = \frac{3}{1024}$
4 $u_1 = 8$, $r = -\frac{3}{4}$, $u_{10} = -0.600\,677\,49$
5 $u_1 = 8$, $r = \frac{1}{\sqrt{2}}$, $u_n = 2^{\frac{7}{2} - \frac{n}{2}}$

6 a $k = \pm 14$ **b** $k = 2$ **c** $k = -2$ or 4

7 a $u_n = 3 \times 2^{n-1}$ **b** $u_n = 32 \times (-\frac{1}{2})^{n-1}$

   c $u_n = 3 \times (\pm\sqrt{2})^{n-1}$ **d** $u_n = 10 \times (\pm\sqrt{2})^{1-n}$

8 a $u_9 = 13\,122$ **b** $u_{14} = 2916\sqrt{3} \approx 5050.66$

   c $u_{18} \approx 0.000\,091\,55$

EXERCISE 2D.2

1 a \$3993.00 **b** \$993.00 **2** € 11 470.39

3 a 43 923 Yen **b** 13 923 Yen **4** \$23 602.32

5 148 024.43 Yen **6** £ 51 249.06 **7** \$14 976.01

8 £ 11 477.02 **9** € 19 712.33 **10** 19 522.47 Yen

EXERCISE 2D.3

1 a i 1550 ants **ii** 4820 ants **b** 12.2 weeks

2 a 278 animals **b** Year 2044

EXERCISE 2E.1

1 a i $S_n = 3 + 11 + 19 + 27 + ... + (8n - 5)$ **ii** 95

   b i $S_n = 42 + 37 + 32 + ... + (47 - 5n)$ **ii** 160

   c i $S_n = 12 + 6 + 3 + 1\frac{1}{2} + ... + 12(\frac{1}{2})^{n-1}$ **ii** $23\frac{1}{4}$

   d i $S_n = 2 + 3 + 4\frac{1}{2} + 6\frac{3}{4} + ... + 2(\frac{3}{2})^{n-1}$ **ii** $26\frac{3}{8}$

   e i $S_n = 1 + \frac{1}{2} + \frac{1}{4} + \frac{1}{8} + ... + \frac{1}{2^{n-1}}$ **ii** $1\frac{15}{16}$

   f i $S_n = 1 + 8 + 27 + 64 + ... + n^3$ **ii** 225

2 a 10 **b** 25 **c** 168 **d** 310 **3** $\sum\limits_{n=1}^{20}(3n - 1) = 610$

5 b $\sum\limits_{k=1}^{n}(k + 1)(k + 2) = \frac{n(n^2 + 6n + 11)}{3}$

EXERCISE 2E.2

1 a 820 **b** 3087.5 **c** -1460 **d** -740

2 a 1749 **b** 2115 **c** $1410\frac{1}{2}$

3 a 160 **b** -630 **c** 135 **4** 203

5 -115.5 **6** 18 **7 a** 65 **b** 1914 **c** 47 850

8 a 14 025 **b** 71 071 **c** 3367

10 a $u_n = 2n - 1$ **c** $S_1 = 1$, $S_2 = 4$, $S_3 = 9$, $S_4 = 16$

11 56, 49 **12** 10, 4, -2 or -2, 4, 10

13 2, 5, 8, 11, 14 or 14, 11, 8, 5, 2

EXERCISE 2E.3

1 a $23.9766 \approx 24.0$ **b** $\approx 189\,134$ **c** ≈ 4.000 **d** ≈ 0.5852

2 a $S_n = \frac{3 + \sqrt{3}}{2}\left((\sqrt{3})^n - 1\right)$ **b** $S_n = 24(1 - (\frac{1}{2})^n)$

   c $S_n = 1 - (0.1)^n$ **d** $S_n = \frac{40}{3}(1 - (-\frac{1}{2})^n)$

3 a 3069 **b** $\frac{4095}{1024} \approx 3.999$ **c** $-134\,217\,732$

4 c \$26 361.59

5 a $\frac{1}{2}$, $\frac{3}{4}$, $\frac{7}{8}$, $\frac{15}{16}$, $\frac{31}{32}$ **b** $S_n = \frac{2^n - 1}{2^n}$

   c $1 - (\frac{1}{2})^n = \frac{2^n - 1}{2^n}$ **d** as $n \to \infty$, $S_n \to 1$

EXERCISE 2E.4

1 a i $u_1 = \frac{3}{10}$ **ii** $r = 0.1$ **b** $S_\infty = \frac{1}{3}$

2 a $\frac{4}{9}$ **b** $\frac{16}{99}$ **c** $\frac{104}{333}$ **4 a** 54 **b** 14.175 **5 a** 1 **b** $4\frac{2}{7}$

6 a convergent, sum = 12 **b** not convergent, $n = 10$

7 $u_1 = 9$, $r = \frac{2}{3}$ **8** $u_1 = 8$, $r = \frac{1}{5}$ and $u_1 = 2$, $r = \frac{4}{5}$

9 b $S_n = 1 + 18(1 - (0.9)^{n-1})$ **c** 19 seconds

EXERCISE 2F

1 34th week (total sold = 2057)

2 After 85 months its value is \$501.88 and after 86 months its value is \$491.84, $\therefore$ during the 86th month its value is \$500.

3 54 or $\frac{2}{3}$ **4** 70 cm

5 The 20th terms are: arithmetic 39, geometric 3^{19}
   or arithmetic $7\frac{1}{3}$, geometric $(\frac{4}{3})^{19}$

6 a 420 **b** 2231.868 211 **7 a** $n = 37$ **b** $n = 11$

8 $x = \frac{1}{2}$ **9 a** $u_1 = 7$, $u_2 = 10$, **b** 64

10 a $A_3 = \$8000(1.03)^3 - (1.03)^2 R - 1.03R - R$

   b $A_8 = \$8000(1.03)^8 - (1.03)^7 R - (1.03)^6 R - (1.03)^5 R$
   $\qquad - (1.03)^4 R - (1.03)^3 R - (1.03)^2 R - (1.03)R - R$
   $\qquad = 0 \qquad R = \$1139.65$

REVIEW SET 2A

1 a $\frac{1}{3}$, 1, 3, 9 **b** $\frac{5}{4}$, $\frac{8}{5}$, $\frac{11}{6}$, 2 **c** 5, -5, 35, -65

2 b $u_1 = 63$, $d = -5$ **c** -117 **d** $u_{54} = -202$

3 a $u_1 = 3$, $r = 4$ **b** $u_n = 3 \times 4^{n-1}$, $u_9 = 196\,608$

4 $k = -\frac{11}{2}$ **5** $u_n = 73 - 6n$, $u_{34} = -131$

6 b $u_1 = 6$, $r = \frac{1}{2}$ **c** 0.000 183

7 $u_n = 33 - 5n$, $S_n = \frac{n}{2}(61 - 5n)$ **8** $k = \pm\frac{2\sqrt{3}}{3}$

9 $u_n = \frac{1}{6} \times 2^{n-1}$ or $-\frac{1}{6} \times (-2)^{n-1}$

10 a $\frac{1331}{2100} \approx 0.634$ **b** $6\frac{8}{15}$ **11** $x > -\frac{1}{2}$

12 a $u_1 = 54$, $r = \frac{2}{3}$ and $u_1 = 150$, $r = -\frac{2}{5}$

   b $|r| < 1$ in both cases.
   For $u_1 = 54$, $r = \frac{2}{3}$, $S = 162$
   For $u_1 = 150$, $r = -\frac{2}{5}$, $S = 107\frac{1}{7}$

13 $a = b = c$

14 $x = 3$, $y = -1$, $z = \frac{1}{3}$ or $x = \frac{1}{3}$, $y = -1$, $z = 3$

REVIEW SET 2B

1 a 81 **b** $-1\frac{1}{2}$ **c** -486 **2** 21, 19, 17, 15, 13, 11

3 a $u_n = 89 - 3n$ **b** $u_n = \frac{2n + 1}{n + 3}$ **c** $u_n = 100(0.9)^{n-1}$

4 a $1 + 4 + 9 + 16 + 25 + 36 + 49$

   b $\frac{4}{3} + \frac{5}{4} + \frac{6}{5} + \frac{7}{6} + \frac{8}{7} + \frac{9}{8} + \frac{10}{9} + \frac{11}{10}$

5 $\sum\limits_{k=1}^{n}(7k - 3)$ **b** $\sum\limits_{k=1}^{n}(\frac{1}{2})^{k+1}$ **6 a** 1587 **b** $47\frac{253}{256} \approx 47.99$

7 a 70 **b** 241.2 **8** $u_{12} = 10\,240$

9 a € 8415.31 **b** € 8488.67 **c** € 8505.75

10 a $10\frac{4}{5}$ **b** $16 + 8\sqrt{2}$

11 $x = \frac{3}{2}$ $\left(x = -\frac{6}{7}\text{ gives a divergent series}\right)$

12 $\frac{64}{1875}$ **14** $S = \dfrac{2 - 2^{-\frac{1}{n+1}}}{2^{\frac{1}{n+1}} - 1}$

REVIEW SET 2C

1 $u_n = (\frac{3}{4})2^{n-1}$ **a** 49 152 **b** 24 575.25 **2** 12

3 $u_{11} = \frac{8}{19\,683} \approx 0.000\,406$ **4 a** 17 **b** $255\frac{511}{512} \approx 256.0$

5 a \$18 726.65 **b** \$18 885.74 **6** \$13 972.28

7 a 3470 **b** Year 2014 **8** 18 metres

9 a $0 < x < 1$ **b** $35\frac{5}{7}$ **10 a** $u_n = 3n + 1$

EXERCISE 3A

1 a $2^1 = 2$, $2^2 = 4$, $2^3 = 8$, $2^4 = 16$, $2^5 = 32$, $2^6 = 64$

   b $3^1 = 3$, $3^2 = 9$, $3^3 = 27$, $3^4 = 81$, $3^5 = 243$, $3^6 = 729$

   c $4^1 = 4$, $4^2 = 16$, $4^3 = 64$, $4^4 = 256$, $4^5 = 1024$, $4^6 = 4096$

2 a $5^1 = 5$, $5^2 = 25$, $5^3 = 125$, $5^4 = 625$

   b $6^1 = 6$, $6^2 = 36$, $6^3 = 216$, $6^4 = 1296$

   c $7^1 = 7$, $7^2 = 49$, $7^3 = 343$, $7^4 = 2401$

EXERCISE 3B

1 a 1 **b** 1–**c** 1 **d** 1 **e** 1–**f** -1 **g** -1
   h -32 **i** -32 **j** -64 **k** 625 **l** -625

2 a 16 784 **b** 2401 **c** -3125 **d** -3125 **e** 262 144
   f 262 144 **g** $-262\,144$ **h** 902.436 039 6
   i $-902.436\,039\,6$ **j** $-902.436\,039\,6$

3 a $0.\overline{1}$ **b** $0.\overline{1}$ **c** $0.02\overline{7}$ **d** $0.02\overline{7}$
   e 0.012 345 679 **f** 0.012 345 679 **g** 1 **h** 1

4 3 5 7

6 1 Yes, $n = 2^{s-1}$ **2** $2^{39} \approx 5.5 \times 10^{11}$ **3** $2^{64} - 1 \approx 1.8 \times 10^{19}$

EXERCISE 3C.1

1 a 2^2 **b** 2^{-2} **c** 2^3 **d** 2^{-3} **e** 2^5 **f** 2^{-5} **g** 2^1
   h 2^{-1} **i** 2^6 **j** 2^{-6} **k** 2^7 **l** 2^{-7}

2 a 3^2 **b** 3^{-2} **c** 3^3 **d** 3^{-3} **e** 3^1 **f** 3^{-1} **g** 3^4
   h 3^{-4} **i** 3^0 **j** 3^5 **k** 3^{-5}

3 a 2^{a+1} **b** 2^{b+2} **c** 2^{t+3} **d** 2^{2x+2} **e** 2^{n-1} **f** 2^{c-2}
   g 2^{2m} **h** 2^{n+1} **i** 2^1 **j** 2^{3x-1}

4 a 3^{p+2} **b** 3^{3a} **c** 3^{2n+1} **d** 3^{d+3} **d** 3^{3t+2} **f** 3^{y-1}
   g 3^{1-y} **h** 3^{2-3t} **i** 3^{3a-1} **j** 3^3

5 a $\dfrac{a}{b^2}$ **b** $\dfrac{1}{a^2b^2}$ **c** $\dfrac{4a^2}{b^2}$ **d** $\dfrac{9b^2}{a^4}$ **e** $\dfrac{a^2}{bc^2}$ **f** $\dfrac{a^2c^2}{b}$

   g a^3 **h** $\dfrac{b^3}{a^2}$ **i** $\dfrac{2}{ad^2}$ **j** $12am^3$

6 a a^{-n} **b** b^n **c** 3^{n-2} **d** $a^n b^m$ **e** a^{-2n-2}

EXERCISE 3C.2

1 a $2^{\frac{1}{5}}$ **b** $2^{-\frac{1}{5}}$ **c** $2^{\frac{3}{2}}$ **d** $2^{\frac{5}{2}}$ **e** $2^{-\frac{1}{3}}$ **f** $2^{\frac{4}{3}}$ **g** $2^{\frac{3}{2}}$
   h $2^{\frac{3}{2}}$ **i** $2^{-\frac{4}{3}}$ **j** $2^{-\frac{3}{2}}$

2 a $3^{\frac{1}{3}}$ **b** $3^{-\frac{1}{3}}$ **c** $3^{\frac{1}{4}}$ **d** $3^{\frac{1}{2}}$ **e** $3^{-\frac{5}{2}}$

3 a $7^{\frac{1}{3}}$ **b** $3^{\frac{1}{4}}$ **c** $2^{\frac{4}{5}}$ **d** $2^{\frac{5}{3}}$ **e** $7^{\frac{2}{7}}$ **f** $7^{-\frac{1}{3}}$ **g** $3^{-\frac{3}{4}}$
   h $2^{-\frac{4}{5}}$ **i** $2^{-\frac{5}{3}}$ **j** $7^{-\frac{2}{7}}$

4 a 2.28 **b** 1.83 **c** 0.794 **d** 0.435
5 a 3 **b** 1.68 **c** 1.93 **d** 0.523
6 a 8 **b** 32 **c** 8 **d** 125 **e** 4 **f** $\frac{1}{2}$ **g** $\frac{1}{27}$ **h** $\frac{1}{16}$
   i $\frac{1}{81}$ **j** $\frac{1}{25}$

EXERCISE 3D.1

1 a $x^5 + 2x^4 + x^2$ **b** $2^{2x} + 2^x$ **c** $x+1$ **d** $e^{2x} + 2e^x$
   e $2(3^x) - 1$ **f** $x^2 + 2x + 3$ **g** $1 + 5(2^{-x})$ **h** $5^x + 1$
   i $x^{\frac{3}{2}} + x^{\frac{1}{2}} + 1$

2 a $4^x + 2^{2+x} + 3$ **b** $9^x + 7(3^x) + 10$ **c** $25^x - 6(5^x) + 8$
   d $4^x + 6(2^x) + 9$ **e** $9^x - 2(3^x) + 1$ **f** $16^x + 14(4^x) + 49$
   g $x - 4$ **h** $4^x - 9$ **i** $x - x^{-1}$ **j** $x^2 + 4 + \dfrac{4}{x^2}$
   k $e^{2x} - 2 + e^{-2x}$ **l** $25 - 10(2^{-x}) + 4^{-x}$

EXERCISE 3D.2

1 a $5^x(5^x + 1)$ **b** $10(3^n)$ **c** $e^n(1 + e^{2n})$ **d** $5(5^n - 1)$
   e $6(6^{n+1} - 1)$ **f** $16(4^n - 1)$ **g** $5(2^n)$ **h** $7(2^n)$ **i** $16(3^{n-1})$

2 a $(3^x + 2)(3^x - 2)$ **b** $(2^x + 5)(2^x - 5)$ **c** $(4 + 3^x)(4 - 3^x)$
   d $(5 + 2^x)(5 - 2^x)$ **e** $(3^x + 2)(3^x - 2^x)$ **f** $(2^x + 3)^2$
   g $(3^x + 5)^2$ **h** $(2^x - 7)^2$ **i** $(5^x - 2)^2$

3 a $(2^x + 3)(2^x + 6)$ **b** $(2^x + 4)(2^x - 5)$ **c** $(3^x + 2)(3^x + 7)$
   d $(3^x + 5)(3^x - 1)$ **e** $(5^x + 2)(5^x - 1)$ **f** $(7^x - 4)(7^x - 3)$

4 a 2^n **b** 10^a **c** 3^b **d** $\dfrac{1}{5^n}$ **e** 5^x **f** $(\frac{3}{4})^a$ **g** 5 **h** 5^n

5 a $3^m + 1$ **b** $1 + 6^n$ **c** $4^n + 2^n$ **d** 6^n **e** 5^n **f** 4
   g $\frac{1}{2}$ **h** $\frac{1}{2}$ **i** $1\frac{1}{2}$

6 a $n2^{n+1}$ **b** -3^{n-1} **7 a** $x = 1$ or 2 **b** $x = 1$ **c** $x = 1$ or 2
   d $x = 1$ **e** $x = 2$ **f** $x = 0$

EXERCISE 3E

1 a $x = 1$ **b** $x = 2$ **c** $x = 3$ **d** $x = 0$ **e** $x = -1$ **f** $x = -1$
   g $x = -3$ **h** $x = 2$ **i** $x = 0$ **j** $x = -4$ **k** $x = 5$ **l** $x = 1$

2 a $x = 2\frac{1}{2}$ **b** $x = -\frac{2}{3}$ **c** $x = -\frac{1}{2}$ **d** $x = -\frac{1}{2}$ **e** $x = -1\frac{1}{2}$

f $x = -\frac{1}{2}$ **g** $x = -\frac{1}{3}$ **h** $x = \frac{5}{3}$ **i** $x = \frac{1}{4}$ **j** $x = \frac{7}{2}$
k $x = -2$ **l** $x = -4$ **m** $x = 0$ **n** $x = \frac{5}{2}$ **o** $x = -2$
p $x = -6$

3 a $x = \frac{1}{7}$ **b** has no solutions **c** $x = 2\frac{1}{2}$

4 a $x = 3$ **b** $x = 3$ **c** $x = 2$ **d** $x = 2$ **e** $x = -2$ **f** $x = -2$

EXERCISE 3F

1 a 1.4 **b** 1.7 **c** 2.8 **d** 0.3 **e** 2.7 **f** 0.4

2 a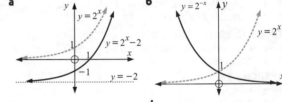

4 a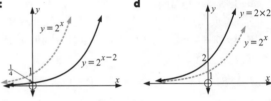

5 a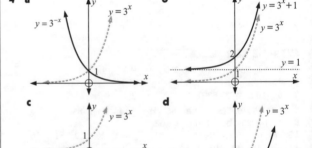

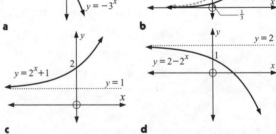

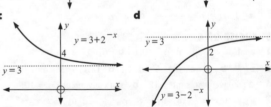

6 a $y \approx 3.67$ **b** $y \approx -0.665$ **c** $y \approx 3.38$ **d** $y \approx 2.62$

7 a as $x \to \infty$, $y \to \infty$
    as $x \to -\infty$, $y \to 1$ (above)   HA is $y = 1$

   b as $x \to \infty$, $y \to -\infty$
    as $x \to -\infty$, $y \to 2$ (below)   HA is $y = 2$

   c as $x \to \infty$, $y \to 3$ (above)
    as $x \to -\infty$, $y \to \infty$ HA is $y = 3$

   d as $x \to \infty$, $y \to 3$ (below)
    as $x \to -\infty$, $y \to -\infty$ HA is $y = 3$

EXERCISE 3G.1

1 a 100 grams **c**

b i 132 g
ii 200 g
iii 528 g

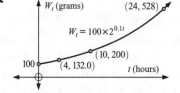

2 a 50 **c**

b i 76
ii 141
iii 400

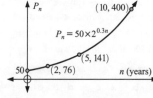

3 a V_0 **b** $2V_0$ **c** 100% **d** 183% increase, percentage increase at $50°C$ compared with $20°C$

4 a 12 bears **b** 146 bears **c** 248% increase

EXERCISE 3G.2

1 a 250 g **b i** 112 g **ii** 50.4 g **iii** 22.6 g
c   **d** ≈ 346 years

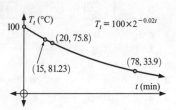

2 a $100°C$ **c**

b i $81.2°C$
ii $75.8°C$
iii $33.9°C$

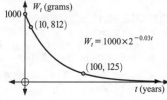

3 a 1000 g **c**

b i 812 g
ii 125 g
iii 9.31×10^{-7} g

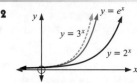

4 a W_0 **b** 12.9%

EXERCISE 3H

1 $e^1 \approx 2.718\,281\,828\,....$ **2**

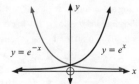

The graph of $y = e^x$ lies between $y = 2^x$ and $y = 3^x$.

3 One is the other reflected in the y-axis.

4 a

5 a $e^x > 0$ for all x **b i** $0.000\,000\,004\,12$ **ii** $970\,000\,000$

6 a ≈ 7.39 **b** ≈ 20.1 **c** ≈ 2.01 **d** ≈ 1.65 **e** ≈ 0.368

7 a $e^{\frac{1}{2}}$ **b** $e^{\frac{3}{2}}$ **c** $e^{-\frac{1}{2}}$ **d** e^{-2}

8 a $e^{0.18t}$ **b** $e^{0.004t}$ **c** $e^{-0.005t}$ **d** $\approx e^{-0.167t}$

9 a 10.074 **b** 0.099\,261 **c** 125.09 **d** 0.007\,994\,5
e 41.914 **f** 42.429 **g** 3540.3 **h** 0.006\,342\,4

10

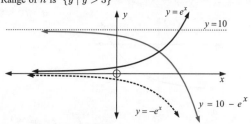

Domain of f, g and h is $\{x \mid x \in \mathbb{R}\}$
Range of f is $\{y \mid y > 0\}$ Range of g is $\{y \mid y > 0\}$
Range of h is $\{y \mid y > 3\}$

11

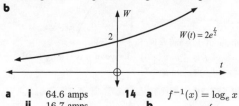

Domain of f, g and h is $\{x \mid x \in \mathbb{R}\}$
Range of f is $\{y \mid y > 0\}$ Range of g is $\{y \mid y < 0\}$
Range of h is $\{y \mid y < 10\}$

12 a i 2 g **ii** 2.57 g **iii** 4.23 g **iv** 40.2 g
b

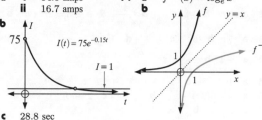

13 a i 64.6 amps
ii 16.7 amps
b

14 a $f^{-1}(x) = \log_e x$
b

c 28.8 sec

REVIEW SET 3A

1 a -1 **b** 27 **c** $\frac{2}{3}$ **2 a** $a^6 b^7$ **b** $\frac{2}{3x}$ **c** $\frac{y^2}{5}$

3 a 2^{-3} **b** 2^7 **c** 2^{12} **4 a** $\frac{1}{b^3}$ **b** $\frac{1}{ab}$ **c** $\frac{a}{b}$

5 a $x = -2$ **b** $x = \frac{3}{4}$ **6 a** 4 **b** $\frac{1}{9}$

7 a 2.28 **b** 0.517 **c** 3.16 **8 a** 3 **b** 24 **c** $\frac{3}{4}$

9

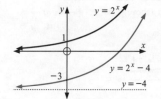

a $y = 2^x$ has y-intercept 1 and horizontal asymptote $y = 0$

b $y = 2^x - 4$ has y-intercept -3 and horizontal asymptote $y = -4$

10 a $80°C$

c

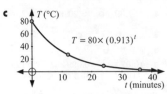

b i $26.8°C$
ii $9.00°C$
iii $3.02°C$

$T = 80 \times (0.913)^t$

d ≈ 12.8 min

REVIEW SET 3B

1 a 8 **b** $-\frac{4}{5}$ **2 a** a^{21} **b** $p^4 q^6$ **c** $\frac{4b}{a^3}$

3 a 2^{-4} **b** 2^{x+2} **c** 2^{2x-3} **4 a** $\frac{1}{x^5}$ **b** $\frac{2}{a^2 b^2}$ **c** $\frac{2a}{b^2}$

5 a $x = 4$ **b** $x = -\frac{2}{5}$

6 a 3^4 **b** 3^0 **c** 3^{-3} **d** 3^{-5} **7 a** 3^{3-2a} **b** $3^{\frac{5}{2}-\frac{9}{2}x}$

8 a

x	-2	-1	0	1	2
y	$-4\frac{8}{9}$	$-4\frac{2}{3}$	-4	-2	4

b as $x \to \infty$, $y \to \infty$; as $x \to -\infty$, $y \to -5$ (above)

c **d** $y = -5$

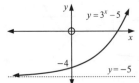

$y = 3^x - 5$

$y = -5$

9 a $x = \frac{1}{3}$ **b** $x = -\frac{4}{5}$

10

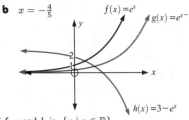

$f(x) = e^x$

$g(x) = e^{x-1}$

$h(x) = 3 - e^x$

Domain of f, g and h is $\{x \mid x \in \mathbb{R}\}$
Range of f is $\{y \mid y > 0\}$ Range of g is $\{y \mid y > 0\}$
Range of h is $\{y \mid y < 3\}$

REVIEW SET 3C

1 a 2^{n+2} **b** $-\frac{6}{7}$ **c** $3\frac{3}{8}$ **d** $\frac{4}{a^2 b^4}$ **2 a** $288 = 2^5 \times 3^2$ **b** 2^{2x}

3 a 5^0 **b** $5^{\frac{3}{2}}$ **c** $5^{-\frac{1}{4}}$ **d** 5^{2a+6}

4 a -4 **b** $\frac{1}{4a^6}$ **c** $-\frac{b^3}{27}$

5 a $1 + e^{2x}$ **b** $2^{2x} + 10(2^x) + 25$ **c** $x - 49$

6 a $9 - 6(2^a) + 2^{2a}$ **b** $x - 4$ **c** $2^x + 1$

7 a $x = 5$ **b** $x = -4$

8 a 1500 g **c**

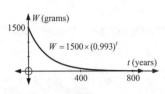

b i 90.3 g
ii 5.4 g

$W = 1500 \times (0.993)^t$

d 386 years

9 $\frac{1}{64}$

10 a

x	-2	-1	0	1	2
y	15.8	6.44	3	1.74	1.27

b as $x \to \infty$, $y \to 1$ (above); as $x \to -\infty$, $y \to \infty$

c **d** $y = 1$

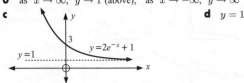

$y = 2e^{-x} + 1$

$y = 1$

EXERCISE 4A

1 a $10^4 = 10\,000$ **b** $10^{-1} = 0.1$ **c** $10^{\frac{1}{2}} = \sqrt{10}$
d $2^3 = 8$ **e** $2^{-2} = \frac{1}{4}$ **f** $3^{1.5} = \sqrt{27}$

2 a $\log_2 4 = 2$ **b** $\log_2(\frac{1}{8}) = -3$ **c** $\log_{10}(0.01) = -2$
d $\log_7 49 = 2$ **e** $\log_2 64 = 6$ **f** $\log_3(\frac{1}{27}) = -3$

3 a 5 **b** -2 **c** $\frac{1}{2}$ **d** 3 **e** 6 **f** 7 **g** 2 **h** 3 **i** -3 **j** $\frac{1}{2}$
k 2 **l** $1\frac{1}{2}$ **m** 5 **n** $\frac{1}{3}$ **o** n **p** $\frac{1}{3}$ **q** -1 **r** $\frac{3}{2}$ **s** 0 **t** 1

4 a ≈ 2.18 **b** ≈ 1.40 **c** ≈ 1.87 **d** ≈ -0.0969

5 a $x = 8$ **b** $x = 2$ **c** $x = 3$ **d** $x = 14$

6 a Let $\log_a a^n = x$ $\therefore$ $a^x = a^n$ $\therefore$ $x = n$
b i 2 **ii** 2 **iii** -1 **iv** $\frac{2}{5}$ **v** $-\frac{1}{2}$ **vi** $\frac{5}{2}$ **vii** $-\frac{1}{2}$ **viii** $-\frac{3}{4}$

EXERCISE 4B

1 a 4 **b** -3 **c** 1 **d** 0 **e** $\frac{1}{2}$ **f** $\frac{1}{3}$ **g** $-\frac{1}{4}$ **h** $1\frac{1}{2}$ **i** $\frac{2}{3}$
j $1\frac{1}{2}$ **k** $1\frac{1}{3}$ **l** $3\frac{1}{2}$ **m** n **n** $a+2$ **o** $1-m$ **p** $a-b$

2 a [log] 10000 [ENTER] , 4 **b** [log] 0.001 [ENTER] , -3
c [log] [2nd] [√] 10 [)] [)] [ENTER] , 0.5
d [log] 10 [^] [(] 1 [÷] 3 [)] [)] [ENTER] , $0.\overline{3}$
e [log] 100 [^] [(] 1 [÷] 3 [)] [)] [ENTER] , $0.\overline{6}$
f [log] 10 [×] [2nd] [√] 10 [)] [)] [ENTER] , 1.5
g [log] 1 [÷] [2nd] [√] 10 [)] [)] [ENTER] , -0.5
h [log] 1 [÷] 10 [^] 0.25 [)] [ENTER] , -0.25

3 a $10^{0.7782}$ **b** $10^{1.7782}$ **c** $10^{3.7782}$ **d** $10^{-0.2218}$ **e** $10^{-2.2218}$
f $10^{1.1761}$ **g** $10^{3.1761}$ **h** $10^{0.1761}$ **i** $10^{-0.8239}$ **j** $10^{-3.8239}$

4 a i 0.477 **ii** 2.477 **b** $\log 300 = \log(3 \times 10^2)$

5 a i 0.699 **ii** -1.301 **b** $\log 0.05 = \log(5 \times 10^{-2})$

6 a $x = 100$ **b** $x = 10$ **c** $x = 1$ **d** $x = \frac{1}{10}$ **e** $x = 10^{\frac{1}{2}}$
f $x = 10^{-\frac{1}{2}}$ **g** $x \approx 6.84$ **h** $x \approx 0.000631$

EXERCISE 4C.1

1 a $\log 16$ **b** $\log 4$ **c** $\log 8$ **d** $\log 20$ **e** $\log 2$ **f** $\log 24$
g $\log 30$ **h** $\log 0.4$ **i** $\log 10$ **j** $\log 200$ **k** $\log 0.4$
l $\log 1$ or 0 **m** $\log 0.005$ **n** $\log 20$ **o** $\log 28$

2 a $\log 96$ **b** $\log 72$ **c** $\log 8$ **d** $\log\left(\frac{25}{8}\right)$ **e** $\log 6$
f $\log \frac{1}{2}$ **g** $\log 20$ **h** $\log 25$ **i** 1

3 a 2 **b** $\frac{3}{2}$ **c** 3 **d** $\frac{1}{2}$ **e** -2 **f** $-\frac{3}{2}$

5 a $p+q$ **b** $2p+3q$ **c** $2q+r$ **d** $r+\frac{1}{2}q-p$ **e** $r-5p$ **f** $p-2q$

6 a $x+z$ **b** $z+2y$ **c** $x+z-y$ **d** $2x+\frac{1}{2}y$ **e** $3y-\frac{1}{2}z$
f $2z+\frac{1}{2}y-3x$ **7 a** 0.86 **b** 2.15 **c** 1.075

EXERCISE 4C.2

1 a $\log y = x \log 2$ **b** $\log y \approx 1.301 + 3 \log b$
c $\log M = \log a + 4 \log d$ **d** $\log T \approx 0.6990 + \frac{1}{2} \log d$
e $\log R = \log b + \frac{1}{2} \log l$ **f** $\log Q = \log a - n \log b$
g $\log y = \log a + x \log b$ **h** $\log F \approx 1.301 - \frac{1}{2} \log n$
i $\log L = \log a + \log b - \log c$ **j** $\log N = \frac{1}{2} \log a - \frac{1}{2} \log b$
k $\log S \approx 2.301 + 0.301t$ **l** $\log y = m \log a - n \log b$

2 a $D = 2e$ **b** $F = \frac{5}{t}$ **c** $P = \sqrt{x}$ **d** $M = b^2 c$
e $B = \frac{m^3}{n^2}$ **f** $N = \frac{1}{\sqrt[3]{p}}$ **g** $P = 10x^3$ **h** $Q = \frac{100}{x}$

3 a $x = 9$ **b** $x = 2$ or 4 **c** $x = 25\sqrt{5}$ **d** $x = 200$
e $x = 5$ **f** $x = 3$

EXERCISE 4D

1 a 3 **b** 0 **c** $\frac{1}{3}$ **d** -2

3 x does not exist such that $e^x = -2$ or 0

4 a a **b** $a + 1$ **c** $a + b$ **d** ab **e** $a - b$

5 a $e^{1.7918}$ **b** $e^{4.0943}$ **c** $e^{8.6995}$ **d** $e^{-0.5108}$ **e** $e^{-5.1160}$
f $e^{2.7081}$ **g** $e^{7.3132}$ **h** $e^{0.4055}$ **i** $e^{-1.8971}$ **j** $e^{-8.8049}$

6 a $x \approx 20.1$ **b** $x \approx 2.72$ **c** $x = 1$ **d** $x \approx 0.368$
e $x \approx 0.006\,74$ **f** $x \approx 2.30$ **g** $x \approx 8.54$ **h** $x \approx 0.0370$

7 a $\ln 45$ **b** $\ln 5$ **c** $\ln 4$ **d** $\ln 24$ **e** $\ln 1 = 0$ **f** $\ln 30$
g $\ln 4e$ **h** $\ln\left(\frac{6}{e}\right)$ **i** $\ln 20$ **j** $\ln 4e^2$ **k** $\ln\left(\frac{20}{e^2}\right)$ **l** $\ln 1 = 0$

8 a $\ln 972$ **b** $\ln 200$ **c** $\ln 1 = 0$ **d** $\ln 16$ **e** $\ln 6$
f $\ln\left(\frac{1}{3}\right)$ **g** $\ln\left(\frac{1}{2}\right)$ **h** $\ln 2$ **i** $\ln 16$

9 e.g., for **a**, $\ln 27 = \ln 3^3 = 3\ln 3$

10 a $D = ex$ **b** $F = \dfrac{e^2}{p}$ **c** $P = \sqrt{x}$ **d** $M = e^3 y^2$

e $B = \dfrac{t^3}{e}$ **f** $N = \dfrac{1}{\sqrt[3]{g}}$ **g** $Q \approx 8.66x^3$ **h** $D \approx 0.518n^{0.4}$

EXERCISE 4E

1 a $x \approx 3.32$ **b** $x \approx 2.73$ **c** $x \approx 3.32$ **d** $x \approx 37.9$
e $x \approx -3.64$ **f** $x \approx -7.55$ **g** $x \approx 7.64$ **h** $x \approx 32.0$
i $x \approx 1150$

2 a $t \approx 6.340$ **b** $t \approx 74.86$ **c** $t \approx 8.384$ **d** $t \approx 132.9$
e $t \approx 121.5$ **f** $t \approx 347.4$

3 a $x \approx 2.303$ **b** $x \approx 6.908$ **c** $x \approx -4.754$ **d** $x \approx 3.219$
e $x \approx 15.18$ **f** $x \approx -40.85$ **g** $x \approx -14.63$
h $x \approx 137.2$ **i** $x \approx 4.868$

EXERCISE 4F

1 a ≈ 2.26 **b** ≈ -10.3 **c** ≈ -2.46 **d** ≈ 5.42

2 a $x \approx -4.29$ **b** $x \approx 3.87$ **c** $x \approx 0.139$

3 a $x \approx 0.683$ **b** $x \approx -1.89$

4 a $x = 16$ **b** $x \approx 1.71$ **5** $x = \dfrac{\log 8}{\log 25}$ or $\log_{25} 8$

EXERCISE 4G.1

1 a i $x \in\ ]-1, \infty[$, **iii**
    $y \in \mathbb{R}$
ii VA is $x = -1$,
    x and y-intercepts 0
iv $x = -\frac{2}{3}$
v $f^{-1}(x) = 3^x - 1$

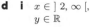

b i $x \in\ ]-1, \infty[$, **iii**
    $y \in \mathbb{R}$
ii VA is $x = -1$,
    x-intercept 2,
    y-intercept 1
iv $x = 8$
v $f^{-1}(x) = 3^{1-x} - 1$

c i $x \in\ ]2, \infty[$, **iii**
    $y \in \mathbb{R}$
ii VA is $x = 2$,
    x-intercept 27,
    no y-intercept
iv $x = 7$
v $f^{-1}(x) = 5^{2+x} + 2$

d i $x \in\ ]2, \infty[$, **iii**
    $y \in \mathbb{R}$
ii VA is $x = 2$,
    x-intercept 7,
    no y-intercept
iv $x = 27$
v $f^{-1}(x) = 5^{1-x} + 2$

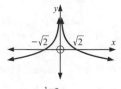

e i $x \in \mathbb{R}$, $x \neq 0$, **iii**
    $y \in \mathbb{R}$
ii VA is $x = 0$,
    x-intercepts $\pm\sqrt{2}$,
    no y-intercept
iv $x = \pm 2$ **v** if $x > 0$, $f^{-1}(x) = 2^{\frac{1-x}{2}}$
    if $x < 0$, $f^{-1}(x) = -2^{\frac{1-x}{2}}$

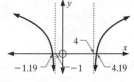

f i $x \in\ ]-\infty, -1[$ **iii**
    or $x \in\ ]4, \infty[$
    $y \in \mathbb{R}$
ii VA $x = 4$, $x = -1$
    x-ints. 4.19, -1.19,
    no y-intercept
iv $x = -1.10$ and 4.10
v if $f(x) = \log_2(x^2 - 3x - 4)$, $x > 4$,
    $$f^{-1}(x) = \frac{3 + \sqrt{25 + 2^{x+2}}}{2}$$
    if $f(x) = \log_2(x^2 - 3x - 4)$, $x < -1$,
    $$f^{-1}(x) = \frac{3 - \sqrt{25 + 2^{x+2}}}{2}$$

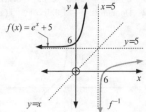

2 a i $f^{-1}(x)$ **ii**
    $= \ln(x - 5)$
iii domain of f is
    $\{x \mid x \in \mathbb{R}\}$,
    range is $\{y \mid y > 5\}$
    domain of f^{-1} is
    $\{x \mid x > 5\}$,
    range is $\{y \mid y \in \mathbb{R}\}$
iv f has a HA $y = 5$,
    f^{-1} has a VA $x = 5$

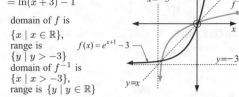

b i $f^{-1}(x)$ **ii**
    $= \ln(x + 3) - 1$
iii domain of f is
    $\{x \mid x \in \mathbb{R}\}$,
    range is
    $\{y \mid y > -3\}$
    domain of f^{-1} is
    $\{x \mid x > -3\}$,
    range is $\{y \mid y \in \mathbb{R}\}$
iv f has a HA $y = -3$, f^{-1} has a VA $x = -3$

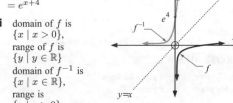

c i $f^{-1}(x)$ **ii**
    $= e^{x+4}$
iii domain of f is
    $\{x \mid x > 0\}$,
    range of f is
    $\{y \mid y \in \mathbb{R}\}$
    domain of f^{-1} is
    $\{x \mid x \in \mathbb{R}\}$,
    range is
    $\{y \mid y > 0\}$
iv f has a VA $x = 0$, f^{-1} has a HA $y = 0$

d i $f^{-1}(x)$
$= 1 + e^{x-2}$

ii

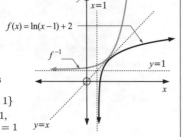

$f(x) = \ln(x-1) + 2$

iii domain of f is
$\{x \mid x > 1\}$,
range is
$\{y \mid y \in \mathbb{R}\}$
domain of f^{-1} is
$\{x \mid x \in \mathbb{R}\}$,
range is $\{y \mid y > 1\}$

iv f has a VA $x = 1$,
f^{-1} has a HA $y = 1$

3 $f^{-1}(x) = \frac{1}{2}\ln x$ **a** $\frac{1}{2}\ln(2x-1)$ **b** $\frac{1}{2}\ln\left(\frac{x+1}{2}\right)$

4 a A is $y = \ln x$ **b**
as its x-inter-
cept is 1

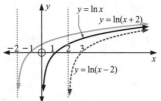

c $y = \ln x$ has
VA $x = 0$
$y = \ln(x-2)$
has VA $x = 2$
$y = \ln(x+2)$
has VA $x = -2$

5 $y = \ln(x^2) = 2\ln x$, so she is correct.
This is because the y-values are twice as large for $y = \ln(x^2)$
as they are for $y = \ln x$.

6 a $f^{-1} : x \mapsto \ln(x-2) - 3$
b i $x < -5.30$ **ii** $x < -7.61$ **iii** $x < -9.91$
iv $x < -12.2$ Conjecture HA is $y = 2$
c as $x \to -\infty$, $e^{x+3} \to 0$ and $y \to 2$ $\therefore$ HA is $y = 2$
d VA of f^{-1} is $x = 2$, domain of f^{-1} is $\{x \mid x > 2\}$

EXERCISE 4G.2

1 a $x < -0.703$ **b** $x < 0.773$ **c** $x < 3.69$
2 Domain is $x \in]\,0, \infty\,[$, $f(x) \leqslant 0$ for $x \in]\,0, 1]$
3 a

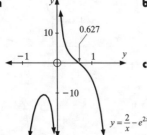

b Domain is
$\{x \mid x \in \mathbb{R}, \; x \neq 0\}$
Range is
$\{y \mid y \in \mathbb{R}\}$
c For $x \in]-\infty, 0\,[$
or $]\,0.627, \infty\,[$

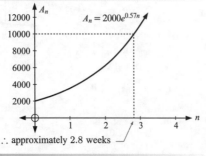

$y = \frac{2}{x} - e^{2x^2 - x + 1}$

EXERCISE 4H.1

1 a 3.90 h
b 15.5 h
2 a 6.9 h
b 13.9 h
3 a see graph
alongside
b $n \approx 2.82$

$\therefore$ approximately 2.8 weeks

EXERCISE 4H.2

1 6.17 years, i.e., 6 years 62 days
2 8.65 years, i.e., 8 years 237 days
3 a $\dfrac{8.4\%}{12} = 0.7\% = 0.007$ $r = 1 + 0.007 = 1.007$
b after 74 months

4 1 € 12 000 **2** A_6 = € 17 919.50
3 $A_{3.25}$ is the value after 2 years 3 months **4** 8.64 years
5

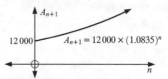

$A_{n+1} = 12\,000 \times (1.0835)^n$

EXERCISE 4H.3

1 a 17.3 years **b** 92.2 years **c** 115 years **2** 8.05 sec
3 a 50.7 min **b** 152 min
4 a 25 years **b** 141 years **c** 166 years
5 a 10 000 years **b** 49 800 years
6 166 seconds **7** 11.6 seconds

REVIEW SET 4A

1 a 3 **b** 8 **c** -2 **d** $\frac{1}{2}$ **e** 0 **f** 1 **g** $\frac{1}{4}$ **h** -1 **i** $\frac{1}{3}$ **j** $\frac{1}{2}$
2 a $\frac{1}{2}$ **b** $-\frac{1}{3}$ **c** $a + b + 1$
3 a $x = \frac{1}{8}$ **b** $x \approx 82.7$ **c** $x \approx 0.0316$
4 a $\log P = \log 3 + x \log b$ **b** $\log m = 3 \log n - 2 \log p$
5 a $k \approx 3.25 \times 2^x$ **b** $Q = P^3 R$ **c** $A = \dfrac{B^5}{400}$
6 a $x \approx 1.209$ **b** $x \approx 1.822$
7 a 2500 g
b 3290 years
c 42.3%
d

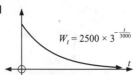

$W_t = 2500 \times 3^{-\frac{t}{3000}}$

8 $x \approx 2.32$
9 $x = 2$ **10** $a = \dfrac{\ln 25}{\ln 2}$

REVIEW SET 4B

1 a $\frac{3}{2}$ **b** $\frac{2}{3}$ **c** $a + b$ **2 a** $x = 1000$ **b** $x \approx 4.70$ **c** $x \approx 6.28$
3 a $\log 144$ **b** $\log_2\left(\frac{16}{9}\right)$ **c** $\log_4 80$
4 a $T = \dfrac{x^2}{y}$ **b** $K = n\sqrt{t}$
5 a $x \approx 5.19$ **b** $x \approx 4.29$ **c** $x \approx -0.839$
6 a $2A + 2B$ **b** $A + 3B$ **c** $3A + \frac{1}{2}B$ **d** $4B - 2A$ **e** $3A - 2B$
7 a $x \in]-2, \infty\,[$, $y \in \mathbb{R}$ **e**
b VA is $x = -2$,
x-intercept is 7,
y-intercept is -1.37
c

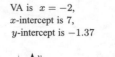

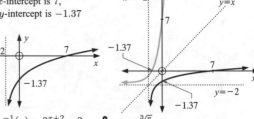

d $g^{-1}(x) = 3^{x+2} - 2$ **8** $a = \sqrt[3]{5}$
9 a $y = -2x + \log_5 3$ **b** $M = 3(5^{-2x})$ **c** $x = \frac{1}{2}\log_5 3 - 1$
10 $x = \frac{1}{2}$, $y = 3$ **11** $x = \pm 3$

REVIEW SET 4C

1 a

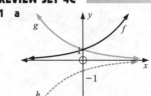

b i g is the reflection
of f in the y-axis
ii h is the reflection
of g in the x-axis

2

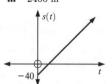

3 a i -40 m **ii** 585 m
  iii 2400 m
  b

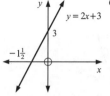

4 a 5 **b** $\frac{1}{2}$ **c** -1 **5 a** $2x$ **b** $2+x$ **c** $1-x$
6 a $\ln 24$ **b** $\ln 3$ **c** $\ln 4$ **d** $\ln 125$
7 a $5\ln 2$ **b** $3\ln 5$ **c** $6\ln 3$
8 a $x \approx 5.99$ **b** $x \approx 0.699$ **c** $x \approx 6.80$ **d** $x \approx 1.10$ or 1.39
9 $x = -2 + \log_2 5$

REVIEW SET 4D

1

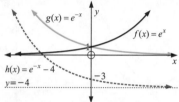

Each function has domain $\{x \mid x \in \mathbb{R}\}$
Range of f is $\{y \mid y > 0\}$, Range of g is $\{y \mid y > 0\}$
Range of h is $\{y \mid y > -4\}$

2

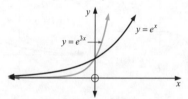

3 a $\frac{3}{2}$ **b** -3 **c** $-\frac{3}{2}$ **4 a** $\approx e^{3.00}$ **b** $\approx e^{8.01}$ **c** $\approx e^{-2.59}$
5 a $\ln 144$ **b** $\ln(\frac{3}{2})$ **c** $\ln(\frac{25}{e})$ **d** $\ln 3$
6 a $P = TQ^{1.5}$ **b** $M = \dfrac{e^{1.2}}{\sqrt{N}}$
7 a $g^{-1}(x)$
  $= \ln\left(\dfrac{x+5}{2}\right)$
  b

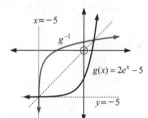

  c domain of g is $\{x \mid x \in \mathbb{R}\}$, range is $\{y \mid y > -5\}$
    domain of g^{-1} is $\{x \mid x > -5\}$, range is $\{y \mid y \in \mathbb{R}\}$
8 a 13.9 weeks **b** 41.6 weeks **c** 138 weeks
9 a $f(x) = \ln\left(\dfrac{x+4}{x}\right)$, $a = 4$
  b $f^{-1}(x) = \dfrac{4}{e^x - 1}$, $0 < x < \ln 2$

EXERCISE 5A

1 a $2x$ **b** $x+2$ **c** $\dfrac{x}{2}$ **d** $2x+3$
2 a $64x^3$ **b** $4x^3$ **c** $x^3 + 3x^2 + 3x + 1$
  d $2x^3 + 6x^2 + 6x - 1$
3 a 4^x **b** $2^{-x} + 1$ **c** $2^{x-2} + 3$ **d** $2^{x+1} + 3$
4 a $-\dfrac{1}{x}$ **b** $\dfrac{2}{x}$ **c** $\dfrac{2+3x}{x}$ **d** $\dfrac{2x+1}{x-1}$

5 a

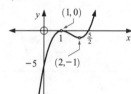

  b i $-1\frac{1}{2}$ **ii** 3
  iii 2

6 a

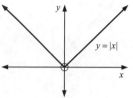

  b x-int's are -1 and 5
    y-int is -5

7 a, b

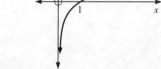

8

9

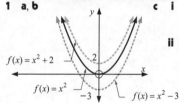

When $x = 0$,
$y = 2^0 = 1$ ✓
$2^x > 0$ for all x as
the graph is always
above the y-axis. ✓

10

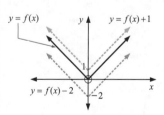

EXERCISE 5B.1

1 a, b

  c i If $b > 0$, the function
    is translated vertically
    upwards through b units.
  ii If $b < 0$, the function
    is translated vertically
    downwards $|b|$ units.

2 a

  b

  c

  d

3 a

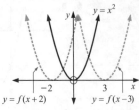

b i If $a > 0$, the graph is translated a units right.
ii If $a < 0$, the graph is translated $|a|$ units left.

4 a

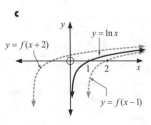

b

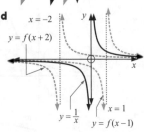

c

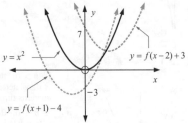

d

$y = f(x-a)$ is a horizontal translation of $y = f(x)$ through $\begin{pmatrix} a \\ 0 \end{pmatrix}$.

5 a

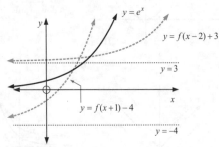

b

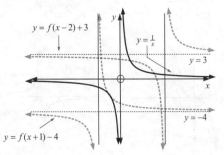

c

6 A translation of $\begin{pmatrix} 2 \\ -3 \end{pmatrix}$.

a

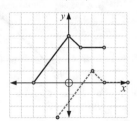

b

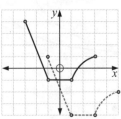

7 a i $(3, 2)$ **ii** $(0, 11)$ **iii** $(5, 6)$
  b i $(-2, 4)$ **ii** $(-5, 25)$ **iii** $(-1\frac{1}{2}, 2\frac{1}{4})$

EXERCISE 5B.2

1 a

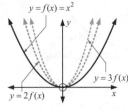

b

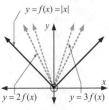

c

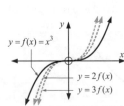

d

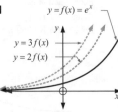

e

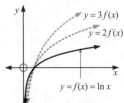

f

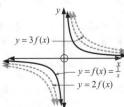

2 a

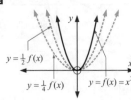

b

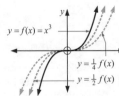

c

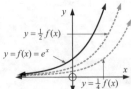

3 p affects the vertical stretching or compressing of the graph of
$y = f(x)$ by a factor of p. If $p > 1$ stretching occurs. If
$0 < p < 1$ compression occurs.

4 a
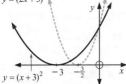

b
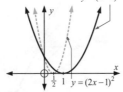

c $y = (2x+3)^2$
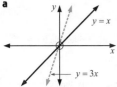

c
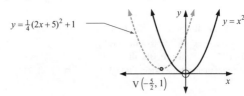
$y = \frac{1}{4}(2x+5)^2 + 1$
$V\left(-\frac{5}{2}, 1\right)$

9 a i $\left(\frac{3}{2}, -15\right)$ **ii** $\left(\frac{1}{2}, 6\right)$ **iii** $(-1, 3)$
  b i $\left(4, \frac{1}{3}\right)$ **ii** $\left(-6, \frac{2}{3}\right)$ **iii** $(-14, 1)$

10 a $f(x)$ is translated horizontally 1 unit left, then horizontally stretched by a factor of 2, then vertically stretched by a factor of 2, then translated 3 units upwards.

  b i $(0, -3)$ **ii** $(2, 5)$ **iii** $(-4, -1)$
  c i $(0, -4)$ **ii** $\left(\frac{3}{2}, -2\right)$ **iii** $\left(\frac{7}{2}, -\frac{3}{2}\right)$

EXERCISE 5B.3

1 a
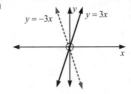

b
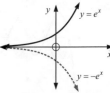

c
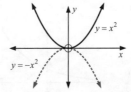

d
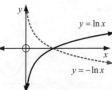

e
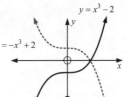

f
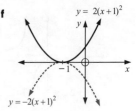

5 a
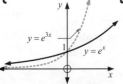

b
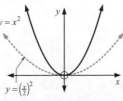

c
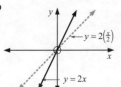

6 a
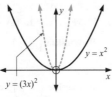

b
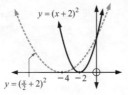

c

7 k affects the horizontal compressing of $y = f(x)$ by a factor of k.
  If $k > 1$ it moves closer to the y-axis.
  If $0 < k < 1$ it moves further from the y-axis.

8 a
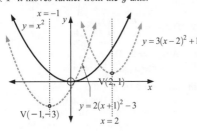

b
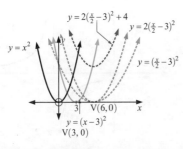

2 $y = -f(x)$ is the reflection of $y = f(x)$ in the x-axis.

3 a i $f(-x) = -2x + 1$ **ii** $f(-x) = x^2 - 2x + 1$
   iii $f(-x) = |-x - 3|$
  b i
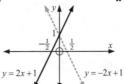
  ii
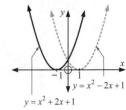

  iii
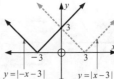

4 $y = f(-x)$ is the reflection of $y = f(x)$ in the y-axis.

5 a i (3, 0) **ii** (2, 1) **iii** (−3, −2)
   b i (7, 1) **ii** (−5, 0) **iii** (−3, 2)

6 a i (−2, −1) **ii** (0, 3) **iii** (1, 2)
   b i (−5, −4) **ii** (0, 3) **iii** (−2, 3)

7 a A rotation about the origin through 180°. **b** (−3, 7)
   c (5, 1)

EXERCISE 5B.4

1 a
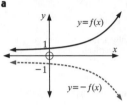

   b
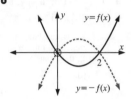

   c
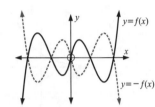

2 a
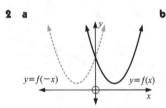

   b
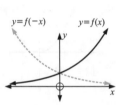

   c
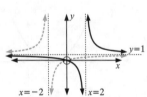

3 a A **b** B **c** D **d** C

4
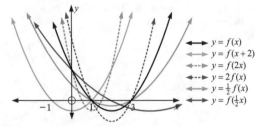

$y = f(x)$
$y = f(x+2)$
$y = f(2x)$
$y = 2f(x)$
$y = \frac{1}{2}f(x)$
$y = f(\frac{1}{2}x)$

5
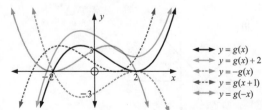

$y = g(x)$
$y = g(x) + 2$
$y = -g(x)$
$y = g(x+1)$
$y = g(-x)$

6
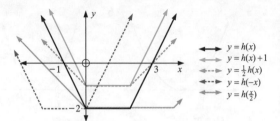

$y = h(x)$
$y = h(x) + 1$
$y = \frac{1}{2}h(x)$
$y = h(-x)$
$y = h(\frac{x}{2})$

EXERCISE 5C

1 a i $y = \dfrac{1}{2x}$ **ii** $y = \dfrac{3}{x}$ **iii** $y = \dfrac{1}{x+3}$

     iv $y = \dfrac{1}{x} + 4$ **v** $y = \dfrac{3}{2(x+3)} + 4$

   b Domain is $\{x \mid x \in \mathbb{R}, \ x \neq -3\}$
      Range is $\{y \mid y \in \mathbb{R}, \ y \neq 4\}$

2 a i VA is $x = 1$, HA is $y = 2$

     ii Translate $\begin{pmatrix} -1 \\ -2 \end{pmatrix}$, then vertically stretch, factor $\frac{1}{6}$.

   b i VA is $x = -1$, HA is $y = 3$

     ii Translate $\begin{pmatrix} 1 \\ -3 \end{pmatrix}$, reflect in the x-axis, then vertically stretch, factor $\frac{1}{5}$.

   c i VA is $x = 2$, HA is $y = -2$

     ii Translate $\begin{pmatrix} -2 \\ 2 \end{pmatrix}$, reflect in the x-axis, then vertically stretch, factor $\frac{1}{5}$.

3 a i VA is $x = -1$, HA is $y = 2$
     ii x-intercept is $-\frac{3}{2}$, y-intercept is 3

     iii as $x \to -1$ (from left), $y \to -\infty$
        as $x \to -1$ (from right), $y \to \infty$
        as $x \to -\infty$, $y \to 2$ (from below)
        as $x \to \infty$, $y \to 2$ (from above)

     iv
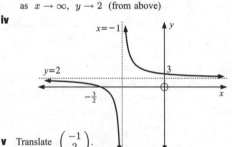

     v Translate $\begin{pmatrix} -1 \\ 2 \end{pmatrix}$.

   b i VA is $x = 2$, HA is $y = 0$
     ii no x-intercept, y-intercept is $-1\frac{1}{2}$

     iii as $x \to 2$ (from left), $y \to -\infty$
        as $x \to 2$ (from right), $y \to \infty$
        as $x \to \infty$, $y \to 0$ (from above)
        as $x \to -\infty$, $y \to 0$ (from below)

     iv
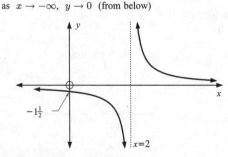

v Vertically stretch with factor 3, then translate $\begin{pmatrix} 2 \\ 0 \end{pmatrix}$.

c i VA is $x = 3$, HA is $y = -2$

ii x-intercept is $\frac{1}{2}$, y-intercept is $-\frac{1}{3}$

iii as $x \to 3$ (from left), $y \to \infty$
as $x \to 3$ (from right), $y \to -\infty$
as $x \to -\infty$, $y \to -2$ (from above)
as $x \to \infty$, $y \to -2$ (from below)

iv

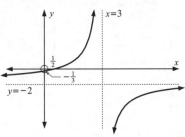

v Vertically stretch, factor 5, reflect in x-axis, then translate $\begin{pmatrix} 3 \\ -2 \end{pmatrix}$.

d i VA is $x = -\frac{1}{2}$, HA is $y = 2\frac{1}{2}$

ii x-intercept is $\frac{1}{5}$, y-intercept is -1

iii as $x \to -\frac{1}{2}$ (from left), $y \to \infty$
as $x \to -\frac{1}{2}$ (from right), $y \to -\infty$
as $x \to \infty$, $y \to 2\frac{1}{2}$ (from below)
as $x \to -\infty$, $y \to 2\frac{1}{2}$ (from above)

iv

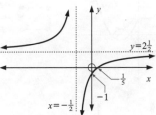

v Vertically stretch, factor $\frac{7}{4}$, reflect in x-axis, then translate $\begin{pmatrix} -\frac{1}{2} \\ \frac{5}{2} \end{pmatrix}$.

4 a 70 weeds/ha **b** 30 weeds/ha **c** 3 days

d

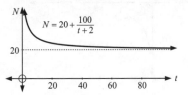

e No, the number of weeds/ha will approach 20 (from above).

EXERCISE 5D.1

1 a

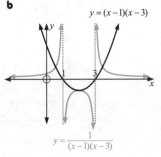

2 a invariant points are $(-1, -1)$ and $(1, -1)$
b invariant points are $(0.586, 1)$, $(2, -1)$ and $(3.414, 1)$

EXERCISE 5D.2

1 a

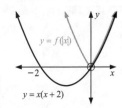

$y = x(x + 2)$

b

$y = x(x + 2)$

2 a

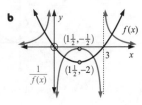

b

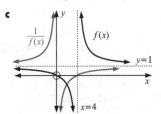

c

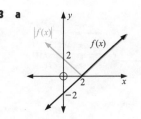

3 a

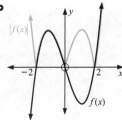

b

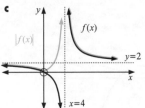

c

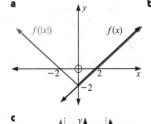

4 a

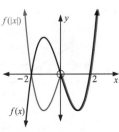

b

c

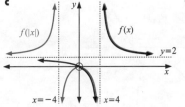

5 a $(3, 0)$ **b** $(5, 2)$ **c** $(0, 7)$ **d** $(2, 2)$

6 a i $(0, 3)$ **ii** $(1, 3)$ and $(-1, 3)$ **iii** $(7, -4)$ and $(-7, -4)$
   b i $(0, 3)$ **ii** $(1, 3)$ **iii** $(10, -8)$

REVIEW SET 5A

1 a 3 **b** 8 **c** $4x^2 - 4x$ **d** $x^2 + 2x$ **e** $3x^2 - 6x - 2$

2 a -15 **b** 5 **c** $-x^2 + x + 5$ **d** $5 - \frac{1}{2}x - \frac{1}{4}x^2$
   e $-x^2 - 3x + 5$

3

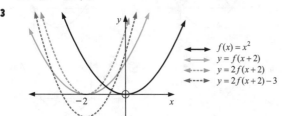

4 $g(x) = 3x^3 - 11x^2 + 14x - 6$

5 a

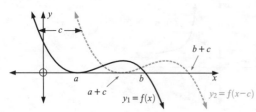

b i 1 and -3 **ii** -3
c $V(-1, -4)$

6 a

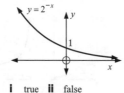

b i true **ii** false **iii** false **iv** true

7

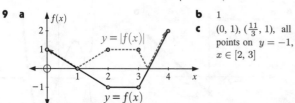

8

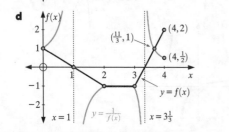

9 a

b 1
c $(0, 1)$, $(\frac{11}{3}, 1)$, all points on $y = -1$, $x \in [2, 3]$

d

10 a $F(x) = 4x - 1$
   b i $(1, 3) \to (1, 6) \to (\frac{1}{2}, 6) \to (1, 6) \to (1, 3)$
   ii $(0, 2) \to (\frac{1}{2}, 1)$ and $(-1, 1) \to (0, -1)$
   iii $F(\frac{1}{2}) = 1$ and $F(0) = -1$

11 $g(x) = -x^2 - 6x - 7$

REVIEW SET 5B

1 a -1 **b** $\dfrac{2}{x}$ **c** $\dfrac{8}{x}$ **d** $\dfrac{10 - 3x}{x + 2}$

2 a

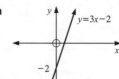

b i $\frac{2}{3}$ **ii** -2 **iii** 3
c i -1.1 **ii** 0.9

3 $x \geqslant a$

4 a, b

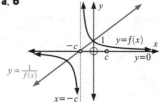

5

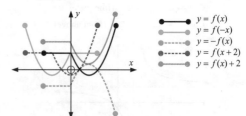

6 a

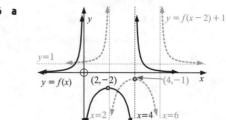

b

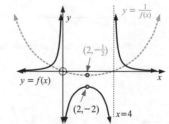

c

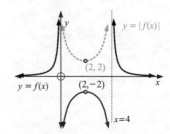

7 a $f(x) = \dfrac{2x-5}{2x-2}$ **b**

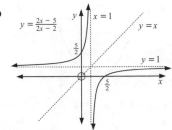

domain of $f(x)$ is $\{x \mid x \neq 1\}$
range of $f(x)$ is $\{y \mid y \neq 1\}$

c Yes, since it is a one-to-one function (passes both the vertical and horizontal line tests).

d Yes, since $f^{-1}(x) = f(x) = \dfrac{2x-5}{2x-2}$. Also, the graph of $f(x)$ is symmetrical about the line $y = x$.

8 $y = \dfrac{2x-3}{3x+5} = \dfrac{2}{3} - \dfrac{\frac{19}{9}}{\left(x+\frac{5}{3}\right)}$ HA is $y = \frac{2}{3}$,
VA is $x = -\frac{5}{3}$,

x-int at $x = \frac{3}{2}$, y-int at $y = -\frac{3}{5}$

as $x \to +\infty$, $y \to \frac{2}{3}$ (from below)
as $x \to -\infty$, $y \to \frac{2}{3}$ (from above)
as $x \to -\frac{5}{3}$ (from the left), $y \to +\infty$
as $x \to -\frac{5}{3}$ (from the right), $y \to -\infty$

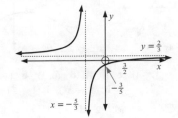

9 $y = \dfrac{-2x}{x-3}$

10 a i $y = 2^{x-1} - 2$
   ii

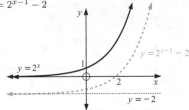

iii For $y = 2^x$, HA is $y = 0$, no VA
For $y = 2^{x-1} - 2$, HA is $y = -2$, no VA

iv For $y = 2^x$,
domain is $\{x \mid x \in \mathbb{R}\}$, range is $\{y \mid y > 0\}$
For $y = 2^{x-1} - 2$,
domain is $\{x \mid x \in \mathbb{R}\}$, range is $\{y \mid y > -2\}$

b i $y = \log_4(x-1) - 2$
   ii

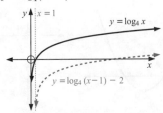

iii For $y = \log_4 x$, VA is $x = 0$, no HA
For $y = \log_4(x-1) - 2$, VA is $x = 1$, no HA

iv For $y = \log_4 x$,
domain is $\{x \mid x > 0\}$, range is $\{y \in \mathbb{R}\}$
For $y = \log_4(x-1) - 2$,
domain is $\{x \mid x > 1\}$, range is $\{y \in \mathbb{R}\}$

11 a, d

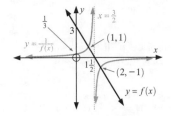

b (1, 1) and (2, −1)   **c** $x = 1\frac{1}{2}, \frac{1}{3}$
e

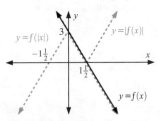

EXERCISE 6A.1

1 a $x = 0, -\frac{7}{4}$ **b** $x = 0, -\frac{1}{3}$ **c** $x = 0, \frac{7}{3}$ **d** $x = 0, \frac{11}{2}$
  e $x = 0, \frac{8}{3}$ **f** $x = 0, \frac{3}{2}$ **g** $x = 3, 2$ **h** $x = 4, -2$
  i $x = 3, 7$ **j** $x = 3$ **k** $x = -4, 3$ **l** $x = -11, 3$

2 a $x = \frac{2}{3}$ **b** $x = -\frac{1}{2}, 7$ **c** $x = -\frac{2}{3}, 6$ **d** $x = \frac{1}{3}, -2$
  e $x = \frac{3}{2}, 1$ **f** $x = -\frac{3}{2}, 2$ **g** $x = -\frac{2}{3}, 4$ **h** $x = \frac{1}{2}, -\frac{3}{2}$
  i $x = -\frac{1}{4}, 3$ **j** $x = -\frac{3}{4}, \frac{5}{3}$ **k** $x = \frac{1}{7}, -1$ **l** $x = -2, \frac{28}{15}$

3 a $x = 2, 5$ **b** $x = -3, 2$ **c** $x = 0, -\frac{3}{2}$ **d** $x = 1, 2$
  e $x = \frac{1}{2}, -1$ **f** $x = 3$

EXERCISE 6A.2

1 a $x = -5 \pm \sqrt{2}$ **b** no real solns. **c** $x = 4 \pm 2\sqrt{2}$
  d $x = 8 \pm \sqrt{7}$ **e** $x = -3 \pm \sqrt{5}$ **f** $x = 2 \pm \sqrt{6}$
  g $x = -1 \pm \sqrt{10}$ **h** $x = -\frac{1}{2} \pm \frac{1}{2}\sqrt{3}$ **i** $x = \frac{1}{3} \pm \frac{\sqrt{7}}{3}$

2 a $x = 2 \pm \sqrt{3}$ **b** $x = -3 \pm \sqrt{7}$ **c** $x = 7 \pm \sqrt{3}$
  d $x = 2 \pm \sqrt{7}$ **e** $x = -3 \pm \sqrt{2}$ **f** $x = 1 \pm \sqrt{7}$
  g $x = -3 \pm \sqrt{11}$ **h** $x = 4 \pm \sqrt{6}$ **i** no real solns.

3 a $x = -1 \pm \frac{1}{\sqrt{2}}$ **b** $x = \frac{5}{2} \pm \frac{\sqrt{19}}{2}$ **c** $x = -2 \pm \sqrt{\frac{7}{3}}$
  d $x = 1 \pm \sqrt{\frac{7}{3}}$ **e** $x = \frac{3}{2} \pm \sqrt{\frac{37}{20}}$ **f** $x = -\frac{1}{2} \pm \frac{\sqrt{6}}{2}$

EXERCISE 6A.3

1 a $x = 2 \pm \sqrt{7}$ **b** $x = -3 \pm \sqrt{2}$ **c** $x = 2 \pm \sqrt{3}$
  d $x = -2 \pm \sqrt{5}$ **e** $x = 2 \pm \sqrt{2}$ **f** $x = \frac{1}{2} \pm \frac{1}{2}\sqrt{7}$
  g $x = \sqrt{2}$ **h** $x = -\frac{4}{9} \pm \frac{\sqrt{7}}{9}$ **i** $x = -\frac{7}{4} \pm \frac{\sqrt{97}}{4}$

2 a $x = -2 \pm 2\sqrt{2}$ **b** $x = -\frac{5}{8} \pm \frac{\sqrt{57}}{8}$ **c** $x = \frac{5}{2} \pm \frac{\sqrt{13}}{2}$
  d $x = \frac{1}{2} \pm \frac{1}{2}\sqrt{7}$ **e** $x = \frac{1}{2} \pm \frac{\sqrt{5}}{2}$ **f** $x = \frac{3}{4} \pm \frac{\sqrt{17}}{4}$

EXERCISE 6B

1 a 2 real distinct roots **b** a repeated root **c** 2 real distinct roots
  d 2 real distinct roots **e** no real roots **f** a repeated root

2 a, c, d, f

3 **a** $\Delta = 16 - 4m$

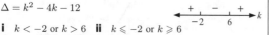

   i $m = 4$ **ii** $m < 4$ **iii** $m > 4$

b $\Delta = 9 - 8m$

   i $m = \frac{9}{8}$ **ii** $m < \frac{9}{8}$ **iii** $m > \frac{9}{8}$

c $\Delta = 9 - 4m$

   i $m = \frac{9}{4}$ **ii** $m < \frac{9}{4}$ **iii** $m > \frac{9}{4}$

4 **a** $\Delta = k^2 + 8k$

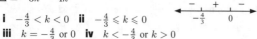

   i $k < -8$ or $k > 0$ **ii** $k \leqslant -8$ or $k \geqslant 0$

   iii $k = -8$ or 0 **iv** $-8 < k < 0$

b $\Delta = 4 - 4k^2$

   i $-1 < k < 1$ **ii** $-1 \leqslant k \leqslant 1$

   iii $k = \pm 1$ **iv** $k < -1$ or $k > 1$

c $\Delta = k^2 + 4k - 12$

   i $k < -6$ or $k > 2$ **ii** $k \leqslant -6$ or $k \geqslant 2$

   iii $k = -6$ or 2 **iv** $-6 < k < 2$

d $\Delta = k^2 - 4k - 12$

   i $k < -2$ or $k > 6$ **ii** $k \leqslant -2$ or $k \geqslant 6$

   iii $k = 6$ or -2 **iv** $-2 < k < 6$

e $\Delta = 9k^2 - 14k - 39$

   i $k < -\frac{13}{9}$ or $k > 3$ **ii** $k \leqslant -\frac{13}{9}$ or $k \geqslant 3$

   iii $k = -\frac{13}{9}$ or 3 **iv** $-\frac{13}{9} < k < 3$

f $\Delta = -3k^2 - 4k$

   i $-\frac{4}{3} < k < 0$ **ii** $-\frac{4}{3} \leqslant k \leqslant 0$

   iii $k = -\frac{4}{3}$ or 0 **iv** $k < -\frac{4}{3}$ or $k > 0$

EXERCISE 6C

1 **a** sum $= \frac{2}{3}$, product $= \frac{7}{3}$ **b** sum $= -11$, product $= -13$

   c sum $= \frac{6}{5}$, product $= -\frac{14}{5}$

2 $k = -\frac{3}{5}$. roots are -1 and $\frac{1}{3}$

3 **a** $3\alpha = \frac{6}{a}$, $2\alpha^2 = \frac{a-2}{a}$

   b $a = 4$, roots are $\frac{1}{2}$ and 1 or $a = -2$, roots are -1 and -2

4 $k = 4$, roots are $-\frac{1}{2}$ and $\frac{3}{2}$ or $k = 16$, roots are $-\frac{5}{4}$ and $\frac{3}{4}$

5 $7x^2 - 48x + 64 = 0$ **6** $a(8x^2 - 70x + 147) = 0$, $a \neq 0$

7 $-8 + \sqrt{60} < k < 0$

EXERCISE 6D.1

1 **a** $y = (x - 4)(x + 2)$ **b** $y = -(x - 4)(x + 2)$

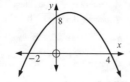

   c $y = 2(x + 3)(x + 5)$ **d** $y = -3x(x + 4)$

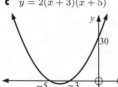
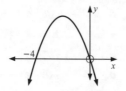

e $y = 2(x + 3)^2$ **f** $y = -\frac{1}{4}(x + 2)^2$

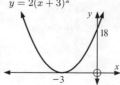
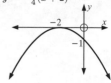

2 **a** $x = 1$ **b** $x = 1$ **c** $x = -4$ **d** $x = -2$ **e** $x = -3$ **f** $x = -2$

3 **a**   **b**

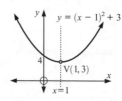

   c   **d**

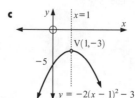
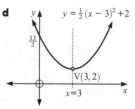

   e   **f**

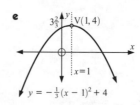
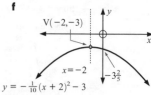

4 **a** $(2, -2)$ **b** $(-1, -4)$ **c** $(0, 4)$ **d** $(0, 1)$ **e** $(-2, -15)$

   f $(-2, -5)$ **g** $(-\frac{3}{2}, -\frac{11}{2})$ **h** $(\frac{5}{2}, -\frac{19}{2})$ **i** $(1, -\frac{9}{2})$

5 **a** ± 3 **b** $\pm\sqrt{3}$ **c** -5 and -2 **d** 3 and -4 **e** 0 and 4

   f -4 and -2 **g** -1 (touching) **h** 3 (touching)

   i $2 \pm \sqrt{3}$ **j** $-2 \pm \sqrt{7}$ **k** $3 \pm \sqrt{11}$ **l** $-4 \pm \sqrt{5}$

6 **a** **i** $x = 1$ **b** **i** $x = -2$

   ii $(1, 4)$ **ii** $(-2, -5)$

   iii no x-intercept,   **iii** x-int. $-2 \pm \sqrt{5}$,

       y-intercept 5 y-intercept -1

   iv   **iv**

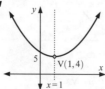
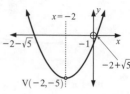

   c **i** $x = \frac{5}{4}$ **d** **i** $x = \frac{3}{2}$

   ii $(\frac{5}{4}, -\frac{9}{8})$ **ii** $(\frac{3}{2}, \frac{1}{4})$

   iii x-intercepts $\frac{1}{2}$, 2,   **iii** x-intercepts 1, 2,

       y-intercept 2 y-intercept -2

   iv   **iv**

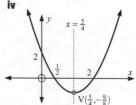
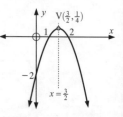

e i $x = \frac{2}{3}$

ii $(\frac{2}{3}, \frac{1}{3})$

iii x-intercepts $\frac{1}{3}$, 1, y-intercept -1

iv

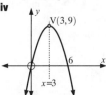

f i $x = \frac{1}{4}$

ii $(\frac{1}{4}, \frac{9}{8})$

iii x-intercepts $-\frac{1}{2}$, 1, y-intercept 1

iv
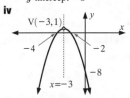

g i $x = 3$

ii $(3, 9)$

iii x-intercepts 0, 6, y-intercept 0

iv
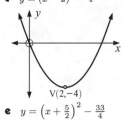

h i $x = -3$

ii $(-3, 1)$

iii x-int. -2, -4, y-intercept -8

iv
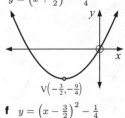

i i $x = 4$

ii $(4, 5)$

iii x-int. $4 \pm 2\sqrt{5}$, y-intercept 1

iv
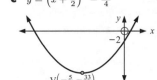

EXERCISE 6D.2

1 a $y = (x - 1)^2 + 2$
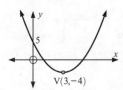

b $y = (x + 2)^2 - 6$
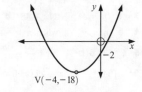

c $y = (x - 2)^2 - 4$

d $y = \left(x + \frac{3}{2}\right)^2 - \frac{9}{4}$

e $y = \left(x + \frac{5}{2}\right)^2 - \frac{33}{4}$

f $y = \left(x - \frac{3}{2}\right)^2 - \frac{1}{4}$

g $y = (x - 3)^2 - 4$

h $y = (x + 4)^2 - 18$

i $y = \left(x - \frac{5}{2}\right)^2 - 5\frac{1}{4}$
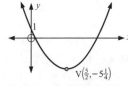
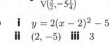

2 a i $y = 2(x + 1)^2 + 3$

ii $(-1, 3)$ **iii** 5

iv
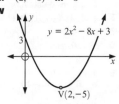

b i $y = 2(x - 2)^2 - 5$

ii $(2, -5)$ **iii** 3

iv

c i $y = 2\left(x - \frac{3}{2}\right)^2 - \frac{7}{2}$

ii $(\frac{3}{2}, -\frac{7}{2})$ **iii** 1

iv
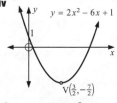

d i $y = 3(x - 1)^2 + 2$

ii $(1, 2)$ **iii** 5

iv
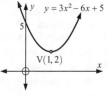

e i $y = -(x - 2)^2 + 6$

ii $(2, 6)$ **iii** 2

iv
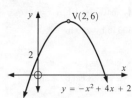

f i $y = -2\left(x + \frac{5}{4}\right)^2 + \frac{49}{8}$

ii $(-\frac{5}{4}, \frac{49}{8})$ **iii** 3

iv
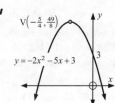

3 a $y = (x - 2)^2 + 3$ **b** $y = (x + 3)^2 - 6$

c $y = -(x - 2)^2 + 9$ **d** $y = 2\left(x + \frac{3}{2}\right)^2 - \frac{17}{2}$

e $y = -2\left(x + \frac{5}{2}\right)^2 + \frac{27}{2}$ **f** $y = 3\left(x - \frac{3}{2}\right)^2 - \frac{47}{4}$

EXERCISE 6D.3

1 a cuts x-axis twice **b** touches x-axis **c** cuts x-axis twice
d cuts x-axis twice **e** cuts x-axis twice **f** touches x-axis

2 a $a = 1$ which is > 0 and $\Delta = -15$ which is < 0
b $a = -1$ which is < 0 and $\Delta = -8$ which is < 0
c $a = 2$ which is > 0 and $\Delta = -40$ which is < 0
d $a = -2$ which is < 0 and $\Delta = -23$ which is < 0

3 $a = 3$ which is > 0 and $\Delta = k^2 + 12$ which is
always > 0 {as $k^2 > 0$ for all k}

4 $a = 2$ which is > 0 and $\Delta = k^2 - 16$ ∴ positive
definite when $k^2 < 16$ i.e., $-4 < k < 4$

EXERCISE 6E

1 a $y = 2(x - 1)(x - 2)$ **b** $y = 2(x - 2)^2$
c $y = (x - 1)(x - 3)$ **d** $y = -(x - 3)(x + 1)$
e $y = -3(x - 1)^2$ **f** $y = -2(x + 2)(x - 3)$

2 a $y = \frac{3}{2}(x - 2)(x - 4)$ **b** $y = -\frac{1}{2}(x + 4)(x - 2)$
c $y = -\frac{4}{3}(x + 3)^2$

3 a $y = 3x^2 - 18x + 15$ **b** $y = -4x^2 + 6x + 4$
c $y = -x^2 + 6x - 9$ **d** $y = 4x^2 + 16x + 16$
e $y = \frac{3}{2}x^2 - 6x + \frac{9}{2}$ **f** $y = -\frac{1}{3}x^2 + \frac{2}{3}x + 5$

4 a $y = -(x-2)^2 + 4$ **b** $y = 2(x-2)^2 - 1$
   c $y = -2(x-3)^2 + 8$ **d** $y = \frac{2}{3}(x-4)^2 - 6$
   e $y = -2(x-2)^2 + 3$ **f** $y = 2(x-\frac{1}{2})^2 - \frac{3}{2}$

EXERCISE 6F

1 a $(1, 7)$ and $(2, 8)$ **b** $(4, 5)$ and $(-3, -9)$
   c $(3, 0)$ (touching) **d** graphs do not meet
2 a $(0.59, 5.59)$ and $(3.41, 8.41)$ **b** $(3, -4)$ touching
   c graphs do not meet **d** $(-2.56, -18.81)$ and $(1.56, 1.81)$
3 a $(2, 4), (-1, 1)$ **b** $(1, 0), (-2, -3)$ **c** $(1, 4)$ **d** $(1, 4), (-4, -1)$
5 $c = -9$
6 $m = 0$ or -8
7 -1 or 11
8 a $c < -9$
   b E.g., $c = -10$

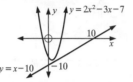

EXERCISE 6G

1 7 and -5 or -7 and 5 **2** 5 or $\frac{1}{5}$ **3** 14
4 18 and 20 or -18 and -20 **5** 15 and 17 or -15 and -17
6 15 sides **7** 3.48 cm **8 b** 6 cm by 6 cm by 7 cm
9 11.2 cm square **10** no **12** 221 ha **13** 2.03 m
14 52.1 km h^{-1} **15** 554 km h^{-1} **16** 61.8 km h^{-1} **17** 32
18 No, tunnel is only 3.79 m wide 4.8 m above ground level.
19 a $y = -\frac{1}{100}x^2 + 70$
   b supports are 21 m, 34 m, 45 m, 54 m, 61 m, 66 m, 69 m

EXERCISE 6H

1 a min. -1, when $x = 1$ **b** max. 8, when $x = -1$
   c max. $8\frac{1}{3}$, when $x = \frac{1}{3}$ **d** min. $-1\frac{1}{8}$, when $x = -\frac{1}{4}$
   e min. $4\frac{15}{16}$ when $x = \frac{1}{8}$ **f** max. $6\frac{1}{8}$, when $x = \frac{7}{4}$
2 40 refrigerators, \$4000 **4** 500 m by 250 m
5 c 100 m by 112.5 m
6 a $41\frac{2}{3}$ m by $41\frac{2}{3}$ m **b** 50 m by $31\frac{1}{4}$ m
7 b $3\frac{1}{8}$ units **8 a** $y = 6 - \frac{3}{4}x$ **b** 3 cm by 4 cm
9 125 **10** 40 **11** 157
12 $m = \dfrac{a_1b_1 + a_2b_2 + \cdots + a_nb_n}{a_1^2 + a_2^2 + \cdots + a_n^2}$
13 $f(x) = x^4 - 2(a^2 + b^2)x^2 + (a^2 - b^2)^2$,
   least value $= -4a^2b^2$

REVIEW SET 6A

1 a $-2, 1$ **b** $x = -\frac{1}{2}$ **2 a** $x = 2$ **b** $(2, -4)$
   c $(-\frac{1}{2}, \frac{9}{2})$ **c** -2
   d 4   **d**
   e

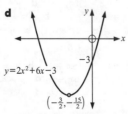

3 a $y = 2\left(x + \frac{3}{2}\right)^2 - \frac{15}{2}$ **d**
   b $(-\frac{3}{2}, -\frac{15}{2})$
   c -3

4 a $x = 15$ or -4 **b** $x = -\frac{5}{3}$ or 2 **c** $x = 0$ or 4
5 a $x = 5$ or 2 **b** $x = 3$ or 4 **c** $x = \frac{1}{2}$ or 3
6 $x = -\frac{7}{2} \pm \frac{\sqrt{65}}{2}$ **7 a** $x = \frac{7}{2} \pm \frac{\sqrt{37}}{2}$ **b** no real roots
8 a $c > -6$ **b** e.g., $c = -2$, $(-1, -5)$ and $(3, 7)$
9 $4x^2 + 3x - 2 = 0$

REVIEW SET 6B

1

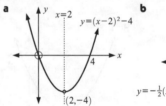

2 $x = \frac{4}{3}$, $V(\frac{4}{3}, 12\frac{1}{3})$
3 a no real solutions
   b two real distinct solutions

4 $a = -2$ which is < 0 $\therefore$ a max.
   max. $= 5$ when $x = 1$
5 $(4, 4)$ and $(-3, 18)$ **6** $k < -3\frac{1}{8}$ **7 b** 15 m by 30 m
8 $m = -5$ or 19 **9** $k = 3$, roots are $-\frac{1}{3}$ and 3

REVIEW SET 6C

1 a $x = -\frac{5}{2} \pm \frac{\sqrt{13}}{2}$ **b** $x = \frac{-11 \pm \sqrt{145}}{6}$
2 a $x = \frac{5}{2} \pm \frac{\sqrt{37}}{2}$ **b** $x = \frac{7}{4} \pm \frac{\sqrt{73}}{4}$
3 a $x \approx 0.586$ or 3.414 **b** $x \approx -0.186$ or 2.686
4 a two distinct real rational roots **b** a repeated root
5 a $m = \frac{9}{8}$ **b** $m < \frac{9}{8}$ **c** $m > \frac{9}{8}$ **6** 12.92 cm
7 17 cm **8** y-int $= \frac{1}{2}$ **9** $a < -9$, $-1 < a < 0$

REVIEW SET 6D

1 a

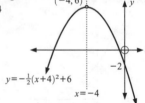

   b

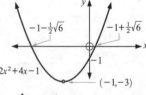

2 a $x = -1$ **d**
   b $(-1, -3)$
   c y-intercept -1,
       x-ints. $-1 \pm \frac{1}{2}\sqrt{6}$

3 a graph cuts x-axis twice **b** graph cuts x-axis twice
4 a neither **b** positive definite
5 a $y = 3(x-3)(x+3)$ **b** $y = -6(x-2)^2 + 25$
6 $\frac{6}{5}$ or $\frac{5}{6}$ **7** 13.48 cm by 13.48 cm **8** touch at $(-2, 9)$
10 $a(6x^2 - 10x - 25) = 0$, $a \neq 0$

REVIEW SET 6E

1 a $y = -6(x+3)(x-1)$ **b** $y = \frac{20}{9}(x-2)^2 - 20$
   c $y = -\frac{2}{7}(x-1)(x-7)$ **d** $y = \frac{2}{9}(x+3)^2$
2 $y = -4x^2 + 4x + 24$
3 a $y = 3x^2 - 24x + 48$ **b** $y = \frac{2}{5}x^2 + \frac{16}{5}x + \frac{37}{5}$
4 a min. $= 5\frac{2}{3}$ when $x = -\frac{2}{3}$ **b** max. $= 5\frac{1}{8}$ when $x = -\frac{5}{4}$
5 $k < 1$ **6 b** $A = x\left(\dfrac{600 - 8x}{9}\right)$ **c** $37\frac{1}{2}$ m by $33\frac{1}{3}$ m **d** 1250 m^2
8 $a(64x^2 - 135x - 27) = 0$, $a \neq 0$

EXERCISE 7A

1 **a** $3i$ **b** $8i$ **c** $\frac{1}{2}i$ **d** $i\sqrt{5}$ **e** $i\sqrt{8}$

2 **a** $(x+3)(x-3)$ **b** $(x+3i)(x-3i)$ **c** $(x+\sqrt{7})(x-\sqrt{7})$
d $(x+i\sqrt{7})(x-i\sqrt{7})$ **e** $(2x+1)(2x-1)$ **f** $(2x+i)(2x-i)$
g $(\sqrt{2}x+3)(\sqrt{2}x-3)$ **h** $(\sqrt{2}x+3i)(\sqrt{2}x-3i)$
i $x(x+1)(x-1)$ **j** $x(x+i)(x-i)$
k $(x+1)(x-1)(x+i)(x-i)$
l $(x+2)(x-2)(x+2i)(x-2i)$

3 **a** $x=\pm5$ **b** $x=\pm5i$ **c** $x=\pm\sqrt{5}$ **d** $x=\pm i\sqrt{5}$ **e** $x=\pm\frac{3}{2}$
f $x=\pm\frac{3}{2}i$ **g** $x=0,x=\pm2$ **h** $x=0,x=\pm2i$
i $x=0,x=\pm\sqrt{3}$ **j** $x=0,x=\pm i\sqrt{3}$ **k** $x=\pm1,x=\pm i$
l $x=\pm3,x=\pm3i$

4 **a** $x=5\pm2i$ **b** $x=-3\pm4i$ **c** $x=-7\pm i$
d $x=\frac{3}{2}\pm\frac{1}{2}i$ **e** $x=\sqrt{3}\pm i$ **f** $x=\frac{1}{4}\pm\frac{i\sqrt{7}}{4}$

5 **a** $x=\pm i\sqrt{3}$ or ±1 **b** $x=\pm\sqrt{3}$ or $\pm i\sqrt{2}$ **c** $x=\pm3i$ or ±2
d $x=\pm i\sqrt{7}$ or $\pm i\sqrt{2}$ **e** $x=\pm1$ **f** $x=\pm i$

EXERCISE 7B.1

1

z	$\mathcal{Re}(z)$	$\mathcal{Im}(z)$	z	$\mathcal{Re}(z)$	$\mathcal{Im}(z)$
$3+2i$	3	2	$-3+4i$	-3	4
$5-i$	5	-1	$-7-2i$	-7	-2
3	3	0	$-11i$	0	-11
0	0	0	$i\sqrt{3}$	0	$\sqrt{3}$

2 **a** $7-i$ **b** $10-4i$ **c** $-1+2i$ **d** $3-3i$
e $4-7i$ **f** $12+i$ **g** $3+4i$ **h** $21-20i$

3 **a** $-3+7i$ **b** $2i$ **c** $-2+2i$ **d** $-1+i$
e $-5-12i$ **f** $-5+i$ **g** $-6-4i$ **h** $-1-5i$

4 $i^0=1,\ i^1=i,\ i^2=-1,\ i^3=-i,\ i^4=1,\ i^5=i,\ i^6=-1,$
$i^7=-i,\ i^8=1,\ i^9=i,\ i^{-1}=-i,\ i^{-2}=-1,\ i^{-3}=i,$
$i^{-4}=1,\ i^{-5}=-i,\ i^{4n+3}=-i$

5 $(1+i)^4=-4,\ (1+i)^{101}=-2^{50}(1+i)$ **6** $a=3,b=-5$

7 **a** $-\frac{1}{10}-\frac{7}{10}i$ **b** $-\frac{1}{5}+\frac{2}{5}i$ **c** $\frac{7}{5}+\frac{1}{5}i$ **d** $\frac{3}{25}+\frac{4}{25}i$

8 **a** $-\frac{2}{5}+\frac{1}{5}i$ **b** $-\frac{1}{13}+\frac{8}{13}i$ **c** $-\frac{2}{5}+\frac{3}{5}i$

9 **a** -2 **b** -4 **c** 3 **d** 0

EXERCISE 7B.2

1 **a** $x=0,y=-2$ **b** $x=-2$ **c** $x=3,y=2$
d $x=-\frac{2}{13},y=-\frac{3}{13}$

2 **a** $x=0,y=0$ **b** $x=3,y=-2$ or $x=4,y=-\frac{3}{2}$
c $x=2,y=-5$ or $x=-\frac{5}{3},y=6$ **d** $x=-1,y=0$

3 $z=5-4i$ **4** $z=65-72i$ **5** $m=-\frac{1}{11},\ n=\frac{8}{11}$ **6** $z=i\sqrt{2}$

EXERCISE 7B.3

1 **a** $a(x^2-6x+10)=0\ \ a\neq0$
b $a(x^2-2x+10)=0,\ a\neq0$
c $a(x^2+4x+29),\ a\neq0$ **d** $a(x^2-2\sqrt{2}x+3)=0,a\neq0$
e $a(x^2-4x+1)=0,\ a\neq0$ **f** $a(3x^2+2x)=0,\ a\neq0$
g $a(x^2+2)=0,\ a\neq0$ **h** $a(x^2+12x+37)=0,\ a\neq0$

2 **a** $a=-6,\ b=10$ **b** $a=-2,\ b=-1$
c $a=-2,\ b=8$ or $a=0,\ b=0$

EXERCISE 7B.4

2 z^* **4** **a** $\left[\dfrac{ac+bd}{c^2+d^2}\right]+\left[\dfrac{bc-ad}{c^2+d^2}\right]i$

7 **a** $[a^2-b^2]+[2ab]i$ **c** $z^3=[a^3-3ab^2]+[3a^2b-b^3]i$

8 **a** $a=0$ or $(b=0,\ a\neq-1)$
b $a^2-b^2=1$ and neither a nor b is 0

EXERCISE 7B.5

1 **c** $(z_1z_2z_3z_4....z_n)^*=z_1^*\,z_2^*\,z_3^*....z_n^*$ **d** $(z^n)^*=(z^*)^n$

EXERCISE 7C.1

1 **a** $3x^2+6x+9$ **b** $5x^2+7x+9$ **c** $-7x^2-8x-9$
d $4x^4+13x^3+28x^2+27x+18$

2 **a** x^3+x^2-4x+7 **b** x^3-x^2-2x+3
c $3x^3+2x^2-11x+19$ **d** $2x^3-x^2-x+5$
e $x^5-x^4-x^3+8x^2-11x+10$
f $x^4-2x^3+5x^2-4x+4$

3 **a** $2x^3-3x^2+4x+3$ **b** $x^4+x^3-7x^2+7x-2$
c $x^3+6x^2+12x+8$ **d** $4x^4-4x^3+13x^2-6x+9$
e $16x^4-32x^3+24x^2-8x+1$
f $18x^4-87x^3+56x^2+20x-16$

4 **a** $6x^3-11x^2+18x-5$ **b** $8x^3+18x^2-x+10$
c $-2x^3+7x^2+13x+10$ **d** $2x^3-7x^2+4x+4$
e $2x^4-2x^3-9x^2+11x-2$
f $15x^4+x^3-x^2+7x-6$ **g** $x^4-2x^3+7x^2-6x+9$
h $4x^4+4x^3-15x^2-8x+16$ **i** $8x^3+60x^2+150x+125$
j $x^6+2x^5+x^4-4x^3-4x^2+4$

EXERCISE 7C.2

1 **a** quotient is x, remainder is -3
b quotient is $x-4$, remainder is -3
c quotient is $2x^2+10x+16$, remainder is 35

2 **a** $x+1+\dfrac{10}{x-4}$ **b** $x+1-\dfrac{14}{x+3}$ **c** $2x-3-\dfrac{4}{x-2}$
d x^2+x-2 **e** $x^2+4x+4+\dfrac{11}{3x-1}$
f $x^3-2x^2+\frac{5}{2}x-\frac{1}{4}+\dfrac{\frac{19}{4}}{2x+3}$

3 **a** $x+2+\dfrac{9}{x-2}$ **b** $2x+1-\dfrac{1}{x+1}$ **c** $3x-4+\dfrac{3}{x+2}$
d x^2+3x-2 **e** $2x^2-8x+31-\dfrac{124}{x+4}$
f $x^2+3x+6+\dfrac{7}{x-2}$

EXERCISE 7C.3

1 **a** quotient is $x+1$, remainder is $-x-4$
b quotient is 3, remainder is $-x+3$
c quotient is $3x$, remainder is $-2x-1$
d quotient is 0, remainder is $x-4$

2 **a** $1-\dfrac{2x}{x^2+x+1}$ **b** $x-\dfrac{2x}{x^2+2}$
c $x^2+x+3+\dfrac{3x-4}{x^2-x+1}$ **d** $2x+4+\dfrac{5x+2}{(x-1)^2}$
e $x^2-2x+3-\dfrac{4x+3}{(x+1)^2}$ **f** $x^2-3x+5+\dfrac{15-10x}{(x-1)(x+2)}$

3 quotient is x^2+2x+3, remainder is 7
4 quotient is x^2-3x+5, remainder is $15-10x$

EXERCISE 7D.1

1 **a** $4,-\frac{3}{2}$ **b** $-3\pm i$ **c** $3\pm\sqrt{3}$ **d** $0,\pm2$ **e** $0,\pm i\sqrt{2}$
f $\pm1,\pm i\sqrt{5}$

2 **a** $x=1,-\frac{2}{5}$ **b** $x=-\frac{1}{2},\pm i\sqrt{3}$ **c** $z=0,1\pm i$
d $x=0,\pm\sqrt{5}$ **e** $z=0,\pm i\sqrt{5}$ **f** $z=\pm i\sqrt{2},\pm\sqrt{5}$

3 **a** $(2x+3)(x-5)$ **b** $(z-3+i\sqrt{7})(z-3-i\sqrt{7})$
c $x(x+1+\sqrt{5})(x+1-\sqrt{5})$ **d** $z(3z-2)(2z+1)$
e $(z+1)(z-1)(z+\sqrt{5})(z-\sqrt{5})$
f $(z+i)(z-i)(z+\sqrt{2})(z-\sqrt{2})$

5 a $P(z) = a(z^2 - 4)(z - 3)$ $a \neq 0$
b $P(z) = a(z + 2)(z^2 + 1)$ $a \neq 0$
c $P(z) = a(z - 3)(z^2 + 2z + 2)$ $a \neq 0$
d $P(z) = a(z + 1)(z^2 + 4z + 2)$ $a \neq 0$

6 a $P(z) = a(z^2 - 1)(z^2 - 2)$ $a \neq 0$
b $P(z) = a(z - 2)(z + 1)(z^2 + 3)$ $a \neq 0$
c $P(z) = a(z^2 - 3)(z^2 - 2z + 2)$ $a \neq 0$
d $P(z) = a(z^2 - 4z - 1)(z^2 + 4z + 13)$ $a \neq 0$

EXERCISE 7D.2

1 a $a = 2$, $b = 5$, $c = 5$ **b** $a = 3$, $b = 4$, $c = 3$
2 a $a = 2$, $b = -2$ or $a = -2$, $b = 2$ **b** $a = 3$, $b = -1$
4 $a = -2$, $b = 2$, $x = 1 \pm i$ or $-1 \pm \sqrt{3}$

5 a $a = -1$, zeros are $\frac{3}{2}$, $\dfrac{-1 \pm i\sqrt{3}}{2}$

b $a = 6$, zeros are $-\frac{2}{3}$, $\dfrac{1 \pm i\sqrt{11}}{2}$

6 a $a = -3$, $b = 6$ zeros are $-\frac{1}{2}$, 2, $\pm 2i$
b $a = 1$, $b = -15$ zeros are -3, $\frac{1}{2}$, $1 \pm \sqrt{2}$

7 a $P(x) = (x + 3)^2(x - 3)$ or $P(x) = (x - 1)^2(x + 5)$
b If $m = -2$, zeros are -1 (repeated) and $\frac{2}{3}$.
   If $m = \frac{14}{243}$, zeros are $\frac{1}{9}$ (repeated) and $-\frac{14}{9}$.

EXERCISE 7D.3

1 a $P(x) = (x - 2)Q(x) + 7$, $P(x)$ divided by $x - 2$ leaves a remainder of 7.
b $P(-3) = -8$, $P(x)$ divided by $x + 3$ leaves a remainder of -8.
c $P(5) = 11$, $P(x) = (x - 5)Q(x) + 11$
2 a 1 **b** 1 **3 a** $a = 3$ **b** $a = 2$ **4** $a = -5$, $b = 6$
5 $a = -3$, $n = 4$ **6 a** -3 **b** 1 **7** $3z - 5$

EXERCISE 7D.4

1 a $k = -8$, $P(x) = (x + 2)(2x + 1)(x - 2)$
b $k = 2$, $P(x) = x(x - 3)(x + \sqrt{2})(x - \sqrt{2})$
2 $a = 7$, $b = -14$
3 a If $k = 1$, zeros are 3, $-1 \pm i$.
   If $k = -4$, zeros are ± 3, 1. **b** $m = -\frac{10}{7}$
4 a i $P(a) = 0$, $x - a$ is a factor **ii** $(x - a)(x^2 + ax + a^2)$
b i $P(-a) = 0$, $x + a$ is a factor **ii** $(x + a)(x^2 - ax + a^2)$
5 b $a = 2$

EXERCISE 7E.1

1 a cuts the x-axis at α **b** touches the x-axis at α
c cuts the x-axis at α with a change in shape
2 a $P(x) = 2(x + 1)(x - 2)(x - 3)$
b $P(x) = -2(x + 3)(2x + 1)(2x - 1)$
c $P(x) = \frac{1}{4}(x + 4)^2(x - 3)$ **d** $P(x) = \frac{1}{10}(x + 5)(x + 2)(x - 5)$
e $P(x) = \frac{1}{4}(x + 4)(x - 3)^2$
f $P(x) = -2(x + 3)(x + 2)(2x + 1)$
3 a $P(x) = (x - 3)(x - 1)(x + 2)$
b $P(x) = x(x + 2)(2x - 1)$ **c** $P(x) = (x - 1)^2(x + 2)$
d $P(x) = (3x + 2)^2(x - 4)$
4 a F **b** C **c** A **d** E **e** D **f** B
5 a $P(x) = 5(2x - 1)(x + 3)(x - 2)$
b $P(x) = -2(x + 2)^2(x - 1)$ **c** $P(x) = (x - 2)(2x^2 - 3x + 2)$

EXERCISE 7E.2

1 a $P(x) = 2(x + 1)^2(x - 1)^2$
b $P(x) = (x + 3)(x + 1)^2(3x - 2)$
c $P(x) = -2(x + 2)(x + 1)(x - 2)^2$
d $P(x) = -\frac{1}{3}(x + 3)(x + 1)(2x - 3)(x - 3)$
e $P(x) = \frac{1}{4}(x + 1)(x - 4)^3$ **f** $P(x) = x^2(x + 2)(x - 3)$
2 a C **b** F **c** A **d** E **e** B **f** D
3 a $P(x) = (x + 4)(2x - 1)(x - 2)^2$
b $P(x) = \frac{1}{4}(3x - 2)^2(x + 3)^2$
c $P(x) = 2(x - 2)(2x - 1)(x + 2)(2x + 1)$
d $P(x) = (x - 1)^2 \left(\frac{8}{3}x^2 + \frac{8}{3}x - 1\right)$

EXERCISE 7E.3

1 a -1, $2 \pm \sqrt{3}$ **b** 1, $1 \pm i$ **c** $\frac{7}{2}$, $-1 \pm 2i$ **d** $\frac{1}{2}$, $\pm i\sqrt{10}$
e $\pm\frac{1}{2}$, 3, -2 **f** 2, $1 \pm 3i$
2 a $x = -2$, $\pm i\sqrt{3}$ **b** $x = -2$, $-\frac{1}{2}$, 1
c $x = 2$ (treble root) **d** $x = -2$, $\frac{3}{2}$, 3
e $x = -3$, 2, $1 \pm \sqrt{2}$ **f** $x = -\frac{1}{2}$, 3, $2 \pm i$
3 a $(x - 1)(x - 1 + i)(x - 1 - i)$ **b** $(x + 3)(x + 2i)(x - 2i)$
c $(2x - 1)(x - 2 - \sqrt{3})(x - 2 + \sqrt{3})$
d $(x - 2)(x - 1 + 2i)(x - 1 - 2i)$
e $(x - 1)(2x - 3)(2x + 1)$
f $(x + 2)(3x - 2)(x - i\sqrt{3})(x + i\sqrt{3})$
g $(x + 1)(2x - 1)(x - 1 - i\sqrt{3})(x - 1 + i\sqrt{3})$
h $(2x + 5)(x + 2i)(x - 2i)$
4 a -3.273, -0.860, 2.133 **b** -2.518, -1.178, 2.696

EXERCISE 7F

1 $P(x) = a(2x + 1)(x^2 - 2x + 10)$ $a \neq 0$
2 $p(x) = 4x^3 - 20x^2 + 36x - 20$
3 $p = -3$, $q = 52$ other zeros are $2 + 3i$, -4
4 $a = -13$, $b = 34$ other zeros are $3 - i$, $-2 \pm \sqrt{3}$
5 $a = 3$, $P(z) = (z + 3)(z + i\sqrt{3})(z - i\sqrt{3})$
6 $k = 2$, $P(x) = (x + i\sqrt{5})(x - i\sqrt{5})(3x + 2)$
7 a $a = 700$, the time at which the barrier has returned to its original position
b $k = \dfrac{85}{36\,000\,000}$, $f(t) = \dfrac{85}{36\,000\,000}t(t - 700)^2$
c 120 mm, at 233 milliseconds
8 March

$V(t) = -t^3 + 30t^2 - 131t + 250$
9 9.938 m or 1.112 m

REVIEW SET 7A

1 a $a = 4$, $b = 0$ **b** $a = 3$, $b = -4$
c $a = 3$, $b = -7$ or $a = 14$, $b = -\frac{3}{2}$
2 a $12 + 5i$ **b** $-1 + i$ **c** $18 + 26i$
3 $\text{Re}(z) = \frac{7\sqrt{3}}{4}$, $\text{Im}(z) = -\frac{3}{4}$ **4** $z = \frac{3}{5} - \frac{1}{5}i$
6 $w = \dfrac{(a + 1)^2 - b^2}{(a + 1)^2 + b^2} + i\left(\dfrac{2(a + 1)b}{(a + 1)^2 + b^2}\right)$
   w is purely imaginary if $b = \pm(a + 1)$, $a \neq -1$
7 a $12x^4 - 9x^3 + 8x^2 - 26x + 15$

b $4x^4 - 4x^3 + 13x^2 - 6x + 9$

8 a $x^2 - 2x + 4 - \dfrac{8}{x+2}$ **b** $x - 5 + \dfrac{19x+30}{(x+2)(x+3)}$

9 "If a polynomial $P(x)$ is divided by $x - k$ until a constant remainder R is obtained then $R = P(k)$."

10 $a = 7,\ b = 0$ or $a = 4,\ b = \pm\sqrt{3}$ **11** $1,\ -\frac{1}{2},\ 1 \pm i\sqrt{5}$

12 $(z+2)^2(z - 1 + i)(z - 1 - i)$

13 $P(z) = z^4 - 6z^3 + 14z^2 - 10z - 7$

14 $k = 3,\ b = 27,\ x = 3,\ -3;\ k = -1,\ b = -5,\ x = -1,\ 5$

15 $k \in\ ] -\infty,\ 10 - 3\sqrt{10}\ [\ $ or $\ k \in\ ] 10 + 3\sqrt{10},\ \infty\ [$

16 $k = -2,\ n = 36$

17 Another hint: Show that: $(\alpha\beta)^3 + (\alpha\beta)^2 - 1 = 0$

REVIEW SET 7B

1 $x = 2,\ y = -2$ **2** $3 - 2i$ **5** 7 **6** $a = 0,\ b = -1$

7 $a = 0,\ b = 0$ or $a = 3,\ b = 18$ **8** 2

9 $P(x) = (x + 2)^2(x - 1)(4x - 3)$

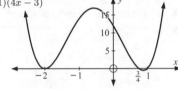

10 $3x - 7$ **11** $P(x) = a(x^4 - 8x^3 + 22x^2 - 16x - 11),\ a \neq 0$

12 $(2z + 1)(z + i\sqrt{5})(z - i\sqrt{5})$

13 $P(z) = a(z^2 - 4z + 5)(z^2 + 2z + 10),\ a \neq 0$

14 $k = -4$, zeros are $3 \pm 2i,\ -1 \pm \sqrt{2}$ **15** $\pm 2i,\ -1 \pm i$ **16** 7

REVIEW SET 7C

1 $x = -1,\ y = 2$ **2** $z = 4 - 2i$ or $2 + i$

4 a $x = 0,\ y = 0$ **b** $x = 5,\ y = -7$

  c $x = 0,\ y = 0,$ or $x = 1,\ y = 0,$

  or $x = -\frac{1}{2},\ y = \frac{\sqrt{3}}{2},$ or $x = -\frac{1}{2},\ y = -\frac{\sqrt{3}}{2}$

6 $z = -\frac{3737}{169} + \frac{4416}{169}i$ **7** 267 214

8 $a = -21$, other zeros are $5 + i,\ \frac{1}{2}$

9 a $P(x) = a(2x - 1)(x^2 + 2),\ a \neq 0$

  b $P(x) = a(x^2 - 2x + 2)(x^2 + 6x + 10),\ a \neq 0$

10 $k = 0,\ 4,\ -\frac{343}{8};\ \ P(x) = (x + 2)^2(2x - 1)$ when $k = 4$

11 $z = -\frac{1}{2},\ 2,\ \pm i\sqrt{2}$ **12 a** a is real, $k > 0$ **b** a is real, $k \leqslant 0$

13 $a = 7,\ b = -20$ **14** $k = 5 \pm 2\sqrt{2}$

15 quotient is $x^2 + 3x - 9$, remainder is $5x + 17,\ a = 4,\ b = -18$

EXERCISE 8A

1 24 **2 a** 4 **b** 8 **c** 24 **3** 6 **4** 42 **5** 1680

6 a 125 **b** 60 **7** 17 576 000 **8 a** 4 **b** 9 **c** 81

EXERCISE 8B

1 a 13 **b** 20 **c** 19 **d** 32

EXERCISE 8C

1 1, 1, 2, 6, 24, 120, 720, 5040, 40 320, 362 880, 3 628 800

2 a 6 **b** 30 **c** $\frac{1}{7}$ **d** $\frac{1}{30}$ **e** 100 **f** 21

3 a n **b** $(n + 2)(n + 1)$ **c** $(n + 1)n$

4 a $\frac{7!}{4!}$ **b** $\frac{10!}{8!}$ **c** $\frac{11!}{6!}$ **d** $\frac{13!}{10!3!}$ **e** $\frac{3!}{6!}$ **f** $\frac{4!16!}{20!}$

5 a $6 \times 4!$ **b** $10 \times 10!$ **c** $57 \times 6!$ **d** $131 \times 10!$ **e** $81 \times 7!$

  f $62 \times 6!$ **g** $10 \times 11!$ **h** $32 \times 8!$

6 a 11! **b** 9! **c** 8! **d** 9 **e** 34 **f** $n + 1$ **g** $(n - 1)!$

  h $(n + 1)!$

EXERCISE 8D

1 a W, X, Y, Z

  b WX, WY, WZ, XW, XY, XZ, YW, YX, YZ, ZW, ZX, ZY

  c WXY, WXZ, WYX, WYZ, WZX, WZY, XWY, XWZ,
    XYW, XYZ, XZW, XZY, YWX, YWZ, YXW, YXZ,
    YZX, YZW, ZWX, ZWY, ZXW, ZXY, ZYW, ZYX

2 a AB, AC, AD, AE, BA, BC, BD, BE, CA, CB, CD, CE, DA,
    DB, DC, DE, EA, EB, EC, ED

  b ABC, ABD, ABE, ACB, ACD, ACE, ADB, ADC, ADE,
    AEB, AEC, AED, BAC, BAD, BAE, BCA, BCD, BCE,
    BDA, BDC, BDE, BEA, BEC, BED, CAB, CAD, CAE,
    CBA, CBD, CBE, CDA, CDB, CDE, CEA, CEB, CED,
    DAB, DAC, DAE, DBA, DBC, DBE, DCA, DCB, DCE,
    DEA, DEB, DEC, EAB, EAC, EAD, EBA, EBC, EBD,
    ECA, ECB, ECD, EDA, EDB, EDC
    2 at a time: 20   3 at a time: 60

3 a 120 **b** 336 **c** 5040 **4 a** 12 **b** 24 **c** 36

5 720 **a** 24 **b** 24 **c** 48 **6 a** 343 **b** 210 **c** 120

7 720, 72 **8 a** 648 **b** 64 **c** 72 **d** 136

9 a 120 **b** 48 **c** 72 **10 a** 3 628 800 **b** 241 920

11 a 48 **b** 24 **c** 15 **12 a** 360 **b** 336 **c** 288

13 a 15 120 **b** 720

14 a i 3 628 800 **ii** 28 800 **b i** 151 200 **ii** 33 600

15 a 40 320 **b** 5760 **c** 8640

EXERCISE 8E

1 a 8 **b** 28 **c** 56 **d** 28 **e** 1 **3** $k = 3$ or 6

4 ABCD, ABCE, ABCF, ABDE, ABDF, ABEF, ACDE, ACDF, ACEF,
   ADEF, BCDE, BCDF, BCEF, BDEF, CDEF, $C_4^6 = 15$

5 $C_{11}^{17} = 12\,376$ **6** $C_5^9 = 126,\ C_1^1 C_4^8 = 70$

7 $C_3^{13} = 286,\ C_1^1 C_2^{12} = 66$

8 $C_5^{12} = 792$ **a** $C_2^2 C_3^{10} = 120$ **b** $C_1^2 C_4^{10} = 420$

9 $C_3^3 C_0^1 C_6^{11} = 462$

10 a $C_1^1 C_3^9 = 84$ **b** $C_0^2 C_4^8 = 70$ **c** $C_0^2 C_1^1 C_3^7 = 35$

11 a $C_5^{16} = 4368$ **b** $C_3^{10} C_2^6 = 1800$ **c** $C_5^{10} C_0^6 = 252$

  d $C_3^{10} C_2^6 + C_4^{10} C_1^6 + C_5^{10} C_0^6 = 3312$

  e $C_5^{16} - C_5^{10} C_0^6 - C_0^{10} C_5^6 = 4110$

12 a $C_2^6 C_1^3 C_2^7 = 945$ **b** $C_2^6 C_3^{10} = 1800$

  c $C_5^{16} - C_0^9 C_5^7 = 4347$

13 $C_2^{20} - 20 = 170$ **14 a i** $C_2^{12} = 66$ **ii** $C_1^{11} = 11$

15 $C_4^9 = 126$ **b i** $C_3^{12} = 220$ **ii** $C_2^{11} = 55$

16 a the different committees of 4 to be selected from 5 men
    and 6 women in all possible ways **b** C_r^{m+n}

17 a $\dfrac{C_6^{12}}{2} = 462$ **b** $\dfrac{C_4^{12} C_4^8 C_4^4}{3!} = 5775$

18 $C_2^{10} \times C_2^7 = 945$ **19** $C_2^{10} C_2^9 + C_2^9 C_2^8 + C_2^{10} C_2^8 + C_2^{10} C_1^9 C_1^8$
   $+ C_1^{10} C_2^9 C_1^8 + C_1^{10} C_1^9 C_2^8 = 12\,528$

EXERCISE 8F

1 a $x^3 + 3x^2 + 3x + 1$ **b** $27x^3 - 27x^2 + 9x - 1$

  c $8x^3 + 60x^2 + 150x + 125$ **d** $8x^3 + 12x + \dfrac{6}{x} + \dfrac{1}{x^3}$

2 a $x^4 - 8x^3 + 24x^2 - 32x + 16$

  b $16x^4 + 96x^3 + 216x^2 + 216x + 81$

  c $x^4 + 4x^2 + 6 + \dfrac{4}{x^2} + \dfrac{1}{x^4}$

  d $16x^4 - 32x^2 + 24 - \dfrac{8}{x^2} + \dfrac{1}{x^4}$

3 a 1 6 15 20 15 6 1

  b i $x^6 + 12x^5 + 60x^4 + 160x^3 + 240x^2 + 192x + 64$

  ii $64x^6 - 192x^5 + 240x^4 - 160x^3 + 60x^2 - 12x + 1$

  iii $x^6 + 6x^4 + 15x^2 + 20 + \dfrac{15}{x^2} + \dfrac{6}{x^4} + \dfrac{1}{x^6}$

4 a $7 + 5\sqrt{2}$ **b** $56 + 24\sqrt{5}$ **c** $232 - 164\sqrt{2}$

5 a $64 + 192x + 240x^2 + 160x^3 + 60x^4 + 12x^5 + x^6$

  b 65.944 160 601 201

6 $2x^5 + 11x^4 + 24x^3 + 26x^2 + 14x + 3$　**7 a** 270　**b** 4320

EXERCISE 8G

1 a $1^{11} + \binom{11}{1}(2x) + \binom{11}{2}(2x)^2 + \ldots + \binom{11}{10}(2x)^{10} + (2x)^{11}$

b $(3x)^{15} + \binom{15}{1}(3x)^{14}\left(\frac{2}{x}\right) + \binom{15}{2}(3x)^{13}\left(\frac{2}{x}\right)^2 + \ldots$

$\quad \ldots + \binom{15}{14}(3x)\left(\frac{2}{x}\right)^{14} + \left(\frac{2}{x}\right)^{15}$

c $(2x)^{20} + \binom{20}{1}(2x)^{19}\left(-\frac{3}{x}\right) + \binom{20}{2}(2x)^{18}\left(-\frac{3}{x}\right)^2 + \ldots$

$\quad \ldots + \binom{20}{19}(2x)\left(-\frac{3}{x}\right)^{19} + \left(-\frac{3}{x}\right)^{20}$

2 a $T_6 = \binom{15}{5}(2x)^{10}5^5$　**b** $T_4 = \binom{9}{3}(x^2)^6\left(\frac{5}{x}\right)^3$

c $T_{10} = \binom{17}{9}x^8\left(-\frac{2}{x}\right)^9$　**d** $T_9 = \binom{21}{8}(2x^2)^{13}\left(-\frac{1}{x}\right)^8$

3 a $\binom{10}{5}3^5 2^5$　**b** $\binom{6}{3}2^3(-3)^3$　**c** $\binom{12}{4}2^8(-1)^4$

4 a $\binom{15}{5}2^5$　**b** $\binom{9}{3}(-3)^3$

5 a

1　1	2
1　2　1	4
1　3　3　1	8
1　4　6　4　1	16
1　5　10　10　5　1	32

b sum　**c** The sum of the numbers in row n of Pascal's triangle is 2^n.

d After the first part let $x = 1$.

6 a $\binom{8}{6} = 28$　**b** $2\binom{9}{3}3^6 - \binom{9}{4}3^5 = 91854$

7 $1 + 10x + 35x^2 + 40x^3 - 30x^4$

8 b $84x^3$　**c** $n = 6$ and $k = -2$　**9** $a = 2$

11 $\displaystyle\sum_{r=0}^{n} 2^r \binom{n}{r} = 3^n$　**12** $(-1)^{100} = 1$

REVIEW SET 8A

1 a $26^2 \times 10^4 = 6\,760\,000$　**b** $5 \times 26 \times 10^4 = 1\,300\,000$
c $26 \times 25 \times 10 \times 9 \times 8 \times 7 = 3\,276\,000$

2 a 45　**b** 120　**3 a** $n(n-1)$　**b** $n + 2$

4 a 3003　**b** 980　**c** 2982　**5** 28

6 a $x^3 - 6x^2 y + 12xy^2 - 8y^3$
b $81x^4 + 216x^3 + 216x^2 + 96x + 16$

7 a 252　**b** 246　**8 a** 24　**b** 6　**9** 20 000　**10** 60

11 $k = -\frac{1}{4}$, $n = 16$　**12** 4320　**13 a** 900　**b** 180

REVIEW SET 8B

1 a 43 758 teams　**b** 11 550 teams　**c** 41 283 teams

2 a $9 \times 9 \times 8 \times 7 = 4536$ numbers　**b** 952 numbers

3 $(a+b)^6 = a^6 + 6a^5 b + 15a^4 b^2 + 20a^3 b^3 + 15a^2 b^4 + 6ab^5 + b^6$

a $x^6 - 18x^5 + 135x^4 - 540x^3 + 1215x^2 - 1458x + 729$

b $1 + \dfrac{6}{x} + \dfrac{15}{x^2} + \dfrac{20}{x^3} + \dfrac{15}{x^4} + \dfrac{6}{x^5} + \dfrac{1}{x^6}$

4 $362 + 209\sqrt{3}$　**5** 64.964 808　**6** It does not have one.

7 $\binom{12}{6} \times 2^6 \times (-3)^6$　**8** $8\binom{6}{2} - 6\binom{6}{1} = 84$　**9** $a = \pm 4$

10 $\binom{6}{2} \times 3^4 \times (-2)^2 = 4860$　**11** $q = \pm\sqrt{\frac{6}{70}}$

EXERCISE 9A

1 a $4n - 1$　**b** all $n \in \mathbb{Z}^+$, $n \geqslant 2$　**c** 10 for all $n \in \mathbb{Z}^+$
d $n(n+1)$, $n \in \mathbb{Z}^+$　**e** $(n+1)! - 1$ for all $n \in \mathbb{Z}^+$

f $\dfrac{(n+1)! - 1}{(n+1)!}$ for all $n \in \mathbb{Z}^+$　**g** 3 for all $n \in \mathbb{Z}^+$

h $\dfrac{1}{n+1}$ for all $n \in \mathbb{Z}^+$　**i** $\dfrac{n}{6n+4}$, $n \in \mathbb{Z}^+$

2 *Proposition:* The number of triangles for n points within the original triangle is given by $T_n = 2n + 1$, $n \in \mathbb{Z}^+$.

EXERCISE 9B

3 a $\frac{11}{210}$　**4 b** $\frac{3\,628\,799}{3\,628\,800}$

8 *Conjecture:* $u_n = n^2$ for $n \in \mathbb{Z}^+$

9 *Conjecture:* $u_n = \dfrac{n}{2n+1}$ for $n \in \mathbb{Z}^+$

10 a $A_1 = 2$, $B_1 = 1$;　$A_2 = 7$, $B_2 = 4$;　$A_3 = 26$, $B_3 = 15$;
$A_4 = 97$, $B_4 = 56$

c For $n = 1, 2, 3, 4$, $(A_n)^2 - 3(B_n)^2 = 1$
Conjecture: $(A_n)^2 - 3(B_n)^2 = 1$ for $n \in \mathbb{Z}^+$

EXERCISE 10A

1 a $\frac{\pi^c}{2}$　**b** $\frac{\pi^c}{3}$　**c** $\frac{\pi^c}{6}$　**d** $\frac{\pi^c}{10}$　**e** $\frac{\pi^c}{20}$　**f** $\frac{3\pi^c}{4}$　**g** $\frac{5\pi^c}{4}$
h $\frac{3\pi^c}{2}$　**i** $2\pi^c$　**j** $4\pi^c$　**k** $\frac{7\pi^c}{4}$　**l** $3\pi^c$　**m** $\frac{\pi^c}{5}$　**n** $\frac{4\pi^c}{9}$　**o** $\frac{23\pi^c}{18}$

2 a 0.641^c　**b** 2.39^c　**c** 5.55^c　**d** 3.83^c　**e** 6.92^c

3 a 36°　**b** 108°　**c** 135°　**d** 10°　**e** 20°　**f** 140°
g 18°　**h** 27°　**i** 150°　**j** 22.5^o

4 a 114.59^o　**b** 87.66^o　**c** 49.68^o　**d** 182.14^o　**e** 301.78^o

5 a

Degrees	0	45	90	135	180	225
Radians	0	$\frac{\pi}{4}$	$\frac{\pi}{2}$	$\frac{3\pi}{4}$	π	$\frac{5\pi}{4}$

Degrees	270	315	360
Radians	$\frac{3\pi}{2}$	$\frac{7\pi}{4}$	2π

b

Degrees	0	30	60	90	120	150	180
Radians	0	$\frac{\pi}{6}$	$\frac{\pi}{3}$	$\frac{\pi}{2}$	$\frac{2\pi}{3}$	$\frac{5\pi}{6}$	π

Degrees	210	240	270	300	330	360
Radians	$\frac{7\pi}{6}$	$\frac{4\pi}{3}$	$\frac{3\pi}{2}$	$\frac{5\pi}{3}$	$\frac{11\pi}{6}$	2π

EXERCISE 10B

1 a i 6.53 cm　**ii** 29.4 cm²　**b i** 10.5 cm　**ii** 25.9 cm²

2 a 3.14 m　**b** 9.30 m²

3 a 5.91 cm　**b** 18.9 cm　**4 a** 39.3^o　**b** 34.4^o

5 a 0.75^c, 24 cm²　**b** 1.68^c, 21 cm²　**c** 2.32^c, 126.8 cm²

6 10 cm, 25 cm²　**7** 65 cm²

8 a 11.7 cm　**b** 11.7　**c** 37.7 cm　**d** 185°

9 a $\alpha = 18.43$　**b** $\theta = 143.1$　**c** 387.3 m²

10 b 2 h 24 min　**11** 227 m²

12 a $\alpha = 5.739$　**b** $\theta = 168.5$　**c** $\phi = 191.5$　**d** 71.62 cm

EXERCISE 10C.1

1 a

b

c

2 a i A$(\cos 26^o, \sin 26^o)$　B$(\cos 146^o, \sin 146^o)$
C$(\cos 199^o, \sin 199^o)$

ii A$(0.899, 0.438)$　B$(-0.829, 0.559)$　C$(-0.946, -0.326)$

b i A$(\cos 123^o, \sin 123^o)$　B$(\cos 251^o, \sin 251^o)$
C$(\cos(-35^o), \sin(-35^o))$

ii A$(-0.545, 0.839)$　B$(-0.326, -0.946)$　C$(0.819, -0.574)$

3

θ (degrees)	0°	90°	180°	270°	360°	450°
θ (radians)	0	$\frac{\pi}{2}$	π	$\frac{3\pi}{2}$	2π	$\frac{5\pi}{2}$
sine	0	1	0	-1	0	1
cosine	1	0	-1	0	1	0
tangent	0	undef	0	undef	0	undef

5 a ≈ 0.6820　**b** ≈ 0.8572　**c** ≈ -0.7986　**d** ≈ 0.9135
e ≈ 0.9063　**f** ≈ -0.6691

6 a $\cos\theta = \pm\frac{\sqrt{3}}{2}$ **b** $\cos\theta = \pm\frac{2\sqrt{2}}{3}$ **c** $\cos\theta = \pm1$ **d** $\cos\theta = 0$

7 a $\sin\theta = \pm\frac{3}{5}$ **b** $\sin\theta = \pm\frac{\sqrt{7}}{4}$ **c** $\sin\theta = 0$ **d** $\sin\theta = \pm1$

8 a

Quad-rant	Degree measure	Radian measure	$\cos\theta$	$\sin\theta$	$\tan\theta$
1	$0 < \theta < 90$	$0 < \theta < \frac{\pi}{2}$	+ve	+ve	+ve
2	$90 < \theta < 180$	$\frac{\pi}{2} < \theta < \pi$	−ve	+ve	−ve
3	$180 < \theta < 270$	$\pi < \theta < \frac{3\pi}{2}$	−ve	−ve	+ve
4	$270 < \theta < 360$	$\frac{3\pi}{2} < \theta < 2\pi$	+ve	−ve	−ve

b i 1 and 4 **ii** 2 and 3 **iii** 3 **iv** 2

9 a $\sin\theta = \frac{\sqrt{5}}{3}$ **b** $\cos\theta = -\frac{\sqrt{21}}{5}$ **c** $\cos\theta = \frac{4}{5}$ **d** $\sin\theta = -\frac{12}{13}$

10 a $-\frac{1}{2\sqrt{2}}$ **b** $-2\sqrt{6}$ **c** $\frac{1}{\sqrt{2}}$ **d** $-\frac{\sqrt{7}}{3}$

11 a $\sin x = \frac{2}{\sqrt{13}}$, $\cos x = \frac{3}{\sqrt{13}}$ **b** $\sin x = \frac{4}{5}$, $\cos x = -\frac{3}{5}$

c $\sin x = -\sqrt{\frac{5}{14}}$, $\cos x = -\frac{3}{\sqrt{14}}$ **d** $\sin x = -\frac{12}{13}$, $\cos x = \frac{5}{13}$

EXERCISE 10C.2

1 a 0 **b** $-2\tan\theta$ **c** $3\cos\theta$ **d** $4\sin\theta$ **e** $\cos^2\alpha$
f $\sin^2\alpha$ **g** 1

2 a $\sin\theta$ **b** $-2\sin\theta$ **c** 0 **d** $-\cos\theta$ **e** $4\cos\theta$ **f** $5\sin\theta$

3 $\phi - \theta = -(\theta - \phi)$

4 a $\tan\theta$ **b** $-\tan\theta$ **c** 1 **d** $\tan\theta$ **e** $\tan\theta$ **f** $\tan\theta$

EXERCISE 10C.3

1

	a	b	c	d	e
$\sin\theta$	$\frac{1}{\sqrt{2}}$	$-\frac{1}{\sqrt{2}}$	$-\frac{1}{\sqrt{2}}$	0	$-\frac{1}{\sqrt{2}}$
$\cos\theta$	$\frac{1}{\sqrt{2}}$	$-\frac{1}{\sqrt{2}}$	$\frac{1}{\sqrt{2}}$	-1	$-\frac{1}{\sqrt{2}}$
$\tan\theta$	1	1	-1	0	1

2

	a	b	c	d	e
$\sin\beta$	$\frac{1}{2}$	$\frac{\sqrt{3}}{2}$	$-\frac{1}{2}$	$-\frac{\sqrt{3}}{2}$	$-\frac{1}{2}$
$\cos\beta$	$\frac{\sqrt{3}}{2}$	$-\frac{1}{2}$	$-\frac{\sqrt{3}}{2}$	$\frac{1}{2}$	$\frac{\sqrt{3}}{2}$
$\tan\beta$	$\frac{1}{\sqrt{3}}$	$-\sqrt{3}$	$\frac{1}{\sqrt{3}}$	$-\sqrt{3}$	$-\frac{1}{\sqrt{3}}$

3 a $\frac{3}{4}$ **b** $\frac{1}{4}$ **c** 3 **d** $\frac{1}{4}$ **e** $-\frac{1}{4}$ **f** 1 **g** $\sqrt{2}$ **h** $\frac{1}{2}$
i $\frac{1}{2}$ **j** 2 **k** -1 **l** $-\sqrt{3}$

4 a $30°, 150°$ **b** $60°, 120°$ **c** $45°, 315°$ **d** $120°, 240°$
e $135°, 225°$ **f** $240°, 300°$

5 a $\frac{\pi}{4}, \frac{5\pi}{4}$ **b** $\frac{3\pi}{4}, \frac{7\pi}{4}$ **c** $\frac{\pi}{3}, \frac{4\pi}{3}$ **d** $0, \pi, 2\pi$ **e** $\frac{\pi}{6}, \frac{7\pi}{6}$
f $\frac{2\pi}{3}, \frac{5\pi}{3}$

6 a $\frac{\pi}{6}, \frac{11\pi}{6}, \frac{13\pi}{6}, \frac{23\pi}{6}$ **b** $\frac{7\pi}{6}, \frac{11\pi}{6}, \frac{19\pi}{6}, \frac{23\pi}{6}$ **c** $\frac{3\pi}{2}, \frac{7\pi}{2}$

7 a $\theta = \frac{\pi}{3}, \frac{5\pi}{3}$ **b** $\theta = \frac{\pi}{3}, \frac{2\pi}{3}$ **c** $\theta = \pi$ **d** $\theta = \frac{\pi}{2}$
e $\theta = \frac{3\pi}{4}, \frac{5\pi}{4}$ **f** $\theta = \frac{\pi}{2}, \frac{3\pi}{2}$ **g** $\theta = 0, \pi, 2\pi$
h $\theta = \frac{\pi}{4}, \frac{3\pi}{4}, \frac{5\pi}{4}, \frac{7\pi}{4}$ **i** $\theta = \frac{5\pi}{6}, \frac{11\pi}{6}$ **j** $\theta = \frac{\pi}{3}, \frac{2\pi}{3}, \frac{4\pi}{3}, \frac{5\pi}{3}$

EXERCISE 10D

1 a 28.9 cm^2 **b** 384 km^2 **c** 28.3 cm^2 **2** $x = 19.0$
3 18.9 cm^2 **4** 137 cm^2 **5** 374 cm^2 **6** 7.49 cm **7** 11.9 m
8 a $48.6°$ or $131.4°$ **b** $42.1°$ or $137.9°$ **9** $\frac{1}{4}$ is not covered
10 a 36.2 cm^2 **b** 62.8 cm^2
11 a i and **ii** 6 cm^2 **b i** 21.3 cm^2 **ii** 30.7 cm^2

REVIEW SET 10A

1 21.1 km^2 **2 a** 118 cm^2 **b** 44.9 cm^2
3 M$(\cos73°, \sin73°) \approx (0.292, 0.956)$
N$(\cos190°, \sin190°) \approx (-0.985, -0.174)$
P$(\cos307°, \sin307°) \approx (0.602, -0.799)$

4 $\theta \approx 102.8°$ **5 a** $\frac{\pi}{3}$ **b** $15°$ **c** $84°$
6 a $133°$ **b** $\frac{14\pi}{15}$ **c** $174°$
7 a 0.358 **b** -0.035 **c** 0.259 **d** -0.731
8 a $1, 0$ **b** $-1, 0$
10 a 0.961 **b** -0.961 **c** -0.961 **d** -0.961
11 a 3 **b** $-\sqrt{2}$ **12** $\frac{1}{\sqrt{15}}$

REVIEW SET 10B

1 a $\frac{2\pi}{3}$ **b** $\frac{5\pi}{4}$ **c** $\frac{5\pi}{6}$ **d** 3π
2 a 1.239^c **b** 2.175^c **c** -2.478^c **d** -0.4416^c
3 a $72°$ **b** $225°$ **c** $140°$ **d** $330°$
4 a $171.89°$ **b** $83.65°$ **c** $24.92°$ **d** $-302.01°$
5 perimeter $= 34.1$ cm, area $= 66.5$ cm^2
6 $r = 8.79$ cm, area $= 81.0$ cm^2 **7** $67.4°$ or $112.6°$
8 a $10\,600$ m^2 **b** 1.06 ha
9 a -0.743 **b** -0.743 **c** 0.743 **d** -0.743 **10** $\pm\frac{\sqrt{7}}{4}$
11 a $\frac{\sqrt{3}}{2}$ **b** 0 **c** $\frac{1}{2}$ **12 a** $-\frac{3}{\sqrt{13}}$ **b** $\frac{2}{\sqrt{13}}$

REVIEW SET 10C

1 a $(0.766, -0.643)$ **b** $(-0.956, 0.292)$

2

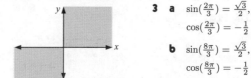

3 a $\sin(\frac{2\pi}{3}) = \frac{\sqrt{3}}{2}$,
$\cos(\frac{2\pi}{3}) = -\frac{1}{2}$

b $\sin(\frac{8\pi}{3}) = \frac{\sqrt{3}}{2}$,
$\cos(\frac{8\pi}{3}) = -\frac{1}{2}$

4 a $0, -1$ **b** $0, -1$ **5 a** $\frac{\sqrt{7}}{4}$ **b** $-\frac{\sqrt{7}}{3}$
6 a $150°, 210°$ **b** $45°, 135°$ **c** $120°, 300°$

7 a $\theta = \pi + k2\pi$ **b** $\theta = \left.\begin{matrix}\frac{\pi}{3}\\\frac{2\pi}{3}\end{matrix}\right\} + k\pi$

8 a $2\frac{1}{2}$ **b** $1\frac{1}{2}$ **c** $-\frac{1}{2}$ **9 a** 0 **b** $\sin\theta$
10 $x = 47.5$, AC $= 14.3$ cm or $x = 132.5$, AC $= 28.1$ cm
11 36.8 cm^2

EXERCISE 11A

1 a 28.8 cm **b** 3.38 km **c** 14.2 m
2 $\angle A = 52.0°$, $\angle B = 59.3°$, $\angle C = 68.7°$ **3** $112°$
4 a $40.3°$ **b** $107°$ **5 a** $\cos\theta = 0.65$ **b** $x = 3.81$
6 a $x = 3 + \sqrt{22}$ **b** $x = \dfrac{-3 + \sqrt{73}}{2}$ **c** $x = \frac{5}{\sqrt{3}}$
7 a $x \approx 10.8$ **b** $x \approx 9.21$ **8 a** $x = 2$ **b** Area $= 2\sqrt{24}$ cm^2

EXERCISE 11B.1

1 a $x = 28.4$ **b** $x = 13.4$ **c** $x = 3.79$
2 a $a = 21.25$ cm **b** $b = 76.9$ cm **c** $c = 5.09$ cm

EXERCISE 11B.2

1 $\angle C = 62.1°$ or $\angle C = 117.9°$
2 a $\angle A = 49.5°$ **b** $\angle B = 72.05°$ or $107.95°$ **c** $\angle C = 44.3°$
3 No, $\dfrac{\sin85°}{11.4} \neq \dfrac{\sin27°}{9.8}$ **4** $\angle ABC = 66°$, BD $= 4.55$ cm
5 $x = 17.7$, $y = 33.1$
6 a $88.7°$ or $91.3°$ **b** $91.3°$
c .... cosine rule as it avoids the ambiguous case.
7 Area ≈ 25.1 cm^2 **8** $x = 8 + \frac{11}{2}\sqrt{2}$

EXERCISE 11C

1 17.7 m **2** 207 m **3** $23.9°$ **4** 77.5 m **5** $9.38°$ **6** 69.1 m
7 a 38.0 m **b** 94.0 m **8** $55.1°$ **9** AC ≈ 11.7 km, BC ≈ 8.49 km
10 a 74.9 km^2 **b** 7490 hectares **11** 9.12 km
12 ≈ 85 mm **13** 10.1 km **14** 29.2 m **15** 37.6 km

REVIEW SET 11A

1 a $x = 34.1$ **b** $x = 18.9$ **2 a** $x = 41.5$ **b** $x = 15.4$

3 AC = 12.55 cm, $\angle A = 48.6^o$, $\angle C = 57.4^o$ **4** 113 cm^2

5 7.32 m **6** 204 m **7** 530 m, bearing 077.2^o

8 179 km, bearing 352°

9 If the unknown is an angle, use the cosine rule to avoid the ambiguous case.

10 **a** $x = 3$ or 5 **b** Kady can draw 2 triangles:

11 **a** The information given could give two triangles:

b ≈ 2.23 m^3

REVIEW SET 11B

1 $\widehat{EDG} \approx 74.4^o$ **2** 3.52 km **4** 42 km **5 a** 2:18 pm **b** 157°

6 **a** $d^2 = x^2 - (10\cos 20^o)x + 25$ **b** $x = 5\cos 20^o$

7 **b ii** $b = 103.8$, $d = 76.2$ **iii** $a = 95.4$, $c = 84.6$

8 **a** max. value 16 when $x = 6$

b i $y = 12 - x$ **ii** $y^2 = x^2 + 64 - 16x\cos\theta$

d max. area $= 8\sqrt{5}$ units^2 when $x = y = 6$ {i.e., isos. Δ}

9 **a** $QS = \sqrt{45 - 36\cos\phi}$

b i $\widehat{RSQ} = 52.5^o$ or 127.5^o **ii** 24.8 units **c** 23.2 units^2

EXERCISE 12A

1 **a**

Data exhibits periodic behaviour.

b

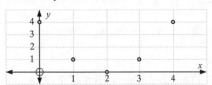

Not enough information to say data is periodic.
It may in fact be quadratic.

c

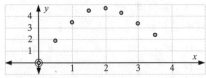

Not enough information to say data is periodic.
It may in fact be quadratic.

d

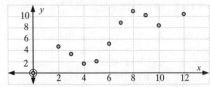

Not enough information to say data is periodic.

2 **a**

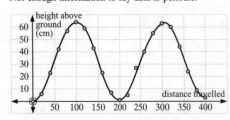

b The data is periodic. **i** $y = 32$ (approx.)
  ii ≈ 64 cm **iii** ≈ 200 cm **iv** ≈ 32 cm

c A curve can be fitted to the data.

3 **a** periodic **b** periodic **c** periodic **d** not periodic
  e periodic **f** periodic

EXERCISE 12B.1

1 **a**

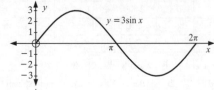

b

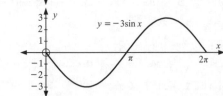

c

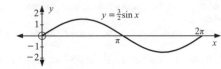

d

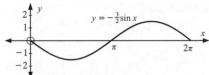

2 **a**

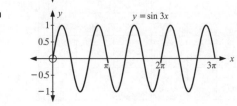

b

c

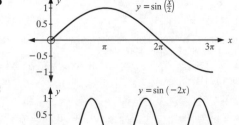

3 **a** $\frac{\pi}{2}$ **b** $\frac{\pi}{2}$ **c** 6π **d** $\frac{10\pi}{3}$

4 **a** $B = \frac{2}{5}$ **b** $B = 3$ **c** $B = \frac{1}{6}$ **d** $B = \frac{\pi}{2}$ **e** $B = \frac{\pi}{50}$

5 **a**

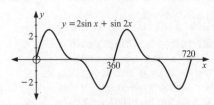

b

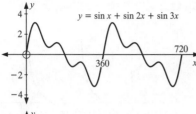

$y = \sin x + \sin 2x + \sin 3x$

c

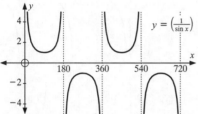

$y = \left(\frac{1}{\sin x}\right)$

6 a

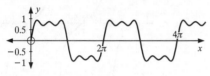

b

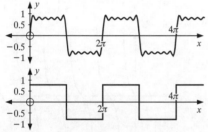

EXERCISE 12B.2

1 a

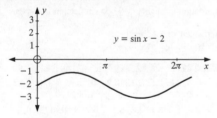

$y = \sin x - 2$

b

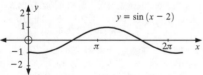

$y = \sin (x - 2)$

c

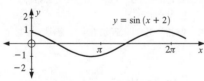

$y = \sin (x + 2)$

d

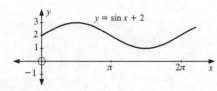

$y = \sin x + 2$

e

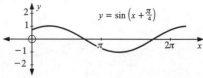

$y = \sin\left(x + \frac{\pi}{4}\right)$

f

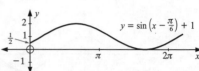

$y = \sin\left(x - \frac{\pi}{6}\right) + 1$

3 a $\frac{2\pi}{5}$ **b** 8π **c** π **4 a** $\frac{2}{3}$ **b** 20 **c** $\frac{1}{50}$ **d** $\frac{\pi}{25}$

5 a vert. translation -1 **b** horiz. translation $\frac{\pi}{4}$ right
c vert. stretch, factor 2 **d** horiz. compression, factor 4
e vert. stretch, factor $\frac{1}{2}$ **f** horiz. stretch factor 4
g reflection in the x-axis **h** translation $\begin{pmatrix} -2 \\ -3 \end{pmatrix}$
i vert. stretch factor 2, followed by a horiz. compression, factor 3
j translation $\begin{pmatrix} \frac{\pi}{3} \\ 2 \end{pmatrix}$

EXERCISE 12C

1 a $T \approx 6.5 \sin \frac{\pi}{6}(t - 4.5) + 20.5$
2 a $T \approx 4.5 \sin \frac{\pi}{6}(t - 10.5) + 11.5$
3 $T \approx 13.1 \sin(0.345)(t + 6.87) - 5.43$
4 a $H \approx 7 \sin(0.507)(t - 3.1)$
b

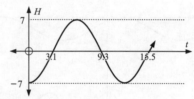

5 $H = 10 \sin \frac{\pi}{50}(t - 25) + 12$

EXERCISE 12D

1 a $y = \cos x + 2$

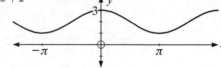

b $y = \cos x - 1$

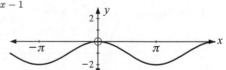

c $y = \cos\left(x - \frac{\pi}{4}\right)$

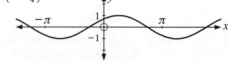

d $y = \cos\left(x + \frac{\pi}{6}\right)$

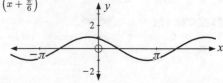

e $y = \frac{2}{3}\cos x$

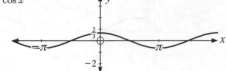

f $y = \frac{3}{2}\cos x$

g $y = -\cos x$

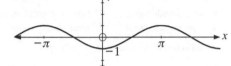

h $y = \cos\left(x - \frac{\pi}{6}\right) + 1$

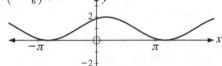

i $y = \cos\left(x + \frac{\pi}{4}\right) - 1$

j $y = \cos 2x$

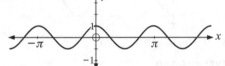

k $y = \cos\left(\frac{x}{2}\right)$

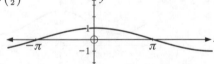

l $y = 3\cos 2x$

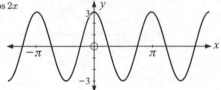

2 a $\frac{2\pi}{3}$ **c** 6π **c** 100

3 A: amplitude, B: $\dfrac{2\pi}{\text{period}}$, C: horizontal translation, D: vertical translation

4 a $y = 2\cos 2x$ **b** $y = \cos\left(\frac{x}{2}\right) + 2$ **c** $y = -5\cos\left(\frac{\pi}{3}x\right)$

EXERCISE 12E.1

1 a 0 **b** 0.27 **c** 0.36 **2** triangle TON is
 d 0.47 **e** 0.70 **f** 1   isosceles, ON = TN
 g 1.19 **h** 1.43

EXERCISE 12E.2

1 a i $y = \tan\left(x - \frac{\pi}{2}\right)$

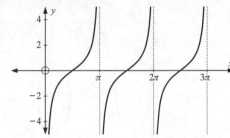

ii $y = -\tan x$

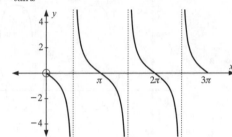

iii $y = \tan 2x$

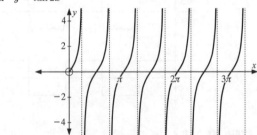

2 a translation through $\begin{pmatrix} 1 \\ 0 \end{pmatrix}$ **b** reflection in x-axis

 c horizontal stretch, factor $k = 2$

3 a π **b** $\frac{\pi}{2}$ **c** $\frac{\pi}{n}$

EXERCISE 12F.1

1 a $x = 0.3, 2.8, 6.6, 9.1, 12.9$ **b** $x = 5.9, 9.8, 12.2$
2 a $x = 1.2, 5.1, 7.4$ **b** $x = 4.4, 8.2, 10.7$
3 a $x = 0.4, 1.2, 3.5, 4.3, 6.7, 7.5, 9.8, 10.6, 13.0, 13.8$
 b $x = 1.7, 3.0, 4.9, 6.1, 8.0, 9.3, 11.1, 12.4, 14.3, 15.6$
4 a i 1.6 **ii** -1.1 **b i** 1.557 **ii** -1.119
 c i $x = 1.1, 4.2, 7.4$ **ii** $x = 2.2, 5.3$

EXERCISE 12F.2

1 a $x = 1.08, 4.35$ **b** $x = 0.666, 2.48$
 c $x = 0.171, 4.92$ **d** $x = 1.31, 2.03, 2.85$
2 $x = -0.951, 0.234, 5.98$

EXERCISE 12F.3

1 a $x = \frac{\pi}{6}, \frac{13\pi}{6}, \frac{25\pi}{6}$ **b** $x = -\frac{\pi}{3}, \frac{5\pi}{3}$
 c $x = -\frac{7\pi}{2}, -\frac{5\pi}{2}, -\frac{3\pi}{2}, -\frac{\pi}{2}, \frac{\pi}{2}, \frac{3\pi}{2}, \frac{5\pi}{2}, \frac{7\pi}{2}$
 d $x = \frac{\pi}{6}, \frac{5\pi}{6}, \frac{4\pi}{3}, \frac{11\pi}{6}, \frac{7\pi}{3}, \frac{17\pi}{6}, \frac{10\pi}{3}, \frac{23\pi}{6}$
2 a $x = \frac{2\pi}{3}, \frac{4\pi}{3}, \frac{8\pi}{3}, \frac{10\pi}{3}, \frac{14\pi}{3}$ **b** $x = -\frac{11\pi}{6}, -\frac{7\pi}{6}, \frac{\pi}{6}, \frac{5\pi}{6}$
 c $x = \frac{5\pi}{6}, \frac{7\pi}{6}, \frac{17\pi}{6}$ **d** $x = -\frac{5\pi}{3}, -\pi, \frac{\pi}{3}, \pi$
 e $x = -\frac{13\pi}{6}, -\frac{3\pi}{2}, -\frac{\pi}{6}, \frac{\pi}{2}, \frac{11\pi}{6}, \frac{5\pi}{2}$ **f** $x = 0, \frac{3\pi}{2}, 2\pi$
3 $X = \frac{\pi}{3} + k\pi$ **a** $x = \frac{\pi}{2} + k\pi$ **c** $x = \left.\begin{array}{c} \frac{\pi}{3} \\ -\frac{\pi}{3} \end{array}\right\} + k\pi$
 b $x = \frac{\pi}{12} + k\frac{\pi}{4}$

4 a $x = 0, \frac{\pi}{2}, \pi$ **b** $x = \frac{\pi}{4}, \frac{5\pi}{4}, \frac{9\pi}{4}$

5 a

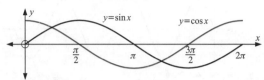

b $x = \frac{\pi}{4}$ or $\frac{5\pi}{4}$ **c** $x = \frac{\pi}{4}$ or $\frac{5\pi}{4}$

6 a $x = \frac{3\pi}{4}$ or $\frac{7\pi}{4}$ **b** $x = \frac{\pi}{12}, \frac{5\pi}{12}, \frac{3\pi}{4}, \frac{13\pi}{12}, \frac{17\pi}{12}, \frac{7\pi}{4}$

   c $x = \frac{\pi}{6}, \frac{2\pi}{3}, \frac{7\pi}{6}, \frac{5\pi}{3}$

EXERCISE 12G

1 a i 7500 **ii** 10 300 **b** 10 500, when $t = 4$ weeks
   c i at $t = 1\frac{1}{3}$ wks and $6\frac{2}{3}$ wks **ii** at $t = 9\frac{1}{3}$ wks
   d $2.51 \leqslant t \leqslant 5.49$

2 a 20 m **b** at $t = \frac{3}{4}$ minute **c** 3 minutes
   d

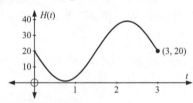

3 a 400 **b i** 577 **ii** 400
   c 650   It is the maximum population.
   d 150, after 3 years **e** $t \approx 0.26$ years

4 a $H(t) = 3\cos(\frac{\pi t}{2}) + 4$ **b** $t \approx 1.46$ sec

5 a i true **ii** true **b** 116.8 cents L^{-1}
   c on the 5th and 11th days
   d 98.6 cents L^{-1} on the 1st and 15th day

EXERCISE 12H

1 a $\csc x = \frac{5}{3}$, $\sec x = \frac{5}{4}$, $\cot x = \frac{4}{3}$
   b $\csc x = -\frac{3}{\sqrt{5}}$, $\sec x = \frac{3}{2}$, $\cot x = -\frac{2}{\sqrt{5}}$

2 a $\frac{2}{\sqrt{3}}$ **b** $-\frac{1}{\sqrt{3}}$ **c** $-\frac{2}{\sqrt{3}}$ **d** undefined

3 a $\sin x = -\frac{\sqrt{7}}{4}$, $\tan x = -\frac{\sqrt{7}}{3}$, $\csc x = -\frac{4}{\sqrt{7}}$,
   $\sec x = \frac{4}{3}$, $\cot x = -\frac{3}{\sqrt{7}}$

   b $\cos x = -\frac{\sqrt{5}}{3}$, $\tan x = \frac{2}{\sqrt{5}}$, $\csc x = -\frac{3}{2}$,
   $\sec x = -\frac{3}{\sqrt{5}}$, $\cot x = \frac{\sqrt{5}}{2}$

   c $\sin x = \frac{\sqrt{21}}{5}$, $\cos x = \frac{2}{5}$, $\tan x = \frac{\sqrt{21}}{2}$,
   $\csc x = \frac{5}{\sqrt{21}}$, $\cot x = \frac{2}{\sqrt{21}}$

   d $\sin x = \frac{1}{2}$, $\cos x = -\frac{\sqrt{3}}{2}$, $\tan x = -\frac{1}{\sqrt{3}}$,
   $\sec x = -\frac{2}{\sqrt{3}}$, $\cot x = -\sqrt{3}$

   e $\sin \beta = -\frac{1}{\sqrt{5}}$, $\cos \beta = -\frac{2}{\sqrt{5}}$, $\csc \beta = -\sqrt{5}$,
   $\sec \beta = -\frac{\sqrt{5}}{2}$, $\cot \beta = 2$

   f $\sin \theta = -\frac{3}{5}$, $\cos \theta = -\frac{4}{5}$, $\tan \theta = \frac{3}{4}$,
   $\csc \theta = -\frac{5}{3}$, $\sec \theta = -\frac{5}{4}$

4 a 1 **b** 1 **c** $\frac{\cos x}{\sin^2 x}$ **d** $\cos x$ **e** $\cos x$ **f** $5\sin x$

5 a

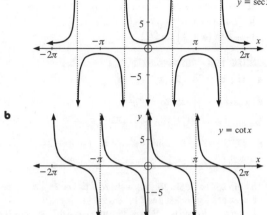

$y = \sec x$

   b

$y = \cot x$

6 a $x = \frac{\pi}{3}, \frac{5\pi}{3}$ **b** $x = \frac{5\pi}{4}, \frac{7\pi}{4}$ **c** $x = 0.245, 3.387$
   d no solutions **e** no solutions
   f $x = 0.232, 1.803, 3.373, 4.944$

EXERCISE 12I

1 a $(1 + \sin \theta)(1 - \sin \theta)$ **b** $\tan \alpha(3\tan \alpha - 2)$
   c $(\sec \beta + \csc \beta)(\sec \beta - \csc \beta)$ **d** $(2\cot x - 1)(\cot x - 1)$
   e $(2\sin x + \cos x)(\sin x + 3\cos x)$

2 a 3 **b** $-\tan^2 \beta$ **c** $4\sin^2 \theta$ **d** $-2\sin^2 \alpha$ **e** 1
   f $\sin^2 \alpha$ **g** 13 **h** $\cos^2 \theta$ **i** 0 **j** $\sin \theta$ **k** $\cos \theta$
   l $\cos \beta + \sin \beta$ **m** $\sec \theta + 1$

EXERCISE 12J

1 a $\cos \theta$ **b** $-\sin \theta$ **c** $\sin \alpha$ **d** $-\cos \alpha$ **e** $-\sin A$
   f $-\sin \theta$ **g** $\frac{1 + \tan \theta}{1 - \tan \theta}$ **h** $\frac{1 + \tan \theta}{1 - \tan \theta}$ **i** $\tan \theta$

2 a $\frac{1}{2}\sin \theta + \frac{\sqrt{3}}{2}\cos \theta$ **b** $\frac{\sqrt{3}}{2}\sin \theta - \frac{1}{2}\cos \theta$
   c $-\frac{1}{\sqrt{2}}\sin \theta + \frac{1}{\sqrt{2}}\cos \theta$ **d** $-\frac{\sqrt{3}}{2}\sin \theta + \frac{1}{2}\cos \theta$

3 a $\cos \theta$ **b** $\sin 3A$ **c** $\sin(B - A)$ **d** $\cos(\alpha - \beta)$
   e $-\cos(\theta + \phi)$ **f** $2\sin(\alpha - \beta)$ **g** $\tan \theta$ **h** $\tan(3A)$

5 a $\cos 2\alpha$ **b** $-\sin 3\phi$ **c** $\cos \beta$

7 a $2 + \sqrt{3}$ **b** $-2 - \sqrt{3}$ **8** $\frac{7}{17}$ **9** 7

10 a -1 **b** $\tan(2A)$ **11** $\sqrt{3}$ **12** $-\frac{1}{21}$

13 $\tan A = \pm 1$ **14** $\tan \alpha = \frac{25}{62}$ **15** $\frac{1}{8}$

16 $\tan(A + B + C)$
   $= \dfrac{\tan A + \tan B + \tan C - \tan A \tan B \tan C}{1 - \tan A \tan B - \tan A \tan C - \tan B \tan C}$

19 b i $\frac{1}{2}\sin 4\theta + \frac{1}{2}\sin 2\theta$ **ii** $\frac{1}{2}\sin 7\alpha + \frac{1}{2}\sin 5\alpha$
   iii $\sin 6\beta + \sin 4\beta$ **iv** $2\sin 5\theta + 2\sin 3\theta$
   v $3\sin 7\alpha - 3\sin \alpha$ **vi** $\frac{1}{6}\sin 8A - \frac{1}{6}\sin 2A$

20 b i $\frac{1}{2}\cos 5\theta + \frac{1}{2}\cos 3\theta$ **ii** $\frac{1}{2}\cos 8\alpha + \frac{1}{2}\cos 6\alpha$
   iii $\cos 4\beta + \cos 2\beta$ **iv** $3\cos 8x + 3\cos 6x$
   v $\frac{3}{2}\cos 5P + \frac{3}{2}\cos 3P$ **vi** $\frac{1}{8}\cos 6x + \frac{1}{8}\cos 2x$

21 b i $\frac{1}{2}\cos 2\theta - \frac{1}{2}\cos 4\theta$ **ii** $\frac{1}{2}\cos 5\alpha - \frac{1}{2}\cos 7\alpha$
   iii $\cos 4\beta - \cos 6\beta$ **iv** $2\cos 3\theta - 2\cos 5\theta$
   v $5\cos 6A - 5\cos 10A$ **vi** $\frac{1}{10}\cos 4M - \frac{1}{10}\cos 10M$

22 $\sin A \cos A = \frac{1}{2}\sin 2A$ $\cos^2 A = \frac{1}{2}\cos 2A + \frac{1}{2}$
   $\sin^2 A = \frac{1}{2} - \frac{1}{2}\cos 2A$

23 d $\cos\left(\frac{S+D}{2}\right)\cos\left(\frac{S-D}{2}\right) = \frac{1}{2}\cos S + \frac{1}{2}\cos D$
   e $\sin\left(\frac{S+D}{2}\right)\sin\left(\frac{S-D}{2}\right) = \frac{1}{2}\cos D - \frac{1}{2}\cos S$

24   **a** $2\sin 3x \cos 2x$ **b** $2\cos 5A \cos 3A$ **c** $-2\sin 2\alpha \sin\alpha$
    d $2\cos 4\theta \sin\theta$ **e** $-2\sin 4\alpha \sin 3\alpha$ **f** $2\sin 5\alpha \cos 2\alpha$
    g $2\sin 3B \sin B$ **h** $2\cos\left(x+\frac{h}{2}\right)\sin\left(\frac{h}{2}\right)$
    i $-2\sin\left(x+\frac{h}{2}\right)\sin\left(\frac{h}{2}\right)$

EXERCISE 12K

1   **a** $\frac{24}{25}$ **b** $-\frac{7}{25}$ **2**   **a** $-\frac{7}{9}$ **b** $\frac{1}{9}$

3   **a** $\cos\alpha = \frac{-\sqrt{5}}{3}$, $\sin 2\alpha = \frac{4\sqrt{5}}{9}$

    b $\sin\beta = \frac{-\sqrt{21}}{5}$, $\sin 2\beta = \frac{-4\sqrt{21}}{25}$

4   **a** $\frac{1}{3}$ **b** $\frac{2\sqrt{2}}{3}$ **5** $\tan A = -\frac{7}{3}$ **6** $\tan A = \frac{3}{2}$

7 $\tan\left(\frac{\pi}{8}\right) = \sqrt{2}-1$ **8**   **a** $\frac{9+5\sqrt{2}}{2}$ **b** $\frac{4\sqrt{2}}{7}$ **9** $\frac{3}{2}$

10   **a** $\sin 2\alpha$ **b** $2\sin 2\alpha$ **c** $\frac{1}{2}\sin 2\alpha$ **d** $\cos 2\beta$ **e** $-\cos 2\phi$
     f $\cos 2N$ **g** $-\cos 2M$ **h** $\cos 2\alpha$ **i** $-\cos 2\alpha$
     j $\sin 4A$ **k** $\sin 6\alpha$ **l** $\cos 8\theta$ **m** $-\cos 6\beta$ **n** $\cos 10\alpha$
     o $-\cos 6D$ **p** $\cos 4A$ **q** $\cos\alpha$ **r** $-2\cos 6P$

12   **a** $\cos A = \frac{7}{10}$ **b** $\cos A = \frac{3}{4}$

13   **a**   Domain $\{x \mid x \neq \frac{\pi}{2} + k\pi, \ k \in \mathbb{Z}\}$,   Range $\{y \mid y \text{ is in } \mathbb{R}\}$

    b   Domain $\{x \mid x \neq \frac{\pi}{4} + \frac{k\pi}{2}, \ k \in \mathbb{Z}\}$,
       Range $\{y \mid y \geqslant 1 \text{ or } y \leqslant -1\}$

    c   Domain $\{x \mid x \neq \frac{k\pi}{3}, \ k \in \mathbb{Z}\}$,   Range $\{y \mid y \text{ is in } \mathbb{R}\}$

16 $k = 2$, $b = \frac{\pi}{6}$ **18**   **b** $\theta = -\frac{8\pi}{9}, -\frac{4\pi}{9}, -\frac{2\pi}{9}, \frac{2\pi}{9}, \frac{4\pi}{9}, \frac{8\pi}{9}$

19   **a** $\sin 3\theta = -4\sin^3\theta + 3\sin\theta$
    b $\theta = 0, \frac{\pi}{4}, \frac{3\pi}{4}, \pi, \frac{5\pi}{4}, \frac{7\pi}{4}, 2\pi, \frac{9\pi}{4}, \frac{11\pi}{4}, 3\pi$

21   **a** $2\cos x - 5\sin x = \sqrt{29}\cos(x+1.19)$ **b** $x = 0.761, \pi$
    d $x = 0.761$ (the solution $x = \pi$ has been lost)

EXERCISE 12L

1   **a** $x = 0, \pi, \frac{7\pi}{6}, \frac{11\pi}{6}, 2\pi$ **b** $x = \frac{\pi}{3}, \frac{\pi}{2}, \frac{3\pi}{2}, \frac{5\pi}{3}$
    c $x = \frac{\pi}{3}, \pi, \frac{5\pi}{3}$ **d** $x = \frac{7\pi}{6}, \frac{3\pi}{2}, \frac{11\pi}{6}$
    e   no solutions   **f** $x = \frac{\pi}{6}, \frac{5\pi}{6}, \frac{7\pi}{6}, \frac{11\pi}{6}$
    g $x = 0, \frac{\pi}{6}, \frac{\pi}{2}, \frac{5\pi}{6}, \pi, \frac{7\pi}{6}, \frac{3\pi}{2}, \frac{11\pi}{6}, 2\pi$ **h** $x = \frac{\pi}{4}$

2   **a** $x = \frac{\pi}{6}, \frac{\pi}{2}, \frac{5\pi}{6}$ **b** $x = -\frac{5\pi}{6}, -\frac{\pi}{6}, 0$
    c $x = -\frac{2\pi}{3}, -\frac{\pi}{3}, \frac{\pi}{3}, \frac{2\pi}{3}$

3   **a** $x \approx 0.896, 2.246$ **b** $x \approx 3.33, 6.10$
    c $x \approx 0.730, 2.412, 3.871, 5.553$

EXERCISE 12M

1   **a** $\frac{1-\sin^n x}{1-\sin x}$ **b** $\frac{1}{1-\sin x}$ as $-1 \leqslant \sin x \leqslant 1$ **c** $\frac{7\pi}{6}$ or $\frac{11\pi}{6}$

2   **b**   **i** $\sin 8x$ **ii** $\frac{\sin 20x}{2\sin x}$ **c** $\frac{\sin 2nx}{2\sin x}$

3   **b**   **i** $\frac{\sin(2^4 x)}{2^4}$ **ii** $\frac{\sin(2^6 x)}{2^6}$
    c $\sin x \cos x \cos 2x \ldots \ldots \cos 2^n x = \frac{\sin(2^{n+1} x)}{2^{n+1}}$

4   **b** $\frac{\sin 32\theta}{2\sin\theta}$ **5** 0

REVIEW SET 12A

1

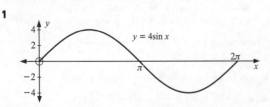

$y = 4\sin x$

2

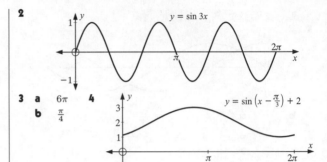

$y = \sin 3x$

3   **a** 6π **4**
    b $\frac{\pi}{4}$

$y = \sin\left(x - \frac{\pi}{3}\right) + 2$

5   **a** $T \approx 7.05\sin\frac{\pi}{6}(t - 10.5) + 24.75$

6   **a** $x \approx 0.392, 2.750, 6.675$ **b** $x \approx 5.42$

7   **a** $x \approx 3.25, 4.69$ **b** $x \approx 1.445, 5.89, 7.73$

8   **a** $x = \frac{7\pi}{6}, \frac{11\pi}{6}, \frac{19\pi}{6}, \frac{23\pi}{6}$ **b** $x = \frac{-7\pi}{4}, \frac{-5\pi}{4}, \frac{\pi}{4}, \frac{3\pi}{4}$

9   **a** $x = \frac{4\pi}{9}, \frac{5\pi}{9}, \frac{10\pi}{9}, \frac{11\pi}{9}, \frac{16\pi}{9}, \frac{17\pi}{9}$ **b** $x = 0, \frac{\pi}{4}, \pi, \frac{5\pi}{4}, 2\pi$

10   **a** 5000 **b** $3000, 7000$
     c $0.5 < t < 2.5$ and $6.5 < t \leqslant 8$

REVIEW SET 12B

1   **a** $x = \frac{3\pi}{2} + k2\pi$ **b** $x = \left.\begin{array}{c}\frac{\pi}{6} \\ \frac{5\pi}{6}\end{array}\right\} + k\pi$

2   **a**

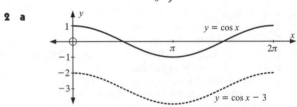

$y = \cos x$
$y = \cos x - 3$

    b

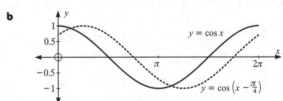

$y = \cos x$
$y = \cos\left(x - \frac{\pi}{4}\right)$

    c

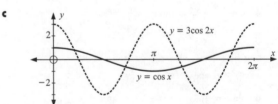

$y = 3\cos 2x$
$y = \cos x$

    d

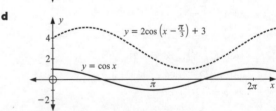

$y = 2\cos\left(x - \frac{\pi}{3}\right) + 3$
$y = \cos x$

3   **a**   28 milligrams per m^3 **b**   8.00 am Monday

4   **a** $y = -4\cos 2x$ **b** $y = \cos\frac{\pi}{4}x + 2$

5   **a** $x \approx 1.12, 5.17, 7.40$ **b** $x \approx 0.184, 4.616$

6   **a** $\frac{-1-\sqrt{3}}{2\sqrt{2}}$ **b** $2 - \sqrt{3}$

7 a $x = \frac{\pi}{2}, \frac{3\pi}{2}, \frac{5\pi}{2}, \frac{7\pi}{2}$ **b** $x = -\pi, -\frac{\pi}{3}, \pi, \frac{5\pi}{3}$

8 a $x = 0, \frac{3\pi}{2}, 2\pi, \frac{7\pi}{2}, 4\pi$ **b** $x = \frac{\pi}{6}, \frac{2\pi}{3}, \frac{7\pi}{6}, \frac{5\pi}{3}$

9 a $\cos\theta$ **b** $-\sin\theta$ **c** $5\cos^2\theta$ **d** $-\cos\theta$ **e** $\sin 2\theta$

10 a $4\sin^2\alpha - 4\sin\alpha + 1$ **b** $1 - \sin 2\alpha$

REVIEW SET 12C

1 a $1 - \cos\theta$ **b** $\dfrac{1}{\sin\alpha + \cos\alpha}$ **c** $\dfrac{-\cos\alpha}{2}$

3 a $\frac{120}{169}$ **b** $\frac{119}{169}$ **4** $\cos\alpha = \frac{-\sqrt{7}}{4}$, $\sin 2\alpha = \frac{3\sqrt{7}}{8}$

5 $\sin\left(\frac{x}{2}\right) = \frac{\sqrt{7}}{2\sqrt{2}}$

6 a i $x \approx 1.33 + k\pi$ **ii** $x \approx 5.30 + k4\pi$ **iii** $x \approx 2.83 + k\pi$

b i $x = \frac{\pi}{2} + k\pi$ **ii** $x = \frac{\pi}{3} + k\frac{\pi}{2}$ **iii** $\left.\begin{array}{c} x = \frac{\pi}{3} \\ \frac{2\pi}{3} \end{array}\right\} + k\pi$

c $x \approx 0.612 + k\pi$

7 $\sin\theta = \frac{2}{\sqrt{13}}$, $\cos\theta = -\frac{3}{\sqrt{13}}$ **9 a** $-\sin\theta$ **b** $\cos\theta$ **10** 1.5 m

REVIEW SET 12D

2 a $-\frac{\sqrt{7}}{4}$ **b** $-\frac{3\sqrt{7}}{8}$ **c** $-\frac{1}{8}$ **d** $3\sqrt{7}$

6 a $x = \frac{\pi}{3}, \frac{2\pi}{3}, \frac{4\pi}{3}$ or $\frac{5\pi}{3}$ **b** $x = \frac{\pi}{3}, \frac{5\pi}{6}, \frac{4\pi}{3}, \frac{11\pi}{6}$

8 $\sin\alpha = \frac{1}{\sqrt{5}}$ **9 c** $x = \frac{16}{3}$ **10** 60 m

EXERCISE 13A

1 a 1×4 **b** 2×1 **c** 2×2 **d** 3×3

2 a $(2 \; 1 \; 6 \; 1)$ **b** $\begin{pmatrix} 1.95 \\ 2.35 \\ 0.15 \\ 0.95 \end{pmatrix}$ **c** total cost of groceries

3 $\begin{pmatrix} 1000 & 1500 & 1250 \\ 1500 & 1000 & 1000 \\ 800 & 2300 & 1300 \\ 1200 & 1200 & 1200 \end{pmatrix}$ **4** $\begin{pmatrix} 40 & 50 & 55 & 40 \\ 25 & 65 & 44 & 30 \\ 35 & 40 & 40 & 35 \\ 35 & 40 & 35 & 50 \end{pmatrix}$

EXERCISE 13B.1

1 a $\begin{pmatrix} 9 & 1 \\ 3 & 3 \end{pmatrix}$ **b** $\begin{pmatrix} 6 & 8 \\ -1 & 1 \end{pmatrix}$ **c** $\begin{pmatrix} 3 & 4 \\ -6 & -1 \end{pmatrix}$ **d** $\begin{pmatrix} 0 & 0 \\ -11 & -3 \end{pmatrix}$

2 a $\begin{pmatrix} 20 & 1 & -8 \\ 8 & 10 & -2 \\ 1 & -5 & 18 \end{pmatrix}$ **b** $\begin{pmatrix} -14 & 9 & -14 \\ 12 & -6 & 14 \\ -5 & 3 & -4 \end{pmatrix}$ **c** $\begin{pmatrix} 14 & -9 & 14 \\ -12 & 6 & -14 \\ 5 & -3 & 4 \end{pmatrix}$

3 a Friday $\begin{pmatrix} 85 \\ 92 \\ 52 \end{pmatrix}$ Saturday $\begin{pmatrix} 102 \\ 137 \\ 49 \end{pmatrix}$ **b** $\begin{pmatrix} 187 \\ 229 \\ 101 \end{pmatrix}$

4 a i $\begin{pmatrix} 1.72 \\ 27.85 \\ 0.92 \\ 2.53 \\ 3.56 \end{pmatrix}$ **ii** $\begin{pmatrix} 1.79 \\ 28.75 \\ 1.33 \\ 2.25 \\ 3.51 \end{pmatrix}$ **b** subtract cost price from selling price **c** $\begin{pmatrix} 0.07 \\ 0.90 \\ 0.41 \\ -0.28 \\ -0.05 \end{pmatrix}$

5 a $\begin{array}{c} \\ \text{fr} \\ \text{st} \\ \text{mi} \end{array}$ $\begin{matrix} \text{L} & \text{R} \\ \begin{pmatrix} 23 & 19 \\ 17 & 29 \\ 31 & 24 \end{pmatrix} \end{matrix}$ **b** $\begin{matrix} \text{L} & \text{R} \\ \begin{pmatrix} 18 & 25 \\ 7 & 13 \\ 36 & 19 \end{pmatrix} \end{matrix}$ fr st mi **c** $\begin{matrix} \text{L} & \text{R} \\ \begin{pmatrix} 41 & 44 \\ 24 & 42 \\ 67 & 43 \end{pmatrix} \end{matrix}$ fr st mi

6 a $x = -2$, $y = -2$ **b** $x = 0$, $y = 0$

7 a $A + B = \begin{pmatrix} 1 & 3 \\ 5 & 2 \end{pmatrix}$ $B + A = \begin{pmatrix} 1 & 3 \\ 5 & 2 \end{pmatrix}$

8 a $(A + B) + C = \begin{pmatrix} 6 & 3 \\ -1 & 6 \end{pmatrix}$ $A + (B + C) = \begin{pmatrix} 6 & 3 \\ -1 & 6 \end{pmatrix}$

EXERCISE 13B.2

1 a $\begin{pmatrix} 12 & 24 \\ 48 & 12 \end{pmatrix}$ **b** $\begin{pmatrix} 2 & 4 \\ 8 & 2 \end{pmatrix}$ **c** $\begin{pmatrix} \frac{1}{2} & 1 \\ 2 & \frac{1}{2} \end{pmatrix}$ **d** $\begin{pmatrix} -3 & -6 \\ -12 & -3 \end{pmatrix}$

2 a $\begin{pmatrix} 3 & 5 & 6 \\ 2 & 8 & 7 \end{pmatrix}$ **b** $\begin{pmatrix} 1 & 1 & 4 \\ 0 & 4 & 1 \end{pmatrix}$

c $\begin{pmatrix} 5 & 8 & 11 \\ 3 & 14 & 11 \end{pmatrix}$ **d** $\begin{pmatrix} 5 & 7 & 14 \\ 2 & 16 & 9 \end{pmatrix}$

3 a $\begin{matrix} \text{A} & \text{B} & \text{C} & \text{D} \\ \begin{pmatrix} 35 & 46 & 46 & 69 \\ 58 & 46 & 35 & 86 \\ 46 & 46 & 58 & 58 \\ 12 & 23 & 23 & 17 \end{pmatrix} \end{matrix}$ **b** $\begin{matrix} \text{A} & \text{B} & \text{C} & \text{D} \\ \begin{pmatrix} 26 & 34 & 34 & 51 \\ 43 & 34 & 26 & 64 \\ 34 & 34 & 43 & 43 \\ 9 & 17 & 17 & 13 \end{pmatrix} \end{matrix}$

4 a $\begin{pmatrix} 75 \\ 27 \\ 102 \end{pmatrix} \begin{array}{l} \leftarrow \text{DVD} \\ \leftarrow \text{VHS} \\ \leftarrow \text{games} \end{array}$ $\begin{pmatrix} 136 \\ 43 \\ 129 \end{pmatrix} \begin{array}{l} \leftarrow \text{DVD} \\ \leftarrow \text{VHS} \\ \leftarrow \text{games} \end{array}$ **b** $\begin{pmatrix} 211 \\ 70 \\ 231 \end{pmatrix} \begin{array}{l} \leftarrow \text{DVD} \\ \leftarrow \text{VHS} \\ \leftarrow \text{games} \end{array}$

c total weekly average hirings **5** 12F

EXERCISE 13B.3

1 a $3A$ **b** O **c** $-C$ **d** O **e** $2A + 2B$

f $-A - B$ **g** $-2A + C$ **h** $4A - B$ **i** $3B$

2 a $X = A - B$ **b** $X = C - B$ **c** $X = 2C - 4B$

d $X = \frac{1}{2}A$ **e** $X = \frac{1}{3}B$ **f** $X = A - B$

g $X = 2C$ **h** $X = \frac{1}{2}B - A$ **i** $X = \frac{1}{4}(A - C)$

3 a $X = \begin{pmatrix} 3 & 6 \\ 9 & 18 \end{pmatrix}$ **b** $X = \begin{pmatrix} \frac{1}{2} & -\frac{1}{4} \\ \frac{3}{4} & \frac{5}{4} \end{pmatrix}$ **c** $X = \begin{pmatrix} -1 & -6 \\ 1 & -\frac{1}{2} \end{pmatrix}$

EXERCISE 13B.4

1 a (11) **b** (22) **c** (16) **2** $(w \; x \; y \; z) \begin{pmatrix} \frac{1}{4} \\ \frac{1}{4} \\ \frac{1}{4} \\ \frac{1}{4} \end{pmatrix}$

3 a $P = (27 \; 35 \; 39)$ $Q = \begin{pmatrix} 4 \\ 3 \\ 2 \end{pmatrix}$

b total cost $= (27 \; 35 \; 39) \begin{pmatrix} 4 \\ 3 \\ 2 \end{pmatrix} = \$291$

4 a $P = (10 \; 6 \; 3 \; 1)$ $N = \begin{pmatrix} 3 \\ 2 \\ 4 \\ 2 \end{pmatrix}$

b total points $= (10 \; 6 \; 3 \; 1) \begin{pmatrix} 3 \\ 2 \\ 4 \\ 2 \end{pmatrix} = 56$ points

EXERCISE 13B.5

1 Number of columns in **A** does not equal number of rows in **B**.

2 a $m = n$ **b** 2×3 **c** **B** has 3 columns, **A** has 2 rows

3 a i does not exist **ii** $(28 \; 29)$

b i (8) **ii** $\begin{pmatrix} 2 & 0 & 3 \\ 8 & 0 & 12 \\ 4 & 0 & 6 \end{pmatrix}$

4 a $(3 \; 5 \; 3)$ **b** $\begin{pmatrix} -2 \\ 1 \\ 1 \end{pmatrix}$

5 a $C = \begin{pmatrix} 12.5 \\ 9.5 \end{pmatrix}$ $N = \begin{pmatrix} 2375 & 5156 \\ 2502 & 3612 \end{pmatrix}$

b $\begin{pmatrix} 78\,669.5 \\ 65\,589 \end{pmatrix}$ income from day 1, income from day 2 **c** $\$144\,258.50$

6 a $R = \begin{pmatrix} 1 & 1 \\ 1 & 2 \\ 2 & 3 \end{pmatrix}$ **b** $P = \begin{pmatrix} 7 & 3 & 19 \\ 6 & 2 & 22 \end{pmatrix}$ **c** $\begin{pmatrix} 48 & 70 \\ 52 & 76 \end{pmatrix}$

d My costs at store A are €48, my friend's costs at store B are €76. **e** store A

EXERCISE 13B.6

1 a $\begin{pmatrix} 16 & 18 & 15 \\ 13 & 21 & 16 \\ 10 & 22 & 24 \end{pmatrix}$ **b** $\begin{pmatrix} 10 & 6 & -7 \\ 9 & 3 & 0 \\ 4 & -4 & -10 \end{pmatrix}$

c $\begin{pmatrix} 22 & 0 & 132 & 176 & 198 \\ 44 & 154 & 88 & 110 & 0 \\ 176 & 44 & 88 & 88 & 132 \end{pmatrix}$ **d** $\begin{pmatrix} 115 \\ 136 \\ 46 \\ 106 \end{pmatrix}$

2 a $(\ 3 \ \ 3 \ \ 2 \ )$ **b** $\begin{pmatrix} 125 & 150 & 140 \\ 44 & 40 & 40 \\ 75 & 80 & 65 \end{pmatrix}$ **c** $(\ 657 \ \ 730 \ \ 670 \ )$

d $(\ 369 \ \ 420 \ \ 385)$ **e** $\begin{pmatrix} 657 & 730 & 670 \\ 369 & 420 & 385 \end{pmatrix}$

3 \$224 660

4 a $(\ 125 \ \ 195 \ \ 225 \ ) \times \begin{pmatrix} 15 & 12 & 13 & 11 & 14 & 16 & 8 \\ 4 & 3 & 6 & 2 & 0 & 4 & 7 \\ 3 & 1 & 4 & 4 & 3 & 2 & 0 \end{pmatrix}$

$- (\ 85 \ \ 120 \ \ 130 \ ) \times \begin{pmatrix} 15 & 12 & 13 & 11 & 14 & 16 & 8 \\ 4 & 3 & 6 & 2 & 0 & 4 & 7 \\ 3 & 1 & 4 & 4 & 3 & 2 & 0 \end{pmatrix}$

$= \$7125$

b $(\ 125 \ \ 195 \ \ 225 \ ) \times \begin{pmatrix} 15 & 12 & 13 & 11 & 14 & 16 & 8 \\ 4 & 3 & 6 & 2 & 0 & 4 & 7 \\ 3 & 1 & 4 & 4 & 3 & 2 & 0 \end{pmatrix}$

$- (\ 85 \ \ 120 \ \ 130 \ ) \times \begin{pmatrix} 20 & 20 & 20 & 20 & 20 & 20 & 20 \\ 15 & 15 & 15 & 15 & 15 & 15 & 15 \\ 5 & 5 & 5 & 5 & 5 & 5 & 5 \end{pmatrix}$

$= -\$9030, \ $ i.e., a loss of \$9030

c $((\ 125 \ \ 195 \ \ 225 \ ) - (\ 85 \ \ 120 \ \ 130 \ ))$

$\times \begin{pmatrix} 15 & 12 & 13 & 11 & 14 & 16 & 8 \\ 4 & 3 & 6 & 2 & 0 & 4 & 7 \\ 3 & 1 & 4 & 4 & 3 & 2 & 0 \end{pmatrix}$

EXERCISE 13B.7

1 $AB = \begin{pmatrix} -1 & 1 \\ -1 & 7 \end{pmatrix}$ $BA = \begin{pmatrix} 0 & 2 \\ 3 & 6 \end{pmatrix}$ $AB \neq BA$

2 $AO = OA = O$ **4 b** $I = \begin{pmatrix} 1 & 0 \\ 0 & 1 \end{pmatrix}$

5 a $\begin{pmatrix} 7 & 0 \\ 0 & 7 \end{pmatrix}$ **b** $\begin{pmatrix} 97 & -59 \\ 118 & 38 \end{pmatrix}$

6 a A^2 does not exist   **b** when A is a square matrix

EXERCISE 13B.8

1 a $A^2 + A$ **b** $B^2 + 2B$ **c** $A^3 - 2A^2 + A$ **d** $A^3 + A^2 - 2A$
e $AC + AD + BC + BD$ **f** $A^2 + AB + BA + B^2$
g $A^2 - AB + BA - B^2$ **h** $A^2 + 2A + I$ **i** $9I - 6B + B^2$

2 a $A^3 = 3A - 2I$ $A^4 = 4A - 3I$
b $B^3 = 3B - 2I$ $B^4 = 6I - 5B$ $B^5 = 11B - 10I$
c $C^3 = 13C - 12I$ $C^5 = 121C - 120I$

3 a i $I + 2A$ **ii** $2I - 2A$ **iii** $10A + 6I$
b $A^2 + A + 2I$ **c i** $-3A$ **ii** $-2A$ **iii** A

4 a $AB = \begin{pmatrix} 0 & 0 \\ 0 & 0 \end{pmatrix}$ **b** $A^2 = \begin{pmatrix} \frac{1}{2} & \frac{1}{2} \\ \frac{1}{2} & \frac{1}{2} \end{pmatrix}$

c false as $A(A - I) = O$ does not imply that $A = O$ or $A - I = O$
d $\begin{pmatrix} 0 & 0 \\ 0 & 0 \end{pmatrix}, \begin{pmatrix} 1 & 0 \\ 0 & 1 \end{pmatrix}, \begin{pmatrix} a & b \\ \frac{a-a^2}{b} & 1-a \end{pmatrix}, b \neq 0$

5 For example, $A = \begin{pmatrix} 0 & 1 \\ 0 & 0 \end{pmatrix}$, gives $A^2 = \begin{pmatrix} 0 & 0 \\ 0 & 0 \end{pmatrix}$

6 a $a = 3, b = -4$ **b** $a = 1, b = 8$
7 $p = -2, q = 1$ **a** $A^3 = 5A - 2I$ **b** $A^4 = -12A + 5I$

EXERCISE 13C.1

1 a $\begin{pmatrix} 3 & 0 \\ 0 & 3 \end{pmatrix} = 3I, \ \begin{pmatrix} 1 & -2 \\ -\frac{2}{3} & \frac{5}{3} \end{pmatrix}$

b $\begin{pmatrix} 10 & 0 \\ 0 & 10 \end{pmatrix} = 10I, \ \begin{pmatrix} 0.2 & 0.4 \\ -0.1 & 0.3 \end{pmatrix}$

2 a -2 **b** -1 **c** 0 **d** 1
3 a 26 **b** 6 **c** -1 **d** $a^2 + a$

4 a -3 **b** 9 **c** -12 **5** Hint: Let $A = \begin{pmatrix} a & b \\ c & d \end{pmatrix}$

6 a $|A| = ad - bc$ $|B| = wz - xy$

b $AB = \begin{pmatrix} aw + by & ax + bz \\ cw + dy & cx + dz \end{pmatrix}$, $|AB| = (ad - bc)(wz - xy)$

7 a i -2 **ii** -8 **iii** -2 **iv** -9 **v** 2

8 a $\frac{1}{14}\begin{pmatrix} 5 & -4 \\ 1 & 2 \end{pmatrix}$ **b** $\begin{pmatrix} 1 & 0 \\ 1 & -1 \end{pmatrix}$ **c** does not exist   **d** $\begin{pmatrix} 1 & 0 \\ 0 & 1 \end{pmatrix}$

e does not exist   **f** $-\frac{1}{15}\begin{pmatrix} 7 & -2 \\ -4 & -1 \end{pmatrix}$ **g** $\frac{1}{10}\begin{pmatrix} 2 & -4 \\ 1 & 3 \end{pmatrix}$ **h** $\begin{pmatrix} -3 & -1 \\ 2 & 1 \end{pmatrix}$

9 a $AB = \begin{pmatrix} 1 & 0 \\ 0 & 1 \end{pmatrix}$ **b** A and B are not inverses since they are not square matrices.

EXERCISE 13C.2

1 a $\begin{pmatrix} 3 & -1 \\ 2 & 3 \end{pmatrix}\begin{pmatrix} x \\ y \end{pmatrix} = \begin{pmatrix} 8 \\ 6 \end{pmatrix}$ **b** $\begin{pmatrix} 4 & -3 \\ 3 & 2 \end{pmatrix}\begin{pmatrix} x \\ y \end{pmatrix} = \begin{pmatrix} 11 \\ -5 \end{pmatrix}$

c $\begin{pmatrix} 3 & -1 \\ 2 & 7 \end{pmatrix}\begin{pmatrix} a \\ b \end{pmatrix} = \begin{pmatrix} 6 \\ -4 \end{pmatrix}$

2 a $x = \frac{32}{7}, \ y = \frac{22}{7}$ **b** $x = -\frac{37}{23}, \ y = -\frac{75}{23}$
c $x = \frac{17}{13}, \ y = -\frac{37}{13}$ **d** $x = \frac{59}{13}, \ y = -\frac{25}{13}$
e $x = -40, \ y = -24$ **f** $x = \frac{1}{34}, \ y = \frac{55}{34}$

3 b i $X = \begin{pmatrix} -1 & 3 \\ 2 & 4 \end{pmatrix}$ **ii** $X = \begin{pmatrix} \frac{13}{7} & \frac{3}{7} \\ -\frac{2}{7} & -\frac{8}{7} \end{pmatrix}$

4 a i $k = -3$ **ii** $\frac{1}{2k+6}\begin{pmatrix} 2 & -1 \\ 6 & k \end{pmatrix}, \ k \neq -3$

b i $k = 0$ **ii** $\frac{1}{3k}\begin{pmatrix} k & 1 \\ 0 & 3 \end{pmatrix}, \ k \neq 0$

c i $k = -2$ or 1
ii $\frac{1}{(k+2)(k-1)}\begin{pmatrix} k & -2 \\ -1 & k+1 \end{pmatrix}, \ k \neq -2$ or 1

5 a i $\begin{pmatrix} 2 & -3 \\ 4 & -1 \end{pmatrix}\begin{pmatrix} x \\ y \end{pmatrix} = \begin{pmatrix} 8 \\ 11 \end{pmatrix}, \ |A| = 10$
ii Yes, $x = 2.5, \ y = -1$

b i $\begin{pmatrix} 2 & k \\ 4 & -1 \end{pmatrix}\begin{pmatrix} x \\ y \end{pmatrix} = \begin{pmatrix} 8 \\ 11 \end{pmatrix}, \ |A| = -2 - 4k$
ii $k \neq -\frac{1}{2}, \ x = \frac{8+11k}{2+4k} \ \ y = \frac{5}{1+2k}$
iii $k = -\frac{1}{2}$, no solutions

EXERCISE 13C.3

1 $X = \begin{pmatrix} \frac{1}{4} & \frac{3}{4} \\ 1 & 0 \end{pmatrix}$

2 b $\begin{pmatrix} 1 & 0 \\ 0 & 1 \end{pmatrix}, \begin{pmatrix} -1 & 0 \\ 0 & -1 \end{pmatrix}, \begin{pmatrix} 0 & 1 \\ 1 & 0 \end{pmatrix}, \begin{pmatrix} 0 & -1 \\ -1 & 0 \end{pmatrix}$

3 a $A^{-1} = \begin{pmatrix} 0 & -1 \\ \frac{1}{2} & \frac{1}{2} \end{pmatrix}, \ (A^{-1})^{-1} = \begin{pmatrix} 1 & 2 \\ -1 & 0 \end{pmatrix}$
b $(A^{-1})^{-1}(A^{-1}) = (A^{-1})(A^{-1})^{-1} = I$
c $(A^{-1})^{-1} = A$

4 a i $\begin{pmatrix} \frac{1}{3} & \frac{1}{3} \\ \frac{2}{3} & -\frac{1}{3} \end{pmatrix}$ **ii** $\begin{pmatrix} \frac{3}{2} & \frac{1}{2} \\ 1 & 0 \end{pmatrix}$ **iii** $\begin{pmatrix} \frac{5}{6} & \frac{1}{3} \\ \frac{1}{3} & \frac{1}{3} \end{pmatrix}$

iv $\begin{pmatrix} \frac{5}{6} & \frac{1}{6} \\ \frac{2}{3} & \frac{1}{3} \end{pmatrix}$ **v** $\begin{pmatrix} \frac{5}{6} & \frac{1}{6} \\ \frac{2}{3} & \frac{1}{3} \end{pmatrix}$ **vi** $\begin{pmatrix} \frac{5}{6} & \frac{1}{3} \\ \frac{1}{3} & \frac{1}{3} \end{pmatrix}$

c $(AB)^{-1} = B^{-1}A^{-1}$ and $(BA)^{-1} = A^{-1}B^{-1}$
d $(AB)(B^{-1}A^{-1}) = (B^{-1}A^{-1})(AB) = I$
AB and $B^{-1}A^{-1}$ are inverses

5 $(k\mathbf{A})\left(\frac{1}{k}\mathbf{A}^{-1}\right) = \left(\frac{1}{k}\mathbf{A}^{-1}\right)(k\mathbf{A}) = \mathbf{I}$

$k\mathbf{A}$ and $\frac{1}{k}\mathbf{A}^{-1}$ are inverses

6 a $\mathbf{X} = \mathbf{ABZ}$ **b** $\mathbf{Z} = \mathbf{B}^{-1}\mathbf{A}^{-1}\mathbf{X}$

7 $\mathbf{A}^2 = 2\mathbf{A} - \mathbf{I}$, $\mathbf{A}^{-1} = 2\mathbf{I} - \mathbf{A}$

8 a $\mathbf{A}^{-1} = 4\mathbf{I} - \mathbf{A}$ **b** $\mathbf{A}^{-1} = 5\mathbf{I} + \mathbf{A}$ **c** $\mathbf{A}^{-1} = \frac{3}{2}\mathbf{A} - 2\mathbf{I}$

10 If $\mathbf{A}^{-1}$ exists, i.e., $|\mathbf{A}| \neq 0$.

EXERCISE 13D.1

1 a 41 **b** -8 **c** 0 **d** 6 **e** -6 **f** -12

2 a $x = 1$ or 5 **b** When $x = 1$ or 5, does not have an inverse.

3 a abc **b** 0 **c** $3abc - a^3 - b^3 - c^3$ **4** $k \neq -3$

5 for all values of k except $\frac{1}{2}$ or -9

6 a $k = \frac{5}{2}$ or 2 **b** $k = 1$ or $\dfrac{-1 \pm \sqrt{33}}{2}$

7 a 16,

$$\begin{pmatrix} -\frac{21}{16} & -\frac{17}{16} & \frac{5}{4} & \frac{11}{16} \\ -\frac{17}{16} & -\frac{29}{16} & \frac{5}{4} & \frac{15}{16} \\ \frac{5}{4} & \frac{5}{4} & -1 & -\frac{3}{4} \\ \frac{11}{16} & \frac{15}{16} & -\frac{3}{4} & -\frac{5}{16} \end{pmatrix}$$

b -34,

$$\begin{pmatrix} -\frac{1}{2} & \frac{1}{2} & -1 & \frac{3}{2} & -\frac{1}{2} \\ -\frac{15}{34} & \frac{1}{2} & -\frac{4}{17} & \frac{29}{34} & -\frac{23}{34} \\ -\frac{29}{34} & \frac{3}{2} & -\frac{61}{17} & \frac{149}{34} & -\frac{83}{34} \\ \frac{39}{34} & -\frac{3}{2} & \frac{58}{17} & -\frac{157}{34} & \frac{87}{34} \\ \frac{1}{17} & 0 & -\frac{4}{17} & \frac{6}{17} & -\frac{3}{17} \end{pmatrix}$$

8 a $\begin{pmatrix} 1 & 2 & 1 & 1 & 1 \\ 2 & 1 & 2 & 1 & 1 \\ 1 & 2 & 3 & 1 & 1 \\ 2 & 2 & 1 & 1 & 3 \\ 3 & 3 & 5 & 2 & 2 \end{pmatrix}\begin{pmatrix} o \\ a \\ p \\ c \\ l \end{pmatrix} = \begin{pmatrix} 6.3 \\ 6.7 \\ 7.7 \\ 9.8 \\ 10.9 \end{pmatrix}$ **b** $|\mathbf{A}| = 0$

c oranges 50 cents, apples 80 cents, pears 70 cents, cabbages $2.00, lettuces $1.50

EXERCISE 13D.2

1 $\begin{pmatrix} 2 & 0 & 0 \\ 0 & 2 & 0 \\ 0 & 0 & 2 \end{pmatrix} = 2\mathbf{I}$, $\begin{pmatrix} -\frac{11}{2} & \frac{9}{2} & \frac{15}{2} \\ -\frac{1}{2} & \frac{1}{2} & \frac{1}{2} \\ 4 & -3 & -5 \end{pmatrix}$

2 a $\begin{pmatrix} \frac{5}{4} & \frac{3}{4} & -\frac{7}{4} \\ -\frac{1}{4} & -\frac{3}{4} & \frac{3}{4} \\ -\frac{3}{4} & -\frac{1}{4} & \frac{5}{4} \end{pmatrix}$ **b** $\begin{pmatrix} -5.5 & 4.5 & 7.5 \\ -0.5 & 0.5 & 0.5 \\ 4 & -3 & -5 \end{pmatrix}$

3 a $\begin{pmatrix} 0.050 & -0.011 & -0.066 \\ 0.000 & 0.014 & 0.028 \\ -0.030 & 0.039 & 0.030 \end{pmatrix}$ **b** $\begin{pmatrix} 1.596 & -0.996 & -0.169 \\ -3.224 & 1.925 & 0.629 \\ 2 & -1.086 & -0.396 \end{pmatrix}$

EXERCISE 13E

1 a $\begin{pmatrix} 1 & -1 & -1 \\ 1 & 1 & 3 \\ 9 & -1 & -3 \end{pmatrix}\begin{pmatrix} x \\ y \\ z \end{pmatrix} = \begin{pmatrix} 2 \\ 7 \\ -1 \end{pmatrix}$ **b** $\begin{pmatrix} 2 & 1 & -1 \\ 0 & 1 & 2 \\ 1 & -1 & 1 \end{pmatrix}\begin{pmatrix} x \\ y \\ z \end{pmatrix} = \begin{pmatrix} 3 \\ 6 \\ 13 \end{pmatrix}$

c $\begin{pmatrix} 1 & 1 & -1 \\ 1 & -1 & 1 \\ 2 & 1 & -3 \end{pmatrix}\begin{pmatrix} a \\ b \\ c \end{pmatrix} = \begin{pmatrix} 7 \\ 6 \\ -2 \end{pmatrix}$

2 $\mathbf{AB} = \mathbf{I}$, $a = 2$, $b = -1$, $c = 3$

3 $\mathbf{MN} = 4\mathbf{I}$, $u = -1$, $v = 3$, $w = 5$

4 a $x = 2.3$, $y = 1.3$, $z = -4.5$ **b** $x = -\frac{1}{3}$, $y = -\frac{95}{21}$, $z = \frac{2}{21}$
c $x = 2$, $y = 4$, $z = -1$

5 a $x = 2$, $y = -1$, $z = 5$ **b** $x = 4$, $y = -2$, $z = 1$
c $x = 4$, $y = -3$, $z = 2$ **d** $x = 4$, $y = 6$, $z = -7$
e $x = 3$, $y = 11$, $z = -7$ **f** $x \approx 0.33$, $y \approx 7.65$, $z \approx 4.16$

6 a x represents the cost per football in dollars,
y represents the cost per baseball in dollars,
z represents the cost per basketball in dollars
b 12 basketballs

7 a $2x + 3y + 8z = 352$
$x + 5y + 4z = 274$
$x + 2y + 11z = 351$
b $x = 42$, $y = 28$, $z = 23$
c €1 201 000

8 $11.80 per kg **9 a** $\begin{aligned} 5p + 5q + 6r &= 405 \\ 15p + 20q + 6r &= 1050 \\ 15p + 20q + 36r &= 1800 \end{aligned}$ **b** $p = 24$, $q = 27$, $r = 25$

10 a $a = 50\,000$, $b = 100\,000$, $c = 240\,000$ **b** yes
c 2007, $\approx$ £284 000, 2009, $\approx$ £377 000

EXERCISE 13F.1

1 a $x = 2$, $y = -3$ **b** $x = -1$, $y = 5$ **c** $x = -2$, $y = -4$

2 a intersecting **b** parallel **c** intersecting **d** coincident
e intersecting **f** parallel

3 a The second equation is the same as the first when divided throughout by 2. The lines are coincident.
b It gives no more information than the first. Gives the same solutions for x and y.
c i when $x = t$, $y = \dfrac{3 - t}{2}$, $t \in \mathbb{R}$
ii when $y = s$, $x = 3 - 2s$, $s \in \mathbb{R}$

4 a The system is inconsistent and so has no solutions. The lines are parallel.
b The lines are coincident. Infinitely many solutions exist of the form $x = t$, $y = \dfrac{5 - 2t}{3}$, $t \in \mathbb{R}$.

5 b If $k \neq -4$, the system is inconsistent and so has no solutions. If $k = -4$, the system has infinitely many solutions of the form $x = t$, $y = 3t - 2$, $t \in \mathbb{R}$.

6 a $\left(\begin{array}{cc|c} 3 & -1 & 8 \\ 0 & 0 & k - 16 \end{array}\right)$ **b** $k = 16$
c $x = t$, $y = 3t - 8$, $t \in \mathbb{R}$
d when $k \neq 16$

7 a $\left(\begin{array}{cc|c} 4 & 8 & 1 \\ 0 & 2a + 8 & -21 \end{array}\right)$ **b** $a \neq -4$
d When $a = -4$, last row is $0\ 0\ |\ -21$. So, the system is inconsistent and $\therefore$ no solutions exist.

8 A unique solution for $m \neq 2$ or -2.
a $x = \dfrac{6}{m + 2}$, $y = \dfrac{6}{m + 2}$
b If $m = 2$, there are infinitely many solutions of the form $x = t$, $y = 3 - t$ (t is real). If $m = -2$, there are no solutions.

EXERCISE 13F.2

1 a $x = 1 + 2t$, $y = t$, $z = 0$, $t \in \mathbb{R}$
b $x = 4$, $y = -2$, $z = 1$ **c** $x = 4$, $y = -3$, $z = 2$
d no solution, system is inconsistent

2 a $x = 2$, $y = -1$, $z = 5$
b no solution, system is inconsistent
c $x = \dfrac{1 - 5t}{3}$, $y = t$, $z = \dfrac{1 - 2t}{3}$, $t \in \mathbb{R}$

3 a $\left(\begin{array}{ccc|c} 1 & 2 & 1 & 3 \\ 0 & -5 & 2 & -5 \\ 0 & 0 & 0 & k - 8 \end{array}\right)$
b If $k \neq 8$, no solutions, if $k = 8$, infinitely many solutions of the form $x = \dfrac{5 - 9t}{5}$, $y = \dfrac{2t + 5}{5}$, $z = t$ (t is real).
c The last row does not enable us to solve for z.

4 a $\left(\begin{array}{ccc|c} 1 & 2 & -2 & 5 \\ 0 & -3 & 5 & -6 \\ 0 & 0 & k - 13 & -k + 13 \end{array}\right)$
b If $k = 13$, infinitely many solutions of the form $x = \dfrac{3 - 4t}{3}$, $y = \dfrac{5t + 6}{3}$, $z = t$ (t is real).
c If $k \neq 13$, $x = \frac{7}{3}$, $y = \frac{1}{3}$, $z = -1$.

5 a $\left(\begin{array}{ccc|c} 1 & 3 & 3 & a - 1 \\ 0 & -7 & -5 & 9 - 2a \\ 0 & 0 & a + 1 & a + 1 \end{array}\right)$
b $x = \dfrac{19 - 6t}{7}$, $y = \dfrac{-5t - 11}{7}$, $z = t$ (t is real)
c $x = \frac{1}{7}a + 2$, $y = \frac{2}{7}a - 2$, $z = 1$

6 $\begin{pmatrix} 1 & 2 & m & | & -1 \\ 0 & -2(m+1) & 1-m^2 & | & 1+m \\ 0 & 0 & (m+1)(m+5) & | & -7(m+1) \end{pmatrix}$

   a if $m = -5$, no solution

   b if $m = -1$, infinitely many solutions

   c if $m \neq -5$ or -1, unique solution

7 a $\begin{pmatrix} 1 & 3 & k & | & 2 \\ 0 & -(2+3k) & 3-k^2 & | & -k \\ 0 & 0 & (3k+25)(k-1) & | & 6(k-1) \end{pmatrix}$

   b $k = 1$, infinitely many solutions of the form

$$x = \frac{7-11t}{5}, \quad y = \frac{1+2t}{5}, \quad z = t \ (t \text{ is real})$$

   c $k = -\frac{25}{3}$ **d** $k \neq 1$ or $-\frac{25}{3}$

EXERCISE 13F.3

1 **a** $x = 2-2t$, $y = t$, $z = 3t+1$, $t \in \mathbb{R}$

   b $x = 18-5t$, $y = t$, $z = 7t-22$, $t \in \mathbb{R}$ **c** no solution

2 $x = \frac{5t}{7}$, $y = \frac{4t}{7}$, $z = t$, $t \in \mathbb{R}$ $x = 5$, $y = 4$, $z = 7$

3 If $a \neq -\frac{2}{7}$, $x = y = z = 0$

   If $a = -\frac{2}{7}$, $x = \frac{-7t}{5}$, $y = \frac{3t}{5}$, $z = t$, $t \in \mathbb{R}$

4 **c** $P(x) = -\frac{29}{9}x^2 + \frac{172}{9}x - \frac{71}{9}$ thousand $

   d Max. profit = $20\,448$ when producing 2966

EXERCISE 13G

1 **a** $\mathbf{M}^2 = \begin{pmatrix} 1 & 4 \\ 0 & 1 \end{pmatrix}$, $\mathbf{M}^3 = \begin{pmatrix} 1 & 6 \\ 0 & 1 \end{pmatrix}$, $\mathbf{M}^4 = \begin{pmatrix} 1 & 8 \\ 0 & 1 \end{pmatrix}$

   b Conjecture is: $\mathbf{M}^n = \begin{pmatrix} 1 & 2n \\ 0 & 1 \end{pmatrix}$

2 a $\mathbf{A}^2 = \begin{pmatrix} 1 & 8 \\ 0 & 9 \end{pmatrix}$, $\mathbf{A}^3 = \begin{pmatrix} 1 & 26 \\ 0 & 27 \end{pmatrix}$, $\mathbf{A}^4 = \begin{pmatrix} 1 & 80 \\ 0 & 81 \end{pmatrix}$,

   $\mathbf{A}^5 = \begin{pmatrix} 1 & 242 \\ 0 & 243 \end{pmatrix}$

   b Conjecture is: $\mathbf{A}^n = \begin{pmatrix} 1 & 3^n - 1 \\ 0 & 3^n \end{pmatrix}$, $n \in \mathbb{Z}^+$

   d Yes as $\mathbf{A}^{-1} = \begin{pmatrix} 1 & -\frac{2}{3} \\ 0 & \frac{1}{3} \end{pmatrix}$.

3 a $\mathbf{P}^2 = \begin{pmatrix} 3 & 2 \\ -2 & -1 \end{pmatrix}$, $\mathbf{P}^3 = \begin{pmatrix} 4 & 3 \\ -3 & -2 \end{pmatrix}$, $\mathbf{P}^4 = \begin{pmatrix} 5 & 4 \\ -4 & -3 \end{pmatrix}$

   b $\mathbf{P}^n = \begin{pmatrix} n+1 & n \\ -n & 1-n \end{pmatrix}$ for all $n \in \mathbb{Z}^+$

REVIEW SET 13A

1 a $\begin{pmatrix} 4 & 2 \\ -2 & 3 \end{pmatrix}$ **b** $\begin{pmatrix} 9 & 6 \\ 0 & -3 \end{pmatrix}$ **c** $\begin{pmatrix} -2 & 0 \\ 4 & -8 \end{pmatrix}$ **d** $\begin{pmatrix} 2 & 2 \\ 2 & -5 \end{pmatrix}$

   e $\begin{pmatrix} -5 & -4 \\ -2 & 6 \end{pmatrix}$ **f** $\begin{pmatrix} 7 & 6 \\ 4 & -11 \end{pmatrix}$ **g** $\begin{pmatrix} -1 & 8 \\ 2 & -4 \end{pmatrix}$ **h** $\begin{pmatrix} 3 & 2 \\ -6 & -8 \end{pmatrix}$

   i $\begin{pmatrix} \frac{1}{3} & \frac{2}{3} \\ 0 & -1 \end{pmatrix}$ **j** $\begin{pmatrix} 9 & 4 \\ 0 & 1 \end{pmatrix}$ **k** $\begin{pmatrix} -3 & -10 \\ 6 & 8 \end{pmatrix}$ **l** $\begin{pmatrix} \frac{1}{3} & \frac{2}{3} \\ \frac{1}{6} & \frac{1}{12} \end{pmatrix}$

2 a $a = 0$, $b = 5$, $c = 1$, $d = -4$ **b** $a = 2$, $b = -1$, $c = 3$, $d = 8$

3 a $\mathbf{Y} = \mathbf{B} - \mathbf{A}$ **b** $\mathbf{Y} = \frac{1}{2}(\mathbf{D} - \mathbf{C})$ **c** $\mathbf{Y} = \mathbf{A}^{-1}\mathbf{B}$

   d $\mathbf{Y} = \mathbf{C}\mathbf{B}^{-1}$ **e** $\mathbf{Y} = \mathbf{A}^{-1}(\mathbf{C} - \mathbf{B})$ **f** $\mathbf{Y} = \mathbf{B}^{-1}\mathbf{A}$

4 a $x = 0$, $y = -\frac{1}{2}$ **b** $x = \frac{12}{7}$, $y = \frac{13}{7}$ **c** $\mathbf{X} = \begin{pmatrix} -1 & 8 \\ -2 & 6 \end{pmatrix}$

   d $\mathbf{X} = \begin{pmatrix} -\frac{1}{2} \\ \frac{3}{2} \end{pmatrix}$ **e** $\mathbf{X} = \begin{pmatrix} \frac{14}{3} \\ \frac{1}{3} \end{pmatrix}$ **f** $\mathbf{X} = \begin{pmatrix} \frac{1}{2} & \frac{3}{2} \\ \frac{3}{2} & -\frac{1}{2} \end{pmatrix}$

5 a $\begin{pmatrix} 4 & 8 \\ 0 & 2 \\ 6 & 4 \end{pmatrix}$ **b** $\begin{pmatrix} 1 & 2 \\ 0 & \frac{1}{2} \\ \frac{3}{2} & 1 \end{pmatrix}$ **c** $(11 \ \ 12)$ **d** BA does not exist.

6 a $\begin{pmatrix} 4 & 2 \\ 2 & 4 \\ 3 & 4 \end{pmatrix}$ **b** $\begin{pmatrix} 2 & -2 \\ 0 & 4 \\ -1 & -2 \end{pmatrix}$ **c** $\begin{pmatrix} -\frac{3}{2} & 3 \\ \frac{1}{2} & -4 \\ 2 & \frac{7}{2} \end{pmatrix}$

7 unique solution if $k \neq \frac{3}{4}$, no solution if $k = \frac{3}{4}$

8 $x = 1$, $y = -2$, $z = -1$

9 a $-2a + 4b + c = -20$
     $a + 3b + c = -10$
     $\therefore \ a = 2 - t$, $b = -4 - 3t$, $c = 10t$ (t is real)

   b There are three unknowns and only two pieces of information.

   c $x^2 + y^2 + 4x + 2y - 20 = 0$

10 When $k \neq 27$, there are no solutions.
    When $k = 27$, there are infinite solutions of the form $x = 2-t$, $y = 2t+3$, $z = t$ (t is real).

11 $x = 3t$, $y = -7t$, $z = 2t$, t is real

REVIEW SET 13B

1 $\begin{pmatrix} 1 & 0 \\ 0 & 1 \end{pmatrix}$ **2 a** (10) **b** $\begin{pmatrix} 4 & 3 & 2 \\ 8 & 6 & 4 \\ 0 & 0 & 0 \end{pmatrix}$ **c** $(15 \ \ 18 \ \ 21)$

   d CA does not exist **e** $\begin{pmatrix} 5 \\ 7 \\ 5 \end{pmatrix}$

3 a $\begin{pmatrix} \frac{7}{2} & -4 \\ \frac{-5}{2} & 3 \end{pmatrix}$ **b** does not exist **c** $\begin{pmatrix} 1 & \frac{5}{3} \\ -2 & -\frac{11}{3} \end{pmatrix}$

4 b $2\mathbf{A} - \mathbf{I}$ **5** 56.30 **6** $\mathbf{AB} = \mathbf{I}$, $\mathbf{BA} = \mathbf{I}$, $\mathbf{A}^{-1} = \mathbf{B}$

7 $x = 2$, $y = 1$, $z = 3$

8 $x = \dfrac{-13t-1}{9}$, $y = \dfrac{20t+14}{9}$, $z = t$, $t \in \mathbb{R}$

9 b when $m \neq \frac{14}{3}$

REVIEW SET 13C

1 Unique solution for $k \neq -3$ or 1. If $k = -3$, infinitely many solutions exist. If $k = 1$, no solutions exist.

2 $x = -1, 2$ or -4 {using technology}

3 a $\begin{pmatrix} 10 & -12 \\ -10 & 4 \end{pmatrix}$ **b** $\begin{pmatrix} 2 & 6 & -3 \\ -4 & -2 & 11 \end{pmatrix}$

   c not possible **d** $\begin{pmatrix} 2.9 & -0.3 \\ -0.3 & 2.1 \end{pmatrix}$

4 $\mathbf{X} = \begin{pmatrix} 1 & 3 & 2 \\ -1 & 1 & 3 \end{pmatrix}$ **5** $\mathbf{A}^{-1} = \frac{5}{3}\mathbf{A} - 2\mathbf{I}$

6 a i $|\mathbf{B}| \neq 0$ **ii** $\mathbf{AB} = \mathbf{BA}$

   b $k \in \mathbb{R}$, but $k \neq 3, -2, 2$ {technology}

7 Does not have unique solutions when $t = 2$ or 3.
   When $t = 3$ there are no solutions.
   When $t = 2$ there are infinite solutions of the form $x = 1 + s$, $y = 4 - s$, $z = s$ (s is real).

   When $t \neq 2$ or 3, $x = \dfrac{3(t-5)}{t-3}$, $y = \dfrac{6t-8}{t-3}$, $z = \dfrac{-8}{t-3}$.

8 a $a = -3$, $b = 18$, $c = 48$ $\Rightarrow s(t) = -3t^2 + 18t + 48$

   b 48 m **c** 8 seconds

REVIEW SET 13D

1 $x = 1$, $y = -1$, $z = 2$

3 $\mathbf{A}^3 = 27\mathbf{A} + 10\mathbf{I}$, $\mathbf{A}^4 = 145\mathbf{A} + 54\mathbf{I}$,
   $\mathbf{A}^5 = 779\mathbf{A} + 290\mathbf{I}$, $\mathbf{A}^6 = 4185\mathbf{A} + 1558\mathbf{I}$

4 a $d = 80$ **b** $a = 2$, $b = 8$, $c = 10$ **5** $\mathbf{X} = \begin{pmatrix} 0 & -2 \\ 1 & 1 \end{pmatrix}$

6 a $x = 6$, $y = -2$, $z = 1$ **b** $x = \frac{3}{2}$, $y = -\frac{7}{6}$, $z = -\frac{7}{6}$

7 If $k = \pm 2$, there are no solutions.

If $k \neq \pm 2$, $x = \dfrac{k+4}{k^2-4}$, $y = \dfrac{-2-2k}{k^2-4}$

8 If $k = 2$ and $m \neq 20$ there are no solutions.

If $k = 2$ and $m = 20$ there are infinite solutions of the

form $x = \dfrac{10+3s-t}{2}$, $y = s$, $z = t$, s, t are real.

If $k \neq 2$, $z = \dfrac{m-20}{k-2}$, $y = s$, $x = \left(\dfrac{10+3s-\frac{m-20}{k-2}}{2} \right)$

9 b $k \neq 2$ or $\frac{2}{3}$

c If $k = 2$, $x = \dfrac{13-t}{9}$, $y = \dfrac{11t+1}{9}$, $z = t$, t is real

d When $k = \frac{2}{3}$, the system is inconsistent and has no solutions.

REVIEW SET 13E

1 a $3x + 2y + 5z = 267$
    $2x + 3y + z = 145$
    $x + 5y + 4z = 230$
b Opera €32   **c** €200
    Play €18
    Concert €27

2 $x = 2$, $y = 1$, $z = 3$

3 a $\begin{pmatrix} -9 & 6 & 6 \\ 3 & -3 & 0 \end{pmatrix}$ **b** $\begin{pmatrix} -10 & -6 \\ 5 & 3 \end{pmatrix}$ **c** $\begin{pmatrix} -2 & 0 & 4 \\ 10 & -7 & -6 \\ -1 & 0 & 2 \end{pmatrix}$

d not possible **e** $\begin{pmatrix} 0 & 22 \\ 7 & -12 \\ 0 & 11 \end{pmatrix}$

5 $\mathbf{A}^3 = -\mathbf{I}$, $\mathbf{A}^4 = -\mathbf{A}$, $\mathbf{A}^5 = -\mathbf{A} + \mathbf{I}$, $\mathbf{A}^6 = \mathbf{I}$, $\mathbf{A}^7 = \mathbf{A}$,
    $\mathbf{A}^8 = \mathbf{A} - \mathbf{I}$

a $\mathbf{A}^{6n+3} = (\mathbf{A}^6)^n \mathbf{A}^3 = -\mathbf{I}$, $\mathbf{A}^{6n+5} = -\mathbf{A} + \mathbf{I}$

b $\mathbf{A}^{-1} = -\mathbf{A} + \mathbf{I}$

6 a $a = 1$, $b = -1$ **b** $x = -5$, $y = 4$, $z = 7$

EXERCISE 14A.1

1 a
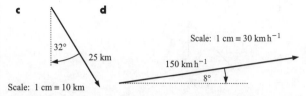
135°
30 N

b
25 m s⁻¹

c
70°
35 m

d
10°
50 m s⁻¹

2 a
100 m s⁻¹

b
45° 75 m s⁻¹

3 a
30 N
N
45°
scale: 1 cm ≡ 10 N

b
N
146°
scale: 1 cm ≡ 10 m s⁻¹
40 m s⁻¹

c
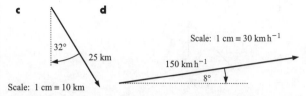
32°
25 km
Scale: 1 cm ≡ 10 km

d
Scale: 1 cm ≡ 30 km h⁻¹
150 km h⁻¹
8°

EXERCISE 14A.2

1 a p, q, s, t **b** p, q, r, t **c** p and r, q and t **d** q, t
    e p and q, p and t
2 a true **b** true **c** false **d** false **e** true **f** false

EXERCISE 14B.1

1 a
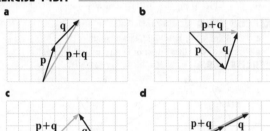
q
p
p+q

b
p+q
p
q

c
p+q
q
p

d
p+q
q
p

e
p
q
p+q

f
q
p+q
p

2 a $\overrightarrow{AC}$ **b** $\overrightarrow{BD}$ **c** $\overrightarrow{AD}$ **d** $\overrightarrow{AD}$

3 a i
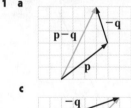
p
q
p+q

ii
q+p
q
p

b yes

EXERCISE 14B.2

1 a
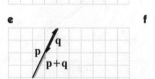
p−q
−q
p

b
p−q
p
−q

c
−q
p
p−q

d
p−q
−q
p

2 a
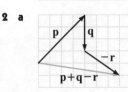
p
q
−r
p+q−r

b
−q
−r
p
p−q−r

c

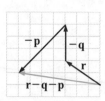

3 a $\overrightarrow{AB}$ **b** $\overrightarrow{AB}$ **c** 0 **d** $\overrightarrow{AD}$ **e** 0 **f** $\overrightarrow{AD}$

4 a $t = r + s$ **b** $r = -s - t$ **c** $r = -p - q - s$
 d $r = q - p + s$ **e** $p = t + s + r - q$
 f $p = -u + t + s - r - q$

5 a i $r + s$ **ii** $-t - s$ **iii** $r + s + t$
 b i $p + q$ **ii** $q + r$ **iii** $p + q + r$

EXERCISE 14B.3

1 a 24.6 km h^{-1} **b** 9.93^o east of south
2 a 82.5 m **b** 23.3^o west of north **c** 48.4 seconds

EXERCISE 14B.4

1 a   **b**   **c**   **d**

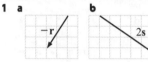 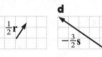

e   **f**

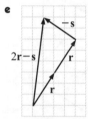 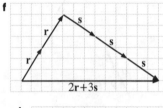

g   **h**

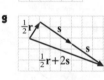 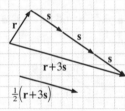

2 a   **b**   **c** $p = 2q$

d

e

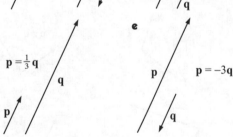

3 a

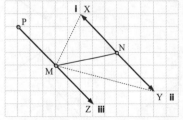

b a parallelogram

EXERCISE 14C.1

1 a   **b**   **c** $\begin{matrix}2\\2\end{matrix}$ **d**

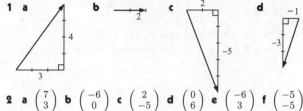

2 a $\begin{pmatrix}7\\3\end{pmatrix}$ **b** $\begin{pmatrix}-6\\0\end{pmatrix}$ **c** $\begin{pmatrix}2\\-5\end{pmatrix}$ **d** $\begin{pmatrix}0\\6\end{pmatrix}$ **e** $\begin{pmatrix}-6\\3\end{pmatrix}$ **f** $\begin{pmatrix}-5\\-5\end{pmatrix}$

EXERCISE 14C.2

1 a $\begin{pmatrix}-2\\6\end{pmatrix}$ **b** $\begin{pmatrix}-2\\6\end{pmatrix}$ **c** $\begin{pmatrix}-1\\-1\end{pmatrix}$ **d** $\begin{pmatrix}-1\\-1\end{pmatrix}$ **e** $\begin{pmatrix}-5\\-3\end{pmatrix}$

 f $\begin{pmatrix}-5\\-3\end{pmatrix}$ **g** $\begin{pmatrix}-6\\4\end{pmatrix}$ **h** $\begin{pmatrix}-4\\1\end{pmatrix}$

2 a $\begin{pmatrix}-3\\7\end{pmatrix}$ **b** $\begin{pmatrix}-4\\-3\end{pmatrix}$ **c** $\begin{pmatrix}-8\\-1\end{pmatrix}$ **d** $\begin{pmatrix}-6\\9\end{pmatrix}$ **e** $\begin{pmatrix}0\\-5\end{pmatrix}$

 f $\begin{pmatrix}6\\-9\end{pmatrix}$ **3 a** $\begin{pmatrix}-5\\4\end{pmatrix}$ **b** $\begin{pmatrix}1\\2\end{pmatrix}$ **c** $\begin{pmatrix}6\\-5\end{pmatrix}$

4 a $\begin{pmatrix}2\\4\end{pmatrix}$ **b** $\begin{pmatrix}-2\\5\end{pmatrix}$ **c** $\begin{pmatrix}3\\-3\end{pmatrix}$ **d** $\begin{pmatrix}1\\-5\end{pmatrix}$ **e** $\begin{pmatrix}6\\-5\end{pmatrix}$ **f** $\begin{pmatrix}1\\3\end{pmatrix}$

EXERCISE 14C.3

1 a $\begin{pmatrix}-3\\-15\end{pmatrix}$ **b** $\begin{pmatrix}-1\\2\end{pmatrix}$ **c** $\begin{pmatrix}0\\14\end{pmatrix}$ **d** $\begin{pmatrix}5\\-3\end{pmatrix}$ **e** $\begin{pmatrix}\frac{5}{2}\\\frac{11}{2}\end{pmatrix}$

 f $\begin{pmatrix}-7\\7\end{pmatrix}$ **g** $\begin{pmatrix}5\\11\end{pmatrix}$ **h** $\begin{pmatrix}3\\\frac{17}{3}\end{pmatrix}$

2 a $\begin{pmatrix}8\\-1\end{pmatrix}$ **b** $\begin{pmatrix}8\\-1\end{pmatrix}$ **c** $\begin{pmatrix}8\\-1\end{pmatrix}$

EXERCISE 14C.4

1 a $\sqrt{13}$ units **b** $\sqrt{17}$ units **c** $5\sqrt{2}$ units **d** $\sqrt{10}$ units **e** $\sqrt{29}$ units
2 a $\sqrt{10}$ units **b** $2\sqrt{10}$ units **c** $2\sqrt{10}$ units **d** $3\sqrt{10}$ units
 e $3\sqrt{10}$ units **f** $2\sqrt{5}$ units **g** $8\sqrt{5}$ units **h** $8\sqrt{5}$ units
 i $\sqrt{5}$ units **j** $\sqrt{5}$ units

4 a $\overrightarrow{AB} = \begin{pmatrix}1\\6\end{pmatrix}$, AB $= \sqrt{37}$ units **b** $\overrightarrow{BA} = \begin{pmatrix}-1\\-6\end{pmatrix}$, BA $= \sqrt{37}$ units

 c $\overrightarrow{BC} = \begin{pmatrix}-4\\-1\end{pmatrix}$, BC $= \sqrt{17}$ units **d** $\overrightarrow{DC} = \begin{pmatrix}3\\7\end{pmatrix}$, DC $= \sqrt{58}$ units

 e $\overrightarrow{CA} = \begin{pmatrix}3\\-5\end{pmatrix}$, CA $= \sqrt{34}$ units **f** $\overrightarrow{DA} = \begin{pmatrix}6\\2\end{pmatrix}$, DA $= 2\sqrt{10}$ units

EXERCISE 14D

1 a   **b**

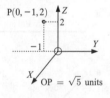

OP $= 3$ units

c   **d**

          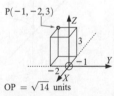

OP $= \sqrt{26}$ units   OP $= \sqrt{14}$ units

2 a i $\sqrt{14}$ units **ii** $(-\frac{1}{2}, \frac{1}{2}, 2)$ **b i** $\sqrt{14}$ units **ii** $(1, -\frac{1}{2}, \frac{3}{2})$
 c i $\sqrt{21}$ units **ii** $(1, -\frac{1}{2}, 0)$ **d i** $\sqrt{14}$ units **ii** $(1, \frac{1}{2}, -\frac{3}{2})$
4 a isosceles **b** right angled **c** right angled **d** straight line
5 $(0, 3, 5)$, $r = \sqrt{3}$ units **6 a** $(0, y, 0)$ **b** $(0, 2, 0)$ and $(0, -4, 0)$

EXERCISE 14E.1

1 a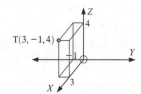

T(3, −1, 4)

b $\overrightarrow{OT} = \begin{pmatrix} 3 \\ -1 \\ 4 \end{pmatrix}$

c $OT = \sqrt{26}$ units

2 a $\overrightarrow{AB} = \begin{pmatrix} 4 \\ -1 \\ -3 \end{pmatrix}$, $\overrightarrow{BA} = \begin{pmatrix} -4 \\ 1 \\ 3 \end{pmatrix}$ **b** $AB = \sqrt{26}$ units

$BA = \sqrt{26}$ units

3 $\overrightarrow{OA} = \begin{pmatrix} 3 \\ 1 \\ 0 \end{pmatrix}$, $\overrightarrow{OB} = \begin{pmatrix} -1 \\ 1 \\ 2 \end{pmatrix}$, $\overrightarrow{AB} = \begin{pmatrix} -4 \\ 0 \\ 2 \end{pmatrix}$

4 a $\overrightarrow{NM} = \begin{pmatrix} 5 \\ -4 \\ -1 \end{pmatrix}$ **b** $\overrightarrow{MN} = \begin{pmatrix} -5 \\ 4 \\ 1 \end{pmatrix}$ **c** $MN = \sqrt{42}$ units

5 a $\overrightarrow{OA} = \begin{pmatrix} -1 \\ 2 \\ 5 \end{pmatrix}$, $OA = \sqrt{30}$ u **b** $\overrightarrow{AC} = \begin{pmatrix} -2 \\ -1 \\ -5 \end{pmatrix}$, $AC = \sqrt{30}$ u

c $\overrightarrow{CB} = \begin{pmatrix} 5 \\ -1 \\ 3 \end{pmatrix}$, $CB = \sqrt{35}$ units

6 a $\sqrt{13}$ units **b** $\sqrt{14}$ units **c** 3 units

EXERCISE 14E.2

1 a $a = 5$, $b = 6$, $c = -6$ **b** $a = 4$, $b = 2$, $c = 1$
2 a $a = \frac{1}{3}$, $b = 2$, $c = 1$ **b** $a = 1$, $b = 2$
c $a = 1$, $b = -1$, $c = 2$
3 a $r = 2$, $s = 4$, $t = -7$ **b** $r = -4$, $s = 0$, $t = 3$
4 a $\overrightarrow{AB} = \begin{pmatrix} 2 \\ -5 \\ -1 \end{pmatrix}$, $\overrightarrow{DC} = \begin{pmatrix} 2 \\ -5 \\ -1 \end{pmatrix}$

b ABCD is a parallelogram **5 a** S = (−2, 8, −3)

EXERCISE 14F.1

1 a $x = \frac{1}{2}q$ **b** $x = 2n$ **c** $x = -\frac{1}{3}p$ **d** $x = \frac{1}{2}(r - q)$
e $x = \frac{1}{5}(4s - t)$ **f** $x = 3(4m - n)$

2 a $y = \begin{pmatrix} -1 \\ \frac{3}{2} \end{pmatrix}$ **b** $y = \begin{pmatrix} 2 \\ 4 \end{pmatrix}$ **c** $y = \begin{pmatrix} \frac{3}{2} \\ -\frac{1}{2} \end{pmatrix}$ **d** $y = \begin{pmatrix} \frac{5}{4} \\ \frac{3}{4} \end{pmatrix}$

4 a B(−1, 10) **b** B(−2, −9) **c** B(7, 4)
5 a M(1, 4) **b** $\overrightarrow{CA} = \begin{pmatrix} 7 \\ 5 \end{pmatrix}$, $\overrightarrow{CM} = \begin{pmatrix} 5 \\ 3 \end{pmatrix}$, $\overrightarrow{CB} = \begin{pmatrix} 3 \\ 1 \end{pmatrix}$

6 a $x = \begin{pmatrix} 4 \\ -6 \\ -5 \end{pmatrix}$ **b** $x = \begin{pmatrix} 1 \\ -\frac{2}{3} \\ \frac{5}{3} \end{pmatrix}$ **c** $x = \begin{pmatrix} \frac{3}{2} \\ -1 \\ \frac{5}{2} \end{pmatrix}$

7 $\overrightarrow{AB} = \begin{pmatrix} 3 \\ 4 \\ -2 \end{pmatrix}$, $AB = \sqrt{29}$ units

9 C(5, 1, −8), D(8, −1, −13), E(11, −3, −18)
10 a parallelogram **b** parallelogram **c** not parallelogram
11 a D(9, −1) **b** R(3, 1, 6) **c** X(2, −1, 0)
12 a $\overrightarrow{BD} = \frac{1}{2}a$ **b** $\overrightarrow{AB} = b - a$ **c** $\overrightarrow{BA} = -b + a$
d $\overrightarrow{OD} = b + \frac{1}{2}a$ **e** $\overrightarrow{AD} = b - \frac{1}{2}a$ **f** $\overrightarrow{DA} = \frac{1}{2}a - b$

13 a $\begin{pmatrix} -1 \\ 5 \\ -1 \end{pmatrix}$ **b** $\begin{pmatrix} -3 \\ 4 \\ -2 \end{pmatrix}$ **c** $\begin{pmatrix} -3 \\ 6 \\ -5 \end{pmatrix}$

14 a $\begin{pmatrix} 3 \\ 1 \\ -2 \end{pmatrix}$ **b** $\begin{pmatrix} 1 \\ -3 \\ 4 \end{pmatrix}$ **c** $\begin{pmatrix} 1 \\ 4 \\ -9 \end{pmatrix}$ **d** $\begin{pmatrix} 2 \\ -4 \\ 10 \end{pmatrix}$ **e** $\begin{pmatrix} 3 \\ 2 \\ -5 \end{pmatrix}$

f $\begin{pmatrix} -1 \\ \frac{3}{2} \\ -\frac{7}{2} \end{pmatrix}$ **g** $\begin{pmatrix} 1 \\ -4 \\ 7 \end{pmatrix}$ **h** $\begin{pmatrix} 4 \\ 2 \\ -2 \end{pmatrix}$

15 a $\sqrt{11}$ units **b** $\sqrt{14}$ units **e** $\begin{pmatrix} \sqrt{11} \\ -3\sqrt{11} \\ 2\sqrt{11} \end{pmatrix}$ **f** $\begin{pmatrix} -\frac{1}{\sqrt{11}} \\ \frac{1}{\sqrt{11}} \\ \frac{3}{\sqrt{11}} \end{pmatrix}$
c $\sqrt{38}$ units **d** $\sqrt{3}$ units

16 a $r = 2$, $s = -5$ **b** $r = 4$, $s = -1$

EXERCISE 14F.2

1 a 1:1 **b** 1:3 **c** 3:1 **d** 1:3 **e** −2:1
f −2:5
2 a $Q(-\frac{1}{3}, 1, \frac{4}{3})$ **b** R(−5, −7, 13) **c** $S(2, \frac{5}{4}, \frac{3}{4})$
d $T(\frac{7}{3}, -3, \frac{20}{3})$ **e** $X(3, \frac{1}{3}, \frac{5}{3})$ **f** Y(−7, 8, −6)
3 a $p = \frac{5}{8}a + \frac{3}{8}b$ **b** $p = \frac{7}{5}a - \frac{2}{5}b$
c $p = \frac{n}{m+n}a + \frac{m}{m+n}b$

EXERCISE 14G

1 $r = 3$, $s = -9$ **2** $a = -6$, $b = -4$

3 a $\begin{pmatrix} \frac{2}{3} \\ -\frac{1}{3} \\ -\frac{2}{3} \end{pmatrix}$ **b** $\begin{pmatrix} -\frac{4}{3} \\ -\frac{2}{3} \\ \frac{4}{3} \end{pmatrix}$ **4 a** $\overrightarrow{AB} \parallel \overrightarrow{CD}$, $AB = 3CD$
b $\overrightarrow{RS} \parallel \overrightarrow{KL}$, $RS = \frac{1}{2}KL$
opposite direction
c A, B and C are collinear and $AB = 2BC$
d A, B and C are collinear and $AC = 3BC$

5 a $\overrightarrow{PR} = \begin{pmatrix} -1 \\ -3 \\ 3 \end{pmatrix}$, $\overrightarrow{QS} = \begin{pmatrix} -2 \\ -6 \\ 6 \end{pmatrix}$ **b** $PR = \frac{1}{2}QS$

6 a −7:2 **b** −1:2
7 a $a = 7$, $b = -1$ **b** $a = -\frac{7}{2}$, $b = -\frac{21}{2}$

EXERCISE 14H

1 a $\begin{pmatrix} 1 \\ -1 \\ 1 \end{pmatrix}$ **b** $\begin{pmatrix} 3 \\ -1 \\ 1 \end{pmatrix}$ **c** $\begin{pmatrix} 1 \\ 0 \\ -5 \end{pmatrix}$ **d** $\begin{pmatrix} 0 \\ \frac{1}{2} \\ \frac{1}{2} \end{pmatrix}$
$\sqrt{3}$ units $\sqrt{11}$ units $\sqrt{26}$ units $\frac{1}{\sqrt{2}}$ units

2 a $k = \pm 1$ **b** $k = \pm 1$ **c** $k = 0$ **d** $k = \pm\frac{\sqrt{11}}{4}$ **e** $k = \pm\frac{2}{3}$
3 a 5 units **b** $\sqrt{6}$ units **c** 3 units **d** ≈ 6.12 units
4 a $\frac{1}{\sqrt{5}}(i + 2j)$ **b** $\frac{1}{\sqrt{13}}(2i - 3k)$ **c** $\frac{1}{\sqrt{33}}(-2i - 5j - 2k)$

5 a $\frac{3}{\sqrt{5}}\begin{pmatrix} 2 \\ -1 \end{pmatrix}$ **b** $-\frac{2}{\sqrt{17}}\begin{pmatrix} -1 \\ -4 \end{pmatrix}$ **c** $\frac{6}{\sqrt{18}}\begin{pmatrix} -1 \\ 4 \\ 1 \end{pmatrix}$ **d** $-\frac{5}{3}\begin{pmatrix} -1 \\ -2 \\ -2 \end{pmatrix}$

EXERCISE 14I

1 a 7 **b** 22 **c** 29 **d** 66 **e** 52 **f** 3 **g** 5 **h** 1
2 a 2 **b** 2 **c** 14 **d** 14 **e** 4 **f** 4
3 a −1 **b** $94.1°$ **4 a** 1 **b** 1 **c** 0
6 a $t = 6$ **b** $t = -8$ **c** $t = 0$ or 2 **d** $t = -\frac{3}{2}$
7 a $t = -\frac{3}{2}$ **b** $t = -\frac{6}{7}$ **c** $t = \frac{-1 \pm \sqrt{5}}{2}$ **d** impossible
8 Show $a \bullet b = b \bullet c = a \bullet c = 0$ **9 b** $t = -\frac{5}{6}$
10 $\overrightarrow{AB} \bullet \overrightarrow{AC} = 0$, ∴ $\widehat{BAC}$ is a right angle
11 b $AB = \sqrt{14}$ units, $BC = \sqrt{14}$ units, ABCD is a rhombus
c 0, the diagonals of a rhombus are perpendicular.
12 a $101.3°$ or $78.7°$ **b** $116.6°$ or $63.4°$ **13 a** 5
c $63.4°$ or $116.6°$ **d** $71.6°$ or $108.4°$ **b** −9

14 a $k\begin{pmatrix} -2 \\ 5 \end{pmatrix}$, $k \neq 0$ **b** $k\begin{pmatrix} -2 \\ 1 \end{pmatrix}$, $k \neq 0$ **c** $k\begin{pmatrix} 1 \\ 3 \end{pmatrix}$, $k \neq 0$
d $k\begin{pmatrix} 3 \\ 4 \end{pmatrix}$, $k \neq 0$ **e** $k\begin{pmatrix} 0 \\ 1 \end{pmatrix}$, $k \neq 0$

15 $\widehat{ABC} \approx 62.5^o$,   the exterior angle 117.5^o

16 a 54.7^o **b** 60° **c** 35.3^o

17 a 30.3^o **b** 54.2^o **18 a** $M(\frac{3}{2}, \frac{5}{2}, \frac{3}{2})$ **b** 51.5^o

19 a $t = 0$ or -3 **b** $r = -2$, $s = 5$, $t = -4$

20 a 74.5^o **b** 72.45^o

21 $\mathbf{a} = \begin{pmatrix} 1 \\ 0 \\ 0 \end{pmatrix}$, $\mathbf{b} = \begin{pmatrix} 0 \\ 1 \\ 0 \end{pmatrix}$, $\mathbf{c} = \begin{pmatrix} 0 \\ 0 \\ 1 \end{pmatrix}$ will do

$\mathbf{a} \bullet \mathbf{b} = \mathbf{a} \bullet \mathbf{c}$, but $\mathbf{b} \neq \mathbf{c}$

23 a Hint: Square both sides.

b Consider the parallelogram. Find $\overrightarrow{AB}$ and $\overrightarrow{OC}$, etc.

24 -7 **25** $\mathbf{a} \bullet \mathbf{b}$ is a scalar and so $\mathbf{a} \bullet \mathbf{b} \bullet \mathbf{c}$ is a scalar 'dotted' with a vector which is meaningless.

EXERCISE 14J.1

1 a $\begin{pmatrix} 2 \\ 5 \\ 11 \end{pmatrix}$ **b** $\begin{pmatrix} 2 \\ 4 \\ 1 \end{pmatrix}$ **c** $-\mathbf{i} - \mathbf{j} - \mathbf{k}$ **d** $\mathbf{i} - 6\mathbf{j} + 2\mathbf{k}$

2 $\mathbf{a} \times \mathbf{b} = \begin{pmatrix} -11 \\ -2 \\ 5 \end{pmatrix}$, $\mathbf{a} \bullet (\mathbf{a} \times \mathbf{b}) = 0 = \mathbf{b} \bullet (\mathbf{a} \times \mathbf{b})$

$\mathbf{a} \times \mathbf{b}$ is a vector perpendicular to both $\mathbf{a}$ and $\mathbf{b}$

3 a $\mathbf{i} \times \mathbf{i} = 0$ $\mathbf{j} \times \mathbf{j} = 0$ $\mathbf{k} \times \mathbf{k} = 0$

b $\mathbf{i} \times \mathbf{j} = \mathbf{k}$ $\mathbf{j} \times \mathbf{i} = -\mathbf{k}$ $\mathbf{j} \times \mathbf{k} = \mathbf{i}$ $\mathbf{k} \times \mathbf{j} = -\mathbf{i}$
$\mathbf{i} \times \mathbf{k} = -\mathbf{j}$ $\mathbf{k} \times \mathbf{i} = \mathbf{j}$
$\mathbf{a} \times \mathbf{a} = 0$ $\mathbf{a} \times \mathbf{b} = -\mathbf{b} \times \mathbf{a}$

5 a $\begin{pmatrix} 1 \\ 4 \\ 2 \end{pmatrix}$ **b** 17 **c** 17

7 a $\begin{pmatrix} 2 \\ -1 \\ -1 \end{pmatrix}$ **b** $\begin{pmatrix} 0 \\ 5 \\ 0 \end{pmatrix}$ **c** $\begin{pmatrix} 2 \\ 4 \\ -1 \end{pmatrix}$ **d** $\begin{pmatrix} 2 \\ 4 \\ -1 \end{pmatrix}$

8 $\mathbf{a} \times (\mathbf{b} + \mathbf{c}) = (\mathbf{a} \times \mathbf{b}) + (\mathbf{a} \times \mathbf{c})$

11 a $\mathbf{a} \times \mathbf{b}$ **b** 0 **c** $2(\mathbf{b} \times \mathbf{a})$ **d** 0

12 a $k\begin{pmatrix} -4 \\ 1 \\ 3 \end{pmatrix}$ **b** $k\begin{pmatrix} 6 \\ 22 \\ -15 \end{pmatrix}$ **c** $(-\mathbf{i} + \mathbf{j} - 2\mathbf{k})n$

d $(5\mathbf{i} + \mathbf{j} + 4\mathbf{k})n$ $n, k \in \mathbb{R}$, $n, k \neq 0$

13 $k\begin{pmatrix} 4 \\ -5 \\ -7 \end{pmatrix}$, $k \neq 0$, $\frac{\sqrt{10}}{6}\begin{pmatrix} 4 \\ -5 \\ -7 \end{pmatrix}$ or $-\frac{\sqrt{10}}{6}\begin{pmatrix} 4 \\ -5 \\ -7 \end{pmatrix}$

14 a $\begin{pmatrix} 2 \\ 5 \\ -1 \end{pmatrix}$ **b** $\begin{pmatrix} 2 \\ 0 \\ 1 \end{pmatrix}$

EXERCISE 14J.2

1 a $\mathbf{i} \times \mathbf{k} = -\mathbf{j}$, $\mathbf{k} \times \mathbf{i} = \mathbf{j}$

2 a $\mathbf{a} \bullet \mathbf{b} = -1$ $\mathbf{a} \times \mathbf{b} = \begin{pmatrix} 1 \\ 5 \\ 1 \end{pmatrix}$

b $\cos\theta = -\frac{1}{\sqrt{28}}$ **c** $\sin\theta = \frac{\sqrt{27}}{\sqrt{28}}$ **d** $\sin\theta = \frac{\sqrt{27}}{\sqrt{28}}$

4 a $\overrightarrow{OA} = \begin{pmatrix} 2 \\ 3 \\ -1 \end{pmatrix}$ $\overrightarrow{OB} = \begin{pmatrix} -1 \\ 1 \\ 2 \end{pmatrix}$

b $\overrightarrow{OA} \times \overrightarrow{OB} = \begin{pmatrix} 7 \\ -3 \\ 5 \end{pmatrix}$ $|\overrightarrow{OA} \times \overrightarrow{OB}| = \sqrt{83}$

c Area $\triangle OAB = \frac{1}{2}|\overrightarrow{OA}||\overrightarrow{OB}|\sin\theta$
$= \frac{1}{2}|\overrightarrow{OA} \times \overrightarrow{OB}| = \frac{\sqrt{83}}{2}$ units^2

5 a $\overrightarrow{OC}$ is parallel to $\overrightarrow{AB}$ **b** $\mathbf{a} \times \mathbf{b} = \mathbf{b} \times \mathbf{c}$

EXERCISE 14J.3

1 a $\frac{\sqrt{101}}{2}$ units^2 **b** $\frac{\sqrt{133}}{2}$ units^2 **c** $\frac{\sqrt{69}}{2}$ units^2

2 $8\sqrt{2}$ units^2 **3 a** $D(-4, 1, 3)$ **b** $\sqrt{307}$ units^2

4 a 4 units^3 **b** $(\sqrt{42} + 2\sqrt{3} + 3\sqrt{2} + 6)$ units^2

5 a $(3, 1, 0), (1, 3, 3), (4, 2, 3), (4, 3, 3)$ **b** $\approx 79.0^o$ **c** 9 units^3

6 $k = 2 \pm 2\sqrt{33}$

7 $S = \frac{1}{2}\{|\mathbf{a} \times \mathbf{b}| + |\mathbf{a} \times \mathbf{c}| + |\mathbf{b} \times \mathbf{c}| + |(\mathbf{b} - \mathbf{a}) \times (\mathbf{c} - \mathbf{a})|\}$

9 a Yes **b** No **10** $k = \frac{23}{10}$

REVIEW SET 14A

1 a

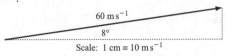

Scale: 1 cm $\equiv$ 10 m s^{-1}

b

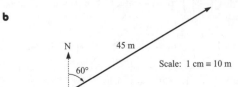

Scale: 1 cm $\equiv$ 10 m

2 a

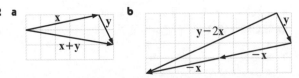

3 a $\overrightarrow{PQ}$ **b** $\overrightarrow{PR}$ **4** 4.845 km, 208° **5 a** $\overrightarrow{AC}$ **b** $\overrightarrow{AD}$

6 a $AB = \frac{1}{2}CD$, $[AB] \parallel [CD]$ **b** C is midpoint AB

7 a $\mathbf{p} + \mathbf{r} = \mathbf{q}$ **b** $\mathbf{l} + \mathbf{m} = \mathbf{k} - \mathbf{j} + \mathbf{n}$

8 a $\mathbf{r} + \mathbf{q}$ **b** $-\mathbf{p} + \mathbf{r} + \mathbf{q}$ **c** $\mathbf{r} + \frac{1}{2}\mathbf{q}$ **d** $-\frac{1}{2}\mathbf{p} + \frac{1}{2}\mathbf{r}$

9 a $\begin{pmatrix} 4 \\ 3 \end{pmatrix}$ **b** $\begin{pmatrix} 3 \\ -5 \end{pmatrix}$ **c** $\begin{pmatrix} 0 \\ -4 \end{pmatrix}$

10 a $\begin{pmatrix} -4 \\ -2 \end{pmatrix}$ **b** $\begin{pmatrix} -1 \\ -13 \end{pmatrix}$ **c** $\begin{pmatrix} -4 \\ 8 \end{pmatrix}$ **11** $\begin{pmatrix} 1 \\ 4 \end{pmatrix}$

12 a $\sqrt{17}$ units **b** $\sqrt{13}$ units **c** $\sqrt{10}$ units **d** $\sqrt{109}$ units

13 a $\mathbf{p} + \mathbf{q}$ **b** $\frac{3}{2}\mathbf{p} + \frac{1}{2}\mathbf{q}$

14 a $\mathbf{x} = \begin{pmatrix} -1 \\ \frac{1}{3} \end{pmatrix}$ **b** $\mathbf{x} = \begin{pmatrix} 1 \\ -10 \end{pmatrix}$ **16** $r = 4$, $s = 7$

17 a $\mathbf{q} + \mathbf{r}$ **b** $\mathbf{r} + \mathbf{q}$, $DB = AC$, $[DB] \parallel [AC]$

REVIEW SET 14B

1 a $\overrightarrow{PQ} = \begin{pmatrix} -3 \\ 12 \\ 3 \end{pmatrix}$ **b** $\sqrt{162}$ units **c** $\sqrt{61}$ units

2 a $\begin{pmatrix} 3 \\ -3 \\ 11 \end{pmatrix}$ **b** $\begin{pmatrix} 7 \\ -3 \\ -26 \end{pmatrix}$ **c** $\sqrt{74}$ units **3** $\begin{pmatrix} 8 \\ -8 \\ 7 \end{pmatrix}$

4 $m = 5$, $n = -\frac{1}{2}$ **5** $2:3$ **6** $t = 2 \pm \sqrt{2}$ **7** 80.3^o

8 40.7^o **9 a** $\begin{pmatrix} -6 \\ 1 \\ 3 \end{pmatrix}$ **b** $\sqrt{46}$ units **c** $(-1, 3\frac{1}{2}, \frac{1}{2})$

10 a -1 **b** $\begin{pmatrix} 4 \\ -1 \\ 7 \end{pmatrix}$ **c** 60°

11 $\widehat{K} \approx 124^o$, $\widehat{L} \approx 11.3^o$, $\widehat{M} \approx 45.0^o$

12 63.95^o **13** $c = \frac{50}{3}$

14 a $\mathbf{a} \bullet \mathbf{b}$ is a scalar, so $\mathbf{a} \bullet \mathbf{b} \bullet \mathbf{c}$ is a scalar dotted with a vector, which is meaningless.

  b $\mathbf{b} \times \mathbf{c}$ must be done first otherwise we have a scalar crossed with a vector which is meaningless.

15 a $k = \pm\frac{7}{\sqrt{33}}$ **b** $k = \pm\frac{1}{\sqrt{2}}$

REVIEW SET 14C

1 a -13 **b** -36 **3** $t = \frac{2}{3}$ or -3 **4** $k = 6$

5 $k \begin{pmatrix} 5 \\ 4 \end{pmatrix}$, $k \neq 0$ **6** $\widehat{K} \approx 64.4^o$, $\widehat{L} \approx 56.9^o$, $\widehat{M} \approx 58.7^o$

7 72.35^o or 107.65^o **8 a i** $\mathbf{p} + \mathbf{q}$ **ii** $\frac{1}{2}\mathbf{p} + \frac{1}{2}\mathbf{q}$

9 a $\overrightarrow{AC} = -\mathbf{p} + \mathbf{r}$, $\overrightarrow{BC} = -\mathbf{q} + \mathbf{r}$

10 a $\begin{pmatrix} 7 \\ -12 \\ -7 \end{pmatrix}$ **b** $\begin{pmatrix} 1 \\ -\frac{5}{3} \\ -\frac{2}{3} \end{pmatrix}$ **11** **a** ± 7 **b** $\frac{\sqrt{14}}{2}$ units^2 **c** $\frac{7}{6}$ units^3

REVIEW SET 14D

1 a $7\mathbf{i} - 3\mathbf{j} + 10\mathbf{k}$ **b** $\sqrt{14}$ units

3 a $\overrightarrow{PQ} = \begin{pmatrix} 5 \\ -2 \\ -4 \end{pmatrix}$ **b** $\approx 41.81^o$ **c** $R(\frac{2}{3}, \frac{4}{3}, \frac{5}{3})$ **4** $a = 4$ or $-\frac{36}{5}$

5 a $(1, 1, 2)$ and $(3, -1, 0)$ **b** $\begin{pmatrix} \frac{2}{\sqrt{3}} \\ -\frac{2}{\sqrt{3}} \\ -\frac{2}{\sqrt{3}} \end{pmatrix}$ **6** $-3 : 2$ **7** $(-\frac{16}{3}, \frac{17}{3}, \frac{23}{3})$ **8** $\frac{3}{2}$ units^3

9 $t = \frac{5}{6}\mathbf{a} - \frac{1}{2}\mathbf{b} + \frac{2}{3}\mathbf{c}$ **10** $\frac{1}{\sqrt{5}}\mathbf{i} + \frac{2}{\sqrt{5}}\mathbf{k}$

11 If θ is acute, $\mathbf{u} \bullet \mathbf{v} = \sqrt{199}$, If θ is obtuse, $\mathbf{u} \bullet \mathbf{v} = -\sqrt{199}$

12 $t = \frac{8}{7}$ **13** $\approx 26.4^o$

REVIEW SET 14E

1 $AB = AC = \sqrt{53}$ units and $BC = \sqrt{46}$ units $\therefore$ Δ is isosceles

2 $r = 3$, $s = -\frac{5}{2}$, $t = \frac{1}{4}$ **3** $(0, 0, 1)$ and $(0, 0, 9)$

4 a $\mathbf{x} = \begin{pmatrix} -11 \\ 5 \\ -10 \end{pmatrix}$ **b** $\mathbf{x} = \begin{pmatrix} 2 \\ 1 \\ 1 \end{pmatrix}$ **5** $a = -2$, $b = 0$ **6 a** 10 **b** $\approx 61.6^o$

7 a $r = -2$, $s = \frac{15}{2}$ **b** $\pm\frac{4}{\sqrt{14}}(3\mathbf{i} - 2\mathbf{j} + \mathbf{k})$

8 a $k = \pm\frac{1}{2}$ **b** $-\frac{5}{\sqrt{14}}\begin{pmatrix} 3 \\ 2 \\ -1 \end{pmatrix}$ **9 a** 8 **b** $\approx 62.2^o$

10 $\approx 16.1^o$ **11 a** $\sqrt{2}\begin{pmatrix} 5 \\ 4 \\ 3 \end{pmatrix}$ **b** $\frac{5}{2}\sqrt{2}$ units^2 **c** $k = 0$

12 a $t = -4$ **b** $\overrightarrow{LM} = \begin{pmatrix} 5 \\ -3 \\ -4 \end{pmatrix}$, $\overrightarrow{KM} = \begin{pmatrix} -2 \\ -2 \\ -1 \end{pmatrix}$

  So, $\overrightarrow{LM} \bullet \overrightarrow{KM} = 0$ $\therefore$ $\widehat{M} = 90^o$

EXERCISE 15A.1

1

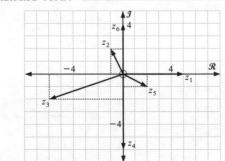

EXERCISE 15A.2

1 a

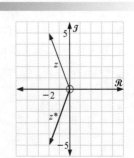

  b

2 a $4 + i$

  c $-1 + 5i$

  d $-7i$

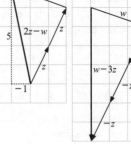

  b $-2 + 3i$

3 a $5 - i$

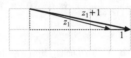

  b $4 + i$

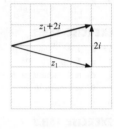

  c $4 + \frac{5}{2}i$

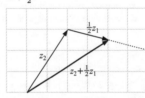

  d $4 - \frac{1}{2}i$

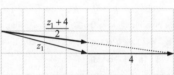

4 a   **b**   **c**

  d   **e**   **f**

  g   **h**

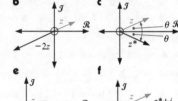
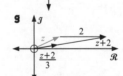
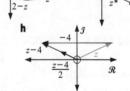

4 $z^* = z$ **5** $a = 11, b = -7$

EXERCISE 15B.1

1 a 5 **b** 13 **c** $2\sqrt{17}$ **d** 3 **e** 4

2 a $\sqrt{5}$ **b** $\sqrt{5}$ **c** 5 **d** 5 **e** $5\sqrt{2}$ **f** $5\sqrt{2}$ **g** $\frac{1}{\sqrt{2}}$

h $\frac{1}{\sqrt{2}}$ **i** 5 **j** 5 **k** $5\sqrt{5}$ **l** $5\sqrt{5}$

3 • $|z^*| = |z|$ • $zz^* = |z|^2$ • $|zw| = |z|\,|w|$ • $\left|\dfrac{z}{w}\right| = \dfrac{|z|}{|w|}$

• $|z^n| = |z|^n$ **5** 1 **6** $\left|\dfrac{z}{w}\right| \times |w| = |z|$

7 b $|z_1 z_2 z_3 .... z_n| = |z_1|\,|z_2| ..... |z_n|$ and that $|z^n| = |z|^n$

e $2^{20} = 1\,048\,576$

8 a 6 **b** 9 **c** $3\sqrt{5}$ **d** 3 **e** $\frac{1}{3}$ **f** $\frac{2}{9}$

9 a $\left[\dfrac{a^2 + b^2 - 1}{(a-1)^2 + b^2}\right] + \left[\dfrac{-2b}{(a-1)^2 + b^2}\right] i$ **b** 0 **10** 3 **11** 2

EXERCISE 15B.2

1 a i $4\sqrt{2}$ units **ii** $(1, 4)$ **b i** $5\sqrt{5}$ units **ii** $\left(-\frac{3}{2}, 2\right)$

2 a i $w + z$ **ii** $w - z$

3 a reflection in the R-axis **b** anti-clockwise rotation of π about 0
c reflection in the I-axis **d** clockwise rotation of $\frac{\pi}{2}$ about 0

4 $z = 2 + 6i$

EXERCISE 15B.3

1 a $4 \operatorname{cis} 0$ **b** $2 \operatorname{cis} \frac{\pi}{2}$ **c** $6 \operatorname{cis} \pi$ **d** $3 \operatorname{cis} \left(-\frac{\pi}{2}\right)$
e $\sqrt{2} \operatorname{cis} \frac{\pi}{4}$ **f** $2\sqrt{2} \operatorname{cis} \left(-\frac{\pi}{4}\right)$ **g** $2 \operatorname{cis} \left(\frac{5\pi}{6}\right)$ **h** $4 \operatorname{cis} \frac{\pi}{6}$

2 0 **3** $k\sqrt{2} \operatorname{cis} \frac{\pi}{4}$ if $k > 0$, $-k\sqrt{2} \operatorname{cis} \left(-\frac{3\pi}{4}\right)$ if $k < 0$,
not possible if $k = 0$

4 a $2i$ **b** $4\sqrt{2} + 4\sqrt{2}i$ **c** $2\sqrt{3} + 2i$ **d** $1 - i$ **e** $-\frac{\sqrt{3}}{2} + \frac{3}{2}i$
f -5 **5 a** 1 **b** 1

EXERCISE 15B.4

1 a $\operatorname{cis} 3\theta$ **b** $\operatorname{cis} 2\theta$ **c** $\operatorname{cis} 3\theta$ **d** $\frac{\sqrt{3}}{2} + \frac{1}{2}i$
e $\sqrt{2} + i\sqrt{2}$ **f** 8 **g** $-2i$ **h** -4 **i** $4i$

2 a -1 **b** -1 **c** $\frac{1}{2} + \frac{\sqrt{3}}{2}i$

3 a $|z| = 2, \arg(z) = \theta$ **b** $2 \operatorname{cis} (-\theta)$ **c** $2 \operatorname{cis} (\theta + \pi)$ **d** $2 \operatorname{cis} (\pi - \theta)$

4 a $\operatorname{cis} \frac{\pi}{2}$ **b** $r \operatorname{cis} \left(\theta + \frac{\pi}{2}\right)$ **d** clock. rotn. of $\frac{\pi}{2}$ about 0

5 a $\operatorname{cis} (-\theta)$ **b** $\operatorname{cis} \left(\theta - \frac{\pi}{2}\right)$ ..... then $z^* = r \operatorname{cis} (-\theta)$

6 a $\cos \left(\frac{\pi}{12}\right) = \frac{\sqrt{2}+\sqrt{6}}{4}$, $\sin \left(\frac{\pi}{12}\right) = \frac{\sqrt{6}-\sqrt{2}}{4}$

b $\cos \left(\frac{11\pi}{12}\right) = \frac{-\sqrt{2}-\sqrt{6}}{4}$, $\sin \left(\frac{11\pi}{12}\right) = \frac{\sqrt{6}-\sqrt{2}}{4}$

EXERCISE 15B.5

2 a $|-z| = 3$, $\arg(-z) = \theta - \pi$ **b** $|z^*| = 3$, $\arg(z^*) = -\theta$
c $|iz| = 3$, $\arg(iz) = \theta + \frac{\pi}{2}$
d $|(1+i)z| = 3\sqrt{2}$, $\arg((1+i)z) = \theta + \frac{\pi}{4}$

3 a $|z - 1| = 2\sin\frac{\phi}{2}$, $\arg(z - 1) = \frac{\phi}{2} + \frac{\pi}{2}$
b $z - 1 = \left(2\sin\left(\frac{\phi}{2}\right)\right)\operatorname{cis}\left(\frac{\phi}{2} + \frac{\pi}{2}\right)$
c $(z - 1)^* = \left(2\sin\left(\frac{\phi}{2}\right)\right)\operatorname{cis}\left(-\frac{\phi}{2} - \frac{\pi}{2}\right)$

4 b $\left|\dfrac{z_2 - z_1}{z_3 - z_2}\right| = 1$ **c** $\arg\left(\dfrac{z_2 - z_1}{z_3 - z_2}\right) = \frac{2\pi}{3}$ **d** 1 **5** $a = -\sqrt{3}$

6 a $e^{i\pi} = -1$, $e^{i\frac{\pi}{2}} = i$
c i $\frac{\theta}{2}$ **ii** $\frac{\pi}{2} + \theta$ **iii** $2\theta - \frac{\pi}{2}$ **iv** $\frac{\pi}{2} - \theta$

EXERCISE 15B.6

1 a $-1.41 + 1.01i$ **b** $1.27 - 3.06i$ **c** $-2.55 - 1.25i$

2 a $5 \operatorname{cis} (-0.927)$ **b** $13 \operatorname{cis} (-1.97)$ **c** $17.7 \operatorname{cis} (2.29)$

3 a $2 \operatorname{cis} \frac{\pi}{4}$ **b** $\sqrt{19} \operatorname{cis} (-2.50)$

4 a $a(x^2 + 2x + 4) = 0, a \neq 0$ **b** $a(x^2 - 2x + 2) = 0, a \neq 0$

EXERCISE 15C

1 a 32 **b** -1 **c** $-64i$ **d** $\sqrt{5} \operatorname{cis}\left(\frac{\pi}{14}\right) \approx (2.180 + 0.498i)$
e $\sqrt{3} + i$ **f** $16 + 16\sqrt{3}i$

2 a $128 - 128i$ **b** $1024 + 1024\sqrt{3}i$ **c** $\frac{1}{524\,288}\left(\frac{-1}{\sqrt{2}} + \frac{1}{\sqrt{2}}i\right)$
d $\frac{1}{64}(1-i)$ **e** $\sqrt{2}\cos\left(-\frac{\pi}{12}\right) + i\sqrt{2}\sin\left(-\frac{\pi}{12}\right)$ **f** $\frac{1}{64}(-\sqrt{3}-i)$

4 a $|z|^{\frac{1}{2}} \operatorname{cis} \frac{\theta}{2}$ **b** $-\frac{\pi}{2} < \phi \leqslant \frac{\pi}{2}$ **c** True **6** $\operatorname{cis} 3\theta$

7 $1 + i = \sqrt{2} \operatorname{cis}\left(\frac{\pi}{4}\right)$ $z^n = 2^{\frac{n}{2}} \operatorname{cis}\left(\frac{n\pi}{4}\right)$
a $n = 4k$, k any integer **b** $n = 2 + 4k$, $k \in \mathbb{Z}$

8 a $|z^3| = 8$, $\arg(z^3) = 3\theta$ **b** $|iz^2| = 4$, $\arg(iz^2) = \frac{\pi}{2} + 2\theta$
c $\left|\frac{1}{z}\right| = \frac{1}{2}$, $\arg\left(\frac{1}{z}\right) = -\theta$ **d** $\left|\frac{-i}{z^2}\right| = \frac{1}{4}$, $\arg\left(\frac{-i}{z^2}\right) = -\frac{\pi}{2} - 2\theta$

10 b $\tan 3\theta = \dfrac{3\tan\theta - \tan^3\theta}{1 - 3\tan^2\theta}$
c i $x = \frac{1}{\sqrt{2}}$, $\cos\left(\frac{5\pi}{12}\right)$, $\cos\left(\frac{11\pi}{12}\right)$
ii $x = \tan\left(\frac{\pi}{9}\right)$, $\tan\left(\frac{4\pi}{9}\right)$, $\tan\left(\frac{7\pi}{9}\right)$

11 a $\overrightarrow{AB} \equiv z_2 - z_1$, $\overrightarrow{BC} \equiv z_3 - z_2$ **Hint:** Notice that $\overrightarrow{BC}$ is a $90°$ rotation of $\overrightarrow{BA}$ about B.
b $\overrightarrow{OD} \equiv z_1 + z_3 - z_2$

12 a $\cos 4\theta = 8\cos^4\theta - 8\cos^2\theta + 1$
b $\sin 4\theta = 4\cos^3\theta \sin\theta - 4\cos\theta \sin^3\theta$

13 c $\left(z + \dfrac{1}{z}\right)^3 = z^3 + 3z + \dfrac{3}{z} + \dfrac{1}{z^3}$

14 Hint: When $n = 1$, $2i\sin\theta = z - \frac{1}{z}$. Now cube both sides.

EXERCISE 15D.1

1 $1, -\frac{1}{2} \pm i\frac{\sqrt{3}}{2}$ **2 a** $z = \sqrt{3} - i$, $2i$, $-\sqrt{3} - i$
b $z = \frac{3\sqrt{3}}{2} - \frac{3}{2}i$, $3i$, $-\frac{3\sqrt{3}}{2} - \frac{3}{2}i$

3 $-1, \frac{1}{2} \pm \frac{\sqrt{3}}{2}i$

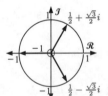

4 a $z = \pm 2$, $\pm 2i$
b $z = \sqrt{2} \pm i\sqrt{2}$, $-\sqrt{2} \pm i\sqrt{2}$

5 $\operatorname{cis}\left(\frac{3\pi}{8}\right)$, $\operatorname{cis}\left(\frac{7\pi}{8}\right)$, $\operatorname{cis}\left(\frac{-\pi}{8}\right)$, $\operatorname{cis}\left(\frac{-5\pi}{8}\right)$

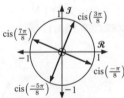

6 a $z = \sqrt{2} \operatorname{cis}\left(\frac{\pi}{12}\right)$, $\sqrt{2}\operatorname{cis}\left(\frac{3\pi}{4}\right) = -1 + i$, $\sqrt{2}\operatorname{cis}\left(\frac{-7\pi}{12}\right)$

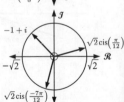

b $z = \sqrt{2}\operatorname{cis}\left(\frac{\pi}{4}\right) = 1 + i$

$\sqrt{2}\operatorname{cis}\left(\frac{11\pi}{12}\right)$,

$\sqrt{2}\operatorname{cis}\left(\frac{-5\pi}{12}\right)$

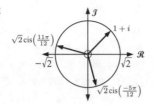

c $z = \frac{\sqrt{3}}{2} + \frac{1}{2}i$ or

$-\frac{\sqrt{3}}{2} - \frac{1}{2}i$

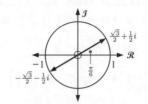

d $z = \sqrt[4]{2}\operatorname{cis}\left(\frac{\pi}{24}\right)$,

$\sqrt[4]{2}\operatorname{cis}\left(\frac{13\pi}{24}\right)$,

$\sqrt[4]{2}\operatorname{cis}\left(\frac{-11\pi}{24}\right)$,

$\sqrt[4]{2}\operatorname{cis}\left(\frac{-23\pi}{24}\right)$

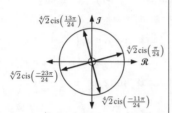

e $z = \sqrt{2}\operatorname{cis}\left(\frac{-3\pi}{20}\right)$,

$\sqrt{2}\operatorname{cis}\left(\frac{\pi}{4}\right) = 1 + i$

$\sqrt{2}\operatorname{cis}\left(\frac{13\pi}{20}\right)$,

$\sqrt{2}\operatorname{cis}\left(\frac{-11\pi}{20}\right)$,

$\sqrt{2}\operatorname{cis}\left(\frac{-19\pi}{20}\right)$

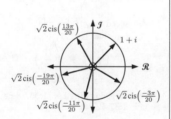

f $z = \sqrt[3]{4}\operatorname{cis}\left(\frac{-5\pi}{18}\right)$,

$\sqrt[3]{4}\operatorname{cis}\left(\frac{7\pi}{18}\right)$,

$\sqrt[3]{4}\operatorname{cis}\left(\frac{-17\pi}{18}\right)$

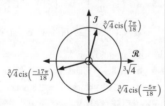

7 $z = \frac{1}{\sqrt{2}} - \frac{1}{\sqrt{2}}i$,

$\frac{1}{\sqrt{2}} + \frac{1}{\sqrt{2}}i$,

$-\frac{1}{\sqrt{2}} + \frac{1}{\sqrt{2}}i$, or

$-\frac{1}{\sqrt{2}} - \frac{1}{\sqrt{2}}i$

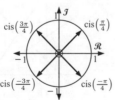

$z^4 + 1 = (z^2 - \sqrt{2}z + 1)(z^2 + \sqrt{2}z + 1)$

8 a $|z| = 1$ and $\arg z = -\frac{2\pi}{3}$ **b** $z^3 = \operatorname{cis}(-2\pi) = 1$

c Simplifies to $2(z + z^*) - 5$ where $z + z^*$ is always real.

9 a $16\operatorname{cis}\left(-\frac{\pi}{2}\right)$ **b i** $2\operatorname{cis}\left(\frac{7\pi}{8}\right)$ **ii** $2\cos\left(\frac{7\pi}{8}\right) + 2i\sin\left(\frac{7\pi}{8}\right)$

EXERCISE 15D.2

1 a i $z = w^n - 3$ $(n = 0, 1, 2)$ and $w = \operatorname{cis}\frac{2\pi}{3}$

ii $z = 2w^n + 1$ $(n = 0, 1, 2)$ and $w = \operatorname{cis}\frac{2\pi}{3}$

iii $z = \frac{1 - w^n}{2}$ $(n = 0, 1, 2)$ and $w = \operatorname{cis}\frac{2\pi}{3}$

2 a Yes **3 a** $z = \operatorname{cis} 0$,

$\operatorname{cis}\left(\frac{2\pi}{5}\right)$,

$\operatorname{cis}\left(\frac{4\pi}{5}\right)$,

$\operatorname{cis}\left(\frac{6\pi}{5}\right)$,

$\operatorname{cis}\left(\frac{8\pi}{5}\right)$

b

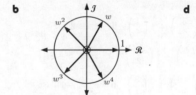

c $1 - w^5$

4 b Hint: The LHS is a geometric series.

EXERCISE 15E

1 $z = 1 + 2i$ or $1 - i$

2 a $y = x$ **b** $y = \frac{1}{\sqrt{3}}x + 1$, $x \geqslant 0$ **c** $7x^2 + 16y^2 = 112$

4 $\dfrac{\cos n\theta - \cos\theta - \cos[(n+1)\theta] + 1}{2 - 2\cos\theta}$

5 $2^n \cos^n\left(\frac{\theta}{2}\right)\cos\left(\frac{n\theta}{2}\right)$

REVIEW SET 15A

1 Real part is $16\sqrt{3}$. Imaginary part is 16.

2 a $2x + 4y = -1$ **b** $y = -x$ **3** $|z| = 4$ **4 a** $\frac{5\pi}{12}$ **b** $-\frac{11\pi}{12}$

5 a $5\operatorname{cis}\left(-\frac{\pi}{2}\right)$ **b** $4\operatorname{cis}\left(-\frac{\pi}{3}\right)$ **c** $-k\sqrt{2}\operatorname{cis}\left(\frac{3\pi}{4}\right)$ **6** $b = \frac{1}{\sqrt{3}}$

7 b $(1 - i)z = 4\operatorname{cis}\left(\alpha - \frac{\pi}{4}\right)$, $\arg((1 - i)z) = \alpha - \frac{\pi}{4}$

8 a $\left|\dfrac{z_1^2}{z_2^2}\right| = 1$, $\arg\left(\dfrac{z_1^2}{z_2^2}\right) = \pi$

9 $\operatorname{Re}\left(\left(\dfrac{z}{w}\right)^4\right) = \dfrac{a}{2b}$, $\operatorname{Im}\left(\left(\dfrac{z}{w}\right)^4\right) = \dfrac{-a\sqrt{3}}{2b}$

10 a $z = 1, w, w^2, w^3$ and w^4 where $w = \operatorname{cis}\left(\frac{2\pi}{5}\right)$

b

d 31

11 $\sqrt{3} - i$, $2i$, $-\sqrt{3} - i$

REVIEW SET 15B

1 $\frac{1}{\sqrt{2}} - \frac{1}{\sqrt{2}}i$ **2 a** $5 + 2i$ **b** $2\sqrt{2}$ **c** 17^5 **d** ≈ -2.034

3 $a = 0, b = -1$ **4 a** $x = 0, y > 1$ **b** $3x^2 + 3y^2 - 20x + 12 = 0$

5 $4\operatorname{cis}\left(-\frac{\pi}{3}\right)$, $n = 3k$, k is an integer **6** $\frac{3}{2} \pm \frac{i3\sqrt{3}}{2}$, -3

7 a $|z^3| = 64$, $\arg(z^3) = 3\theta$ **b** $\left|\frac{1}{z}\right| = \frac{1}{4}$, $\arg\left(\frac{1}{z}\right) = -\theta$

c $|iz^*| = 4$, $\arg(iz^*) = \frac{\pi}{2} - \theta$

9 a $n = 3$ **b** $n = -2$ **c** $n = -1$

10 $z = 2^{0.3}\operatorname{cis}\left(\frac{\pi}{20}\right)$, $2^{0.3}\operatorname{cis}\left(\frac{9\pi}{20}\right)$, $2^{0.3}\operatorname{cis}\left(\frac{17\pi}{20}\right)$,

$2^{0.3}\operatorname{cis}\left(\frac{-7\pi}{20}\right)$, $2^{0.3}\operatorname{cis}\left(\frac{-3\pi}{4}\right)$

13 a $a\left(z^2 - 2\cos\left(\frac{2\pi}{5}\right)z + 1\right) = 0$, $a \neq 0$

b $a(z^2 + z - 1) = 0$, $a \neq 0$

15 b i

ii $\cos\theta = \frac{1}{2} \Rightarrow \theta = \frac{\pi}{3}$

$\therefore \ \arg v = \frac{2\pi}{3}$

iii $\arg w = -\frac{2\pi}{3}$

c i $\dfrac{\pi(4m - 7)}{6}$

ii $m = \frac{7}{4}$

REVIEW SET 15C

1 a reflection in $\mathcal{R}$-axis
b anti-clockwise rotation of π about 0
c anti-clockwise rotation of $\frac{\pi}{2}$ about 0

5 b $z = \dfrac{\alpha+2}{\alpha-1}, \dfrac{\alpha^2+2}{\alpha^2-1}, \dfrac{\alpha^3+2}{\alpha^3-1}, \dfrac{\alpha^4+2}{\alpha^4-1}$ where $\alpha = \text{cis}\left(\frac{2\pi}{5}\right)$

8 $-1 + i\sqrt{3} = 2\,\text{cis}\left(\frac{2\pi}{3}\right), \quad m = \frac{3k}{2}, \quad k$ is an integer

10 $2\sqrt{3} - 2i, \ -2\sqrt{3} - 2i, \ 4i$

11 a $\left|(2z)^{-1}\right| = \frac{1}{2}, \quad \arg\left((2z)^{-1}\right) = -\theta$
b $|1 - z| = 2\sin\left(\frac{\theta}{2}\right), \quad \arg(1-z) = \frac{\theta}{2} - \frac{\pi}{2}$

12 $2 \leqslant |z| \leqslant 5$,
$-\frac{\pi}{4} < \arg z \leqslant \frac{\pi}{2}$

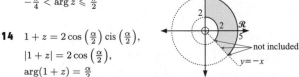

not included
$y = -x$

14 $1 + z = 2\cos\left(\frac{\alpha}{2}\right)\text{cis}\left(\frac{\alpha}{2}\right)$,
$|1 + z| = 2\cos\left(\frac{\alpha}{2}\right)$,
$\arg(1 + z) = \frac{\alpha}{2}$

15 b $\left|\dfrac{z_2 - z_1}{z_3 - z_2}\right| = 1, \quad \arg\left(\dfrac{z_2 - z_1}{z_3 - z_2}\right) = \frac{2\pi}{3}$

16 $a = -3, \ b = -8, \ c = 30$

17 $z = 1, w, w^2, w^3, w^4$ where $w = \text{cis}\left(\frac{2\pi}{5}\right)$
a $\frac{3}{2}, \ w + \frac{1}{2}, \ w^2 + \frac{1}{2}, \ w^3 + \frac{1}{2}, \ w^4 + \frac{1}{2}$
b $0, \ w - 1, \ w^2 - 1, \ w^3 - 1, \ w^4 - 1$
c $\dfrac{w+1}{w-1}, \dfrac{w^2+1}{w^2-1}, \dfrac{w^3+1}{w^3-1}, \dfrac{w^4+1}{w^4-1}$

EXERCISE 16A.1

1 a i $\begin{pmatrix} x \\ y \end{pmatrix} = \begin{pmatrix} 3 \\ -4 \end{pmatrix} + t\begin{pmatrix} 1 \\ 4 \end{pmatrix}$ **ii** $x = 3 + t$
$y = -4 + 4t, \ t \in \mathbb{R}$

b i $\begin{pmatrix} x \\ y \end{pmatrix} = \begin{pmatrix} 5 \\ 2 \end{pmatrix} + t\begin{pmatrix} -8 \\ 2 \end{pmatrix}$ **ii** $x = 5 - 8t$
$y = 2 + 2t, \ t \in \mathbb{R}$

c i $\begin{pmatrix} x \\ y \end{pmatrix} = \begin{pmatrix} -6 \\ 0 \end{pmatrix} + t\begin{pmatrix} 3 \\ 7 \end{pmatrix}$ **ii** $x = -6 + 3t$
$y = 7t, \ t \in \mathbb{R}$

d i $\begin{pmatrix} x \\ y \end{pmatrix} = \begin{pmatrix} -1 \\ 11 \end{pmatrix} + t\begin{pmatrix} -2 \\ 1 \end{pmatrix}$ **ii** $x = -1 - 2t$
$y = 11 + t, \ t \in \mathbb{R}$

2 $x = -1 + 2\lambda, \ y = 4 - \lambda, \ \lambda \in \mathbb{R}$
Points are: $(-1, 4), \ (1, 3), \ (5, 1), \ (-3, 5), \ (-9, 8)$
3 a When $t = 1, \ x = 3, \ y = -2 \ \therefore$ yes **b** $k = -5$
When $t = -2, \ x = 0, \ y = 7 \ \therefore$ no

4 a $(1, 2)$ **b**
c $\sqrt{29}$ cm s^{-1}

$y \uparrow (1,2)$
x
$(3, -3)$
$(5, -8)$
$(7, -13)$

EXERCISE 16A.2

1 a $\begin{pmatrix} x \\ y \\ z \end{pmatrix} = \begin{pmatrix} 1 \\ 3 \\ -7 \end{pmatrix} + t\begin{pmatrix} 2 \\ 1 \\ 3 \end{pmatrix} \quad t \in \mathbb{R}$

b $\begin{pmatrix} x \\ y \\ z \end{pmatrix} = \begin{pmatrix} 0 \\ 1 \\ 2 \end{pmatrix} + t\begin{pmatrix} 1 \\ 1 \\ -2 \end{pmatrix}, \quad t \in \mathbb{R}$

c $\begin{pmatrix} x \\ y \\ z \end{pmatrix} = \begin{pmatrix} -2 \\ 2 \\ 1 \end{pmatrix} + t\begin{pmatrix} 1 \\ 0 \\ 0 \end{pmatrix}, \quad t \in \mathbb{R}$

2 a $x = 5 - t, \ y = 2 + 2t, \ z = -1 + 6t, \ t \in \mathbb{R}$
b $x = 2t, \ y = 2 - t, \ z = -1 + 3t, \ t \in \mathbb{R}$
c $x = 3, \ y = 2, \ z = -1 + t, \ t \in \mathbb{R}$
3 a $x = 1 - 2t, \ y = 2 + t, \ z = 1 + t, \ t \in \mathbb{R}$

b $x = 3t, \ y = 1, \ z = 3 - 4t, \ t \in \mathbb{R}$
c $x = 1, \ y = 2 - 3t, \ z = 5, \ t \in \mathbb{R}$
d $x = 5t, \ y = 1 - 2t, \ z = -1 + 4t, \ t \in \mathbb{R}$

4 a $\left(-\frac{1}{2}, \frac{9}{2}, 0\right)$ **b** $(0, 4, 1)$ **c** $(4, 0, 9)$

5 $(0, 7, 3)$ and $\left(\frac{20}{3}, -\frac{19}{3}, -\frac{11}{3}\right)$ **6 a** $(1, 2, 3)$ **b** $\left(\frac{7}{3}, \frac{2}{3}, \frac{8}{3}\right)$

EXERCISE 16A.3

1 $75.5°$ **2** $75.7°$ **3** $\begin{pmatrix} 5 \\ -2 \end{pmatrix} \bullet \begin{pmatrix} 4 \\ 10 \end{pmatrix} = 0, \ \therefore$ perpendicular **4** $28.6°$

EXERCISE 16B.1

1 a i $(-4, 3)$ **ii** $\begin{pmatrix} 12 \\ 5 \end{pmatrix}$ **iii** 13 m s^{-1}

b i $(0, -6)$ **ii** $\begin{pmatrix} 3 \\ -4 \end{pmatrix}$ **iii** 5 m s^{-1}

c i $(-2, -7)$ **ii** $\begin{pmatrix} -6 \\ -4 \end{pmatrix}$ **iii** $\sqrt{52}$ m s^{-1}

2 a $\begin{pmatrix} 120 \\ -90 \end{pmatrix}$ **b** $\begin{pmatrix} 12 \\ 3.5 \end{pmatrix}$ **c** $\begin{pmatrix} 20\sqrt{5} \\ 10\sqrt{5} \end{pmatrix}$ **d** $\begin{pmatrix} -60 \\ 80 \end{pmatrix}$

3 a A is at $(4, 5)$, B is at $(1, -8)$
b For A it is $\begin{pmatrix} 1 \\ -2 \end{pmatrix}$. For B it is $\begin{pmatrix} 2 \\ 1 \end{pmatrix}$.
c For A, speed is $\sqrt{5}$ km h^{-1}. For B, speed is $\sqrt{5}$ km h^{-1}.
d 10:12 am **e** $\begin{pmatrix} 1 \\ -2 \end{pmatrix} \bullet \begin{pmatrix} 2 \\ 1 \end{pmatrix} = 0, \ \therefore$ direction vectors are $\perp$

4 a $\begin{pmatrix} x_1 \\ y_1 \end{pmatrix} = \begin{pmatrix} -5 \\ 4 \end{pmatrix} + t\begin{pmatrix} 3 \\ -1 \end{pmatrix} \ \therefore \quad x_1(t) = -5 + 3t,$
$y_1(t) = 4 - t$
b speed $= \sqrt{10}$ km min^{-1}
c a minutes later, $(t - a)$ min have elapsed.
$\therefore \ \begin{pmatrix} x_2 \\ y_2 \end{pmatrix} = \begin{pmatrix} 15 \\ 7 \end{pmatrix} + (t - a)\begin{pmatrix} -4 \\ -3 \end{pmatrix}$
$\therefore \ x_2(t) = 15 - 4(t - a), \ y_2(t) = 7 - 3(t - a)$
d Torpedo is fired at 1:35:28 pm and the explosion occurs at 1:37:42 pm.

5 a $\begin{pmatrix} -120 \\ -40 \end{pmatrix}$ **b** $\begin{pmatrix} x \\ y \end{pmatrix} = \begin{pmatrix} 200 \\ 100 \end{pmatrix} + t\begin{pmatrix} -120 \\ -40 \end{pmatrix}$ **c** $\begin{pmatrix} 80 \\ 60 \end{pmatrix}$
d $\left|\begin{pmatrix} 80 \\ 60 \end{pmatrix}\right| = 100$ km **e** at 1:45 pm and $d_{\min} \approx 31.6$ km
f at 2:30 pm
6 a A$(3, -4)$ and B$(4, 3)$ **b** For A $\begin{pmatrix} -1 \\ 2 \end{pmatrix}$, for B $\begin{pmatrix} -3 \\ -2 \end{pmatrix}$
c $97.1°$ **d** at $t = 1.5$ hours

EXERCISE 16B.2

1 a
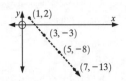
b A$(2, 4)$, B$(8, 0)$, C$(4, 6)$
c BC = BA $= \sqrt{52}$ units $\therefore$ isosceles $\triangle$

2 a
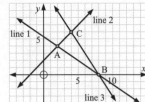

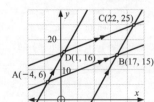
b A$(-4, 6)$, B$(17, 15)$, C$(22, 25)$, D$(1, 16)$

3 a A is at $(2, 3)$, B$(8, 6)$, C$(5, 0)$ **b** $AB = BC = \sqrt{45}$ units

4 a P is at $(10, 4)$, Q$(3, -1)$, R$(20, -10)$

  b $\overrightarrow{PQ} = \begin{pmatrix} -7 \\ -5 \end{pmatrix}$, $\overrightarrow{PR} = \begin{pmatrix} 10 \\ -14 \end{pmatrix}$, $\overrightarrow{PQ} \bullet \overrightarrow{PR} = 0$

  c $\angle QPR = 90^o$ **d** 74 units^2

5 a A is at $(2, 5)$, B$(18, 9)$, C$(14, 25)$, D$(-2, 21)$

  b $\overrightarrow{AC} = \begin{pmatrix} 12 \\ 20 \end{pmatrix}$ and $\overrightarrow{DB} = \begin{pmatrix} 20 \\ -12 \end{pmatrix}$

    i $\sqrt{544}$ units **ii** $\sqrt{544}$ units **iii** 0

  c Diagonals are perpendicular and equal in length, and as their midpoints are the same, i.e., $(8, 15)$, ABCD is a square.

EXERCISE 16C

1 a They intersect at $(1, 2, 3)$, angle $\approx 10.9^o$.

  b Lines are skew, angle $\approx 62.7^o$.

  c They are parallel, $\therefore$ angle 0°.

  d They are skew, angle $\approx 11.4^o$.

  e They intersect at $(-4, 7, -7)$, angle $\approx 40.2^o$.

  f They are parallel, $\therefore$ angle $= 0^o$.

2 If $k \neq 16$, the lines are parallel and so there are no solutions. If $k = 16$, the lines are coincident. We $\therefore$ have infinitely many solutions of the form $x = t$, $y = 3t - 8$, $t \in \mathbb{R}$.

3 If $a \neq -4$, we have a unique solution. The lines meet at $\left(\frac{a+88}{4a+16}, \frac{-21}{2a+8} \right)$. If $a = -4$, the lines are parallel and so do not intersect (no solns). No case for infinite number of solns.

4 $\frac{5}{\sqrt{10}}$ units **5** $3\sqrt{3}$ units **6** $\sqrt{\frac{3}{2}}$ units

7 a $\frac{2}{\sqrt{26}}$ units **b** $2\sqrt{2}$ units

8 a 0 units **b** $\frac{111}{\sqrt{1498}} \approx 2.87$ units **c** $\frac{\sqrt{2769}}{13} \approx 4.05$ units

  d $\frac{3\sqrt{2}}{4}$ units **e** 0 units **f** $\frac{\sqrt{6180}}{10} \approx 7.86$ units

EXERCISE 16D

1 a $2x - y + 3z = 8$ **b** $3x + 4y + z = 19$

  c $x - y - 2z = -1$ **d** $x + 3y + z = 10$

2 a $\begin{pmatrix} 2 \\ 3 \\ -1 \end{pmatrix}$ **b** $\begin{pmatrix} 3 \\ -1 \\ 0 \end{pmatrix}$ **c** $\begin{pmatrix} 0 \\ 0 \\ 1 \end{pmatrix}$ **d** $\begin{pmatrix} 1 \\ 0 \\ 0 \end{pmatrix}$

3 a $y = 0$ **b** $z = 4$

4 a ii $-2x + 6y + z = 18$ **b ii** $-5x + 3y + 12z = 12$

  c ii $-y + z = 3$ {many vector forms exist}

5 a $x = 1 + t$, $y = -2 - 3t$, $z = 4t$, $t \in \mathbb{R}$

  b $x = 3 + t$, $y = 4 - t$, $z = -1 - 2t$, $t \in \mathbb{R}$

6 $x = 2 - t$, $y = -1 + 3t$, $z = 3 - 3t$, $t \in \mathbb{R}$ $(1, 2, 0)$

7 $x = 1 + t$, $y = -2 + 2t$, $z = 4 - 5t$, $t \in \mathbb{R}$

  a $(0, -4, 9)$ **b** $(1, -2, 4)$ **c** $(-5, -14, 34)$

8 a $(-1, -1, 4)$; 3 units **b** $(0, 1, -3)$; $2\sqrt{11}$ units

  c $(-\frac{1}{7}, -\frac{26}{7}, -\frac{17}{7})$; $2\sqrt{\frac{3}{7}}$ units

9 $(1, -3, 0)$ **10** X axis at $(2, 0, 0)$

11 a $y - 3z = -7$ **b** $x - z = -2$ **c** $3x - y = 1$ **12** $y - 2z = 8$

13 a $k = -\frac{3}{2}$ **b** B$(3, 6, -\frac{11}{2})$ or $(-1, -2, \frac{5}{2})$

14 a N$(3.4, 1.2, 1)$, $d = \frac{2}{\sqrt{5}}$ units **b** N$(\frac{1}{6}, \frac{5}{6}, -\frac{1}{3})$, $d = \frac{5}{\sqrt{6}}$ units

16 a $\frac{10}{\sqrt{6}}$ units **b** $2\sqrt{3}$ units

17 a $\frac{19}{2\sqrt{6}}$ units **b** $\frac{|d_2 - d_1|}{\sqrt{a^2 + b^2 + c^2}}$ units **18** $\frac{26}{\sqrt{138}}$ units

19 $2x - y + 2z = -1$ and $2x - y + 2z = 11$

EXERCISE 16E

1 a $\approx 13.1^o$ **b** the line and plane are parallel $\therefore$ 0°

  c $\approx 11.3^o$ **d** $\approx 30.7^o$

2 a $\approx 83.7^o$ **b** $\approx 84.8^o$ **c** $\approx 86.2^o$ **d** $\approx 73.2^o$ **e** $\approx 62.3^o$

EXERCISE 16F

1 a Either no solutions or an infinite number of solutions.

  b i $a_1 = ka_2$, $b_1 = kb_2$, $c_1 = kc_2$ for some k

    ii $a_1 = ka_2$, $b_1 = kb_2$, $c_1 = kc_2$, $d_1 = kd_2$ for some k

  c i Planes meet in a line $x = -2 + 3t$, $y = t$, $z = 5$, $t \in \mathbb{R}$

    ii Planes meet in a line $x = 2 - 2t$, $y = t$, $z = 1 + 3t$, $t \in \mathbb{R}$

    iii Planes are coincident
      $\therefore$ $x = 6 - 2s + 3t$, $y = s$, $z = t$, $s, t \in \mathbb{R}$

2 a If $k = -2$, planes are coincident with infinitely many solutions. If $k \neq -2$, planes meet in a line with infinitely many solutions.

  b If $k = 16$, planes are coincident, with infinitely many solutions. If $k \neq 16$, planes are parallel with no solutions.

4 a Meet at a point $(1, -2, 4)$

  b Meet in a line $x = \frac{9 - t}{3}$, $y = \frac{6 + 5t}{3}$, $z = t$, $t \in \mathbb{R}$

  c Meet in a line $x = 3t - 3$, $y = t$, $z = 5t - 11$, $t \in \mathbb{R}$

  d No solutions as 2 planes are parallel and intersected by 3rd plane.

  e Two planes are coincident and the other cuts obliquely at the line $x = \frac{5}{2} + \frac{1}{2}t$, $y = -\frac{3}{2} + \frac{3}{2}t$, $z = t$, $t \in \mathbb{R}$

  f Meet at the point $(3, -2, 0)$

5 If $k = 5$ the planes meet in a line $x = -10t$, $y = -1 - 7t$, $z = t$, $t \in \mathbb{R}$. If $k \neq 5$, the line of intersection of any two planes is parallel to the third $\therefore$ no solutions.

6 A unique solution exists if $m \neq -1$ or $m \neq -5$.

  If $m = -1$, planes meet in a line $x = \frac{t + 7}{3}, y = \frac{t - 5}{3}$, $z = t$,

  $t \in \mathbb{R}$. If $m = -5$, the system is inconsistent $\therefore$ no solutions.

7 They meet at the point $\left(\frac{94}{29}, \frac{-68}{29}, \frac{64}{29} \right)$

REVIEW SET 16A

1 a $\begin{pmatrix} x \\ y \end{pmatrix} = \begin{pmatrix} -6 \\ 3 \end{pmatrix} + t \begin{pmatrix} 4 \\ -3 \end{pmatrix}$ **b** $x = -6 + 4t$, $y = 3 - 3t$, $t \in \mathbb{R}$

2 $\begin{pmatrix} x \\ y \end{pmatrix} = \begin{pmatrix} 0 \\ 8 \end{pmatrix} + t \begin{pmatrix} 5 \\ 4 \end{pmatrix}$, $t \in \mathbb{R}$ **3** $m = 10$

4 $2\sqrt{10}(3i - j)$

5 a $(-4, 3)$ **b** $(28, 27)$ **c** 10 m s^{-1} **d** $\begin{pmatrix} 8 \\ 6 \end{pmatrix}$

6 a i $-6i + 10j$ **ii** $-5i - 15j$ **iii** $(-6 - 5t)i + (10 - 15t)j$

  b $t = 0.48$ h **c** shortest dist. ≈ 8.85 km, so, will miss reef.

7 a X23, $x_1 = 2 + t$, $y_1 = 4 - 3t$, $t \geqslant 0$

  b Y18, $x_2 = 13 - t$, $y_2 = 3 - 2a + at$, $t \geqslant 2$

  c interception occurred at 2:22:30 pm

  d $\theta = 192.7^o$, ≈ 4.54 units per minute

8 a KL is parallel to MN as $\begin{pmatrix} 5 \\ -2 \end{pmatrix}$ is parallel to $\begin{pmatrix} -5 \\ 2 \end{pmatrix}$

  b KL is perpendicular to NK as $\begin{pmatrix} 5 \\ -2 \end{pmatrix} \bullet \begin{pmatrix} 4 \\ 10 \end{pmatrix} = 0$

  and NK is perpendicular to MN as $\begin{pmatrix} 4 \\ 10 \end{pmatrix} \bullet \begin{pmatrix} -5 \\ 2 \end{pmatrix} = 0$

  c K$(7, 17)$, L$(22, 11)$, M$(33, -5)$, N$(3, 7)$ **d** 261 units^2

REVIEW SET 16B

1 a $3x + 2y - z = -1$ **b** $(0, 1, 3)$

2 a $\begin{pmatrix} x \\ y \\ z \end{pmatrix} = \begin{pmatrix} 3 \\ 2 \\ -1 \end{pmatrix} + t \begin{pmatrix} -4 \\ 0 \\ 5 \end{pmatrix}$, $t \in \mathbb{R}$ **b** $-4x + 5z = 24$

  c $(-5, 2, 9)$ or $(11, 2, -11)$

3 a $\approx 15.8^o$ **b** $\approx 65.9^o$

4 a $\begin{pmatrix} x \\ y \\ z \end{pmatrix} = \begin{pmatrix} 3 \\ -1 \\ 1 \end{pmatrix} + t \begin{pmatrix} -3 \\ 3 \\ -2 \end{pmatrix}$, $t \in \mathbb{R}$ **b** P$(\frac{6}{7}, \frac{8}{7}, -\frac{3}{7})$

5 $(6, -1, -10)$ **6 b** $\approx 28.6^o$ **c** 14 units

7 a $\frac{17}{3}$ units **b** $(\frac{8}{3}, \frac{7}{3}, \frac{4}{3})$

8 a $\overrightarrow{PQ} = \begin{pmatrix} 1 \\ 4 \\ -3 \end{pmatrix}$ $|\overrightarrow{PQ}| = \sqrt{26}$ units, $\overrightarrow{QR} = \begin{pmatrix} -4 \\ -1 \\ 4 \end{pmatrix}$

b $x = 2 + t$, $y = 4t$, $z = 1 - 3t$, $t \in \mathbb{R}$

c $\begin{pmatrix} x \\ y \\ z \end{pmatrix} = \begin{pmatrix} 2 \\ 0 \\ 1 \end{pmatrix} + \lambda \begin{pmatrix} 1 \\ 4 \\ -3 \end{pmatrix} + \mu \begin{pmatrix} -4 \\ -1 \\ 4 \end{pmatrix}$, $\lambda, \mu \in \mathbb{R}$

9 a 3 units **b** $(1, 2, 4)$ **c** $\sqrt{116}$ units

10 a $5x + y + 4z = 3$ **b** $x = 5t$, $y = t$, $z = 4t$, $t \in \mathbb{R}$

c $(\frac{5}{14}, \frac{1}{14}, \frac{2}{7})$

11 If $k = -2$, the planes meet in the line
$x = \frac{4}{3}$, $y = -\frac{11}{3} + t$, $z = t$, $t \in \mathbb{R}$. If $k \neq -2$ the planes meet at the point $(\frac{4}{3}, -\frac{14}{3}, -1)$.

12 a $5 \begin{pmatrix} -1 \\ 1 \\ 1 \end{pmatrix}$ **b** $m = 1$ **c** $x - y - z = 0$ **d** $t = 2$

e $\frac{4}{\sqrt{114}}$

REVIEW SET 16C

1 a $14x + 29y - 4z = 32$ **b** $\approx 55.9°$ **c** $r = \frac{2 \pm \sqrt{10}}{2}$

2 a They do not meet, the line is parallel to the plane. **b** $\frac{16}{\sqrt{14}}$ units

3 a $n = \begin{pmatrix} 5 \\ -1 \\ 3 \end{pmatrix}$ **b** $D(-1, -1, 2)$ **c** $(\frac{1}{6}, \frac{5}{6}, \frac{2}{3})$

4 $\frac{31}{\sqrt{110}}$ units **5 a** intersecting **b** $\cos \theta = \frac{10}{3\sqrt{14}}$

6 a $\begin{pmatrix} x \\ y \\ z \end{pmatrix} = \begin{pmatrix} 2 \\ -1 \\ 3 \end{pmatrix} + t \begin{pmatrix} -2 \\ 2 \\ -4 \end{pmatrix}$, $t \in \mathbb{R}$

b $\left(2 - \frac{2}{\sqrt{6}}, -1 + \frac{2}{\sqrt{6}}, 3 - \frac{4}{\sqrt{6}} \right)$ and
$\left(2 + \frac{2}{\sqrt{6}}, -1 - \frac{2}{\sqrt{6}}, 3 + \frac{4}{\sqrt{6}} \right)$

7 $4x + 2y + z = 3$, $\approx 64.1°$

8 a $\begin{pmatrix} \sqrt{3} \\ -\sqrt{3} \\ \sqrt{3} \end{pmatrix}$ and $\begin{pmatrix} -\sqrt{3} \\ \sqrt{3} \\ -\sqrt{3} \end{pmatrix}$

b $\frac{1}{\sqrt{74}}\mathbf{i} + \frac{8}{\sqrt{74}}\mathbf{j} + \frac{3}{\sqrt{74}}\mathbf{k}$ or $-\frac{1}{\sqrt{74}}\mathbf{i} - \frac{8}{\sqrt{74}}\mathbf{j} - \frac{3}{\sqrt{74}}\mathbf{k}$

c $k = -7$ or 11

9 $\approx 26.4°$ **10 a** $\overrightarrow{PQ} = \begin{pmatrix} 5 \\ -2 \\ -4 \end{pmatrix}$ **b** $\approx 41.8°$

11 a $\overrightarrow{OM} = \frac{1}{2}(\overrightarrow{OB} + \overrightarrow{OC})$ **d** $2 : 1$

12 a $A(2, -1, 0)$ **c** $r = \begin{pmatrix} 0 \\ -3 \\ 2 \end{pmatrix} + u \begin{pmatrix} 3 \\ 1 \\ -4 \end{pmatrix}$ **d** $3x - y + 2z = 7$

e $\sqrt{14}$ units^2 **f** normal is $\begin{pmatrix} x \\ y \\ z \end{pmatrix} = \begin{pmatrix} 3 \\ -2 \\ -2 \end{pmatrix} + \lambda \begin{pmatrix} 3 \\ -1 \\ 2 \end{pmatrix}$

g $\frac{28}{3}$ units^3

REVIEW SET 16D

1 a $\overrightarrow{AB} = \begin{pmatrix} -2 \\ -1 \\ 6 \end{pmatrix}$ and $\overrightarrow{AC} = \begin{pmatrix} 5 \\ 2 \\ 2 \end{pmatrix}$ and $\overrightarrow{AB} \bullet \overrightarrow{AC} = 0$, $\therefore$ $\overrightarrow{AB} \perp \overrightarrow{AC}$

b $14x - 34y - z = -11$, ≈ 2.42 units

c $x = 4 - 2t$, $y = 2 - t$, $z = -1 + 6t$, $t \in \mathbb{R}$ **d** $6\sqrt{2}$ units

2 a $(\frac{1}{5}, \frac{17}{5}, \frac{9}{5})$ **b** $(-1, 3, 1)$ **c** $6x - 8y - 5z = -35$

3 b $k = -1$

---

c $t(p + 10) = q + 2$ has infinitely many solutions for t when
$p + 10 = 0$ and $q + 2 = 0$, $\therefore$ $p = -10$, $q = -2$

4 a
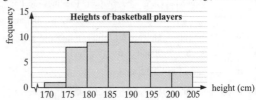
OABC is a rhombus.
So, its diagonals
bisect its angles.

b $x = 7$, $y = 3 + \frac{1}{3}t$, $z = -4 + \frac{1}{3}t$, $t \in \mathbb{R}$ **c** $M(7, 3\frac{3}{4}, -3\frac{1}{4})$

5 $(4, 1, -3)$ and $(1, -5, 0)$ **6** $7.82°$ **7** $\frac{9\sqrt{2}}{2}$ units^2

8 a $X(7, 3, -1)$, $D(7, 1, -2)$ **b** $Y(5, 3, -2)$

c $\overrightarrow{BD} = \begin{pmatrix} 3 \\ -3 \\ 0 \end{pmatrix}$ and $\overrightarrow{BY} = \begin{pmatrix} 1 \\ -1 \\ 0 \end{pmatrix}$ So, $\overrightarrow{BD} = 3\overrightarrow{BY}$, etc.

10 a $t = \frac{2}{3}$ **b** $t = -\frac{1}{3}$

11 b $2x + 3y + 6z = 147$ **c** 14 units
d $(5, 7, 3)$ and $(9, 13, 15)$

EXERCISE 17A

1 a Heights can take any value from 170 cm to 205 cm, e.g., 181.37 cm.

b
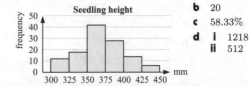

c The modal class is 185-190 cm, as this occurred the most frequently.
d slightly positively skewed

2 a Continuous numerical, but has been rounded to become discrete numerical data.

b

Stem	Leaf
0	3 6 8 8 8 8
1	0 0 0 0 2 2 2 4 4 4 4 5 5 5 5 6 6 6 6 7 8 8 8 8 9
2	0 0 0 1 2 4 5 5 5 6 7 7 8
3	1 2 2 2 3 4 5 7 8
4	0 2 5 5 5 6

$1 \mid 2$ means 12 minutes

c positively skewed
d The modal travelling time was between 10 and 20 minutes.

3 a column graph **b** histogram

4 a Seedling height **b** 20 **c** 58.33% **d i** 1218 **ii** 512

EXERCISE 17B.1

1 a i 5.61 **ii** 6 **iii** 6 **b i** 16.3 **ii** 17 **iii** 18
c i 24.8 **ii** 24.9 **iii** 23.5

2 a $A : 6.46$ $B : 6.85$ **b** $A : 7$ $B : 7$

c The data sets are the same except for the last value, and the last value of A is less than the last value of B, so the mean of A is less than the mean of B.

d The middle value of the data sets is the same, so the median is the same.

3 a mean: $29 300, median: $23 500, mode: $23 000
  b The mode is the lowest value, so does not take the higher values into account.
  c No, since the data is positively skewed, the median is not in the centre.
4 a mean: 3.19, median: 0, mode: 0
  b The data is very positively skewed so the median is not in the centre.
  c The mode is the lowest value so does not take the higher values into account.
  d yes, 21 and 42 **e** no
5 a 44 **b** 44 **c** 40.2 **d** increase mean to 40.3
6 116 **7** 3144 km **8** $185 604 **9** $x = 15$ **10** $a = 5$
11 37 **12** 14.77 **13** 9 and 7

EXERCISE 17B.2

1 a 1 **b** 1 **c** 1 43
2 a i 2.96 **ii** 2 **iii** 2 **b**

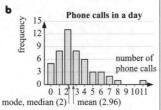

Phone calls in a day

mode, median (2)   mean (2.96)

  c positively skewed with data value 11 as an outlier
  d The mean takes into account the larger numbers of phone calls.
  e the mean

3 a i 49 **ii** 49 **iii** 49.03 **b** no
  c The sample of only 30 is not large enough. The company could have won its case by arguing that a larger sample would have found an average of 50 matches per box.
4 a i 2.61 **ii** 2 **iii** 2 **b** This school has more children per family than the average Australian family. **c** positive
  d The mean is larger than the median and the mode.
5 a i 69.1 **ii** 67 **iii** 73 **b i** 5.86 **ii** 5.8 **iii** 6.7
6 a i 5.63 **ii** 6 **iii** 6 **b i** 6.81 **ii** 7 **iii** 7
  c the mean **d** yes
7 a mean = $163 770, median = $147 200 (differ by $16 570)
  b i mean selling price **ii** median selling price
8 a ≈ 70.9 g **b** ≈ 210 g **c** 139 g **9** 10.1 cm
10 a mean for A ≈ 50.8, mean for B ≈ 49.9
  b No, as to the nearest match, A is 51 and B is 50.
11 17.25 goals per game **12** 6 and 12
13 a i $31 500 **ii** $28 000 **iii** $33 300 **b** The mean.

EXERCISE 17B.3

1 31.7 **2 a** 70 **b** ≈ 411 000 litres, i.e., ≈ 411 kL **c** ≈ 5870 L
3 a 125 people **b** ≈ 119 marks **c** $\frac{3}{25}$ **d** 137 marks

EXERCISE 17C

1 a 8   **2 a**
  b i 40
  ii 40

Length (x cm)	Frequency	C. frequency
$24 \leqslant x < 27$	1	1
$27 \leqslant x < 30$	2	3
$30 \leqslant x < 33$	5	8
$33 \leqslant x < 36$	10	18
$36 \leqslant x < 39$	9	27
$39 \leqslant x < 42$	2	29
$42 \leqslant x < 45$	1	30

  b

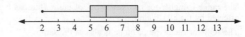

c median ≈ 35 cm **d** actual median = 34.5, i.e., a good approx.

3

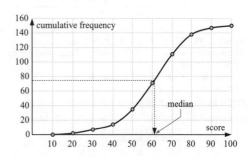

a ≈ 61 **b** ≈ 87 students **c** ≈ 76 students
d 24 (or 25) students **e** 76 marks
4 a 26 years **b** 36% **c i** 0.527 **ii** 0.030
5 a 2270 h **b** ≈ 69% **c** 62 or 63

EXERCISE 17D.1

1 a i 6 **ii** $Q_1 = 4$, $Q_3 = 7$ **iii** 7 **iv** 3
  b i 17.5 **ii** $Q_1 = 15$, $Q_3 = 19$ **iii** 14 **iv** 4
  c i 24.9 **ii** $Q_1 = 23.5$, $Q_3 = 26.1$ **iii** 7.7 **iv** 2.6
2 a median = 2.45, $Q_1 = 1.45$, $Q_3 = 3.8$
  b range = 5.2, IQR = 2.35
  c i ...... greater than 2.45 min **ii** ...... less than 3.8 min
    iii The minimum waiting time was 0 minutes and the maximum waiting time was 5.2 minutes. The waiting times were spread over 5.2 minutes.
3 a 3 **b** 42 **c** 20 **d** 13 **e** 29 **f** 39 **g** 16
4 a i 124 cm **ii** $Q_1 = 116$ cm, $Q_3 = 130$ cm
  b i ...... 124 cm **ii** ...... 130 cm tall
  c i 29 cm **ii** 14 cm **d** .... over 14 cm
5 a i 7 **ii** 6 **iii** 5 **iv** 7 **v** 2
  b i 10 **ii** 7 **iii** 6 **iv** 8 **v** 2

EXERCISE 17D.2

1 a i 35 **ii** 78 **iii** 13 **iv** 53 **v** 26 **b i** 65 **ii** 27
2 a ...... was 98, ... was 25
  b .... greater than or equal to 70 **c** .... at least 85 marks
  d ...... between 55 and 85 ...... **e** 73 **f** 30 **g** ≈ 67
3 a i min = 3, $Q_1 = 5$, median = 6, $Q_3 = 8$, max = 10
    ii

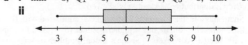

    iii range = 7 **iv** IQR = 3
  b i min = 0, $Q_1 = 4$, median = 7, $Q_3 = 8$, max = 9
    ii

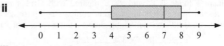

    iii range = 9 **iv** IQR = 4
  c i min = 117, $Q_1 = 127$, med. = 132, $Q_3 = 145.5$, max = 151
    ii

    iii range = 34 **iv** IQR = 18.5
4 a

Statistic	Year 9	Year 12
min value	1	6
Q_1	5	10
median	7.5	14
Q_3	10	16
max value	12	17.5

  b i Year 9: 11, Year 12: 11.5
  ii Year 9: 5, Year 12: 6
  c i true **ii** true
5 a median = 6, $Q_1 = 5$, $Q_3 = 8$ **b** 3
  c

6 a $\text{Min}_x = 33$, $Q_1 = 35$, $Q_2 = 36$, $Q_3 = 37$, $\text{Max}_x = 40$

b i 7 **ii** 2 **c**

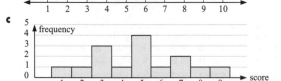

30 31 32 33 34 35 36 37 38 39 40 41

7 a 9 **b** $\approx 28.3\%$ **c** 7 cm **d** IQR ≈ 2.4 cm

e 10 cm, which means that 90% of the seedlings have a height of 10 cm or less.

8 a 27 min **b** 29 min **c** 31.3 min **d** IQR ≈ 4.3 min

e 28 min 10 s

EXERCISE 17E

1 a $\overline{x} \approx 4.87$, $\text{Min}_x = 1$, $Q_1 = 3$, $Q_2 = 5$, $Q_3 = 7$, $\text{Max}_x = 9$

b

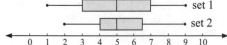

1 2 3 4 5 6 7 8 9 10

c

5
4 frequency
3
2
1
0
        1 2 3 4 5 6 7 8 9 → score

d $\overline{x} \approx 5.24$, $\text{Min}_x = 2$, $Q_1 = 4$, $Q_2 = 5$, $Q_3 = 6.5$, $\text{Max}_x = 9$

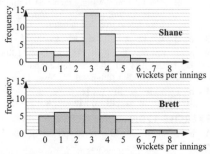

set 1

set 2

0 1 2 3 4 5 6 7 8 9 10

2 a discrete **c**

frequency (Shane)
15
10
5
0
  0 1 2 3 4 5 6 7 8
             wickets per innings

frequency (Brett)
15
10
5
0
  0 1 2 3 4 5 6 7 8
             wickets per innings

d There are no outliers for Shane. Brett has outliers of 7 and 8 which must not be removed.

e Shane's distribution is reasonably symmetrical.
Brett's distribution is positively skewed.

f Shane has a higher mean (≈ 2.89 wickets) compared with Brett (≈ 2.67 wickets). Shane has a higher median (3 wickets) compared with Brett (2.5 wickets). Shane's modal number of wickets is 3 (14 times) compared with Brett, who has a bi-modal distribution of 2 and 3 (7 times each).

g Shane's range is 6 wickets, compared with Brett's range of 8 wickets. Shane's IQR is 2 wickets, compared with Brett's IQR of 3 wickets. Brett's wicket taking shows greater spread or variability.

h

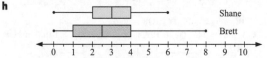

Shane

Brett

0 1 2 3 4 5 6 7 8 9 10

i Generally, Shane takes more wickets than Brett and is a more consistent bowler.

3 a continuous

c For the 'New type' globes, 191 hours could be considered an outlier. However, it could be a genuine piece of data, so we will include it in the analysis.

d

	Old type	New type
Mean	107	134
Median	110.5	132
Range	56	84
IQR	19	18.5

The mean and median are $\approx 25\%$ and $\approx 19\%$ higher for the 'new type' of globe compared with the 'old type'.

The range is higher for the 'new type' of globe (but has been affected by the 191 hours).

The IQR for each type of globe is almost the same.

e

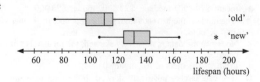

'old'

* 'new'

60 80 100 120 140 160 180 200
                          lifespan (hours)

f For the 'old type' of globe, the data is bunched to the right of the median, hence the distribution is negatively skewed.

For the 'new type' of globe, the data is bunched to the left of the median, hence the distribution is positively skewed.

g The manufacturer's claim, that the 'new type' of globe has a 20% longer life than the 'old type' seems to be backed up by the 25% higher mean life and 19.5% higher median life.

EXERCISE 17F.1

1 a Sample A

b

	A	B
$\overline{x}$	8	8
s	2	1.06

c

2 a

	$\overline{x}$	s
Andrew	25	4.97
Brad	30.5	12.6

b Andrew

3 a Rockets: range = 11, $\overline{x} = 5.7$;
Bullets: range = 11, $\overline{x} = 5.7$

b We suspect the Rockets, they have two zeros.

c Rockets: $s = 3.9$ ← greater variability   Bullets: $s = 3.29$

d standard deviation

4 a We suspect variability in standard deviation since the factors may change every day.

b i sample mean **ii** sample standard deviation

c less variability

5 a $\overline{x} = 69$, $s = 6.05$ **b** $\overline{x} = 79$, $s = 6.05$

c The distribution has simply shifted by 10 kg. The mean increases by 10 kg and the standard deviation remains the same.

6 a $\overline{x} = 1.01$ kg; $s = 0.17$ **b** $\overline{x} = 2.02$ kg; $s = 0.34$

c Doubling the values doubles the mean and the standard deviation.

7 $p = 6$, $q = 9$ **8** $a = 8$, $b = 6$ **9 b** $\overline{x} = 8.7$

10 a 0.809 **b** 0.150

c the extreme value greatly increases the standard deviation

EXERCISE 17F.2

1 a $s_n \approx 6.77$ kg **b** $\mu \approx 93.8$ kg, $\sigma^2 \approx 46.4$ kg^2

2 a $\overline{x} \approx 77.5$ g, $s_n \approx 7.44$ g **b** $\mu = 77.5$ g, $\sigma^2 = 58.9$ g^2

3 a 32.4 min **b** 9.86 min^2

EXERCISE 17F.3

1 a $\overline{x} \approx 1.72$ children, $s \approx 1.67$ children

b $\mu \approx 1.72$ children, $\sigma^2 \approx 2.83$ children^2

2 a $\overline{x} = 14.5$ years, $s \approx 1.75$ years

b $\mu \approx 14.5$ years, $\sigma^2 \approx 3.18$ years^2

3 a $\overline{x} = 37.3$ toothpicks, $s \approx 1.45$ toothpicks

b $\mu \approx 37.3$ toothpicks, $\sigma^2 \approx 2.16$ toothpicks^2

4 a $\overline{x} = 47.8$ cm, $s \approx 2.66$ cm

b $\mu \approx 47.8$ cm, $\sigma^2 \approx 7.31$ cm^2

5 a $\overline{x} = \$390.30$, $s \approx \$15.87$

b $\mu \approx \$390.30$, $\sigma^2 \approx 253.18$ dollars^2

EXERCISE 17G

1 a 16% **b** 84% **c** 97.4% **d** 0.15% **2** 3 times

3 a 5 **b** 32 **c** 136 **4 a** 458 babies **b** 444 babies

REVIEW SET 17A

1 a Diameter of bacteria colonies

0	4 8 9
1	3 5 5 7
2	1 1 5 6 8 8
3	0 1 2 3 4 5 5 6 6 7 7 9
4	0 1 2 7 9

leaf unit: 0.1 cm

b i 3.15 cm
ii 4.5 cm

c The distribution is slightly negatively skewed.

2 a highest = 97.5 m, lowest = 64.6 m
b use groups 60 - < 65, 65 - < 70, 70 - < 75, etc.
c

A frequency distribution table for distances thrown by Thabiso		
distance (m)	tally	freq. (f)
60 - < 65	I	1
65 - < 70	III	3
70 - < 75	HHT	5
75 - < 80	II	2
80 - < 85	HHT III	8
85 - < 90	HHT I	6
90 - < 95	III	3
95 - < 100	II	2
	Total	30

d

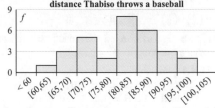

Frequency histogram displaying the distance Thabiso throws a baseball

e i ≈ 81.1 m **ii** 83.1 m

3 $a = 8$ and $b = 6$ or $a = 6$ and $b = 8$
4 a

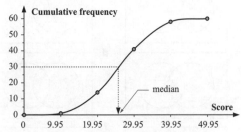

b ≈ 25.9 **c** ≈ 12.0 **d** $\bar{x} \approx 26.0$, $s \approx 8.31$

5 a

	Girls	Boys
shape	pos. skewed	approx. symm.
centre (median)	36.3 sec	34.9 sec
spread (range)	7.7 sec	4.9 sec

b The girls' distribution is positively skewed and boys' distribution is approximately symmetrical. The median swim times for boys is 1.4 seconds lower than for girls but the range of the girls' swim times is 2.8 seconds higher than for boys. The analysis supports the conjecture that boys generally swim faster than girls with less spread of times.

6 a

	A	B
Min	11	11.2
Q_1	11.6	12
Median	12	12.6
Q_3	12.6	13.2
Max	13	13.8

b

		A	B
i	Range	2	2.6
ii	IQR	1	1.2

c i We know the members of squad A generally ran faster because their median time is lower.
ii We know the times in squad B are more varied because their range and IQR is higher.

7 a i 101.5 **ii** 98 **iii** 105.5 **b** 7.5 **c** $\bar{x} = 100.2$, $s \approx 7.59$
8 a $\bar{x} \approx 33.6$ L, $s \approx 7.63$ L **b** $\mu \approx 33.6$ L, $\sigma^2 \approx 58.7$ L^2
9 a $2\frac{1}{2}\%$ **b** 95% **c** 68% **10 a** 58.5 sec **b** 6 sec
11 a 88 students **b** $m \approx 24$

REVIEW SET 17B

1

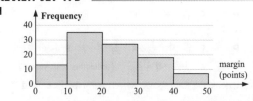

2 $\bar{x} \approx 49.6$, $s \approx 1.60$ Does not justify claim. Need a larger sample.
3 ≈ 414 customers
4 range = 19, lower quartile = 119, upper quartile = 130, $s \approx 6.38$
5

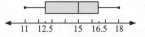

6 a $\bar{x} = \$103.50$, $s \approx \$19.40$ **b** $\mu = \$103.50$, $\sigma \approx 378.15$ $\$^2$
7 a 68% **b** 95% **c** 81.5% **d** 13.5%
8 a mean is 18.8, standard deviation is 2.6 **b** 13.6 to 24.0
9 a 2.5% **b** 84% **c** 81.5%
10 a i $\bar{x} \approx 3.88$ cm **ii** $s^2 \approx 0.0571$ cm^2
b $\mu \approx 3.88$ cm, $\sigma^2 \approx 0.0591$ cm^2
11 a $a = 4$, $b = 6$ **b** 5 **c** 2.5
12 a 120 students **b** 65 marks **c** 54 and 75
d 21 marks **e** 73% of them **f** 81 marks

EXERCISE 18A

1 a 0.78 **b** 0.22 **2 a** 0.487 **b** 0.051 **c** 0.731
3 a 43 days **b i** ≈ 0.047 **ii** ≈ 0.186 **iii** 0.465
4 a ≈ 0.089 **b** ≈ 0.126

EXERCISE 18B

1 a {A, B, C, D} **b** {BB, BG, GB, GG}
c {ABCD, ABDC, ACBD, ACDB, ADBC, ADCB, BACD, BADC, BCAD, BCDA, BDAC, BDCA, CABD, CADB, CBAD, CBDA, CDAB, CDBA, DABC, DACB, DBAC, DBCA, DCAB, DCBA}
d {GGG, GGB, GBG, BGG, GBB, BGB, BBG, BBB}

2 a 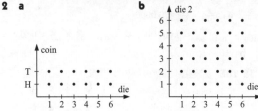 **b**

c **d**

3 a 5-cent   10-cent **b** coin   spinner
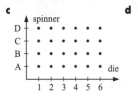
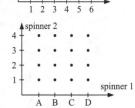

c spinner 1   spinner 2 **d** draw 1   draw 2

EXERCISE 18C.1

1 a $\frac{1}{5}$ b $\frac{1}{3}$ c $\frac{7}{15}$ d $\frac{4}{5}$ e $\frac{1}{5}$ f $\frac{8}{15}$

2 a 4 b i $\frac{2}{3}$ ii $\frac{1}{3}$

3 a $\frac{1}{4}$ b $\frac{1}{9}$ c $\frac{4}{9}$ d $\frac{1}{36}$ e $\frac{1}{18}$ f $\frac{1}{6}$ g $\frac{1}{12}$ h $\frac{1}{3}$

4 a $\frac{1}{7}$ b $\frac{2}{7}$ c $\frac{124}{1461}$ d $\frac{237}{1461}$ {remember leap years}

5 {AKN, ANK, KAN, KNA, NAK, NKA} a $\frac{1}{3}$ b $\frac{1}{3}$ c $\frac{1}{3}$ d $\frac{2}{3}$

6 a {GGG, GGB, GBG, BGG, GBB, BGB, BBG, BBB}
b i $\frac{1}{8}$ ii $\frac{1}{8}$ iii $\frac{1}{8}$ iv $\frac{3}{8}$ v $\frac{1}{2}$ vi $\frac{7}{8}$

7 a {ABCD, ABDC, ACBD, ACDB, ADBC, ADCB,
BACD, BADC, BCAD, BCDA, BDAC, BDCA,
CABD, CADB, CBAD, CBDA, CDAB, CDBA,
DABC, DACB, DBAC, DBCA, DCAB, DCBA}
b i $\frac{1}{2}$ ii $\frac{1}{2}$ iii $\frac{1}{2}$ iv $\frac{1}{2}$

EXERCISE 18C.2

1

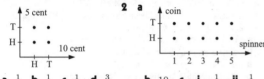

a $\frac{1}{4}$ b $\frac{1}{4}$ c $\frac{1}{2}$ d $\frac{3}{4}$

2 a

b 10 c i $\frac{1}{10}$ ii $\frac{1}{5}$
iii $\frac{3}{5}$ iv $\frac{3}{5}$

3 a $\frac{1}{36}$ b $\frac{1}{18}$ c $\frac{5}{9}$ d $\frac{11}{36}$ e $\frac{5}{18}$ f $\frac{25}{36}$ g $\frac{1}{6}$
h $\frac{5}{18}$ i $\frac{2}{9}$ j $\frac{13}{18}$

EXERCISE 18D.1

1 a $\frac{6}{7}$ b $\frac{36}{49}$ c $\frac{216}{343}$ **2** a $\frac{1}{8}$ b $\frac{1}{8}$

3 a 0.0096 b 0.8096 **4** a $\frac{1}{16}$ b $\frac{15}{16}$

5 a 0.56 b 0.06 c 0.14 d 0.24 **6** a $\frac{8}{125}$ b $\frac{12}{125}$ c $\frac{27}{125}$

EXERCISE 18D.2

1 a $\frac{14}{55}$ b $\frac{1}{55}$ **2** a $\frac{7}{15}$ b $\frac{7}{30}$ c $\frac{7}{15}$

3 a $\frac{3}{100}$ b $\frac{3}{100} \times \frac{2}{99} \approx 0.0006$
c $\frac{3}{100} \times \frac{2}{99} \times \frac{1}{98} \approx 0.000\,006$ d $\frac{97}{100} \times \frac{96}{99} \times \frac{95}{98} \approx 0.912$

4 a $\frac{4}{7}$ b $\frac{2}{7}$

EXERCISE 18E

1 a

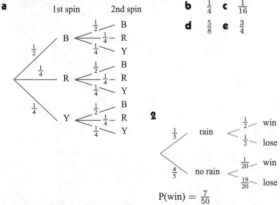

b $\frac{1}{4}$ c $\frac{1}{16}$
d $\frac{5}{8}$ e $\frac{3}{4}$

2

$$P(\text{win}) = \frac{7}{50}$$

3 0.032 **4** $\frac{17}{40}$ **5** a $\frac{11}{30}$ b $\frac{19}{30}$

EXERCISE 18F

1 a $\frac{20}{49}$ b $\frac{10}{21}$ **2** a $\frac{3}{10}$ b $\frac{1}{10}$ c $\frac{3}{5}$

3 a $\frac{2}{9}$ b $\frac{5}{9}$ **4** a $\frac{1}{3}$ b $\frac{2}{15}$ c $\frac{4}{15}$ d $\frac{4}{15}$

These are all possibilities, so their probabilities must sum to 1.

5 a $\frac{1}{5}$ b $\frac{3}{5}$ c $\frac{4}{5}$ **6** $\frac{19}{45}$ **7** a $\frac{2}{100} \times \frac{1}{99} \approx 0.0002$
b $\frac{98}{100} \times \frac{97}{99} \approx 0.9602$ c $1 - \frac{98}{100} \times \frac{97}{99} \approx 0.0398$

8 $\frac{7}{33}$ **9** 7 to start with

EXERCISE 18G

1 a $(p+q)^4 = p^4 + 4p^3q + 6p^2q^2 + 4pq^3 + q^4$ b $4(\frac{1}{2})^3(\frac{1}{2}) = \frac{1}{4}$

2 a $(p+q)^5 = p^5 + 5p^4q + 10p^3q^2 + 10p^2q^3 + 5pq^4 + q^5$
b i $5(\frac{1}{2})^4(\frac{1}{2}) = \frac{5}{32}$ ii $10(\frac{1}{2})^2(\frac{1}{2})^3 = \frac{5}{16}$ iii $(\frac{1}{2})^4(\frac{1}{2}) = \frac{1}{32}$

3 a $(\frac{2}{3} + \frac{1}{3})^4 = (\frac{2}{3})^4 + 4(\frac{2}{3})^3(\frac{1}{3}) + 6(\frac{2}{3})^2(\frac{1}{3})^2 + 4(\frac{2}{3})(\frac{1}{3})^3$
$+ (\frac{1}{3})^4$ b i $(\frac{2}{3})^4 = \frac{16}{81}$ ii $6(\frac{2}{3})^2(\frac{1}{3})^2 = \frac{8}{27}$ iii $\frac{8}{9}$

4 a $(\frac{3}{4} + \frac{1}{4})^5 = (\frac{3}{4})^5 + 5(\frac{3}{4})^4(\frac{1}{4})^1 + 10(\frac{3}{4})^3(\frac{1}{4})^2$
$+ 10(\frac{3}{4})^2(\frac{1}{4})^3 + 5(\frac{3}{4})(\frac{1}{4})^4 + (\frac{1}{4})^5$
b i $10(\frac{3}{4})^3(\frac{1}{4})^2 = \frac{135}{512}$ ii $\frac{53}{512}$ iii $\frac{47}{128}$

5 a ≈ 0.154 b ≈ 0.973 **6** a ≈ 0.0305 b ≈ 0.265

7 $\approx 0.000\,864$ **8** ≈ 0.0341 **9** 4 times

EXERCISE 18H.1

1 a $A = \{1, 2, 3, 6\}$, $B = \{2, 4, 6, 8, 10\}$
b i $n(A) = 4$ ii $A \cup B = \{1, 2, 3, 4, 6, 8, 10\}$
iii $A \cap B = \{2, 6\}$

2 a

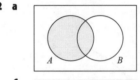

b

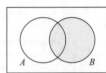

c

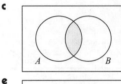

d

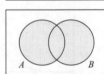

e

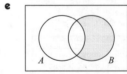

f

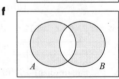

3 a 29 b 17 c 26 d 5 **4** a 65 b 9 c 4 d 52

5 a $\frac{19}{40}$ b $\frac{1}{2}$ c $\frac{4}{5}$ d $\frac{5}{8}$ e $\frac{13}{40}$ f $\frac{7}{20}$

6 a $\frac{19}{25}$ b $\frac{13}{25}$ c $\frac{6}{25}$ d $\frac{7}{19}$ **7** a $\frac{7}{15}$ b $\frac{1}{15}$ c $\frac{2}{15}$ d $\frac{6}{7}$

8 a

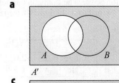

A'

b

$A' \cap B$

c

$A \cup B'$

d

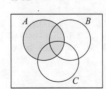

$A' \cap B'$

9 a

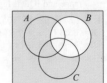

b

c
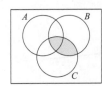

d

e

f
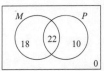

EXERCISE 18H.2

1 For each of these draw **two** diagrams, shade the first with the LHS set and the second with the RHS set.

2 a $A = \{7, 14, 21, 28, 35, \ldots, 98\}$
   $B = \{5, 10, 15, 20, 25, \ldots, 95\}$
   i $n(A) = 14$ **ii** $n(B) = 19$ **iii** 2 **iv** 31

3 a i $\frac{b+c}{a+b+c+d}$ **ii** $\frac{b}{a+b+c+d}$ **iii** $\frac{a+b+c}{a+b+c+d}$ **iv** $\frac{a+b+c}{a+b+c+d}$
   b $P(A \text{ or } B) = P(A) + P(B) - P(A \text{ and } B)$

EXERCISE 18I

1 a

22 study both

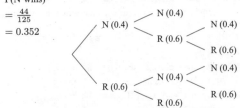

M: 18, 22, P: 10, 0

b i $\frac{9}{25}$ **ii** $\frac{11}{20}$

2 a $\frac{3}{8}$ **b** $\frac{7}{20}$ **c** $\frac{1}{5}$ **d** $\frac{15}{23}$

3 a $\frac{14}{25}$ **b** $\frac{4}{5}$ **c** $\frac{1}{5}$ **d** $\frac{5}{23}$ **e** $\frac{9}{14}$ **4** $\frac{5}{6}$

5 a $\frac{13}{20}$ **b** $\frac{7}{20}$ **c** $\frac{11}{50}$ **d** $\frac{7}{20}$ **e** $\frac{4}{7}$ **f** $\frac{1}{4}$

6 a $\frac{3}{5}$ **b** $\frac{2}{3}$ **7 a** 0.46 **b** $\frac{14}{23}$ **8** $\frac{70}{163}$

9 a 0.45 **b** 0.75 **c** 0.65 **10 a** 0.0484 **b** 0.3926

11 $\frac{2}{3}$ **12** $\frac{1}{5}$

13 $P(A \cup B \cup C) = P(A) + P(B) + P(C) - P(A \cap B)$
$- P(B \cap C) - P(A \cap C) + P(A \cap B \cap C)$

EXERCISE 18J

1 $P(R \cap S) = 0.2$ and $P(R) \times P(S) = 0.2$
   $\therefore$ are independent events

2 a $\frac{7}{30}$ **b** $\frac{7}{12}$ **c** $\frac{7}{10}$ No, as $P(A \cap B) \neq P(A) \times P(B)$

3 a 0.35 **b** 0.85 **c** 0.15 **d** 0.15 **e** 0.5

4 $\frac{14}{15}$ **5 a** $\frac{91}{216}$ **b** 26

6 Hint: Show $P(A' \cap B') = P(A') P(B')$
   using a Venn diagram and $P(A \cap B)$

7 a i $\left(\frac{12}{13}\right)^4 \left(\frac{1}{13}\right)$ **iii** $\frac{13}{25}$ **b** ≈ 0.544 **8** 0.9

9 a i $\frac{13}{20}$ **ii** $\frac{7}{10}$ **b** No, as $P(C \cap D) \neq P(C) P(D)$ **10** $\frac{63}{125}$

EXERCISE 18K

1 ≈ 0.655 **2** $\frac{1}{12}$ **3** ≈ 0.318 **4** ≈ 0.530

5 a $\frac{1}{10}$ **b** $\frac{2}{5}$ **6 a** ≈ 0.0288 **b** ≈ 0.635 **c** ≈ 0.966

7 $\frac{1}{5}$ **8 a** ≈ 0.0962 **b** ≈ 0.0962

EXERCISE 18L

1 a 0.0435 **b** ≈ 0.598 **2 a** ≈ 0.773 **b** ≈ 0.556

3 $\frac{10}{13}$ **4** ≈ 0.424 **5** 0.0137 **6** $\frac{15}{83}$ **7** $\frac{99}{148}$

8 a $\frac{9}{19}$ **b** $\frac{10}{19}$ **10 a** 0.95 **b** ≈ 0.306 **c** 0.6

11 a 0.104 **b** ≈ 0.267 **c** ≈ 0.0168

REVIEW SET 18A

1 ABCD, ABDC, ACBD, ACDB, ADBC, ADCB, BACD, BADC, BCAD, BCDA, BDAC, BDCA, CABD, CADB, CBAD, CBDA, CDAB, CDBA, DABC, DACB, DBAC, DBCA, DCAB, DCBA

a $\frac{1}{2}$ **b** $\frac{1}{3}$

2 a $\frac{3}{8}$ **b** $\frac{1}{8}$ **c** $\frac{5}{8}$ **3 a** $\frac{3}{25}$ **b** $\frac{24}{25}$ **c** $\frac{11}{12}$

4 P(N wins)
   $= \frac{44}{125}$
   $= 0.352$

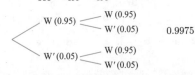

N (0.4) — N (0.4) — N (0.4), R (0.6)
N (0.4) — R (0.6)
R (0.6) — N (0.4) — N (0.4), R (0.6)
R (0.6) — R (0.6)

5 a $\frac{2}{5}$ **b** $\frac{13}{15}$ **c** $\frac{4}{15}$

6 a $10(\frac{4}{5})^3(\frac{1}{5})^2 \approx 0.205$ **b** $5(\frac{4}{5})^4(\frac{1}{5}) + (\frac{4}{5})^5 \approx 0.737$

7 a $\frac{4}{500} \times \frac{3}{499} \times \frac{2}{498} \approx 0.000\,000\,193$
   b $1 - \frac{496}{500} \times \frac{495}{499} \times \frac{494}{498} \approx 0.023\,86$

8

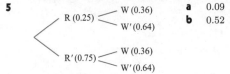

W (0.95) — W (0.95), W' (0.05)   0.9975
W' (0.05) — W (0.95), W' (0.05)

9 a ≈ 0.0238 **b** ≈ 0.976 **10 a** $\frac{1}{10}$ **b** $\frac{1}{5}$

11 a ≈ 0.259 **b** ≈ 0.703

REVIEW SET 18B

1 BBBB, BBBG, BBGB, BGBB, GBBB, BBGG, BGBG, BGGB, GGBB, GBBG, GBGB, BGGG, GBGG, GGBG, GGGB, GGGG
   $\frac{3}{8}$

2 a $\frac{1}{4}$ **b** $\frac{37}{40}$ **c** $\frac{10}{25} = \frac{2}{5}$ **3 a** $\frac{5}{33}$ **b** $\frac{19}{66}$ **c** $\frac{5}{11}$ **d** $\frac{16}{33}$

4 a Two events are independent if the occurrence of each event does not influence the occurrence of the other.
   For A and B independent, $P(A) \times P(B) = P(A \text{ and } B)$

   b Two events, A and B, are disjoint if they have no common outcomes. $P(A \text{ or } B) = P(A) + P(B)$

5
R (0.25) — W (0.36), W' (0.64)
R' (0.75) — W (0.36), W' (0.64)
   a 0.09
   b 0.52

6 $1 - 0.9 \times 0.8 \times 0.7 = 0.496$

7 a $\frac{31}{70}$ **b** $\frac{21}{31}$

8 a $\left(\frac{3}{5} + \frac{2}{5}\right)^4 = \left(\frac{3}{5}\right)^4 + 4\left(\frac{3}{5}\right)^3\left(\frac{2}{5}\right) + 6\left(\frac{3}{5}\right)^2\left(\frac{2}{5}\right)^2$
   $+ 4\left(\frac{3}{5}\right)\left(\frac{2}{5}\right)^3 + \left(\frac{2}{5}\right)^4$ **b i** $\frac{216}{625}$ **ii** $\frac{328}{625}$

9 $(0.6 + 0.4)^6$
   $= (0.6)^6 + 6(0.6)^5(0.4) + 15(0.6)^4(0.4)^2 + 20(0.6)^3(0.4)^3$

   X wins 6   X wins 5   X wins 4   X wins 3
   Y wins 1   Y wins 2   Y wins 3

   $+15(0.6)^2(0.4)^4 + 6(0.6)(0.4)^5 + (0.4)^6$

   X wins 2   X wins 1   Y wins 6
   Y wins 4   Y wins 5

   a $20(0.6)^3(0.4)^3 \approx 0.276$ **b** $6(0.6)(0.4)^5 + (0.4)^6 \approx 0.0410$

10 a ≈ 0.0205 **b** ≈ 0.205

REVIEW SET 18C

1 a $P(M \cap C) = 0.85$, $P(M)P(C) \approx 0.801$, so not independent **b** $\frac{3}{88}$

2 $\frac{3}{14}$ **3 a** ≈ 0.692 **b** ≈ 0.558 **4** ≈ 0.127 **5** $\frac{4}{9}$

6 $\frac{4}{15}$ **7** $\frac{5}{9}$ **8** 8 **9 a** $\frac{5}{8}$ **b** $\frac{1}{4}$ **c i** $\frac{6}{13}$ **ii** $\frac{7}{13}$

10 a 1.54×10^{-6} **b** 1.28×10^{-8} **11** $\frac{1}{2}$

REVIEW SET 18D

1 a The occurrence of each event does not affect the occurrence of the other.

3 b $P(0) = \frac{1}{32}$, $P(1) = \frac{5}{32}$, $P(2) = \frac{10}{32}$, $P(3) = \frac{10}{32}$, $P(4) = \frac{5}{32}$, $P(5) = \frac{1}{32}$

4 a 0.93 **b** 0.8 **c** 0.2 **d** 0.65 **5** $n = 11$

6 a 0.07831 **b** 0.07663

7 B [probability $p(1-q)(1+q)$] is more likely than
A [probability $p(1-q)(2-p)$]

8 a 0 **b** $\frac{3}{14}$ **c** $\frac{2}{15}$ **9** $\frac{5}{8}$ **10** $(\frac{1}{3} + \frac{2}{3})^5$, ≈ 0.313

11 $\frac{148}{243}$ **12 a** $\frac{1}{50}$ **b** $\frac{13}{50}$

EXERCISE 19A

1 a 7 **b** 7 **c** 11 **d** 16 **e** 0 **f** $\frac{3}{2}$ **g** 5 **h** -2 **i** -3
j 6 **k** -8 **l** $1\frac{1}{2}$ **m** $\frac{1}{2}$ **n** 5 **o** $\frac{20}{17}$ **p** $\frac{3}{2}$ **q** 6 **r** $\frac{7}{6}$

2 $\lim\limits_{x \to \infty} \frac{1}{x} = 0$ **3 a** 3 **b** $-\frac{2}{3}$ **c** -1 **d** 1 **e** 1 **f** $\frac{1}{3}$

EXERCISE 19B

1 a vertical asymptote $x = -3$, horizontal asymptote $y = 3$
as $x \to -3^-$, $f(x) \to \infty$ as $x \to \infty$, $f(x) \to 3^-$
as $x \to -3^+$, $f(x) \to -\infty$ as $x \to -\infty$, $f(x) \to 3^+$

b vertical asymptote $x = 0$, oblique asymptote $y = 2x$
as $x \to 0^-$, $y \to -\infty$ as $x \to \infty$, $y \to (2x)^+$
as $x \to 0^+$, $y \to \infty$ as $x \to -\infty$, $y \to (2x)^-$

c horizontal asymptote $W = 5000$ **d** horizontal asymptote $y = 1$
as $t \to \infty$, $W \to 5000^-$ as $x \to \infty$, $y \to 1^-$
                                          as $x \to -\infty$, $y \to 1^-$

e horizontal asymptote $y = 0$ as $x \to \infty$, $f(x) \to 0^+$
                                      as $x \to -\infty$, $f(x) \to 0^-$

f vertical asymptotes $x = -2$, $x = 1$,
horizontal asymptote $y = 0$
as $x \to -2^-$, $f(x) \to -\infty$ as $x \to \infty$, $f(x) \to 0^+$
as $x \to -2^+$, $f(x) \to \infty$ as $x \to -\infty$, $f(x) \to 0^-$
as $x \to 1^-$, $f(x) \to \infty$
as $x \to 1^+$, $f(x) \to -\infty$

g oblique asymptote $y = x$ as $x \to \infty$, $y \to x^-$
                                   as $x \to -\infty$, $y \to x^+$

h vertical asymptote $x = 0$, horizontal asymptote $y = 0$
as $x \to 0^-$, $f(x) \to \infty$ as $x \to \infty$, $f(x) \to \infty$
as $x \to 0^+$, $f(x) \to 0^+$ as $x \to -\infty$, $f(x) \to 0^+$

i vertical asymptote $x = 0$ as $x \to 0^+$, $y \to -\infty$

j horizontal asymptote $y = 12$ as $x \to \infty$, $f(x) \to \infty$
                                       as $x \to -\infty$, $f(x) \to 12^-$

k oblique asymptote $y = -x$ as $x \to \infty$, $y \to \infty$
                                    as $x \to -\infty$, $y \to (-x)^+$

l horizontal asymptotes $y = 0$, $y = 1000$
as $x \to \infty$, $y \to 1000^-$ as $x \to -\infty$, $y \to 0^+$

EXERCISE 19C

1 a 2 **b** 1 **c** 1 **d** 4 **e** $\frac{1}{2}$ **f** 2π

2 b πr^2 **c** Area of circle $= \pi r^2$ **3 c** $-\sin x$

EXERCISE 19D.1

1 a

b maximum speed is 100 km h^{-1}, minimum speed is 68.4 km h^{-1}
c **Hint:** $V(t) \geqslant 68.4$ km h^{-1}
d 4.84 km $<$ distance from Adelaide $<$ 20.64 km
e 9.28 km $<$ distance from Adelaide $<$ 17.18 km

2 a

b **Hint:** $P(n) \leqslant 10\,000$ **c** \$375\,000 $<$ profit $<$ \$875\,000
d \$531\,250 $<$ profit $<$ \$781\,250
e Use upper sum with 100 intervals.

EXERCISE 19D.2

1

n	A_L	A_U
10	2.1850	2.4850
25	2.2736	2.3936
50	2.3034	2.3634
100	2.3184	2.3484
500	2.3303	2.3363

converges to $\frac{7}{3}$

2 a i

n	A_L	A_U
5	0.16000	0.36000
10	0.20250	0.30250
50	0.24010	0.26010
100	0.24503	0.25503
500	0.24900	0.25100
1000	0.24950	0.25050
10000	0.24995	0.25005

ii

n	A_L	A_U
5	0.40000	0.60000
10	0.45000	0.55000
50	0.49000	0.51000
100	0.49500	0.50500
500	0.49900	0.50100
1000	0.49950	0.50050
10000	0.49995	0.50005

iii

n	A_L	A_U
5	0.54974	0.74974
10	0.61051	0.71051
50	0.65610	0.67610
100	0.66146	0.67146
500	0.66565	0.66765
1000	0.66616	0.66716
10000	0.66662	0.66672

iv

n	A_L	A_U
5	0.61867	0.81867
10	0.68740	0.78740
50	0.73851	0.75851
100	0.74441	0.75441
500	0.74893	0.75093
1000	0.74947	0.75047
10000	0.74995	0.75005

b **i** $\frac{1}{4}$ **ii** $\frac{1}{2}$ **iii** $\frac{2}{3}$ **iv** $\frac{3}{4}$ **c** area $= \dfrac{1}{a+1}$

3 **a**

n	Rational bounds for π
10	$2.9045 < \pi < 3.3045$
50	$3.0983 < \pi < 3.1783$
100	$3.1204 < \pi < 3.1604$
200	$3.1312 < \pi < 3.1512$
1000	$3.1396 < \pi < 3.1436$
10 000	$3.1414 < \pi < 3.1418$

b $n = 10\,000$

EXERCISE 19D.3

1 **a**

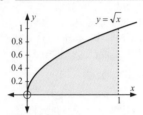

b

n	A_L	A_U
5	0.5497	0.7497
10	0.6105	0.7105
50	0.6561	0.6761
100	0.6615	0.6715
500	0.6656	0.6676

c $\int_0^1 \sqrt{x}\,dx \approx 0.67$

2 **a**

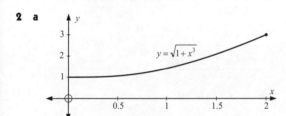

b

n	A_L	A_U
50	3.2016	3.2816
100	3.2214	3.2614
500	3.2373	3.2453

c $\int_0^2 \sqrt{1+x^3}\,dx \approx 3.24$

3 **a** 18 **b** 4.5 **c** 2π

REVIEW SET 19

1 **a** -4 **b** $\frac{6}{5}$ **c** $\frac{1}{4}$ **d** 8 **e** -1 **f** $-\frac{1}{2}$

2 **a** vertical asymptote $x = 2$, oblique asymptote $y = x + 3$
  as $x \to 2^-$, $f(x) \to -\infty$ as $x \to \infty$, $f(x) \to (x+3)^+$
  as $x \to 2^+$, $f(x) \to \infty$ as $x \to -\infty$, $f(x) \to (x+3)^-$
b horizontal asymptote $y = -3$
  as $x \to \infty$, $y \to \infty$ as $x \to -\infty$, $y \to -3^+$
c no asymptotes
d vertical asymptote $x = 0$, horizontal asymptote $y = 0$
  as $x \to 0^+$, $f(x) \to -\infty$ as $x \to \infty$, $f(x) \to 0^+$
e vertical asymptote $x = \frac{3}{2}$ as $x \to \frac{3}{2}^+$, $y \to -\infty$
f vertical asymptote $x = 0$ as $x \to 0^-$, $y \to -\infty$

3 **a** 4 **b** $\frac{2}{3}$ **c** π
4 **a**

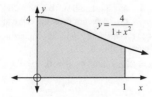

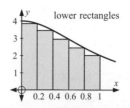
lower rectangles

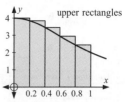
upper rectangles

b

n	A_L	A_U
5	2.9349	3.3349
50	3.1215	3.1615
100	3.1316	3.1516
500	3.1396	3.1436

c $\displaystyle\int_0^1 \frac{4}{1+x^2}\,dx \approx 3.1416$

5 **a**

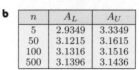
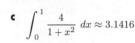

b **Hint:** $10\text{ mg} \leqslant r(t) \leqslant 25\text{ mg}$
c $35.9\text{ mg} < \text{amount} < 50.5\text{ mg}$
d Use more intervals of shorter length.

6 $\cos x$, h and x are in radians   **7** **c** $\cos x$

8 **a**

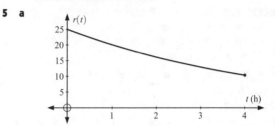

b maximum is 0.5, minimum is 0.167
c $0.95 < \text{area} < 1.28$
d Use more intervals of shorter length.

9 **a**

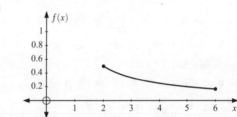

b $A_U \approx 0.977$ units^2, $A_L \approx 0.761$ units^2
c $A_U \approx 0.8733$ units^2, $A_L \approx 0.8560$ units^2

10 **a** 2π **b** 4
12 **a** $A = \frac{17}{4}$, $B = \frac{25}{4}$ **b** $\int_0^2 (4-x^2)\,dx \approx \frac{21}{4}$
13 **a**

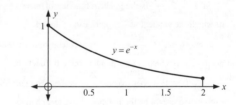

EXERCISE 20A

1 **a** 1 **b** 0 **c** $3x^2$ **d** $4x^3$
2 **a** 2 **b** $2x - 3$ **c** $3x^2 - 4x$

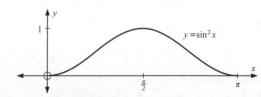

3 a $\dfrac{-1}{(x+2)^2}$ **b** $\dfrac{-2}{(2x-1)^2}$ **c** $-\dfrac{2}{x^3}$ **d** $-\dfrac{3}{x^4}$

4 a $\dfrac{1}{2\sqrt{x+2}}$ **b** $-\dfrac{1}{2x\sqrt{x}}$ **c** $\dfrac{1}{\sqrt{2x+1}}$

5

Function	Derivative	Function	Derivative
x	1	x^{-2}	$-2x^{-3}$
x^2	$2x^1$	x^{-3}	$-3x^{-4}$
x^3	$3x^2$	$x^{\frac{1}{2}}$	$\frac{1}{2}x^{-\frac{1}{2}}$
x^4	$4x^3$	$x^{-\frac{1}{2}}$	$-\frac{1}{2}x^{-\frac{3}{2}}$
x^{-1}	$-x^{-2}$	x^n	nx^{n-1}

EXERCISE 20B

1 a -4 **b** 1 **c** -12 **d** 3

2 a -1 **b** $\frac{3}{4}$ **c** $-\frac{1}{32}$ **d** -12 **e** -1 **f** $-\frac{45}{289}$

3 a $\frac{1}{4}$ **b** 1 **c** $-\frac{1}{27}$ **d** $\frac{1}{4}$

4 a 9 **b** 10 **c** $-\frac{2}{25}$ **d** $-\frac{2}{27}$ **e** $\frac{1}{4}$ **f** $-\frac{1}{2}$

5 a 12 **b** 108

EXERCISE 20C

1 a $3x^2$ **b** $6x^2$ **c** $14x$ **d** $2x+1$ **e** $-4x$ **f** $2x+3$

g $3x^2+6x+4$ **h** $20x^3-12x$ **i** $\dfrac{6}{x^2}$ **j** $-\dfrac{2}{x^2}+\dfrac{6}{x^3}$

k $2x-\dfrac{5}{x^2}$ **l** $2x+\dfrac{3}{x^2}$ **m** $-\dfrac{1}{2x\sqrt{x}}$ **n** $8x-4$

o $3x^2+12x+12$

2 a $6x^2-14x$ **b** $2\pi x$ **c** $-\dfrac{2}{5x^3}$ **d** 100 **e** 10 **f** $12\pi x^2$

3 a 6 **b** $\dfrac{3\sqrt{x}}{2}$ **c** $2x-10$ **d** $2-9x^2$ **e** $4+\dfrac{1}{4x^2}$

f $6x^2-6x-5$

4 a 4 **b** $-\frac{16}{729}$ **c** -7 **d** $\frac{13}{4}$ **e** $\frac{1}{8}$ **f** -11

5 a $\dfrac{2}{\sqrt{x}}+1$ **b** $\dfrac{1}{3\sqrt[3]{x^2}}$ **c** $\dfrac{1}{x\sqrt{x}}$ **d** $2-\dfrac{1}{2\sqrt{x}}$

e $-\dfrac{2}{x\sqrt{x}}$ **f** $6x-\frac{3}{2}\sqrt{x}$ **g** $\dfrac{-25}{2x^3\sqrt{x}}$ **h** $2+\dfrac{9}{2x^2\sqrt{x}}$

6 a $\dfrac{dy}{dx}=4+\dfrac{3}{x^2}$, $\dfrac{dy}{dx}$ is the gradient function of $y=4x-\dfrac{3}{x}$ from which the gradient at any point can be found.

b $\dfrac{dS}{dt}=4t+4$ ms^{-1}, $\dfrac{dS}{dt}$ is the instantaneous rate of change in position at the time t, i.e., it is the velocity function.

c $\dfrac{dC}{dx}=3+0.004x$ \$ per toaster, $\dfrac{dC}{dx}$ is the instantaneous rate of change in cost as the number of toasters changes.

EXERCISE 20D.1

1 a $f(g(x))=(2x+7)^2$ **b** $f(g(x))=2x^2+7$

c $f(g(x))=\sqrt{3-4x}$ **d** $f(g(x))=3-4\sqrt{x}$

e $f(g(x))=\dfrac{2}{x^2+3}$ **f** $f(g(x))=\dfrac{4}{x^2}+3$

2 a $f(x)=x^3$, $g(x)=3x+10$ **b** $f(x)=\dfrac{1}{x}$, $g(x)=2x+4$

c $f(x)=\sqrt{x}$, $g(x)=x^2-3x$ **d** $f(x)=\dfrac{10}{x^3}$, $g(x)=3x-x^2$

EXERCISE 20D.2

1 a u^{-2}, $u=2x-1$ **b** $u^{\frac{1}{2}}$, $u=x^2-3x$

c $2u^{-\frac{1}{2}}$, $u=2-x^2$ **d** $u^{\frac{1}{3}}$, $u=x^3-x^2$

e $4u^{-3}$, $u=3-x$ **f** $10u^{-1}$, $u=x^2-3$

2 a $8(4x-5)$ **b** $2(5-2x)^{-2}$ **c** $\frac{1}{2}(3x-x^2)^{-\frac{1}{2}}\times(3-2x)$

d $-12(1-3x)^3$ **e** $-18(5-x)^2$

f $\frac{1}{3}(2x^3-x^2)^{-\frac{2}{3}}\times(6x^2-2x)$ **g** $-60(5x-4)^{-3}$

h $-4(3x-x^2)^{-2}\times(3-2x)$ **i** $6(x^2-\dfrac{2}{x})^2\times(2x+\dfrac{2}{x^2})$

3 a $-\dfrac{1}{\sqrt{3}}$ **b** -18 **c** -8 **d** -4 **e** $-\frac{3}{32}$ **f** 0

4 a $\dfrac{dy}{dx}=3x^2$, $\dfrac{dx}{dy}=\frac{1}{3}y^{-\frac{2}{3}}$ **Hint:** Substitute $y=x^3$

b $\dfrac{dy}{dx}\times\dfrac{dx}{dy}=\dfrac{dy}{dy}=1$

EXERCISE 20E.1

1 a $2x(2x-1)+2x^2$ **b** $4(2x+1)^3+24x(2x+1)^2$

c $2x(3-x)^{\frac{1}{2}}-\frac{1}{2}x^2(3-x)^{-\frac{1}{2}}$

d $\frac{1}{2}x^{-\frac{1}{2}}(x-3)^2+2\sqrt{x}(x-3)$

e $10x(3x^2-1)^2+60x^3(3x^2-1)$

f $\frac{1}{2}x^{-\frac{1}{2}}(x-x^2)^3+3\sqrt{x}(x-x^2)^2(1-2x)$

2 a -48 **b** $406\frac{1}{4}$ **c** $\frac{13}{3}$ **d** $\frac{11}{2}$ **3** $x=3$ or $\frac{3}{5}$

EXERCISE 20E.2

1 a $\dfrac{3(2-x)+(1+3x)}{(2-x)^2}$ **b** $\dfrac{2x(2x+1)-2x^2}{(2x+1)^2}$

c $\dfrac{(x^2-3)-2x^2}{(x^2-3)^2}$ **d** $\dfrac{\frac{1}{2}x^{-\frac{1}{2}}(1-2x)+2\sqrt{x}}{(1-2x)^2}$

e $\dfrac{2x(3x-x^2)-(x^2-3)(3-2x)}{(3x-x^2)^2}$

f $\dfrac{(1-3x)^{\frac{1}{2}}+\frac{3}{2}x(1-3x)^{-\frac{1}{2}}}{1-3x}$

2 a 1 **b** 1 **c** $-\frac{7}{324}$ **d** $-\frac{28}{27}$

3 b i never (note: $\dfrac{dy}{dx}$ is undefined at $x=-1$)

ii $x\leqslant 0$ and $x=1$

4 b i $x=-2\pm\sqrt{11}$ **ii** $x=-2$

c $\dfrac{dy}{dx}$ is zero when the tangent to the function is horizontal (gradient 0), i.e., at its turning points or points of horizontal inflection.

$\dfrac{dy}{dx}$ is undefined at vertical asymptotes.

EXERCISE 20F

1 a $y=-7x+11$ **b** $4y=x+8$ **c** $y=-2x-2$

d $y=-2x+6$

2 a $6y=-x+57$ **b** $7y=-x+26$ **c** $3y=x+11$

d $x+6y=43$

3 a $y=21$ and $y=-6$ **b** $(\frac{1}{2},2\sqrt{2})$ **c** $k=-5$

d $y=-3x+1$

4 a $a=-4$, $b=7$ **b** $a=2$, $b=4$

5 a $3y=x+5$ **b** $9y=x+4$ **c** $16y=x-3$ **d** $y=-4$

6 a $y=2x-\frac{7}{4}$ **b** $y=-27x-\frac{242}{3}$

c $57y=-4x+1042$ **d** $2y=x+1$

7 $a=4$, $b=3$ **8 a** $(-4,-64)$ **b** $(4,-31)$

c does not meet the curve again

9 a $y=(2a-1)x-a^2+9$; $y=5x$, contact at $(3,15)$

$y=-7x$, contact at $(-3,21)$

b $y=0$, $y=27x+54$ **c** $y=0$, $y=-\sqrt{14}x+4\sqrt{14}$

10 a

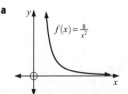

$f(x) = \frac{8}{x^2}$

b $16x + a^3y = 24a$

c A is $(\frac{3}{2}a, 0)$,
B is $(0, \frac{24}{a^2})$

d Area $= \frac{18}{a}$ units^2,
area $\to 0$ as $a \to \infty$

11 a Domain $\{x \mid x < 2\}$ **c** $8x + 3y = -19$

12 $a = \frac{1}{4}$, point of intersection $(\frac{1}{2}, \frac{\sqrt{3}}{2})$ **13** $b = 3$

EXERCISE 20G

1 a 6 **b** $12x - 6$ **c** $\dfrac{3}{2x^{\frac{5}{2}}}$ **d** $\dfrac{12 - 6x}{x^4}$ **e** $24 - 48x$ **f** $\dfrac{20}{(2x-1)^3}$

2 a $\dfrac{d^2y}{dx^2} = -6x$, $\dfrac{d^3y}{dx^3} = -6$ **b** $\dfrac{d^2y}{dx^2} = 2 - \dfrac{30}{x^4}$, $\dfrac{d^3y}{dx^3} = \dfrac{120}{x^5}$

c $\dfrac{d^2y}{dx^2} = -\dfrac{9}{4}x^{-\frac{5}{2}}$, $\dfrac{d^3y}{dx^3} = \dfrac{45}{8}x^{-\frac{7}{2}}$

d $\dfrac{d^2y}{dx^2} = \dfrac{8}{x^3}$, $\dfrac{d^3y}{dx^3} = \dfrac{-24}{x^4}$

e $\dfrac{d^2y}{dx^2} = 6(x^2 - 3x)(5x^2 - 15x + 9)$,

$\dfrac{d^3y}{dx^3} = 6(2x - 3)(5x^2 - 15x + 9) + 6(x^2 - 3x)(10x - 15)$

f $\dfrac{d^2y}{dx^2} = 2 + \dfrac{2}{(1-x)^3}$, $\dfrac{d^3y}{dx^3} = \dfrac{6}{(1-x)^4}$

3 a $x = 1$ **b** $x = 0, \pm\sqrt{6}$ **4 a** $\dfrac{dy}{dx} = \dfrac{1}{(1-x)^2}$

REVIEW SET 20A

1 $y = 4x + 2$ **2 a** $6x - 4x^3$ **b** $1 + \dfrac{1}{x^2}$ **3** $2x + 2$

4 $x = 1$ **5** $(-2, -25)$ **6** $a = \frac{5}{2}, b = -\frac{3}{2}$ **7** $a = \frac{1}{2}$

8 $y = 16x - \frac{127}{2}$

9 a $\dfrac{dM}{dt} = 8t(t^2 + 3)^3$ **b** $\dfrac{dA}{dt} = \dfrac{\frac{1}{2}t(t+5)^{-\frac{1}{2}} - 2(t+5)^{\frac{1}{2}}}{t^3}$

10 a $-\dfrac{2}{x\sqrt{x}} - 3$ **b** $4\left(x - \dfrac{1}{x}\right)^3\left(1 + \dfrac{1}{x^2}\right)$

c $\frac{1}{2}(x^2 - 3x)^{-\frac{1}{2}}(2x - 3)$

11 a $-2(5 - 4x)^{-\frac{1}{2}}$ **b** $-4(5 - 4x)^{-\frac{3}{2}}$ **c** $-24(5 - 4x)^{-\frac{5}{2}}$

REVIEW SET 20B

1 a $\dfrac{dy}{dx} = 5 + 3x^{-2}$ **b** $\dfrac{dy}{dx} = 4(3x^2 + x)^3(6x + 1)$

c $\dfrac{dy}{dx} = 2x(1 - x^2)^3 - 6x(1 - x^2)^2(x^2 + 1)$

2 $y = 7$, $y = -25$ **3** $5y = x - 11$

4 a $f'(x) = \dfrac{3(x+3)^2\sqrt{x} - \frac{1}{2}x^{-\frac{1}{2}}(x+3)^3}{x}$

b $f'(x) = 4x^3\sqrt{x^2 + 3} + x^5(x^2 + 3)^{-\frac{1}{2}}$

5 a $f''(x) = 6 - \dfrac{2}{x^3}$ **b** $f''(x) = -\frac{1}{4}x^{-\frac{3}{2}}$

6 area $= \frac{3267}{152}$ units^2 **Hint:** tangent is $4y = -57x - 99$

7 $a = -1$, $b = 2$

8 $a = 2$ and the tangent is $y = 3x - 1$ which meets the curve again at $(-4, -13)$

9 $A = -14$, $B = 21$

REVIEW SET 20C

1 a $\dfrac{dy}{dx} = 3x^2(1 - x^2)^{\frac{1}{2}} - x^4(1 - x^2)^{-\frac{1}{2}}$

b $\dfrac{dy}{dx} = \dfrac{(2x - 3)(x + 1)^{\frac{1}{2}} - \frac{1}{2}(x^2 - 3x)(x + 1)^{-\frac{1}{2}}}{x + 1}$

2 $x = -\frac{1}{2}, \frac{3}{2}$

3 BC $= \frac{8\sqrt{10}}{3}$ **(Hint:** normal is $y = -3x + 8$)

4 a $\dfrac{d^2y}{dx^2} = 36x^2 - \dfrac{4}{x^3}$ **b** $\dfrac{d^2y}{dx^2} = 6x + \frac{3}{4}x^{-\frac{5}{2}}$

5 $a = 9$, $b = -16$ **6** $A = 9$, $B = 2$, $f''(-2) = -18$

7 $a = 64$ **8** $4y = 3x + 5$

9 a

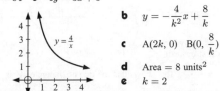

$y = \frac{4}{x}$

b $y = -\dfrac{4}{k^2}x + \dfrac{8}{k}$

c A$(2k, 0)$ B$(0, \dfrac{8}{k})$

d Area $= 8$ units^2

e $k = 2$

EXERCISE 21A

1 a \$118 000 **b** $\dfrac{dP}{dt} = 4t - 12$ \$1000 per year

c $\dfrac{dP}{dt}$ is the rate of change in profit with time

d i $0 \leqslant t \leqslant 3$ years **ii** $t \geqslant 3$ years

e minimum profit is \$100 000 when $t = 3$

f $\left.\dfrac{dP}{dt}\right]_{t=4} = 4$ Profit is increasing at \$4000 per year after 4 years.

$\left.\dfrac{dP}{dt}\right]_{t=10} = 28$ Profit is increasing at \$28 000 per year after 10 years.

$\left.\dfrac{dP}{dt}\right]_{t=25} = 88$ Profit is increasing at \$88 000 per year after 25 years.

2 a 19 000 m^3 per minute **b** 18 000 m^3 per minute

3 a 1.2 m **b** $\dfrac{ds}{dt} = 28.1 - 9.8t$ represents the instantaneous velocity of the ball

c $t = 2.867$ secs. The ball has stopped and reached its maximum height. **d** 41.49 m

e i 28.1 m s^{-1} **ii** 8.5 m s^{-1} **iii** -20.9 m s^{-1}
$s'(t) \geqslant 0$ ball travelling upwards
$s'(t) \leqslant 0$ ball travelling downwards

f 5.777 sec **g** $\dfrac{d^2s}{dt^2}$ is the rate of change of $\dfrac{ds}{dt}$, i.e., the instantaneous acceleration. **4 b** 69.58 m s^{-1}

EXERCISE 21B

1 a i $Q = 100$ **ii** $Q = 50$ **iii** $Q = 0$

b i decr. 1 unit per year **ii** decr. $\frac{1}{\sqrt{2}}$ units per year

c Hint: Consider the graph of $\dfrac{dQ}{dt}$ against t.

$\dfrac{dQ}{dt} = \dfrac{-5}{\sqrt{t}} < 0$
for all $t > 0$

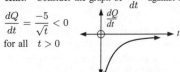

2 a 0.5 m **b** $t = 4$; 9.17 m, $t = 8$; 12.5 m, $t = 12$; 14.3 m

c $t = 0$: 3.9 m year^{-1} $t = 5$: 0.975 m year^{-1}
$t = 10$: 0.433 m year^{-1}

d as $\dfrac{dH}{dt} = \dfrac{97.5}{(t+5)^2} > 0$, for all $t \geqslant 0$, the tree is always growing, and $\dfrac{dH}{dt} \to 0$ as t increases

3 a i €4500 **b i** decr. of €210.22 per km h^{-1}
ii €4000 **ii** incr. of €11.31 per km h^{-1}

c $\dfrac{dC}{dt} = 0$ at $v = \sqrt[3]{500\,000}$ i.e., 79.4 km h^{-1}

4 a The near part of the lake is 2 km from the sea, the furthest part is 3 km.

b $\dfrac{dy}{dx} = \dfrac{3}{10}x^2 - x + \dfrac{3}{5}$ $x = \dfrac{1}{2}$; $\dfrac{dy}{dx} = 0.175$,   height of
hill is increasing as gradient is positive

$x = 1\frac{1}{2}$; $\dfrac{dy}{dx} = -0.225$,   height of hill is decreasing as
gradient is negative

∴   top of the hill is between $x = \frac{1}{2}$ and $x = 1\frac{1}{2}$

c 2.55 km from the sea, 63.1 m deep

5 a $\dfrac{dV}{dt} = -1250\left(1 - \dfrac{t}{80}\right)$

b at $t = 0$ (when the tap was first opened)

c $\dfrac{d^2V}{dt^2} = \dfrac{125}{8}$ This shows that the rate of change of V is
constantly increasing, i.e., the outflow is decreasing at a
constant rate.

6 a When $\dfrac{dP}{dt} = 0$, the population is not changing over time,
i.e., it is stable.   **b**   4000 fish   **c**   8000 fish

7 a $C'(x) = 0.0009x^2 + 0.04x + 4$ dollars per pair

b $C'(220) = \$56.36$ per pair. This estimates the additional cost
of making one more pair of jeans if 220 pairs are currently being
made.

c \$56.58   This is the actual increase in cost to make an extra pair
of jeans (221 rather than 220).

d $C''(x) = 0.0018x + 0.04$, $C''(x) = 0$ when $x = -22.2$
This is where the rate of change is a minimum, however it is out
of the bounds of the model (you cannot make < 0 jeans!).

EXERCISE 21C.1

1 a 7 m s^{-1} **b** $(h+5)$ m s^{-1} **c** 5 m s^{-1} $= s'(1)$

d av. velocity $= (2t + h + 3)$ m s^{-1},

$\lim\limits_{h \to 0}(2t + h + 3) = s'(t) \to 2t + 3$ as $h \to 0$

2 a -14 cm s^{-1} **b** $(-8 - 2h)$ cm s^{-1}

c -8 cm s^{-1} $= s'(2)$ i.e., velocity $= -8$ cm s^{-1} at $t = 2$

d $-4t = s'(t) = v(t)$

3 a $\frac{2}{3}$ cm s^{-2} **b** $\left(\dfrac{2}{\sqrt{1+h}+1}\right)$ cm s^{-2} **c** 1 cm s^{-2} $= v'(1)$

d $\dfrac{1}{\sqrt{t}}$ cm s^{-2} $= v'(t)$ i.e., the instantaneous accn. at time t

4 a velocity at $t = 4$ **b** acceleration at $t = 4$

EXERCISE 21C.2

1 a $v(t) = 2t - 4$, $a(t) = 2$

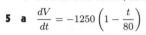

b The object is initially 3 cm to the right of the origin and is moving
to the left at 4 cm s^{-1}. It is accelerating at 2 cm s^{-2} to the right.

c The object is instantaneously stationary, 1 cm to the left of the
origin and is accelerating to the right at 2 cm s^{-2}.

d At $t = 2$, $s(2) = 1$ cm to the left of the origin.

e

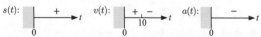

f $0 \leqslant t \leqslant 2$

2 a $v(t) = 98 - 9.8t$, $a(t) = -9.8$

b $s(0) = 0$ m above the ground, $v(0) = 98$ m s^{-1} skyward

c $t = 5$ Stone is 367.5 m above the ground and moving skyward
at 49 m s^{-1}. Its speed is decreasing. $t = 12$ Stone is 470.4
m above the ground and moving groundward at 19.6 m s^{-1}. Its
speed is increasing.

d 490 m   **e** 20 seconds

3 a $v(t) = 12 - 6t^2$, $a(t) = -12t$

b $s(0) = -1$, $v(0) = 12$, $a(0) = 0$
Particle started 1 cm to the left of the origin and was travelling
to the right at a constant speed of 12 cm s^{-1}

c $t = \sqrt{2}$, $s(\sqrt{2}) = 8\sqrt{2} - 1$ **d i** $t \geqslant \sqrt{2}$ **ii** never

4 a $v(t) = 3t^2 - 18t + 24$ $a(t) = 6t - 18$

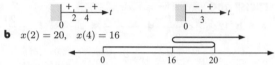

b $x(2) = 20$, $x(4) = 16$

c i $0 \leqslant t \leqslant 2$ and $3 \leqslant t \leqslant 4$ **ii** $0 \leqslant t \leqslant 3$ **d** 28 m

5 Hint: $s'(t) = v(t)$ and $s''(t) = a(t) = g$

Show that $a = \frac{1}{2}g$ $b = v(0)$ $c = 0$

EXERCISE 21D.1

1 a i $x \geqslant 0$ **ii** never   **b i** never **ii** $-2 < x \leqslant 3$

c i $x \leqslant 2$ **ii** $x \geqslant 2$ **d i** all real x **ii** never

e i $1 \leqslant x \leqslant 5$ **ii** $x \leqslant 1, x \geqslant 5$

f i $2 \leqslant x < 4$, $x > 4$ **ii** $x < 0$, $0 < x \leqslant 2$

2 a increasing for $x \geqslant 0$, decreasing for $x \leqslant 0$

b decreasing for all x

c increasing for $x \geqslant -\frac{3}{4}$, decreasing for $x \leqslant -\frac{3}{4}$

d increasing for $x \geqslant 0$, never decreasing

e decreasing for $x > 0$, never increasing

f incr. for $x \leqslant 0$ and $x \geqslant 4$, decr. for $0 \leqslant x \leqslant 4$

g increasing for $-\sqrt{\frac{2}{3}} \leqslant x \leqslant \sqrt{\frac{2}{3}}$,

decreasing for $x \leqslant -\sqrt{\frac{2}{3}}$, $x \geqslant \sqrt{\frac{2}{3}}$

h decr. for $x \leqslant -\frac{1}{2}$, $x \geqslant 3$, incr. for $-\frac{1}{2} \leqslant x \leqslant 3$

i increasing for $x \geqslant 0$, decreasing for $x \leqslant 0$

j increasing for $x \geqslant -\frac{3}{2} + \frac{\sqrt{5}}{2}$ and $x \leqslant -\frac{3}{2} - \frac{\sqrt{5}}{2}$

decreasing for $-\frac{3}{2} - \frac{\sqrt{5}}{2} \leqslant x \leqslant -\frac{3}{2} + \frac{\sqrt{5}}{2}$

k increasing for $x \leqslant 2 - \sqrt{3}$, $x \geqslant 2 + \sqrt{3}$

decreasing for $2 - \sqrt{3} \leqslant x \leqslant 2 + \sqrt{3}$

l increasing for $x \geqslant 1$, decreasing for $0 \leqslant x \leqslant 1$

m increasing for $-1 \leqslant x \leqslant 1$, $x \geqslant 2$
decreasing for $x \leqslant -1$, $1 \leqslant x \leqslant 2$

n increasing for $1 - \sqrt{2} \leqslant x \leqslant 1$, $x \geqslant 1 + \sqrt{2}$
decreasing for $x \leqslant 1 - \sqrt{2}$, $1 \leqslant x \leqslant 1 + \sqrt{2}$

3 a i

ii increasing for $-1 \leqslant x \leqslant 1$
decreasing for $x \leqslant -1$, $x \geqslant 1$

b i

ii increasing for $-1 \leqslant x < 1$
decreasing for $x \leqslant -1$, $x > 1$

c i

ii increasing for $-1 \leqslant x < 1$, $1 < x \leqslant 3$
decreasing for $x \leqslant -1$, $x \geqslant 3$

4 a increasing for $x \geqslant \sqrt{3}$ and $x \leqslant -\sqrt{3}$

decreasing for $-\sqrt{3} \leqslant x < -1$, $-1 < x \leqslant 0$,

$0 \leqslant x < 1$, $1 < x \leqslant \sqrt{3}$

b increasing for $x \geqslant 2$ decreasing for $x < 1$, $1 < x \leqslant 2$

EXERCISE 21D.2

1 a A - local min   B - local max   C - horiz. inflection

b

c i $x \leqslant -2, x \geqslant 3$ **ii** $-2 \leqslant x \leqslant 3$

d

e For **b** we have intervals where the function is increasing $(+)$ or decreasing $(-)$. For **d** we have intervals where the function is above $(+)$ and below $(-)$ the x-axis.

2 a

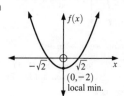

b

horizontal inflection $(0,1)$

c

local max. $(-1,4)$

$(1,0)$ local min.

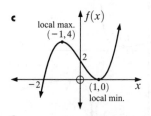

d

local max. $(0,0)$

$(-1,-1)$ local min. $(1,-1)$ local min.

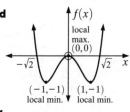

e

$(2,9)$ horizontal inflection

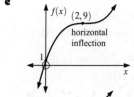

f

(no stationary points)

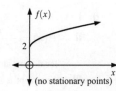

g

$(\frac{1}{4},-\frac{1}{4})$ local min.

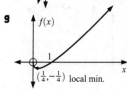

h

$(1,0)$ horizontal inflection

$(-2,-27)$ local min.

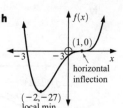

i

$(0,1)$ local max.

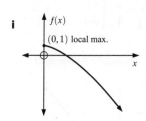

j

local max. $(0,-8)$

$(-1,-9)$ local min. $(1,-9)$ local min.

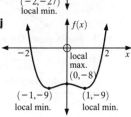

3 $x = -\dfrac{b}{2a}$, local min if $a > 0$, local max if $a < 0$ **4** $a = 9$

5 a $a = -12$, $b = -13$ **b** $(-2, 3)$ local max. $(2, -29)$ local min

6 $P(x) = -9x^3 - 9x^2 + 9x + 2$

7 a greatest value 63 (at $x = 5$) least value -18 (at $x = 2$)
b greatest value $= 4$ (at $x = 3$ and $x = 0$)
least value $= -16$ (at $x = -2$)

8 Maximum hourly cost $= \$680.95$ when 150 hinges are made per hour. Minimum hourly cost $= \$529.80$ when 104 hinges are made per hour.

EXERCISE 21E

1 a H.A. $y = 0$, V.A. $x = 2$ and $x = -2$
b H.A. $y = 0$, V.A. $x = -2$ **c** H.A. $y = 0$, no V.A

d V.A. $x = 1$ and $x = -1$, H.A. $y = 2$
e no V.A.'s, H.A. $y = -1$ **f** V.A. $x = -2$, H.A. $y = 3$
g V.A. $x = 2$, parabolic asymptote $y = 3x^2 + 7x + 14$
h V.A. $x = -1$, OA $y = 2x - 7$
i V.A. $x = \frac{1}{2}$, OA $y = \frac{3}{2}x + \frac{5}{4}$

2 a i H.A. $y = 1$,   V.A.s $x = 3$ and $x = -2$
ii $\left(\frac{1}{2}, \frac{1}{25}\right)$ is a local maximum
iii x-intercepts are 0 and 1, y-intercept is 0
iv

local max $\left(\frac{1}{2}, \frac{1}{25}\right)$

$y = 1$

$y = \dfrac{x^2 - x}{x^2 - x - 6}$

$x = -2$ $x = 3$

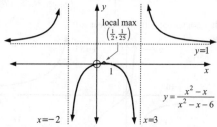

b i H.A. $y = 1$,   no V.A.
ii $(0, -1)$ is a local minimum
iii x-intercepts are 1 and -1, y-intercept is -1
iv

$y = 1$

local min $(0, -1)$

$y = \dfrac{x^2 - 1}{x^2 + 1}$

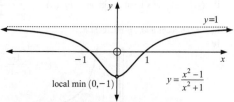

c i H.A. $y = 1$,   V.A.s $x = -4$ and $x = -1$
ii $(2, -\frac{1}{9})$ is a local min., $(-2, -9)$ is a local max.
iii x-intercepts are 4 and 1, y-intercept is 1
iv

$y = \dfrac{x^2 - 5x + 4}{x^2 + 5x + 4}$

$y = 1$

local max $(-2, -9)$

local min $(2, -\frac{1}{9})$

$x = -4$ $x = -1$

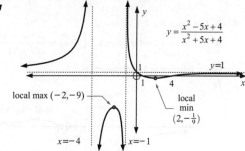

d i H.A. $y = 1$,   V.A. $x = -1$
ii $(2, -\frac{1}{3})$ is a local minimum
iii x-intercepts are 5 and 1, y-intercept is 5
iv

$y = \dfrac{x^2 - 6x + 5}{(x + 1)^2}$

$y = 1$

$x = -1$ local min $(2, -\frac{1}{3})$

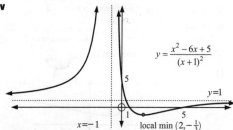

3 a i H.A. $y = 0$
ii $(1, 2)$ is a local max. $\left[f'(x) = \dfrac{-4(x + 1)(x - 1)}{(x^2 + 1)^2}\right]$
$(-1, -2)$ is a local min.
iii x-intercept is 0, y-intercept is 0

iv

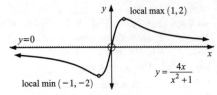

local max $(1, 2)$
$y = 0$
$y = \dfrac{4x}{x^2 + 1}$
local min $(-1, -2)$

b **i** H.A. $y = 0$, V.A.s $x = 5$ and $x = -1$

ii no stationary points $\left[f'(x) = \dfrac{-4(x^2 + 5)}{(x - 5)^2 (x + 1)^2} \right]$

iii x-intercept is 0, y-intercept is 0

iv

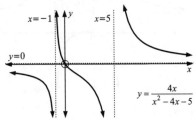

$x = -1$ $x = 5$
$y = 0$
$y = \dfrac{4x}{x^2 - 4x - 5}$

c **i** H.A. $y = 0$, V.A. $x = 1$

ii $(-1, -1)$ is a local minimum $\left[f'(x) = \dfrac{-4(x + 1)}{(x - 1)^3} \right]$

iii x-intercept is 0, y-intercept is 0

iv

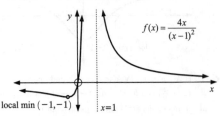

$f(x) = \dfrac{4x}{(x - 1)^2}$
local min $(-1, -1)$ $x = 1$

d **i** H.A. $y = 0$, V.A. $x = -2$

ii $(4, \frac{1}{4})$ is a local maximum $\left[f'(x) = \dfrac{-3(x - 4)}{(x + 2)^3} \right]$

iii x-intercept is 1, y-intercept is $-\frac{3}{4}$

iv

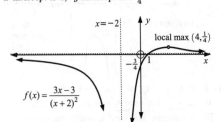

$x = -2$
local max $(4, \frac{1}{4})$
$-\frac{3}{4}$
$f(x) = \dfrac{3x - 3}{(x + 2)^2}$

4 **a** VA $x = -2$, oblique asymptote $y = x + 2$

ii $f'(x) = \dfrac{(x + 1)(x + 3)}{(x + 2)^2}$, local min. at $(-1, 2)$, local max. at $(-3, -2)$

iii no x-intercept, y-intercept is $2\frac{1}{2}$

iv

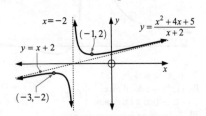

$x = -2$ $(-1, 2)$ $y = \dfrac{x^2 + 4x + 5}{x + 2}$
$y = x + 2$
$(-3, -2)$

b **i** VA $x = -1$, oblique asymptote $y = x + 2$

ii $f'(x) = \dfrac{x^2 + 2x + 3}{(x + 1)^2}$, no turning points

iii x-intercepts 0 and -3, y-intercept 0

iv

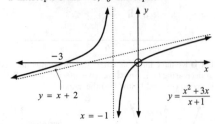

-3
$y = x + 2$
$y = \dfrac{x^2 + 3x}{x + 1}$
$x = -1$

c **i** VA $x = 2$, oblique asymptote $y = -2x + 1$

ii $f'(x) = \dfrac{-2(x - 3)(x - 1)}{(x - 2)^2}$, local min. at $(1, 1)$, local max. at $(3, -7)$

iii no x-intercept, y-intercept is 2

iv

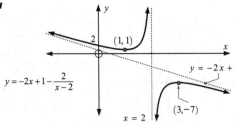

2 $(1, 1)$
$y = -2x + 1$
$y = -2x + 1 - \dfrac{2}{x - 2}$
$x = 2$ $(3, -7)$

d **i** VA $x = 1$, $x = -1$ OA $y = x$

ii $f'(x) = \dfrac{x^2(x^2 - 3)}{(x + 1)^2(x - 1)^2}$, local max. at $(-\sqrt{3}, \frac{-3\sqrt{3}}{2})$, local min. at $(\sqrt{3}, \frac{3\sqrt{3}}{2})$, horizontal inflection at $(0, 0)$

iii x-intercept is 0, y-int. is 0

iv

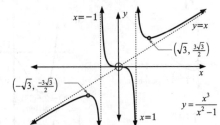

$x = -1$ $y = x$
$(\sqrt{3}, \frac{3\sqrt{3}}{2})$
$(-\sqrt{3}, \frac{-3\sqrt{3}}{2})$
$y = \dfrac{x^3}{x^2 - 1}$ $x = 1$

e **i** No VA exists, OA is $y = x$

ii $f'(x) = \dfrac{x^2(x^2 + 3)}{(x^2 + 1)^2}$, horizontal inflection at $(0, 0)$

iii x and y intercepts of 0

iv

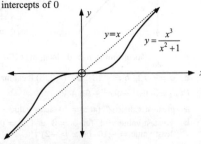

$y = x$ $y = \dfrac{x^3}{x^2 + 1}$

EXERCISE 21F

1 **a** no inflection   **b** horizontal inflection at $(0, 2)$
c non-horizontal inflection at $(2, 3)$
d horizontal inflection at $(-2, -3)$
e horizontal inflection at $(0, 2)$
non-horizontal inflection at $(-\frac{4}{3}, \frac{310}{27})$ **f** no inflection

2 a i local minimum at $(0, 0)$ **v**
  ii no points of inflection
  iii decreasing for $x \leqslant 0$,
       increasing for $x \geqslant 0$
  iv function is concave up
       for all x

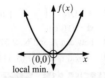

b i horizontal inflection at $(0, 0)$
  ii horizontal inflection at $(0, 0)$
  iii increasing for all **v**
       real x
  iv concave down for $x \leqslant 0$,
       concave up for $x \geqslant 0$

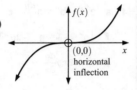

c i $f'(x) \neq 0$, no stationary points
  ii no points of inflection
  iii incr. for $x \geqslant 0$, **v**
       never decr.
  iv concave down for $x \geqslant 0$,
       never concave up

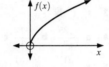

d i local max. at $(-2, 29)$ local min at $(4, -79)$
  ii non-horizontal inflection at $(1, -25)$
  iii increasing for **v**
       $x \leqslant -2$, $x \geqslant 4$
       decreasing for
       $-2 \leqslant x \leqslant 4$
  iv concave down for
       $x \leqslant 1$,
       concave up for $x \geqslant 1$

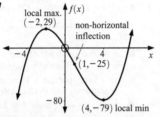

e i horiz. inflection at $(0, -2)$ local min. at $(-1, -3)$
  ii horizontal inflection at $(0, -2)$
       non-horizontal inflection at $(-\frac{2}{3}, -\frac{70}{27})$
  iii increasing for $x \geqslant -1$, decreasing for $x \leqslant -1$
  iv concave down for **v**
       $-\frac{2}{3} \leqslant x \leqslant 0$
       concave up for
       $x \leqslant -\frac{2}{3}$, $x \geqslant 0$

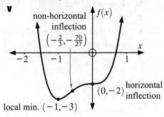

f i local min. at $(1, 0)$
  ii no points of inflection
  iii increasing for $x \geqslant 1$, decreasing for $x \leqslant 1$
  iv concave up **v**
       for all x

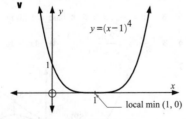

g i local minimum at $(-\sqrt{2}, -1)$ and $(\sqrt{2}, -1)$,
       local maximum at $(0, 3)$,
  ii non-horizontal inflection at $(\sqrt{\frac{2}{3}}, \frac{7}{9})$
       non-horizontal inflection at $(-\sqrt{\frac{2}{3}}, \frac{7}{9})$
  iii increasing for $-\sqrt{2} \leqslant x \leqslant 0$, $x \geqslant \sqrt{2}$
       decreasing for $x \leqslant -\sqrt{2}$, $0 \leqslant x \leqslant \sqrt{2}$

iv concave down for $-\sqrt{\frac{2}{3}} \leqslant x \leqslant \sqrt{\frac{2}{3}}$
    concave up for $x \leqslant -\sqrt{\frac{2}{3}}$, $x \geqslant \sqrt{\frac{2}{3}}$
v

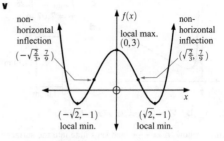

h i no stationary points **v**
  ii no inflections
  iii increasing for $x > 0$,
       never decreasing
  iv concave down for $x > 0$,
       never concave up

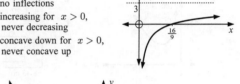

3 a

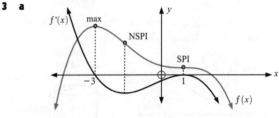

b

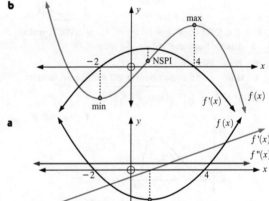

4 a

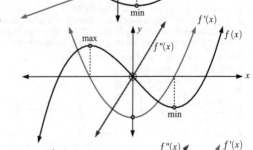

b

c

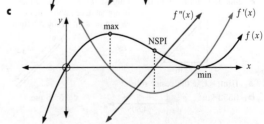

EXERCISE 21G

1 50 fittings   **2** 250 items   **3** 10 blankets   **4** 25 km h^{-1}

5 b
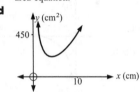
  c $L_{\min} = 28.28$ m, $x = 7.07$ m
  d

6 a $2x$ cm   **b** $V = 200 = 2x \times x \times h$

  c **Hint:** Show $h = \dfrac{100}{x^2}$ and substitute into the surface area equation.

  d
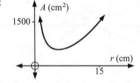
  e $SA_{\min} = 213.4$ cm^2, $x = 4.22$ cm

  f

7 a recall that $V_{\text{cylinder}} = \pi r^2 h$ and that 1 L $= 1000$ cm^3

  b recall that $SA_{\text{cylinder}} = 2\pi r^2 + 2\pi rh$

  c
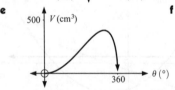
  d $A = 554$ cm^2, $r = 5.42$ cm

  e

8 b 6 cm $\times$ 6 cm

9 a $0 \leqslant x \leqslant 63.66$ **c** $x = 63.66$ m, $l = 0$ m (i.e., circular)

10 a **Hint:** Show that $AC = \frac{\theta}{360} \times 2\pi \times 10$

  b **Hint:** Show that $2\pi r = AC$

  c **Hint:** Use the result from **b** and Pythagoras' theorem.

  d $V = \frac{1}{3}\pi \left(\frac{\theta}{36}\right)^2 \sqrt{100 - \left(\frac{\theta}{36}\right)^2}$

  e
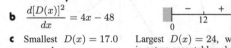
  f $\theta = 293.9°$

11 a For $x < 0$ or $x > 6$, X is not on AC.

  c $x = 2.67$ km   This is the distance from A to X which minimises the time taken to get from B to C. (Proof: Use sign diagram or second derivative test. Be sure to check the end points.)

12 3.33 km   **13** $r = 31.7$ cm, $h = 31.7$ cm

14 4 m from the 40 cp globe

15 a $D(x) = \sqrt{x^2 + (24 - x)^2}$

  b $\dfrac{d[D(x)]^2}{dx} = 4x - 48$

  c Smallest $D(x) = 17.0$ Largest $D(x) = 24$, which is not an acceptable solution as can be seen in the diagram.

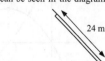

16 a **Hint:** Use the cosine rule.

  b 3553 km^2

  c 5:36 pm

17 a $QR = \left(\dfrac{2 + x}{x}\right)$ m   **c** **Hint:** All solutions < 0 can be discarded as $x \geqslant 0$.

  d 416 cm

18 between A and N, 2.578 m from N

19 at grid reference $(3.544, 8)$ **20** $\sqrt{\frac{3}{2}} : 1$ **21 e** 63.7%

EXERCISE 21H

1 a $2\dfrac{dy}{dx}$ **b** $-3\dfrac{dy}{dx}$ **c** $3y^2\dfrac{dy}{dx}$ **d** $-y^{-2}\dfrac{dy}{dx}$ **e** $4y^3\dfrac{dy}{dx}$

  f $\frac{1}{2}y^{-\frac{1}{2}}\dfrac{dy}{dx}$ **g** $-2y^{-3}\dfrac{dy}{dx}$ **h** $y + x\dfrac{dy}{dx}$ **i** $2xy + x^2\dfrac{dy}{dx}$

  j $y^2 + 2xy\dfrac{dy}{dx}$

2 a $-\dfrac{x}{y}$ **b** $-\dfrac{x}{3y}$ **c** $\dfrac{x}{y}$ **d** $\dfrac{2x}{3y^2}$ **e** $\dfrac{-2x - y}{x}$ **f** $\dfrac{3x^2 - 2y}{2x}$

3 a 1   **b** $-\frac{1}{9}$

4 a $\dfrac{-25}{y^3}$ **b** $\dfrac{-1}{y^3}$ **c** $\dfrac{8}{y^3}$ **d** $\dfrac{6y^3 - 8x^2}{9y^5}$ **e** $\dfrac{2x + 2y}{x^2}$ **f** $\dfrac{2y}{x^2}$

5 a $\dfrac{dV}{dq} = \dfrac{V - 1}{3V - q}$ **b** $\dfrac{d^2q}{dV^2} = \dfrac{2q - 3V - 3}{(1 - V)^2}$

REVIEW SET 21A

1 a $v(t) = (6t^2 - 18t + 12)$ cm s^{-1} $a(t) = (12t - 18)$ cm s^{-2}

  b $s(0) = 5$ cm to left of origin, $v(0) = 12$ cm s^{-1} towards origin $a(0) = -18$ cm s^{-2} (reducing speed)

  c At $t = 2$, particle is 1 cm to the left of the origin, is stationary and is accelerating towards the origin.

  d $t = 1$, $s = 0$ and $t = 2$, $s = -1$

  e
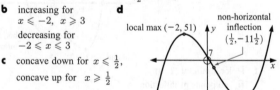

  f Speed is increasing for $1 \leqslant t \leqslant 1\frac{1}{2}$ and $t \geqslant 2$.

2 a i \$535   **ii** \$1385.79

  b i $-\$0.27$ per km h^{-1} **ii** \$2.33 per km h^{-1}

  c 51.3 km h^{-1}

3 a local maximum at $(-2, 51)$, local minimum at $(3, -74)$ non-horizontal inflection at $(\frac{1}{2}, -11.5)$

  b increasing for $x \leqslant -2$, $x \geqslant 3$ decreasing for $-2 \leqslant x \leqslant 3$

  c concave down for $x \leqslant \frac{1}{2}$, concave up for $x \geqslant \frac{1}{2}$

  d
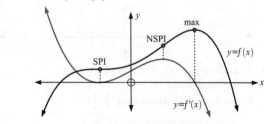

local max $(-2, 51)$; non-horizontal inflection $(\frac{1}{2}, -11\frac{1}{2})$; local min $(3, -74)$

4 b $k = 9$

5 a $y = \dfrac{1}{x^2}$, $x > 0$ **c** base is 1.26 m square, height 0.630 m

6 a $\dfrac{dy}{dx} = \dfrac{-2y(x + y^2)}{x(x + 6y^2)}$ **b** $4x - 5y = 14$

7

REVIEW SET 21B

1 b $\dfrac{d[A(x)]^2}{dx} = 5000x - 4x^3$

Area is a maximum when $x \approx 35.4$, $A = 1250$ m^2.

2 a $v(t) = 15 + \dfrac{120}{(t-1)^3}$ cm s^{-1}, $a(t) = \dfrac{-360}{(t-1)^4}$ cm s^{-2}

b At $t = 3$, particle is 30 cm to the right of the origin, moving to the right at 30 cm s^{-1} and decelerating at 22.5 cm s^{-2}.

c $0 \leqslant t < 1$

3 6 cm from each end

4 a $k = -1$ **b** $\dfrac{dy}{dx} = \dfrac{2y^2 - 2x}{3y^2 - 4xy}$ **c** $11x - 2y = 24$

5 a $v(t) = 3 - \dfrac{1}{2\sqrt{t}}$, $a(t) = \dfrac{1}{4t\sqrt{t}}$

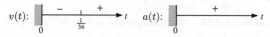

b $x(0) = 0$, $v(0)$ is undefined, $a(0)$ is undefined

c Particle is 24 cm to the right of the origin and is travelling to the right at 2.83 cm s^{-1}. Its speed is increasing.

d Changes direction at $t = \frac{1}{36}$, 0.083 cm to the left of the origin.

e Particle's speed is decreasing for $0 \leqslant t \leqslant \frac{1}{36}$.

6 a y-int. at $y = -1$ x-int. at $x = 1$, $x = -1$

b $x^2 + 1 > 0$ for all real x (i.e., denominator is never 0)

c local minimum at $(0, -1)$

e

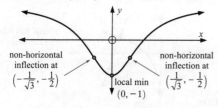

non-horizontal inflection at $\left(-\frac{1}{\sqrt{3}}, -\frac{1}{2}\right)$

non-horizontal inflection at $\left(\frac{1}{\sqrt{3}}, -\frac{1}{2}\right)$

local min $(0, -1)$

7

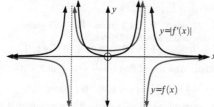

$y = |f'(x)|$

$y = f(x)$

REVIEW SET 21C

1 a y-intercept at $y = 0$, x-intercept at $x = 0$ and $x = 2$

b local maximum at $\left(\frac{2}{3}, \frac{32}{27}\right)$, local minimum at $(2, 0)$,

non-horizontal inflection at $\left(\frac{4}{3}, \frac{16}{27}\right)$

c

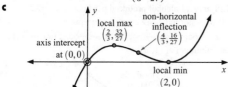

local max $\left(\frac{2}{3}, \frac{32}{27}\right)$

non-horizontal inflection $\left(\frac{4}{3}, \frac{16}{27}\right)$

axis intercept at $(0,0)$

local min $(2,0)$

2 b $A = 200x - 2x^2 - \frac{1}{2}\pi x^2$ **c**

28.0 m

56.0 m

3 a VA at $x = 2$ OA is $y = x + 4$

b local max. at $(-0.828, 0.343)$

local min. at $(4.828, 11.66)$

c x-intercepts at $x = 0$ and $x = -2$, y-intercept at $y = 0$

d

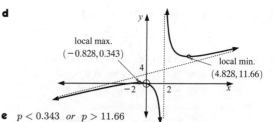

local max. $(-0.828, 0.343)$

local min. $(4.828, 11.66)$

e $p < 0.343$ or $p > 11.66$

4 a **Hint:** Use Pythagoras to find h as a function of x and then substitute into the equation for the volume of a cylinder.

b radius $= 4.08$ cm, height $= 5.77$ cm

5 a $LQ = \dfrac{8}{x}$ km **b** **Hint:** Show that

(length of pipe)$^2 = (LQ + 1)^2 + (8 + x)^2$ then simplify.

c 11.2 km (when $x = 2$ km)

6 When $x = \frac{k}{2}\left(1 - \frac{1}{\sqrt{3}}\right)$

7

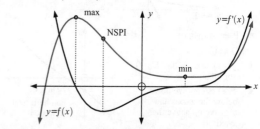

max

NSPI

$y = f'(x)$

min

$y = f(x)$

EXERCISE 22A

1 a $4e^{4x}$ **b** e^x **c** $-2e^{-2x}$ **d** $\frac{1}{2}e^{\frac{x}{2}}$ **e** $-e^{-\frac{x}{2}}$ **f** $2e^{-x}$

g $2e^{\frac{x}{2}} + 3e^{-x}$ **h** $\dfrac{e^x - e^{-x}}{2}$ **i** $-2xe^{-x^2}$ **j** $e^{\frac{1}{x}} \times \dfrac{-1}{x^2}$

k $20e^{2x}$ **l** $40e^{-2x}$ **m** $2e^{2x+1}$ **n** $\frac{1}{4}e^{\frac{x}{4}}$ **o** $-4xe^{1-2x^2}$

p $-0.02e^{-0.02x}$

2 a $e^x + xe^x$ **b** $3x^2e^{-x} - x^3e^{-x}$ **c** $\dfrac{xe^x - e^x}{x^2}$ **d** $\dfrac{1 - x}{e^x}$

e $2xe^{3x} + 3x^2e^{3x}$ **f** $\dfrac{xe^x - \frac{1}{2}e^x}{x\sqrt{x}}$ **g** $\frac{1}{2}x^{-\frac{1}{2}}e^{-x} - x^{\frac{1}{2}}e^{-x}$

h $\dfrac{e^x + 2 + 2e^{-x}}{(e^{-x} + 1)^2}$

3 a $4e^x(e^x + 2)^3$ **b** $\dfrac{-e^{-x}}{(1 - e^{-x})^2}$ **c** $\dfrac{e^{2x}}{\sqrt{e^{2x} + 10}}$

d $\dfrac{6e^{3x}}{(1 - e^{3x})^3}$ **e** $-\dfrac{e^{-x}}{2}\left(1 - e^{-x}\right)^{-\frac{3}{2}}$ **f** $\dfrac{1 - 2e^{-x} + xe^{-x}}{\sqrt{1 - 2e^{-x}}}$

4 b $\dfrac{d^n y}{dx^n} = k^n y$

5 Hint: Find $\dfrac{dy}{dx}$ and $\dfrac{d^2 y}{dx^2}$ and substitute into the equation.

6 $\dfrac{dy}{dx} = \dfrac{-(54e^{-2x} + 3x^2e^{3y} + 8xy^3)}{3x^2(xe^{3y} + 4y^2)}$

7 a local maximum at $(1, e^{-1})$

b local max. at $(-2, 4e^{-2})$, local min. at $(0, 0)$

c local minimum at $(1, e)$ **d** local maximum at $(-1, e)$

EXERCISE 22B

1 a $\ln N = \ln 50 + 2t$ **b** $\ln P = \ln 8.69 - 0.0541t$

c $\ln S = 2\ln a - kt$

2 a 2 **b** $\frac{1}{2}$ **c** -1 **d** $-\frac{1}{2}$ **e** 3 **f** 9 **g** $\frac{1}{5}$ **h** $\frac{1}{4}$

3 a $e^{\ln 2}$ **b** $e^{\ln 10}$ **c** $e^{\ln a}$ **d** $e^{x \ln a}$

4 a $x = \ln 2$ **b** no real solutions **c** no real solutions

d $x = \ln 2$ **e** $x = 0$ **f** $x = \ln 2$ or $\ln 3$ **g** $x = 0$

h $x = \ln 4$ **i** $x = \ln\left(\dfrac{3 + \sqrt{5}}{2}\right)$ or $\ln\left(\dfrac{3 - \sqrt{5}}{2}\right)$

5 a $2^x \ln 2$ **b** $5^x \ln 5$ **c** $2^x + x2^x \ln 2$

d $\dfrac{3x^2 - x^3 \ln 6}{6^x}$ **e** $\dfrac{x2^x \ln 2 - 2^x}{x^2}$ **f** $\dfrac{1 - x \ln 3}{3^x}$

6 a $(\ln 3, 3)$ **b** $(\ln 2, 5)$ **c** $(0, 2)$ and $(\ln 5, -2)$

7 a $f(x)$: x-int. at $x = \ln 3$, y-int. at $y = -2$

  $g(x)$: x-int. at $x = \ln\left(\frac{5}{3}\right)$, y-int. at $y = -2$

b $f(x)$:   as $x \to \infty$, $f(x) \to \infty$

     as $x \to -\infty$, $f(x) \to -3$ (above)

  $g(x)$:   as $x \to \infty$, $g(x) \to 3$ (below)

     as $x \to -\infty$, $g(x) \to -\infty$

c intersect at $(0, -2)$ and $(\ln 5, 2)$

d

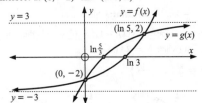

8 a $P = (\frac{1}{2}\ln 3, 0)$

  $Q = (0, -2)$

b $f'(x) = e^x + 3e^{-x} > 0$
  for all x

c $f(x)$ is concave down
  below the x-axis and
  concave up above the
  x-axis

d

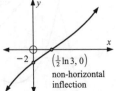

$(\frac{1}{2}\ln 3, 0)$

non-horizontal
inflection

9 a x-intercept at $x = 0$, y-intercept at $y = 0$

b as $x \to \infty$, $y \to \infty$, as $x \to -\infty$, $y \to 0^-$

c local minimum at $(-1, -\frac{1}{4})$

d concave down for $x \le -2$, concave up for $x \ge -2$

e

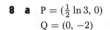

$y = 4^x - 2^x$

inflection
$(-2, -\frac{3}{16})$
$(-1, -\frac{1}{4})$
$(0, 0)$

EXERCISE 22C

1 a $\dfrac{1}{x}$ **b** $\dfrac{2}{2x+1}$ **c** $\dfrac{1-2x}{x-x^2}$ **d** $-\dfrac{2}{x}$ **e** $2x \ln x + x$

f $\dfrac{1-\ln x}{2x^2}$ **g** $e^x \ln x + \dfrac{e^x}{x}$ **h** $\dfrac{2\ln x}{x}$ **i** $\dfrac{1}{2x\sqrt{\ln x}}$

j $\dfrac{e^{-x}}{x} - e^{-x}\ln x$ **k** $\dfrac{\ln(2x)}{2\sqrt{x}} + \dfrac{1}{\sqrt{x}}$ **l** $\dfrac{\ln x - 2}{\sqrt{x}(\ln x)^2}$

2 a $\ln 5$ **b** $\dfrac{3}{x}$ **c** $\dfrac{4x^3+1}{x^4+x}$ **d** $\dfrac{1}{x-2}$ **e** $\dfrac{6}{2x+1}[\ln(2x+1)]^2$

f $\dfrac{1-\ln(4x)}{x^2}$ **g** $-\dfrac{1}{x}$ **h** $\dfrac{1}{x\ln x}$ **i** $\dfrac{-1}{x[\ln x]^2}$

3 a $\dfrac{-1}{1-2x}$ **b** $\dfrac{-2}{2x+3}$ **c** $1 + \dfrac{1}{2x}$ **d** $\dfrac{1}{x} - \dfrac{1}{2(2-x)}$

e $\dfrac{1}{x+3} - \dfrac{1}{x-1}$ **f** $\dfrac{2}{x} + \dfrac{1}{3-x}$ **g** $\dfrac{9}{3x-4}$

h $\dfrac{1}{x} + \dfrac{2x}{x^2+1}$ **i** $\dfrac{2x+2}{x^2+2x} - \dfrac{1}{x-5}$

4 a i $\dfrac{1}{x\ln 2}$ **ii** $\dfrac{1}{x\ln 10}$ **iii** $\log_3 x + \dfrac{1}{\ln 3}$ **b** $\dfrac{dy}{dx} = 2^x \ln 2$

---

5 a $x = \dfrac{e^3+1}{2}$ (≈ 10.54) **b** no, $\therefore$ there is no y-int.

c gradient $= 2$ **d** $x > \frac{1}{2}$ **e** $f''(x) = \dfrac{4}{(2x-1)^2} < 0$ for

all $x > \frac{1}{2}$, so $f(x)$ is concave down

f

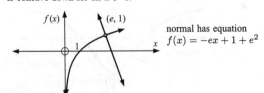

$f(x)$ $x = \frac{1}{2}$

$\frac{e^3+1}{2}$ x

6 Hint: Show: $x \to 0$, $f(x) \to -\infty$, and as $x \to \infty$, $f(x) \to 0$.

7 Hint: Show that $f(x) \ge 1$ for all $x > 0$.

8 $\dfrac{da}{db} = \dfrac{a^4b - 2ae^{2a} - a}{4abe^{2a}\ln b - 3a^3b^2 + b}$

EXERCISE 22D

1 $y = -\dfrac{1}{e}x + \dfrac{2}{e}$ **2** $3y = -x + 3\ln 3 - 1$

3 A is $\left(\frac{2}{3}, 0\right)$, B is $(0, -2e)$ **4** $y = -\dfrac{2}{e^2}x + \dfrac{2}{e^4} - 1$

5 $y = e^ax + e^a(1-a)$ so $y = ex$ is the tangent to $y = e^x$
from the origin

6 a $x > 0$

b $f'(x) > 0$ for all $x > 0$, so $f(x)$ is always increasing.
Its gradient is always positive. $f''(x) < 0$ for all $x > 0$, so $f(x)$
is concave down for all $x > 0$.

c

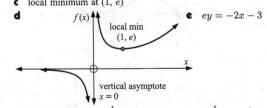

$f(x)$ $(e, 1)$

normal has equation
$f(x) = -ex + 1 + e^2$

7 $\approx 63.43°$

8 a $k = \frac{1}{50}\ln 2$ (≈ 0.0139)

b i 20 grams **ii** 14.3 grams **iii** 1.95 grams

c 9 days and 6 minutes (216 hours)

d i -0.0693 g h^{-1} **ii** -2.64×10^{-7} g h^{-1}

e Hint: You should find $\dfrac{dW}{dt} = -\dfrac{1}{50}\ln 2 \times 20e^{-\frac{1}{50}\ln 2t}$

9 a $k = \dfrac{-1}{15}\ln\left(\frac{95}{15}\right)$ (≈ 0.123) **b** $100°C$

d i decreasing by 11.7°C/min **ii** decreasing by 3.42°C/min
iii decreasing by 0.998°C per minute

10 a 43.9 cm **b** 10.4 years

c i growing by 5.45 cm per year
ii growing by 1.88 cm per year

11 a $A = 0$ **b** $k = \dfrac{\ln 2}{3}$ (≈ 0.231)

c 0.728 units of alcohol produced per hour

12 a $f(x)$ does not have any x or y-intercepts

b as $x \to \infty$, $f(x) \to \infty$, as $x \to -\infty$, $f(x) \to 0$ (below)

c local minimum at $(1, e)$

d

$f(x)$

local min
$(1, e)$

x

vertical asymptote
$x = 0$

e $ey = -2x - 3$

13 a $v(t) = 100 - 40e^{-\frac{t}{5}}$ cm s^{-1}, $a(t) = 8e^{-\frac{t}{5}}$ cm s^{-2}

b $s(0) = 200$ cm on positive side of origin

$v(0) = 60$ cm s^{-1} $a(0) = 8$ cm s^{-2}

c as $t \to \infty$, $v(t) \to 100$ cm s^{-1} (below)   **e** after 3.47 sec

d

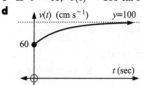

14 a at 4.41 months old **b**

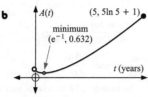

15 a There is a local maximum at $\left(0, \frac{1}{\sqrt{2\pi}}\right)$.

$f(x)$ is incr. for all $x \leqslant 0$ and decr. for all $x \geqslant 0$.

b Inflections at $\left(-1, \frac{1}{\sqrt{2e\pi}}\right)$ and $\left(1, \frac{1}{\sqrt{2e\pi}}\right)$

c as $x \to \infty$, $f(x) \to 0$ (positive)
  as $x \to -\infty$, $f(x) \to 0$ (positive)

d

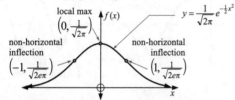

16 20 kettles   **17** $C = \left(\frac{1}{\sqrt{2}}, e^{\left(-\frac{1}{2}\right)}\right)$ **18** 267 torches

19 a Hint: They must have the same y-coordinate at $x = b$
  and the same gradient. **c** $a = \frac{1}{2e}$ **d** $y = e^{-\frac{1}{2}}x - \frac{1}{2}$

20 after 13.8 weeks **21** $a = \frac{\sqrt{e}}{2}$, $b = -\frac{1}{8}$

23 a i $-e^{-x}(x+1)$ **ii** $e^{-x}(x)$ **iii** $-e^{-x}(x-1)$ **iv** $e^{-x}(x-2)$
  b $f^{(n)}(x) = (-1)^n e^{-x}(x - n + 2)$

24 a $e^{ax}(ax+1)$, $ae^{ax}(ax+2)$, $a^2 e^{ax}(ax+3)$, $a^3 e^{ax}(ax+4)$
  b $f^{(n)}(x) = a^{n-1} e^{ax}(ax + n)$

EXERCISE 22E

1 a

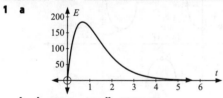

b i 177.1 units **ii** 74.7 units
c When $t \approx 0.667$ hours = 40 min
d i 0.1728 h $\approx$ 10 min **ii** 91 min
e $t = \frac{4}{3}$ or 80 min. This is when the effectiveness is
  decreasing the fastest.

2 a i Show that $f'(t) = Ae^{-bt}(1 - bt)$
  ii Show that $f''(t) = Abe^{-bt}(bt - 2)$
  b Local max. in **c** is at $t = \frac{2}{3}$
  Point of inflection in **e** is at $t = \frac{4}{3}$

3 a

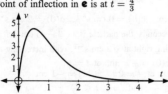

c $0 \leqslant t \leqslant \frac{1}{2}$ **d** Point of inflection is at (1, 3.38). This is when
  the velocity is decreasing the fastest.
e $t \geqslant 1$

4 a

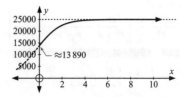

b $\approx 13\,900$ ants **c** $\approx 24\,000$ ants
d Yes, 25 000 ants **e** after 3.67 months

5 a $\frac{2C}{3}$ bees **b** 37.8% increase **c** Yes, C bees **d** 3047 bees
e $B'(t) = \dfrac{0.865C}{e^{1.73t}(1 + 0.5e^{-1.73t})^2}$ and so $B'(t) > 0$ for all $t \geqslant 0$
  $\therefore$ $B(t)$ is incr. over time.

f

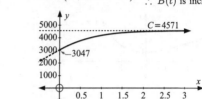

6 a as $t \to \infty$, $e^{-bt} \to 0$, etc.

REVIEW SET 22A

1 a $3x^2 e^{x^3 + 2}$ **b** $\dfrac{xe^x - 2e^x}{x^3}$ **c** $\dfrac{e^y(2y+1)}{2 - xe^y(2y+1)}$

2 $y = \dfrac{e}{2}x + \dfrac{1}{e} - \dfrac{e}{2}$

3

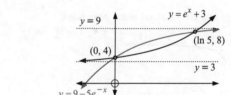

4 a y-intercept at $y = -1$, no x-intercept
  b $f(x)$ is defined for all $x \neq 1$
  c $f'(x) < 0$ for $x < 1$ and $1 < x \leqslant 2$ and $f'(x) > 0$ for $x \geqslant 2$.
    $f''(x) > 0$ for $x > 1$, $f''(x) < 0$ for $x < 1$.
    So, the gradient of the curve is negative for all defined values of
    $x \leqslant 2$ and positive for all $x \geqslant 2$. The curve is concave down
    for $x < 1$ and concave up for $x > 1$.
  d tangent is $y = e^2$

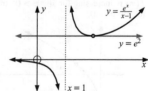

5 a 60 cm **b i** 4.244 years **ii** 201.2 years
  c i 16 cm per year **ii** 1.95 cm per year
6 a $v(t) = -8e^{-\frac{t}{10}} - 40$ m s^{-1}, $a(t) = \frac{4}{5}e^{-\frac{t}{10}}$ m s^{-2} $\{t \geqslant 0\}$
  b $s(0) = 80$ m,   **d**
    $v(0) = -48$ m s^{-1},
    $a(0) = 0.8$ m s^{-2}

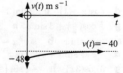

  c as $t \to \infty$,
    $v(t) \to -40$ m s^{-1} (below)
  e $t = 6.93$ seconds

7 $A(\frac{1}{2}, e^{-1})$ **8** 100 or 101 shirts, \$938.63 profit

9 Tangent is $y = \ln 3$, so never cuts x-axis.

10 **a** $2^x(1 + x \ln 2)$

    b $\dfrac{(x^2+2)(x-3)}{1-x^3}\left[\dfrac{2x}{x^2+2} + \dfrac{1}{x-3} + \dfrac{3x^2}{1-x^3}\right]$

REVIEW SET 22B

1 **a** $\dfrac{dy}{dx} = \dfrac{3x^2-3}{x^3-3x}$ **b** $\dfrac{dy}{dx} = \dfrac{1}{x+3} - \dfrac{2}{x}$

    c $\dfrac{dy}{dx} = \dfrac{e^{x+y}(y^2+1)}{2y - e^{x+y}(y^2+1)}$ **d** $x^{x^2+1}(2\ln x + 1)$

2 $(0, \ln 4 - 1)$ **3** **a** $x = \ln 3$ **b** $x = \ln 4$ or $\ln 3$

4 **a** local minimum at $(0, 1)$

    b As $x \to \infty$, $f(x) \to \infty$, as $x \to -\infty$, $f(x) \to -x$ (above)

    c $f''(x) = e^x$, 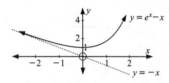 thus $f(x)$ is concave up for all x.

    d

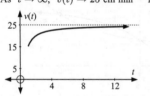

5 **a** $f'(x) = \dfrac{e^x}{e^x+3}$ **b** $f'(x) = \dfrac{3x-(x+2)}{x(x+2)}$

6 **a** $x = \ln\left(\frac{2}{3}\right)$ or 0 **b** $x = e^2$

7 **a** $v(t) = 25 - \dfrac{10}{t}$ cm min^{-1}, $a(t) = \dfrac{10}{t^2}$ cm min^{-2}

    b $s(e) = 25e - 10$, $v(e) = 25 - \dfrac{10}{e}$, $a(e) = \dfrac{10}{e^2}$

    c As $t \to \infty$, $v(t) \to 25$ cm min^{-1} from below

    d   **e** $t = \frac{10}{13}$ min

8 197 or 198 clocks per day   **9** P is $(\ln a, 1)$

10 **a** $x > 0$ **b** Sign diag of $f'(x)$ Sign diag of $f''(x)$

    $f(x)$ is increasing for all $x > 0$ and is concave downwards for all $x > 0$.

    c

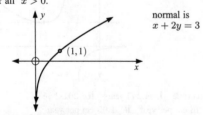

    normal is $x + 2y = 3$

EXERCISE 23A

1 **a** $2\cos(2x)$ **b** $\cos x - \sin x$ **c** $-3\sin(3x) - \cos x$

    d $\cos(x+1)$ **e** $2\sin(3-2x)$ **f** $5\sec^2(5x)$

    g $\frac{1}{2}\cos(\frac{x}{2}) + 3\sin x$ **h** $3\pi\sec^2(\pi x)$ **i** $4\cos x + 2\sin(2x)$

2 **a** $2x - \sin x$ **b** $\sec^2 x - 3\cos x$ **c** $e^x\cos x - e^x\sin x$

    d $-e^{-x}\sin x + e^{-x}\cos x$ **e** $\cot x$ **f** $2e^{2x}\tan x + e^{2x}\sec^2 x$

    g $3\cos(3x)$ **h** $-\frac{1}{4}\sin(\frac{x}{2})$ **i** $6\sec^2(2x)$

---

    j $\cos x - x\sin x$ **k** $\dfrac{x\cos x - \sin x}{x^2}$ **l** $\tan x + x\sec^2 x$

3 **a** $2x\cos(x^2)$ **b** $-\dfrac{1}{2\sqrt{x}}\sin(\sqrt{x})$ **c** $-\dfrac{\sin x}{2\sqrt{\cos x}}$

    d $2\sin x\cos x$ **e** $-3\sin x\cos^2 x$

    f $-\sin x\sin(2x) + 2\cos x\cos(2x)$ **g** $\sin x\sin(\cos x)$

    h $-12\sin(4x)\cos^2(4x)$ **i** $-\dfrac{\cos x}{\sin^2 x}$ **j** $\dfrac{2\sin(2x)}{\cos^2(2x)}$

    k $-\dfrac{8\cos(2x)}{\sin^3(2x)}$ **l** $\dfrac{-12}{\cos^2(\frac{x}{2})\tan^4(\frac{x}{2})}$

4 **a** $\dfrac{dy}{dx} = \cos x$, $\dfrac{d^2y}{dx^2} = -\sin x$, $\dfrac{d^3y}{dx^3} = -\cos x$, $\dfrac{d^4y}{dx^4} = \sin x$

    b The answers of **a** are cycled over and over.

6 **a** $y = x$ **b** $y = x$ **c** $2x - y = \frac{\pi}{3} - \frac{\sqrt{3}}{2}$ **d** $x = \frac{\pi}{4}$

7 **a** rising   **b** rising at 2.731 m per hour

8 **a** $-34\,000\pi$ units per second   **b** $V'(t) = 0$

9 **b** **i** 0 ms^{-1} **ii** 1 ms^{-1} **iii** ≈ 1.11 ms^{-1}

10 **a**

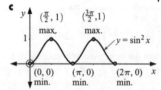

    c

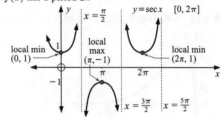

11 **a** $x = \frac{\pi}{2}, \frac{3\pi}{2}$

    b $(0, 1)$ is a local minimum, $(\pi, -1)$ is a local maximum
    $(2\pi, 1)$ is a local minimum

    c $f(x)$ has a period 2π

    d

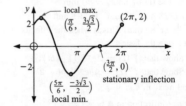

12 $y = \sin(2x) + 2\cos x$ $[0, 2\pi]$

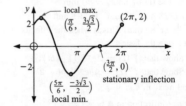

13 **a** $x(0) = -1$ cm $v(0) = 0$ cm s^{-1} $a(0) = 2$ cm s^{-2}

    b At $t = \frac{\pi}{4}$ seconds, the particle is $(\sqrt{2} - 1)$ cm left of the origin, moving right at $\sqrt{2}$ cm s^{-1}, with increasing speed.

    c At $t = 0$, $x(0) = -1$ cm, at $t = \pi$, $x(\pi) = 3$ cm, at $t = 2\pi$, $x(2\pi) = -1$ cm

    d for $0 \leqslant t \leqslant \frac{\pi}{2}$ and $\pi \leqslant t \leqslant \frac{3\pi}{2}$

EXERCISE 23B

2 a $\sec x + x \sec x \tan x$ **b** $e^x(\cot x - \csc^2 x)$

c $8 \sec(2x) \tan(2x)$ **d** $-e^{-x}\left[\cot\left(\frac{x}{2}\right) + \frac{1}{2}\csc^2\left(\frac{x}{2}\right)\right]$

e $x \csc x[2 - x \cot x]$ **f** $\sqrt{\csc x}\left[1 - \frac{x}{2}\cot x\right]$

g $\tan x$ **h** $\csc(x^2)\left[1 - 2x^2 \cot(x^2)\right]$

i $\dfrac{-\sqrt{x}\csc^2 x - \frac{1}{2}x^{-\frac{1}{2}}\cot x}{x} \equiv -\dfrac{\cos x \sin x + 2x}{2\sqrt{x}\sin^2 x}$

3 a $\sqrt{2}x - y = \sqrt{2}\left(\frac{\pi}{4} - 1\right)$ **b** $2x + y = \frac{2\pi}{3} + \sqrt{3}$

4 a $x - 2\sqrt{3}y = \frac{\pi}{6} - 4\sqrt{3}$ **b** $\sqrt{6}x + y = \pi\sqrt{6} + \sqrt{2}$

EXERCISE 23C.1

2 a 0 **b** $-\frac{\pi}{2}$ **c** $\frac{\pi}{4}$ **d** $-\frac{\pi}{4}$ **e** $\frac{\pi}{6}$ **f** $\frac{5\pi}{6}$ **g** $\frac{\pi}{3}$

h $\frac{3\pi}{4}$ **i** $-\frac{\pi}{6}$ **j** ≈ -0.874 **k** ≈ 1.238 **l** ≈ -1.551

3 a $x = \frac{\sqrt{3}}{2}$ **b** $x = -\frac{1}{3}$

4 Hint: Let $\theta = \arctan(5)$ $\therefore$ $\tan \theta = 5$, etc. **6** $\frac{\pi}{4}$

EXERCISE 23C.2

3 a $\dfrac{2}{1 + 4x^2}$ **b** $\dfrac{-3}{\sqrt{1 - 9x^2}}$ **c** $\dfrac{1}{\sqrt{16 - x^2}}$ **d** $\dfrac{-1}{\sqrt{25 - x^2}}$

e $\dfrac{2x}{1 + x^4}$ **f** -1

4 a $\dfrac{dy}{dx} = \arcsin x + \dfrac{x}{\sqrt{1 - x^2}}$ **b** $\dfrac{dy}{dx} = e^x \arccos x - \dfrac{e^x}{\sqrt{1 - x^2}}$

c $\dfrac{dy}{dx} = -e^{-x}\arctan x + \dfrac{e^{-x}}{1 + x^2}$

5 c $\dfrac{dy}{dx} = -\dfrac{1}{\sqrt{a^2 - x^2}}, \quad x \in \,]-a, a[$

6 a $\tan \alpha = \dfrac{2}{x}$ and $\tan(\alpha + \theta) = \dfrac{3}{x}$

b $\theta = \arctan\left(\dfrac{3}{x}\right) - \arctan\left(\dfrac{2}{x}\right)$ **c** $x = \sqrt{6}$

d The maximum angle of view (θ) occurs when Sonia's eye is $\sqrt{6}$ m from the wall.

EXERCISE 23D

1 $\approx 109.5°$ **2 c** $\theta = 30°$

3 1 hour 34 min 53 sec when $\theta = 36.9°$

4 c $4\sqrt{2}$ m **5** 9.866 m **6** 1.340 m from A

7 e AP + PB is a minimum when $\theta = \phi$

EXERCISE 23E

1 a is decreasing at 7.5 units per second

2 increasing at 1 cm per minute

3 a 4π m^2 per second **b** 8π m^2 per second

4 increasing at 6π m^2 per minute

5 decreasing at 0.16 m^3 per minute **6** $\frac{20}{3}$ cm per minute

7 $\frac{25\sqrt{3}}{6}$ cm per minute **8** decreasing at $\frac{250}{13}$ m s^{-1}

9 a 0.2 m s^{-1} **b** $\frac{8}{90}$ m s^{-1}

10 decreasing at $\frac{\sqrt{2}}{100}$ radians per second

11 a decr. at $\frac{3}{100}$ rad sec^{-1} **b** decr. at $\frac{1}{100}$ rad sec^{-1}

12 increasing at 0.128 radians per second

13 0.12 radians per minute **14** $4\sqrt{37}$ m s^{-1}

15 a $\frac{\sqrt{3}}{2}\pi$ cm s^{-1} **b** 0 cm s^{-1}

16 a $\frac{200}{\sqrt{13}}\pi$ rad sec^{-1} **b** 100π rad sec^{-1} **17 b** $\frac{\sqrt{3}}{120}$ m min^{-1}

REVIEW SET 23A

1 a $5\cos(5x)\ln(x) + \dfrac{\sin(5x)}{x}$

b $\cos(x)\cos(2x) - 2\sin(x)\sin(2x)$

c $-2e^{-2x}\tan x + e^{-2x}\sec^2 x$

3 a $f'(x) = 3\cos x + 8\sin(2x)$, $f''(x) = -3\sin x + 16\cos(2x)$

b $f'(x) = \frac{1}{2}x^{-\frac{1}{2}}\cos(4x) - 4x^{\frac{1}{2}}\sin(4x)$,
$f''(x) = -\frac{1}{4}x^{-\frac{3}{2}}\cos(4x) - 4x^{-\frac{1}{2}}\sin(4x) - 16x^{\frac{1}{2}}\cos(4x)$

4 a $x(0) = 3$ cm, $x'(0) = 2$ cm s^{-1}, $x''(0) = 0$ cm s^{-2}

b $t = \frac{\pi}{4}$ sec and $\frac{3\pi}{4}$ sec **c** 4 cm

5 a for $0 \leqslant x \leqslant \frac{\pi}{2}$ and $\frac{3\pi}{2} \leqslant x \leqslant 2\pi$

b increasing for $\frac{3\pi}{2} \leqslant x \leqslant 2\pi$, decreasing for $0 \leqslant x \leqslant \frac{\pi}{2}$

c

6 a $v(0) = 0$ cm s^{-1}, $v(\frac{1}{2}) = -\pi$ cm s^{-1}, $v(1) = 0$ cm s^{-1},
$v\left(\frac{3}{2}\right) = \pi$ cm s^{-1} $v(2) = 0$ cm s^{-1}

b $0 \leqslant t \leqslant 1$, $2 \leqslant t \leqslant 3$, $4 \leqslant t \leqslant 5$, etc.
i.e., for $2n \leqslant t \leqslant 2n + 1$, $n \in \{0, 1, 2, 3, ...\}$

7 a $\dfrac{x^2}{9} + \dfrac{y^2}{4} = 1$ **b** $\dfrac{dy}{dx} = -\dfrac{2\cos\theta}{3\sin\theta}$

c 6 units^2, when $\theta = \frac{\pi}{4}, \frac{3\pi}{4}, \frac{5\pi}{4}, \frac{7\pi}{4}$

8 a $a^2 + b^2 - 2ab\cos\theta = c^2 + d^2 - 2cd\cos\phi$

9 b $\frac{1}{\sqrt{2}}$ m above the floor

REVIEW SET 23B

1 a $\dfrac{dy}{dx} = \sqrt{\cos x} - \dfrac{x\sin x}{2\sqrt{\cos x}}$

b $\dfrac{dy}{dx} = e^x[\cot(2x) - 2\csc^2(2x)]$ **c** $\dfrac{dy}{dx} = \dfrac{-1}{\sqrt{4 - x^2}}$

2 a $2\sqrt{3}x - y = \frac{2\sqrt{3}\pi}{3} - 2$ **b** $4x + y = 4\sqrt{3} + \frac{\pi}{3}$

3 $\frac{20\sqrt{10}}{3} \approx 21.1$ m per minute **4** 3.60 m s^{-1}

5 a $f'(x) = 0$ for all x, so $f(x)$ is a constant $(\frac{\pi}{2})$.

b $\frac{\pi}{4} + k\pi$, $k \in \mathbb{Z}$ **c** $\frac{\pi}{4}$

6 a i 5 km **ii** $2\sqrt{10}$ km

7 a $V(r) = \frac{8}{9}\pi r^3$ m^3 **b** $\dfrac{dr}{dt} = -\dfrac{8}{375\pi} \approx -0.006\,79$ m min^{-1}

EXERCISE 24A

1 a i $\dfrac{x^2}{2}$ **ii** $\dfrac{x^3}{3}$ **iii** $\dfrac{x^6}{6}$ **iv** $-\dfrac{1}{x}$ **v** $-\dfrac{1}{3x^3}$ **vi** $\frac{3}{4}x^{\frac{4}{3}}$ **vii** $2\sqrt{x}$

b the antiderivative of x^n is $\dfrac{x^{n+1}}{n + 1}$.

2 a i $\frac{1}{2}e^{2x}$ **ii** $\frac{1}{5}e^{5x}$ **iii** $2e^{\frac{1}{2}x}$ **iv** $100e^{0.01x}$ **v** $\frac{1}{\pi}e^{\pi x}$

vi $3e^{\frac{x}{3}}$ **b** the antiderivative of e^{kx} is $\dfrac{1}{k}e^{kx}$

3 a $\dfrac{d}{dx}(x^3 + x^2) = 3x^2 + 2x$
$\therefore$ antiderivative of $6x^2 + 4x = 2x^3 + 2x^2$

b $\dfrac{d}{dx}(e^{3x+1}) = 3e^{3x+1}$
$\therefore$ antiderivative of $e^{3x+1} = \frac{1}{3}e^{3x+1}$

c $\dfrac{d}{dx}(x\sqrt{x}) = \frac{3}{2}\sqrt{x}$
$\therefore$ antiderivative of $\sqrt{x} = \frac{2}{3}x\sqrt{x}$

d $\dfrac{d}{dx}(2x + 1)^4 = 8(2x + 1)^3$
$\therefore$ antiderivative of $(2x + 1)^3 = \frac{1}{8}(2x + 1)^4$

EXERCISE 24B

2 a $\frac{1}{4}$ units^2 **b** $3\frac{3}{4}$ units^2 **c** $24\frac{2}{3}$ units^2 **d** $\frac{4\sqrt{2}}{3}$ units^2
e 3.48 units^2 **f** 2 units^2 **g** 3.96 units^2
3 a 4.06 units^2 **b** 2.41 units^2 **c** 2.58 units^2
4 c i $-\frac{1}{3}$ **ii** $-\frac{1}{6}$ **iii** -6 **d** $-\pi$

EXERCISE 24C.1

1 $\frac{dy}{dx} = 7x^6$; $\int x^6\,dx = \frac{1}{7}x^7 + c$

2 $\frac{dy}{dx} = 3x^2 + 2x$; $\int(3x^2 + 2x)\,dx = x^3 + x^2 + c$

3 $\frac{dy}{dx} = 2e^{2x+1}$; $\int e^{2x+1}\,dx = \frac{1}{2}e^{2x+1} + c$

4 $\frac{dy}{dx} = 8(2x+1)^3$; $\int(2x+1)^3\,dx = \frac{1}{8}(2x+1)^4 + c$

5 $\frac{dy}{dx} = \frac{3}{2}\sqrt{x}$; $\int\sqrt{x}\,dx = \frac{2}{3}x\sqrt{x} + c$

6 $\frac{dy}{dx} = -\frac{1}{2x\sqrt{x}}$; $\int\frac{1}{x\sqrt{x}}\,dx = -\frac{2}{\sqrt{x}} + c$

8 $\frac{dy}{dx} = \frac{-2}{\sqrt{1-4x}}$; $\int\frac{1}{\sqrt{1-4x}}\,dx = -\frac{1}{2}\sqrt{1-4x} + c$

9 $2\ln(5-3x+x^2) + c$ $(5 - 3x + x^2$ is $> 0)$ **10** $\frac{1}{\ln 2}2^x + c$

11 $x\ln x - x + c$

EXERCISE 24C.2

1 a $\frac{x^5}{5} - \frac{x^3}{3} - \frac{x^2}{2} + 2x + c$ **b** $\frac{2}{3}x^{\frac{3}{2}} + e^x + c$
c $3e^x - \ln|x| + c$ **d** $\frac{2}{5}x^{\frac{5}{2}} - 2\ln|x| + c$
e $-2x^{-\frac{1}{2}} + 4\ln|x| + c$ **f** $\frac{1}{8}x^4 - \frac{1}{5}x^5 + \frac{3}{4}x^{\frac{4}{3}} + c$
g $\frac{1}{3}x^3 + 3\ln|x| + c$ **h** $\frac{1}{2}\ln|x| + \frac{1}{3}x^3 - e^x + c$
i $5e^x + \frac{1}{12}x^4 - 4\ln|x| + c$

2 a $\frac{1}{3}x^3 + \frac{3}{2}x^2 - 2x + c$ **b** $\frac{2}{3}x^{\frac{3}{2}} - 2x^{\frac{1}{2}} + c$ **c** $2e^x + \frac{1}{x} + c$
d $-2x^{-\frac{1}{2}} - 8x^{\frac{1}{2}} + c$ **e** $\frac{4}{3}x^3 + 2x^2 + x + c$
f $\frac{1}{2}x^2 + x - 3\ln|x| + c$ **g** $\frac{4}{3}x^{\frac{3}{2}} - 2x^{\frac{1}{2}} + c$
h $2x^{\frac{1}{2}} + 8x^{-\frac{1}{2}} - \frac{20}{3}x^{-\frac{3}{2}} + c$ **i** $\frac{1}{4}x^4 + x^3 + \frac{3}{2}x^2 + x + c$

3 a $y = 6x + c$ **b** $y = \frac{4}{3}x^3 + c$ **c** $y = \frac{5}{2}x^2 - \frac{1}{3}x^3 + c$
d $y = -\frac{1}{x} + c$ **e** $y = 2e^x - 5x + c$ **f** $y = x^4 + x^3 + c$

4 a $y = x - 2x^2 + \frac{4}{3}x^3 + c$ **b** $y = \frac{2}{3}x^{\frac{3}{2}} - 4\sqrt{x} + c$
c $y = x + 2\ln|x| + \frac{5}{x} + c$

5 a $f(x) = \frac{1}{4}x^4 - \frac{5}{2}x^2 + 3x + c$ **b** $f(x) = \frac{4}{3}x^{\frac{3}{2}} - \frac{12}{5}x^{\frac{5}{2}} + c$
c $f(x) = 3e^x - 4\ln|x| + c$

6 a $f(x) = x^2 - x + 3$ **b** $f(x) = x^3 + x^2 - 7$
c $f(x) = e^x + 2\sqrt{x} - 1 - e$ **d** $f(x) = \frac{1}{2}x^2 - 4\sqrt{x} + \frac{11}{2}$

7 a $f(x) = \frac{1}{3}x^3 + \frac{1}{2}x^2 + x + \frac{1}{3}$ **b** $f(x) = 4x^{\frac{5}{2}} + 4x^{\frac{3}{2}} - 4x + 5$
c $f(x) = \frac{1}{3}x^3 - \frac{16}{3}x + 5$

EXERCISE 24D

1 a $\frac{1}{8}(2x+5)^4 + c$ **b** $\frac{1}{2(3-2x)} + c$ **c** $\frac{-2}{3(2x-1)^3} + c$
d $\frac{1}{32}(4x-3)^8 + c$ **e** $\frac{2}{9}(3x-4)^{\frac{3}{2}} + c$ **f** $-4\sqrt{1-5x} + c$
g $-\frac{3}{5}(1-x)^5 + c$ **h** $-2\sqrt{3-4x} + c$

2 a $y = \frac{1}{3}(2x-7)^{\frac{3}{2}} + 2$ **b** $(-8, -19)$

3 a $\frac{1}{2}(2x-1)^3 + c$ **b** $\frac{1}{5}x^5 - \frac{1}{2}x^4 + \frac{1}{3}x^3 + c$
c $-\frac{1}{12}(1-3x)^4 + c$ **d** $x - \frac{2}{3}x^3 + \frac{1}{5}x^5 + c$
e $-\frac{8}{3}(5-x)^{\frac{3}{2}} + c$ **f** $\frac{1}{7}x^7 + \frac{3}{5}x^5 + x^3 + x + c$

4 a $2e^x + \frac{5}{2}e^{2x} + c$ **b** $\frac{3}{5}e^{5x-2} + c$ **c** $-\frac{1}{3}e^{7-3x} + c$
d $\frac{1}{2}\ln|2x-1| + c$ **e** $-\frac{5}{3}\ln|1-3x| + c$
f $-e^{-x} - 2\ln|2x+1| + c$ **g** $\frac{1}{2}e^{2x} + 2x - \frac{1}{2}e^{-2x} + c$
h $-\frac{1}{2}e^{-2x} - 4e^{-x} + 4x + c$ **i** $\frac{1}{2}x^2 + 5\ln|1-x| + c$

5 a $y = x - 2e^x + \frac{1}{2}e^{2x} + c$ **b** $y = x - x^2 + 3\ln|x+2| + c$
c $y = -\frac{1}{2}e^{-2x} + 2\ln|2x-1| + c$

6 Both are correct.
Recall that: $\frac{d}{dx}(\ln|Ax|) = \frac{d}{dx}(\ln|A| + \ln|x|) = \frac{1}{x}$

7 a $f(x) = -e^{-2x} + 4$ **b** $f(x) = x^2 + 2\ln|1-x| + 2 - 2\ln 2$
c $f(x) = \frac{2}{3}x^{\frac{3}{2}} - \frac{1}{8}e^{-4x} + \frac{1}{8}e^{-4} - \frac{2}{3}$

8 $\int\frac{2x-8}{x^2-4}\,dx = 3\ln|x+2| - \ln|x-2| + c$

9 $\int\frac{2}{4x^2-1}\,dx = \frac{1}{2}\ln|2x-1| - \frac{1}{2}\ln|2x+1| + c$

EXERCISE 24E

1 a $\frac{1}{5}(x^3+1)^5 + c$ **b** $2\sqrt{x^2+3} + c$ **c** $\frac{2}{3}(x^3+x)^{\frac{3}{2}} + c$
d $\frac{1}{4}(2+x^4)^4 + c$ **e** $\frac{1}{5}(x^3+2x+1)^5 + c$ **f** $-\frac{1}{27(3x^3-1)^3} + c$
g $\frac{1}{8(1-x^2)^4} + c$ **h** $-\frac{1}{2(x^2+4x-3)} + c$ **i** $\frac{1}{5}(x^2+x)^5 + c$

2 a $e^{1-2x} + c$ **b** $e^{x^2} + c$ **c** $\frac{1}{3}e^{x^3+1} + c$ **d** $2e^{\sqrt{x}} + c$
e $-e^{x-x^2} + c$ **f** $e^{1-\frac{1}{x}} + c$

3 a $\ln|x^2+1| + c$ **b** $-\frac{1}{2}\ln|2-x^2| + c$ **c** $\ln|x^2-3x| + c$
d $2\ln|x^3-x| + c$ **e** $-2\ln|5x-x^2| + c$ **f** $-\frac{1}{3}\ln|x^3-3x| + c$

4 a $f(x) = -\frac{1}{9}(3-x^3)^3 + c$ **b** $f(x) = 4\ln|\ln x| + c$
c $f(x) = -\frac{1}{3}(1-x^2)^{\frac{3}{2}} + c$ **d** $f(x) = -\frac{1}{2}e^{1-x^2} + c$
e $f(x) = -\ln|x^3-x| + c$ **f** $f(x) = \frac{1}{4}(\ln x)^4 + c$

EXERCISE 24F.1

1 a $-3\cos x - 2x + c$ **b** $2x^2 - 2\sin x + c$ **c** $\frac{4}{3}x^{\frac{3}{2}} + 4\tan x + c$
d $\tan x - 2\cos x + c$ **e** $\frac{x^2}{4} - \tan x + c$
f $-\cos x - 2\sin x + e^x + c$ **g** $\frac{2}{7}x^3\sqrt{x} + 10\cos x + c$
h $\frac{1}{9}x^3 - \frac{1}{6}x^2 + \sin x + c$ **i** $5\tan x + \cos x + \frac{4}{3}x\sqrt{x} + c$

2 a $\frac{2}{3}x^{\frac{3}{2}} + \frac{1}{2}\sin x + c$ **b** $\frac{\theta^2}{2} + \cos\theta + c$ **c** $\frac{2}{5}t^{\frac{5}{2}} + 2\tan t + c$
d $2e^t + 4\cos t + c$ **e** $3\sin t - \ln|t| + c$ **f** $3\theta - 2\ln|\theta| + \tan\theta + c$

3 a $e^x\sin x + e^x\cos x$, $e^x\sin x + c$
b $-e^{-x}\sin x + e^{-x}\cos x$, $e^{-x}\sin x + c$
c $\cos x - x\sin x$, $\sin x - x\cos x + c$ **d** $\frac{1}{\cos x} + c$

4 a $f(x) = \frac{x^3}{3} - 4\sin x + 3$ **b** $f(x) = 2\sin x + 3\cos x - 2\sqrt{2}$
c $f(x) = \frac{2}{3}x^{\frac{3}{2}} - 2\tan x - \frac{2}{3}\pi^{\frac{3}{2}}$

EXERCISE 24F.2

1 a $-\frac{1}{3}\cos(3x) + c$ **b** $\frac{1}{2}\sin(4x) + c$ **c** $\frac{1}{2}\tan(2x) + c$
d $6\sin\left(\frac{x}{2}\right) + c$ **e** $-\frac{3}{2}\cos(2x) + e^{-x} + c$

f $\frac{1}{2}e^{2x} - 4\tan\left(\frac{x}{2}\right) + c$ **g** $-\cos\left(2x + \frac{\pi}{6}\right) + c$

h $3\sin\left(\frac{\pi}{4} - x\right) + c$ **i** $-2\tan\left(\frac{\pi}{3} - 2x\right) + c$

j $\frac{1}{2}\sin(2x) - \frac{1}{2}\cos(2x) + c$ **k** $-\frac{2}{3}\cos(3x) + \frac{5}{4}\sin(4x) + c$

l $\frac{1}{16}\sin(8x) + 3\cos x + c$

2 a $\frac{1}{2}x + \frac{1}{4}\sin(2x) + c$ **b** $\frac{1}{2}x - \frac{1}{4}\sin(2x) + c$

c $\frac{3}{2}x + \frac{1}{8}\sin(4x) + c$ **d** $\frac{5}{2}x + \frac{1}{12}\sin(6x) + c$

e $\frac{1}{4}x + \frac{1}{32}\sin(8x) + c$ **f** $\frac{3}{2}x + 2\sin x + \frac{1}{4}\sin(2x) + c$

3 $\frac{1}{32}\sin(4x) + \frac{1}{4}\sin(2x) + \frac{3}{8}x + c$

4 a $\frac{1}{5}\sin^5 x + c$ **b** $-2(\cos x)^{\frac{1}{2}} + c$ **c** $-\ln|\cos x| + c$

d $\frac{2}{3}(\sin x)^{\frac{3}{2}} + c$ **e** $-(2 + \sin x)^{-1} + c$ **f** $\frac{1}{2}(\cos x)^{-2} + c$

g $\ln|1 - \cos x| + c$ **h** $\frac{1}{2}\ln|\sin(2x) - 3| + c$

i $-\frac{1}{2}\cos(x^2) + c$ **j** $\frac{1}{4}\tan^4 x + c$ **k** $-\frac{1}{6}\operatorname{cosec}^3(2x) + c$

l $-\frac{1}{3}\sin^3 x + \sin x + c$

5 a $-\cos x + \frac{2}{3}\cos^3 x - \frac{1}{5}\cos^5 x + c$ **b** $\frac{1}{5}\sin^5 x - \frac{1}{7}\sin^7 x + c$

6 a $-e^{\cos x} + c$ **b** $\frac{1}{8}\sin^4(2x) + c$ **c** $\ln|\sin x - \cos x| + c$

d $e^{\tan x} + c$

7 a $\ln|\sin x| + c$ **b** $\frac{1}{3}\ln|\sin(3x)| + c$ **c** $-\cot x + c$

d $\sec x + c$ **e** $-\csc x + c$ **f** $\frac{1}{3}\sec(3x) + c$

g $-2\csc\left(\frac{x}{2}\right) + c$ **h** $\frac{1}{2}\sec^2 x + c$ **i** $-2\sqrt{\cot x} + c$

EXERCISE 24G.1

1 a $\frac{1}{4}$ **b** $\frac{2}{3}$ **c** $e - 1 \;(\approx 1.718)$ **d** $1\frac{1}{2}$ **e** $6\frac{2}{3}$

f $\ln 3 \;(\approx 1.099)$ **g** 1.524 **h** 2 **i** $e - 1 \;(\approx 1.718)$

2 a $\frac{1}{2}$ **b** $\frac{1}{2}$ **c** $\sqrt{3} - 1$ **d** $\frac{1}{3}$ **e** $\frac{\pi}{8} + \frac{1}{4}$ **f** $\frac{\pi}{4}$

3 a $\frac{1}{12}$ **b** 1.557 **c** $20\frac{1}{3}$ **d** 0.0337 **e** $\frac{1}{2}\ln(\frac{2}{7}) \;(\approx -0.6264)$

f $\frac{1}{2}(\ln 2)^2 \;(\approx 0.2402)$ **g** 0 **h** $2\ln 7 \;(\approx 3.892)$ **i** $\frac{3^{n+1}}{2n+2}, n \neq -1$

4 a $2 - \sqrt{2}$ **b** $\frac{1}{24}$ **c** $\frac{1}{2}\ln 2$ **d** $\ln 2$ **e** $\ln 2$ **f** $\frac{1}{4}$

EXERCISE 24G.2

1 a $\int_1^4 \sqrt{x}\,dx = 4.67$ $\int_1^4 (-\sqrt{x})\,dx = -4.67$

b $\int_0^1 x^7\,dx = \frac{1}{8}$ $\int_0^1 (-x^7)\,dx = -\frac{1}{8}$

2 a $\frac{1}{3}$ **b** $\frac{7}{3}$ **c** $\frac{8}{3}$ **d** 1 **3 a** -4 **b** 6.25 **c** 2.25

4 a $\frac{1}{3}$ **b** $\frac{2}{3}$ **c** 1 **5 a** 6.5 **b** -9 **c** 0 **d** -2.5

6 a 2π **b** -4 **c** $\frac{\pi}{2}$ **d** $\frac{5\pi}{2} - 4$

7 a $\int_2^7 f(x)\,dx$ **b** $\int_1^9 g(x)\,dx$ **8 a** -5 **b** 4

REVIEW SET 24A

1 a $8\sqrt{x} + c$ **b** $-\frac{3}{2}\ln|1 - 2x| + c$ **c** $-\frac{1}{2}e^{1-x^2} + c$ **d** $-\frac{1}{3}e^{4-3x} + c$

2 a $\frac{1}{8}\sin^8 x + c$ **b** $-\frac{1}{2}\ln|\cos(2x)| + c$ **c** $e^{\sin x} + c$

3 a $12\frac{4}{9}$ **b** $\frac{5}{54}$ **4** $\frac{dy}{dx} = \frac{x}{\sqrt{x^2 - 4}}$; $\int$ is $\sqrt{x^2 - 4} + c$

5 $f(x) = 3x^3 + 5x^2 + 6x - 1$ **6 a** $\frac{\pi}{6} + \frac{\sqrt{3}}{4}$ **b** $\ln 2$

7 a $A = 2$,   **b** $\int_0^2 \frac{4x - 3}{2x + 1}\,dx = 4 - \frac{5}{2}\ln 5 \;(\approx -0.0236)$

$B = -5$

8 a $3 - \sqrt{7}$ **b** $\frac{1}{3}(e^9 - e)$ **9** $\tan x$, $\int \tan x\,dx = \ln(\sec x) + c$

10 $a = \ln\sqrt{2}$ **11** $e^{-\pi}$

REVIEW SET 24B

1 a $-2e^{-x} - \ln|x| + 3x + c$ **b** $\frac{1}{2}x^2 - 2x + \ln|x| + c$

c $9x + 3e^{2x-1} + \frac{1}{4}e^{4x-2} + c$ **2 a** $2\frac{8}{15}$ **b** $4\frac{1}{2}$

3 a $2x - 2\sin x + c$ **b** $\frac{9x}{2} - 4\sin x + \frac{1}{4}\sin(2x) + c$

4 $\frac{d}{dx}(3x^2 + x)^3 = 3(3x^2 + x)^2(6x + 1)$

$\int (3x^2 + x)^2 (6x + 1)\,dx = \frac{1}{3}(3x^2 + x)^3 + c$

5 $f(x) = \frac{1}{3}x^3 - \frac{3}{2}x^2 + 2x + 2\frac{1}{6}$ **6** $\frac{1}{2}\sin(x^2) + c$

7 $\frac{2}{3}(\sqrt{5} - \sqrt{2})$

8 a $f(x) = \frac{1}{4}x^4 + \frac{1}{3}x^3 - \frac{10}{3}x + 3$ **b** $3x + 26y = 84$ **9** $\ln 2$

10 $A = 1, B = 2, C = 1, D = 4,$ $\frac{(x+1)^3}{3} + 4\ln|x - 2| + c$

11 a $\ln\left(\frac{|x+2|}{(x-1)^2}\right) + c$ **b** $\ln\left(\frac{(x-1)^2}{|x+2|}\right) + c$

12 a $A = 4, \quad B = -2, \quad C = -2$

b $4\ln|x| - 2\ln|x + 1| - 2\ln|x - 1| + c$ **c** $\ln\left(\frac{16}{25}\right)$

REVIEW SET 24C

1 a $y = \frac{1}{5}x^5 - \frac{2}{3}x^3 + x + c$ **b** $y = 400x + 40e^{-\frac{x}{2}} + c$

2 a $-2\ln 5$ **b** $3\frac{1}{3}$ **3** $\frac{1}{3\cos^3 x} + c$

4 $\frac{2(\ln x)}{x}$, $\frac{1}{2}(\ln x)^2 + c$ **5** $23\frac{1}{6}$ **6** $x\tan x + \ln|\cos x| + c$

7 if $n \neq -1$, $\frac{1}{2(n+1)}(2x + 3)^{n+1} + c$

if $n = -1$, $\frac{1}{2}\ln|2x + 3| + c$

8 a $e^{3x} + 6e^{2x} + 12e^x + 8$ **b** $\frac{1}{3}e^3 + 3e^2 + 12e - 7\frac{1}{3}$

9 a $\frac{\pi}{12} - \frac{1}{4}$ **b** $\frac{1}{2}\ln 3$

10 $a = \frac{1}{3}$, $f'(x) = 2\sqrt{x} + \frac{1}{3\sqrt{x}}$ is never 0

as $\sqrt{x} \geqslant 0$ for all x, $\therefore$ $f'(x) > 0$ for all x

11 $a = 0$ or ± 3 **12** $1 - \frac{1}{4e}$

13 $\frac{\cos^{1-\frac{n}{2}} x}{\frac{n}{2} - 1} + c$, for $n \neq 2$, $-\ln|\cos x| + c$, for $n = 2$

EXERCISE 25A

1 a $\frac{1}{3}$ units^2 **b** $63\frac{3}{4}$ units^2 **c** $e - 1 \;(\approx 1.718)$ units^2

d $20\frac{5}{6}$ units^2 **e** $3\frac{1}{3}$ units^2 **f** $12\frac{2}{3}$ units^2

2 a 18 units^2 **b** $\ln 4 \;(\approx 1.39)$ units^2 **c** $\ln 3 \;(\approx 1.10)$ u^2

d $4\frac{1}{2}$ u^2 **e** $2e - \frac{2}{e} \;(\approx 4.70)$ u^2 **f** $\ln\left(\frac{27}{4}\right) - 1$ u^2

3 a 1 u^2 **c** $\frac{\pi}{2}$ u^2

4 a $4\frac{1}{2}$ u^2 **b** $1 + e^{-2} \;(\approx 1.14)$ u^2 **c** $1\frac{5}{27}$ u^2 **d** $2\frac{1}{4}$ u^2

5 $(\sqrt{2} - 1)$ u^2

6 a $10\frac{2}{3}$ units^2

b i, ii

iii $1\frac{1}{3}$ units^2

c $\frac{1}{3}$ units^2

d

enclosed area $= 3\ln 2 - 2 \;(\approx 0.0794)$ units^2 **e** $\frac{1}{2}$ units^2

7

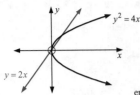

enclosed area $= \frac{1}{3}$ units^2

8 a $(\frac{\pi}{4}, 1)$ **b** $\ln\sqrt{2}$ u^2

9 a

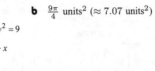

b $\frac{9\pi}{4}$ units^2 (≈ 7.07 units^2)

10 a $40\frac{1}{2}$ units^2 **b** 8 units^2 **c** 8 units^2

11 a C_1 is $y = \sin 2x$, C_2 is $y = \sin x$ **b** $A(\frac{\pi}{3}, \frac{\sqrt{3}}{2})$ **c** $2\frac{1}{2}$ u^2

12 a i $A = \int_{-2}^{-1} (x^3 - 7x - 6)\, dx + \int_{-1}^{3} (7x + 6 - x^3)\, dx$

ii $A = \int_{-2}^{3} \left| x^3 - 7x - 6 \right| dx$

b Area $= 32\frac{3}{4}$ units^2

13 a $21\frac{1}{12}$ units^2 **b** 8 units^2 **c** $101\frac{3}{4}$ units^2

14 a $\int_3^5 f(x)\, dx = -$ (area between $x = 3$ and $x = 5$)

b $\int_1^3 f(x)\, dx - \int_3^5 f(x)\, dx + \int_5^7 f(x)\, dx$

15 a C_1 is $y = \cos^2 x$, C_2 is $y = \cos(2x)$

b A$(0, 1)$ B$(\frac{\pi}{4}, 0)$ C$(\frac{\pi}{2}, 0)$ D$(\frac{3\pi}{4}, 0)$ E$(\pi, 1)$

16 a 2.88 units^2 **b** 4.97 units^2 **17** $k \approx 1.7377$

18 $b \approx 1.3104$ **19** $k \approx 2.3489$ **20** $a = \sqrt{3}$

EXERCISE 25B.1

1 110 m **2 a i** travelling forwards

ii travelling backwards (i.e., opposite direction)

b 16 km

c 8 km from starting point (on positive side)

3 9.75 km

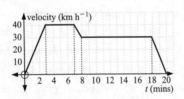

EXERCISE 25B.2

1 a $\frac{1}{2}$ cm **b** 0 cm **2 a** $5\frac{1}{6}$ cm **b** $1\frac{1}{2}$ cm left

3 a 41 units **b** 34 units **4 b** 2 units

EXERCISE 25B.3

1 a 40 m s^{-1} **b** 47.77 m s^{-1} **c** 1.386 seconds

d as $t \to \infty$, $v(t) \to 50$ **f**

e $a(t) = 5e^{-0.5t}$ and as $e^x > 0$ for all x, $a(t) > 0$ for all t.

g 134.5 m

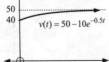

2 900 m

3 a Show that $v(t) = 100 - 80e^{-\frac{1}{20}t}$ m s^{-1} and as $t \to \infty$, $v(t) \to 100$ m s^{-1} **b** 370.4 m

EXERCISE 25C

1 €4250 **2 a** $P(x) = 15x - 0.015x^2 - 650$ dollars

b maximum profit is \$3100, when 500 plates are made

c $46 \leqslant x \leqslant 954$ plates (you can't produce part of a plate)

3 14 400 calories **4** 76.3° C

5 a $y = -\frac{1}{120}(1 - x)^4 - \frac{x}{30} + \frac{1}{120}$ **b** 2.5 cm (at $x = 1$ m)

6 a $y = \left(\frac{0.01}{3}x^3 - \frac{0.005}{12}x^4 - \frac{0.08}{3}x \right)$ metres **b** 3.33 cm

c 2.375 cm **d** 1.05°

7 Extra hint: $\dfrac{dC}{dV} = \frac{1}{2}x^2 + 4$ and $\dfrac{dV}{dx} = \pi r^2$

8 3.82020 units **9 e** 0.974 km $\times$ 2.05 km

REVIEW SET 25A

1 a $2 + \pi$ **b** -2 **c** π

2 a $A = \int_a^b [f(x) - g(x)]dx + \int_b^c [g(x) - f(x)]\, dx + \int_c^d [f(x) - g(x)]\, dx$

b $\int_a^d |f(x) - g(x)|\, dx$ or $\int_a^d |g(x) - f(x)|\, dx$

3 269 cm

4

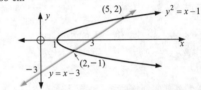

a $(2, -1)$ and $(5, 2)$ **b** 4.5 units^2

5 $k = \sqrt[3]{16}$ **6** **Hint**: Show that the areas represented by the integrals can be arranged to form a $1 \times e$ unit rectangle.

7 a $v(0) = 25$ m s^{-1}, $v(3) = 4$ m s^{-1} **b** as $t \to \infty$, $v(t) \to 0$

c

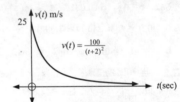

d 3 seconds **e** $a(t) = \dfrac{-200}{(t + 2)^3}$, $t \geqslant 0$ **f** $k = \frac{1}{5}$

8 $21\frac{1}{12}$ units^2 **9** $a = \ln 3$, $b = \ln 5$ **10** $\dfrac{kL^4}{4}$ m

11 $\left(2 - \frac{\pi}{2} \right)$ units^2 **12 a** $b \approx -0.7292$ **b** 0.2009 units^2

13 a $\sec x$, $\ln|\tan x + \sec x| + c$

b i

ii 0.965 units^2

REVIEW SET 25B

1 29.6 cm **2** 4.5 units^2 **3** π units^2

4 $I(t) = \dfrac{100}{t} + 100$ **a** 105 milliamps **b** as $t \to \infty$, $I \to 100$

5 no, $\int_1^3 f(x)\, dx = -$ (area from $x = 1$ to $x = 3$)

6 a local maximum at $(1, \frac{1}{2})$, local minimum at $(-1, -\frac{1}{2})$

b as $x \to \infty$, $f(x) \to 0$ (above)
as $x \to -\infty$, $f(x) \to 0$ (below)

c

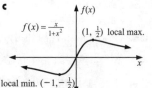

$f(x) = \frac{x}{1+x^2}$

$(1, \frac{1}{2})$ local max.

local min. $(-1, -\frac{1}{2})$

d $\frac{1}{2} \ln 5$ (≈ 0.805) units^2

7 $k = 1\frac{1}{3}$ **8 a**

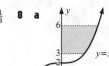

$y = x^3 + 2$

b $f(y) = \sqrt[3]{y - 2}$

c $3\sqrt[3]{4} - \frac{3}{4} \approx 4.01$ units^2

9 31.2 units^2

10 a

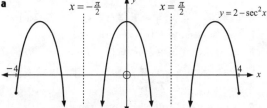

$x = -\frac{\pi}{2}$ $x = \frac{\pi}{2}$ $y = 2 - \sec^2 x$

b $x = -\frac{\pi}{2}$ and $x = \frac{\pi}{2}$

c x-intercepts are $x = -\frac{5\pi}{4}, -\frac{3\pi}{4}, -\frac{\pi}{4}, \frac{\pi}{4}, \frac{3\pi}{4}, \frac{5\pi}{4}$
y-intercept is $y = 1$

d $(\pi - 2)$ units^2

12 $\ln 2$ units^2 **13** ≈ 2.35 m

REVIEW SET 25C

1 a $v(t)$:

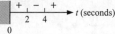

b The particle moves in the positive direction initially, then at $t = 2$, $6\frac{2}{3}$ m from its starting point, it changes direction. It changes direction again at $t = 4$, $5\frac{1}{3}$ m from its starting point, and at $t = 5$, it is $6\frac{2}{3}$ m from its starting point.

c $6\frac{2}{3}$ m **d** $9\frac{1}{3}$ m

2 ≈ 2.59 units^2 **3 a** $a = -3$ **b** A has x-coordinate $\sqrt[3]{4}$

4 a

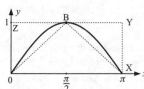

From the graph,
area $\triangle$OBX $<$ area under the curve $<$ area OXYZ
$\therefore$ $\frac{1}{2}\pi(1) <$ $\int_0^\pi \sin x \, dx$ $< \pi(1)$
i.e., $\frac{\pi}{2} <$ $\int_0^\pi \sin x \, dx$ $< \pi$

b partition as

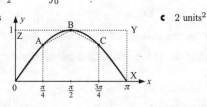

c 2 units^2

5 c $\int_0^4 y_A \, dx = 2\pi$, $\int_4^6 y_B \, dx = -\frac{\pi}{2}$ **d** $\frac{3\pi}{2}$ **6** $m = 1$, $c = 1$

7 a

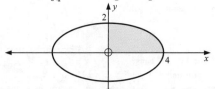

8 $40\frac{1}{2}$ units^2

9 Hint:

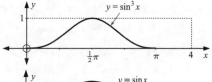

$y = \sin^3 x$

10 a

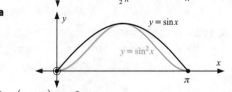

$y = \sin x$

$y = \sin^2 x$

b $\left(1 - \frac{\pi}{4}\right)$ units^2

11 $\left(\frac{\pi^2}{2} - 2\right)$u^2 **12** $m = \frac{\pi}{3}$ **13 a** $a \approx 0.8767$ **b** ≈ 0.1357 u^2

14 b 8.66 years **c** 12.21% p.a.

EXERCISE 26A

1 a 36π units^3 **b** 8π units^3 **c** $\frac{127\pi}{7}$ units^3 **d** $\frac{255\pi}{4}$ units^3
 e $\frac{992\pi}{5}$ units^3 **f** $\frac{250\pi}{3}$ units^3 **g** $\frac{\pi}{2}$ units^3 **h** $\frac{40\pi}{3}$ units^3

2 a 18.6 units^3 **b** 30.2 units^3

3 a 186π units^3 **b** $\frac{146\pi}{5}$ units^3 **c** $\frac{\pi}{2}(e^8 - 1)$ units^3

4 a 63π units^3 **b** ≈ 198 cm^3

5 a a cone of base radius r and height h
 b $y = -\left(\frac{r}{h}\right)x + r$ **c** $V = \frac{1}{3}\pi r^2 h$

6 a a sphere of radius r

7 a 8π units^3 **b** $\frac{1024\pi}{5}$ units^3 **c** $\frac{\pi}{2}(e^4 - 1)$ units^3
 d $\frac{483\pi}{5}$ units^3 **e** $\frac{256\pi}{5}$ units^3

8 48π units^3

9 a $\frac{\pi^2}{4}$ units^3 **b** $\frac{\pi^2}{8}$ units^3 **c** 2π units^3 **d** $\pi\sqrt{3}$ units^3
 e $\frac{\pi}{3}$ units^3 **f** $\pi\left(2 - \frac{\pi}{2}\right)$ units^3

10 a

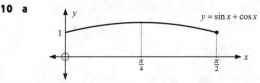

$y = \sin x + \cos x$

b $\pi\left(\frac{\pi}{4} + \frac{1}{2}\right)$ units^3

11 a

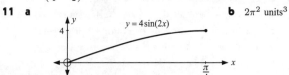

$y = 4\sin(2x)$

b $2\pi^2$ units^3

EXERCISE 26B

1 a A is at $(-1, 3)$, B$(1, 3)$ **b** $\frac{136\pi}{15}$ units^3

2 a A is at $(2, e)$ **b** $\pi(e^2 + 1)$ units^3

3 a A is at $(1, 1)$ **b** $\frac{11\pi}{6}$ units^3 **4** $\frac{162\pi}{5}$ units^3

5 a A is at (5, 1) **b** $\frac{9\pi}{2}$ units^3

6 b see diagram alongside:

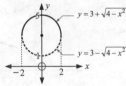

$y = 3 + \sqrt{4 - x^2}$

$y = 3 - \sqrt{4 - x^2}$

c $24\pi^2 \approx 237$ units^3

8 $V = 36\pi$ units^3, which is independent of r.

REVIEW SET 26

1 a 312π units^3 **b** 402π units^3 **c** $\frac{\pi^2}{2}$ units^3 **d** 18π units^3

2 a $\pi\left(\frac{3\pi}{32} - \frac{1}{8\sqrt{2}}\right)$ units^3 **b** ≈ 124 units^3 **3** 2π units^3

4 a $\frac{31\pi}{5}$ units^3 **b** $\frac{65\pi}{4}$ units^3 **c** $\frac{93\pi}{5}$ units^3 **5** $\frac{128\pi}{5}$ units^3

6 $\frac{\pi}{2}$ units^3 **7 a** $\frac{128\pi}{3}$ units^3 **b** $\frac{128\pi}{3}$ units^3 **8** $\frac{96\pi}{5}$ units^3

EXERCISE 27A

1 a $4\arcsin x + c$ **b** $3\arcsin\left(\frac{x}{2}\right) + c$ **c** $\frac{1}{4}\arctan\left(\frac{x}{4}\right) + c$

d $\frac{1}{2}\arctan(2x) + c$ **e** $\frac{1}{2}\arcsin(2x) + c$ **f** $\frac{2}{3}\arcsin\left(\frac{3x}{2}\right) + c$

g $\frac{1}{2\sqrt{2}}\arctan\left(\frac{x}{\sqrt{2}}\right) + c$ **h** $\frac{5}{6}\arctan\left(\frac{2x}{3}\right) + c$

2 a

b i $f(-x) = \frac{1}{\sqrt{1-(-x)^2}}$

$= \frac{1}{\sqrt{1-x^2}}$

$= f(x)$ for all x

ii For y to have meaning $1 - x^2 > 0$ which has solution $x \in\ ]-1, 1[$

c Area $= \frac{\pi}{6}$ units^2

EXERCISE 27B

1 a $\frac{2}{5}(x-3)^{\frac{5}{2}} + 2(x-3)^{\frac{3}{2}} + c$

b $\frac{2}{7}(x+1)^{\frac{7}{2}} - \frac{4}{5}(x+1)^{\frac{5}{2}} + \frac{2}{3}(x+1)^{\frac{3}{2}} + c$

c $-(3-x^2)^{\frac{3}{2}} + \frac{1}{5}(3-x^2)^{\frac{5}{2}} + c$ **d** $\frac{1}{5}(t^2+2)^{\frac{5}{2}} - \frac{2}{3}(t^2+2)^{\frac{3}{2}} + c$

e $2\sqrt{x-1} - 2\arctan\left(\sqrt{x-1}\right) + c$

2 a $\frac{28\sqrt{3}}{5} - \frac{44\sqrt{2}}{5}$ **b** $\frac{48\sqrt{6}-54}{5}$ **c** $\frac{1054\sqrt{3}}{35}$

3 a $x - 3\arctan\left(\frac{x}{3}\right) + c$ **b** $\frac{1}{2}\arcsin x - \frac{1}{2}x\sqrt{1-x^2} + c$

c $\ln(x^2 + 9) + c$ **d** $2\ln(1 + [\ln x]^2) + c$

e $\sqrt{x^2 - 4} - 2\arccos\left(\frac{2}{x}\right) + c$ **f** $\cos x - \frac{2}{3}\cos^3 x + c$

g $\frac{1}{2}\arcsin\left(\frac{2x}{3}\right) + c$ **h** $\frac{1}{2}x^2 - \frac{1}{2}\ln(1 + x^2) + c$

i $\frac{1}{6}\arctan\left(\frac{2}{3}\ln x\right) + c$ **j** $\frac{1}{16}\ln\left(\frac{|x|}{\sqrt{x^2+16}}\right) + c$

k $\frac{-1}{16x}\sqrt{16 - x^2} + c$ **l** $2\arcsin\left(\frac{x}{2}\right) - \frac{1}{4}x(2-x^2)\sqrt{4-x^2} + c$

EXERCISE 27C

1 a $xe^x - e^x + c$ **b** $-x\cos x + \sin x + c$

c $\frac{1}{3}x^3\ln x - \frac{1}{9}x^3 + c$ **d** $-\frac{1}{3}x\cos 3x + \frac{1}{9}\sin 3x + c$

e $\frac{1}{2}x\sin 2x + \frac{1}{4}\cos 2x + c$ **f** $x\tan x + \ln|\cos x| + c$

g $x\ln x - x + c$ **h** $x(\ln x)^2 - 2x\ln x + 2x + c$

i $x\arctan x - \frac{1}{2}\ln(x^2 + 1) + c$

2 a $-x^2 e^{-x} - 2xe^{-x} - 2e^{-x} + c$ **b** $\frac{1}{2}e^x(\sin x + \cos x) + c$

c $-\frac{1}{2}e^{-x}(\cos x + \sin x) + c$

d $-x^2\cos x + 2x\sin x + 2\cos x + c$

3 a $u^2 e^u - 2ue^u + 2e^u + c$ **b** $x(\ln x)^2 - 2x\ln x + 2x + c$

4 a $-u\cos u + \sin u + c$ **b** $-\sqrt{2x}\cos\sqrt{2x} + \sin\sqrt{2x} + c$

5 $\frac{2}{3}\sqrt{3x}\sin\sqrt{3x} + \frac{2}{3}\cos\sqrt{3x} + c$

EXERCISE 27D

1 a $\ln\left|e^x - e^{-x}\right| + c$ **b** $\frac{7^x}{\ln 7} + c$ **c** $\frac{(3x+5)^6}{18} + c$

d $\ln|2 - \cos x| + c$ **e** $x\tan x + \ln|\cos x| + c$ **f** $\frac{1}{2}\ln|\sin 2x| + c$

g $\frac{(x+3)^5}{5} - \frac{3}{4}(x+3)^4 + c$ **h** $\frac{x^3}{3} + \frac{3}{2}x^2 + 3x + \ln|x| + c$

i $-x^2 e^{-x} - 2xe^{-x} - 2e^{-x} + c$ **j** $\frac{2}{5}(1-x)^{\frac{5}{2}} - \frac{2}{3}(1-x)^{\frac{3}{2}} + c$

k $\frac{x^3\sqrt{1-x^2}}{4} - \frac{x\sqrt{1-x^2}}{8} + \frac{\arcsin x}{8} + c$ **l** $\frac{3}{2}\arccos\left(\frac{2}{x}\right) + c$

m $\frac{2}{7}(x-3)^{\frac{7}{2}} + \frac{12}{5}(x-3)^{\frac{5}{2}} + 6(x-3)^{\frac{3}{2}} + c$

n $\ln|\cos x| + \frac{1}{2\cos^2 x} + c$ **o** $-\frac{\ln(x+2)+1}{x+2} + c$

p $\frac{1}{\sqrt{2}}\arctan\left(\frac{x+1}{\sqrt{2}}\right) + c$

2 a $\frac{1}{3}\arctan\left(\frac{x}{3}\right) + c$ **b** $8\arcsin\left(\sqrt{x}\right) + c$ **c** $x\ln 2x - x + c$

d $\frac{1}{2}e^{-x}(\sin x - \cos x) + c$ **e** $\ln\left|\frac{x}{\sqrt{x^2+1}}\right| + c$

f $\frac{\arctan^2 x}{2} + c$ **g** $\frac{9}{2}\arcsin\left(\frac{x}{3}\right) + \frac{x\sqrt{9-x^2}}{2} + c$

h $-\frac{(\ln x)^2 + 2\ln x + 2}{x} + c$ **i** $\frac{2}{3}(x-3)^{\frac{3}{2}} + 6\sqrt{x-3} + c$

j $-\frac{1}{15}(\sin x\sin 4x + 4\cos x\cos 4x) + c$

k $\ln\left|x^2 - 2x + 5\right| + \frac{5}{2}\arctan\left(\frac{x-1}{2}\right) + c$

l $\sin x - \frac{1}{3}\sin^3 x + c$ **m** $\frac{1}{2}\ln\left|x^2 + 4\right| + 2\arctan\left(\frac{x}{2}\right) + c$

n $\arcsin\left(\frac{x}{2}\right) + 2\sqrt{4 - x^2} + c$

o $2 - x - 6\ln|2 - x| - \frac{12}{2-x} + \frac{4}{(2-x)^2} + c$

p $\frac{\sin^6 x}{6} - \frac{\sin^8 x}{8} + \frac{\sin^{10} x}{10} + c$

EXERCISE 27E.1

1 a $y = Ae^{5x}$ **b** $M = Ae^{-2t}$ **c** $y^2 = 4x + c$

d $P^{\frac{1}{2}} = \frac{3}{2}t + c$ **e** $Q = Ae^{2t} - \frac{3}{2}$ **f** $t = Q^2 + 3Q + c$

2 a $y = 10e^{4x}$ **b** $M = 20e^{-3t}$ **c** $\sqrt{y} = \frac{1}{6}t - 1$

d $P = \frac{7}{2}e^{2n} - \frac{3}{2}$ **e** $y = (x-3)^2$

3 $y = Ae^{2x}$ **4 a** $p = \frac{10}{e}$ **b** $r = \ln 2$

6 a $y = Ax^3$ **b** $y = Ae^{\frac{x^2}{8}}$ **c** $y = Ae^{e^x}$ **d** $y = -\ln(-\frac{x^2}{2} + c)$

7 $z = e^{\frac{1}{3}r^3 + r}$ **8** $y = e^{-x^2}$ **9** $y = \sqrt{6 - 2(x+1)e^{-x}}$

10 $y = \frac{e^{2x+2}}{(x+1)^2}$ **11** $y = 2x^2 + 2$ **12** $y = 2\tan\left(x^2 + \frac{\pi}{4}\right)$

13 $f(x) = 2e^{-\frac{1}{3}x}$ **14** $y^2 = x^2 - 9$, $a = \pm 3\sqrt{2}$

15 a $y = \frac{-2}{x^2 + 2x - 4}$ **b** Horizontal asymptote $y = 0$, vertical asymptotes $x = -1 \pm \sqrt{5}$

16 b $x^2 + y^2 = c$ circle centre $(0, 0)$, radius $= \sqrt{c}$ $y = dx$ line passing through $(0, 0)$, gradient d "diameter meets the tangent to the circle at right angles".

17 $v = 4(1.5)^{\frac{t}{4}}$ m s^{-1}, $v \approx 6.64$ m s^{-1} **18** 0.8% **19** $t = 3$ sec

20 a $v \to \frac{g}{4}$ m s^{-1} **b** $t = \frac{1}{4}\ln\left(\frac{5}{3}\right) \approx 0.128$ sec

21 a V_0 is the original volume of water, V is the volume of water that has evaporated. $\therefore\ V_0 - V$ is the volume remaining.

b $\approx 17.7\%$

22 4 hours **23 a** $\frac{dh}{dt} = \frac{r^2}{\pi h^2 - 2\pi rh}$ **b** ≈ 14.4 hours

24 ≈ 12.5 minutes **25** 12 midnight

EXERCISE 27E.2

1 $y = e^x(x^2 + c)$ **2** $y = e^x(x + c)$ or $y = Ae^{-x} - \frac{1}{2}e^x$

3 $x(x^2 + 5y^2)^2 = k$ **4** $y = Axe^{2x^2}$

REVIEW SET 27A

1 $-\frac{32}{3}(4-x)^{\frac{3}{2}} + \frac{16}{5}(4-x)^{\frac{5}{2}} - \frac{2}{7}(4-x)^{\frac{7}{2}} + c$

2 $x\arctan x - \frac{1}{2}\ln(x^2+1) + c$

3 a $\frac{1}{2}e^{-x}(\sin x - \cos x) + c$ **b** $e^x(x^2 - 2x + 2) + c$

  c $\frac{1}{3}(9-x^2)^{\frac{3}{2}} - 9\sqrt{9-x^2} + c$

4 $y^2 = 20 - 4e^x$ **5** $\approx 0.005\,27$ sec **6** $f(x) = 3e^{\frac{1}{3}x}$

7 $y^2 = x^2 + Ax$

REVIEW SET 27B

1 a $5\arcsin(\frac{x}{3}) + c$ **b** $\frac{1}{6}\arctan(\frac{2x}{3}) + c$ **c** $\frac{80}{3}\sqrt{5} - \frac{124}{15}\sqrt{2}$

2 a $\cos x + x\sin x + c$ **b** $\sqrt{x^2-4} + 2\arccos(\frac{2}{x}) + c$

5 b 0.0248 metres **c** $m_H = -2$, $m_L \approx -0.00496$

6 a $\dfrac{dN}{dt} = kN$ (k a constant) **b** $\approx 8.97 \times 10^6$ bacteria

7 a $y = 1 - \dfrac{2}{x^2+4x+1}$ **b** HA $y = 1$,
                                           VA $x = -2+\sqrt{3}$, $x = -2-\sqrt{3}$

8 $\frac{1}{8}$ remains

EXERCISE 28A

1 a continuous **b** discrete **c** continuous **d** continuous
  e discrete **f** discrete **g** continuous **h** continuous

2 a i height of water in the rain gauge **ii** $0 \leqslant x \leqslant 200$ mm
    iii continuous
  b i stopping distance **ii** $0 \leqslant x \leqslant 50$ m **iii** continuous
  c i number of switches until failure **ii** any integer ≥ 1
    iii discrete

3 a $0 \leqslant x \leqslant 4$ **b** YYYY YYYN YYNN NNNY NNNN
                                        YYNY YNYN NNYN
                                        YNYY YNNY NYNN
                                        NYYY NNYY YNNN
                                              NYNY
                                              NYYN
                               $(x=4)$ $(x=3)$ $(x=2)$ $(x=1)$ $(x=0)$

  c i $x = 2$ **ii** $x = 2, 3$ or 4

4 a $x = 0, 1, 2, 3$ **b** HHH   HHT   TTH   TTT
                                HTH   THT
                                THH   HTT
                        $(x=3)$ $(x=2)$ $(x=1)$ $(x=0)$

  c $P(x=3) = \frac{1}{8}$, **d**
    $P(x=2) = \frac{3}{8}$,
    $P(x=1) = \frac{3}{8}$,
    $P(x=0) = \frac{1}{8}$

EXERCISE 28B

1 a $k = 0.2$ **b** $k = \frac{1}{7}$

2 a $P(2) = 0.1088$
  b $a = 0.5488$, the probability that Jason does not hit a home run
    in a game.
  c $P(1) + P(2) + P(3) + P(4) + P(5) = 0.4512$ and is the
    probability that Jason will hit one or more home runs in a game.
  d

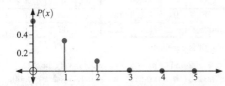

3 a $\sum P(x_i) > 1$ **b** $P(5) < 0$ which is not possible

4 a The random variable represents the number of hits that Sally
    has in each game.
  b $k = 0.23$ **c i** $P(x \geqslant 2) = 0.79$ **ii** $P(1 \leqslant x \leqslant 3) = 0.83$

5 a

roll 1						
6	(6, 1)	(6, 2)	(6, 3)	(6, 4)	(6, 5)	(6, 6)
5	(5, 1)	(5, 2)	(5, 3)	(5, 4)	(5, 5)	(5, 6)
4	(4, 1)	(4, 2)	(4, 3)	(4, 4)	(4, 5)	(4, 6)
3	(3, 1)	(3, 2)	(3, 3)	(3, 4)	(3, 5)	(3, 6)
2	(2, 1)	(2, 2)	(2, 3)	(2, 4)	(2, 5)	(2, 6)
1	(1, 1)	(1, 2)	(1, 3)	(1, 4)	(1, 5)	(1, 6)
	1	2	3	4	5	6
			roll 2			

  b $P(0) = 0$; $P(1) = 0$; $P(2) = \frac{1}{36}$; $P(3) = \frac{2}{36}$; $P(4) = \frac{3}{36}$;
    $P(5) = \frac{4}{36}$; $P(6) = \frac{5}{36}$; $P(7) = \frac{6}{36}$; $P(8) = \frac{5}{36}$;
    $P(9) = \frac{4}{36}$; $P(10) = \frac{3}{36}$; $P(11) = \frac{2}{36}$; $P(12) = \frac{1}{36}$

  c

6 a $k = \frac{1}{12}$ **b** $k = \frac{12}{25}$

7 a $P(0) = 0.1975k$; $P(1) = 0.0988k$; $P(2) = 0.0494k$;
    $P(3) = 0.0247k$; $P(4) = 0.0123k$
  b $k = 2.6130$ $P(x \geqslant 2) = 0.2258$

8 a $P(0) = 0.6648$ **b** $P(x \geqslant 1) = 0.3352$

9 a

X	0	1	2
$P(X=x)$	$\frac{3}{28}$	$\frac{15}{28}$	$\frac{10}{28}$

  b

X	0	1	2	3
$P(X=x)$	$\frac{1}{56}$	$\frac{15}{56}$	$\frac{30}{56}$	$\frac{10}{56}$

10 a

Die 2

Die 1	1	2	3	4	5	6
1	2	3	4	5	6	7
2	3	4	5	6	7	8
3	4	5	6	7	8	9
4	5	6	7	8	9	10
5	6	7	8	9	10	11
6	7	8	9	10	11	12

  b $\frac{1}{6}$ **d** $\frac{15}{26}$

  c

D	2	3	4	5	6	7
$P(D=d)$	$\frac{1}{36}$	$\frac{2}{36}$	$\frac{3}{36}$	$\frac{4}{36}$	$\frac{5}{36}$	$\frac{6}{36}$

D	8	9	10	11	12
$P(D=d)$	$\frac{5}{36}$	$\frac{4}{36}$	$\frac{3}{36}$	$\frac{2}{36}$	$\frac{1}{36}$

11 a i ≈ 0.819 **ii** ≈ 0.164 **iii** ≈ 0.0164 **b** $0.001\,15$

12 a

Die 2

Die 1	1	2	3	4	5	6
1	0	1	2	3	4	5
2	1	0	1	2	3	4
3	2	1	0	1	2	3
4	3	2	1	0	1	2
5	4	3	2	1	0	1
6	5	4	3	2	1	0

  b

N	0	1	2	3	4	5
Probability	$\frac{6}{36}$	$\frac{10}{36}$	$\frac{8}{36}$	$\frac{6}{36}$	$\frac{4}{36}$	$\frac{2}{36}$

  c $\frac{1}{6}$ **d** $\frac{2}{5}$

EXERCISE 28C

1 102 days **2 a** $\frac{1}{8}$ **b** 25 **3** 30 times **4** $1.50 **5** 15 days

6 a i 0.55 **ii** 0.29 **iii** 0.16 **b i** 4125 **ii** 2175 **iii** 1200

7 a $3.50 **b** No

8 a i $\frac{1}{6}$ **ii** $\frac{1}{3}$ **iii** $\frac{1}{2}$ **b i** $1.33 **ii** $0.50 **iii** $3.50
  c lose 50 cents **d** lose $50

9 a $2.75 **b** $3.75

EXERCISE 28D.1

1 a $k = 0.03$ **b** $\mu = 0.74$ **c** $\sigma = 0.9962$

2 $P(1) = \frac{1}{10}$, $P(2) = \frac{3}{10}$, $P(3) = \frac{6}{10}$, $\mu = 2.5$, $\sigma = 0.6708$

3 a $P(0) = 0.216$, $P(1) = 0.432$, $P(2) = 0.288$, $P(3) = 0.064$

x_i	0	1	2	3
$P(x_i)$	0.216	0.432	0.288	0.064

b $\mu = 1.2$, $\sigma = 0.8485$

5 a

x_i	1	2	3	4	5
$P(x_i)$	0.1	0.2	0.4	0.2	0.1

b $\mu = 3.0$,
$\sigma = 1.0954$

c i $P(\mu - \sigma < x < \mu + \sigma) \approx 0.8$
ii $P(\mu - 2\sigma < x < \mu + 2\sigma) \approx 1$

6 \$390 **7 a**

M	1	2	3	4	5	6
$P(M_i)$	$\frac{1}{36}$	$\frac{3}{36}$	$\frac{5}{36}$	$\frac{7}{36}$	$\frac{9}{36}$	$\frac{11}{36}$

b $\mu = 4.472$, $\sigma = 1.404$

8 Tossing a coin $P(\text{head}) = P(\text{tail}) = \frac{1}{2}$ or rolling a die
$P(1) = P(2) = P(3) = ... = P(6) = \frac{1}{6}$

9 In **1**, median = 0, mode = 0   In **2**, median = 3, mode = 3
In **3**, median = 1, mode = 1   In **5**, median = 3, mode = 3
In **7**, median = 5, mode = 6

EXERCISE 28D.2

1 a 3.4 **b** 1.64 **c** ≈ 1.28 **2 a** $k = 0.3$ **b** 6.4 **c** 0.84
3 a 2 **b** 5 **c** 1 **d** 1 **e** 3 **f** 1 **g** 9
4 a $a = 0.15$, $b = 0.35$ **5 a** $a = -\frac{1}{84}$ **b** 4 **c** $\sqrt{3}$

6 a

x	0	1	2	3	4
p_x	$\frac{1}{16}$	$\frac{4}{16}$	$\frac{6}{16}$	$\frac{4}{16}$	$\frac{1}{16}$

b i 2 **ii** 1

7 a

x	0	1	2
p_x	$\frac{7}{15}$	$\frac{7}{15}$	$\frac{1}{15}$

b i 0.6 **ii** ≈ 0.611

8 a $a = 0.25$, $b = 0.35$ **b** 0.99
9 $a = \frac{1}{4}$, $E(X) = 2\frac{11}{12}$, $\text{Var}(X) = \frac{275}{144} \approx 1.91$

EXERCISE 28D.3

1 17 and 4 respectively
2 a $E(aX + b) = E(aX) + E(b) = aE(X) + b$
  b i 13 **ii** -5 **iii** $3\frac{1}{3}$
3 a i 13 **ii** 16 **b i** -7 **ii** 16 **c i** 0 **ii** 1
4 a $2E(X)+3$ **b** $4E(X^2)+12E(X)+9$ **c** $4E(X^2)-4\{E(X)\}^2$

EXERCISE 28E.1

1 a The binomial distribution applies, as tossing a coin has one of two possible outcomes (H or T) and each toss is independent of every other toss.
  b The binomial distribution applies, as this is equivalent to tossing one coin 100 times.
  c The binomial distribution applies as we can draw out a red or a blue marble with the same chances each time.
  d The binomial distribution does not apply as the result of each draw is dependent upon the results of previous draws.
  e The binomial distribution does not apply, assuming that ten bolts are drawn without replacement. We do not have a repetition of independent trials.

2 a ≈ 0.268 **b** ≈ 0.800 **c** ≈ 0.200
3 a ≈ 0.476 **b** ≈ 0.840 **c** ≈ 0.160 **d** ≈ 0.996
4 a ≈ 0.0280 **b** ≈ 0.00246 **c** ≈ 0.131 **d** ≈ 0.710
5 a ≈ 0.998 **b** ≈ 0.807

EXERCISE 28E.2

1 a i $\mu = 3$, $\sigma = 1.2247$

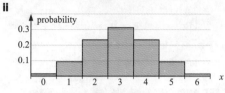

x_i	0 or 6	1 or 5	2 or 4	3
$P(x_i)$	0.0156	0.0938	0.2344	0.3125

ii

iii The distribution is bell-shaped.

b i $\mu = 1.2$, $\sigma = 0.980$

x_i	0	1	2	3	4	5	6
$P(x_i)$	0.262	0.393	0.246	0.082	0.015	0.002	0.000

ii

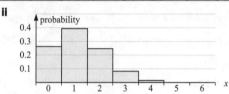

iii The distribution is positively skewed.

c i $\mu = 4.8$, $\sigma = 0.980$

ii

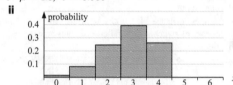

iii This distribution is negatively skewed and is the exact reflection of **b**.

2 $\mu = 5$, $\sigma = 1.58$

3 a

x_i	0	1	2	3
p_i	q^3	$3pq^2$	$3p^2q$	p^3

4 $\mu = 1.2$, $\sigma = 1.07$ **5** $\mu = 0.65$, $\sigma = 0.752$

EXERCISE 28F

1 a 1.5 **b** $p_x = \dfrac{(1.5)^x e^{-1.5}}{x!}$ for $x = 0, 1, 2, 3, 4, 5, 6, ...$

X	0	1	2	3	4	5	6
f	12	18	12	6	3	0	1
$52p_x$	11.6	17.4	13.0	6.5	2.4	0.7	0.2

The fit is excellent.

2 a i ≈ 7.13 **ii** $p_x = \dfrac{(7.13)^x e^{-7.13}}{x!}$, $x = 0, 1, 2, 3, ...$
  b i ≈ 0.0204 **ii** ≈ 0.0752 **iii** ≈ 0.839 **iv** ≈ 0.974

3 a 1.694, so $p_x = \dfrac{(1.694)^x e^{-1.694}}{x!}$, $x = 0, 1, 2, 3, ...$
  b

X	0	1	2	3	4	5	6	7
f	91	156	132	75	33	9	3	1
$500p_x$	92	156	132	74	32	11	3	1

The fit is excellent.

  c $\sigma \approx 1.292$ and $\sqrt{m} \approx 1.302$, so, σ is very close to $\sqrt{m}$ in value.
4 a ≈ 0.0498 **b** ≈ 0.577 **c** ≈ 0.185 **d** ≈ 0.440
5 a $m = \dfrac{3+\sqrt{33}}{2}$ **b i** ≈ 0.506 **ii** ≈ 0.818
6 a 0.271 **b** 0.271 **c** 0.677 **7 a** 0.901 **b** 6 years
8 a ≈ 0.150 **b** ≈ 0.967 **c** mode = 1 flaw per metre
9 a $m \approx 6.8730$ **b** ≈ 0.177 **c** ≈ 0.417

90 **a** $a = (r + \frac{1}{r})\cos\theta$, $b = (r - \frac{1}{r})\sin\theta$

 b $r = 1$ or z is real and non-zero

91 **a** $2p^2 - p^4$ **b** $p \approx 0.541$

92 **a** $\mathbf{A}^2 = \begin{pmatrix} 4 & 4 \\ 0 & 4 \end{pmatrix}$ **b** $\mathbf{A}^3 = \begin{pmatrix} 8 & 12 \\ 0 & 8 \end{pmatrix}$

94 **a** $1 - (1-p)^n$ **b** $\dfrac{\binom{n}{k}p^k(1-p)^{n-k}}{\displaystyle\sum_{r=k}^{n}\binom{n}{r}p^r(1-p)^{n-r}}$ **c** $p = 1$

 d no real solutions

95 **a** $n\binom{n}{2}$ committees **b** $\binom{n}{3}$ committees **d** **i** $\frac{4}{11}$ **ii** $\frac{1}{8}$

96 **a** $\frac{3}{5}$ **b** 5 cm or 2.2 cm **c** AB = 5 cm is not possible

98 **b** 1, 1, 1

101 **a**

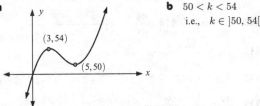

(3, 54)

(5, 50)

 b $50 < k < 54$

 i.e., $k \in\ ]50, 54[$

102 **b** $x = 2\cos(\frac{2\pi}{9})$, $2\cos(\frac{8\pi}{9})$, $2\cos(\frac{14\pi}{9})$

103 **a** $y^2 = x^2 + 64 - 16x\cos\theta$, $\cos\theta = \dfrac{3x - 10}{2x}$

 c $8\sqrt{5}$ cm^2 when Δ is isosceles

104 **a** $\mathbf{A}^n = \begin{pmatrix} 2^n & 2^n - 1 \\ 0 & 1 \end{pmatrix}$ for all $n \in \mathbb{Z}^+$

 c $\mathbf{S}_n = \begin{pmatrix} 2^{n+1} - 2 & 2^{n+1} - 2 - n \\ 0 & n \end{pmatrix}$

 $\mathbf{S}_{20} = \begin{pmatrix} 2\,097\,150 & 2\,097\,130 \\ 0 & 20 \end{pmatrix}$

105 $f(n) = 3n^2 - 3n + 4$ **106** ≈ 6.40 cm

107 **a** ≈ 0.34 **b** $\sigma \approx 5$ **108** **a** $\sigma \approx 3.599\,86$ **b** ≈ 0.781

109 $\frac{17}{32}$ **110** ≈ 0.114 **111** **a** ≈ 0.242 **b** ≈ 0.769

112 ≈ 0.842 **113** $a = \frac{3}{5}$ **114** $\frac{7}{10}$

115 **a** $k = \frac{1}{3}$ **b** mean = 800, sd = $\frac{40\sqrt{3}}{3}$

116 **a** ≈ 0.549 **b** $\approx 0.001\,72$ **117** $\sigma = \sqrt{1 + \sqrt{7}}$

118 **a** ≈ 375 **b** ≈ 0.0366 **119** **a** 66 **b** ≈ 275

120 **a** $x\ln x - x + c$ **b** $k = e$

 c m is the solution of $\int_1^m \ln x\ dx = \frac{1}{2}$

123 **b**

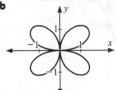

124 **a** $u_n = \cos\theta\tan^{n-2}\theta$

 b $u_1 = 1$ and $u_{n+1} = u_n^2\cos\theta$, $n \in \mathbb{Z}^+$

125 **a** $k = 2$ **b** $u_n = \dfrac{3n - 8}{2}$, $n \in \mathbb{Z}^+$ **126** **a** $k\sqrt{3}$

128 **b** r km **c** $1000\sqrt{3}$ kmh^{-1} **130** **b** 1

131 $x = -\frac{11\pi}{12}$, $-\frac{3\pi}{4}$, $-\frac{7\pi}{12}$, $\frac{\pi}{12}$, $\frac{\pi}{4}$, $\frac{5\pi}{12}$

132 $x = \frac{\pi}{6}$, $\frac{5\pi}{6}$, $\frac{4\pi}{3}$, $\frac{5\pi}{3}$ **133** 3

135 **a** $x = -\frac{10}{9}$ **b** $x = -1$ **c** $x = e^e$ **d** $x = \frac{1}{5}$

136 **a** $x < 2$ **b** $x < \frac{1}{2}$ **c** $x < 2$ **138** $2\sin\theta$, $\theta - \frac{\pi}{2}$

139 $a = \frac{4}{3}$, $b = \frac{2}{3}$ or $a = -\frac{4}{3}$, $b = -\frac{2}{3}$ **140** $x = \frac{15}{7}$, $y = \frac{10}{7}$

141 $w = \dfrac{[a^2 - 1 - b^2] + i[2ab]}{(a + 1)^2 + b^2}$, purely imaginary if $a^2 - b^2 = 1$ and $ab \neq 0$

142 $\frac{8}{x}$ **143** **a** $\frac{25\pi}{2}$ units^2 **b** $25\pi\sin(\frac{\alpha}{2})$ units^2

144 $9b = 2a^2$ **145** $a = -1$, $b = -7$ **146** $a = 2$, $n = 3$

147 **a** $P(x) = (ax + b)(2x^2 - 3x + 1)$

 c $P(x) = (3x + 7)(2x^2 - 3x + 1)$

148 $f(x) = (x + 1)^2(2x - 5)$, $x = -1$ or $x \geqslant \frac{5}{2}$

149 $f(x) = \frac{1}{3}(x + 3)(4x + 1)(2x - 3)^2$

150 **a** $x^2 + 4x + 5$ **b** $a = -4$, real zero is 4

151 **b** $h(x) = (x - t)(x - 2t)(x - 3t)$

 c $(-3, 27)$, $(-2, 16)$, $(-1, 5)$

152 **a** **i** $x^2 - 2x + (1 + k^2)$ **ii** $k = 0, \pm1, \pm2, \pm3$

 b $pq = -1, -2, -5, -10$ **c** $x = 1, -2, 1 \pm 2i$

153 $P(z) = (z^2 + 2)(z^2 - 2z + 5)$

154 **a** $(0, 4)$. A translation of $\binom{2}{1}$.

 b $(0, 6)$. A translation of $\binom{2}{0}$ followed by a vertical stretch of factor 2.

 c $(-2, -5)$

 d $(\frac{1}{2}, 3)$. A horizontal compression factor 2 followed by a translation of $\binom{1.5}{0}$.

 e $(-2, \frac{1}{3})$ **f** $(3, -2)$. A reflection in $y = x$.

155

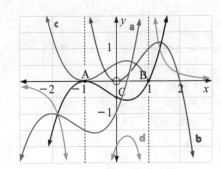

156 **a** $f(x) = -x^2 + 6x - 13$ **b** $f(x) = -(x - 3)^2 - 4$

157 $y = 4\sin(\frac{\pi}{2}x) - 1$ **158** $x = 2$, $y = 4$, $z = -1$

159 **a** $a = 13$, $b = 12$, $c = \frac{\pi}{30}$, $d = 15$ **b** ≈ 24.93 m

160 **a** $(\frac{1}{5}, \frac{17}{5}, \frac{9}{5})$ **c** $(-1, 3, 1)$ **d** $6x - 8y - 5z = -35$

161 $\approx 7.82°$

162 **a** $\begin{pmatrix} 1 & -2 & 3 & | & 1 \\ 1 & p & 2 & | & 0 \\ -2 & p^2 & -4 & | & q \end{pmatrix}$ **c** **i** $p \neq 0$ **ii** $p = 0$, $q \neq 0$ **iii** $p = q = 0$

 d $x = -2 - 4t$, $y = t$, $z = 1 + 2t$, $t \in \mathbb{R}$

163 **b** $k = -1$ **c** $p = -2$, $q = 6$

164 $\mathbf{AB} = \mathbf{I}$ $a = 2$, $b = -1$, $c = 3$

166 **a** $5\mathbf{i} - 2\mathbf{j} + \mathbf{k}$ **b** $\frac{\sqrt{30}}{6}(5\mathbf{i} - 2\mathbf{j} + \mathbf{k})$ **167** $\frac{5}{2}\sqrt{6}$ units^2

168 **a** D(7, 1, -2) X(7, 3, -1) Y(5, 3, -2)

 b Hint: Show $\overrightarrow{BD} = k\overrightarrow{BY}$

170 **a** $t = \frac{2}{3}$ **b** $t = -\frac{1}{3}$

171 **a** $x = 0$ **b** $x = 0.2$ or 0.3

172 **a** $x < \frac{1}{5}$ or $x > \frac{2}{7}$ **b** $-6 < x < 1$ or $x \geqslant 2$

173 **a** ≈ 0.785 **b** ≈ 0.995 **174** $y = \frac{1}{2}x + \frac{1}{4}\sin 2x + 4$

175 $y^2 = \frac{1}{4}x^2 - 1$ **177** $\approx 50\,000$ guinea pigs

178 b $y = \dfrac{624}{1 + 311(\frac{51}{311})^t}$

   c i 624 people **ii** about 67 people **iii** $\approx$ 4:24 pm

179 a $\frac{1}{\sqrt{2}}e^{i(-\frac{7\pi}{12})}$ **b** 12

180 a 479 001 600

   b i 43 545 600 **ii** 7 257 600 **iii** 159 667 200

   iv 58 060 800

   c i 5775 **ii** 1575

181 20.6 cm **182 a** 8008 **b** 5320 **c** 2211

183 $n = 3$ or 8 **184 a** -224 **b** 880 **c** -40

185 a when $x = \frac{\pi}{2}$

   b $\sin^2 2x + 2\cos 2x = 0$ needs to be solved

   c (0.999, 2.028) and (2.143, 2.028)

186 $x = 4$ or 2 **187** $a = \sqrt{e^6 - 1}$ **188** $\frac{\sqrt{13}-2}{3}$

189 $a = 5$, $b = 9$

190

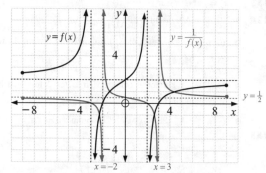

191 $x = 0$ or 4 **192** $a = -2$, $b = 3$; $\mathbf{A}^{11} = \begin{pmatrix} -2 & -1 \\ 3 & 2 \end{pmatrix}$

193 $x = \sqrt{5}$ ($y = 0$) **194** $1 + 2i$, $-1 \pm 3i$

195 $\frac{\pi}{6}(e^2 - 1)$ units^3

196 Translate through $\begin{pmatrix} 1 \\ -10 \end{pmatrix}$ then reflect in x-axis.

197 $\frac{1}{2}$ unit^2 **198** $2x\sqrt{1-x^2}$, $\frac{2}{3}$ unit^2

199 a $a = 0$ **b** $a = 4$; $x = \dfrac{5-5t}{2}$, $y = 1 - 2t$, $z = t$, $t \in \mathbb{R}$

   c $a \neq 0$ or 4; $x = -\dfrac{a}{2} - \dfrac{12}{a}$, $y = -1 - a$, $z = \dfrac{a+8}{a}$

   when $a = 2$; $x = -7$, $y = -3$, $z = 5$

200 a VA is $x = -1$, HA is $y = 1$

   b $f'(x) = \dfrac{2(x-1)}{(x+1)^3}$; local min $(1, \frac{1}{2})$

   c $f''(x) = \dfrac{-4(x-2)}{(x+1)^4}$; inflection $(2, \frac{5}{9})$

   d

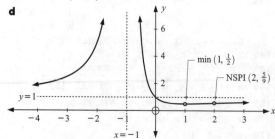

201 a $v = \dfrac{-2}{t+2}$ **b** 1.39 units

202 $x \in [-1, 0] \cup [1, 2]$ $f'(x) = \dfrac{2x-1}{\sqrt{1-(1+x-x^2)^2}}$

203 $\frac{3}{4}$ unit^2

204 VAs $x = -\frac{\pi}{2}$, $x = -\frac{\pi}{4}$, $x = \frac{\pi}{2}$, $x = \frac{3\pi}{4}$ No HAs

205 $(\frac{\pi}{4}, \frac{\sqrt{2}}{4})$, $(-\frac{3\pi}{4}, -\frac{\sqrt{2}}{4})$ **206** $47\frac{6}{7}$ or $31\frac{1}{7}$

207 a $\dfrac{3x}{x-2}$ **b** $\dfrac{2x+1}{x-1}$

208 a $\dfrac{dy}{dx} = \dfrac{3y - 2x}{2y - 3x}$ **b** $(\sqrt{7}, 0)$, $(-\sqrt{7}, 0)$

209 a i $\frac{13}{21}$ **ii** $\frac{11}{21}$ **b** $\frac{2}{3}$

210 a A(2, −3, 1) **b** B(−1, 2, 3) **c** $p = 0$ or $\frac{62}{371}$

211 $x = \dfrac{2}{a^2 - 1}$ **212** $y = -1 + 3e^{\arctan x}$

213 $-x^2 \cos x + 2x \sin x + 2 \cos x + c$ **214** $\dfrac{2x+29}{5}$

215 3.76 units^2 **216** $\dfrac{dy}{dx} = \dfrac{-y^2 - ye^{xy}}{xe^{xy} + 2xy - \cos y}$

217 $x < \dfrac{-\sqrt{65} - 7}{2}$ or $-5 < x < -1$

218 $\frac{2}{3}(x+2)^{\frac{3}{2}} - x - 2 - 2\sqrt{x+2} + 2\ln(\sqrt{x+2} + 1) + c$

219 $\dfrac{dy}{dx} = \dfrac{1 - y\cos(xy)}{x\cos(xy) + 2y}$

220 a P(0, 3, −8) **b** $\theta \approx 18.8^o$ **c** $5x - 11y - 7z = 23$

221 $a < -8$ or $a > 4$ **222** $\frac{1}{40\pi}$ cm s^{-1} **223** $a = 2$

224 a

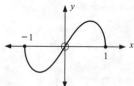

   b $V = \pi \displaystyle\int_0^1 \left(x \tan\sqrt{1 - x^2}\right)^2 dx$

225 a $f'(x) = e^{1-2x^2}(1 - 4x^2)$ $f''(x) = e^{1-2x^2}(16x^3 - 12x)$

   b local min at $(-\frac{1}{2}, -\frac{\sqrt{e}}{2})$ local max at $(\frac{1}{2}, \frac{\sqrt{e}}{2})$

   c $x = 0$ or $\pm\frac{\sqrt{3}}{2}$

   d as $x \to \infty$, $f(x) \to 0$ (above)

     as $x \to -\infty$, $f(x) \to 0$ (below)

   e

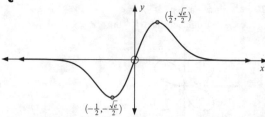

   f $k = \frac{1}{\sqrt{2}}$

226 a $k = -2$, $a = -1$

   c $x = 3 + t$, $y = -3 - 2t$, $z = t$, $t \in \mathbb{R}$ **d** (3, −3, 0)

   e $\approx 61.9^o$

228 $a = 8$, $b = 25$, $c = 26$; $z \geqslant -2$

229 a $\frac{\pi}{3}$ **b** $x \approx -0.571$, $t \approx 0.476$

   c A horizontal stretch factor $\frac{1}{3}$, followed by a vertical stretch factor 2, followed by a translation $\begin{pmatrix} 1 \\ 4 \end{pmatrix}$.

   d $x \in [-1, 1]$ but $x \not\approx -0.571$ or 0.476; range $y \in \mathbb{R}$

INDEX